ALL THINGS NUCLEAR

second edition

by

JAMES C. WARF

ALL THINGS NUCLEAR
second edition

by JAMES C. WARF

Published by
FIGUEROA PRESS
Suite 401E
840 Childs Way
Los Angeles, CA 90089
Phone: (213) 740-3570
Fax: (213) 740-5203
www.figueroapress.com

Figueroa Press is a division of the USC University Bookstore

Cover, text and layout design by Jeff Ratto, USC GraphicDesign

Author cover photos: James C. Warf

Produced by Crestec Los Angeles, Inc.

Printed in the United States of America

Library of Congress Cataloguing-in-Publication Data
Warf, James C.
All Things Nuclear, second edition
Includes bibliographical references (p.) and index
ISBN: 1-932800-00-X
Library of Congress Number: 2004111890

We may be likened to two scorpions in a bottle, each capable of killing the other, but only at the risk of his own life.

—J. Robert Oppenheimer, 1947

Every day I saw huge material, intellectual, and nervous resources of thousands of people being poured into the creation of a means of total destruction, something capable of annihilating all human civilization. I noticed that the control levers were in the hands of people who, though talented in their own ways, were cynical.

—Andrei Sakharov, 1974

CONTENTS

CREDITS FOR ILLUSTRATIONS

Chapter 3

3-6. The first nuclear reactor.
Courtesy of Argonne National Laboratory, Argonne, IL.

3-10. The Trinity test, the world's first nuclear explosion.
Courtesy of the Los Alamos National Laboratory.

3-10D. Color Plate I.
The photo of the author and a replica of the Nagasaki bomb was taken by the author.

3-11. The photograph of Hiroshima made two months after the bombing is from the book *Atomic Bomb Documents: Hiroshima*, reproduced by courtesy of the publisher, Chugoku Shimbunsha, Hiroshima City.

3-21. First Soviet nuclear bomb test.
Courtesy of The General Board of Global Ministries of The United Methodist Church (USA and Kazakhstan), 1994.

Chapter 4

4-15. Cartoon, "Chapter 7. The Structure of the Nucleus."
Reproduced by permission of the cartoonist, Sidney Harris.

4-16. Fission yield graph.
From Samuel Glasstone, *Sourcebok on Atomic Energy,* 3rd edition, Van Nostrand Reinhold Co., 1967.

4-29E. Photo of wind turbines,
From The Los Angeles Times, July 10, 1997. Photographer: Tony Barnard.

Chapter 5

5-1. Color Plate I. Model of DNA molecule.
Published in *Science*, volume 230, 1985, Reproduced by permission of Dr. Alexander Rich, Massachusetts Institute of Technology.

5-7. Bottle of Radithor,
From *The New Scientist*, Sept. 28, p.3, 1996, London.

5-17. Graphs A and B were copied with permission from John W. Gofman,
Radiation-Induced Cancer from Low-Dose Exposure, 1990, Committee for Nuclear Responsibility, Inc., San Francisco.

Chapter 6

Title page. Peace dove logo.
From *Nuclear Science Journal*, Taiwan, Volume 1.32, No. 1. February 1995.

6-9. Radioautograph of a leaf of a bean plant containing phosphorus-32.
From *Sourcebook on Atomic Energy,* by Samuel Glasstone, U. S. Atomic Energy Commission, Van Nostrand Reinhold Co., New York, NY, 1967, p. 683.

6-11. Screw-worm fly.
Reproduced from *Traite d'Entomologie Medicale et Veterinaire*, by Maurice Neveu-Lemaire, Vigot Freres, Paris, 1938, Figure 378, page 848.

6-19-1 and 6-19-2, Color Plate I. Images of cerebral glioma and of ocular melanoma.
From the research of Giovanni Paganelli, M.D., of Milan, Italy.

6-23, Color Plate II. Thyroid and parathyroid glands.
Reproduced by permission of Milton Gross from *Diagnostic Nuclear Medicine,* M. P. Sandler, Ed., Williams and Wilkins, 1996.

6-24. Images of the spleen of an injured boy.
Courtesy of Naomi P. Alazraki and Fred S. Mishkin, *Fundamentals of Nuclear Medicine*, first edition, 1984, Fig. 11–1, page 107. Reproduced by permission of The Society of Nuclear Medicine.

6-25. Gallium-67 image showing cancer of the lung.
Courtesy of Naomi P. Alazraki and Fred S. Mishkin, *Fundamentals of Nuclear Medicine*, first edition, 1984, Fig. 13–2, page 124. Reproduced by permission of The Society of Nuclear Medicine.

6-25F. Color Plate II. PET of brains of normal and abused children, 1997.
Reproduced by permission of Harry Chugani, M.D., of Children's Hospital, Wayne State University.

6-29. Sketch of commercial food irradiation unit.
Supplied by MDS Nordion, Ontario, Canada, and reproduced by permission.

6-38D. Home smoke detector.
Design adapted from an advertisement.

6-38J. Neutron moisture meter.
Data courtesy of U.S. Department of Agriculture, Soil Conservation Service, Davis, CA 95616; sketch from Nyle C. Brady, *The Nature and Properties of Soils,* Macmillan Publishing Co., New York, NY, p. 134, 1990.

6-39A. Low resolution NMR spectrum of water.
Adapted from standard chemical sources; the high resolution NMR spectrum of ethanol is from *Nuclear Magnetic Resonance Spectroscopy,* 2nd ed., by Frank Bovey, Lynn Jelinski, and Peter Mirau, Academic Press, NY, 1988, p. 120.

6-39B. Color Plate II. Tomograph of MRI image of human brain.
Courtesy of John Belliveau, who sent an original photograph, and *Science*, vol. 254, page 716, 1991, copyright by AAAS.

6-39F. Mössbauer spectrum.
Adapted from *Mössbauer Isomer Shifts,* G. K. Shenoy and F. E. Wagner, eds., North-Holland Publishing Co., N.Y., 1978, page 54.

Chapter 7

7-4G. Pressurized Water Reactor Plant.
From NUCREG-0956 (1986), U.S. Department of Energy.

7-7. CANDU reactor.
From Atomic Energy of Canada, Ltd.

7-10D. Molten salt reactor.
From ORNL-4812, by M. W. Rosenthal, P. N. Haubenreich, and R. B. Briggs, U.S. Department of Energy, 1972.

7-12. Fuel element.
From Idaho National Nuclear Engineering Laboratory, Argonne-West, U.S. Department of Energy.

7-14. Superphénix Fast Breeder Reactor.
Courtesy of Electricité de France, Centre Nucléaire de Production d'Électricité, Creys-Malville, France.

7-19C. The N Reactor.
U.S. Department of Energy, Richland, WA. Reproduced from NUSAR, Volume 2, Fig. 3.2–8, 1978.

7-20. High-temperature gas-cooled reactor.
Reproduced with permission, Office of Technology Assessment, *Nuclear Power in an Age of Uncertainty,* OTA-E-216, Washington, DC., U.S. Government Printing Office, 1984.

7-25. RMBK reactor at Chernobyl.
Reproduced with permission from *Chernobyl: Errors and Design Flaws*, by Colin Norman, *Science*, Vol. 233, pp. 102–1031, sketch, September 5, 1986. Copyright 1986 by AAAS.

7-38. Tokamak.
Adapted from sketch by Matt Moody, Los Angeles Times, May 8, 1989.

Chapter 8.

8-31B. Sketch of Nirex nuclear waste repository.
Courtesy of Nirex Limited, Harwell, United Kingdom.

8-33. Graph of radioactivity of spent fuel vs. time.
Adapted from data in High-Level Radioactive Waste Alternatives, Battelle Pacific Northwest Laboratories, BNWL-1900, 1974.

Chapter 9

9-5. Trinity fission bomb.
Drawn by the author; based on many non-classified sources.

9-6. Hiroshima gun-assembly fission bomb (Little Boy).
Reproduced from *US Nuclear Weapons: the Secret History,* with permission from its author, Chuck Hansen, Orion Books (Crown Publishers, NY), 1988, page 121. The sketch was drawn by Mike Wagnon.

9-15. Hydrogen bomb.
Drawn by the author; based on many non-classified sources.

9-16. Three-stage hydrogen bomb.
Drawn by the author; based on many non-classified sources.

9-19. Circulation pattern of nuclear bomb explosion.
Reproduced from *The Effects of Nuclear Weapons*, by Samuel Glasstone and Philip J. Dolan, Department of Defense and the Energy Research and Development Administration, Washington, DC, 1977, page 29.

9-19. Hydrogen bomb test Mike.
Courtesy of Nuclear War Graphics Project, Northfield, MN, 1986.

9-23. Soviet hydrogen bomb test.
Courtesy of The General Board of Global Ministries of the United Methodist Church (USA and Kazakhstan), 1994.

9-30. Color Plate II. Nuclear artillery test, Grable shot Color Plate II.
Courtesy of Nuclear War Graphics Project, Northfield, MN, 1986.

9-59. Graph drawn by the author.
Based on data from the Natural Resources Defense Committee and published in *The Bulletin of the Atomic Scientists*, Nov./Dec., 1997.

Chapter 10

10-6. The MX missile.
Reproduced with permission from *Chemical & Engineering News*, American Chemical Society, March 16, page 27, 1981.

10-8. The W84 cruise missile.
From Cochran, Arkin, and Hoenig's *Nuclear Weapons Databook, Volume I: U.S. Nuclear Forces and Capabilities,* The Natural Resources Defense Council. Reprinted with permission of Ballinger Publishing Company,1984.

10-15. Pop-up version of anti-missile laser weapon.
Courtesy of Robert M. Bowman, *Star Wars: Defense or Death Star?* Reproduced from page 19 with permission of Institute for Space and Security Studies, 1985.

10-15. Orbiting mirrors.
Courtesy of Robert M. Bowman, *Star Wars: Defense or Death Star?* Reproduced from page 22 with permission of Institute for Space and Security Studies, 1985.

10-15. X-ray laser battle station.
Courtesy of Robert M. Bowman, *Star Wars: Defense or Death Star?* Reproduced from page 24 with permission of Institute for Space and Security Studies, 1985.

10-18. Quick-burning launching.
Courtesy of Robert M. Bowman, *Star Wars: Defense or Death Star?* Reproduced from page 29 with permission of Institute for Space and Security Studies, 1985.

10-43. Total dose contours from local fallout.
Reproduced from *The Effects of Nuclear Weapons*, by Samuel Glasstone and Philip J. Dolan, page 426. Department of Defense and Energy Research and Development Administration, Washington, DC, 1977.

10-44. Real fallout patterns from the 15 megaton hydrogen bomb test at Bikini and Patterns of local fallout, Boltzman and Turk shots.
Reproduced from *The Effects of Nuclear Weapons*, by Samuel Glasstone and Philip J. Dolan, pages 437 and 421, Department of Defense and Energy Research and Development Administration, Washington, DC, 1977.

10-58. Fallout pattern for only ten bombing areas in an attack on the United States.
Courtesy of Lawrence Livermore National Laboratory, Livermore, CA. Reproduced with permission from UCRL-98348, March, 1988, by Kendall R. Peterson, Charles S. Shapiro, and Ted F. Harvey. This was also published in *The Medical Implications of Nuclear War*, The National Academy Press, 1986, which also granted permission to reproduce the figure.

Chapter 12

12-11. Photo reproduced with permission from the book *Haha to Ko de Miru Tokyo Daikúshú*, published by Kusanone Publishing Co., Tokyo, Japan, 1983 and 1986.
ISBN 4-7945-0043-2.

ACKNOWLEDGMENTS

In writing any treatise on a convoluted subject covering hundreds of aspects of the topic, each author needs as much help as possible. It is a pleasure to acknowledge the assistance of quite a number of individuals who have contributed their skills in making this work possible.

First, my patient wife, Kyoko, was a sort of nuclear widow during the years required to write this book, and the author wants to express his deeply-felt appreciation to her.

Two dedicated people scrutinized the first drafts of the entire book. One of these is the author's late sister, Ms. Lois Warf Hilton. Her criticisms clarified many obscure parts and pointed out ways to improve numerous sections of the text. The second is Dr. Sheldon Plotkin, an engineer, who corrected a large number of technical errors and made suggestions for adding information or amplifying numerous other points. Both gave constant support for the writing effort.

Professor Raymond Wilson, a physicist, supplied a great deal of raw material, especially on the atomic bombings of Japan (Chapter 3). He also contributed one part of the text in Chapter 12, "Ways to Peace." Prof. Wilson gave continuing encouragement to the author all through the years devoted to writing this treatise.

Dr. Tomio Kawata, of the Japan Nuclear Cycle Development Institute, supplied valuable information about Japanese reprocessing procedures.

Fred Blair, an electronics and computer expert, performed much appreciated services by keeping the author's computers (including e-mail and the web), printers, scanners, copiers, and other equipment in trim running condition.

The dedicated work of Ms. Laura Lee Carter as editor of the entire book proved to be extremely valuable and is profoundly esteemed.

For the Chapters, the following acknowledgments are thankfully made: Chapters 1 through 5: Dr. Antonie Churg, a physical chemist, contributed many valuable criticisms and corrections in the five chapters.

Chapter 3: The Road to the Bomb. Arnold Kramish, a Manhattan Project physicist and historian of nuclear events, supplied valuable help in matters concerning wartime Soviet and German espionage on the American Manhattan Project, the status of nuclear reactors, the German submarine U-234, and a variety of related matters.

Chapter 4: Nuclear Science, Radioactivity, and Energy. Professor Charles Shapiro, of San Francisco State University, and the late Dr. Robert Cornog, a veteran of the Manhattan Project, both nuclear physicists, supplied authoritative information and ways to improve the sections on subnuclear particles, and also the sections on energy. Professor Nina Byers, a physicist at UCLA, made constructive criticisms of the sections on subnuclear particles.

Chapter 5: Biological Effects of Ionizing Radiation. Three physicians read and corrected errors of commission and omission in this chapter. They are: Earl Budin,

M.D.; John Gofman, M.D., Ph.D.; and Curren W. Warf, M.D. Dr. Stuart Salot, a chemist, critiqued and contributed to the information on exposure to radon.

Chapter 6: Radioactivity in Human Service. Four experts checked the text and contributed valued criticisms on sterilization of foodstuffs using ionizing radiation. They are: Dr. Joseph Borsa, of MDS Nordion, Ontario, Canada; Mr. William Hargraves, of Food Technology Service, Mulberry, Florida; Mr. Russell Stein, Vice President of Gray*Star; and Dr. Donald W. Thayer, U.S. Department of Agriculture.

The author is also indebted to the following physicians for sending me original medical images: J. W. Belliveau, M.D., of Massachusetts General Hospital (MRI image of human head); Harry Chugani, M.D., of Children's Hospital of Michigan, Wayne State University (PET tomographs of the brains of abused children); and Milton Gross, M.D., of the University of Michigan Medical Center (thyroid and parathyroid imaging using technetium-99m).

Chapter 7: Nuclear Reactors. Bruce Hoglund, a nuclear physicist, supplied abundant and highly appreciated data concerning molten-salt reactors, as well as the technology of processing to recover the uranium-233 produced.

Dr. Tetsuji Imanaka, a nuclear physicist at the Research Reactor Institute near Osaka, furnished important information on Japanese reactors representing data difficult to find in English. He has studied the Chernobyl accident for years, and supplied the author with much of the data on that dreadful event. He also was co-author of the article clarifying Hagiwara's role in the concept of hydrogen bombs (Chapter 9), along with Professor Shuji Fukui, of the University of Nagoya.

The late Professor Paul Kuroda, a nuclear chemist for many years at the University of Arkansas, gave helpful advice concerning natural nuclear reactors, as well as a variety of other topics.

Chapter 9: Nuclear Weapons. Concerning the matter of Hagiwara, Mr. Kazuya Hosaka, a Tokyo engineer, made the preliminary search of the Japanese literature. Professor Tatsuo Namba, of the Hiroshima Prefectural University, contributed further details in this matter. Professor Paul Kuroda supplied the author with a copy of the Tonizo document concerning Hagiwara, and helped with many other details on nuclear matters. Later, nuclear physicists Dr. Tetsuji Imanaka, of the Research Reactor Institute, Kyoto University, and Professor Shuji Fukui, of Nagoya University, and the author researched all the literature and other sources concerning Hagiwara, and finally unraveled the facts of the matter, which were published in *The Bulletin of the Atomic Scientists*, July-August, 2000.

Additional acknowledgments are below. Ms. Linda Sandoval, Archivist's Assistant, Los Alamos National Laboratory, kindly supplied a copy of the original Smyth Report.

Ms. Theresa Strottman, Archivist at the Los Alamos Historical Museum, furnished sketches concerning the early history of the Manhattan Project.

The author is happy to acknowledge the invaluable help of various offices of the Department of Energy in matters such as nuclear reactors and radioactive waste disposal. In addition, Mr. Daniel Hirsch and Dr. Bennett Ramberg of the Committee to Bridge the Gap, located in Los Angeles, kindly supplied many essential documents on nuclear issues.

The analytical scrutiny by all these specialists, reviewers, literature searchers, historians, and others, greatly strengthened the manuscript. The author is strongly appreciative.

The author also acknowledges with gratitude the financial assistance from the University of Southern California Emeriti College, which made possible a grant from the Rita H. Small Foundation to purchase some essential computer equipment. The Emeriti College also sponsored grants from the Kenneth T. and Eileen L. Norris Foundation to help cover the costs for an editor of the text, and this is also gratefully acknowledged.

JAMES C. WARF
Los Angeles, California

PREFACE

The United States and the former Soviet Union carried out a forty-year (1950–1990) Cold War in which a total of nearly 70,000 nuclear warheads accumulated. Our world had never before experienced such peril. What are these nuclear or atomic bombs? How were they developed? Would an all-out nuclear war have wiped humanity from the face of the earth? How can the bombs be reliably destroyed now that the Cold War is over? Is the human race stupid enough to do it all over again? Did anything of value come from all this?

Answers to or observations on these questions and thousands more are presented in this book. The author's view is to learn what we can from the past and then move on to a better, more secure future. The facts are that enormous benefits to the human race can be gained by the studies and applications of the sciences involved in radioactivity and other nuclear properties. In fact, this is the main mission of this publication, although of necessity considerable space is devoted to nuclear weapons and related matters.

This book is intended to serve readers without excessively detailed knowledge of each subject, and thus from the technical point of view is not too demanding. There is some mathematics in two chapters; these parts are not difficult, but can be skipped without excessive loss of continuity.

Thousands of books on nuclear energy and radioactivity in their various aspects are available. Many are rather specialized in nature. In this work, the topics are generally covered in a pithy manner. A number of subjects are controversial. An endeavor was made to avoid scarring the text with too many acronyms.

This volume serves as a resource to look up each topic dealing with nuclear issues and science. You might want to know something just about neutron bombs, or disposal of waste products from nuclear reactors, or the probable consequences of a nuclear war, or nuclear medicine, or the nature of the earth's ozone layer. Peace groups, environmental societies, those working in the relation of science to society, students, and others will find the book informative. After all, if nuclear war is to be prevented, an informed electorate is best prepared to do this.

Our world still harbors a vast arsenal of nuclear bombs and related weapons systems. The hostilities between the world's countries continue unabated, although the patterns of alliance keep shifting. Most people in all countries have only rudimentary knowledge of what a massive nuclear war would mean. Make no mistake: while such a cataclysm would probably not erase the human race, it would be devastating beyond belief, far, far worse than the most morbid pessimist could dream. The development of bantam nuclear bombs, as compared to those of the Hiroshima type, has enhanced the probability of their use. Such a trigger could ignite events leading to world catastrophe. Especially over the next two or three generations, the governments of the world have the responsibility to cope competently with these matters, but the outlook for this is hardly promising.

An extensive range of topics is covered in this volume, such as how the atomic nucleus was discovered, what radioactivity is, how atomic bombs were developed and their effects on Hiroshima and Nagasaki, nuclear reactors, coping with radioactive waste, plutonium, cancer and radiation, and many other such matters. Peaceful applications of radioactive materials and related techniques include: generation of electricity; small thermoelectric generators to power space craft; determination of the age of the Earth, of the bones of our pre-human ancestors and of artifacts, and carbon-14 dating of many materials; determination of temperatures which prevailed millions of years ago; control of certain obnoxious insects; neutron moisture meters for use in agriculture; and developing improved strains of crops. In the field of nuclear medicine, making images of living, moving human organs in order to examine them for disease; looking into the human mind and studying thought processes and emotions; researching brain disorders such as dyslexia, Parkinson's disease, and Alzheimer's disease; preservation of food by irradiation; all of these and more exemplify the practice and the promise. In addition, there are nuclear properties which do not depend on radioactivity. These include magnetic resonance imaging and atomic clocks accurate to one second in more than a billion years.

All values of half-lives were taken from the exhaustive and authoritative book by E. Browne and R. Firestone, *Table of Radioactive Isotopes*, V. Shirley, editor (see reference, end of Chapter 4). Cross-references are frequently inserted into the manuscript as chapter and section numbers, for example (4-20).

The first edition was selected as a text at five universities for courses concerning war and peace in the nuclear age. A shortened form of ATN is to be prepared as a text and a guide for students and professors in such courses.

At the end of each chapter is a list of important reference books covered in that chapter. At the end of the text there is a list of more general references, and two color plates. There is a series of appendices: Appendix I shows a modern periodic table of the elements, II is a table of the more important radioactive isotopes and their properties, III gives some useful physical constants and data, IV is a list of some names and organizations in the nuclear field, and V identifies quite a number of books and other literature on nuclear topics.

The spelling of geographical names in general conforms to those in the National Geographic *ATLAS OF THE WORLD*. Opinions expressed in this work are those of the author alone. Please send any inquiries, comments, or suggestions to: Prof. James C. Warf, Department of Chemistry, University of Southern California, Los Angeles, CA 90089–1062, or by e-mail to: warf@usc.edu.

JAMES C. WARF
Los Angeles, California
2004

ALL THINGS NUCLEAR

Chapter 1: INTRODUCTION

Nuclear science is a technical matter, but the nonprofessional can still learn its fascinating essentials. Since nuclear energy for both military and civilian purposes profoundly affects us all, by both threat and benefit, it is not just an issue for the experts. Citizens have the right and responsibility to make informed choices. The whole subject is not some monopoly of the priesthood of atomic weapons. You can understand the main ideas and make your voice heard. In a democracy, informed citizens can exert significant influence. In Einstein's words, "There is no secret and there is no defense; there is no possibility of control except through the aroused understanding and insistence of the peoples of the world."

Citizens and nuclear Issues

The issues of war and peace are primarily political, but they cannot be addressed meaningfully in modern times without some knowledge of nuclear weapons and their effects and of other scientific matters. Studies of radioactivity have greatly modified, even transfigured, our concepts of the Earth and Universe. Within the last 35 years these studies have profoundly revolutionized medical diagnosis.

We often complain that the populace wants peace, but our leaders prepare for war. But in a democracy, leaders are elected, and thus we have abundant opportunities to change them. This can best be done by a public well informed, not only in politics, and economics, but also in issues of war and peace and nuclear questions, hence this book, a modest contribution.

Three subjects have been added to this edition because they have important bearings on nuclear issues and also are of immense interest to the public. Thus the subject of energy in general is covered, in view of nuclear reactors being only one source of power. The greenhouse effect is summarized in part because operating reactors do not emit carbon dioxide, while burning fossil fuels do. The ozone layer is concisely discussed because it could be drastically affected by a nuclear war, and also has a connecting link with the greenhouse effect.

About 60% of the first edition of this book, printed in 1989 just before the Cold War faded away, was devoted to nuclear weapons and war in its various aspects. This might seem disproportionate, but considering its seriousness and consequences, it was warranted. The topic war and peace in the nuclear age is an issue of utmost importance in our lives and times. In 1990 the Union of Soviet Socialist Republics began to crumble, and profound political convulsions took place. These events provided a rare opportunity for the world to restructure in order to assure continuing peace, and it would be a shame to waste it. The basic and underlying origins of international conflicts have not been addressed, and after 20 years or less we might be back to normal bellicosity. Mini Cold Wars and worse are evident in several regions of the Third World. Beware.

Strong, unrelenting effort is required for real peace.

Chapter 2: THE BEGINNINGS

ABSTRACT—The most remote origins of the Universe, stars, our Earth, and the human species are sketched, as best known at present. The essentials of the Big Bang theory are presented, being a partial explanation of the origins of matter, stars, galaxies, and of the formation of nuclei of the heaviest elements in supernovae. An ever-so-brief account of the origin of life on Earth and its evolution into higher forms, including humans, is outlined.

2-1 Stars, Nuclear Energy, and the Origin of the Earth

All peoples have wondered about our most remote origins and ultimate fate. Religious leaders and philosophers have always been fascinated by questions about how the Universe came into being. In recent years scientists have been able to get at least partial answers to these questions, though complete answers may remain forever beyond our grasp. We can, however, be quite sure that stars were the first nuclear reactors, and that life on our Earth evolved into the human species, which invented a new kind of nuclear reactor—and bombs.

Since the term "Big Bang" is singularly unimaginative, Calvin, of Calvin and Hobbes, prefers the title "The Horrendous Space Kablooie."

In the 1920s astronomers deduced that the known Universe is expanding, that is, the stars are receding from each other. If we make a movie of this expansion, and then run it backwards, the stars would appear to converge toward a single point. This evidence and more indicate that all matter exploded from this incredibly hot and dense point long, long ago. Light from distant galaxies carry images of the remote past. The most reliable determination of age of the universe, announced in 1999 and based on data gained using the Hubble Space Telescope, is between 12.0 and 13.4 billion years; a little later the spectra of uranium and thorium in the star known as CS31082-001 revealed that the minimum age is 12.5 ± 3 billion years. In the point of origin, called a singularity, the density was so high that space-time was distorted, and the familiar laws of physics as we know them were not accurate. Atoms began to form after some hundreds of thousands of years, and stars and galaxies somewhat later. This is the Big Bang theory, introduced by George Gamow in 1948. Various ancient tribal accounts of the origin of the Universe are fantastic, but for the really weird, wild, and bizarre, try that cosmic sneeze, the Big Bang.

The process of expansion of the Universe; a uniform background of weak microwave radiation; the observed proportions of helium, deuterium, lithium, beryllium, and boron; these are all factors which also support the Big Bang theory. While there are competing hypotheses, such as the steady-state theory, Big Bang makes the best explanation of the currently available observational data, in fact, no other theory even comes close. The theory does unify a wealth of observations and has genuine predictive power. It predicts a weak background radiation left over from the Big Bang itself, and its existence was verified in 1964 and again in 2000. Each cubic centimeter of space contains about 400 of these photons. Recently the theory came under attack, mainly because this fossil microwave radiation seemed to be much too uniform, and because a few primeval, iron-poor stars have far too much beryllium to be in harmony with Big Bang constraints. In addition, early versions of the Big Bang theory did not give any really satisfactory account of how galaxies formed. Another worrisome topic is evidence that 90% or so of the Universe consists of "cold, dark matter," and while this point is still not certain, evidence for its existence was gained recently from studies of star cluster NGC 2300. The research was carried out using an orbiting X-ray observatory (ROSAT). Maybe the expanding Universe will contract and collapse into another point (the "Big Crunch"), and explode again. This point, whether the universe is "open" or "closed," is highly controversial, although the "open" view seems more likely. While a number of astronomers and astrophysicists find the Big Bang theory unconvincing, the great majority subscribe to one variant or another of its basic tenets. Nevertheless, there remains the real problem of explaining exactly how the Big Bang started in the first place. Beginning from just nothing violates all our common sense. Clearly, new and different developments and concepts are needed.

In 1999, the Kansas Board of Education, dominated by religious literalists, voted to remove evolution as well as the Big Bang theory from testing, thus undercutting teaching of these scientific subjects.

2-2 Aftermath of the Big Bang

Strong new evidence supporting the Big Bang theory was gained in 1992 using the Cosmic Background Explorer, a satellite in polar orbit. Its evidence disclosed that the weak background ("fossil") radiation is not quite as uniform as previously thought, and that the existence of the dark matter is less in doubt. This strengthens the idea that gravitational attractions will eventually arrest expansion, and the Universe will shrink to a point again. Later in the same year, a team of investigators announced that independent observations by instruments launched in a balloon going 25 miles high in 1989 had reached the same conclusions. It required much longer to analyze the data, hence the delay in publishing. Higher and higher resolution in analysis of the cosmic background radiation revealed convincing evidence that it is blotchy, that is, there are undulations in an otherwise smooth sea of photons. It is important that the "ripples"—hotter and colder spots in the cosmic background—occurred in the same places in the two sets of measurements (satellite and balloon). These areas represent the slightly denser regions in the early Universe which eventually became galaxies.

Directly after the Big Bang, the fantastically high temperatures (trillions of degrees) began to moderate, and the explosion site was surrounded by a rapidly expanding subnuclear plasma-like material (see subnuclear particles, 4-13). This captured all internal radiation. Only after cooling some 300,000 years could ordinary atoms begin to form, and these were the lightest elements; this process gave birth to our future. Our Universe is about 25% helium, most of which, so far as is known, was created right after the earliest flash of the Big Bang. Deuterium, a heavier form of hydrogen, was also formed at this time, but in trace quantities. Helium is formed continually from hydrogen in stars, but not deuterium, whose nuclei are too fragile. Some older stars appeared to have too much boron to be compatible with Big Bang theory, but Japanese astrophysicists have shown that formation of boron from lithium and helium nuclei could account for this. The abundant helium referred to is the heavier form, helium-4. Traces of light helium atoms (helium-3) were also generated during the Big Bang. Most of it which was originally present on Earth has been lost by diffusion into space. Interplanetary dust is constantly falling on Earth, and it is 200 times richer in adsorbed helium-3 than our atmosphere.

Birth of light atoms

Data from the Cosmic Background Explorer gives clues on how vast swaths of space became organized into gigantic sheets and filaments with clusters of galaxies. In 2002 additional data, confirming the earlier conclusions, came from research by Cal Tech scientists. They used a cluster of 13 radio telescopes connected to an interferometer on a frigid peak in the Chilean Andes, 16,700 feet high. They also contributed evidence that the Universe is not truly spherical, but a flattened sphere in the infinite vacuum of empty space. Clearly there is much about these events which we do not understand, but whatever happened there on the rooftop of the Universe, it stupefies the imagination.

Thus vast quantities of the simplest chemical element, hydrogen, were born in the Big Bang and rapidly expanded. In the enormity of space, great clouds of hydrogen began to congregate and coalesce, resulting in galaxies of stars. Gravitational energy of falling hydrogen in each star's prenatal cloud produced heat by impact and increased axial spin of each new star. There was a whole range of sizes of stars, some colossal and some relatively small. We know today that when the internal temperature of these stars reached 15 to 20 million degrees C, a nuclear reaction began to take place. This is the formation of the next simplest chemical element, helium, from primordial hydrogen, with the liberation of enormous amounts of heat (4-11 and 4-12). The entire body of each stellar mass became a white hot body of plasma, and light streamed extravagantly from the new-born star out into space for billions of years. Chemical elements (or rather the nuclei of their atoms) up to iron and nickel in the periodic table, meaning the lightest one-fourth of the elements, were synthesized inside these stellar ovens. Thus it is not nuclear energy which is new in this Universe; what is new is the human race.

Stars were the first nuclear reactors.

Most of the more massive stars go through a stage called a supernova, in which the brightness becomes that of a billion suns. This is a cataclysmic explosion which lasts only a few days or weeks, and during this time the temperature and pressure in the core reach absolutely fantastic magnitudes, which become momentarily reinforced by shock waves. Temperatures might reach 3.5 billion degrees C. Under these conditions lighter nuclei, including helium, are fused together to form the heavier chemical elements, all the way to uranium and plutonium, and even beyond. These heavy elements were scattered by the gigantic explosion into space, along with the unchanged hydrogen, so that when new, second-generation stars were born, this cosmic debris was incorporated, a sort of stellar

Formation of uranium

recycling. Occasional supernovae are seen in modern times. Related events are gamma ray bursts (hypernovae; see 4-12). These events benumb challenge the imagination. An American chemist, F. W. Clarke, was the first to suggest something along the lines of the above account of the synthesis of the chemical elements, and this was as early as 1873.

In this way our Sun had its genesis about 5 billion years ago. It is believed that a gigantic flattened ring of gas and dust (the solar nebula) first formed about the new star, a ring which collapsed and by accretion formed the solar system we know today. This process required about 400 million years, so our Earth, as well as Mercury, Venus, and Mars are about 4.6 billion years old (6-3). The outer planets probably were formed somewhat later. Analyses of rocks on Mars by the Pathfinder probe and its rover (July 1997) confirmed that the composition of the red planet is strongly similar to that of Earth. While a great deal about these processes is poorly understood, there is evidence that the dust, after reaching a certain critical density, began to clump and these eventually reached a size big enough to be called planetesimals, perhaps 10 kilometers in size, and their gravity began to play an important local role. The collapsing impacts of these bodies heated the nascent Earth to around 4500 degrees C, melting most of it. At this temperature, a white heat, loss of energy by radiation was rapid. Earth's Moon appeared later, perhaps 300 million years after Earth itself. One plausible theory for the birth of the Moon was a glancing collision with a large planetoid, almost as big as Mars. This crashing blow to the still-liquid Earth would scoop up a total mass equal to that of the present Moon, and put it into orbit. This hypothesis would explain why none of the new Earth's molten metal core was lost, and thus why the Moon has no magnetic field such as the Earth does. Gradually the two bodies cooled and solidified on the outside. The meteoroids and asteroids, as well as those celestial tadpoles we call comets, had their origins along with that of the Earth. The innermost planets, being nearer the Sun and thus hotter, lost most of their lighter elements (hydrogen and helium), and consist principally of residual oxygen (not in the free state), silicon, aluminum, iron, etc.; these are in the form of silicates, from which most rocks are made. Jupiter and planets still further from the sun retain enormous quantities of hydrogen, helium, and other light elements.

Why the Moon has no magnetic field

In 1995 the orbiting Hubble telescope captured photographs which revealed the violent birth throes of stars and planets. Five ordinary stars, in different galaxies, were examined; each was in the process of coalescing from gas and dust. These events were about five billion years ago and the light is just now reaching our Earth. In several regions of the cosmos most of the young stars show signs that they are surrounded by disks of gas and dust, appearing to be the forerunners of planets.

By selecting and studying a few elements which have radioactive isotopes whose half-lives are several million years, it has proven possible to gain much information about the earliest stages of evolution of the nascent solar system in the time interval between the last synthesis of heavy elements in a supernova and the formation of the first solid bodies. The samples are taken from fresh lava, from ancient minerals, and from meteorites. Thus evidence for the existence of at least ten such isotopes has helped to explain the heating of our Earth in its earliest stages, permitting a liquid metallic core to form. The first nuclide to be studied was iodine-129, with half-life 16 million years, and the most recent was iron-60, with half-life 1.5 million years. It is their final disintegration products which are actually determined.

2-3 New Observations

With anything as complicated as the Big Bang and the origin of the Universe, doubts, new data, and new interpretations always arise. In 1994 astronomers at Indiana University and at Harvard University presented evidence that the Universe might be much younger than 15 billion years, perhaps 12 billion years, as mentioned earlier. The observations depend on new measurements using the Hubble space telescope of the rate of expansion of the Universe.

The interior of our Earth contains the elements potassium, uranium, and thorium, each of which is slightly radioactive. Their radioactive decay liberates heat, which keeps the Earth's core hot. The consequence of a hot, liquid core (with a metallic center, possibly solid by now) is movement of tectonic plates, and formation of mountain ranges and continents. Were this not the case, mountains and all land would weather down, and our planet would be covered with water. Without this radioactivity, we would not exist. Geologists have known for years that beneath the Himalayan mountain range the temperature was exceptionally high, and strangely was lower below the hot zone, contrary to the usual pattern. Analysis of outcroppings for uranium, thorium, and potassium revealed relatively high concentrations and this has led to a better understanding of the phenomenon. The Indian tectonic plate was subducted under the Asian plate some 20 to 30 kilometers deep, and the emerging mountains served as a thick insulator. The evidence indicates that the rocks from the outcroppings had been baked at about 650 °C, a dull red heat. Over billions of years, the rocks have been churned and cooked. Today, some 10 million years later, the temperature is around 400 °C (752 °F).

Thanks, Mother Nature, for radioactivity.

We need not let ourselves be overwhelmed by the immensity of space. True, our Earth, even our galaxy, is but the merest dust mote in the cosmos, but immensity is not the same as quality. We have a good Earth, and it is the only one we have. Let's take good care of it.

2-4 The Origin and Evolution of Life

The Earth cooled slowly, the steam condensed, and torrential rains carried the spoils of the Earth to the new oceans. There is today a considerable body of information on the origin of life. In general it deals with chemical evolution of the substances which constitute living cells, which are made of carbon, hydrogen, oxygen, nitrogen, phosphorus, sulfur, and a few other chemical elements. Evidently, there in the kitchen of creation, molecules of growing complexity evolved in patterns ever more intricate, possibly in or near hot springs. It took about a billion years for the first living microbial life form to appear. Long afterwards, blue-green algae evolved and this began generating oxygen gas from the abundant carbon dioxide, with the aid of sunlight. Eventually green plants manufactured enough oxygen to make about 21% of our atmosphere this element.

Our Earth at that time was a much more violent and radioactive place than today. Cosmic debris left over from formation of the planets pummeled the surface relentlessly. The Moon experienced similar bombardment, and the scars are still visible today. It might well have been that the first life on Earth was wiped out by sterilizing steam from oceans vaporized by the impacts of asteroids, some perhaps 150 miles in diameter. But if so, life started again, maybe requiring as short a time as 165 million years. More and more complex organisms appeared as a consequence of evolution. There are compelling similarities in the protein and DNA structural and molecular patterns of related species, etc., correlated with measurements of age. If we condense the 4.6 billion year period our Earth has existed down to a single year, then the following approximate schedule prevails:

Earth is tame, today, compared to its youth.

January 1	Earth is born
March 15	First life appears, microbial
October 15	Abundant life in many forms
December 15	Age of dinosaurs
December 23	Mammals appear
December 31	At 11:55 p.m. the human race emerges

Recent (1996) determination of carbon-12/carbon-13 ratios in microfossils from ancient rocks from Greenland have given strong suggestions that the first life on Earth appeared 4.0 billion years ago, when our Earth was only 600 million years old. This would correspond to about February 17 on the calendar above.

The human species, emerging from its simian shadows, evolved in Africa through quite a number of hominid ancestors who invented ways to make and use fire (the term hominid generally refers to two-legged mammals). Emergence of a new humanlike species was followed a number of times by a sort of evolutionary cusp in which either the older or the newer branch became extinct. We, Homo sapiens, are the most recent in the series, and the only survivors who are truly human. This new upstart species, a big-brained primate who could eat anything, spread over the Earth, dominating. About 10,000 years ago a second world-shaking development took place, namely agriculture. Two more important ingenious inventions appeared just at the dawn of recorded history; these were the wheel and the manufacture of iron. Centuries later the Chinese prepared gunpowder, a simple chemical mixture which was destined to change the course of history. War had become institutionalized. A few hundred years ago the industrial revolution took place, and in time this included the generation of electricity. Three additional pivotal developments occurred in our own age: nuclear energy and weapons, space travel, and the electronic revolution,

The human race is recent.

especially the communications explosion (the Big Byte?). Any one of these features illustrates the wonder of an exceedingly clever species.

All of life's adventures involve change and uncertainty, which means a certain degree of anxiety. Bewildering new technology causes some people to seek solace in resisting change, which might bring temporary comfort. But in the long run, we should learn and judge from a viewpoint of understanding, accepting that which seems genuinely beneficial, and rejecting that which is not. Science and engineering and their fruits have come to occupy a commanding position in American culture; these are often seen as an anchor of our past, the power of the present, and the hope of our future. But it is wise to beware of any technological fix, and be skeptical of the idea that more and more scientific knowledge alone will be our salvation. It is clear that nuclear processes offer us mortal threats, but that enormous benefits are also at hand, something like the roles of fire. To make thoughtful decisions about nuclear technology, one needs an overview of theoretical and applied nuclear science. Providing such a compendium is the main objective of this book. Unavoidably, the author's opinions are injected here and there: writing in a completely objective manner is an illusion.

Chapter 3: THE ROAD TO THE BOMB—AND BEYOND

ABSTRACT—The origins and early development of science and the important findings which made harnessing nuclear energy possible are outlined. These include the discoveries of uranium, X-rays, radioactivity, the mass-energy equation, and nuclear fission. The surcharged mission to develop atomic bombs (Manhattan Project) during World War II and their use against Japan are recounted tersely. The corresponding German, Japanese, and Soviet projects are covered briefly. Short biographical sketches of important personalities are inserted. The chapter concludes with the high points concerning the nuclear arms race, treaties to prohibit testing nuclear warheads, spread of the bomb, and the end of the Cold War.

3-1 The Origins of Science

The Egyptian civilization was one of the earliest, and its north African site may have been the birthplace of alchemy. The ancient Egyptians developed arithmetic from a practical viewpoint. They invented paper, making it from papyrus. Independently, the Chinese prepared paper, using another process. The Chinese also made gunpowder, rockets, silk fabrics, and porcelain. The Hittites, the early Armenians, and an early civilization of Blacks in Africa developed smelting of iron and other metals. The ancient civilizations of India contributed much to our knowledge of astronomy and mathematics, including the concept of zero. Some Native American Indian peoples, such as the Mayans, also were expert astronomers and independently conceived the mathematical idea of zero. Another tribe invented the compass.

But it is the early Greeks to whom we are indebted for what developed into the scientific method. This occurred on the mainland and islands of the eastern Aegean Sea. One of the most prominent islands was Samos, near the coast of Turkey. The time was in the period 600-300 BC. Why this area? Because the conditions happened to be favorable there. These conditions were: the Aegean Sea was a crossroads of commerce and several civilizations, with a diversity of peoples. Many foreigners and languages mingled there. No single power enforced conformity of thought. Free inquiry was permitted. The Phoenician alphabet was adapted to Greek, and written records could be kept. Thus the revolutionary ideas came into being that the Universe is knowable, that there is order in Nature and it is understandable, and that rules of Nature permit prediction. These philosophers became convinced that the world is not run by capricious gods, a thought considered by some as blasphemous. Thus science, which is organized knowledge and is committed to reality, progressed and eventually became one of the exalted intellectual achievements of the human race. While it has its limits, the scientific method is one antidote to ignorance.

Three of these Greeks who are best known were Thales, Democritus, and Pythagoras. They and their compatriots figured out that the Earth is a sphere, that light travels extremely fast but not infinitely fast, and that higher animals evolved from lower ones. They understood the origin of eclipses. If the methods of science had not evolved in the Aegean, surely they would have in some other region. But later on, with the decline of Greek civilization, its science was submerged.

About 430 B.C. Democritus observed thoughtfully how water could run through his fingers and reunite into a stream, a property which also characterized air. He also considered how odors, such as from baking bread, could travel through the air. Analyzing the properties as well as he could, on the foundation of his exceedingly limited experimental database, he concluded that all fluids, that is, liquids and gases, were not continuous but consisted of minute particles. Since he knew that water would freeze into ice, a solid, and it did not seem reasonable that particulate nature would suddenly disappear, Democritus concluded that all matter consists of these tiny, indiscernible specks. He called them *atoms*, from the Greek *a-* (not), and *tomos* (divide), that is, indivisible. He considered that atoms were the smallest units of matter. A somewhat similar idea arose in India several hundred years earlier, but Democritus was not aware of this.

Origins of the scientific method

This theory of atomism has had a rough time in most of its history. With the fall of Greek civilization, the concept fell into disrepute, especially in ecclesiastical circles. About 1600, Galileo found the atomic theory reasonable and concluded that no other concept could explain the properties of matter. Galileo thought light consisted of corpuscles, called photons today. All this got him into trouble with the Church. In seventeenth-century France, anyone who publicly announced a belief that matter consisted of atoms was subject to the death penalty. The Englishman Dalton, around the year 1800, revised and extended the now hazy Greek ideas of atoms. Nevertheless, the concepts of atoms of matter became widely accepted by chemists, and in modern times, since images of atoms and molecules have been made and there is overwhelming other evidence, the ideas are taught everywhere.

Arabic scientists, in their golden age some 1500 years later than the Greeks, became the world's intellectual leaders and made important achievements in chemistry, physics, and mathematics. The Muslim scholars built upon the knowledge of the Greeks and employed the analytical approach of the Indian Hindus. Actually, many of these scientists were of Persian origin, but had assumed Arabic names. Arabic science reached its zenith about the year 1000, with a galaxy of great intellects. One of them, Ibn al-Haitham was a gifted student of optics. His manuscript, Kitab al-manazir (The Optics), described the nature of reflection and refraction of light. Al-Haitham understood that the change of direction of light entering glass results from its change of speed inside the glass. He analyzed reflection by concave mirrors, both spherical and parabolic, which he had made on a lathe. He understood spherical aberration and the exact focus of the paraboloid. The Arabs invented algebra, and al-Haitham was able to solve equations of the fourth degree. Arabic scientists also studied rainbows, magnetism, meteorology, and a great deal of chemistry.

In Europe, Renaissance alchemists were attempting to transmute base metals such as lead into gold. While they never succeeded with this, other important discoveries were made.

3-2 The Road to Nuclear Energy—to 1900

The industrial revolution, beginning in England about 1760, led to numerous unpredictable events, first in Europe and later the world over. As is always the case in science, no one country had a monopoly on discovery, and many nationalities played a part. Some of the highlights are outlined below. Frequently a discovery was made independently by two different investigators, often at about the same time.

1789: The Discovery of Uranium—At the time just a few years after the American Revolution, a number of chemical elements were known. These included many metals, such as iron, tin, copper, silver, and gold. In 1789, the German chemist Martin Klaproth, studying the black mineral pitchblende, identified a new metal. He named it *uranium*, after the recently discovered planet Uranus. Pitchblende had only a minor importance as a coloring agent for glass and glazes. Traces impart a lovely chartreuse color to glass, a practice in use for centuries. Later some types of alloy steel were made using uranium up to about 5%.

Uranium, a new element

1805: The New Atomic Theory—Shortly after the English chemist John Dalton redefined the concepts of atoms and elements, he then extended his ideas to chemical compounds. Since many more different substances were known than the few elements, he concluded that these different materials consisted of diverse combinations of atoms bonded together. From this standpoint, millions of substances could result from various combinations. Dalton's main contribution, published in 1805 and which distinguished his ideas from the speculations of the Greeks, was that there is some sort of bonding between atoms, connecting them in definite proportions. This was the idea of a *molecule*, an assembly of atoms bonded together. Dalton also realized that atoms had different weights or masses, and he published a scale of relative atomic weights. An element in pure form came to be considered a substance of all of whose atoms were alike.

1869: The Periodic Table—The Russian chemist Dmitri Mendeleyev, intimately acquainted with the chemistry of all the 63 elements known in his time, devised an ingenious table which systematized their properties. The elements were arranged into families of similar chemical nature in order of increasing atomic weight, with metals on one side, nonmetals on the other. So powerful was the new periodic table that Mendeleyev successfully predicted the existence and properties of yet undiscovered elements. The table again illustrated that there is order in Nature, and no lasting secrets in science. Indeed, the German chemist Meyer arrived at about the same conclusions independently only a little later. The great unifying idea of the periodic table later contributed importantly to understanding the sequence of elements in radioactive decay. Today 116 elements are known in Mendeleyev's garden, and more are expected. More than 99% of the Earth's crust is made of only ten elements. A modern form of the periodic table is given in section 4-4 and in Appendix I.

1895: The Discovery of X-Rays—By this date European physicists had long been studying electric discharge tubes, which resemble modern neon signs to some degree. The German physicist Wilhem Roentgen discovered that certain substances, such as barium cyanoplantinate, would luminesce strongly when inside an operating cathode ray tube. He noticed that letters on a paper, made using a solution of barium cyanoplatinate as ink, emitted light even though it was some distance from the tube. When a sheet of opaque cardboard was placed between the cathode ray tube and the paper, it continued to fluoresce. Clearly, some sort of radiation must be generated which could penetrate the cardboard. Roentgen found that the new type of radiation, which he called *X-rays* (because their nature was unknown and the symbol X was used in algebra to represent an unknown), also affected photographic film. He made the first X-ray photograph (also called a radiograph) of a human organ, his wife's hand. The bones and a ring were clearly visible. News of X-rays traveled fast, and soon they were used in many branches of science and medicine. In 1901 the shy German scientist was awarded the first Nobel prize in physics. Roentgen couldn't have known it, but his discovery opened the door to one of the most innovative periods in the history of science and technology. For the first time we could "see" things which were once inaccessible to natural vision. Images that result from natural vision, even those made using microscopes and telescopes, provide only an incomplete view of objects, including human bodies or their parts.

Actually, several other scientists working with electric discharge tubes had noticed the darkening of photographic film stored nearby, and observation so close—just a fairy's jump away—to the discovery of X-rays. But they didn't allow the thought to bubble to the surface of their minds. It didn't take long for the harmful effects of excessive X-rays, that is, an overdose, to be discovered. In fact the first malpractice award was made in 1899. But these negative features should not overwhelm the great beneficial consequences of the discovery of X-rays. It set off extreme excitement among scientists and engineers and triggered an avalanche of inventions of other non-optical imaging techniques. The responsible use of X-rays in medicine has greatly exceeded the shortcomings.

Important discoveries: periodic table, X-rays, radioactivity

1896: The Discovery of Radioactivity—The French physicist Becquerel had been studying luminescence and fluorescence. He suspected that there might be a connection between luminescence and the recently discovered X-rays. One of the luminescent materials he used was potassium uranyl sulfate, a uranium salt. Becquerel wrapped a sheet of photographic film in black paper, put a crystal of the uranium compound on it, and exposed it to the sunlight for activation. On developing the film, he was gratified to see an image in the shape of the crystal. He repeated the experiment, but as the Sun was obscured by clouds for a few days, he stored the new film, wrapped in black paper, in a drawer with the uranium salt crystal resting on it. Following good scientific procedure, he decided to use this packet as a control; it had not been exposed to sunlight. On developing, the film again distinctly showed the image of the crystal! Sunlight had nothing to do with it. He was forced to the conclusion that some sort of radiation must be emitted by the uranium salt which, like X-rays, could penetrate paper. Becquerel soon showed that every uranium compound he had on hand behaved similarly. The rays could also go through aluminum and thin copper foils.

Antoine Becquerel (1852–1908), French physicist. Discoverer of radioactivity. Research in phosphorescence, magnetism, etc. Nobel prize, 1903, jointly with the Curies

Other scientists soon showed that thorium salts had the same amazing property (thorium is another heavy metal considerably more abundant than uranium). In 1898, Marie Curie named the new phenomenon *radioactivity*, the root *radio-* meaning ray; later, when radios were invented, the same root word was used. The process which occurs when an element self-destructs by radioactivity is called decay or disintegration.

It is amazing that such a seemingly innocuous discovery as that of Becquerel could have such earth-shaking consequences. It is sometimes asked what would have happened if he had not discovered radioactivity. The answer is that certainly someone else would have done the same thing a little later, maybe by a different means. In fact, another Frenchman, Niépce, an inventor of photographic processes, came close. He had observed a similar effect of uranium salts on film in the 1850s, but he failed to follow up his findings.

1897: The Discovery of Electrons—The English physicist J. J. Thomson was conducting experiments with electric discharge tubes, and observed a ray which was attracted to a positive electrode, and therefore was negatively charged. This involved using a certain voltage to pass an electric current through a tube of gas at low pressure. He carried out thorough studies and characterized the rays in great detail. His results showed that the "rays" were in reality a stream of particles, and that they are fundamental components of atoms. These subatomic particles came to be known as *electrons*. In 1899 he was able to determine the mass of the electron. An electric current in a wire is a stream of electrons. Thomson was awarded the Nobel Prize in physics in 1906. Ernest Rutherford was one of his students. The idea that atoms are indivisible was shattered.

The discovery of the electron led to the development, directly or indirectly, of revolutionary advances in communication, transportation, medicine, and other fields. It permitted a new theory of atomic structure and pointed the way to quantum theory and the understanding of the periodic table. The invention of the electron microscope and of the transistor was made possible, and a myriad of other instruments.

If an electron, which has a unit negative charge, is removed from a neutral atom, then the atom must become positively charged. Such an atom is called an *ion*, and the process is *ionization*. Atoms can be ionized by high-energy sources, such as electric discharges or radiations from radioactive substances. The electron which is displaced comes from those which surround the nucleus, and the nucleus itself is not directly involved in ionization. Certain neutral atoms can accept one or more electrons as well, and this too is ionization. This process forms negatively charged ions.

1898: The Discovery of Protons—Since the negatively charged electron was a constituent of atoms, a positively charged particle must also exist. Work by several European physicists showed that this idea is correct. Evidence for these particles was obtained using electric discharge tubes containing residual hydrogen. The particles were called *protons*. Measurements showed that the proton is 1837 times heavier than the electron.

1898: The Discovery of Radium—In the city of Warsaw more than a hundred years ago, a young Polish woman, Marie Sklodovska, became science oriented through family influences. She also became involved in student revolutionary movements, and soon found it advisable to leave. The intense scientific activities in Paris beckoned her. There she met a professor of physics, Pierre Curie and they were married in 1895.

Pierre Curie (1859–1906), French physicist. With wife, Marie Curie, discovered polonium and radium. Much research in electricity and magnetism. Nobel prize shared with wife and Becquerel in 1903.

Marie Sklodowska Curie (1867–1934), Polish-French chemist and physicist. With husband Pierre Curie, discovered several elements. Many advances in theory and practice of radioactivity. Second Nobel in chemistry, 1911.

Marie Curie, excited by the phenomenon of radioactivity which Becquerel had recently discovered, noted that uranium ores such as pitchblende were much more active (that is, *radioactive*) than purified uranium. She suspected that some unknown, much more active element must be present in the ores. Pierre Curie had constructed a device which could measure levels of radioactivity more accurately than earlier instruments. The husband/wife team decided to find out why the radioactivity of pitchblende is higher than the level corresponding to its uranium content. They dissolved some of the ore in nitric acid and subjected the solution to a variety of chemical processes, finally separating a new element named *polonium*, after Marie Curie's native land. Pure polonium is more than a billion times as radioactive as uranium. Estimates today indicate that the maximum amount of polonium the Curies had was only about 6 nanograms (6 billionths of a gram), so small it was virtually invisible. In December of the same year, further work disclosed a second new element of completely different chemical properties. It was called *radium*. Starting with one ton of pitchblende residues, they obtained about a quarter of a gram of radium bromide, an amount equal to the mass of a few grains of rice. It required four years of hard labor. The material glowed in the dark, and was always hotter than its surroundings.

Discrimination on account of gender is nothing new.

Historically, women in science have been generally subjected to relentless sex discrimination. Starting at an early age, most experienced scant career motivation, and even if they were talented and industrious, they still faced poor job opportunities and recognition. Moreover, women scientists have been generally neglected by historians. Yet the average intellectual and creative abilities of women are as high as those of men. In modern times the injustices mentioned are being slowly addressed. Marie Curie was never admitted to the French Academy of Sciences. In 1919 the American Association of University Women raised more than $156,000 to enable her to buy a gram of radium so that she could continue her laboratory work. Another woman who won grudging acceptance by her male colleagues was the Norwegian chemist Ellen Gleditsch. She worked in Paris during the period 1907 to 1912, and made an accurate determination of the half-life of radium (this was essential in defining the unit of radioactivity, the *curie*; see 4-22).

3-3 The Road to Nuclear Energy—1900 through World War II

1900: The Quantum Theory—The German physicist Max Planck conceived a revolutionary idea, the quantum theory. According to this concept, radiation comes in packets called *quanta* or *photons*. In general, atoms hold energy in fixed, discrete units, not a continuous range. The quantum theory was destined to play crucial roles in the development of nuclear energy.

1900-1905: Types of Radioactive Emissions—The work of quite a number of physicists showed that the radiations from various radioactive materials are comprised of at least three types. One type, called *alpha rays*, consists of positively charged particles, is deflected by a powerful magnetic field (see sketch), and can penetrate aluminum only a very short distance. Within a few years Ernst Rutherford and Frederick Soddy demonstrated that alpha rays consist of helium nuclei traveling at high velocity. A Canadian woman who played an important role in understanding these transmutations was Harriet Brooks, a physicist who studied under Rutherford.

The second type, called *beta rays*, is negatively charged, and is deflected by a magnetic field in the opposite direction from alpha rays. Beta rays can penetrate much thicker sheets of aluminum than alpha rays can. They consist of streams of extremely fast (that is, energetic) electrons. The *gamma rays*, proved to be closely related to X-rays. They are uncharged and are extremely penetrating. These observations further eroded the doctrine that atoms were immutable.

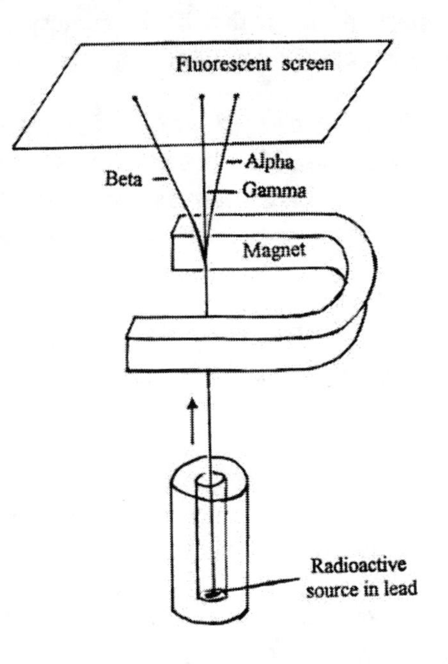

Alpha, beta, and gamma rays in a magnetic field

Ernest Rutherford (1871–1937), Born in New Zealand, worked in England and Canada. Discoverer of atomic nuclei. Developed laws of radioactive decay (with F. Soddy). Nobel Prize in chemistry, 1908. Investigated nuclear reactions and many other such processes.

Frederick Soddy (1877–1956), English chemist. Working with Rutherford, laid foundations of radioactive decay series, first definitively published in 1902. Predicted existence of isotopes in 1912. Nobel Prize, 1921. Soddy, a sensitive and warm-hearted man, lived to see the Cold War, and this shattered his hopes for a peaceful world.

1905: The Mass-Energy Equation—Albert Einstein, German-born physicist, was one of the most creative thinkers of all time. He was pursuing his seminal theory of relativity, one of whose consequences was the mass-energy relationship. As early as 1905 Einstein's incandescent intellect derived the equation

$$E = mc^2$$

where E is *energy*, m is *mass* (really, change in relativistic mass), and c is the *velocity* of light. Since light travels at the incredible speed of 300 million meters per second (186 thousand miles per second), and this value is squared, the amount of energy equivalent to even a small mass is almost incomprehensible. We will see later that this equation governs energy changes in radioactive decay and in nuclear reactors and weapons. Little did Einstein dream that half a century later, other scientists tampering with his equation would bring calamitous new weapons systems into our world.

The mass-energy equation

Albert Einstein (1879–1955), German-American theoretical physicist. Renowned for his theories of relativity, time, and gravitation; relationships between mass and energy; much work in photochemistry and quantum mechanics. Nobel Prize in 1922. He entered the United States in 1933.

1911: The Discovery of the Atomic Nucleus—With all of the above discoveries, the old view that atoms are indivisible, hard spheres had to be discarded. Several fanciful theories were advanced. The first to suggest a nuclear atom was the Japanese physicist H. Nagaoka, in 1903, but he presented no evidence.

Rutherford, as noted earlier, was exceptionally prolific in this field. He observed that images in photographic film exposed to alpha particles had diffuse edges, meaning that the particles were scattered or deflected. In 1909 he and Hans Geiger carried out detailed studies of the scattering of alpha particles from a radioactive source by gold foil (or foil of other heavy metals). Most of the particles just go through the foil unimpeded, but a small fraction is deflected, and a few of these bounce directly back toward the source. After two more years of research, Rutherford concluded that the atoms of gold are mostly void. Deflecting or scattering a heavy alpha particle would not be expected by electrons, whose mass was minute. The deflection of the positively charged alpha particles must be caused by a much heavier, positively charged core or nucleus, since like charges repel. Rutherford and his coworkers were even able to estimate the size of the gold nucleus at about 1/10,000th of the atom's diameter. This work provided some fundamental insight into atomic structure. Much later he said, concerning the back scattering of alpha particles by gold foil, "It was quite the most incredible event that has ever happened to me in my life. It was almost as incredible as if you fired a 15-inch shell at a piece of tissue paper and it came back and hit you."

Imagine measuring the diameter of nuclei by such simple experiments.

1911: The Wilson Cloud Chamber—The Englishman C. T. R. Wilson invented a vapor-filled vessel which, when radiation of any type entered, caused the paths of the particles to become visible and photographable. The chamber, containing some water or other liquid, was equipped with a piston. In use, sudden movement of the piston caused the air inside the chamber to expand and cool. This makes it momentarily supersaturated. Energetic particles under these conditions ionize the air, which causes microscopic droplets of liquid to form. This condensate appears as a visible streak through the chamber. The device was often employed using a strong magnetic field to make charged particles curve in their travel. The *Wilson cloud chamber* played a significant role in early nuclear research, and is still extensively used.

1913: Atomic Structure—By this time, through years of diligent and often frustrating research, physicists and chemists had made many important advances in understanding atomic structure and radioactivity. English physicist Ostwald Moseley used X-ray spectra to demonstrate a regular increase in the nuclear charge of elements in their order in the periodic table. This nuclear charge is the number of protons in the nucleus, and is called *atomic number*.

When a nucleus emits a beta particle, which is an electron, the result is that the new nucleus, having lost one negative unit of charge, is now more positive by one unit. This means that the original element has transmuted itself into a new one, which is its neighbor to the right in the periodic table. Thus, when an atom of *tritium* (hydrogen-3, atomic number 1) decays by emitting a beta particle, it becomes an atom of atomic number 2, that is, *helium*, and in this case the mass number is 3 (helium-3; more on this in 4–5).

Mass number, isotopes, and nuclides

Atomic nuclei were supposed at that time to be made of protons and proton-electron pairs; the equivalent idea today is that the neutral proton-electron pairs are replaced with particles called *neutrons*. The total number of protons and neutrons in a *mass number*, and thus we can write terms like helium-4 or uranium-238. If two atoms of the same element contain different numbers of neutrons, they are called *isotopes*, for example uranium-238 and uranium-235 (atomic number the same, mass number different). A more general term is the word *nuclide*, which designates any specific nuclear species. Any atom of specified atomic number and mass number is a nuclide, whether it is radioactive or not. The constituents of nuclei, that is, protons and neutrons, are together called *nucleons*, and their sum for each nucleus is the mass number of that atom. An isotope is one of a group of nuclides which happen to have the same atomic number, that is, are all different forms of the same element. Thus C-12 is one of the eight known isotopes of carbon, and Mg-24 is one of the twelve known isotopes of magnesium.

The electrons, sufficient in number to make the atom neutral, are arranged outside the nucleus, something like a miniature, three-dimensional solar system. The Danish physicist, Niels Bohr at this time, applying the quantum theory to atomic structure, began to make the electronic structure of atoms intelligible.

By 1913, the mathematics describing radioactive decay had been worked out to a quite sophisticated level. The concept of *half-life* (the time required for half of a given quantity of a radioactive substance to decay, introduced by Rutherford) was becoming widely used.

1913: Cosmic Rays—Coming from outer space, a new type of radiation was discovered by the Austrian physicist Victor Hess of extremely energetic fundamental particles, atoms, and electromagnetic radiation, and impinge on Earth from all directions.

1914: A New Type of Bomb?—Nuclear science had advanced by this date so far that author H. G. Wells wrote a chilling novel, *The World Set Free* in which the world's great cities were obliterated by atomic bombs the size of beach balls. This occurrence was

Prophesy in a novel

about the first time when the texture of events related to nuclear science took an ominous turn. In 1914 the human race entered another of those periodic catastrophes it is so prone to; this was much worse than any natural disaster. In World War I, the scientists of each side (as well as the religious and other leaders) lent their talents to their respective governments, the better to kill their supposed enemies.

3-4 The Road to Nuclear Energy—Between World Wars I and II

1919: The Mass Spectrograph—This is an instrument devised more or less simultaneously but independently by the physicists F. W. Aston and A. J. Dempster. The vapor of any element was introduced into a chamber in a magnetic field, where it was ionized by high-energy electrons. The ions (which are electrically charged) then curved in their movement to a degree depending on their mass and charge, the lighter ones curving more sharply. Thus isotopes could be separated and their exact masses measured. It was shown, for example, that ordinary neon consists mostly of neon-20 (90.51%), with a trace of neon-21 (0.27%), and the rest (9.22%) neon-22. Mass spectrographs became common in all nuclear research. The mass spectrometer is a similar, more advanced instrument.

More instruments which accelerated research

Later, the common isotope of carbon, carbon-12, was chosen as the standard for the atomic weight scale, being assigned the exact value twelve atomic mass units. Modern mass spectrometers are capable of measuring the relative masses of all nuclides with extremely high accuracy. Examples are: hydrogen-1 = 1.007825 and uranium-238 = 238.050770. These are in atomic mass units (amu), and they refer to neutral atoms; all are relative to carbon-12.

In 1919 Rutherford demonstrated that the nuclei of nitrogen atoms are broken up by very energetic alpha particles. One product was *protons*, which are hydrogen nuclei.

1928: The Geiger Counter—Various kinds of meters had been in use to measure levels of radioactivity. They were slow and cumbersome. The German scientist Hans Geiger had worked with Rutherford in England before World War I, and his coworker W. Mueller devised a relatively inexpensive radioactivity meter. It proved to be versatile and convenient and it accelerated all lines of research in the field (see description in 4-21).

1932: The Cyclotron—The year 1932 was a productive one in nuclear research. The American E. O. Lawrence, working in Berkeley, California, fabricated an instrument called the cyclotron (*cyclo and -tron, Greek for instrument)*. It could accelerate charged particles to very high energies and use them to achieve nuclear reactions (see description in 4-18).

1932: More Particles—Two more fundamental particles were discovered, the *neutron* and the *positron,* or positive electron, by the Englishman James Chadwick. Neutrons have about the same mass as protons. Being neutral, they are not repelled by atomic nuclei, and are thus very penetrating. Use of neutrons as probes made detailed studies of nuclei possible. Free neutrons break down rapidly into protons and electrons. The nuclear equation showing Chadwick's production of neutrons (n) is:

$$^{9}_{4}\text{Be} + ^{4}_{2}\text{He} \Rightarrow ^{12}_{6}\text{C} + ^{1}_{0}\text{n}$$

Note that the left superscripts indicate the mass numbers and that subscripts indicate the atomic numbers, that is, nuclear charge. The sums of these sets of numbers on each side of the arrow are the same.

The positron, discovered by the American Carl Anderson in 1932, has the same mass as ordinary negatively charged electrons, but the opposite electric charge (also see subnuclear particles, 4-15).

1932: Deuterium—Harold Urey discovered a heavier isotope of hydrogen called *hydrogen-2, heavy hydrogen*, or *deuterium*. Its nucleus consists of a proton and a neutron. This nuclide began to be used as a tracer of hydrogen (tracers are treated in section 6-7).

1934: Artificial Radioactivity—One of the Curies' two daughters, Irene, had also entered nuclear research. She and her physicist husband, Frederic Joliot-Curie, performed experiments which created the first artificial radioactive isotope. They bombarded aluminum with alpha particles from polonium and produced minute traces of phosphorus-30 (half-life 2.5 minutes), an emitter of positrons (this is also beta radioactivity). They received the Nobel Prize in chemistry in 1937. The nuclear equations for the formation and decay of phosphorus-30 are:

$$^{27}_{13}\text{Al} + ^{4}_{2}\text{He} \Rightarrow ^{30}_{15}\text{P} + ^{1}_{0}\text{n}$$

$$^{30}_{15}\text{P} \Rightarrow ^{30}_{14}\text{Si} + ^{0}_{+1}\text{e}$$

The letter e, with the left subscript +1 in this case, indicates a positive electron, that is, a positron. The silicon formed is stable (nonradioactive).

1934: Concept of a Nuclear Chain Reaction—Leo Szilard was an inventive and resourceful scientist. He migrated from his Hungarian homeland and worked at the Kaiser Wilhelm Institute in Berlin; later he moved to England and to the United States. In England in 1934 he conceived the idea of energy liberated from splitting atoms in a chain reaction, and was even able to patent the concept. Along with Enrico Fermi he is credited with developing the first nuclear reactor in Chicago. Szilard was an iconoclastic genius and visionary idealist, given to acrobatic thinking.

About the same time Soviet physicist Lev Landau pointed out that controlled release of atomic energy using neutrons might now be possible.

Leo Szilard (1898–1964), Hungarian physicist, came to the United States in 1938. He carried out nuclear research in Germany and later in England. One of the first to propose self-sustaining nuclear reactors. Participated in the Manhattan Project. Opposed nuclear bombing of Hiroshima. Early campaigner for nuclear arms control.

1934: Early Attempts to Make Element 93—Soon after the discovery of the neutron, the gifted Italian physicist Fermi was attempting to change ordinary uranium into a heavier isotope of uranium by neutron bombardment. His objective in prying into the secret soul of the atom was to create a new isotope of uranium (atomic number 92) which would beta decay to the unknown new element, number 93. This sort of transformation had already been found with several lighter elements. He came to no definite conclusions, but his research stimulated many investigations around the world.

Enrico Fermi (1901–1954), Italian physicist who was especially intellectually supple. After receiving the Nobel Prize in 1938, he left for the United States rather than return to fascist Italy. Contributed to theories of beta decay and neutrinos. Carried out many investigations of artificial radioactive elements via neutron bombardment. Responsible for construction of first nuclear reactor (1942) and thus the controlled release of nuclear energy. Important roles in the Manhattan Project. Opposed development of hydrogen bomb.

1935: The Meson—The Japanese Hideki Yukawa, on theoretical grounds, predicted that the incredibly enormous forces which hold the nucleus together involved a new particle, now known as the *meson*. This was later confirmed experimentally. Each meson has a mass some 200 times that of the electron. Whole families of related particles have since been discovered (4-15). Yukawa also predicted a new kind of radioactivity, namely capture of the innermost electron of an atom by its nucleus; this was also confirmed experimentally by the American Luis Alvarez years later.

Electron capture by the nucleus

Hideki Yukawa (1907–1991), Japanese physicist. Professor at Kyoto, Osaka, Princeton, and Columbia Universities. Nobel Prize 1949. Originated idea of the meson and predicted a new kind of beta decay, namely inner-orbit electron capture by the nucleus, which was confirmed experimentally.

3-5 Nuclear Fission

Lise Meitner was a brilliant Austrian physicist who worked with German chemists Otto Hahn and Fritz Strassmann at the Kaiser Wilhelm Institute near Berlin. She became the actual but unofficial intellectual leader of the team. While working in Berlin before World War I, Meitner had to cope with deep-seated prejudices against women in science. She was banished to a dismal laboratory made in a carpentry shop in the basement because women were not allowed in the research institute proper. Despite all these barriers, she succeeded in burrowing into the conservative physics establishment. Aside from carrying out research with Hahn and Strassmann, she exchanged ideas with scientific luminaries of her time: Planck, Franck, Pauli, Max Born, Bohr, and Einstein.

In the mid-1930s Hahn, Strassman, and Meitner undertook a series of experiments designed to make sense out of the baffling results from irradiation of uranium with neutrons, especially the work of Fermi. A bewildering array of radioactive nuclides had been reported over the previous half dozen years or so. Meanwhile, in late 1938, Hahn and Strassmann repeated Fermi's experiments using a stronger neutron source. This was after Meitner had been forced to leave. They found that a component of the neutron-exposed uranium sample was carried by barium and thought it must be radium. Hahn just couldn't understand it. This defied all common sense. He informed Meitner of this observation in October and sought guidance from her during a secret meeting in Copenhagen and also

Lise Meitner (1878–1968), nuclear physicist. Born Vienna, in 1907 went to Berlin, the world center of physics at that time. During her years in Germany, she wrote several treatises on physics. In 1918 Meitner and Otto Hahn published a paper describing the isolation of protactinium-131, the most important isotope of this element. Co-discoverer of fission. The Nazi government tightened up implementation of its shameful policies, and since some of Meitner's forbearers were Jews, she was forced to leave Germany. This was in July 1938, after 31 years of dedicated work in Germany. Through the efforts of Niels Bohr, and aided by Paul Rosbaud, a spy for the British in the German Reich throughout the war, she found a haven in Sweden. Meitner shared the Fermi Award of 1966 with Hahn and Strassmann. Element 109 was named meitnerium.

Otto Hahn (1878–1968), German physicist. Productive work with radioactive elements. Co-discoverer of fission. Captured after Germany was overrun by Allied troops, he was interned in England when the announcement was made that he had won the Nobel Prize for 1944. Shared the Fermi Award in 1966. Helped develop the rubidium-strontium technique of dating materials.

Fritz Strassmann (1902–1980), German chemist. Co-discoverer of fission. A superb analytical and radiochemist. Worked with Hahn and Meitner. At great personal risk, helped Jews escape from the Nazis duuring WW II. After WW II, became Director of the Max Planck Istitute for Chemistry. Shared the Fermi Award in 1966.

by exchange of letters. Meitner strongly urged Hahn to recheck this point exhaustively, and he and Strassmann did so. Using fractional crystallization known to separate radium from barium, they soon found that the material first thought to be radium was actually a radioactive isotope of barium (radiobarium). Meitner hypothesized to herself, in a brilliant inspiration, that the only way to explain the results was that the radiobarium was formed from the uranium nucleus by its actually splitting in two, forming two new atoms, one of which was barium. At once, Meitner informed Hahn of this development (German chemist Ida Noddack had earlier suggested something like this idea of nuclear breakup, but she had no hard evidence). In the publication announcing this astounding discovery, Hahn was not allowed by the Nazis to include the name of Meitner on account of her Jewish heritage. She was deeply saddened by not being able to share recognition for this "beautiful discovery." In December Otto Frisch, Meitner's nephew and also a nuclear physicist, was visiting his aunt in Sweden, and the two pondered the meaning of this apparent rupture of the uranium nucleus. It wasn't long before they provided the correct mathematical interpretation (calculation of the energy evolved) and also provided the word *fission* to describe the process.

Natural uranium is 99.284% uranium-238, 0.711% uranium-235, and 0.005% uranium-234 by weight. Not only does the fragile nucleus of the lighter isotope, uranium-235, undergo fission, but extra neutrons and an enormous amount of energy are released. Meitner calculated the amount of that energy (see 4-9). Each fission step, it was found, consumes one neutron and releases two or three extra ones (details in 4-16). They became aware that a nuclear chain reaction is possible. The two heavier fragments of the split nucleus became known as fission products, and are radioactive isotopes of long-known chemical elements. From the viewpoint of the nucleus, fission is the ultimate catastrophe.

Splitting the atom

These ideas at once explained all the earlier confusing experimental data. After Hahn learned of Meitner's calculations, he submitted a paper on the subject in late December 1938; it was published on January 6, 1939. Sad to relate, after World War II, Hahn began to downplay Meitner's contributions to solving the problem. In 1996 the Royal Swedish Academy of Sciences released the records of the circumstances of the Nobel decision made at the end of WW II. These revealed Sweden's scientific isolation during that time, and thus the failure to understand Meitner's contributions.

Danish physicist Niels Bohr, brought news of nuclear fission to the United States in January, 1939, and it electrified the physics community. Gamow told Teller "Bohr has gone crazy. He says uranium splits." Within a few weeks the fission of uranium-235 had been confirmed in several laboratories such as the one at Columbia University. Another was that of Joliot-Curie in France; he also observed the production of neutrons and predicted that chain reactions could be realized. Another was the laboratory of Igor Kurchatov the Soviet Union. In 1939, shortly after fission became known world-wide, Tokutaro Hagiwara published a paper in Japan in which he described his measurements of the number of neutrons released on fission of each atom of uranium-235 by a slow neutron, getting 2.6 as the result; the modern figure is 2.4 to 2.5 (the value varies with the energy of the incoming neutrons). The next year he devised an ingenious technique for counting thermal neutrons based on their decomposition of hydrogen peroxide. Scientists in all of these sites were quite aware of the possibility of nuclear bombs. In fact, the Russians Yuli Khariton and Yakov Zel'dovich proved that a chain reaction in natural uranium, with 0.7% uranium-235, was possible, provided the fast fission neutrons are slowed down. Moreover, they demonstrated that is not the case with fast-neutron chain reaction of uranium-238, and thus separation of the isotope uranium-235 is essential for the purpose of manufacturing bombs.

Niels Bohr (1885–1962), Danish theoretical physicist. Applying quantum mechanics to atoms, he proposed a model for their electronic structures, and later was active in the theories of nuclear structure. Nobel Prize in 1922. Fleeing Nazi-occupied Denmark, Bohr was flown in the bomb bay of a British Mosquito plane from Sweden to Scotland in 1943. Served at Los Alamos. Later he led the Atoms for Peace program.

What if Hahn, Strassmann, and Meitner had not discovered nuclear fission? Then someone else would have. Like an island, it was there, and discovery was only a matter of time. Thus scientific discoveries differ from artistic creations, such as musical compositions.

3-6 The Road to Nuclear Energy and Weapons During World War II—The American Nuclear Program

In September of 1939, Europe once again broke out into bloody military madness, seemingly having learned little from the preceding wars except how to be even more destructive. But the course of World War II was destined to be the catalyst which changed the nature of large-scale war forever. The nuclear enterprises of four countries are described in the following sections: the monumental Manhattan Project in the United States, the efforts in Germany, Japan, and the Soviet Union.

1939: Nuclear Chain Reactions—The discovery of nuclear fission profoundly excited and disturbed the arcane world of nuclear scientists. By March, several groups almost simultaneously had suggested that since more neutrons were released than consumed in the fission process, a nuclear chain reaction should be possible. Some of the men who described this concept were Szilard (Hungarian), von Halban, (Austrian), Joliot and Lew Kowarski, (both French), Fermi (Italian), Hagiwara (Japanese), and Hanle (German).

The significance was that practical, controlled release of atomic energy (more accurately, nuclear energy) now seemed attainable, and uncontrolled release in bombs seemed possible (this was less certain at the time). To get a better idea of a chain reaction, consider the familiar example of a natural gas flame. If the gas comes through a pipe and draws air into a stove-top burner, the blue flame is quiet and steady: controlled combustion. Some type of activation, such as a spark or match flame, is required to start the process. The burning zone heats the incoming gas to ignition, making the process self-propagating; this is a chemical chain reaction. But if the gas accumulates and mixes with air, filling a room, and a spark or flame is introduced, the chain reaction occurs in an uncontrolled manner: an explosion.

Chain reactions, controlled and uncontrolled

By 1939 several European physicists had conferred with Einstein and convinced him to endorse and send a letter to President Franklin Roosevelt which explained the general situation. The letter was mostly composed by Szilard. Einstein urged support of research in this field, mentioning the possibility of "extremely powerful bombs of a new type." In addition, Peierls and Rudolf Frisch wrote a supporting document. The President appointed an Advisory Committee on Uranium, which met in October 1939. Its report mentioned atomic energy and atomic bombs specifically. By 1940 the Committee had learned that the Germans had started a new nuclear research program at the Kaiser Wilhelm Institute in Berlin. It was tormenting and simply unacceptable to think of atomic bombs exclusively in the hands of the Nazis, with their ruttish hankering for war. Werner Heisenberg, a Nobelist in physics and best known for his uncertainty principle, had attempted to calculate the amount of uranium-235 necessary to make a bomb, but he made an important error.

A contract with Columbia University in New York was made in 1940. Research concerning fission, interaction of neutrons with matter, nuclear chain reactions, isotope separation, the chemistry of plutonium (see below), and related studies were undertaken in 1941.

Physicist Arthur H. Compton headed the chain-reaction project. Information was exchanged with the British, who sent many of their top scientists to the U.S. It looked more and more probable that atomic bombs were feasible. With the attack on Pearl Harbor in December 1941, the United States entered the war.

Arthur H. Compton (1892–1962), American physicist. Research in X-rays and cosmic rays. Discoverer of change in wavelength of X-rays on scattering (Compton effect). Nobel Prize in 1927. Program Chief, Chain Reaction Physics, Metallurgical Laboratory of Manhattan Project, University of Chicago.

1940-41: **Elements Beyond Uranium**—Edwin McMillan and Philip Abelson at the University of California in Berkeley, exposed uranium to cyclotron-produced neutrons (using deuterons) and were able to show that the unknown but predicted element, number 93, had been formed in trace quantities. Thus the soundness of Fermi's idea had been experimentally proven. On absorbing a neutron, uranium-238 formed uranium-239, an atom which decayed by beta emission to element 93. The new element was named *neptunium* after the planet Neptune.

In February of 1941, Berkeley scientists J. W. Kennedy, McMillan, and A. C. Wahl, under the direction of Glenn Seaborg discovered another isotope of neptunium (mass number 238) using the cyclotron. This material was also beta active, and thus gave birth to element 94. This new element was alpha active and could be separated chemically from uranium and neptunium. It was at this point that the overriding military importance of this work was realized, and secrecy rules were self-imposed. Element 94 was confirmed, and named *plutonium*, after the planet Pluto. Its chemistry was investigated by radiochemical techniques. Most importantly, isotope plutonium-239 was made, and it proved to undergo fission readily. It was clear for the first time that if a chain-reacting nuclear reactor could be made, plutonium in quantity would result, and that recovery of this element would be easier than separation of uranium-235 from uranium-238. Thus two avenues toward nuclear power and weapons were now evident: Uranium-235 Road and Plutonium-239 Road.

Glenn Seaborg (1912–1999), American physicist. Co-discoverer of plutonium, americium, curium, and seven other transuranium elements. Prominent in Manhattan Project. Nobel Prize in 1951, shared with McMillan. Fermi Award in 1959. Chair, Atomic Energy Commission, 1961–1971. Element 106 was named after him.

By mid 1940 enough experimental work had been done to be reasonably sure a nuclear chain reaction could be controlled under the proper conditions, and also that a nuclear bomb could be constructed. In particular, physicists Otto Frisch and Rudolf Peierls (Fermi Award in 1980) early realized the potential of a bomb, and calculated its size and energy release. Frisch, the nephew of Meitner, had taken refuge in England, where he met Peierls, a refugee from Germany. The necessary amount of uranium-235 they calculated was small; the energy release was vast. Frisch began some experiments to study the separation of uranium-235 from the much more abundant uranium-238. This work employed the readily-volatile compound, uranium hexafluoride (8-12).

The Frisch-Peierls report, dated March 1940, made the following conclusions: A facility based on gaseous-diffusion aided by a temperature differential for separating U-235 from U-238, employing uranium hexafluoride vapor, would be successful; a mechanism could be devised to bring two subcritical pieces of U-235 metal together quickly to initiate the nuclear chain reaction by fast neutrons and consequent explosion; it would be feasible to separate a sufficient amount of U-235; the explosion yield would be enough to destroy a city; a great deal of radioactivity would be released; practically nothing could resist such an explosion; and finally, Germany might be working on such a weapon.

The study led to establishment of a British atomic bomb effort. In April 1940 a committee of British scientists, chaired by G. P. Thomson examined the feasibility of manufacturing nuclear bombs. This group became known as the MAUD Committee, a name designed to conceal its purpose; it was not an acronym, but was taken from a telegram from Meitner, referring to Maud Ray, the governess who taught the Bohr children English. Within a year it confirmed that a bomb was indeed possible. The report concluded the critical mass of uranium-235 was approximately 8 kilograms without a neutron reflector, and a bit more than half that amount with a neutron reflector. The suggestion was made that at least 11 kilograms be employed. The yield was estimated at 1800 tons of TNT, which would bring a quick end to the war. A copy of the report was sent to the American Office of Scientific Research and Development. The MAUD Committee was informed of Seaborg's work in California in which he and his group discovered plutonium.

One of the most important contributions made by the MAUD Committee, made possible by a memorandum from Peierls, was that to be successful a nuclear bomb must be based on chain-reaction fission by "fast" (unmoderated) neutrons, that is, without being slowed down. Evidently Heisenberg did not realize this point in his calculation of the critical size (3-17).

Meanwhile a remarkable Austrian physicist, Fritz Houtermans had been considering nuclear bombs. By August 1941 he had clearly postulated that, in a critical mass of uranium-235, a nuclear chain reaction involving fission by fast neutrons would lead to a nuclear explosion. He did not publicize these ideas.

In late 1941, Soviet physicist Georgi Flerov urged his government to undertake research in fast-neutron fission. He had studied fission of uranium nuclei by fast neutrons in 1940.

1942: The Manhattan Project—In January 1942 President Roosevelt decided to begin a rigorous project to develop nuclear bombs. Research programs were started at Columbia University in New York, the University of Chicago, Iowa State College (now University), the Massachusetts Institute of Technology, and the University of California in Berkeley. Under the official code name Manhattan Engineer District (usually referred to as the Manhattan Project), a gigantic program was authorized in June 1942, involving many university, government, and military agencies. This provided the necessary priorities for manpower and materials and the priority level was the highest, at the AAA rating. The vast resources of the American chemical industries were made available. At its peak, the Manhattan Project was almost a state within a state. It had its own airplanes, factories, cities, and secrets. The history of the Manhattan Project is best told by Richard Rhodes in his *The Making of the Atomic Bomb* (see bibliography at end of chapter).

While the Manhattan Project was primarily an American enterprise, its basic ideas were of international origin, mostly European, although Canadians played important roles. English scientists were especially numerous. Many French, German, Italian, Hungarian, and other scientists participated actively in the United States during the war. Research at the universities continued on purification of uranium, manufacture of uranium metal, processing of plutonium, separation of uranium-235, nuclear chain reactions, instrumentation, analytical problems, corrosion studies, biological and health investigations, development of auxiliary materials such as beryllium, and endless other matters.

The nuclear effort gears up.

At Iowa State College in Ames, a process of producing ultra pure uranium metal was developed, and by the end of the war two million pure uranium ingots, weighing more than 1000 tons, had been produced. These fueled the first reactor in Chicago. The process consisted of reduction of uranium tetrafluoride ("green salt") with magnesium.

Meanwhile, the first visible amount of plutonium, about one microgram, was isolated in August, 1942, and the first weighable amount was available the next month. These observations lent confidence to large-quantity production of plutonium, in which the scale was daringly scaled upwards by a factor of around ten billion at a later time. Seaborg once wrote that an overloaded shelf gave way and broke a vial containing one-quarter of the world's supply of plutonium, which soaked into the *Sunday Tribune.*

The first nuclear reactor was constructed under the bleachers of Stagg Field at the University of Chicago. Directed by Fermi and Eugene Wigner, built by stacking pure graphite bricks with holes in them to accommodate metallic uranium ingots or uranium oxide. This was natural uranium, containing only 0.711% uranium-235. Cadmium control rods were left inside (cadmium is a metal which strongly absorbs neutrons). The assembly was referred to as a "pile," and this first reactor was named CP-1, for Chicago Pile number 1. It contained 385 tons of graphite, 6.2 tons of pure uranium as metal and 34 tons of uranium as oxide. CP-1 was built in the shape of a flattened sphere 20 feet high and 25 feet in diameter. On December 2, 1942, the last control rod was cautiously pulled out. The neutron counters inside disclosed a buildup of neutron density, disclosing that the first self-sustaining nuclear chain reaction was a success. A squad of three stood on a platform and

Eugene Wigner (1902–1995), Hungarian physicist. Educated in Germany, entered the United States in 1930. Member of Manhattan Project 1942–1945 at University of Chicago and Oak Ridge. Many studies of nuclei and the structure of metals. Fermi Award in 1958, shared Nobel Prize in 1963.

they were prepared to flood the pile with a solution of a cadmium salt if necessary. The power was kept to only half a watt for 28 minutes. Physicist Wigner presented Fermi a bottle of Chianti wine. Using small paper cups the group toasted their success. A few days later the pile was operated at 200 watts. The reactor was disassembled and rebuilt with adequate shielding outside Chicago, where it eventually operated at 2000 watts, and for a full hour at 100,000 watts. In 1943 another reactor was constructed at Argonne, near Chicago, under the direction of Fermi. It was used for research purposes. This site developed into a major National Laboratory for nuclear research and development. The author lectured there in 1989 on analysis of nuclear materials during Manhattan Project times.

CP-1 the first man-made nuclear reactor

The way in which plutonium was synthesized in the nuclear reactors is just indicated here, and treated more fully in section 4-5. There was a chain reaction of fission of uranium-235 atoms by neutrons which themselves arose from the fission. Two or three neutrons were formed per fission, but only one was needed to cause a new fission event. Thus the chain reaction was self-sustaining. The newly created neutrons were terribly energetic and had to be moderated (slowed down) by the graphite. Some of these neutrons were used to propagate the chain reaction, while the rest were absorbed by the abundant uranium-238, forming uranium-239. This isotope of uranium is beta active and has a short half-life (23.5 minutes). It decays quickly into the next element, neptunium, which also undergoes quite rapid beta decay (half-life 2.36 days). This process results in formation of plutonium, more specifically plutonium-239. This nuclide has a long half-life (23,110 years), and therefore accumulates.

3-7 Oak Ridge

At a site near Clinton, Tennessee, about 20 miles from Knoxville, an immense complex of nuclear facilities was constructed during World War II. Situated in the Tennessee Valley, this Clinton Engineer Works held three facilities for separating uranium-235 from uranium-238 (K-25 site), a prototype nuclear reactor (X-10 site), and a facility to fabricate uranium-235 (Y-12 site). Eventually the complex became known simply as Oak Ridge.

Separation of uranium isotopes

One of the uranium isotope separation plants was based on the electromagnetic principles of the *mass spectrograph*. Lawrence, inventor of the cyclotron, had altered one of these instruments into a 180° mass spectrograph which could be scaled upward in capacity. These were called calutrons (after *Cal*ifornia *U*niversity, and *-tron*). The plant in Tennessee contained a series of tanks within gigantic magnets; they were arranged in the shape of an oval, and wistfully nicknamed "racetracks." Since copper was in short supply during wartime, silver (13,540 tons!) was borrowed from the Treasury Department. Enormous amounts of electric power were consumed. By January 1945 production of 80% uranium-235 amounted to 204 grams per day.

The second plant used the principle of *thermal diffusion*. A vertical tube full of the isotopic mixture to be processed contained a central wire, which was heated electrically. The lighter isotope tends to concentrate around the wire, and convection currents draw the enriched material upward. While crude, the technique accomplished partial enrichment of uranium-235.

The third isotope separation plant exploited the *gaseous diffusion* principle. In any gas, lighter molecules diffuse faster than heavier ones. If a series of containers is set up, each divided into two parts by porous barriers, and one side is filled with the gas, the lighter component diffuses through the pores slightly faster. Natural uranium hexafluoride, which becomes a gas at slightly elevated temperatures. The molecular weights (sum of atomic weights) of uranium-235 hexafluoride and uranium-238 hexafluoride are 349 and 352 respectively. Therefore the lighter U-235 compound becomes slightly enriched on one side of the porous barrier. By setting up a cascade of these chambers, containing acres of porous barrier surface, each unit equipped with a pump, sufficient enrichment was finally achieved. It was a notable triumph, taxing the scientific talents of the personnel.

Uranium enriched in U-235 from both the electromagnetic separation plant and the thermal diffusion plant was used as feed for the gaseous diffusion plant. The difficult task of upgrading natural uranium (0.711% U-235) to weapons-grade material was eventually successful. By July 1945, 60 kilograms (132 pounds) of uranium whose uranium-235 content was 60% to 90% had been produced.

A fourth technique used centrifuges and uranium hexafluoride vapor. While it did not reach production level, tests did demonstrate that the process is feasible. It has since become the method of choice.

In an adjacent valley, a prototype production nuclear reactor was constructed. Like the first reactor in Chicago, it contained graphite to slow down fast neutrons, and was air-cooled. The structure was shaped like a cube 30 feet on edge. The reactor was turned on in November, 1943. It was a large one, operating first at 1800 kilowatts and later at about 2,000,000 watts (2000 kilowatts or 2 megawatts). A separation plant for plutonium was built; the processing was problem plagued, but successful. Today the separation of plutonium from reactor fuel is known as reprocessing (8-4). These early pilot plants served as training centers. First, milligrams of plutonium, then grams, and finally kilograms, were produced. Today the reactor is a prized museum piece.

In these efforts, it was necessary to build housing, schools, medical facilities, and all the infrastructure of a city, this during wartime. The turmoil was almost overpowering.

3-8 Hanford

Meanwhile, a nearly uninhabited area was chosen on which to build the main nuclear reactors to produce plutonium in quantity. At that time physicists could not be positive that either uranium-235 or plutonium-239 could be produced in sufficient purity or quantity to produce a bomb, and so both objectives were undertaken to double the probability of success. The plutonium facility was constructed near Hanford, southeast of central Washington on the Columbia River, which arcs gracefully through the sagebrush. The complex covers 530 square miles. From the 4100-foot summit of Rattlesnake Mountain, the view stretches to a horizon broken by Mount St. Helens and other volcanoes. Abundant electricity from Grand Coulee Dam was available. Construction of this Hanford Engineer Works was started in April, 1943. Again, facilities to accommodate about 42,000 people had to be erected. Gigantic nuclear reactors were constructed, each well shielded in steel and concrete. One of the most challenging problems was developing a means of cladding ("canning") the metallic uranium ingots in aluminum. The material used had to be water-resistant, not absorb too many neutrons, and capable of being bonded to the uranium to facilitate heat transfer. A sort of solder was developed which proved to be satisfactory. This cladding process had only been perfected the month before the reactor was started up.

Mass production of plutonium

The first reactor, called B Pile, started in September 1944 under Fermi's direction and had a maximum thermal power of 250 megawatts. Water from the Columbia River entered at a cool 10 °C and exited at a hot 60 °C, which is a few degrees higher than that which the human skin can tolerate (the °C here means degrees Celsius, formerly centigrade, on which scale water freezes at zero degrees and boils at one hundred degrees). Operation of the reactor was erratic at first owing to "poisoning" by fission products (4-16). The A, D, and modified B piles soon were producing plutonium too.

Chemical processing facilities to separate the plutonium were constructed in concrete canyons, each remote-controlled on account of the dangerous radioactivity of fission products and transuranium elements. These processes were boldly scaled up from studies of trace amounts of plutonium. These early processes used bismuth phosphate to coprecipitate the plutonium, and thus separate it from most other substances; final purification was achieved via coprecipitation with lanthanum fluoride. The success of this process depended on manipulating the plutonium into various states of oxidation (that is, Pu^{3+}, Pu^{4+}, and PuO_2^{2+}). As mentioned earlier, to protect the metallic uranium fuel from corrosion each ingot had to be clad in aluminum, which proved to be exceptionally difficult. The first plutonium from Hanford was delivered to Los Alamos in early 1945.

The tenor of post-Cold War times is embodied in the status of nine decaying reactors left from the war years. Flocks of bats now use their labyrinths to roost. The radioactive contamination has helped to keep humans at bay, permitting a return of an astonishing diversity of wildlife. There are many deer and elk, and the Columbia River is teeming with salmon. A survey in 1996 revealed a wide variety of ducks, egrets, blue herons, hawks, quail, pheasants, peregrine falcons, bald eagles, sage grouse, and many other birds making their homes on the Hanford reservation, 205 species in all.

3-9 Los Alamos

Early in 1943, under a shroud of secrecy, a laboratory was constructed for the final delicate research and fabrication of the bombs. The site selected was a remote plateau at Los Alamos, New Mexico. Housing, power plants, etc. had to be built; the population reached 6000. At the end, in those vapory days, a galaxy of scientific luminaries under the

Y's guys were wise guys.

direction of J. Robert Oppenheimer had been assembled. Theoretical and practical work on nuclear explosions proceeded. Code words were often used to identify the various sites. Thus the Tennessee installation was Site X, and Los Alamos was Site Y. This laboratory was destined to become the cradle of the first nuclear bomb.

J. Robert Oppenheimer (1904–1967), American physicist. Worked in field of cosmic rays, nuclear physics, fundamental particles and relativity, neutron stars, and black holes. Director of Los Alamos Laboratory 1943–1945, and of the Institute for Advanced Study at Princeton in 1947. A leader in developing fission bombs, but opposed hydrogen bombs. Fermi Award in 1963.

3-10 The First Nuclear Explosion

The Site—By late 1944 it was clear that enough plutonium-239 and uranium-235 would be accumulated in the spring of 1945 to conduct a test. The physicists concluded that a test of the implosion principle (9-5) using plutonium was necessary, and if successful, then the simpler gun-assembly technique (9-6) using uranium-235 would surely work as well.

A site in the New Mexico desert was chosen on account of its remoteness and isolation. It is 156 miles south of Los Alamos and 58 miles northwest of Alamogordo. The territory, covered with mesquite and yucca, is at the north end of La Jornada del Muerto (The Journey of the Dead). The site and the upcoming test were named Trinity in 1944 by Oppenheimer. On May 7, 1945, a test was carried out in which 100 tons of TNT was exploded on a wooden trestle. This was about half a mile south of ground zero of the future nuclear test. The purpose was to check and calibrate the photographic, electrical, and seismic instruments to be used in the planned nuclear explosion. Some radioactive material, namely uranium and its fission products which had been irradiated 100 days in a Hanford reactor, had been put into the huge stack of explosive to give an idea of the distribution of radioactive material in the upcoming blast.

Early on in the work, there was considerable doubt whether the bomb would work. Since so much had been spent on manufacturing the plutonium, it was decided to make a giant steel shell in which to make the first test. Then, if no nuclear explosion occurred, much of the plutonium could be recovered. A massive 25-foot cylinder with thick walls was cast for this purpose, and transported to the site. The cylinder, dubbed Jumbo, was wrapped with steel bands to increase its strength. It weighed 217 tons and cost around $50 million to manufacture. But it was never used because confidence in the implosion technique had grown to a high level. The huge cylinder still lies nearby.

A steel tower 100 feet tall had been built. It had a heavy oaken platform at the top to hold the bomb. Three half-buried concrete bunkers were constructed, each 5.7 miles from ground zero. These housed instrumentation, including high-speed cameras protected by thick bulletproof glass in portholes. The northwest bunker can still be seen near the access road to the site. Base camp was about 10 miles south.

The Bomb—The warhead consisted of a duralumin shell about five feet in diameter, enclosing 5000 pounds of high explosive just inside; the next layer was a heavy uranium sphere (the tamper), a spacer, and a plutonium sphere in the center (more details in Chapter 9).

The chemical explosive was of two kinds, one fast burning and the second slow. The explosive was separated from the aluminum shell by, of all things, a layer of cork. Some of the high explosive was cast into the form of lenses (or shaped charges). The explosives expert George Kistiakowsky was in charge of choosing the high explosives to effect the implosion and to form them into lens-shaped charges. One of the most important objectives of the *Trinity* explosion was to test the performance of the explosive lenses. There were 32 detonators regularly spaced on the outside of the assembly (one for each of the 32 lenses), a procedure devised by Luis Alvarez (Fermi Award, 1987). They led to wires embedded in the explosive. For detonation, a high-voltage capacitor discharged through the wires, vaporizing the filaments simultaneously in all detonators and initiating the explosion. The uniform inward force resulting would compress the interior: an implosion.

Focusing a shock wave

George Kistiakowsky (1900–1982), Ukranian-born physical chemist. Trained in Germany, immigrated to the United States, and eventually became professor at Harvard. Leader of explosives division at Los Alamos. Perfected machining of precision-cast high explosive lenses for implosion.

An uninhabited ranch dwelling, known as the McDonald house, was rented by the Army since it was only two miles from the steel tower. The final assembly of the interior portion of the bomb was carried out in the adobe-and-stone house.

The plutonium was 93-94% of isotope 239 and weighed close to 6 kilograms. It was in the shape of two hemispheres which together were about the size of a billiard ball, slightly subcritical. They had been electroplated with nickel to prevent corrosion; the flat surfaces were further protected by a layer of gold leaf. Each half-sphere had a hemispherical depression in the center to accommodate the neutron generator. To the touch, the plutonium has been described as feeling as warm as a live rabbit, the heat coming from the alpha decay. The two-ton bomb was hoisted up the tower and secured. Every step was checked and rechecked through July 15.

The Blast—A rain forced postponement of the test a few hours until 5:30 a.m. Mountain War Time on July 16, 1945. Thunder and lightning heightened the drama. Many observers had assembled on Compañia Hill, 20 miles northwest of ground zero. These included Hans Bethe, Edward Teller, Richard Feynman, and James Chadwick, discoverer of the neutron. At the base camp were Oppenheimer, Fermi, Leslie Groves, Isador Rabi, Emilio Segrè, Kistiakowsky, K. T Bainbridge, Philip Morrison, and others.

The controls for the firing were in the south bunker. At 5:09:45 a.m. the arming party set it for 20 minutes. At 5:25 a green rocket was sent up, alerting all observers, including those 20 miles distant on Compañia Hill. Shallow depressions had been bulldozed at the base camp so the observers could lie down behind protective mounds.

Another rocket fired at 5:29, when the precise automatic timer was turned on. Tension among the scientists became almost unbearable. Oppenheimer was stressed out.

On count down to zero, an appalling burst of heat and light appeared, as if from the very vortex of hell. The mountains for miles around were brilliantly illuminated. The only journalist present, William L. Lawrence, wrote "From the east came the first signs of dawn. And, just at that moment, there arose as if from the bowels of the

Test explosion: a chunk of hell on earth

Earth a light not of this world, the light of many Suns in one." He went on to add that "It was like a grand finale of a mighty symphony of the elements, fascinating, . . . uplifting, crushing, ominous, devastating, . . . full of foreboding." The light was dazzling almost beyond comparison. Even at ten miles the heat was scorching. A blind girl being driven near Albuquerque felt the heat, and asked "What was that?" The flash was visible from 250 miles. Later a ferocious rumble rolled across the ancient desert: a shock wave. Echoes reflected repeatedly from the hills. The shock wave broke windows 120 miles away. High-speed cameras showed that the fireball contacted the earth in 0.65 millisecond after the firing. The first photo (above) shows the explosion 0.025 second after detonation, and the second was taken 15 seconds later. A special camera took a million frames per second.

The men viewed the light using welder's goggles. The first flash was an eerie light which then became multicolor: orange, golden, peach, purple, blue-green, and finally gray. A mushroom-shaped cloud—or perhaps better, toadstool-shaped—formed, surging and billowing, and rose to 40,000 feet within minutes, carrying most of the radioactive fission products upward. The tower had been vaporized, and a shallow crater lay in its place; the desert sand had become jade-colored, radioactive glass. Oppenheimer wrote the world would never be the same.

The army had lined two tanks with two-inch-thick lead and equipped them with scoops to collect samples. An hour and a half after the blast, physicists Fermi and Herbert Anderson entered the tanks, each with its driver; Fermi's tank broke down after a mile, and he had to walk back. Anderson was driven on to ground zero, and saw that the entire tower and its accessories had vanished. Only the stubs of the tower footings remained; this was in the middle of a depression about 2400 feet across. The surface near ground zero was covered with a green glassy substance formed when the sand had been melted and had resolidified. This substance has been dubbed "trinitite." Anderson collected a scoop of the rubble, but had to leave at once because the gamma radiation was too intense in spite of the shielding. Radiochemical analysis for unfissioned plutonium and fission products indicated that the yield was 18,600 tons of TNT (18.6 kilotons). Later measurements showed that this first estimate was a bit low, and a more reliable estimate is between 20 and 22 kilotons.

A pivotal event in the history of humanity

In this first test nuclear explosion, approximately 17% of the plutonium had been sundered by the fission process. Between 1 and 2% of the fission products remained at the site, the rest being lofted away. Some of this settled as radioactive fallout, whitening the hair on the backs of cattle. An unexpected result of this first nuclear bomb test was that photographic film in Eastman's factory in Rochester, NY, was fogged. This was finally traced to fission products from the test; radioactive substances had been carried a great distance and had become lodged in the raw material from which the paper used to wrap the film was made.

From the cold scientific viewpoint, the bomb must be considered superb physics. But Pandora's nuclear tinderbox had been opened.

A coded message on the success of the bomb was sent to President Truman in Potsdam, Germany, where he was meeting with Churchill and Stalin. President Truman mentioned that the United States had "a new weapon of unusual destructive force," to which Stalin responded that he hoped the U.S. would make "good use of it against the

Japanese." Espionage had already supplied considerable information about the American bomb to Stalin, who pretended ignorance.

Four hours after the *Trinity* test, a ship sailed under the Golden Gate bridge with its cargo of the uranium-235 gun-assembly bomb. It had the heavy cannon and projectile parts; the target rings were flown out later. That bomb was destined for Hiroshima.

Exactly 50 Years Later—On July 16, 1995, there was a special opening of the Trinity site, and the author made a visit, entering shortly after 5:00 a.m. There was a circular fenced area whose center was ground zero. The bomb in 1945 began to explode at 5: 29:45. The point marking fifty years later to the second came and went; there was no sounding on a ram's horn, no announcement or ceremony, nothing except a moment of meditative silence. Maybe that was best.

A black obelisk about 15 feet high has been built on ground zero. A low shelter about 20 by 40 feet in size was constructed over a portion of the crater floor to maintain it in an undisturbed condition. Windows in the slanting roof permit a view inside, and some of the fused, blue-green glassy globules ("trinitite") can be seen. These were formed where the fireball touched the ground.

Using a sensitive Geiger counter, the author measured the level of radioactivity (gamma rays, mostly from cesium-137 and barium-133) at many points in the site. Radioactivity levels in excess of background were clearly evident. The level near ground zero at *Trinity* was about 50 times background. A replica of the Nagasaki bomb was on display (see Fig. 3-10D on Color Plate I).

3-11 Hiroshima

Three weeks after the *Trinity* test, on August 6, 1945, a B-29 bomber flew from Tinian Island, headed for the Japanese city of Hiroshima. It carried the nuclear bomb with the code name "Little Boy." The bomb was originally named *Thin Man* by physicist Robert Serber but he changed it to Little Boy after its canon was shortened. Hiroshima was devastated at 8:15 in the morning, Japanese time. As mentioned above, this bomb contained not plutonium, but uranium-235, and the gun-assembly (9-6) technique was used, not implosion. The physicists had learned enough from many tests, most importantly the Trinity test, to be sure that the much simpler gun-assembly procedure would almost certainly be successful.

Annihilation of Hiroshima

Release of the uranium-235 bomb started its timer, activated the height detector (through air pressure), and at 7000 feet the barometric switch closed the first part of the firing circuit. At 5000 feet the small radar transmitter was turned on. Radar waves which reflected from the ground closed the final switch, causing the bomb to explode at 1900 feet. The flash reached the surface instantly, and the shock wave arrived a second or so later. The American airmen felt two blows, one from the direct shock wave and the second from its reflection from the ground. After approximately nine seconds, Hiroshima was essentially destroyed. So many small fires were started that they grew into a firestorm in the center of the city, and the burning continued for several days. During this time

Absolute destruction

black rain fell: the rain had washed out some of the air-borne soot, the radioactive plume from the products. The yield of the Hiroshima bomb was 15 kilotons (9-7), that is, equivalent to 15,000 tons of TNT. The city was simply pulverized (photo). The photo shows a small section of the wasteland which was Hiroshima, and was taken about two months after the bomb exploded. A few ferroconcrete structures remained standing, but these were so damaged they were useless. One should keep in mind that all this destruction was caused by one bomb, which was small and primitive by comparison to today's warheads. The photo cannot reveal the effects on people, that is, the human suffering; that too must be included in the true dimensions of a nuclear bomb blast. The destruction of Hiroshima was so extensive that communications with the outside were lost and it required considerable time for the news to reach Tokyo.

The element thorium, of atomic number two units lower than that of uranium, was named after Thor, the Norse god of thunder and war. We see today that those ancients might better have named their god, Uran.

In Tokyo, the control officer of the Japanese Broadcasting Corporation was surprised to find that the Hiroshima station had suddenly ceased operations. His phone calls could not get through to Hiroshima. The railroad telegraph service in Hiroshima had stopped working. Soon baffling reports from railway stops some distance north of Hiroshima began to come in, and they reported a huge explosion. The Japanese military headquarters sent a young officer to fly at once to

Hiroshima two months after the Blast.
The building whose shell remains is now called the Atomic Dome.

Hiroshima and find out what was happening. About 100 miles from his destination, the officer and his pilot saw a gigantic cloud of smoke. All of Hiroshima seemed to be burning. The first information from outside Japan came 16 hours after the bombing: it was the report broadcast from the White House that an atomic bomb had had been employed.

Akira Iwasaki and his film crew made some movies of Hiroshima shortly after the bomb exploded. Most of his film was confiscated by the U. S. Army and classified secret, but some footage found its way into a movie, "Hiroshima, Mon Amour." Its stupefying scenes caused some of its American audience to vomit or faint. An artist couple, Iri and Toshi Maruki, entered Hiroshima a short time after the explosion. The scenes gnawed at their souls. For years, they committed their impressions to canvas; the best known is a 15-panel series which required more than 30 years to complete. Today these paintings are in a special museum.

A comprehensive study which examined all available data on the toll of the Hiroshima bomb up to the 50th anniversary on August 6, 1995, gave the following results:

69,000 people killed on August 6, 1945
19,000 more died by the end of September, 1945
104,000 more people died of bomb-related causes up to August 6, 1995
192,000 total number of deaths over 50 years

The intensive incendiary bombing of Japan began in March 1945, and by July approximately 500,000 people had been killed. Of course, this involved thousands of bombs.

Hiroshima had about 350,000 inhabitants at the time of the attack. The immediate deaths were caused by blast effects (40%) and fire (60%). In addition to the deaths listed above, another 20,000 people were missing, again illustrating how unfair life (or death) can be. The effects of the blast were more extreme than the physicists had anticipated. Oppenheimer had estimated death toll at about 20,000. Survival depended primarily on distance from the hypocenter, the point on the surface directly below the explosion, and on the degree of shielding by buildings.

All the American prisoners of war who were in Hiroshima perished.

The Japanese have constructed the Peace Memorial Park at Hiroshima. At one end is the Atomic Dome (sketch below), a ferroconcrete structure housing a government bureau until it was shattered by the blast. It has been left untouched as a reminder of the folly of war.

A visit to this Park and its Memorial Museum by the author was a wrenching emotional experience. The Museum displayed photos of victims in shock walking around like zombies, with strips of skin blackened by burns dangling from their bodies. Flesh was burned away from eyes, noses, and mouths, leaving ghastly holes from which oozed fluids. Infection fouled injuries with pus and caused bloating. Kimono patterns were graven into women's backs. The outlines of human beings were imprinted onto asphalt by gamma rays. The internal organs of people a mile away were ruptured, largely by shock waves reflecting from the ground. Broken glass embedded in bodies caused agonizing death. Exposed persons within 3000 feet of the hypocenter received a radiation dose of 700 rads, much higher than the fatal dose. The flash of heat caused granite to exfoliate,

The nature of nuclear war

roof tiles to melt, and gravel to turn to glass. Packages of nails or needles were fused into a single mass. Metal structures were converted to lumps resembling meteorites. Hiroshima Castle was toppled into its moat. Rails were twisted, bridge girders were fractured.

Instantly reducing a city to rubble was the introduction of atomic energy to the world: an invention of the devil, so to speak. The Nobelist Japanese writer, Kenzaburo Oe, wrote: "Hiroshima is like a nakedly exposed wound inflicted on all mankind." Nothing, no passing passion, no threat, no rivalry, nothing at all justifies the unblemished evil of a nuclear war. Those who think nuclear war is winnable commit cosmic blasphemy.

Hiroshima, the Atomic Dome

Einstein was in a small cabin on a lake in the Adirondack Mountains in New York when his secretary heard the news broadcast. After she informed him of the destruction of a Japanese city by an atomic bomb, Einstein was interviewed by a journalist, during which he summed up the matter succinctly: "Ach! The world is not ready for it."

3-12 Nagasaki

Three days after Hiroshima was destroyed, another B-29 bomber with an escort left Tinian Island for Kokura in northern Kyushu, but that target city was obscured by clouds. The city of Nagasaki (population 280,000) was the second choice. Owing to failure of a valve in a reserve fuel tank, the plane could make only a single pass over the target. The sky was cloudy, but visibility was possible for a few seconds at a couple of minutes past 11 o'clock in the morning. The bomb which the plane carried, called *Fat Man*, contained 6.2 kilograms of plutonium, used the implosion principle, and was a twin of the *Trinity* bomb with the same energy as the *Trinity* test. This bomb was a bit more than 11 feet long and weighed about 5 tons, half of which was high explosive (more details in Chapter 9). The bomb detonated 1650 feet above the hilly city, annihilating most the Urakami area. Another death machine had done its work. Approximately 74,000 people died in the searing flash and shock wave. A second plane dropped three radiosensors suspended from parachutes when the nuclear bomb was released, signaling successful explosion and also radiation and pressure measurements. The U.S. was prepared to deliver a third bomb at the end of August, and several more in September, had the capitulation not come, thus prolonging the rain of ruin. Further demoralized by the declaration of war by the USSR on that same day, Japan surrendered a few days later.

At dawn on August 10, the day after the bomb exploded over Nagasaki, photographer Yosuke Yamahata was sent by the Japanese Army to the devastated area. In one day he took 95 photographs, the most extensive record of the immediate aftermath of a nuclear bomb exploding over a city. These photos are in the public domain today. X-ray film at a Red Cross hospital 1.5 kilometers from the hypocenter was blackened by radiation.

Hiroshima had been spared earlier damage by ordinary bombs so that the effects of nuclear bombs alone would be clear and not obscured or made ambiguous. General Groves, the director of the military aspects of the Manhattan Project, had favored Kyoto as the first target. "It is large enough for an experiment to test the effects of an atomic bomb," he wrote. The minutes of the meetings in which these decisions were made were examined after the war by Prof. Akira Yamagiwa. He wrote his impression that the Target Committee members acted as if they were "selecting some vegetables or fish" and that they were "exceedingly cold and unfeeling, as if these cities were uninhabited." American physicist Robert Serber described the ruined city as "our manufactured hell."

By 1995, approximately 300,000 deaths had occurred from the Hiroshima and Nagasaki bombings. This figure includes delayed deaths from cancer and other malignancies, that is, the number above the rates in unexposed cities in Japan. Some of these casualties were people who had been mobilized to help clear rubble after the attacks, and thus were exposed to radiation induced in the soil and other materials by neutrons from the explosions. Most developed leukemia and expired within five years. Survivors of the attack are referred to as *hibakusha* (literally, victim-of-bomb persons).

Six shipbuilders had been sent from Nagasaki to Hiroshima, and all survived the August 6 bombing. They returned to Nagasaki at once, and experienced the bombing of that city. They were lucky in one way: all survived.

After the war, The Atomic Bomb Casualty Committee was established to study long-term effects of the bombings on human beings, especially any genetic effects. In 1975 it was replaced by the Radiation Effects Research Foundation, a nonprofit Japanese organization financed equally by the United States and Japan.

The reactions of the scientists who created the bomb are varied. Oppenheimer's judgment was expressed in this way: "In some sort of crude sense, which no vulgarity, no humor, no overstatement can quite extinguish, the physicists have known sin, and this is a knowledge which they cannot lose."

The author's visit in 2000 to Nagasaki and its Atomic Bomb Museum was another wrenching experience. The exhibits sear one's soul. A monument stands on the hypocenter and sensitive memorials to a peaceful world cover a large park. The Museum has a Peace Promotion Office with a number of international scholars. Memories of the horror are fading.

3-13 The Franck Report

James Franck was a Nobel-Prize-winning German physicist and chemist who played a prominent role in the Manhattan Project. He chaired a committee of scientists to examine the impact of nuclear weapons on the world. The Franck Report, delivered to Secretary of War Henry Stimson on June 11, 1945 (more than a month before the first test explosion at the *Trinity* site), was written by seven scientists, including Szilard and Seaborg. Here are a few quotes from this remarkable document:

> In the past, science has often been able to provide new methods of protection against new weapons of aggression it made possible, but it cannot promise such efficient protection against the destructive use of nuclear power. This protection can come only from the political organization of the world . . . Nuclear bombs cannot possibly remain a "secret weapon" at the exclusive disposal of this country for more than a few years. The scientific facts on which their construction is based are well known to scientists of other countries . . . We believe that these considerations make the use of nuclear bombs for an early unannounced attack against Japan inadvisable . . . Much more favorable conditions for the eventual achievement of such an agreement could be created if nuclear bombs were first revealed to the world by a demonstration in an appropriately selected uninhabited area . . . To sum up, we urge that the use of nuclear bombs in this war be considered as a problem of long-range national policy rather than of military expediency . . .

The report entreated the political leaders to regard the use of the bomb as a fateful political decision rather than merely a matter of military tactics. A number of informed military leaders opposed use of the bomb directly. General Dwight Eisenhower voiced his opposition, saying "First, the Japanese were ready to surrender and it wasn't necessary to hit them with that awful thing. Second, I hated to see our country be the first to use such a weapon." Admiral William Leahy, chairman of the Joint Chiefs of Staff, believed that bombing Japan with this new weapon would make it more likely that someday an enemy might act the same way, and attack American cities with nuclear bombs. The point was that nuclear warheads were a qualitative change in warfare, not just more firepower. Letting the nuclear genie out of the bottle would profoundly and irrevocably change our world, and not necessarily for the better.

Politicians ignore competent advice.

A few months before the blast, British physicist William Penney had produced convincing calculations that a bomb of the *Trinity* type could reduce a city of three or four hundred thousand people to rubble. This information was available to the President and other leaders if they had wanted to review and consider it.

President Harry Truman and his advisors, however, believed that winning the war quickly was necessary to save American lives and was of overriding importance. The possibility that this same objective might be achieved without introducing this revolutionary to the world as a weapon of war apparently was considered to be unimportant. The advice of the scientists was ignored. The long and bitter war had corroded basic human values. The atomic bombing of Hiroshima and Nagasaki played a strong role in shaping the nuclear age.

3-14 The Smyth Report

After the war the American military establishment was fearful that "atomic secrets" would be leaked. To preempt this possibility, publication of an account of the main developments of the Manhattan Project was authorized. This report, *Atomic Energy for Military Purposes*, had been written by Princeton physicist Henry DeWolf Smyth and was approved by General Groves and President Truman. It described the administrative history of the work, the Metallurgical Laboratory at the University of Chicago, research at the universities in Columbia (NY), Ames (Iowa), and Berkeley (CA), the development of the facilities at Oak Ridge, Los Alamos, and Hanford, and summaries of the manufacture of plutonium-239 and uranium-235, complete with sketches and photographs. If the Smyth report had not been published, nearly all of this information would have been dug out anyway by enterprising journalists, historians, and spies. The report defined much of what was secret and what was public. Its appearance dismayed the British and pleased the Soviets. The first release, a lithoprint based on a typescript, was published about the middle of August, 1945.

The demand for the Smyth report was so great that the Princeton Press prepared a typeset edition in September. Soviet intelligence, of course, had copies of both versions, and compared them sentence by sentence. This revealed a number of changes, the most important being omission of a sentence from the lithoprint in its later versions concerning a problem in the operation of a large reactor for plutonium production (4-16). This omission was evidently at the order of Groves, who was dimayed that he himself had authorized the lithoprint version, according to physicist Arnold Kramish, one of Groves' advisors. Below is a copy of this section, from its Chapter VIII, with the deleted sentence underlined. The effect of the change was to alert the Soviets to a problem which they almost certainly could not have predicted, and thus prevent a delay in their production of their first nuclear warhead. Thus its effect was the exact opposite of what was intended.

At the end of the war, the contingent of British scientists who had worked on Manhattan Project installations returned home, bringing with them an essentially complete knowledge of how to separate uranium-235, to build nuclear reactors, to separate plutonium, to manufacture fission bombs, etc.

The Effects of Reaction Products on the Multiplication Factor

8.15. Even at the high power level used in the Hanford piles, only a few grams of U-238 and of U-235 are used up per day per million grams of uranium present. Nevertheless the effects of these changes are very importan As the U-235 is becoming depleted, the concentration of plutonium is increasing. Fortunately, plutonium itself is fissionable by thermal neutrons and so tends to counterbalance the decrease of U-235 as far as maintaining the chain reaction is concerned. However, other fission products are being produced also. These consist typically of unstable and relatively unfamiliar nuclei so that it was originally impossible to predict how great an undesirable effect they would have on the multiplication constant. Such deleterious effects are called poisoning. In spite of a great deal of preliminary study of fission products, an unforeseen poisoning effect of this kind very nearly prevents operation of the Hanford piles, as we shall see later.

Paragraph copied from the original (lithoprint) Smyth Report

3-15 Scientists' Organizations

Just after the end of the war, in September 1945, groups of scientists at the various Manhattan Project installations and independently formed organizations with the objective of helping to educate the American public concerning this great new force. On learning of each others' existence, the groups amalgamated into the Federation of

Atomic Scientists; later, the name was changed to the Federation of American Scientists, which has become quite influential. Similarly, in Great Britain, the Atomic Scientists Association was formed. Other organizations devoted to addressing the impact of science (especially nuclear issues) on society are of later origin. Three of them are the Union of Concerned Scientists, the Southern California Federation of Scientists (both outgrowths of the Federation of American Scientists), and Physicians for Social Responsibility. The Bulletin of the Atomic Scientists was founded by Eugene Rabinowitch and Hyman Goldsmith shortly after World War II.

3-16 The Controversy on the Bombing

Was it necessary?

Were there genuine alternatives to bombing Hiroshima? It is utterly unrealistic to expect a nation possessing atomic bombs to hurl more than a million of its soldiers against a heavily fortified enemy which has none. Nevertheless, there were several alternatives, and these were discussed at several levels of authority. One possibility was to make a demonstration explosion on the top of Mt. Fuji, or over Tokyo Bay, or on a desert island. Another possibility was to devastate an area in Japan after warning and urging prior evacuation. Incidentally, a memorandum from Roosevelt and Churchill, issued from Hyde Park on September 18, 1944, said that if a nuclear bomb is used against the Japanese, they "should be warned." Still another alternative was to permit captured Japanese officers to observe the Trinity test explosion, to inspect some of the bomb's manufacturing facilities, and then to see that they were repatriated with instructions to inform the Emperor and the military what fate Japan faced unless surrender came promptly. This plan might not have been effective, considering the fanatical nature of the Japanese military leadership. While there were objections to all of these steps, the last would probably have been best, and just might have been successful, although some Americans with long experience in Japan felt that the Imperial High Command would be willing to sacrifice millions of Japanese citizens and even the nation. There is evidence that Japan was about to surrender before the bombing and that it would have occurred before the planned American invasion in the fall.

But the decision to use the weapon on a Japanese city was already implicit in the Manhattan Project. The thrust of history and war compelled its use. Some say the desire to make the Soviet Union more manageable in the future played a role. An unspoken concern was that the United States had just invested $2 billion (equal to perhaps 20 billion present-day dollars) in the Manhattan Project, and if no wartime benefits accrued, then future funding might be endangered. Few leaders in a position to decide expressed doubts, although Edward Teller said that the city of Hiroshima should not have been destroyed. Perhaps the overtures submitted indirectly by the Japanese a few weeks prior to the bombing of Hiroshima, and which offered surrender provided the emperor heritage and system was preserved, should have been taken more seriously.

Edward Teller (1908–2003), Hungarian-American physicist. Higher education in Germany. Later became American. Played a pivotal role in Manhattan Project, and became director of the laboratory at Livermore, California in 1952. A controversial scientist, he was largely responsible for hydrogen bomb development. He opposed most arms-control treaties. Fermi Award in 1962.

Probably most Americans who lived through those times feel that dropping the bomb on Japanese cities was primarily to avoid a bloody invasion and loss of innumerable American lives. Certainly large numbers of American veterans became convinced that they survived the war because the bomb forced Japan to surrender promptly. These feelings surface often, as for example during preparation of the Smithsonian exhibit in 1994 concerning the bombing; in the end, display and commentary were sharply curtailed. The original script had contained archival text of alternatives to the bombings. In any case, the bombing of the Japanese was not primarily inspired by racial prejudice, as is sometimes alleged. If that had been the case, then how explain the fact that the original undertaking of the bomb was to counterbalance the possible development of the weapon by the Germans? So far as the scientists were concerned, fear that Nazi Germany might succeed in manufacturing nuclear bombs was a driving force in the Americans' diligent work. Still, a high-level military committee in May 1943 indicated that the Japanese were the primary target.

No one can say for certain whether the Japanese phase of the war could have been brought to a quick end by just a credible threat to use the bomb, as suggested above. Even if it had, the Cold War would almost certainly have taken place anyway. All informed views deserve our respectful attention. Incidentally, the Nagasaki Atomic Bomb Museum now includes exhibits of the attack on Pearl Harbor and the Japanese invasion of Asia.

As late as 1994 Japanese sensitivities concerning Hiroshima and Nagasaki had hardly subsided. When the U.S. Postal Service revealed a plan to mint a stamp bearing the mushroom cloud of a nuclear explosion, a furor of protest broke out in Japan. The mayor of Hiroshima described the stamp as "heartless." In the end, the design was replaced. Americans tend to perceive the bombing of Hiroshima and Nagasaki as primarily to end the war quickly, while the Japanese tend to view the matter as the main tragic advent of the nuclear age. Just a few years ago a Gallup Poll indicated that one in four adult Americans did not know that atomic bombs had been dropped on Japan.

An exercise in global politics is to imagine American reactions if the Soviet Union had developed a nuclear bomb first and used it against Germany.

3-17 The German Nuclear Program

Despite the discovery of fission in Germany and the related studies begun at the Kaiser Wilhelm Institute in Berlin, the German nuclear program never amounted to much. A few months after the discovery of fission, Austrian chemist Paul Harteck studied the possibility of making an atomic bomb. He wrote Adolf Hitler that the newest development would "make it possible to produce an explosive many orders of magnitude more powerful than conventional ones." While Hitler could not understand this, he did not forbid further research. The Germans knew that nuclear reactors were possible. The two main laboratories, at Hechingen and Haigerloch in southern Germany, were occupied by American troops in April, 1945. A principal leader in Germany's nuclear effort, physicist Werner Heisenberg had declared that "It was from September 1941 that we saw an open road ahead of us, leading to the atomic bomb." But he became very pessimistic about succeeding and this seems to have been a factor in the decision to abandon the work. While Heisenberg was never a member of the Nazi party, he made several public statements to the effect that he had wished for a German victory. The German scientists considered graphite as a neutron moderator, but concluded that it was not suitable; it turned out that the graphite they used to make their measurements was not pure. On the advice of Heisenberg, they decided to use heavy water instead. German orders required production of heavy water in occupied Norway to be expanded; the story of attempts to destroy the plant at Vemork by heroic resistance fighters and the Allies is well known. A cave near Haigerloch was selected as the site for construction of a reactor. This involved the use of 1.5 tons of metallic uranium cubes suspended in an equal amount of heavy water, and a certain degree of neutron multiplication was observed. Heisenberg calculated that the assembly would have to be increased about 50% in size to become critical.

If Hitler had delayed the start of the war, German scientists might well have succeeded in making reactors and plutonium.

Directly after the War in Europe ended, American forces confiscated a substantial amount of uranium ore and ore concentrates from a variety of sites in Germany. The ores were from Joachimstal mines and also from Belgian stock brought in from the Congo. They were shipped to the United States for the nuclear effort underway. Similarly, the Soviets took about 45 tonnes of uranium ore from eastern Germany. American warplanes destroyed a metal refining factory at Oranianburg, near Berlin, which had fabricated uranium metal parts for the German nuclear effort. This was in March, 1945, and involved more than 1500 tons of bombs. Soviet teams were also scouting for German uranium ore, as well as surviving scientists. Most German scientists had fled to areas where they knew they would fall into the hands of the Western powers.

In the early stages of the war, American and British scientists were concerned that Germany might successfully make a nuclear bomb. The supposedly secret implosion principle was known to German researchers, and actual attempts to achieve nuclear fusion were made, using deuterium but no uranium. Since the distempered ideology of the Nazis was about the worst the world has ever known, the German efforts provided a considerable impetus to the Allies to undertake the task. In 1943, the British came to the conclusion that the Germans had given up on making a nuclear bomb, but it was summer 1944 before the highest leadership of the American Manhattan Project became convinced on this point. When it became known that worries about the Germans were unfounded, the technological imperative of the Manhattan Project provided its own driving force. In any case, the U.S. military wanted the bomb for its own sake.

What if Nazi policy, with its unrelenting evil, had not driven out many of Germany's best brains? While the actual discovery of element 94, that is, plutonium, in the United States had not been published, the fact that it must be formed from the beta decay of neptunium (element 93) was appreciated, and also German physicists knew on theoretical grounds that it is easily fissionable by both slow and fast neutrons. Plenty of uranium ore was available in Czechoslovakia. Germany potentially had all the necessary means to make plutonium or uranium-235 bombs. Given the Nazi view of the world, they could conceivably have become victorious technological barbarians, but the wartime demands on their economy and bombing by the Allies would probably have prevented their success. One of the principal reasons why the Germans did not put a major effort into developing nuclear bombs was that Heisenberg grossly overestimated

A fateful error in calculation

Incidentally, after WW II ended, construction of nuclear reactors in Germany started. A company was created to manufacture uranium fuel elements for them. Its name was The Nukem Company.

the critical mass (4-16) of uranium-235. Incidentally, German scientists were simply astounded at the end of the war to learn of the Manhattan Project in the United States and what happened to Hiroshima. Ten captured German scientists, including Hahn and Heisenberg, were overheard and recorded in England in1945 discussing the new bomb. Heisenberg especially was skeptical and disbelieving that a nuclear weapon had been developed. After finally being convinced, the scientists quickly figured out the basic principles. Their conversations revealed the speed and resilience of the scientific mind, and also its conceit and self-absorption.

A curious incident in the German and Japanese nuclear programs took place in March to May, 1945. A German submarine, the U-234, was carrying war materiel to Japan; its manifest showed items such as proximity fuses, rockets, anti-aircraft shells, etc. Surprisingly, there were also ten canisters filled with 1200 pounds of uranium oxide. The submarine U-234 left northern Germany in March bound for Japan. After Hitler's death, the crew surrendered to American forces and the submarine was taken to a base in New Hampshire. There seems to be no conclusive information available on the intended purpose of the shipment to Japan, but it was probably to be used as a component in specialty steels or to replace tungsten in artillery shells. The captured uranium oxide evidently ended up in Oak Ridge.

3-18 The Japanese Nuclear Program

The nuclear program in Japan amounted to even less than that in Germany. A military scientist, Lt. General Takeo Yasuda, eagerly followed research on fission in Europe and in the United States. He had an aide find out whether uranium ores would be available to Japan if needed, and the answer was that adequate supplies were available in Korea, Manchuria, and Burma. Yasuda contacted Japan's leading nuclear physicist, Yoshio Nishina, who had studied under Rutherford in England and under Bohr in Denmark. Nishina had a cyclotron in Tokyo, one of five in Japan. He and his coworkers had discovered that uranium nuclei can be fissioned by fast neutrons as well as slow ones; this was in 1940. Nishina was one of several scientists in Japan who realized that in principle a nuclear bomb was possible. Nishina was authorized to explore the matter with a small team, which was financed with a grant equivalent to about $500,000. In addition, the Imperial Japanese Navy, recognizing that enormous amounts of nuclear energy were potentially available, authorized research to see if a means of propulsion of ships could be developed. This was led by Yoji Ito, a captain in the Navy Technology Research Institute. Hagiwara, mentioned earlier, was a member of the team making this investigation. The Navy also sponsored a project to investigate fission and possible nuclear bombs. It was headed by Professor Bunsaku Arakatsu, and was financed with an amount equal to $150,000.

Japanese scientists realized nuclear bombs are possible.

By 1943 several Japanese physicists were convinced that efforts to develop a nuclear bomb were underway in the United States. When they saw that a similar effort in Japan would consume 10% of their electrical energy and maybe half of their copper production in separating uranium from enormous quantities of uranium ore, followed by the even more difficult separation of uranium-235 from uranium-238, they concluded that success would be beyond the reach of both countries. But no really substantial support was forthcoming. Some research continued through 1944 on separation of uranium isotopes based on gaseous diffusion of uranium hexafluoride. In April, 1945, the laboratories in Tokyo were fire bombed out of existence, and that ended the modest research program.

The Prime Minister's office in Tokyo was informed of the destruction of Hiroshima, and at once phoned the University of Tokyo to get an opinion of a scientist. Radiochemist Kasuo Kuroda was available and expressed the opinion that the bomb used must have been atomic. Nishina was flown over Hiroshima two days after devastation of the city. The pattern of annihilation and the massive destruction by a single explosion convinced him and other physicists that the bomb had to have been nuclear since one or more thousand tons of TNT, far too much for any plane, would have been necessary. That flight must have induced intense emotions as Nishina watched. The first actual detection of radioactivity in a sample from Hiroshima, a piece of copper wire from a downed electric line, was conducted by Professor Motoharu Kimura on August 10, 1945. It had been activated by exposure to neutrons. Since his Geiger counter was out of order and no spare parts were available, Kimura used an electroscope, a simple but reliable instrument. A physician, Taro Takemi, worked with Nishina and found that human bones from the Hiroshima fatalities were also radioactive, in fact 2500 times background. It was Takemi who initiated contacts with the Emperor to inform him of these developments and to convince the military to come to their senses and accept surrender. Most records of the nuclear efforts in Japan were destroyed at the end of the war.

A couple of months after the war, orders from Gen. Groves' office in Tokyo were issued to destroy all the cyclotrons in Japan. In a mindless act, the instruments were cut to pieces and dumped into Tokyo Bay.

Rumors have been circulating for decades to the effect that Japan actually did succeed in making and test-exploding a uranium-235 bomb. They were started by David Snell, who published an article in the *Atlanta Constitution* on October 3, 1945. According to the story, facilities to construct the bomb had been moved to Hungnam, a city with an industrial complex in northern Korea. The nuclear test was alleged to have been made on a small island 20 miles from the mainland about the date when Nagasaki was destroyed. Hungnam was occupied by the Soviet military on August 22, 1945. Japan had the necessary scientific talent but, suffering unending bombing, simply did not have sufficient time and resources to build and operate a gaseous diffusion plant, using uranium hexafluoride vapor. They had not carried out the research necessary to make the porous barriers or to reduce the enriched material to uranium metal, or to master the multitude of other necessary steps. Nearly all of Japan's top nuclear scientists were occupied with the aftermath of the bombings of Hiroshima and Nagasaki, and thus were not in Korea, where most would have been if a nuclear bomb had been built and tested. After the American occupation, numerous investigations were made of the matter, all indicating that Japan had not constructed a uranium-235 bomb. Almost certainly, the claims of a Japanese nuclear bomb are in error. A critical analysis of the myth has been written by Grunden (see bibliography at end of chapter).

3-19 The Soviet Nuclear Program

The Soviets were alert.

Early Soviet Program—During the turbulent 1930s, Soviet scientists had made noteworthy progress in the nascent field of nuclear physics. As early as 1930 the Soviets had three nuclear research institutes. By 1937 their research was in areas such as absorption of gamma rays, nature of beta decay, cosmic rays, and interactions of nuclei with neutrons. Directly after the publication of the discovery of nuclear fission in Berlin in January 1939, physicist Frédéric Joliot-Curie, son-in-law of Madam Marie Curie, sent a letter to Abram F. Yoffe, an influential Russian physicist in Leningrad, which described this event. The letter produced a sensation. Shortly thereafter, Soviet physicist Igor Tamm, wrote that it "means a bomb can be built that will destroy a city out to a radius of maybe 10 kilometers." The Soviet bomb program did not become well known in the West until after World War II. This was due to both extreme secrecy on the part of the Russians and to poor intelligence work by the West. In 1939 a Commission on Uranium was appointed in Moscow. A year later, at the Lenin Radium Institute, calculations showed that a few kilograms of uranium-235 could form a bomb. Indeed, the newspaper *Izvestia* (December 21, 1940) published an article titled "Uranium" on this topic and named many Soviet scientists working on the matter. These included Igor V. Kurchatov, a brilliant physicist, who two years later was appointed manager of the nuclear effort. He enlisted the aid of two theoretical physicists, Khariton and Zel'dovich, who knew a great deal about nuclear chain reactions. The American Embassy in Moscow remained blissfully unaware of the Izvestia article.

Igor V. Kurchatov (1903–1960), Russian physicist. Educated in physics and mathematics at the University of the Crimea, he began studying nuclear physics in 1932 and supervised the construction of the largest cyclotron in Europe. He discovered nuclear isomers and piezoelectricity, and later studied nuclear chain reactions. In 1943 he headed a large part of the Soviet nuclear weapons program. Kurchatov supervised the first Soviet fission bomb and worked with Sakharov on their hydrogen bomb. He directed construction of the first nuclear reactor for civilian production of electricity in 1954.

By 1940 the Commission on Uranium, with V. G. Khlopin as chairman, undertook studies of isotope separation, production of heavy water, and exploration for uranium. Even before World War I, rich deposits of uranium ore were being mined in the Fergana Valley of Uzbekistan. Additional sources were quickly discovered in the Ural Mountains, in the Altai Mountains, and in Turkmenistan.

Soviets discover spontaneous fission

In 1940 Russian physicists Flerov and Konstantin Petrzhak discovered the phenomenon of spontaneous fission of uranium-238. This is remarkable because the exceedingly long half-life of this process (close to 10 thousand trillion years) requires that the most sensitive instruments be used. Even though the Soviet Union was invaded by Germany in 1941, much research continued, although work on the cyclotron at Leningrad was interrupted by the war. In 1942, Flerov wrote Stalin that all the big names in Western nuclear physics had suddenly stopped publishing, reinforcing suspicions of a giant undertaking. Flerov had tried to calculate the critical mass of pure uranium-235, getting 2.5 kilograms, which was too low. He also suggested the gun-assembly technique of detonating a bomb, as well as the implosion (compression) procedure.

In 1943 a research center was constructed in the Chelyabinsk-Zlatoust region in the Urals. Kurchatov and his group began plans to manufacture pure uranium metal and pure graphite, clearly with the objective of building a nuclear reactor. This was before the Soviets had learned (late in 1943) of the successful reactor built at the University of Chicago. Later that year through espionage the Soviets learned of an element of mass number 239 made in reactors (plutonium). Kurchatov also soon realized that the new element 93 (neptunium), being beta active, must yield element 94, which Seaborg and others had discovered. Using a cyclotron, the Russians produced some plutonium in 1944, remarkable considering wartime conditions. They also began to consider ways for separation of uranium-235 from the natural element. Despite receiving reports via espionage on the wartime American nuclear effort, Stalin had not taken the matter seriously until after Hiroshima. On August 20, 1945, he authorized an all-out, relentless initiative to develop a nuclear bomb and to break the American monopoly.

Kurchatov's brother Boris, a chemist, produced the first batch of the new element in October, 1944. A few micrograms of it had been made in the Leningrad cyclotron. Igor Kurchatov designed a small graphite-moderated reactor called F-1 (probably from *fizika*, Russian for physics, but maybe from Fursov, a physicist), built in Moscow. The reactor began operation on Christmas day, 1946. Its design was suspiciously similar to that of the small test reactor built in 1944 at Hanford, known as Hanford 305, and almost certainly incorporated features based on espionage.

The enlarged post-war project was directed by B. L. Vannikov. By 1948 extraction of plutonium from the uranium in this reactor was underway. In June 1948 a task force was formed at the Physics Institute to investigate the feasibility of a hydrogen bomb; Sakharov was a member. This was at a virulent period of the Cold War, when a number of American military officers made appeals to destroy the Soviet Union in a preventive war using nuclear bombs.

A city renamed Arzamas-16, about 250 miles east of Moscow, can be regarded as a sort of Russian Los Alamos (see 9-24). It was begun in 1946, and was fenced off and guarded. It could be not found on any map although it had a population of 100,000.

About the time the first American bomb test was being readied in New Mexico, Soviet troops had overrun Czechoslovakia and eastern Germany. Within a short time uranium ores from these areas began to flow to the Soviet Union. News of American nuclear explosions was a blow to the Soviets, and must have seemed threatening to them.

Captured Scientists—By the end of the war in Europe, American forces had captured many German scientists, and, after sanitizing their Nazi records when needed, employed them; the most famous of these was SS Colonel Wernher von Braun, an expert in rocketry. The Soviets had also captured German and Austrian scientists, the number said to be more than 3000, and had sent them to their scientific centers. These included Manfried von Ardenne, and Gustav Herz, (a Nobelist), Hans Barwich, Friedrich Walter, Germot Zippe, Max Volmer, and Nikolaus Riehl. Considerable detail is available about the case of Riehl, since he wrote an autobiographical account. He was sent first to Elektrostal east of Berlin, and was allowed to send for his wife and two children, a common practice with the other scientists. He helped develop a technique for preparing pure uranium metal in ton quantities; the procedure strongly resembled the American process, that is, it used uranium tetrafluoride "green salt" and calcium or magnesium metal. In 1950 Riehl was sent to Sungul, east of the Ural Mountains, and worked in radiochemistry and radiation biology. In 1952 he was transferred to Sukhumi, in Soviet Georgia, and helped Zippe develop the centrifugal method of separating uranium-235 (4-30), work which was not classified secret. Riehl and his family were repatriated in 1955. The German scientists enjoyed a much higher living standard than Soviet citizens did. Soviet programs were accelerated by these foreign scientists, but did not depend critically on them.

Captured German scientists

Spies—A Canadian physicist, Alan N. May, acted in the role of a spy, and funneled information on the bomb to the Soviets. He received a ten-year prison sentence. Ted Hall, a young American physicist working at Los Alamos, volunteered to provide the Soviets with considerable classified information, especially about the implosion principle. A British physicist of German origin, Klaus Fuchs, had been feeding information about American nuclear bomb manufacture to the Soviets from 1942 to 1949. Suspicion first fell on Fuchs after the U.S. Signal Corps, using new techniques, began decoding old messages. One, sent in 1944 from a Soviet Consulate to Moscow, referred to a helpful British scientist. Fuchs had sent a rather detailed cross-sectional sketch of the first American nuclear bomb. This spying was discovered in Britain in 1950, and Fuchs was imprisoned for nine years; upon release, he went to East Germany. The motives of these three men were ideological, not mercenary. While the data which Fuchs supplied the Soviets must have been of considerable aid to them, it is well not to overemphasize its importance. It is known that much of the information concerning hydrogen bombs which Fuchs gave to the Soviets was wrong. With or without his help, the situation today would probably be about the same. After all, it is very probable that the Soviets gained a great deal of useful information from analysis of fission products, tritium, and especially transuranium elements from fallout arising from the 1952 American hydrogen bomb test. The data revealed that an extremely high pressure must have been generated and that it was a two-stage device, leaving a distinctive signature. The British made similar analyses of debris from the Soviet test, and thus accelerated production of their own hydrogen bomb.

The Soviets worked furiously to develop a nuclear bomb program, making great sacrifices and toiling night and day. Just as the thought of the mere possibility of nuclear bombs in the hands of the Nazis was simply intolerable to Americans and the English, so also the proven nuclear bomb capacity of the United States was wholly unacceptable to the Soviets.

3-20 The Cold War Begins

For a short time after the war ended, something like a state of euphoria set in among the nuclear community in the U.S.: the ultimate weapon had been achieved, so nuclear weapons would never be used again against human beings, and the world would now have an abundance of energy. But the nation-state political structure of the world survived, and now, with no common enemy, the jealousies of sovereign nations began to be evident. It was inevitable that the Cold War would reappear, and that this would lead to a nuclear arms race.

The American military forces tested a number of nuclear bombs in the Pacific Ocean during the years immediately after World War II. These weapons were in the 10 to 20 kiloton range. The vulnerability of battleships to nuclear bombs was demonstrated. Tests were begun at Bikini in the Pacific, using old American, Japanese, and German warships as steel guinea pigs. Tests code-named *Able* and *Baker* were made in 1946, sinking 12 ships. An aircraft carrier, the Saratoga, which had seen service at Wake Island, Guadalcanal, and Iwo Jima, is today an underwater hulk, submerged more than 50 years, and encrusted with rust and marine growth. In retrospect, it appears as if Operation Crossroads, as the exercises were called, were really a consequence of interservice rivalry. The Navy was desperate to prove that the new bomb had not made their ships obsolete.

Nuclear weapons began to be integrated into the armed forces. To accelerate production of implosion warheads, tests were conducted to see whether some or all of the plutonium-239 could be replaced with the more abundant uranium-235. Tests at Eniwetak in the spring of 1948 showed that this was possible. These trials and others permitted building smaller warheads. The Nagasaki bomb weighed 10,000 pounds. The bombs made a few years later, some with yield five times that of its ancestor, were smaller in diameter and considerably lighter. The Mark 5 was about 43 inches in diameter and weighed 3300 pounds. The Mark 7 was only 32 inches in diameter and was still lighter. Its yield ranged from 10 to 60 kilotons. The Mark 12 was as little as 22 inches across. This warhead was the first which could be carried by a plane externally and at supersonic velocity. Advances in compression of the pit or core of a bomb led to more powerful explosions and higher efficiency. Mark 18 was the most powerful fission bomb built. Its yield was 500 kilotons, thus rivaling hydrogen bombs.

In 1947 Congress authorized formation Atomic Energy Commission, which was charged with overseeing both civilian and military nuclear activities.

By 1948 the American inventory of nuclear bombs had reached approximately 50. The American Secretary of State, Dean Acheson, and the chairman of the new Atomic Energy Commission, David Lilienthal sought to share scientific knowledge with the Soviets in order to achieve international control over this dreadful new force. But many military leaders, ignoring advice of the scientists, naively thought that American monopoly in the field would endure. American officials employed the bomb as a sort of trump card in diplomatic bargaining, which the Soviets interpreted as attempts to intimidate them. Excessive reliance on nuclear weapons fostered a climate of secrecy and suspicion, and caused the role of spies to be much overemphasized.

More bombs, more destructive bombs

In 1954 President Eisenhower directed the Joint Chiefs of Staff to devise strategic plans to bombard military targets with nuclear warheads if the Chinese resumed the war in Korea or invaded Vietnam. The chair of the Joint Chiefs of Staff, Admiral A.W. Radford, favored donating nuclear weapons to the French for use in Indo-China, but Eisenhower wisely vetoed the idea. But contradictory information is that Peter Davis, in his 1974 documentary "Hearts and Minds," the U.S. offered two nuclear bombs to the French before their defeat at Dien Bien Phu, but that France declined this overture.

3-21 Continued Nuclear Developments in the Soviet Union

First Soviet nuclear explosion

Predictably, the Soviets had restructured and greatly strengthened their own nuclear weapons program. A great advantage was the certainty that nuclear bombs could be made. It required about the same length of time for success as the American program did. Forced labor of prisoners was used in mining uranium, and to some extent in construction of nuclear reactors and plutonium processing facilities. The compelling rush to make a bomb was so intense that fresh, extraordinarily dangerous spent fuel from the reactor was processed. The deadly radioactive waste was simply dumped into the Techa River, afflicting the people downstream (8-7). By late spring 1949, the Soviets had accumulated enough plutonium to make a test explosion, but the wily Stalin ordered waiting until enough more had been prepared for a second bomb. He evidently felt the need for a deterrent in case Americans behaved irrationally after the first test. By August a second bomb was ready.

The first Soviet test, August 29, 1949

Kurchatov, in a state of nervous tension, directed the first Soviet test explosion. Code-named *Pervaya Molniya* (meaning *First Lightning*), it was conducted in the early morning of August 29, 1949, at the Semipalatinsk test site in the eastern part of the Kazakh Republic (9-22). Analyses of particulate matter from the atmosphere in Alaska and Canada revealed unmistakable evidence of traces of fission products (from fission of plutonium-239, not uranium-235) coming from Asia, revealing the first test explosion of a Soviet nuclear bomb. Washington was shocked. The fruits of this work were shown in the result: the percentage of atoms which underwent fission, reportedly around 35%, was higher than that in the first American test. Thus the atomic bomb gave the U.S. only a transient superiority. The Soviet test (photo) was irreverently dubbed *Joe 1* by Arnold Kramish after Joseph Stalin. The excessive dependence of the United States on atomic deterrence meant that news of a Soviet weapon was particularly shocking to American policy makers. The arms race took a giant step forward when they decided that nuclear superiority could only be achieved through a superbomb. The quest became a new psychological and military imperative.

The idea of shaped charges (9-5), to effect extraordinary compression of the plutonium in the cores of both American and Soviet bombs, was already quite well developed by the Soviets. Its importance was brought home to them in 1942, when they examined captured German anti-tank munitions and found that the principles of shaped charges had been incorporated in the projectiles. They even studied the impact of shaped-charge projectiles on steel using microsecond X-ray radiography.

That the Soviets had also developed facilities for separation of uranium-235 was shown by explosion of a bomb in 1951 containing this material and plutonium-239. Each side in effect goaded the other into an arms race. Americans, with more resources and facilities, generally took the first step and the Soviets followed or reacted.

3-22 The Hydrogen Bomb

Nuclear physicists had been aware from prewar times that the nuclear reaction which drives the Sun and other stars is the joining of hydrogen nuclei together to form helium; this is called nuclear or thermonuclear fusion. A novel idea occurred to physicist Enrico Fermi in September, 1941, namely that it might be possible to use a fission bomb as a trigger to cause the fusion of hydrogen, resulting in a truly monstrous explosion. He shared the concept with his colleague Edward Teller, who enthusiastically accepted it almost to the point of obsession. By 1950, after the first Soviet nuclear explosion, pressures for building such a hydrogen bomb were intense. The wisdom of embarking on a hydrogen bomb program was debated fiercely. After all, hydrogen bombs were expected to have a thousand times more energy than Hiroshima-type fission bombs. Teller feared the Russians might be working on this possibility and advised that it be given urgent attention. Physicists Robert J. Oppenheimer, and Hans Bethe, felt that there was no demonstrable need for a hydrogen bomb, and agonized over the question. But President Truman, prompted by the Soviet nuclear developments, ordered full speed ahead. There was never any real doubt about the decision; it was foreordained by the institutionalized habit of war which the human species has adopted. In this case, the United States, being richer but insecure, took the lead in both quality and quantity of weapons. The story of the hydrogen bomb is best told by Richard Rhodes, in his "Dark Sun: The Making of the Hydrogen Bomb" (see bibliography at end of chapter).

Hans Bethe (1906–), German-born physicist, came to the United States in 1935. Clarified origin of the sun's energy by fusion. Active in theories of supernovae and mesons. Theoretical physicist at Los Alamos, 1943–1946. Supported bombing of Hiroshima, but not Nagasaki. Opposed development of hydrogen bomb and Strategic Defense Initiative. Fermi Award in 1961. Nobel Prize in physics in 1967.

Mechanical calculating machines had been used in generating models of the chain reaction involved in *fission* bombs, but a much more elaborate mathematical model of the progress of events on detonation of a *fusion* bomb was needed. This step in creating a hydrogen bomb entailed coupling a fission device as a trigger to initiate fusion in the fuel. This computer program was formidable indeed, and its analysis was one of the most challenging tasks ever undertaken by mathematicians. It had to accommodate the evolution of a thermonuclear explosion in stages of a fraction of a microsecond.

One of the mathematicians concerned with this problem was John von Neumann, a most talented genius. He adopted Herman Goldstine's vacuum-tube calculator built at the University of Pennsylvania in 1944. This was called ENIAC (for Electronic Numerical Integrator And Computer). Von Neumann later designed and built MANIAC I (an advanced version) in 1952, the first computer with a flexible program. A British mathematician, Alan Turing, had come up with the idea of computers in 1935 (he also suggested artificial intelligence), but it was von Neumann who wrote a paper early in 1945 suggesting the concept of a stored, programmable calculating system. This development gave rise, in time, to hand-held calculators and giant computers. These developments stimulated Teller to pursue the idea of hydrogen bombs further, work which continued after the end of the war in 1945.

John von Neumann (1903–1957), Born in Hungary, recognized as a talented mathematician as a young boy. Came to the United States in 1930 and became professor at Princeton in 1933. Equally at home in pure and in applied mathematics and in mathematical physics. Joined the Manhattan Project in 1943. Founded a new branch of mathematics, theory of games. Fermi Award in 1956.

Stanislaw Ulam (1909–1984), Born in Poland, immigrated to the United States in the 1930s. Mathematician and early computer scientist. Worked at Institute for Advanced Studies at Princeton University. Went to Los Alamos in 1943. Studied hydrodynamics of implosions. Contributed to mathematics of many branches of science. Taught briefly at the University of Southern California.

The mathematician Stanislaw Ulam undertook the problem, and his results disclosed that the bomb design suggested by Teller in 1950 would probably fail. By February 1951 Ulam and Teller had evolved a new principle, which can properly be described as a critical breakthrough, namely to employ the X-rays from the fission bomb to compress and ignite the fusion mass. This idea, along with the use of uranium-238 as a reflector of X-rays, was the development described by Oppenheimer's famous phrase "technically . . . sweet." Teller became "the father of the hydrogen bomb" in folk history.

The hydrogen bomb—a new horror

The new principles for the hydrogen bomb (also called thermonuclear bomb) were subjected to preliminary tests and the first thermonuclear device was exploded on one of the islands at Enewetak Atoll in the Pacific on October 31, 1952. This blast was code-named *Mike*. Weighing 65 tons, the "device" was not a deliverable bomb. Since it contained liquid deuterium with some tritium, it had to be equipped with cryogenic refrigeration, using liquid hydrogen. But its energy or yield was unexpectedly high, 10.4 megatons. This number is a celestial statistic. It means 10,400,000 tons of TNT equivalency, a sum almost outside of human comprehension. The explosion eliminated the island of Elugelab, and created a crater in its place 175 feet deep and 6240 feet across. The fireball was several miles across. The radiation flash of this and other tests was intense enough to ignite the feathers of birds flying miles away.

In addition, the political temperature of the world was raised. Einstein expressed his heartache: "If I had known that the Germans would not succeed in constructing the atom bomb, I would never have lifted a finger." The 1954 tests proved that tritium in large quantities is not necessary for a hydrogen bomb. In 1951 Teller and Hoffmann issued a report showing that the light isotope of lithium (mass number 6) is expected to serve as a tritium generator inside an exploding nuclear bomb.

Priming the Cold War pump

Lithium-6 on irradiation by fast neutrons splits into tritium and helium. Thus a hydrogen bomb using this nuclide would generate part of its own fuel since the tritium formed fuses with deuterium.

Incidentally, two new chemical elements were discovered in the debris from the *Mike* shot described above. They were elements 99 and 100, later named einsteinium (Es-254) and fermium (Fm-257), respectively.

3-23 Nuclear Developments in China and India

All this time, the Chinese were developing their nuclear capacity. In the early 1960s, American U-2 spy planes flew from Taiwan and photographed a factory constructed to separate uranium-235. On October 16, 1964, China's first fission bomb was tested in a dry lake at Lop Nor, Xinjiang (Sinkiang). Its fissionable material was uranium-235, not plutonium-239, indicating a more sophisticated technology than was generally expected. Along with this test, China announced that it would never be the first to use nuclear weapons. Other tests soon followed. In 1966 they launched their first guided missile, and exploded a 20 kiloton weapon carried by missile. The first Chinese hydrogen bomb was exploded in June,1967. Its energy was at least three megatons.

China and India join the nuclear club.

India carried out a successful nuclear bomb test in 1974 at its Pokaran site in the western Rajasthan Desert. It was a plutonium-239 bomb detonated 320 feet underground (more data in 9-45). The test was called "Smiling Buddha."

3-24 The Nuclear Arms Race Heats Up

The development of nuclear bombs by the United States and the Soviet Union, and especially the explosion of an incredibly potent hydrogen bomb by the Americans, goaded other powers to join the competition. The war in Korea was raging, further stimulating military expenditures. There was talk of dropping nuclear waste or cobalt-60, both radioactive enough to be deadly, across the Korean peninsula to seal off troop movements. The chronology below summarizes important points in nuclear developments.

1951: Spies? —The Cold War, now bolstered by the war in Korea, had spawned a fearful and ghastly political climate in the United States, commonly identified by the name of one of its enthusiastic instigators, Sen. Joseph McCarthy. In this atmosphere a New York couple, Julius and Ethel Rosenberg, were charged with implication in spying and passing information on nuclear bombs to the Soviets. In the trial in 1951, they were convicted not of spying, but of conspiracy to spy, under the Espionage Act of 1917. The circumstances were complicated and many people were involved. The matter involved was a sketch which was alleged to show the implosion principle for detonation of bombs; this concept in modified forms had already been long known to German and Soviet scientists. After many years the sketch was made public and it proved to be erroneous and worthless.

For those too young to have lived through those years, it is difficult to communicate the virtually paranoid mood of the times. For example, William Rehnquist, now chief justice but then a law clerk, wrote "It is too bad that drawing and quartering has been abolished." This was just before the Rosenbergs were executed in 1953. Their young children were even prohibited from attending public school.

In 1995, the National Security Agency declassified Soviet messages concerning the Rosenberg case which had been intercepted and decoded in 1943-45. These revelations, assuming they are authentic, confirm that Julius Rosenberg, but not his wife, had indeed been involved in transfer of information, nearly all nonnuclear, to the Soviets. But these disclosures could not be used in the trial without compromising the fact that the Soviet code had been broken. The Justice Department and FBI therefore framed the Rosenbergs using false evidence, and by co-opting one of the defendants' lawyers to act as informer. The case against Ethel Rosenberg was particularly weak. A retired Soviet spy, Alexander Feklisov, who had many contacts with Fuchs in London in 1947, wrote in his detailed memoirs that Julius Rosenberg played almost no role in atomic espionage, and that his wife had no role. Many, perhaps most, observers familiar with the case feel that a miscarriage of justice took place.

1951: The Korean War—Albert Gore, father of Vice President Gore in the Clinton Administration, regarded that war as a "meat grinder of American manhood." As a Senator he had taken an aggressive stance in the Korean War. He advocated creating a dangerously radioactive belt across the Korean peninsula, a view with which General Douglas MacArthur, agreed. Still, Gore Sr. became a progressive in social affairs, and later opposed the war in Vietnam. Passions ran so high during the Korean War that Commandant Orville Anderson, of the Air War College announced that the Air Force was ready and awaited orders to drop nuclear bombs on Moscow.

1952: The First Hydrogen-Fusion Explosion—The first thermonuclear device was exploded on Eniwetak near Bikini, as described earlier.

1952: The First British test—On October 3, the British exploded a fission device suspended 90 feet under a frigate near the Monte Bello Islands, just west of Australia. The ship was obliterated. The United Kingdom nuclear facility was called the Atomic Weapons Establishment, with the appropriate acronym AWE. In the next year, the British constructed their first deliverable nuclear warhead, in a family of weapons called the Blue Danube. It had both plutonium-239 and uranium-235 in an implosion assembly.

1952: Another Bomb Lab—A second nuclear facility was created at Livermore laboratory California, at the urging of Edward Teller and Ernest Lawrence. Two years later Teller undermined Oppenheimer by providing damaging and odious assertions about him to the Atomic Energy Commission. Oppenheimer was stripped of his security clearance; he was essentially another victim of McCarthyism. No one benefited from this.

More expensive steps in the Cold War

1953:The Soviet Hydrogen Bomb—On August 12, the Russians carried out their first test of a hydrogen bomb. This was at the Semipalatinsk test site in Kazakhstan. It used lithium deuteride and tritium. The yield has been variously reported, but a credible value is 400 to 470 kilotons.

1953-54: Bomb China?—American intelligence agencies seriously weighed the possibility of dropping nuclear bombs on China in an attempt to bring the Korean War to a conclusion favorable to the U.S. William C. Bullitt, a former ambassador to the Soviet Union, using inflammatory language, supported such attacks on China, and also bombing Soviet nuclear facilities.

1954: The Mightiest American Bomb—A second hydrogen bomb or, second device (one that could be considered to be a bomb) was detonated on March 1, this time at Bikini Atoll. Code-named *Bravo* it was even more powerful than the first, being approximately 15 megatons (details in 9-19). It weighed 21 tons and could be delivered by plane. It contained no liquid deuterium, but lithium deuteride solid. The radioactive fallout, as a fine ash, exposed 250 Marshallese people and 23 Japanese fishermen 80 miles away. Residual radioactivity was to cause grievous problems for decades, and continues to this day.

1954-55: Influential Scientists—One of the more remarkable physicists working at Los Alamos was Joseph Rotblat. He went from his native Poland to London for a research project, and became a British citizen after the Nazi armies occupied most of his homeland. By early 1944 Rotblat knew that the Germans would not finish a nuclear bomb before being defeated by the Allies. He became convinced that the world would be worse off with nuclear weapons. He quit the Manhattan Project in 1945, the only such case in which the person cited moral reasons. (His Soviet counterpart was Lev Landau, who quit his country's nuclear bomb program as soon as practical; 9-23). After the war his fears materialized: Cold War became reality. Rotblat devoted his energies to nuclear disarmament, but he also studied the effects of ionizing radiation on the human body.

Joseph Rotblat (1908–), Polish physicist. Director, Institute of Atomic Research, Warsaw, 1937–1939, after which he went to England. Manhattan Project (Los Alamos) 1943–1945. Returning to England, he became director of nuclear physics at the universities of Liverpool and London, mostly in medical physics. Secretary-general of the Pugwash Conference. Long active in science and world affairs. Nobel prize in 1995.

Toward the end of 1954 British philosopher Bertrand Russell, stimulated by Rotblat's dogged pursuit of disarmament, drafted a manifesto which cited the Bikini tests and the danger from hydrogen bombs (American and Soviet) as "stark and dreadful and inescapable." Rotblat was one of eleven prominent signatories; seven were Nobel Prize winners who endorsed the manifesto, including Linus Pauling, Frederic Joliot-Curie, and Alber Einstein. It was April 1955 when Einstein signed the manifesto, two days before his death. The papers became known as the Einstein-Russell Accords. These events led Rotblat to arrange a now-famous meeting. Twenty-four international scientists met at Pugwash, Nova Scotia in 1957 to formulate means for confronting the new threat. Leo Szilard was another moving spirit behind these conferences. Going beyond fission bombs, fusion bombs appeared to take the destiny of the world beyond human control. From the outset, in a series of conferences bearing the Pugwash label, the scientists' efforts began to bear fruit. Methods of effectively monitoring arms control agreements emerged. It was the Pugwash meetings which suggested seismic monitoring of underground tests. In 1995, Rotblat himself was awarded the Nobel Peace Prize, along with his Pugwash Conferences on Science and World Affairs.

1955: Soviet Hydrogen Bombs—Late in the year (November 6) the Soviets exploded a hydrogen bomb (details in 9-23). The bomb was on a tower, although it was light enough to be delivered by plane. It contained uranium-235 and a uranium-238 tamper, as well as lithium deuteride. Its yield was 215 kilotons. The leading Soviet scientist in this work was Andrei Sakharov, a pained intellectual. Sakharov independently devised more or less the same principles used in American hydrogen bombs.

Andrei Sakharov (1921–1989), Russian physicist. He published on cosmic rays, electron-positron annihilation, and many nuclear matters, as well as a luminous **samizdat** ***on intellectual freedom. Sakharov was a principal figure in the development of the Soviet hydrogen bomb. This towering scientist was exiled to Gorky from 1980 to 1986 because he attacked calcified government policies, such as censorship (a chastity belt for the mind). Nobel Peace Prize in 1975.***

Shortly after the above test, the Soviets exploded a second hydrogen bomb (November 22). Curiously enough, it contained both uranium-233 and uranium-235, but no plutonium. It was carried by plane. The weather turned cloudy and the pilot could not see the target. He requested permission to land. After a hurried conference between Sakharov and Kurchatov, this was granted, and the plane landed safely. The next day the fog had lifted, and the bomb was exploded; its yield was 1.6 megatons.

A few years later Sakharov regretted the whole endeavor, and became an advocate of disarmament and stopping all atomic tests. Concerning nuclear warheads, Sakharov wrote, "But understanding something in an abstract way is different from feeling it with your whole being, like the reality of life and death." He was awarded the Nobel Peace Prize in 1975, but was so out of favor with the Soviet government that he was not allowed to receive it personally. Although he had been branded a "dupe of the CIA," he was freed from exile by Gorbachev, and became a strong human-rights advocate. His colleague Igor Tamm, also a Nobelist (physics, 1958) played an important role in Soviet weapons development.

1957: The British Hydrogen Bomb—In May the British carried out fusion experiments with explosions in the Christmas Islands. It might have been that these were their first two attempts to detonate hydrogen bombs and they were duds, pushing the British to collaborate more fully with American scientists. The British analyzed fallout from American thermonuclear blasts to aid in their research. Subsequently the British successfully tested hydrogen bombs, the first in November 1957. These were the Mosaic series, and were single stage, like Sakharov's *Sloika* (9-23). They developed hydrogen bombs at a later date (April 1958; see 9-15).

1957: The Soviet Satellite—Scientists in the Soviet Union shocked the world by sending the first satellite (called Sputnik) into orbit around the Earth. This epochal event was interpreted as impending ability to launch nuclear weapons to any point on Earth. Another dimension was added to the arms race. Both superpowers commenced energetic research programs with the objective of developing a series of intercontinental and other missiles.

1957: IAEA—The International Atomic Energy Agency was established, with headquarters in Vienna. It runs the safeguards inspection for the world, and offers technical assistance in a wide variety of nonmilitary nuclear-related efforts.

1960: French Bombs—The French had never felt that the United States would risk its own destruction to save France, and so were driven to build their own nuclear deterrent. Their first fission weapon was tested in the Algerian Sahara Desert on February 13, 1960. In later years the French carried out many explosions, over the protests of the New Zealanders and Australians, in the South Pacific around Moruroa Atoll. They used both uranium-235 and plutonium-239. During this period, the attitude of the great powers is illustrated by Charles de Gaulle. Informed that the winds would blow fallout from a proposed test onto nearby islands and their populations, de Gaulle is reported to have answered, "I'm a busy man. Conduct the test anyway."

1961: The Mightiest Bomb Ever—On October 30, the Soviets exploded the mightiest bomb ever created by human beings. This monster was detonated at 12,000 feet on the island Novaya Zemlya in the Arctic, and had the power of 58 million tons of TNT. The power and energy of this explosion is almost unimaginable (see 9-14). The Soviets must have realized that such a bomb would have minimal military value, but a huge political effect.

"My bomb is bigger than your bomb."

1968: French H-Bomb—The French exploded their first hydrogen bomb in August.

1974-77: Weapons Centers and National Labs—The Atomic Energy Commission was converted into the Energy Research and Development Administration in 1974, and this in turn was transmuted into the Department of Energy by Congress in 1977. This agency regulates commercial nuclear reactors (via the Nuclear Regulatory Commission) and the nuclear weapons centers, such as those at Hanford, Rocky Flats, Pantex, and Savannah River (Chapter 9), but also the venerable National Laboratories. In 1996, the nine principal such Laboratories had an annual budget exceeding $6.5 billion and about 47,200 employees. These Laboratories and their sponsors are:

Argonne National Laboratory, Illinois (University of Chicago)
Brookhaven National Laboratory, Long Island, NY (Associated Universities, Inc.)
Lawrence Berkeley National Laboratory, Berkeley, CA (University of California)
Lawrence Livermore Laboratory, California (University of California)
Los Alamos National Laboratory, New Mexico (University of California)
National Engineering Laboratory, Idaho (multiple sponsors)
Oak Ridge National Laboratory, Tennessee (Martin Marietta Energy Systems)
Pacific Northwest National Laboratory, Hanford, WA (Battelle Memorial Institute)
Sandia National Laboratory, New Mexico (Martin Marietta Corp.)

3-25 The Limited Test Ban and Non-Proliferation Treaties

By 1963 a great deal of public protest against nuclear testing in the atmosphere had taken place. One fission product, strontium-90, became especially notorious; resembling calcium chemically, it entered the world's food supply, and milk for children became suspect owing to the radioactivity. Linus Pauling, a recipient of two Nobel Prizes (chemistry, peace) was a leader in the drive to ban atmospheric tests. He personally submitted a petition with the signatures of 11,000 prominent scientists worldwide to the United Nations. This was a key stimulus which led to the 1963 treaty. Its full name is Treaty Banning Nuclear Weapon Tests in the Atmosphere, in Outer Space and Under Water, but it is generally referred to as the Limited Test Ban Treaty or the Partial Test Ban Treaty. It was signed by J.F. Kennedy and Nikita Khruschev. France and China and others declined to sign, but by 1991 the French changed their mind and signed.

The Non-Proliferation Treaty, instituted in 1970, had over 160 signatory nations by the year 1994. Under its terms, the original nuclear powers (USA, USSR, UK, France, and China) agreed not to transfer nuclear weapons to nonnuclear states. Likewise, these states agreed not to receive, manufacture, or acquire nuclear weapons in any way. The Treaty calls for complete nuclear disarmament by all states, but it gave no schedule on this point.

3-26 Role of Nuclear Weapons Today

By 1990, our world had become a teetering nuclear powder keg. The total nuclear fire-power was about 13,000 megatons, several thousand times the combined firepower spent in all previous wars combined. Physicist Richard L Garwin said that if he "could wave a wand" and make the nuclear age go away, "he would do that." The basic concept of nuclear deterrence had become a profound paradox. It was based on the illusion that nuclear conflagration can only be prevented by arming to the teeth and threatening to use one's arsenal. The demise of the Soviet Union and thus the Cold War in the period 1989 to 1991 precipitated substantial changes in political

The end of the Cold War gives us time. Let's use it wisely.

orientation and nuclear policies of not only the principal powers, but also of many other countries. The Comprehensive Test Ban of 1996, despite its flaws and without American ratification, will help put a damper on further growth of nuclear bombs in our world, and will contribute to reduction of the numbers. Nevertheless, nuclear weapons and deterrence still play a strong role in American national security policies. Accounts of the status of a number of nations which aspired to acquire the bomb, as well as related matters, are given chapter 9.

3-27 Our Responsibility Today

In 1991 the Soviet government crumbled, and the Cold War ended. Our overriding obligation since that time is to commit ourselves in every way possible to insure that never again do we indulge in another mindless nuclear arms race which would pose such dreadful consequences for the human species. The world had some good luck last time; if we allow this lunacy to take place again, our fates could well be different—and fatal.

3- 28 Bibliography for Chapter 3: The Road to the Bomb—and Beyond

Tatsuichiro Akizuki, *NAGASAKI 1945 (an eyewitness account),* Quartet Books, London, 1981.

Jeremy Bernstein, *HITLER'S URANIUM CLUB*, American Institute of Physics, Williston, VT, 1995.

Hans A. Bethe, *THE ROAD FROM LOS ALAMOS*, American Institute of Physics, Williston, VT, 1991.

Kai Bird and Lawrence Lifschultz, Eds., *HIROSHIMA'S SHADOW: Writings on the Denial of History and the Smithsonian Controversy*, The Pamphleteer's Press, Box 3374, Stony Creek, CT 06405,1998.

Farhataziz and M. A. J. Rodgers, *RADIATION CHEMISTRY*, VCH Publishers, 1987.

Rachel Fermi and Esther Samra, *PICTURE THE BOMB: PHOTOGRAPHS FROM THE SECRET WORLD OF THE MANHATTAN PROJECT*, Harry N. Abrams, Publisher, NY, 1995.

Richard L. Garwin and Georges Charpak, *MEGAWATTS AND MEGATONS*, Alfred A. Knopf, 2001.

Walter E. Grunden, *INTELLIGENCE AND NATIONAL SECURITY*, Vol. 13, No. 2, p. 32, 1998.

Gregg Herken, *BROTHERHOOD OF THE BOMB: THE HUNT FOR OPPENHEIMER*, Smithsonian Institution, 2002.

Hiroshima Peace Museum, *THE SPIRIT OF HIROSHIMA*, a modern pictorial review, 1-2 Nakajima-cho, Naka-ku, Hiroshima City 730-0811, Japan, 1999.

Lillian Hoddeson et al., *CRITICAL ASSEMBLY: A TECHNICAL HISTORY OF LOS ALAMOS DURING THE OPPENHEIMER YEARS 1943–1945*, Cambridge University Press, 1993/94.

Darleane C. Hoffman, Albert Ghiorso, and Glenn T. Seaborg, *THE TRANSURANIUM PEOPLE: THE INSIDE STORY*, Imperial College Press, 2000.

Vincent C. Jones, *MANHATTAN: THE ARMY AND THE ATOMIC BOMB*, Center for Military History, U.S. Army, Washington, DC, 1985.

Kawade Shobo Shin-Sha Editorial Staff, *DEAD SPEAK OF WAR*. Published by Masaru Shimizu, 2-32-29 Sendagaya, Shibuya-Ku, Tokyo, 1993.

Motoharu Kimura with John M. Carpenter, *LIVING WITH NUCLEI*, Tsukiji Shokan Publishers, Tokyo, 1993.

William Lanouette with Bela Szilard, *GENIUS IN THE SHADOWS: A BIOGRAPHY OF LEO SZILARD, THE MAN BEHIND THE BOMB*, Charles Schribner's Sons, 1992.

Marlene Rayner-Canham and Geoffrey Rayner-Canham, *A DEVOTION TO THEIR SCIENCE: PIONEER WOMEN OF RADIOACTIVITY*, Chemical Heritage Foundation and McGill-Queen University Press, Montreal, 1997.

Richard Rhodes, *THE MAKING OF THE ATOMIC BOMB*, Simon & Schuster, N. Y, 1986.

Richard Rhodes, *DARK SUN: THE MAKING OF THE HYDROGEN BOMB*, Simon & Schuster, 1995.

Mark B. Schneider, *NUCLEAR WEAPONS AND AMERICAN STRATEGY, 1945–1953*, a Ph. D. dissertation, The University of Southern California, Los Angeles, 1974.

Glenn T. Seaborg, *THE PLUTONIUM STORY*, Battelle Press, Columbus, OH, 1994.

Robert Serber with Robert P. Crease, *PEACE AND WAR: REMINISCENSES OF A LIFE ON THE FRONTIERS OF SCIENCE*, Columbia University Press, 1998.

Naomi Shohno, *THE LEGACY OF HIROSHIMA*, Kosei Publishing Co., 2-7-1 Wada, Suginami-ku, Tokyo 166, 1986.

Ruth L. Sime, *LISE MEITNER, A LIFE IN PHYSICS*, University of California Press, Berkeley, 1996.

Henry DeWolf Smyth, *ATOMIC ENERGY FOR MILITARY PURPOSES* (The Official Report on the Atomic Bomb), Princeton University Press, 1947.

Hans Tammemagi and David Jackson, *UNLOCKING THE ATOM*, McMaster University Press, Hamilton, Ontario, Canada, 2001.

Stanislaw Ulam, *ADVENTURES OF A MATHEMATICIAN: MEMOIRS OF THE MANHATTAN PROJECT*, Schribner, 1976.

Mark Walker, *GERMAN NATIONAL SOCIALISM AND THE QUEST FOR NUCLEAR POWER*, Cambridge University Press, 1989.

C. W. J. Wilson, Ed., *WORLD NUCLEAR DIRECTORY*, Sixth Edition, (A guide to organizations and research in nuclear energy), Longman, Essex, United Kingdom.

Peter Wyden, *DAY ONE: BEFORE AND AFTER HIROSHIMA*, Simon & Schuster, 1984.

Chapter 4: NUCLEAR SCIENCE, RADIOACTIVITY, AND ENERGY: A REVIEW

ABSTRACT—The structures of atoms and their nuclei are examined, as well as the way Nature has arranged them in an orderly manner. Vignettes of the chronicles of atomic theory and the periodic table are presented, including the newest elements (through atomic number 118). The main processes of radioactivity (including the basis of beta emission of both negative and positive electrons), as well as fission, are detailed, and the meanings of half-life, isotopes, and nuclides are explained. The production of energy is shown using the mass-energy equation, including the processes in stars. Important terms are defined, including units of radioactivity and units of absorbed radiation. Some other important topics covered include: Geiger counters, synthetic elements, particle accelerators, and subnuclear particles. Discussions of closely related topics of great interest and importance are included, namely energy and power, the greenhouse effect, and Earth's ozone layer.

4-1 An Overview of Atoms

We have seen that scientific research during the past century has revealed a great deal about atoms, which were once thought to be indivisible. Each atom is now known to consist of a tiny positively charged nucleus holding more than 99.9% of the atom's mass, surrounded by one or more orbiting electrons, which are negatively charged. The forces between the opposite charges are gigantic when one takes into account the infinitesimal scale of an atom. Much is known today about the structure of nuclei and the arrangement of electrons outside them.

Atoms are incredibly small. In spite of their infinitesimal size, atoms and molecules (which are assemblies of atoms bonded together) have been photographed by special techniques. To get an idea of how minute atoms are, consider a teaspoonful of carbon. This carbon may be charcoal, graphite, or a diamond and it weighs 12 grams, which is less than half an ounce. Suppose we shape this carbon in the form of ten little balls 1 centimeter in diameter, somewhat less than half an inch. Now put the ten balls in a line, each touching its neighbor. The line of balls, like this,

OOOOOOOOOO

is 10 centimeters in length, enough to stretch across an adult's palm. Let's again shape the 12 grams of carbon into balls, but this time 50 of them. Now they are 6 millimeters in diameter and the line of them, with 50 balls or beads aligned like this,

OOOOOOOOOOOOOOOOOOOOOOOOOOOOOOOOOOOOOOOOOOOOOOOOOO

Just how small are atoms?

is 30 centimeters long, about a foot. If we keep repeating this process of reforming the carbon into smaller and smaller balls, they become more and more numerous, and the chain of balls grows longer and longer. By the time the balls reach the size of carbon atoms, the chain would stretch from the Earth to the Moon 241,000 times!

In this work we will be using some huge numbers, and some unbelievably small ones. Many people have little experience with them, and tend either not to appreciate their magnitude or to be intimidated by them. Neither response is necessary. Take the number one billion, for example, the number 1 followed by nine zeros: 1,000,000,000. How long is a billion seconds? It's longer than you would suppose at first guess; it comes out to be almost 32 years.

To put relative dimensions into perspective, imagine a carbon atom enlarged until it is as big as one of those huge hot-air balloons which adventure-loving people use to carry them to the Land of Oz or wherever. Then the nucleus would be only the size of a pinhead (1 millimeter)! So it is clear that nearly all of an atom is empty space.

The element hydrogen has the simplest atoms. Each nucleus is only a single proton, and there is a single electron whirling around it. Sometimes atoms are compared with our solar system, but this is inappropriate for at least two reasons: the solar system is more nearly flat than spherical, whereas isolated atoms are more nearly spherical than flat; and the proportions are very different (atoms have much, much less matter per unit volume). The nuclear charge is +1 for hydrogen (this is also called the atomic number), and the hydrogen nucleus is simply a proton. The full name of this particular atom is hydrogen-1, abbreviated H-1 or ^{1}H, and it is one of the three *isotopes* of hydrogen. The second isotope has a proton fused to a neutron as a nucleus, and the nuclear charge is still +1; there is a single planetary electron. This isotope is hydrogen-2 or ^{2}H, which has the name deuterium (symbol D). It weighs twice as much as hydrogen-1. The third isotope of hydrogen has a proton fused to two neutrons in the nucleus and a single electron outside. This is hydrogen-3 or ^{3}H, called tritium (symbol T). All three isotopes have the same atomic number, 1; their *mass numbers* (sum of protons and neutrons) are 1, 2, and 3, respectively. Thus all isotopes of a given element have the same atomic number, but different mass numbers. Incidentally, hydrogen-1 also has a special name, protium, but it is not often used.

Three sibling isotopes of hydrogen: one light-weight (H-1), one heavy (H-2), and one obese (H-3)

All isotopes of a given element have practically the same chemical properties, but slightly different physical properties. Their separation is in general quite difficult. The separation of the two main isotopes of uranium, U-235 and U-238, was a challenging problem, but has been solved by a number of techniques; advantage is taken of slightly different physical properties. The pair of isotopes which are more different than any other case is helium-3 and helium-4. Below a temperature of 0.827 degrees absolute (or kelvin), a mixture of helium-3 and helium-4 condenses to a liquid which actually separates into two phases, like oil and water! This unique behavior is associated with a strange property of liquid helium-4 at these extremely low temperatures, namely, it becomes a superfluid.

Another term we will be using occasionally is *nuclide*. Any atom characterized by its atomic and mass numbers is a nuclide. If it is radioactive, the term radionuclide is used.

4-2 A Touch of History

As discussed earlier, the theory of atoms was slowly being accepted, even though it was strongly opposed by the more conservative elements of society. Galileo demonstrated some impure barium sulfide which was activated by sunlight and then glowed in the dark (the material was engagingly called "solar sponge" in those days). Galileo thought light consisted of corpuscles, called photons today. He explained how this was in harmony with the existence of atoms. The Englishman Dalton, around the year 1800, revised and extended the ideas of atoms, and considered a chemical element as a material all of whose atoms were alike. But even as late as 1900, a number of notable physicists and engineers rejected the atomic theory. An example was Ernst Mach, of speed-of-sound fame. Nevertheless, the concepts of atoms of elements became widely accepted by chemists, and in modern times the ideas are taught everywhere.

Much ado about almost nothing

4-3 Radioactivity and Atomic Nuclei

That atoms have nuclei was realized about 15 years after the discovery of radioactivity, and it at once became apparent that radioactivity is a nuclear property. Radioactive decay (alpha, beta, gamma, and other types) is the consequence of a nucleus spontaneously going from an energetic, unstable state to a less energetic one. It is convenient to have a word that means both protons and neutrons in a nucleus, and this word, which is in common usage, is *nucleon*. Imagine the process of building a nucleus by collecting two types of particles (protons and neutrons) together. Since the neutrons are neutral, no repulsive force from them is expected, but the positively-charged protons would repel each other forcefully, and break any assembly of particles apart. Since most nuclei are stable (meaning not radioactive), there must be another force which overcomes this repulsion. This is the strong nuclear force (4-14). Approximately 99.98 % of the mass of each atom is in its nucleus.

Most atomic nuclei are less than a millionth of a millionth of a centimeter across. Despite this next to nothing size, physicists have been able to ascertain that not all of them are spherical in shape, as formerly thought. Today it is known that nuclei of atoms are spheres, or oblate ellipsoids (flattened spheres), or prolate ellipsoids (stretched out spheres). Spherical nuclei are in general most stable. Excited (energy-rich) nuclei are deformed by, among other factors, incredibly rapid spin (rotation), up to 10^{20} revolutions per second in some cases. Just consider that number. Our Earth is 4.6 billion years old, which is 1.45×10^{17} seconds! On radioactive decay nuclei frequently emit gamma rays, sometimes in steps, to approach a more stable state. Nuclei seem to be oscillating or pulsating constantly.

Screwball-shaped nuclei

Another consequence of nuclear spin was predicted by Heisenberg in 1927. The nuclei of hydrogen atoms are just protons. Since molecules of hydrogen have two atoms, that is, H_2, there are two modifications possible. In one, called para-hydrogen, the two nuclei spin in opposite directions; in the other, ortho-hydrogen, the two nuclei spin in the same direction. The two forms exist in equilibrium and are thus interconvertible. They have slightly different physical properties. Ortho and para forms of deuterium, D_2, are also known.

Stimulated by a question from Fermi, mathematical physicist Maria Goeppert Mayer worked out a theory of nuclear structure based on filling energy shells with nucleons. Accordingly, nuclei exist in a ground state (most stable) and a series of excited states (richer in energy). They have been likened to a liquid drop and to shell-like structures, patterned on the model of electron shells in atoms. Neither model is satisfactory, but both have their uses. Nuclei with filled shells are spherical; the others are ellipsoidal. Owing to human perceptions of stones, balls, and other such objects, we tend to transfer their qualities to electrons, protons, neutrons, etc. While the full truth may never be known, these fundamental particles are not just hard balls, but something more

Maria Goeppert Mayer (1906–1972), German physicist. Immigrated to the United States in the early 1930s. Married Joseph Mayer, a chemist. Experienced the usual discrimination against women in science, but was so quick-minded and tenacious that she maintained a high level of scientific activity without formal appointments at universities. Worked on the Manhattan Project on uranium isotope separation and the physics of isotope effects. Her theory of nuclear structure weighed heavily in winning the Nobel Prize in 1962 (with J. H. D. Jensen).

subtle. Actually, Japanese physicist Tadayoshi Hikosaka had proposed a theory similar to Mayer's in the mid 1930s. He tried to publish his theory in the journal Physical Review, but his paper was rejected.

Thus an electron in an atomic orbit is not truly just a particle (if that is what these marvelous things are), but a sort of standing wave. This means that it is smeared out in space into a continuous blur of some geometric shape around the nucleus, gossamer-like.

An electron has no physical dimensions in the ordinary sense. As components of nuclei, subnuclear particles are evidently fused together through some sort of exchange forces. Without these forces, an assembly of protons and neutrons would blow itself apart on account of mutual repulsion of the positive charges. A nucleus is much more complicated than a mere collection of little grains. We should be aware that particles and events on the atomic scale do not correspond to our concepts of large objects and their behavior. Modern quantum mechanics helps in understanding these counterintuitive concepts, but it is clear that much remains to be discovered.

Might as well get used to weird ideas

Another manifestation of nuclei is revealed by what has been termed halo nuclei. The best studied example is lithium-11, which is very unstable (half-life 8.7 milliseconds). This instability is expected considering that the nucleus consists of three protons and eight neutrons. Six of the neutrons are bound into the nucleus normally, but the remaining two have binding energies of only about 10% of normal. They are evidently beyond the boundary of the main nucleus, skimming along just outside its surface and forming a sort of halo. If one of these two neutrons is removed, the other immediately follows. Other nuclides with halo neutrons are helium-6, beryllium-11, beryllium-14, carbon-19, and carbon-22. All have short half-lives. Clearly, we have much to learn about atomic nuclei.

4-4 The Periodic Table of Chemical Elements

A complete modern form of Mendeleyev's periodic table is shown in Appendix I and an abbreviated form is shown later in this section. It shows families of elements of related chemical character and lists 116 known elements in order of increasing nuclear charge (atomic number); the heaviest is number 118, but numbers 113 and 117 have not yet been discovered. The bottom number in each square is the atomic weight or mass, which is the average of the isotopic weights taking into account the relative abundance of the natural isotopes. Certain of the elements are made synthetically and all of their isotopes are radioactive; in these cases, the mass number of the most stable (longest half-life) isotope is given in parentheses. Note that two series of elements are inserted at the bottom. This is done only because the paper is not large enough to accommodate the series in the proper numerical order of atomic number. Lanthanum and the 14 elements following it (cerium to lutetium) are called the lanthanides or rare-earth metals. The other series at the bottom, actinium to lawrencium, are referred to as the actinide elements. Both of these series are important in nuclear work. Each element requires a whole periodic table of adjectives to describe its chemical behavior.

Order in nature

The periodic table helps systematize the chemistry of all the elements, and is an indispensable tool to all chemists. It introduces order into an area of science which was previously chaos. How wonderful the periodic table is!

There are 116 chemical elements known to date. Some of them, namely those of atomic number 102 and higher, have experienced considerable controversy regarding their names (see also 4-19).

Discovery of element 102 was first claimed by the Swedes, who chose the name nobelium, but this work was later found to be in error. But by the time it was determined that the Swedish discovery was mistaken, the name nobelium was so deeply entrenched that it was kept as the official name. Seaborg and coworkers in 1958 discovered the error and found the true isotope of element 102, and this was confirmed by the Soviets.

A bit of historical information for the elements 104 through 109 is below.

Element 104, discovered in 1969 in USA and in USSR
Element 105, discovered in 1970 in USA and in USSR
Element 106, discovery claimed by American and by Russian scientists in 1974; confirmed by American group
Element 107, discovered in 1976 in Germany
Element 108, discovered in 1984 in Germany
Element 109, discovered in 1982 in Germany

The 20-member nomenclature committee of the International Union of Pure & Applied Chemistry (IUPAC) provided the arena for officially deciding the names, a process which took 20

Brand new elements

years. Some scientists displayed narrow nationalistic views more befitting to politicians, and there were many acrimonious debates. Finally, in summer 1997, an agreement was reached which the IUPAC described as "a fair compromise between the various claims and suggestions." These official names are:

> *Element 104*, Rutherfordium, Rf, after Ernest Rutherford;
> *Element 105*, Dubnium, Db, after Dubna, Russia, site of a major nuclear research center;
> *Element 106*, Seaborgium, Sg, after Glenn Seaborg;
> *Element 107*, Bohrium, Bh, after Niels Bohr;
> *Element 108*, Hassium, Hs, after the Latin Hassias, meaning the German state, Hessen;
> *Element 109*, Meitnerium, Mt, after Lise Meitner.

In August 2003, element 110 was officially named darmstadtium, after the city in which it was discovered.

Glenn Seaborg at age 85 appeared at an American Chemical Society meeting in 1997 wearing a T-shirt bearing the periodic table symbol* Sg *with its atomic number (106) and the message "I am in my element."

An abbreviated periodic table of the elements, presenting most of the above changes, is below.

PERIODIC TABLE OF THE ELEMENTS

1 H																	2 He
3 Li	4 Be											5 B	6 C	7 N	8 O	9 F	10 Ne
11 Na	12 Mg											13 Al	14 Si	15 P	16 S	17 Cl	18 Ar
19 K	20 Ca	21 Sc	22 Ti	23 V	24 Cr	25 Mn	26 Fe	27 Co	28 Ni	29 Cu	30 Zn	31 Ga	32 Ge	33 As	34 Se	35 Br	36 Kr
37 Rb	38 Sr	39 Y	40 Zr	41 Nb	42 Mo	43 Tc	44 Ru	45 Rh	46 Pd	47 Ag	48 Cd	49 In	50 Sn	51 Sb	52 Te	53 I	54 Xe
55 Cs	56 Ba	57– La	72 Hf	73 Ta	74 W	75 Re	76 Os	77 Ir	78 Pt	79 Au	80 Hg	81 Tl	82 Pb	83 Bi	84 Po	85 At	86 Rn
87 Fr	88 Ra	89– Ac	104 Rf	105 Db	106 Sg	107 Bh	108 Hs	109 Mt	110	111	112	(113)	(114)	(115)	(116)	(117)	(118)

Series														
Lanthanide series	58 Ce	59 Pr	60 Nd	61 Pm	62 Sm	63 Eu	64 Gd	65 Tb	66 Dy	67 Ho	68 Er	69 Tm	70 Yb	71 Lu
Actinide series	90 Th	91 Pa	92 U	93 Np	94 Pu	95 Am	96 Cm	97 Bk	98 Cf	99 Es	100 Fm	101 Md	102 No	103 Lr

As might be expected, these superheavy isotopes are exceedingly unstable and have very short half-lives. For example, the half-life of meitnerium-266 is 3.4 milliseconds. Most of the isotopes of elements 107 to 116 do not undergo spontaneous fission, as was first expected, but rather are alpha active.

Using only a few atoms, American, German, and Swiss chemists have shown that seaborgium chemically resembles tungsten and bohrium resembles rhenium, as predicted by the periodic table. Thus the compound BhO_3Cl, analogous to ReO_3Cl, has been prepared. It has been long known that ruthenium and osmium, below iron in the periodic table, form tetroxides which are volatile. In 2001, another international team of chemists demonstrated that hassium, just below osmium, behaves similarly.

Element 110 was synthesized in 1994 at the Heavy-Ion Research laboratory in Darmstadt, Germany. The 12 principal scientists in the team were German, Russian, Slovak, and Finnish. The new element was made by bombarding lead-208 nuclei with very energetic nuclei of nickel-62 from a heavy-ion accelerator. This forged the nucleus of element 110 with a mass number of 269; one neutron was also generated. A sophisticated apparatus was employed which separated atoms of the new element by recoil from the lead and incoming nickel nuclei. Only a few atoms were made, but the evidence of their existence was "superb" and "very convincing," according to American physicist Ghiorso. Element 110 decays rapidly by a series of alpha emissions.

A month later the Darmstadt team succeeded in producing a few atoms of element 111 using the same technique, but with a bismuth-209 target instead of lead. A beam of nickel-64 atoms was employed, and a neutron was emitted from each nucleus on collision. The new element, with mass number 272 and a half-life of perhaps 1.5 milliseconds, was found to disintegrate by a long series of alpha emissions but no spontaneous fission. The trick is to choose a neutron-rich bombarding projectile and accelerate it the to just the energy needed to overcome the repulsion of the target nucleus, and no more.

In early 1996 the productive Darmstadt team made element 112 using the same techniques. This time the projectile particles were zinc nuclei and the target was lead. The isotope had a mass number of 277. Thus the new element flashed into existence for about a third of a millisecond and decayed by a series of alpha emissions to fermium (number 100), where the physicists lost its trail.

Extending the periodic table

According to Mayer's theory, nuclei are constructed in shells of different energy levels, and certain isotopes might show extra stability because the shells are exactly filled with nucleons. This is somewhat analogous to electronic shells surrounding the nuclei of atoms, which become filled periodically to form stable, inert atoms such as argon.

The Soltan Institute for Nuclear Studies, situated in Warsaw, Poland, has several scientists studying the details of nuclear structure from a theoretical point of view. Prof. Adam Sobiczewski and his group have concluded that certain deformed transactinide nuclei (of elements of atomic number 104 and higher) are actually stabilized by shell effects. For example one isotope of hassium, namely the one with mass number 270, has an oddly-shaped nucleus which is stabilized by nuclear shell closing. The prediction had been made that element 114 with mass number 289 will be stabilized.

In early 1999, two Russian scientists, Yuri Organessian and Vladimir Utyonkov at the Joint Institute for nuclear Research in Dubna reported the synthesis of element 114, the isotope with mass number 289. This new radionuclide was made by bombarding plutonium-244 (obtained from Lawrence Livermore National Laboratory) with nuclei of calcium-48, a rare natural isotope of that element. It proved to have the properties mentioned above, namely a half-life of 30.4 seconds, millions of time longer than the half-lives of most elements in the 104 to 109 range. Its decay product is element 112, with a half life of 15.4 minutes. The work must be replicated and confirmed by other laboratories before it can be fully accepted. In 1999 the Russian team announced synthesis of another isotope of element 114, namely the one with mass number 287. It is said to have a half-life of about 5 seconds, by alpha decay.

Researchers at Lawrence Berkeley Laboratory in June 1999 reported synthesis of element number 116 and element number 118. In summer 2000, the Russian laboratory also reported the synthesis of element 116, namely the one with mass number 292. Element 118 was said to be made in a cyclotron in Berkeley by directing a stream of krypton-86 ions at a target of lead-208. Visiting theorist Robert Smolanczuk, from Warsaw's Soltan Institute, predicted by calculation that the krypton-lead reaction would be successful. Judging from the periodic table, element 118 is expected to be a noble gas, like radon and xenon. But in 2001, an announcement was made that the results could not be confirmed, and the original claim for both 116 and 118 was withdrawn. All such research must be confirmed and reconfirmed. More discoveries along these lines are expected.

4-5 The Nature of Beta Radioactivity

Free neutrons are not stable. Within a short time free neutrons disintegrate into protons and electrons. This decay can be represented by the following equation:

neutron ⇒ proton + electron

Hydrogen-1 and hydrogen-2 are stable (the term radiostable is sometimes used), but hydrogen-3 is radioactive. Its nucleus has too many neutrons to be stable. The same disintegration indicated above takes place, but at a different rate. The energetic electron ejected from the nucleus of hydrogen-3 (or any other nucleus) is a beta particle. The nucleus formed now has two protons and one neutron instead of the original one proton and two neutrons. The sketch below summarizes the change (solid circles represent neutrons; open circles represent protons).

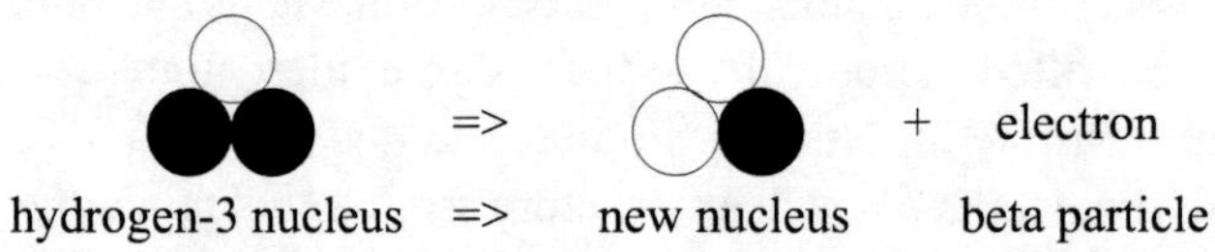

=> + electron

hydrogen-3 nucleus => new nucleus beta particle

Since the new nucleus contains two protons its charge or atomic number is two, and the element must be helium (reference to the periodic table will always show which element has a given atomic number). Thus helium-3 is produced by the radioactive decay of hydrogen-3 (helium-3 is rare; common helium has mass number 4; these terms were explained in 4-1). This example of radioactivity illustrates an important point: whenever a negative electron is ejected from a nucleus during beta decay the element of one higher atomic number results, that is, it moves one unit to the right in the periodic table. Scientists would write the above equation as follows:

Emission of beta particles

$$^{3}_{1}H \Rightarrow ^{3}_{2}He + ^{0}_{-1}e$$

In equations of this type, the left subscript gives the electric charge of the particle or nucleus, while the left superscript gives the total of the number of protons and neutrons.

The sum of the superscripts on each side of the arrow must be equal, and the same is true for the subscripts. Nuclei formed by radioactive decay may be in their normal state of energy ("ground state"), but generally have excess energy ("excited state"). In the second case, one or more gamma ray photons is emitted, until the ground state is attained. In the case of tritium, the helium-3 nucleus is born in the ground state, so no gamma rays are emitted. Radiochemists and physicists often speak affectionately of helium-3 as the "daughter" of tritium. Two nuclides which have different atomic numbers but the same mass number, such as H-3 and He-3, are called *isobars*.

There is another, less common, kind of beta radioactivity, namely that in which the electron ejected from the nucleus has a positive charge instead of negative. A positively charged electron is called a *positron* (4-14). This kind of radioactive decay occurs when the nucleus contains too many protons, relative to neutrons, to be stable. An example of this kind of decay is shown by boron-8, whose nucleus has five protons and three neutrons. In this case, the decay product has an atomic number one less than that of the parent element (a shift one unit to the left in the periodic table, to beryllium):

B-8 (atomic no. 5) ⇒ Be-8 (atomic no. 4) + positron, or

$$^{8}_{5}B \Rightarrow ^{8}_{4}Be + ^{0}_{+1}e$$

Subnuclear particles are discussed in section 4-15. Among them are the electron, neutrino, and antineutrino. In 1934 Fermi presented a more complete theory of beta decay taking neutrinos into account. In beta decay resulting in negative electrons, an antineutrino is released; when a positive electron is ejected, a neutrino accompanies it.

The stable, lighter atoms (up to about mass number 22) have a ratio of neutrons to protons (n/p) of approximately unity. For example, the isotope of phosphorus (atomic number 15) found in nature is P-31, and n/p is (31-15)/15 = 1.07. The known heavier isotopes, of mass numbers 32, 33, 34, and 35, are all radioactive. Each of the four isotopes decays by emitting beta particles. In P-32, the n/p ratio is 1.13, too high for stability. When an atom of P-32 decays, loss of the beta particle (electron) raises the atomic number to 16, sulfur. Thus the product is sulfur-32, with n/p = 1.00. The heaviest four isotopes of phosphorus have too many neutrons to be stable. Going below mass number 31, we find that P-30, P-29, and P-28 are all known, and all are radioactive, emitting positrons in these cases. The nuclei do not have enough neutrons compared to protons to be stable, and throw off the excess positive charge as positrons. This results in formation of silicon, atomic number 14. Going on to heavier and heavier atoms, it takes higher and higher neutron-to-proton ratios for stability, the ratios being about 1.4 or 1.5. The heaviest nonradioactive atom known, bismuth-209, has n/p = 1.52.

Plutonium is synthesized in reactors as follows. In the chain reaction fission of uranium-235, energetic neutrons are generated, and are moderated, or slowed down. Some of these neutrons are used to propagate the chain reaction, while the rest are absorbed by the abundant uranium-238, forming uranium-239 and emitting a gamma ray:

$$^{238}_{92}U + ^{1}_{0}n \Rightarrow ^{239}_{92}U + \gamma$$

This uranium-239 is beta active and has a short half-life (23.5 minutes). Thus it transforms quickly into the next element, neptunium:

$$^{239}_{92}U \Rightarrow ^{239}_{93}Np + ^{0}_{-1}e$$

The neptunium-239 also displays short-lived beta activity (half-life 2.35 days), and so within a few weeks nearly all goes over to the desired plutonium-239:

$$^{239}_{93}Np \Rightarrow ^{239}_{94}Pu + ^{0}_{-1}e$$

The plutonium-239 has the long half-life of 24,110 years, so only a tiny fraction decays per year.

4-6 Half-Life and the Rate of Radioactive Decay

The shorter the half-life, the more rapid decay is.

Half-Life, an Important Concept—The level of activity (that is, radioactivity) of a given material depends on how much of it there is and how fast it decays: the greater the amount and the higher the decay rate, the higher the activity is. The half-life of a radionuclide is the length of time required for half of a specified starting amount to decay. One might have chosen the one-third life, the three-fourths life, or the 90%-life, but half-life is most convenient. Alternative names for half-life are half-time and half-period.

The half-life of a radioactive nuclide in a given environment is constant; so immutable and unchanging is the value that heating white hot or chilling to the temperature of liquid nitrogen does not change its value. There is one factor which causes a slight variation in half-life, and that is a contraction in the distance from the nucleus to the innermost orbital electrons held in its grasp. Thus if technetium-99, the first synthetic element (4-19), is squeezed at a pressure of 100,000 times atmospheric pressure, its radioactive decay rate is raised by 0.025% above the rate at normal pressure. Changing the chemical environment of radioactive atoms results in much greater changes, arising from the same basic cause. Thus the half-life

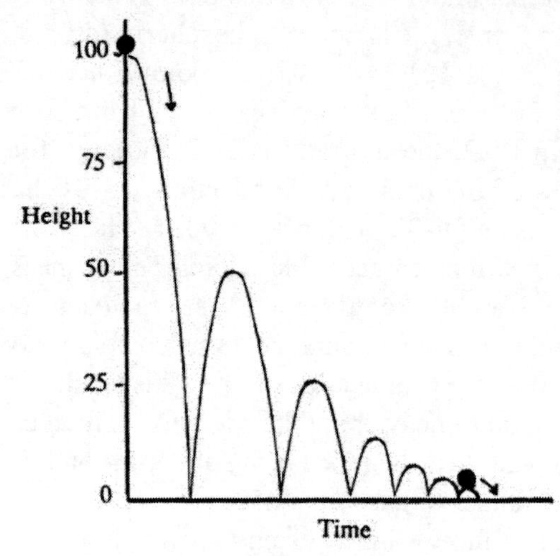

Bouncing ball analogy to half-life (the starting height is 100 units)

of beryllium-7 is near 53.3 days, but there is a variation of about 0.1% depending on whether the element is in the metallic form, or the fluoride, or some other compound. Similarly, the 6.006-hour half-life of technetium-99m varies 0.3% between technetium sulfide and potassium pertechnetate.

An analogy to the concept of half-life is a bouncing ball. Suppose we have an elastic ball which, when dropped, rebounds to half its original height. Then it falls back, and bounces up to half the height of the second bounce. On the next bounce, it returns to half of its previous height, and this process repeats many times. By giving the ball a sideways push, we can see its path more clearly, as illustrated.

Mathematical and Graphical Representation of Half-Life—An accurate parallel to half-life can also be made using money. Suppose we invest $100 in a risky investment, which then loses 5% of its value each year, which is the same as saying that at the end of each year, 95% of its remaining value is left. Then,

after year 1, $100.00 x 0.95 = $95.00 remains
after year 2, 95.00 x .95 = 90.25 remains
after year 3, 90.25 x .95 = 85.74 remains, etc.

after 13 years, 0.95 has been multiplied by itself 13 times, giving 0.5133, and thus $51.33 is left of the original unwise investment. Let's round this to $50, half of the original $100. Then the half-life of the investment is 13 years. After a second 13-year period, only $25 remains, etc.

The measured half-life of hydrogen-3 (tritium) is roughly 13 years (actually, 12.3 years), so its decay is closely similar to the above financial decay. [Incidentally, the half-life of free neutrons, discussed briefly in section 4-5, is 10 minutes and 16 seconds.] The decay of tritium can be shown graphically (below; in this case we start with 100 grams or 100 ounces or any other units). It is as though at the end of each half-life period, we start afresh with a new observation. The rate of formation of helium-3 must be numerically the same as the rate of decay of tritium, except that the rate for tritium is negative (its amount decreases) and the rate for helium-3 is positive (its amount increases).

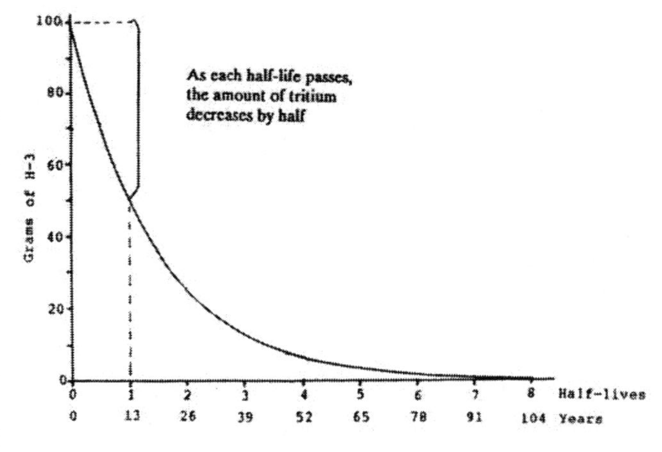

Plot of amount of tritium against time

Mathematically it is simpler to use the logarithm of the amount of decaying element rather than the amount itself, for then the graph is a straight line and much easier to handle. This is also shown (below). The level of radioactivity is always proportional to the amount of decaying material. We could have used number of disintegrations per second or its equivalent in place of the number of grams of tritium in the graphs. Since the logarithm of 2 is very nearly 0.3, after every half-life the value of the logarithm of the amount of tritium drops by this amount, as indicated in the second plot (below).

A useful rule of thumb is as follows: Starting with any given amount of radioactive material, after ten half-lives only 1 part in 2^{10} is left. This number evaluates to 1/1024, that is, about one thousandth or 0.1% of the original amount survives.

Given a starting amount of a radioactive material, some atoms disintegrate at once and others last for centuries. In time, the substance decays toward extinction, and all atoms eventually disintegrate. The sum of all their lives divided by the initial number of atoms is the mean or average life; the value of the average life turns out to be 1.443 times the half-life. The longest half-life of any radioactive nuclide known so far is that of one of the natural isotopes of the metal vanadium. This is vanadium-50; one atom in 400 of ordinary vanadium is this isotope. Its half-life is 4 x 10^{17} years, which is about 87 million times the age of the Earth. One gram of natural vanadium, containing only 0.0025 gram of vanadium-50, exhibits a rate of radioactive decay of only one beta particle per week. Another extremely long-lived nuclide is cadmium-113; one atom in eight of ordinary cadmium is this isotope. Its half-life is just under 10^{16} years, about the same as the half-life corresponding to the spontaneous fission of uranium-238.

Successive Radioactive Decay—How about the case where substance A decays to substance B, which in turn decays to substance C? This situation is often encountered, in fact, it is the usual one. For illustration let's examine the case of three important transuranium elements, namely plutonium-241 decaying by beta emission to americium-241, which in turn decays by alpha emission to neptunium-237. A look at the periodic table helps here. Plutonium-241 has the comparatively short half-life of 14.4 years. It forms americium-241, which has the much longer half-life of 433 years. It too decays, this time by alpha emission, forming neptunium-237. The neptunium is of course also radioactive, but its half-life is very long, namely 2,140,000 years.

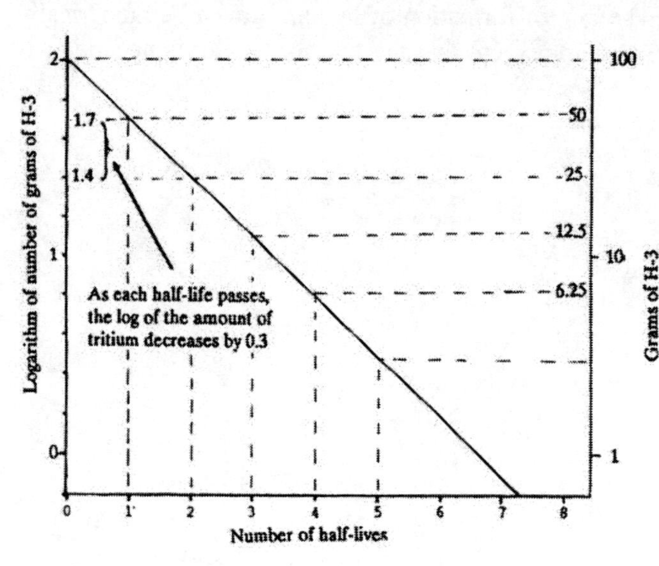

Plot of logarithm of amount of tritium against time

The plutonium-241 decays in exactly the same manner as the previous cases we have studied, such as tritium. As pointed out before, decay of tritium forms helium-3, whose rate of formation must be the same as the rate of decay of its parent. This would also be true in the case of americium-241 forming from plutonium-241 except that unlike stable helium-3, the americium itself is decaying while it is being formed. Since the half-life of the americium is much longer than that of its parent plutonium, it does build up, but not quite at the rate it would if it were stable. On balancing out the rate of formation versus the rate of decay, it becomes clear that the amount of americium must build up to a maximum and then fall off. This is shown in the graph below, in which we start with 10 moles of plutonium-241. The amount of americium reaches a maximum after 73 years from the start. The rate of growth of neptunium is roughly the same as the rate of decay of americium since neptunium has such a long half-life.

Recently a computer program has appeared on the market *(http: chemsw.com)* which facilitates such calculations. It consists of a periodic table on which to choose an element, and then the desired isotope. The decay processes are automatically displayed until a stable nuclide is reached.

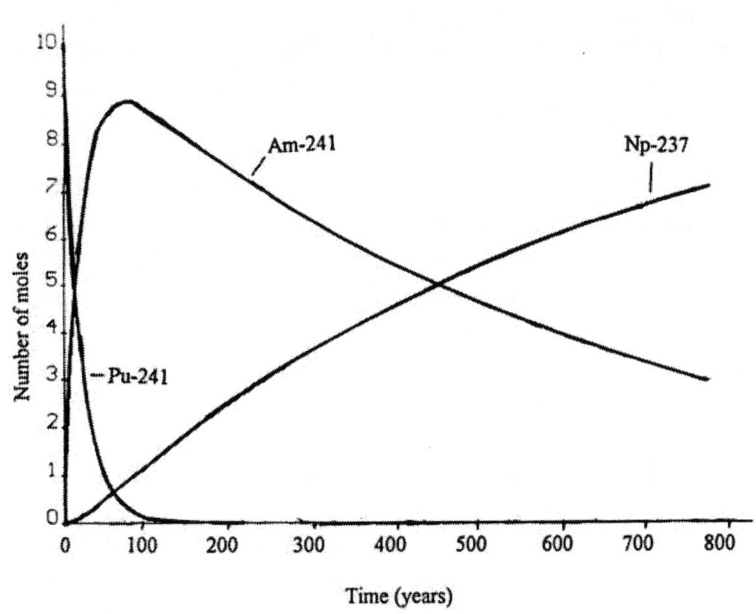

The decay sequence Pu-241 => Am => Np-237

4-7 Alpha Decay

The rate of alpha decay follows the same laws as that for beta decay discussed above, but the rules governing the products are different. The alpha mode of decay is usually characteristic of the very heaviest elements of the periodic table such as uranium (atomic number 92). The common isotope of uranium has mass number 238, meaning that in the nucleus there are 92 protons and 238 - 92 = 146 neutrons. Remember that an alpha particle is the nucleus of helium-4, which contains 2 protons (bearing charge +2) and 2 neutrons. Thus when uranium-238 nuclei eject alpha particles (the half-life is very long, 4.47 billion years) each loses 2 units of charge, and the atomic number falls from 92 to 90. This means that the new-born element falls two units to the left in the periodic table. In ordinary beta activity the shift is one unit to the right. Since the alpha particle (helium nucleus) has a mass number of 4, the element produced on decay must have a mass number 4 units less than 238. Element 90, a glance at a periodic table reveals, is thorium, and in this case it is the isotope with mass number 238 - 4 = 234, that is, thorium-234. In the decay of uranium-238 in Nature there are 13 successive alpha or beta decay steps, and the final product is lead-206, which is stable (see the uranium series, 4-9).

Each nuclide is the daughter of the one preceding it; the whole series is the "progeny" of uranium-238. One of the intermediates in the decay series is the common isotope of radium (Ra-226, half-life 1600 years), and its decay product is radon-222, a gas. Curiously, some of the intermediate elements, such as polonium-218, exhibit both modes of decay, a certain fraction of the atoms emitting alpha particles and the rest beta particles. Each of the two processes takes place with its own half-life. Immediately after ejecting an alpha particle, the new-born decay product usually blows off excess energy by emitting a gamma-ray or X-ray photon. An atom of radium can take up residence in a cell of the human body, or exist thousands of years in, say, the ocean, and not disintegrate. Until the instant of decay, there is no radiation at all coming from that atom. Of course, there are in general colossal numbers of atoms, so some will always be decaying.

Radioactive decay series or chains

Every element has at least one isotope which is radioactive. Every isotope of all elements of atomic number 84 and higher is radioactive; thus bismuth, atomic number 83, is the heaviest element with a stable isotope. In stable nuclides there is no empty energy state to receive the proton which would result if decay of an internal neutron occurred. With heavier and heavier nuclei, the repulsion of the increasing numbers of protons becomes more difficult to overcome via binding energy (4-15), and this leads to a limit in the size of stable nuclei.

4-8 Other Types of Radioactive Decay

There are still other modes of radioactive disintegration. Gamma rays often, but not always, accompany alpha or beta decay. Certain excited nuclei emit gamma rays without a beta particle. An example, exceptionally important in nuclear medicine, is the excited form of technetium-99; it is identified by the letter m, for metastable, after the mass number, that is, technetium-99m. It gives off pure gamma rays with a half-life of 6 hours. Many nuclei, for example calcium-41, capture an orbiting electron from the outside; this of course, decreases the atomic number one unit, shifting one space leftward in the periodic table. A few rare cases of proton emission are known, for example cobalt-53 (this isotope mostly emits positrons, but in a tiny fraction of its atoms, protons are ejected). Spontaneous fission, without prior capture of a neutron, is common in the very heavy atoms. An example is californium-252, which displays alpha decay (97%) and spontaneous fission (3%). Another is californium-254, which undergoes spontaneous fission to the extent of 99.7%, with a half-life of 60.5 days. In 1984 the first instance of superasymmetric spontaneous fission was discovered. In this case, radium-223, the two fission fragments have gross differences in mass and charge. For every billion cases of alpha emission, one atom of radium-223 ejects an entire carbon-14 nucleus; the other product is lead-209. Even in the case of ordinary radium-226, one decay in ten billion yields carbon-14 nuclei. There are a dozen or so cases of superasymmetric fission in which nuclei such as oxygen-20, neon-24, or even one as heavy as sulfur-38, are released. Ordinary uranium-238, in addition to undergoing alpha decay and a trifling degree of spontaneous fission, was shown in 1991 to display an exceedingly low level of double beta decay. In this case, two beta particles are ejected simultaneously, and plutonium-

238 results. Uranium-234 is bizarre in that it decays in three different modes, spitting out nuclei of helium-4 (alpha particles), or neon-24, or magnesium-28. Although not in the uranium series, the case of copper-64 is also remarkable in that it undergoes three types of decay, namely beta (negative electrons), beta (positrons), and orbital electron capture.

Peculiar kinds of radioactivity

4-9 The Uranium Decay Series

Eventually, the complete chain of nuclides in the decay of uranium-238 was determined, and each step was clarified. The series is shown in the figure below. Note that in three cases branched decay take place, and a given nuclide, such as polonium-218, disintegrates by both alpha and beta emission. Each process has its own half-life. The final product in the uranium-238 series is lead-206, which is stable (nonradioactive).

Other decay series start with plutonium-239, thorium-232, or plutonium-241. Such decay series disclose the genetic relationships which exist in radioactive nuclides. The thorium-232 series is identified as the 4n series, since its mass number, and the mass numbers of all its decay products, are evenly divisible by 4. Similarly, plutonium-241 starts the 4n + 1 series, since its mass number and those of its progeny are divisible by 4 with a remainder of 1. Uranium-238 starts the 4n + 2 series, and plutonium-239 starts the 4n + 3 series.

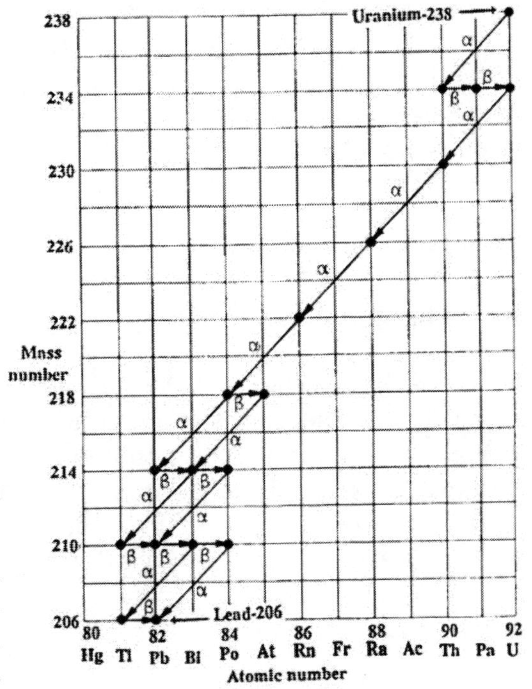

The uranium-238 series

4-10 Atomic Masses

To understand energy changes in nuclear processes, we need to know the masses (or weights) of the various elements (actually their isotopes) involved. For historical reasons, neutral atoms of the common isotope of carbon, which is carbon-12, has been assigned a value of exactly 12 atomic mass units. This is a definition, and the same amount, expressed in grams, is known as one mole of carbon. One mole of any pure substance has the same number of atoms or molecules as in 12 grams of carbon-12. This number, 602,204,000,000,000,000,000,000, called Avogadro's number, is truly enormous. If we had that number of dollars, and spent 1 million dollars every second, it would take 19 billion years to complete the task! This is 4 times the age of our Earth,

4,600,000,000 years. Such huge numbers as Avogadro's are best written in exponential form: 6.02204×10^{23}.

The atomic masses relative to carbon-12 of all atoms can be measured using the mass spectrometer, and tables of these results, known with a high degree of accuracy, have been assembled. The corresponding values for the proton, neutron, electron, etc., are also known. Some of these are given below; note that except for the very light electron (which is not an atom), all values are close to whole numbers.

Atomic Masses

carbon-12	=	12.0000000	atomic mass units
electron	=	0.0005486	atomic mass units
neutron	=	1.008665	atomic mass units
proton (H-1 nucleus)	=	1.007276	atomic mass units
hydrogen-1 (neutral atom)	=	1.00783	atomic mass units
helium-4	=	4.00260	atomic mass units
oxygen-16	=	15.99492	atomic mass units
nickel-58	=	57.93535	atomic mass units
uranium-235	=	235.04392	atomic mass units
uranium-238	=	238.05077	atomic mass units

4-11 Energy and Power

In most of this book, the idea of energy plays a prominent role. We all have a general idea of what energy is. In science, energy is the capacity to do work. The most primitive form of energy is heat, and other forms tend to degrade into it. Potential energy is that which is stored and can be released. Water in a high lake has potential energy because gravitational force can pull it downward, and convert the energy to mechanical work, electricity, or heat. Mechanical energy is force multiplied by the distance through which it operates. Kinetic energy is that which a mass has by virtue of its motion. Electric energy may be stored in a battery or capacitor, and it can move through conductors as electricity. Chemical energy is stored in various substances such as fuels, and can be released when bonds between atoms are broken and formed during such processes as combustion or electrolysis using electric current from a battery. Electromagnetic radiation is energy comprising a continuous spectrum from gamma rays, through X-rays, ultraviolet, visible light, infrared, microwaves, to radio waves, etc. Nuclear energy is stored in atomic nuclei and involves enormous forces at very short distances. In general, one form of energy can be converted to another, but with 100% efficiency only when heat is the final form.

Mostly we will stick to one energy unit, the joule (abbreviated J), or its multiples, such as the kilojoule (kJ or 1000 J). Some other units of energy are the calorie, the British thermal unit, the electron volt (eV), and the kilowatt-hour. One kilowatt-hour is 3.6 million joules (see Appendix III).

What's a watt?

Power is the rate of expenditure or conversion of energy. The expenditure of one joule per second is defined as a unit of power of one watt (abbreviated W). Thus an ordinary 60-watt electric light bulb gives off 60 joules of energy (heat and light) each second, an observation which enables one to imagine about how much energy a joule is. To lift a one-pound weight to a height of about 9 inches requires 1 joule. If this is done in 1 second, the power is 1 J divided by 1 sec, or 1 W; if the time is only ½ second, the power is 1 J divided by ½ sec, or 2 W. The average human body at rest expends energy at a power level of about 140 watts; heavy manual labor can raise this to 700 watts until curtailed by exhaustion.

In view of the overwhelming importance of energy and the enormous public interest in the subject, it is discussed in more detail in section 4-25 ff. This includes standard and renewable sources of energy, means of energy storage such as batteries, and related topics. Since the production of vast amounts of energy by burning coal or petroleum products might produce a greenhouse effect, this topic is analyzed in section 4-31. Whether the use of more nuclear reactors could lessen this possible threat is addressed in Chapter 7. The ozone layer, its importance, and relation to these factors is discussed and evaluated in section 4-32. This topic could also play a role in the event of nuclear war (Chapter 10, Part III).

4-12 Thermonuclear Fusion

Our Sun consists mostly of hydrogen, and the second most abundant element is helium. In the center of the Sun the temperature and the pressure are so high that ordinary atoms do not exist; there are only atomic nuclei (mostly hydrogen nuclei, which are protons), helium nuclei, and free electrons. This state of matter is called a *plasma.* The conditions are suitable to continuously force four hydrogen nuclei together to form helium nuclei, a process known as thermonuclear fusion. This actually occurs stepwise, not all at once (see 4-13 below). In analyzing the energy evolved by the fusion process quantitatively, we must choose the particles in the plasma in such a way that electric charge is neither created nor destroyed.

First we'll use Einstein's equation to compute the energy evolved by the fusion reaction based on four nuclei of hydrogen (that is, protons) to produce one nucleus of helium. We select whatever components of the plasma conserve the numbers of nucleons (protons and neutrons), as well as electric charge. The four hydrogen nuclei have a total electric charge of +4 units and the single helium nucleus formed has a charge of only +2 units, so we must include two electrons, represented as ^{0}e. In the fusion equation we write the two kinds of nuclei as usual, but in this case we'll attach a right superscript to emphasize their electric charges. The thermonuclear fusion equation is:

$$4\,{}^{1}_{2}\mathrm{H}^{+1} + 2\,{}^{0}_{-1}\mathrm{e} \Rightarrow {}^{4}_{2}\mathrm{He}^{+2}$$

Now we must determine the mass change in this reaction in order to use Einstein's equation:

$$E = mc^2$$

The masses of hydrogen nuclei (protons), helium nuclei, and electrons have been measured with extreme accuracy using mass spectrometers and are known out to 7 or 8 digits.

We expect the mass change to be small, and to be the difference between two much larger quantities. Therefore we'll use the masses quite accurately, rounding off at 4 digits after the decimal point. In the equation $E = mc^2$, it is best to express all the masses in kilograms since to compute the energy in joules (J) we must use the mass in kilograms (kg) and the velocity of light (c) in meters (m) per second (s). (The definition of a joule comes from elementary physics, that is, a joule is in units of $(kg)(m/s)^2$.) The velocity of light is 2.9979×10^8 m/s. Expressed in kilograms, the required masses are

proton, 1.6726×10^{-27} kg
helium nucleus 6.6448×10^{-27} kg
electron, 9.1099×10^{-31} kg

So, the mass of the four hydrogen nuclei (which are protons) totals

$$4 \times 1.6726 \times 10^{-27} \text{ kg} = 6.6904 \times 10^{-27} \text{ kg}$$

And, that of the two electrons is

$$2 \times 9.1099 \times 10^{-31} \text{ kg} = 1.8220 \times 10^{-30} \text{ kg} = 0.0018 \times 10^{-27} \text{ kg}$$

making a total of 6.6922×10^{-27} kg. Thus the starting materials have a mass greater than that of the product by

$$6.6922 \times 10^{-27} - 6.6448 \times 10^{-27} = 0.0474 \times 10^{-27} = 4.74 \times 10^{-29} \text{ kg}$$

This makes the energy E liberated

$$E = mc^2 = 4.74 \times 10^{-29} \text{ kg} \times (2.9979 \times 10^8 \text{ m/s})^2 = 4.260 \times 10^{-12} \text{ J}$$

This is the amount of energy (heat and radiation) released per nucleus of helium formed. We can scale the operation upward to that of one mole (4-10), that is, Avogadro's number of atoms of helium formed. This number is 6.0220×10^{23} atoms per mole. Thus

$$E = 4.260 \times 10^{-12} \text{ J per atom} \times 6.0220 \times 10^{23} \text{ atoms per mole}$$
$$= 2.565 \times 10^{12} \text{ J per mole}$$

On a molar basis, it is simpler to conduct the above calculations based on the known atomic masses; in this case, the electrons are automatically accommodated. The four neutral hydrogen atoms together have four electrons; two of these are consumed during fusion, and the other two eventually are captured by the newly-formed helium nucleus, giving neutral helium atoms.

We use the known atomic masses of neutral hydrogen-1 and helium-4, which are classically in grams per mole, that is, H = 1.0078 and He = 4.0026 atomic mass units or grams per mole. This means that one mole of H-1 weighs 1.0078 grams and contains Avogadro's number of atoms. Based on the fusion equation above, the mass of starting material is

4 H-1 = 4 x 1.0078 = 4.0312 atomic mass units or grams.

The mass of product is

1 He-4 = 4.0026 atomic mass units or grams.

The loss in mass is

4.0312 - 4.0026 = 0.0286 atomic mass units or grams.

We change the 0.0286 grams to kilograms and get the energy in the same way as before

$$
\begin{aligned}
E &= mc^2 \\
&= 0.000{,}028{,}6 \text{ kg } (2.9979 \times 10^8 \text{ m/s})^2 \\
&= 2.570 \times 10^{12} \text{ J} \\
&= 2{,}570{,}000{,}000 \text{ kJ}
\end{aligned}
$$

Note that the number of kilojoules is the same as that from the first calculation based on atoms, within the small errors stemming from rounding off some digits. This amount of energy is a bit more than 2½ billion kilojoules, and it arises from only a few milligrams of mass! The number is so large because the velocity of light is very high, and even this tremendous value is squared. In the core of our Sun this reaction occurs continuously, and the heat works its way to the surface, where electromagnetic energy is radiated away at a furious pace. The role of neutrinos (4-15C) has been ignored in this discussion. Our Sun loses approximately 4.3 million metric tonnes of mass each second by the above process in its frenzied production of energy. But in its 4.6 billion years, this amounts to less than 0.1% of its total mass. The power of our Sun is a staggering 3.86×10^{26} watts.

Lots of energy from a tiny mass

Our Earth intercepts a tiny fraction of the light emitted by the Sun. If we express this amount of energy as its equivalent in mass, it comes out to be a surprising 1.93 kilograms (4.25 pounds) per second. But the Earth re-radiates infrared at about the same rate (4-31B).

Compare the above thermonuclear reaction to a corresponding chemical reaction, say the burning of charcoal. If we take carbon (charcoal) in the amount of 12 grams (because the number of atoms is the same as in 4 grams of helium, making the comparison valid), burning it in air or oxygen to carbon dioxide yields only a puny 393 kJ of heat. Actually Einstein's equation is valid in this case too, but the loss of mass equivalent to 393 kJ is simply too small to measure by direct weighing. In general, nuclear reactions give off several million times as much energy as the same amounts of material in chemical reactions.

If you think that the energy generated by the Sun is huge, just consider certain events astronomers have discovered in distant space, namely gamma-ray bursts or hypernovae. These are super-intense sources of gamma rays lasting a few seconds or minutes. The amount of energy thrown out into space during that short span of time exceeds the total amount of energy our Sun has generated since its birth 4.6 billion years ago plus all its expected energy for the next five billion years! An example is the event labeled GRB 970228 (for Gamma-Ray Burst 1997 February 28) in the Orion constellation. Such events might be binary neutron stars collapsing to form black holes. Some astronomers suspect that the gamma rays from some of the nearer bursts have affected evolution on Earth.

4-13 Stars, the First Nuclear Reactors

In 1920 astrophysicists began to understand the nuclear processes which occur in our Sun and other stars. The Sun today consists of about 70% hydrogen, 28% helium, and 2% elements heavier than helium. The plasma in the center has a temperature of around 15,000,000 °C. The primary mechanism of fusion of four protons (that is, hydrogen nuclei) to a helium-4 nucleus is as follows. There is a statistical distribution of velocity among the various particles in the plasma, the fastest being the most energetic. Two of the fastest protons, on colliding, have sufficient energy to overcome the mutual repulsion of their positive charges, and fuse together, one positive charge being thrown off as a positron. A neutrino (4-15) is also released. The result is a newly-created deuterium nucleus (deuteron). Note that loss of the positron has in effect converted one proton into a neutron. In a second step, the deuteron fuses with another proton, forming a helium-3 nucleus and a gamma-ray photon. The third step is collision of two of these energetic helium-3 nuclei (together having four protons and two neutrons) to form a helium-4 nucleus (two protons and the two neutrons); two protons are released. Thus the net process consists of fusing four protons into one helium nucleus. It was as late as 1938 when this process came to be fairly well understood. In stars which are bigger and hotter than our Sun, the main process is different. There are traces of carbon-12 nuclei, and successive collisions with protons yield nitrogen-13, carbon-13, nitrogen-14, oxygen-15, and nitrogen-15. This last nuclide, on impact with a proton, breaks off a helium-4 nucleus, and forms carbon-12, which begins the cycle over again. Each step involves appropriate numbers of positron, neutrino, and gamma releases. The net effect of this carbon-nitrogen-oxygen cycle is the same: fusion of four protons to one helium nucleus.

4-14 Energy Produced in Forming Heavier Nuclei

We have seen that when 4 moles (close to 4 grams) of hydrogen atoms fuse to form helium, 2.57 billion kilojoules of energy is released. A nearly identical operation is the calculation of a term known as the binding energy of nuclei. This is the energy evolved when the constituent components of neutral atoms (protons, neutrons, and electrons) fuse to form heavier atoms. For example, a neutral helium atom consists of two protons, two neutrons, and two electrons. The various atomic masses are:

2 p = 2 x 1.00728 = 2.01456 atomic mass units
2 n = 2 x 1.00866 = 2.01732 atomic mass units
2 e = 2 x 0.00055 = 0.00110 atomic mass units

These total 4.03298 amu. The measured atomic mass of helium-4 is 4.00260 amu. Thus the mass of helium-4 is less than that of its constituents by 4.03298 - 4.00260 = 0.03038 amu. This mass has been converted into energy. Instead of working with huge numbers of kilojoules per mole, it is more convenient to calculate megaelectron volts (MeV) per atom or nucleus formed. Conversion of one atomic mass unit into energy yields 931.5 MeV (per atom), as can be easily shown using Einstein's equation. Thus the above 0.03038 amu corresponds to 0.03038 x 931.5 = 28.32 MeV as the binding energy of helium-4. (A fine point is that energy evolved has a negative sign; the strictly correct definition of binding energy is the energy required to break a nucleus into its components, a positive quantity).

Suppose we extend this sort of calculation to all other known elements in all their isotopic forms, right up through uranium and beyond. Let's illustrate this with the case of, say, nickel-58, the most abundant isotope of this metal. From the periodic table we see that nickel has an atomic number (nuclear charge) of 28. We need 28 protons and 28 electrons. The number of neutrons must be 58 - 28 = 30. Proceeding in the same way as in the case of helium, the final result is that the amount of mass converted to energy is 0.54305 atomic mass units, and the total binding energy is 505.85 MeV. This is enormous, and indicates how stable nickel nuclei are. For uranium-235, the amount of mass lost on forming the atom figures out to be 1736.5 MeV or 1.8642 amu.

The trouble with the above results is that each case is based on a different number of nucleons (protons and neutrons), and so they cannot be compared. The total of the protons and neutrons is the mass number. To overcome the problem we merely divide each amount of energy by the mass number concerned, and this normalizes the energy to one particle. Thus the normalized results, rounded to one or two figures past the decimal point, are as below:

helium-4: $$\frac{28.32\text{MeV}}{4} = 7.08 \text{ Mev per nucleon}$$

nickel-58: $$\frac{505.85 \text{ MeV}}{58} = 8.72 \text{ MeV per nucleon}$$

uranium-235: $$\frac{1736.5\text{MeV}}{235} = 7.39 \text{ MeV per nucleon}$$

Curiously, as we go across the periodic table to heavier and heavier elements, the amounts of energy evolved per nucleon on forming their nuclei first rise and then go down, with some irregularities (figure below). When the above type of calculation is carried out for all kinds of atoms the results are best seen graphically. Helium is above the curve since its nucleus (an alpha particle) is extraordinarily stable. Fusion of hydrogen to form nickel would liberate more energy than fusion to helium, but this formation of nickel has not been done artificially. Note that there

Our nuclear energy has been stored in uranium for eons.

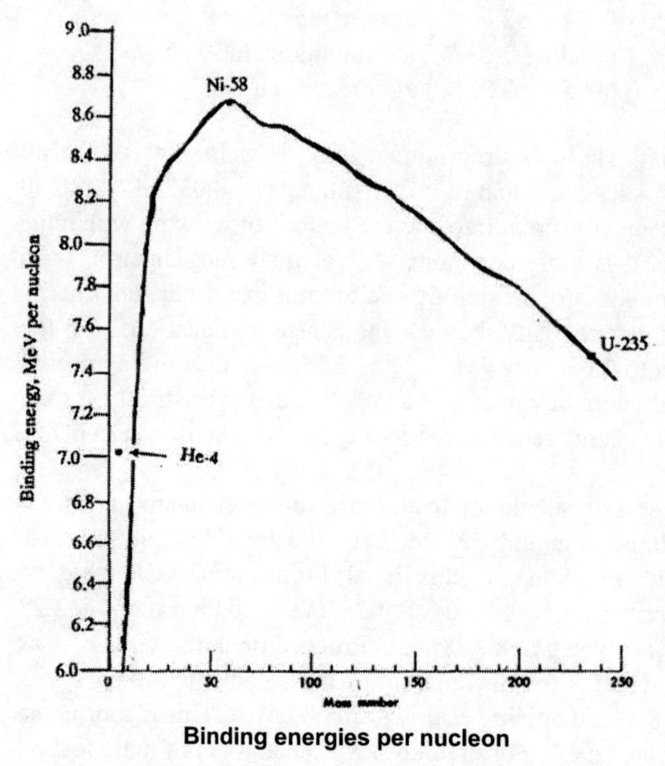

Binding energies per nucleon

is a maximum in the curve in the region of mass number 58 or 59, after which the curve declines. The nuclei at the maximum are lowest in energy, which means they are most stable. The heaviest nuclei, like uranium-235, are energy-rich, and represent energy stored since their formation in ancient stars. In building up a nucleus from protons and neutrons, the positive charge repels each incoming proton. It requires enormous energy to overcome this repulsion, but once that is accomplished, the strong short-range nuclear force takes over, and with sufficient neutrons, binding energy is sufficient to hold the assembly together.

The shape of the curve suggests two avenues to nuclear energy: fusion of light elements such as hydrogen to heavier ones, and splitting or fission of the heavier nuclei to form two lighter ones. The second method was achieved before the first by scientists.

4-15 Subnuclear Particles

Background—By about 1930 physicists had become quite convinced that the only fundamental particles were protons, electrons, and photons (assuming these last count as particles). They were reluctant at first to accept the neutron, discovered by the English physicist Chadwick in 1932, as a genuine particle, and not just a combination of an electron and proton. Yet, the discovery of the neutron permitted a breakthrough in understanding nuclear structure which can be likened to Copernicus' view of celestial motion. A second new particle, discovered by an American, Philip Anderson, in the same year, was the positive electron or positron. Actually, the positron had been predicted a year earlier by the English physicist Dirac. Another, called the neutrino, had been suggested in 1930 by Pauli, then a 30-year-old, superbly keen-witted Austrian-born professor teaching in Switzerland. Still another, as mentioned previously, was the meson, predicted in 1935 by the Japanese physicist Yukawa. Since those days a bewildering array of new particles has been discovered or postulated.

Wolfgang Pauli (1900–1958), Theoretical physicist. Born in Austria, but professionally international. Best known for his exclusion principle and ideas about nuclear spin and the neutrino.

Particles and Antiparticles—In general, to each particle there corresponds an antiparticle with opposite electric charge or different ways of attaining neutrality, a sort of mirror world. Positrons are the antiparticles of ordinary electrons, which have negative charges. When these two particles come together, their opposite charges attract and cause them to form a neutral spinning pair, something like a hydrogen atom. This combination ("positronium") is unstable, and exists less than a millionth of a second. What happens is that mutual annihilation takes place, and the two electron masses become their equivalent in energy, according to the equation $E = mc^2$. Since each electron mass is equivalent to 0.51 megaelectron volts (Appendix III; mega means one million), two gamma ray photons are born, each with the energy 0.51 megaelectron volts; they recoil in opposite directions. Contrariwise, a gamma ray photon of energy at least 1.02 megaelectron volts, under the proper conditions, disappears, and a positron and an electron are born. In1997 physicists at the Stanford Linear Accelerator Center achieved the same result, that is, converting energy to matter, by focusing an intense electron beam onto rays of light from a powerful laser. Positrons appeared. A curiosity is that physicist Hans Dehmelt of the University of Washington trapped a single positron in a magnetic field and held it rotating in a circular orbit for three months. He became so fond of his positron that he named her Priscilla.

A positron named Priscilla

Negative protons (antiprotons) are known; they are the antiparticles of ordinary protons. A deuteron consists of a proton and a neutron; antideuterons, with negative charge, are also known. Antiprotons, made in massive linear accelerators, can be trapped a few days in cylinders cooled with liquid helium; they circulate in a ring controlled by powerful magnets. Antimatter, atoms with negative nuclei and positive electrons, was not known until recently. A contract was awarded to the Stanford Linear Accelerator Center in California in 1993 to investigate antimatter. Additional efforts to make antihydrogen are underway at the Tevatron in the Fermi National Accelerator Laboratory (Fermilab) near Chicago. But it was the laboratory of the European Center for Nuclear Research (Conseil Européen pour la Recherche Nucléaire, or CERN) near Geneva which first succeeded in making antihydrogen just as the year1995 graduated into 1996. Antiprotons, stored by circulating in a ring-shaped track by controlling with magnetic fields, were allowed to impinge on a jet of xenon gas. This generated both positive and negative electrons (from the relativistic energy of the swift antiprotons). In a few rare instances, the antiprotons (with negative charge) and antielectrons (that is, positrons, with positive charge) had speed and direction close together. This permitted formation of neutral antihydrogen atoms, which, having no net charge, continued on a linear trajectory in a strong magnetic field. Accompanying charged particles curved away in both left and right directions. The antihydrogen atoms,

Chapter 7. THE STRUCTURE OF THE NUCLEUS

"What?" exclaimed Roger, as Karen rolled on the bed and rested her warm body against his. "I know some nuclei are spherical and some are ellipsoidal, but where did you find out that some fluctuate in between?"

Karen pursed her lips. "They've been observed with a short-wavelength probe. . ."

An antiperiodic table?

which are a sort of Through-the-Looking-Glass version of ordinary hydrogen, lasted only some 40 microseconds until they were annihilated by collision with atoms of ordinary matter. At most only 11 atoms of antihydrogen were made, but the evidence that they had been formed is strong. In fall 1996 Fermilab also generated antihydrogen. The hope now is to prepare enough antihydrogen to examine its spectrum and other properties. In theory, a whole antiperiodic table is possible, but don't bother to wait for one.

In spring 1997 American astronomers, using the Compton Gamma Ray Observatory orbiting Earth, announced the identification of what might be a huge cloud of antimatter near the center of the Milky Way. It is some 25,000 light years from Earth. Electron-positron annihilation is constantly taking place there, as evidenced by the gamma-ray photons of characteristic energy (1.02 megaelectron volt; see 4-15B).

Speaking of antiprotons, we should mention here a weird form of helium. In 1991 Japanese physicists discovered that when they fired antiprotons into liquid helium, about 3% of the new atoms formed lived a relatively long time, namely 15 microseconds. This observation encouraged investigators at the European center for particle physics, including Japanese visitors, who used laser beams to study the products from the antiproton experiments. The result was a new form of helium. Ordinary helium consists of a nucleus with a mass number of 4 and a charge of +2, with two planetary electrons orbiting outside. Now imagine the atom in which one of these electrons is replaced with an antiproton, which also has a negative charge of 1, but is much heavier. This bizarre new atom, referred to as antiprotonic helium, lives a few microseconds.

Neutrinos—Radioactive decay results when a nucleus goes from one energy state to a lower one, and the emitted particle takes up the difference in energy. Thus one would expect that beta particles (negative or positive) would display fixed, quantized, energy levels. Yet it was early observed that in fact there is a continuous span or spectrum of beta-particle energies, up to a certain maximum for each case. This is true whether a gamma ray is emitted or not. In 1927 the heat liberated during beta decay of bismuth-210 was measured in a calorimeter. The result was that the total heat detected corresponded to the average beta-particle energy, not the maximum energy. So where did the extra energy go?

And thus Pauli begat another member of a growing menagerie of particles.

Addressing the paradox, Pauli boldly proposed that the energy released in beta decay is divided between the electron emitted and a previously unknown, highly-penetrating particle, later named the neutrino ("little neutral one") by Fermi. Its energy could not be detected by ordinary heat measurements.

The type of decay which emits positrons yields neutrinos, while decay which emits negative electrons yields antineutrinos. Neutrinos have either no mass or almost no mass, that is, less than 10^{-5} electron mass and thus detecting and counting them is truly a challenging task. This is equivalent to less than 5 electron volts. These ghostly particles are so penetrating that they can pass right through the Earth. In fact, Japanese physicists fired a beam of neutrinos, generated in a particle accelerator, through the Earth and picked up signals of emerging particles a distance of 250 kilometers away. One could say these bantam phantoms barely exist.

Experiments starting in the 1950s were undertaken to detect the elusive neutrinos. They were first observed by Frederick Reines in 1956, working near a nuclear reactor at the Savannah River Site. He described them as "listening to a gnat's whisper in a hurricane." Further work in the United States, as well as American-Soviet and American-Japanese studies, has been able to confirm indirectly the existence of these shy, wraith-like neutrinos, and to measure their abundance with some accuracy. Neutrinos stream out from the Sun and other stars, from supernovae (which are neutrino-dominated), from nuclear reactors, and from nuclear explosions. About 10^{15} neutrinos from the Sun reach the Earth per square meter each second, carrying several percent of the solar energy reaching the Earth. High-energy neutrino beams were first produced in the 1950s using 30 gigaelectron volt proton accelerators. A neutrino detector, built by chemist Raymond Davis (Nobel Prize, 2002) in the Homestake Gold Mine in South Dakota, contained 100,000 gallons of a chlorinated hydrocarbon, namely tetrachloroethylene. About one quarter of the chlorine atoms is chlorine-37, and these interact weakly with neutrinos to form radioactive argon-37, which is metered. Another neutrino-measuring device was built deep in a mountain in the Soviet Caucasus; it contains 60 metric tonnes of liquid gallium. This was started in 1984, when Cold-War mistrust was intense. Underground sites screen out cosmic rays. The rather rare metal gallium was chosen because it was known that the neutrons in the nucleus of gallium-71 are readily converted into germanium-71 by neutrinos. The germanium produced is radioactive, with a half-life of about 11 days. Thus chemical extraction of the germanium (with hydrochloric acid containing hydrogen peroxide) permits monitoring neutrinos. As few as 20 atoms of germanium-71 per experiment are formed.

Other instruments are under construction in Canada and in Italy. The Canadian instrument, situated in an old nickel mine, uses 1000 metric tonnes of heavy water. The Italian device uses 30 metric tonnes of gallium as a solution of its chloride. An American group plans an "ice telescope" in the Antarctic, using a cubic kilometer of ice with embedded sensors. The Japanese built a neutrino detector in an old mine near Kamiokande, in the Japanese Alps. It has a tank holding 680 metric tonnes of ultra-pure water, which interacts with neutrinos to yield a faint blue-white light (the Cherenkov effect); the light is measured using 11,200 photomultiplier tubes. The leader in this work, Masatoshi Koshiba, received a Nobel Prize in 2002 for this work. Another American team plans construction of a neutrino detector based on liquid helium-4 at a temperature just above absolute zero. Interaction of a neutrino from the Sun with one of the electrons of helium would cause detectable evaporation of helium. Still another neutrino-detecting chamber has been built in Los Alamos. It holds 200 metric tonnes of mineral oil in a tank 30 meters long. The walls are studded with 1220 photomultiplier tubes and the oil contains 30 parts per million of a scintillator. Neutrinos are generated and allowed to pass through the oil; any interaction with the protons (nuclei of hydrogen in the oil) are expected to cause flashes of light.

Something like finding a given grain of sand in the Sahara Desert

Results to date from the various detectors described above indicate that the number of neutrinos coming from the Sun is only a third to a half the number predicted from fusion theories. There is evidence that there are at least three types of neutrinos (each with its antiparticle), and some of these are not measured by current detectors. These are: the neutrino associated with beta decay (the electron neutrino); the muon neutrino; and the tau neutrino. Results in early 1992 from the gallium neutrino detectors also failed to find the expected number of solar neutrinos. Until recently, the exceedingly important but vexing question of whether neutrinos have mass could not be answered for certain: it is very difficult, maybe impossible, to measure zero. But the Los Alamos experiments using mineral oil suggest that neutrinos do have mass, in the range of 0.5 to 5 electron volts, somewhere around a hundred thousandth of the mass of an electron. Moreover, the masses of the muon and tau neutrinos would be 2.4 electron volts. If this is true, neutrinos could make up 20% or more of the mass of the Universe, since they exist in space to the extent of perhaps a billion per cubic meter. In fall 1995 *Physical Review Letters* published two papers, one claiming neutrinos have mass, the other claiming the opposite.

The various neutrino detectors have found only about a third of the theoretical number of these specks of mirage, so to speak, and this inconsistency stimulated particle physicists to critically reexamine the theories. By the fall of 1992 several groups had improved the old calculations using advanced computers, basing their work on a better understanding of the composition of the Sun. The results indicate agreement, more or less, between predicted and observed numbers of neutrinos.

In 1998 the question of neutrino mass was answered at the Kamiokande neutron research facility in Japan. The technique is to count neutrons coming from opposite directions, one group from the atmosphere above the huge tanks of water and the other coming through the Earth diametrically opposite. The idea is that neutrons can oscillate between the tau and muon types only if they have mass and are traveling through material substance, such as the Earth. The usual detectors do not register tau neutrons. The experiments registered a significant difference between the muon neutrons coming directly from the atmosphere and those which had passed through the Earth, which confirms oscillation, thus proving their property of mass. In 2000, an international team of physicists at Fermilab finally succeeded in demonstrating that the tau neutrino does exist. They snared the elusive subparticle by first sending a beam of protons from a particle accelerator through tungsten, which formed many kinds of subparticles, including a few tau neutrinos. All particles except the tau neutrinos were absorbed by a filter, and these were allowed to impinge on iron. About one-trillionth of these tau neutrons were absorbed, forming tau leptons (see 4-15D), which decayed in flight. These were detected using an emulsion technology developed in Japan. For every electron in our universe, there are at least 50 billion neutrinos. Clearly, there is a great deal to be learned about these matters. Stay tuned.

Subparticles in General—According to the most recent physical theories, all particles are one of two types, fermions or bosons. Fermions are basic matter itself, while bosons mediate the forces between fermions. The material in the point which exploded in the Big Bang supposedly consisted of fermions and bosons. Physicists today recognize four fundamental types of forces, namely:

Strong force—Overcomes proton-proton repulsion in nuclei. Very short range (less than 10^{-15} meter).

Weak force—Involved in beta activity. Even shorter range (10^{-18} meter). Strength: 10^{-13} of strong force.

Electromagnetic force—Quite long range. Holds electrons in orbit within atoms. Strength: 10^{-2} of strong force.

Gravitational force—Weakest of all. Very long range. Strength: 10^{-40} of strong force.

Modern theoretical physics has spouted a veritable zoo of particles. It recognizes three fundamental families: the electron family, the muon family, and the tau family. Each is composed of fermions and bosons. The electron family is the least massive, and the tau family is the most massive. Each family is subdivided into two groups, one called quarks and the other leptons. These subparticles are the most fundamental or elementary ones known, the building blocks of all matter. Protons and neutrons consist of three quarks, and are thought to have been formed shortly after the Big Bang. It is those short-range forces mentioned above which hold them together. Photons are bosons, while neutrinos are fermions. Many particles are not discussed here, such as heavy fermion-antifermion pairs. Another subnuclear particle considered only briefly here is the gluon, a rather uncreative name. These are the carriers of the strong exchange force between the quarks which make up protons and neutrons. The American physicist and Nobelist Henry Kendall, working with Jerome Friedman and Richard Taylor, are credited with the discovery that protons and neutrons are made up of still smaller particles, namely quarks. The property of spin, in the cases of protons and neutrons, is much more complex than first thought, and is the result of interactions among their subnuclear constituents.

As fundamental as you can get (at least so far)

Discovery of quarks

With the aid of ultra-high-energy accelerators physicists have been probing progressively deeper into the structure of matter. Studies of this type have revealed the families of subatomic particles mentioned above; some of them exist in the free state for a millionth of a second or less. A Superconducting Super Collider, capable of achieving energy levels of 500 megaelectron volts to around 40 trillion electron volts, was canceled. In 1993 Congress voted to stop financing this project, but in 1996 decided to contribute $530 million towards the Large Hadron Collider at the European center for particle physics (CERN) in Geneva.

A new accelerator, the Relativistic Heavy Ion Collider, has been built at Brookhaven National Laboratory. Among its first experiments, one is the generation of beams consisting of accelerated nuclei of gold atoms. Two beams will go in opposite directions, having been accelerated to an incredible 99.9% of the speed of light. On collision, the two nuclei have an energy of some 40 trillion electron volts. This results in a sort of quark-gluon plasma, like an infinitesimal speck from the inside of an exploding super nova. Thus the nature of material formed in the Big Bang can be studied.

After Yukawa's prediction of mesons in 1935, physicists discovered several kinds of particles with masses between those of electrons and protons. One (the pi meson, or pion), could be positively charged (273 electron masses or 140 MeV) or negatively charged (264 electron masses or 135 MeV). Another kind of pion was found to have 264 electron masses or 135 MeV, and no charge. Pions are unstable, decomposing into muons and neutrinos or antineutrinos. Atomic nuclei are composed of protons, neutrons, and pions. It might be that the same forces which hold nuclei together also are manifested in neutron stars, which in this view could be regarded as giant nuclei, perhaps 2 kilometers in radius. A table of the most important subnuclear particles is presented below.

The following are mostly the ideas of Gell-Mann and Zweig. The most fundamental subparticles are the quarks (non-scientists suspect that physicists are fascinated by a whimsical lexicon). The first evidence for the existence of quarks was gained in 1968 during studies at the Stanford Linear Accelerator which revealed the presence of hard, pointlike subparticles within protons. The experiments involved collisions of electrons from the accelerator with protons (hydrogen nuclei in the liquid element). Thus the building blocks of protons are two quarks with charge +2/3 (up quarks) and one with charge -1/3 (down quark), the sum being +1. Neutrons consist of one quark with charge +2/3 and two with charge -1/3, the sum being zero. The antiproton and antineutron have quarks of the opposite sign, respectively. These three-quark assemblies are referred to as baryons. Thus an intricate world within protons and neutrons has been revealed. Physicists at the Fermilab in 1996 announced evidence that quarks might consist of still smaller components, but this was evidently in error.

The deuterium nucleus consists of a proton and a neutron, making six quarks altogether. Quarks are subject to the strong force, which leptons do not feel. Experiments at the CERN particle-physics laboratory in Geneva have confirmed the existence of fractional electronic charges. The six subnuclear particles are still grouped into two 3-quark assemblies. Of the six kinds of quarks, experimental evidence for their existence is available for five; the sixth, called the top quark was still at large until the spring of 1994, when the other shoe finally dropped. The nature of decay of the bottom quark indicates that it must have a partner, the top quark. This conclusion stimulated the search in which strong evidence for it was found. The successful quest for the top quark was at the Fermilab, where protons and antiprotons were forced to collide in the Tevatron particle accelerator with a ring four miles in circumference. The evanescent top quark, with a mass of about 200 proton masses (approximately 176 gigaelectron volts, the mass of a gold atom), proved to have a life of around 10^{-24} second. This high mass corresponds to the extreme relativistic energy which characterizes the top quark. It decomposes in several ways, yielding fragments which were detected. In 1995 the final evidence pinning down the existence of the top quark was discovered.

Leptons, as mentioned above, span all three families (electron family, muon family, and tau family); they have no internal structure. They interact within nuclei through the weak forces. Electrons fall into the lepton class, as do neutrinos, muons and a few others. The concept of radius is hazy in these cases. Photons, which are bosons, interact with electrons, which are leptons. The electrons are generally in orbits about atomic nuclei, and on absorbing the energy are excited into orbits richer in energy, or are expelled altogether (ionization). Of the various kinds of force listed above, it is the electromagnetic force which is involved. Neutrinos, which are leptons, interact poorly with matter because weak nuclear forces operate.

There is some evidence that neutrinos oscillate between the electron neutrino and the muon neutrino while traveling through space. The two modifications have different masses and therefore different wave frequencies. Thus beats can result, as in sound. It is clear that much remains to be learned about these subparticles.

Baryons are clusters of quarks. Mesons are one subclass, with quark-antiquark pairs. An assembly of three quarks is another subclass, the hadrons. These include protons and neutrons. They interact within nuclei via the strong force. It might be that protons, that is, hydrogen nuclei, are not entirely stable. One theory, proposed by Andrei Sakharov, is that they disintegrate with the incredibly long half-life of more than 10^{32} years, forming positrons, neutrinos, and photons. Attempts to detect decay of protons have been carried out using thousands of tons of water, an amount which contains an astronomical numbers of protons. The American detector was near Cleveland, but it has been shut down and parts sent to Japan's detector at Kamiokande. No definite conclusions have been reached.

Advances in the field of subparticle physics are being made constantly. The picture will probably become still more complex before a fully coherent framework is achieved through some sort of grand unified theory. Eventually these studies will without doubt eventually have practical applications.

Summary—A simplified table outlining the more important subnuclear particles and some of their properties is given below. Their antiparticles are omitted. Their rest masses are given as the equivalent in energy (electron volts, eV, or megaelectron volts, MeV). In the case of photons, the theoretical rest mass is zero, but moving in vacuum, the mass, which is small, is proportional to the frequency. The composition of hadrons in terms of quarks is not indicated in the table; and bosons are not described.

	Rest Mass	**Charge**	**Half-Life**
Photon	0	0	stable
Gluon	0	0	stable
Leptons			
Electron	0.511 MeV	-1	stable
Electron neutrino	0 to 2.4eV	0	stable
Muon	106 MeV	-1	2.2 x 10^{-6} second
Muon neutrino	0 to 2.4 eV	0	stable
Tau	1,700 MeV	-1	unstable
Tau neutrino	0 to 2.4 eV	0	—
Quarks			
Up	300 MeV	+2/3	—
Down	300 MeV	-1/3	—
Charm	1,500 MeV	+2/3	—
Strange	500 MeV	-1/3	—
Top	175,000 MeV	+2/3	extremely unstable
Bottom	4,500 MeV	-1/3	unstable
Hadrons			
Mesons			
Pion	140 MeV	+1	2.6 x 10^{-8} second
Baryons			
Proton	938.3 MeV	+1	stable
Neutron	939.6 MeV	0	616 seconds

Thus there are twelve basic or fundamental subnuclear particles known today, six leptons and six quarks; in addition there are photons, gluons, and W and Z bosons.

In 1973, Fermi said, "If I could remember the names of all these particles I'd be a botanist."

The top quark is an essential element of modern subnuclear particle theory. Our human sense of symmetry demands that the top quark exists. When asked, before the confirming discovery at Fermilab, whether it could be that it does not really exist, veteran quark hunter Burton Richter considered the question a while and answered: "It better."

4-16 Fission and Cross Section

The radii of the nuclei of heavy elements are around 6 x 10^{-15} meter. If we visualize a nucleus sliced through its center and thus cross sectioned, a circle results whose area comes out to be close to 10^{-28} square meter. If a neutron comes by, it is not attracted or repulsed electrostatically by the nuclear charge. Therefore at first glance one might think that the probability of collision (and thus penetration of the nucleus) is proportional to this geometrical cross sectional area. It turns out that this is not really the case. Some nuclei absorb neutrons readily, as if their cross-sectional area were much bigger than that calculated above. This effect arises from complicated quantum and resonance phenomena.

According to the folklore of early Manhattan Project days, physicists Holloway and Baker referred to a large cross section as "bigger than a barn," and this terminology has stuck. The area 10^{-28} square meter became known as one barn (abbreviation: b). The barn unit, with dimensions of area, is a useful measure of the probability of many kinds of nuclear reactions. With billions of billions of nuclei and neutrons, the laws of probability hold exactly. One must specify which nuclear process is meant, whether it is capture of neutrons with fission, capture of neutrons without fission, etc. The energy of the neutrons must also be specified.

"Slow" or "thermal" neutrons are those with energies in the range of the kinetic energies of atoms or molecules at ordinary temperatures. The average energy value is only about 0.025 electron volt (eV). An electron volt is the amount of energy an electron acquires when it falls through a potential difference of 1 volt. Below are some cross sections in barns for fission by thermal neutrons of several important nuclides:

uranium-233, 525 b
uranium-235, 577 b
uranium-238, zero to 0.00005 b
plutonium-239, 741 b
plutonium-240, 290 b

For capture of thermal neutrons, a few values are:

carbon-12, 0.0035 b
sodium-23. 0.43 b

iron-56, 2.6 b
cobalt-59, 20.7 b
zirconium (natural), 0.18 b
hydrogen, 0.33 b
nitrogen, 1.75 b

Note that even though nuclei of the three isotopes of uranium listed have virtually the same physical size, their cross sections for neutron capture are very different.

As the energy of the incoming neutrons rises, the fission cross sections change. Energies of these particles are often in the thousands of electron volts (kiloelectron volts, keV) or millions of electron volts (megaelectron volts, MeV). For uranium-238, for example, the fission cross section for very low energy neutrons is practically zero, but when 2.5 megaelectron volt neutrons are used, it rises to about 1 barn, and becomes still higher when the energy is tens of megaelectron volts (as in a hydrogen bomb explosion). Heavy atoms with odd mass numbers (233, 235, 239, 241) undergo fission much more easily than those with even mass numbers (232, 238, 240).

The cross section of boron-10 for capture of thermal neutrons is high, 3838 barns. For cadmium-113 the value is an enormous 20,000 barns (for high-energy neutrons, the cross section is far lower). Such materials are therefore used in control rods to choke off the nuclear chain reaction in reactors by absorbing neutrons.

There's no substitute for experience.

A lesson in nuclear cross sections for neutron absorption was learned when the first of three giant reactors was turned on at Hanford in September 1944. This one, known as the B pile, had 1500 aluminum-clad uranium ingots in graphite. Cooling was by water from the Columbia River. On withdrawing the control rods the reactor went critical and began producing energy; the temperature of the cooling water rose from 10 to 60 °C. The thermal power rose to the predetermined value of 100 megawatts and held steady; the maximum designed power was 250 megawatts. But after three hours, unexpectedly and alarmingly, the power began to fall, despite further withdrawal of control rods. The reactor was simply dying; after 12 or 15 hours it had essentially closed down. After another period of similar length, the power started up again and reached 100 megawatts. This sort of oscillation promised to continue indefinitely, and was just not tolerable. Physicist Fermi, mathematician Wheeler, and a team of other scientists puzzled over this and soon found the cause. One fission product is tellurium-135, which decays to iodine-135, which decays to xenon-135. The three radionuclides have half-lives of 19 seconds, 6.6 hours, and 9.1 hours, respectively. It turns out that xenon-135 has the largest known cross section for slow neutron capture, a colossal 9.1 million barns! This cross section is so huge that one might think of the xenon-135 nucleus as a sort of octopus with tentacles which reach far out and hungrily ensnare passing neutrons. Thus it poisons the reactor, arresting the chain reaction as if more control rods had been inserted. After some hours, the xenon decays away to the degree that the reactor can begin the chain reaction again. This "xenon effect" was then reproduced in a 300-kilowatt reactor at Argonne, near Chicago by running it at full power. The problem was overcome by a combination of techniques, including addition of more fuel elements. An identical reactor, D pile, was altered by adding 504 extra ingots of uranium. It was started up a few days before

Christmas,1944, and operated without trouble. B pile was similarly modified, and also worked normally a few days after Christmas.

One can visualize the fission process of a U-235 nucleus after it captures a neutron and is set into violent vibratory motion. This convulsion results in its splitting, something like a large drop of water dividing into two smaller drops of unequal size. The sketch below illustrates fission of a U-235 nucleus. The two just-born fission products, which are nuclei having large positive charges, repel each other forcefully and recoil away with enormous energy (about 200 MeV). This little event displays the greatest increase in energy known: an incoming slow neutron, of energy 0.025 eV, provokes the release of 200 million eV, an increase by a factor of 200,000,000 eV/0.025 eV or 8 billion! Note that while one neutron is consumed, three are produced, in this instance.

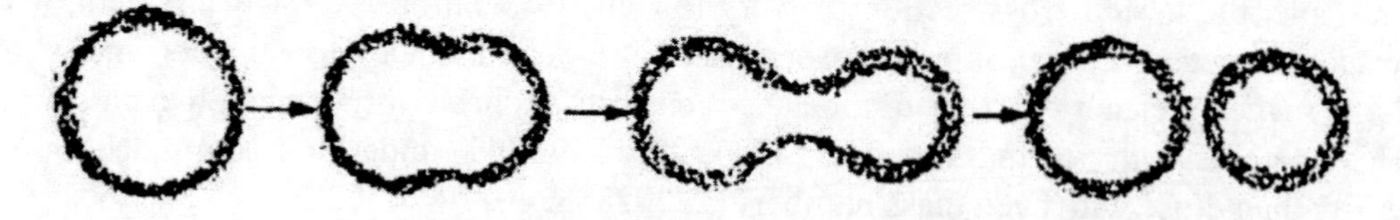

Fission visualized by a liquid drop model

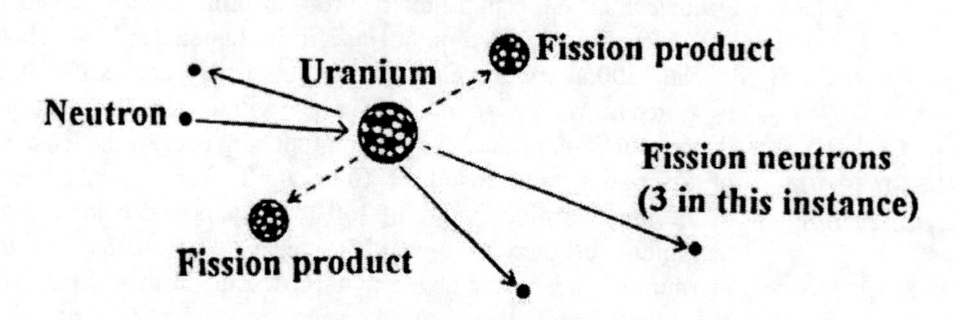

Fission of uranium-235.
More neutrons are produced than consumed.

The lighter group of fission products (remember that the splitting is asymmetric) has mass numbers of about 92 to 102, while the heavier ones peak at 132 to 142. During the couple of years after the discovery of fission, Japanese researcher Nishina and his coworkers showed that with very energetic neutrons, the fission fragments become almost equal in mass, that is, fission becomes more nearly symmetric. The figure below showing fission yield as a function of mass number illustrates the two groups of fission products of uranium-235 by slow (thermal) neutrons and by fission of uranium-238 by fast neutrons. Note that in the U-235 case the light group of fission products and the heavy group are quite well defined, as revealed by the deep valley between the two peaks. In the U-238 case, the asymmetry remains, but the valley is shallow, meaning that considerable numbers of fission events occur in which the two products have nearly the same mass numbers.

Strontium-90 and cesium-137 are important fission products because they are dangerous to health and are produced abundantly on fission. Actually, strontium-90 and cesium-137 result from beta decay of primary fission products, that is, those formed directly by fission. For the series with mass number 90, bromine-90 is the isotope first born by fission. It decays successively in seconds to short-lived krypton-90, to rubidium-90, and to strontium-90, where there is a long pause owing to the much longer half-life of this radionuclide (28.5 years). It decays to yttrium-90 and finally to stable zirconium-90 (refer to the periodic table). All these nuclides have the same mass number (90), and so are isobars (section 4-5). The emission of a beta particle by strontium-90 is not accompanied by gamma rays. In the case of the decay chain of mass number 137, the primary fission product is tellurium-137. This disintegrates rapidly to iodine to xenon to cesium-137 (half-life 30.0 years), which finally goes to stable barium-137. The last step emits both beta and gamma rays. Note that because the primary fission products, Br-90 and Te-137, have such large n/p ratios (1.57 and 1.63) that they are unstable and achieve stability by a series of beta emissions.

Approximate values of fission yields for a few important series, identified by mass number, are given below. This is for uranium-235 fissioned by slow neutrons. The yields for plutonium-239 are closely similar. Helpful words which specifically describe the fission properties of heavy nuclei (atomic numbers 90 and higher) are in common use. Nuclei are said to be *fissile* if they undergo fission on being struck by neutrons of any velocity, fast or slow. The most important examples are uranium-235, uranium-233, and plutonium-239. Only these can sustain chain reactions. This means that for each metal in the pure state, a certain critical mass exists, above which a self-sustaining chain reaction can take place. It was Szilard who first conceived of critical mass (1934). These points are important in nuclear explosions.

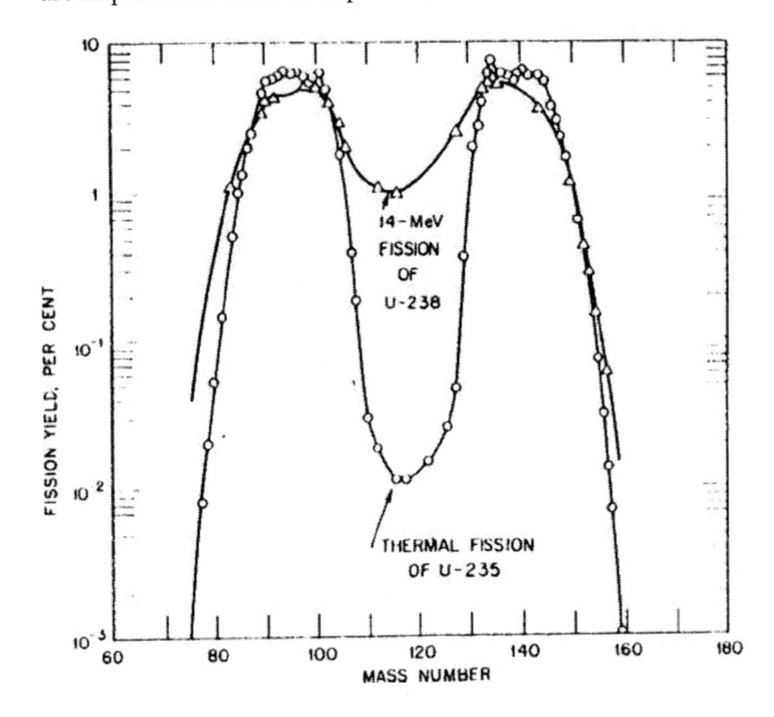

Fission yield curves of uranium.

The thermal neutron fission of U-235 shows two distinct peaks, corresponding to light and heavy fission products.

The fission curve of U-238 by 14 MeV neutrons has a much more shallow valley between the peaks, showing a higher degree of symmetry.

Two nuclides, described by the word *fertile*, have nuclei which are not fissile themselves, but can be converted into those which are. These are uranium-238 and thorium-232. For example, inside a reactor, some of the uranium-238 is converted into fissile plutonium-239, some of which undergoes fission and furnishes additional power. Exposure of thorium-232 leads to uranium-233 (7-10D). Fertile materials are important in breeder reactors. Another word, *fissionable*, can refer to any nucleus in which a neutron induces fission, but usually the word is used when referring to nuclei which are fissioned only by high-energy neutrons (above 1 million electron volts), such as uranium-238 and thorium-232 (which are also fertile). Plutonium-240 is also in this class.

Mass number	Fission yield	Important nuclides
90	5.9%	Sr-90, Y-90
93	6.0	Y-93, Zr-93
99	5.6	Mo-99, Tc-99
129	1.2	Te-129, I-129
131	2.8	Te-131, I-131
135	6.1	I-135, Xe-135
137	6.6	Xe-137, Cs-137
140	5.8	Ba-140, La-140

4-17 Energy Released on Fission of Uranium-235

Consider the nucleus of a uranium-235 atom when it absorbs a neutron and suffers fission. Two fission products are formed, these being neutron-rich nuclides of well-known chemical elements. Each has too many neutrons to be stable, and some atoms fire off some of this excess at once; these are the neutrons which sustain the chain reaction. The number of neutrons released during each fission is sometimes 1, sometimes 2, sometimes 3 or more, but averages around 2.4 or 2.5 for fission caused by slow neutrons. Some 700 to 800 different nuclides result from nuclear fission.

These fission products are fiercely radioactive by beta emission, and many emit gamma rays as well. Their half-lives range from a millionth of a second to over a million years. Each fission product is the starting point of a decay chain; the half-lives of the nuclides in the chain tend to become longer as the final, stable end product is approached. In some cases, a stable isotope results after only one or two beta decay steps with very short half-lives. A few fission products atoms are stable (nonradioactive).

For illustration we will choose an instance in which 3 neutrons are formed, and one fission product is zirconium-97 and the other is tellurium-136. This is typical in that one product is in the atomic mass range of 90 to 100, and the other is in the range 136 to 144, that is, the two fission products are of unequal mass. The fission equation is:

$$\text{U-235} + \text{n} \Rightarrow \text{Zr-97} + \text{Te-136} + 3\text{n}$$

If one figures out the total number of neutrons (free and in the nuclei of the three radionuclides), it comes out to be 144 on each side of the arrow. The energy-rich fission products rapidly undergo beta decay. The first emits an electron and forms niobium-97 (the periodic table helps here). The second similarly emits an electron and forms iodine-136 (each atom must have a positive charge since it lost a negative charge). The nuclei of Nb-97 and I-136 are still radioactive; emitting electrons results respectively in molybdenum-97 and xenon-136 (each now with a double positive charge). These last two nuclides are stable. After some time, the four electrons, now slowed down, are taken up by the positively charged atoms and neutral atoms result. The energy of fission is consequently based on the formation of the two stable, neutral atoms and the 3 neutrons. The fission equation is written to show the final products, as below; the atomic masses are also recorded.

U-235	+ n	=>	Mo-97	+	Xe-136	+ 3 n
235.04392	1.00867		96.90602		135.90722	3 x 1.00867

The masses of the starting materials and of the products (including the 3 neutrons) are calculated, and the difference is obtained. These steps show that 0.21334 atomic mass unit is lost (converted to energy). Applying Einstein's equation as before reveals an energy yield which is the equivalent of 19.20 billion kilojoules per mole; when this amount is divided by 235 (to put it on a per-gram basis so it can be compared with the fusion energy of hydrogen), it comes out to be 81.7 million kilojoules per gram. Approximately 94% of the fission energy is associated with the two fission products, 2.5% with the neutrons, and 3.5% with gamma rays and neutrinos produced by the fission process.

A uranium-235 atom can be crudely compared to a spring-type mouse trap. The trap when baited and set stores a certain amount of energy which is released suddenly on stimulation (by a mouse). An atom of U-235 holds energy, which is released on stimulation (by a neutron).

Each fission of an atom of uranium-235 liberates approximately 200 megaelectron volts (MeV). Remember that each atomic mass unit on conversion to energy yields 931.5 MeV per atom (4-14). When an atom of uranium-235 undergoes fission by a slow neutron, the energy released is approximately as follows:

Kinetic energy of fission products	168 MeV
Kinetic energy of fission neutrons	5
Instantaneous gamma-ray energy	5
Gamma-ray energy from fission product decay	6
Beta particles from fission product decay	7
Neutrinos from fission product decay	10
Total	201 MeV

The last three entries in the table above, totaling 23 MeV, are delayed somewhat since it takes time for the fission products to undergo radioactive decay.

When 1 gram of hydrogen undergoes fusion to helium, 0.718% of the mass is converted to energy. When 1 gram of uranium-235 undergoes fission, 0.090% of the mass is converted to energy. The fission yield of energy is only one-eighth that of the fusion yield, but is still a gigantic amount.

4-18 Particle Accelerators

At this point it is useful to discuss briefly a series of instruments known as particle accelerators which have been developed by physicists during the past century and a half. In these devices, charged particles, such as electrons or protons, are generated in an evacuated chamber and then accelerated by attraction to an electrode with the opposite electric charge. In this manner, using high voltages (commonly 5000 to 60,000 volts), a stream of energetic particles can be produced. Electrons can be accelerated to speeds approaching that of light.

The electric discharge tube which Roentgen used in the discovery of X-rays (3-2) is a simple particle accelerator. Electrons are forced to leave one electrode by (a) keeping the electrode at a white heat, (b) giving a negative electric charge to this electrode so that it repels the negative charge of the electrons, and (c) placing the other electrode nearby and giving it a positive charge to attract the electrons. The negative electrode is termed the cathode; the positive one, called the anode, serves as a target. In early days, what appeared to be rays were observed streaming out of the cathode, hence the term cathode ray tube. By putting auxiliary charged electrodes or permanent magnets or electromagnets along the path of the electron stream, the electron beam can be bent or focused. In time, many useful devices were invented based on these cathode ray tube/particle accelerators, including oscilloscopes, radio tubes, television tubes, Geiger counters, radar, electron microscopes, and computer terminals. Van de Graaff generators are highly modified, gigantic particle accelerators.

The first machine to accelerate charged particles using an alternating field was built by the Norwegian Wideroe in 1928. This employed a straight tube with hollow cylindrical electrodes strategically spaced and alternatively charged, drawing packets of charged particles to ever higher velocities and energy. The largest such accelerator ever built is at the Stanford Linear Accelerator Center; it is 3 kilometers long, and can energize electrons up to 50,000 megaelectron volts (50 gigaelectron volts).

In the early 1930s, the American physicist Lawrence constructed an instrument called a cyclotron, a device for accelerating charged particles such as hydrogen-1 nuclei (protons). The first model was only five inches in diameter. As sketched below, it is seen to consist of a split cylinder, something like a capital letter D with a second D placed to its back. The cylinder was situated between the poles of a huge magnet. The cylinder was evacuated and protons were generated in the center by electron bombardment of hydrogen. By charging the two half-cylinders alternately positively and negatively, the protons could be drawn into a spiral orbit, picking up energy on each shift between the two D's. They would be

A cyclotron is a type of souped-up merry-go-round.

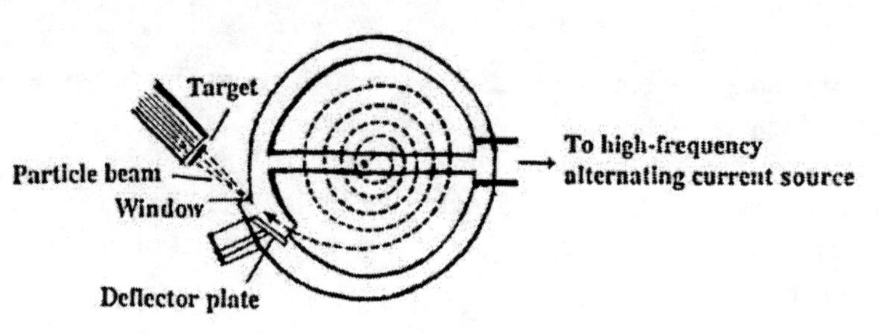

Cross-section of a cyclotron

exceedingly energetic on emer-ging (up to about 25 megaelectron volts). They could be used to bombard a target material in nuclear research. Other charged particles could be similarly accelerated, such as hydrogen-2 nuclei (deuterons, consisting of a proton and a neutron), or helium-4 nuclei (alpha particles). For best performance cyclotrons are designed differently for various particles.

Synchrotrons, which accelerate electrons, overcome certain limitations of cyclotrons. They keep the particles in a circular path of constant radius, not a spiral. The strength of the confining magnetic field must be raised as the particles accelerate. There are several other machines. The Large Electron-Positron Collider is in Switzerland. An accelerator at Fermilab, near Chicago, energizes protons and antiprotons to more than a trillion electron volts (a teraelectron volt, TeV; T = tera = 10^{12}). This accelerator is called the Tevatron. It is buried beneath the prairie whose surface is home to trumpeter swans, Canada geese, and sandhill cranes. A much debated Superconducting Super Collider was started in Texas, but its funding was stopped by Congress. To synthesize the heaviest elements more energetic accelerators and other instruments were necessary, such as the Heavy Ion Linear Accelerator. In any case, no particle accelerators on Earth can even come near matching the energies occurring naturally in astrophysical processes.

4-19 Missing Elements and Transuranium Elements

The periodic table of the year 1939 had spaces for 92 chemical elements. Four vacancies in the table indicated four elements not yet discovered, despite many efforts to find them; these were elements of atomic numbers 43, 61, 85, and 87. The last, francium, was discovered in 1939 by Marguerite Perey in the Curie Institute. The heaviest element known to chemists at that time was uranium, atomic number 92. In the year 1940 at the University of California in Berkeley, the American physicists McMillan and Abelson were studying the newly discovered phenomenon of nuclear fission, as already mentioned in the preceding chapter. After exposing uranium-238 to slow neutrons, they were able to show that some uranium-239 had been formed (despite the high nuclear charge of uranium the neutrons, being neutral, are not repelled). This new isotope of uranium proved to have a half-life of 23.5 minutes and to be beta active. Beta activity must lead to the next higher element, that is, to unknown element 93. Using radiochemical techniques which are based on trace quantities they showed that the new nuclide, of mass number 239 and atomic number 93, has a half-life of 2.36 days, and they examined some of its chemical properties. They gave the new element the name neptunium, after the planet Neptune.

A discovery that shook the world

Using the Berkeley cyclotron to bombard uranium-238 with deuterons, Seaborg, McMillan, Kennedy, and Wahl in 1940-41, prepared neptunium-238 and additional neptunium-239, and showed that both are beta active. This meant that unknown element 94 must result. They identified this new material and studied its chemical properties. The new element, named plutonium after the planet Pluto, proved to undergo fission readily, like uranium-235, and therefore to have the potential for use in a bomb. Its half-life (24.1 thousand years for Pu-239, alpha activity) is long enough for it to be reasonably stable. On fission by slow neutrons, plutonium-239 was found to release even more neutrons than uranium-235, namely an average of 2.88 neutrons per atom fissioned; this figure increases with increasing energy of the incident neutrons, and reaches about 3.5 with 4 megaelectron volt neutrons. Uranium-235 behaves similarly, the value being 2.4 to 2.5 for slow neutrons, and 2.8 for 4 megaelectron volt neutrons. Uranium ores are now known to contain the most minute traces of plutonium. It arises from uranium-238 and stray neutrons from a number of natural events. If plutonium-239 could be produced from uranium-238 (which is abundant) in a nuclear reactor, it would not be too difficult to separate chemically since it is not an isotope of uranium, but a different element. This would be a distinct advantage over uranium-235, which, being an isotope of uranium, is exceedingly difficult to separate from uranium-238. Natural uranium contains only 0.711% U-235, nearly all of the rest being U-238.

On beyond uranium

By using uranium-238 as a target for bombardment with helium-4 nuclei in a cyclotron, element 95, named americium, was synthesized in 1944. When plutonium-239 was similarly targeted, element 96, curium, resulted. The early work with traces of americium and curium was so frustrating that chemists referred to them as "pandemonium" and "delirium," respectively. Related techniques gave elements 97 (berkelium) and 98 (californium). Debris collected from the first hydrogen bomb explosion in 1952 was found to contain elements 99 (einsteinium) and 100 (fermium). Evidently some uranium-238 nuclei had captured as many as 17 neutrons in the potent explosion, something like the conditions under which the heaviest elements were made during a supernova episode of a giant star eons ago. Indeed, optical spectra characteristic of americium and curium have been observed in the light from certain stars. Elements 101, 102, and 103 (mendelevium, nobelium, and lawrencium) have been made by helium nuclei bombardment of einsteinium-253 in the cyclotron. Nine elements beyond number 103 have also been recently synthesized (section 4-4).

Some chemical properties of transfermium elements have been determined. A knowledge of the periodic table suggests that nobelium (element 102) might have a chemically stable ion with a charge of +2, and indeed this proved to be the case, even in aqueous solution. Similarly rutherfordium (element 104) is expected to behave like hafnium and zirconium, all forming ions with a charge of +4, and this also proved to be true. In some respects dubnium (element 105) was found to resemble its prototype tantalum, but it also differs in some important ways. In 1997 German researchers, using only a few atoms of seaborgium (element 106) demonstrated that chemically it resembles tungsten, the element above it in the periodic table.

There is evidence that during supernova occurrences billions of years ago, all of the above and probably still higher transuranium elements were formed. But they were all highly radioactive elements with relatively short half-lives and thus are extinct today. The longest-lived transuranium nuclide known is plutonium-244, with a half-life of 83 million years. Calculations disclosed that with a half-life this long, a few primordial atoms would be expected to survive to the present. Once the chemical properties of plutonium became known through studies of synthetic isotopes, American radiochemist Darleane Hoffman actually detected primordial plutonium-244 in some southern California rocks.

The three missing elements in the periodic table with lower atomic numbers have also been discovered, and every one of their nuclides is radioactive. These elements are number 43 (technetium, Tc), number 61 (promethium, Pm), and number 85 (astatine, At).

Technetium was discovered in 1937 by Perrier and Segrè in Italy in some molybdenum bombarded with deuterons in the Berkeley cyclotron. Once its emission spectrum was known, it was identified in the atmospheres of a number of stars by the American astronomer Charlotte Moore. Promethium was discovered by Marinsky, Glendenin, and Coryell in 1945 among fission products of uranium-235. Although the half-life of its longest-lived isotope is only 17.7 years, it too has been detected by its spectrum in the atmosphere of the star HR465 in Andromeda, the galaxy nearest to the Milky Way. There must be some process which generates it continuously. Astatine was first made in 1940 by Corson, MacKenzie, and Segrè by bombarding bismuth with alpha particles.

Filling in the last empty spaces of the atomic crossword puzzle

A historical footnote concerns elements 43 and 75. In 1925 three German scientists determined to find the two missing elements just below manganese in the periodic table. These were the husband-wife team, Walter and Ida Noddack, and Otto Berg. They worked up hundreds of kilograms of the manganese-rich ores, platinerz, and columbite, suspecting that these might contain traces of the undiscovered elements. Their analyses employed the X-ray spectral technique developed by the British physicist Moseley in 1913. After several years of laborious concentration steps, they announced the discovery of element 75, which they named rhenium, and also, in a few samples, evidence of element 43. Rhenium was verified by other chemists, but element 43 was not. Recently indications have been found that the weak spectral signals indicating element 43 might have been real, the material originating from uranium in the minerals undergoing fission to form technetium-99. The half-life of this isotope, 4.2 million years, is long enough for a small concentration to accumulate.

4-20 Enriched Uranium

After World War II, uranium enriched in U-235 was in demand primarily for nuclear bomb production, but also for commercial nuclear reactors. Natural uranium is 0.711% U-235. To make weapon-grade material in modern times, this level is boosted to 93 to 95% uranium-235; reactor grade material is generally 2.5 to 4.6%.

Four principal post-war techniques for enriching uranium in its U-235 content have been perfected: gaseous diffusion, the centrifuge method, atomic vapor laser isotope separation, and molecular vapor laser isotope separation. A few other less important methods are also known.

Most of the methods employ a uranium compound which vaporizes easily, namely uranium hexafluoride, UF_6. In the gaseous diffusion procedure, a series of chambers equipped with pumps and heaters is assembled. Each chamber or stage contains a porous membrane in which the pores are about 10 nanometers in diameter, a distance shorter than the average distance between collisions of the gaseous molecules. Since the mass of the uranium-235 is 3 units less than that of the uranium-238, the uranium hexafluoride molecules containing the lighter isotope move or diffuse a bit faster, and pass through the porous membrane more often. This accomplishes a slight enrichment in U-235, generally by a factor of about 1.004. By using many cascades of diffusion chambers, enrichment to any desired degree can be achieved. Enormous quantities of electrical energy are required. The cost of the process to make material 3% in U-235 is approximately $150 per kilogram. The uranium left over, impoverished in its normal U-235 content, called *depleted uranium*, is 0.2 to 0.3% U-235. Huge amounts (approximately 700,000 tons) of depleted uranium, much in the form of UF_6, are left over from enrichment processes. Some depleted uranium is also found in nature (7-18).

The centrifuge technique for separating uranium-235 from its heavier isotope is today a mature process employed in a number of countries. One of its primary promoters was Austrian physicist Germot Zippe, who was captured by the Soviets at the end of World War II. He was taken to the resort city of Sukhumi, in Soviet Georgia on the coast of the Black Sea; it is the provincial capital of Abkhazia, a region which in 1992 began a revolution to secede. During those early post-war years a group of captured scientists, in a laboratory situated among tangerine groves, was assigned the task of perfecting a technique of separating uranium-235 from the heavier isotope. Repatriation was the promise of success. Zippe and his colleagues Steenbeck and Riehl, completed and perfected the centrifuge method. Zippe was later transferred to Leningrad to build a prototype centrifuge plant. By the end of 1953 the pilot plant was working well. The Soviets built several enormous enrichment plants containing hundreds of thousands of centrifuges. The Soviets kept their side of the bargain, and Zippe and his coworkers were allowed to return home in 1956. He went to the United States in 1958 and built a centrifuge for the Atomic Energy Commission. He returned to Germany and designed centrifuges for civilian nuclear reactor fuel. The technology became the basis of Urenco, an industrial consortium of Germany, Holland, and Britain.

This tale sounds sort of romantic, but it was in reality another huge step in the Cold War.

The centrifuge procedure requires several times less electrical energy than the diffusion process. The material of construction may be aluminum, steel, fiberglass, or a composite containing carbon fibers. A rapidly rotating vertical cylinder enclosed in a larger evacuated cylinder is equipped with an inlet at the center. Gaseous uranium hexafluoride is fed through this inlet when it is rotating rapidly. Simultaneously, one end of the vertical tube is heated. Centrifugal force causes the heavier isotope to concentrate near the outer rim; the uneven heating causes countercurrent flow, further enhancing the separation. A scoop at the bottom rim conducts the depleted uranium out, while another at the top removes the material enriched in uranium-235. Separation factors of 1.2 to 1.5 are achieved. A cascade of centrifuges in series is necessary, and banks of these in parallel are generally employed.

The atomic vapor laser isotope separation procedure may be applied to U-235/U-238 or to any other similar problem. It is described briefly in section 9-9 in conjunction with the separation of plutonium-240 from plutonium-239.

In the molecular vapor laser isotope procedure, the gaseous mixture of U-235 and U-238 hexafluorides is irradiated with laser light of such a sharply defined wavelength that only the U-235 compound is affected. The pentafluoride is formed by breaking off one fluorine atom. The U-235 pentafluoride is a solid, which precipitates out and is filtered off. This method is also capable of being applied to other isotopic separations.

The best of the less unimportant techniques for separating uranium-235 from uranium-238 depends on slight differences in chemical behavior. Thus, if an aqueous solution contains uranium in both oxidation state four (U^{4+}) and six (UO_2^{2+}), the uranium-235 concentrates slightly in the UO_2^{2+}. The two forms can be separated by extraction or ion exchange. In Japan and in France pilot plants were built which could produce 100 to 400 kilograms of uranium per year which is enriched to 3% in the 235 isotope.

4-21 Radioactivity Counters

A Geiger counter has a tube or probe connected to a box of electronic circuitry. While there are many types, all are based on more or less the same principle. The probe consists of a tungsten wire running along the axis of a glass tube with a metallic coating inside, or section of metal tubing, (see sketch). One end is made of very thin glass (or mica or similar material), and acts as a window to admit the particles or radiation to be monitored. The tube is filled with a gas at a low pressure; a suitable gas is argon containing a percent or two of bromine vapor, chlorine, oxygen, or an organic compound such as methane. The tube is electrically charged so that a difference of several hundred volts exists between the wire and the tube wall. The central wire is positive and the wall is negative. When radiation enters the window, it ionizes some of the gas, forming positive ions and free electrons. These are attracted to the electrodes of opposite charge. The electrons become energized by the voltage difference to the degree that during their movement they ionize other gas atoms, and the electrons from these are accelerated and ionize still more. Thus an avalanche of ions results, discharging as a spark along the length of the wire. This results in a measurable pulse which arose from a single ion at the start, the amplification factor being many millions. These pulses are recorded. Geiger counters are best suited for counting gamma radiation.

How Geiger counters work

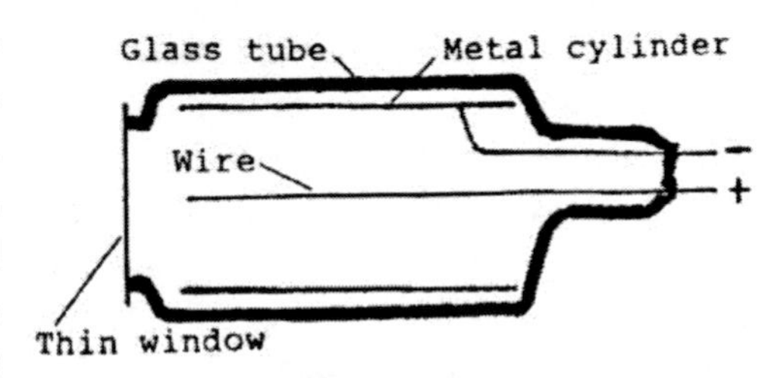

A simple Geiger tube

Today many kinds of detectors and counters are in use, based on film, semiconductors, scintillations, etc. Low intensity gamma rays and weak betas are best counted using scintillation counters. In this case, the sample, generally in a suitable solvent, is mixed in a glass vial with a compound which emits flashes of light when a molecule is struck by a beta particle or gamma ray photon. The light is amplified using a photomultiplier tube; electrical impulses are generated in proportion to the level of radioactivity. There are numerous types of scintillation counters.

Counters for fast neutrons depend on their colliding with protons in hydrogen, that is, their nuclei; the free protons, being charged, can be manipulated and measured. Slow neutrons are counted through their interaction with an element which absorbs them readily and emits a charged particle. Boron-10 is an example; with neutrons it forms alpha particles and these are easily detected. Another method employs uranium-235, which undergoes fission by neutrons. The fission particles or gamma rays are counted. Certain materials absorb neutrons and gain energy; on heating, light is evolved, which is measured.

4-22 Units of Radioactivity

In a given amount of radioactive substance, some of the atoms decay (disintegrate) every second. No one can predict which particular atoms will decay; the process is random. The laws of probability are obeyed exactly because there are so many billions of atoms. Mathematical (statistical) equations describe very precisely the decay behavior of samples with billions of atoms. It might be alpha, beta, gamma, or other kinds of radioactive decay. The number of atoms which disintegrate per second (which must be the same as the number of particles produced per second) is a measure of the degree of activity (that is, radioactivity). If the amount of substance is doubled, the larger sample gives off twice as many particles or rays per second as before, and the activity is twice as high. By correct use of a Geiger counter, the activity can be measured. Activity is not the same as intensity. If the radioactive substance is concentrated at one point, the radiations from it may be intense; if the same amount is spread out over a large area, the radiation is of course much less intense.

One gram of pure radium-226 (half-life 1600 years) emits 37 billion alpha particles per second. This level of radioactivity was defined as one curie unit. The unit has been extended to all radioactive materials, regardless of the nature of decay. The amount of any radioactive substance in which 37 billion disintegrations per second occur is one curie (Ci) of that nuclide. If the substance has a long half-life, a large amount of it will be required to furnish one curie; if the half-life is short, it is decaying rapidly, so only a small amount has one curie of radioactivity. The specific activity (that is, radioactivity) of any nuclide is the number of curies (or other specified unit) of radioactivity per gram (or other specified unit) of material. A table of selected nuclides and their radiological properties is given in Appendix II. More complete information, including exact isotopic masses, binding energies, modes of decay, half-lives, cross-sections for various reactions, and other nuclear properties is available at web site:

http://necs01.dne.bnl.gov/CoN/index.html.

The Curie unit

The curie unit is divided according to the metric system. One millicurie (mCi) is the activity of a thousandth of a gram (1 milligram) of radium, and corresponds to 37 million disintegrations per second. One microcurie (μCi) is 37 thousand disintegrations per second. Each 150-pound human body contains about 0.2 microcuries of radioactivity (potassium-40, carbon-14, etc.); this is around 7400 disintegrations per second. Additional exposure to radioactivity for every person derives from radon in the air, and its daughter products.

Other units are used for exceedingly low levels of radioactivity. A nanocurie (nCi) is a billionth of a curie, and is only 37 disintegrations per second. A picocurie (pCi; pico = 10^{-12}) is 1000 times smaller, and is thus less than one disintegration per second. In this case, it is clearest to calculate the average time between disintegrations. It comes out to be 1 disintegration every 27 seconds. Similarly, a femtocurie (fCi, femto = 10^{-15}) is one disintegration every 7.5 hours.

Another unit of radioactivity is the becquerel (Bq), defined as one disintegration per second, that is, 37 billion becquerels is one curie. Thus the nanocurie mentioned above, being 37 disintegrations per second, is 37 becquerels. A gigabecquerel (GBq) is a billion disintegrations per second, and accordingly 37 of them make one curie. The becquerel unit is especially useful when very low levels of activity are encountered. The use of the becquerel unit and its multiples is slowly replacing the curie unit.

Since almost everything has at least some radioactivity, a limit was set by the Department of Transportation of 2 nanocuries per gram (2 billionths of a curie or 74 becquerels per gram). Below this level, a substance is said not to be radioactive for purposes of transportation.

A gram of radium (1 curie), if in a concentrated form, keeps itself hot from the energy generated. The energies of particles and gamma ray photons emitted by various nuclei differ vastly, some being of low energy ("soft"), and others of high energy ("hard"). In general, a curie of radioactivity is a dangerous amount, and shielding must be used. Heavy metals such as lead are ordinarily used for shielding. A millicurie, if unshielded, is enough to be dangerous if the radiation emitted is hard; if it is soft, as is the case with tritium, little shielding would be required. One curie of radium (an alpha emitter) is more dangerous than one curie of tritium or carbon-14, both of which are soft beta emitters. The international logo which identifies hazardous amounts of radioactivity is shown.

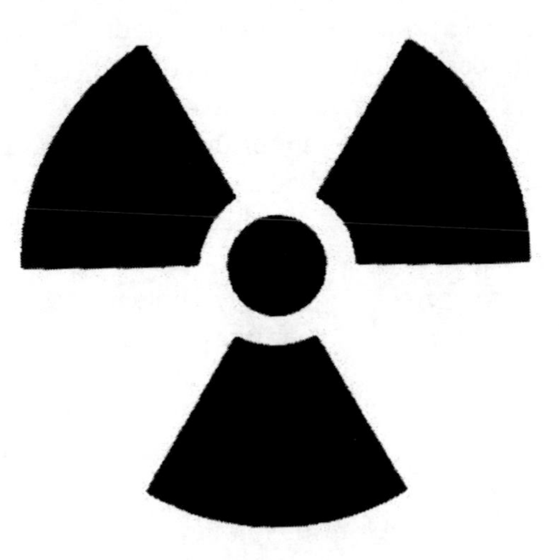

International logo identifying hazardous radioactivity

The half-life of the common isotope of radium (radium-226) is 1600 years. Suppose we have one gram of another isotope, say, radium-228, whose half-life is only 5.76 years. Since now the decay is far faster, the level of activity must be far higher. It comes out to be around 272 curies for this one gram, high enough to melt itself if it is in concentrated form. The activity of any short-lived nuclide dies off rapidly. On the other hand, a material with a very long half-life, such as uranium-238, is comparatively only slightly radioactive. The half-life of this nuclide is 4.468 billion years, and its activity is very close to a third of a microcurie per gram. It takes three metric tonnes to amount to one curie, and most of the radiation is self-absorbed. There is some danger in picking up pieces of the pure metal and handling them for a short time with little or no protection, but gloves should be worn to stop the alpha particles and protect against contamination by the oxide. In the case of uranium, the activity is low, but increases as decay products accumulate.

Natural uranium consists of three isotopes; their percentages by weight are: U-238, 99.284%; U-235, 0.711%; and U-234, 0.005%. The half-life of U-235 is 704 million years, and that of U-234 is 245 thousand years. Using these figures, we can calculate that one gram of pure metallic natural uranium consists of 0.3336 microcurie of U-238, 0.01536 microcurie of U-235, and 0.3115 micro curie of U-234. Note that even though the U-234 is present in only a trace amount, its level of radioactivity is nearly the same as that of U-238. This is because its half-life is so much shorter. The total radioactivity of the one gram of natural uranium amounts to 0.6605 microcurie (the specific activity).

4-23 Absorbed Radiation: the RAD Unit

When radiation of any type strikes matter, a fraction is reflected away, a fraction is absorbed, and a fraction passes through (is transmitted). Chemical changes or damage results only from absorbed radiation. In the parlance of radiologists, the amount of radiation which is absorbed is called the *dose* or, sometimes, the dosage. Here we consider primarily high-energy radiation: X-rays, gamma rays, alpha rays, beta rays, and neutrons, although protons and others are sometimes involved.

When matter absorbs radiation, it is absorbing energy, and the amount of energy per gram or kilogram of matter is a measure of the amount of absorbed radiation. The earliest unit was called the roentgen, but the more modern term is the *rad*, an acronym for "radiation, absorbed dose." One rad unit is the amount of radiation which, absorbed by one kilogram of any matter, increases the energy content of the matter by 0.01 joule. The radiation reflected or transmitted is not counted, only that absorbed. The process might be instantaneous or might be spread over a long time. The number of rads depends not only on the number of curies of the radiation source, but also on the nature and energy of the radiation, the distance, etc. Absorption of high-energy radiation causes breaking some chemical bonds (a process called radiolysis) in the absorbing material, which results in new substances. The number of rads causing a given dose is equivalent to the word concentration, since it measures or is proportional to the amount of radiation-produced (radiolytic) substances per kilogram of matter. The dose is a measure of the amount of radiation damage suffered by the target material. Dose rate has units of rads per unit time, such as rads/hour. When a radiation dose to a person is expressed in rads, it is important to specify whether it is to some organ or to the whole body. A feeling for rads and dose rate can be gained from some examples:

Radiation dose and the rad unit

A. Cobalt-60 emits beta particles and gamma rays with a half-life of 5.27 years. It is frequently used in hospitals to irradiate tumors, to sterilize foods, etc. The beta particles are absorbed by air within a few centimeters, but the gamma rays penetrate a much greater distance. Consider a 0.1 curie source of cobalt-60, which if pure is only a speck weighing less than a tenth of a milligram. At a distance of 48 cm (19 inches), the dose rate is 1 rad per hour. A one-kilogram object at this distance can absorb enough gamma rays to increase its energy content by 0.01 joule in one hour (1 rad/hr), or 0.02 joule in two hours.

B. Ordinary potassium is ever so slightly radioactive (by beta and gamma emission), owing to the presence of about a hundredth of a percent of the isotope potassium-40. The body of a human being of average weight contains enough potassium to show an activity of approximately a tenth of a microcurie. Each year this exposes the body internally to a dose of around 15 millirads. That is to say, the whole body absorbs an amount of energy every year calculated as follows:

$$15 \text{ mrad} \times \frac{1 \text{ rad}}{1000 \text{ mrad}} \times \frac{0.01 \text{J/kg}}{1 \text{ rad}} \times \frac{1000 \text{ mJ}}{1 \text{J}} = 0.15 \text{ mJ/kg}$$

C. In a typical X-ray of the lungs, the dose is usually around 0.05 rad (50 millirad).

D. Picking up a bar of pure uranium metal with the bare hands gives the tissues a dose of 4 or 5 millirads per minute.

E. When Hiroshima was bombed, the soil at the hypocenter received a dose of 10,300 rads from gamma rays and 14,100 rads from neutrons. One kilometer distant, the figures were 255 and 191 respectively.

F. Another unit increasingly used to measure absorbed radiation dose is the *gray* (Gy). One gray is 100 rads, that is, the energy absorbed per kilogram of absorbing material is exactly 1 joule, not 0.01 joule. Thus 1 rad is 1 centigray.

Louis Harold Gray (1895–1965), English physicist and radiobiologist. His research involved interaction of radiation with matter. Gray established a procedure at a hospital to measure quantitatively the amount of energy absorbed during irradiation for cancer. This was done for X-rays, gamma rays, and neutrons, and is universally employed today.

4-24 Measuring Absorbed Dose

A dosimeter is a device to measure the number of rads which matter absorbs, whether the matter is living or nonliving. The most common dosimeter is a small badge holding sensitive X-ray film. On development, the darkness of the film is measured and compared with standards. The film holder contains several filters of various densities which selectively absorb low-energy X- and gamma rays and beta particles. The use of filters extends the range of the film badge. The range of such dosimeters is roughly 0.01 to 1800 rads.

More accurate instruments which are made to monitor personnel are about the size of a pen and are carried in a shirt pocket. The older types depend on the rate of discharge of an electrical capacitor and usually measure up to 300 millirads. Some types measure up to 1000 rads. The newer dosimeters contain substances which, if exposed to ionizing radiation, emit light when heated later. This light is measured in a photometer. Such thermoluminescent dosimeters register from 0.1 millirad to 1000 rads. This type can be made small enough to be worn on a finger like a ring. Dosimeters usually measure beta and gamma rays. Beta particles from tritium are so low in energy that they are absorbed at once by air and do not register on ordinary dosimeters. Measurements in such cases are made using scintillation counters. Doses of living tissues are measured in rem units (5-5).

Alpha particles are stopped quickly by air and do not present much problem by external radiation. If inhaled or consumed, alpha-active substances are terribly dangerous and difficult to monitor. Beta rays penetrate further than alpha rays, but at low intensity present only minor problems unless the source is adjacent to tissue, as it must be if ingested. The number of rads a material absorbs depends not only on the number of particles or photons it absorbs, but also on the energy of these particles or photons.

Soviet scientists developed a sensitive technique for measuring absorbed dosage which employs a crystal of aluminum oxide the size of an aspirin tablet. The material is made by incorporating certain trace materials into the crystals. The method is sensitive to 100 microrads. A joint venture to manufacture the crystals in the U.S. has been arranged.

4-25 Energy Sources—Traditional and Renewable

To place nuclear energy in perspective, a general overview of energy sources is useful. Four chief energy sources can be distinguished: fossil fuels (coal, natural gas, petroleum); geothermal; nuclear; and contemporary solar energy, either direct (heat and electricity from sunlight) or indirect (hydroelectric, wind, movement of ocean water, fermenting or burning wood and other biomass). Quite a number of forms of energy exist, as listed below:

Heat, the most primitive
Light and other radiation (X- and gamma rays, ultraviolet, infrared, micro -waves, radio waves, etc.)
Electricity
Sound
Chemical bonds between atoms
Combustion of fuels breaks and forms bonds, liberating energy
Biological energy, as in work by muscles
Batteries to store energy
Potential energy, as held by water in a high lake or river
Kinetic energy, as in moving mass
Nuclear energy; and still other forms

Thermodynamics is the science which deals with the performance of physical work, the interactions of force and energy with matter, and the movement or transfer of heat (and other forms of energy) to, from, and within matter.

The Department of Energy employs more than 100,000 people, and is responsible for many aspects of energy development, as well as the nuclear weapons programs. Its budget is more than $20 billion annually. Regrettably, the energy policy of the first Bush administration, called the National Energy Strategy and announced in February 1991, emphasized more petroleum consumption and less research on alternative energy sources. It left our country increasingly dependent on imported petroleum. This policy favored squandering natural resources, increasing air pollution, and possibly enhancing a greenhouse effect. The policies of the second Bush administration are not very different. Relaxed energy efficiency standards do not encourage industry to innovate. We could and should do better.

No modern society can function robustly without abundant energy. The world's consumption of energy in all its forms has about doubled every fifteen years since 1925, but has been leveling off recently in the U.S. All means of energy production have undesirable side effects, some worse than others. A lower population on our Earth would alleviate these problems. It seems wise to diversify energy sources and to avoid over-dependence on any one. (Related sections are on standard energy sources, 4-27; renewable energy sources, 4-28; human use of energy in perspective, 4-29; the greenhouse effect, 4-31; and the ozone layer, 4-32.)

Conservation measures in energy consumption would be by far the most profitable way to insure future supplies, and one need not be an energy evangelist to appreciate that. Countries such as Germany, Sweden, Switzerland, and Japan, whose standards of living are as high as that in the U.S., consume only half as much energy per person. With effort, renewable energy sources could supply half of the country's need by 2030. The United States spends more than $500 billion per year on energy and we're not devoting even 1% of that amount on research in alternative sources; this negligence should be corrected.

One form of energy in great demand is electricity. It operates electric motors in thousands of devices, is used for cooking, heating, cooling, refrigeration, and makes all those electronic appliances possible. To bring the poorer countries up to the standard of living of the West would require 1 to 2 gigawatts per million people. The table below identifies energy sources for generating electricity in the United States during 1993, and gives the percentage each contributes to the total. Oil and gas used in transportation, space heating, etc., are not included.

Coal	54.0 %
Nuclear	22.5
Natural gas	8.5
Hydro	8.4
Oil	4.1
Other	2.5

Total electricity production in the U.S. was about 3330 billion kilowatt-hours during 1999, about 22.5% coming from nuclear reactors. Counting all energy production in the U.S., not just electricity, nuclear sources amounted to 6.6% of the total in 1990. Oil accounted for 40.4%, coal for 22.3%, and gas for 23.1%. Only 7.4% of the total energy came from renewable sources, and most of that was hydroelectric. Electricity from nuclear sources had dropped to about 20% of the total by 2002.

In the United States, the average rate of electricity use, counting industrial, commercial, and residential consumption, very roughly averages 1200 watts per person; over the entire world, this figure is about 250 watts. American residential use alone is generally around 250 watts per person, or 1000 watts per household. The total power consumption, counting electricity, heating, transportation, industry, etc., was 6300 watts per person in 1980, and is falling. By the year 2020, it could drop to half that value through use of improved home insulation, better lighting technologies, more efficient transportation, etc. Engineers often express electricity in terms of kilowatt-hours per day rather than watts. (To convert watts into kilowatt-hours per day, multiply by 24 and divide by 1000.) Vigorous conservation measures offer immediate and viable benefits. Thus mass transit and energy-efficient products could save almost half the electricity produced in the United States.

Americans pay rates for residential electricity which vary between averages of 5.0 cents per kilowatt-hour (Washington state, where water power is abundant) and 14.4 cents per kilowatt-hour (New York). The average rate for the entire United States was

8.80 cents in 1998, but this began to rise in late 2000. It appears as if deregulation will be extended to the electric industries, leaving consumers to choose between many suppliers. Deregulation in California in 2001 proved to be disastrous.

An example of conservation is given by the "superwindow." It has double panes holding a mixture of argon and krypton sealed between them; the glass surfaces have multiple coatings of glazing and fused metal oxides, causing them to reflect more light. These panes collect heat in winter and are highly insulating. Another type of window changes color to allow sunshine inside on cold days and becomes reflective on scorching days. Owing to more efficient insulation and electric motors, a refrigerator made in 1990 costs $64 less per year to operate than one of the same capacity made in 1970. The Whirlpool Corporation has built a still more efficient model, and it uses an ozone-friendly refrigerant. The new refrigerator has vacuum insulation and uses only 25% of the electricity that the corresponding 1978 model did.

Lighting consumes 25% of all electrical power in the United States. The EPA reports that if all businesses upgraded their lighting, it could save about $18 billion per year. Only about 10% of the energy of an ordinary incandescent bulb is converted to light. Fluorescent lamps consume much less electricity for the same amount of light. An important new example of electricity-saving devices is the electronic light, or E-lamp, which is a light bulb consuming only a quarter of the electricity which an incandescent bulb uses to generate the same amount of light. E-lamps have no filaments, but rather an energy-coupling antenna which generates a high-frequency radio signal. Provisions are made so that the radio signal does not interfere with other electronic devices. The radio-frequency radiation is absorbed by a trace of mercury vapor in argon; the energy-rich mercury atoms then re-radiate ultraviolet. The ultraviolet radiation is absorbed by a phosphor coating on the inside of the bulb, resulting in visible light. The life of such a bulb is 20,000 hours. Still another revolutionary lamp was announced in fall, 1994. This is the sulfur bulb, made of quartz, and is about the size of a golf ball. Developed under contract with the Department of Energy, the lamp has no electrodes, and is powered by microwaves. The radiation emitted resembles sunlight, but has much less ultraviolet. The operational cost is about one-third that of mercury lamps for the same amount of light. The lamps are best suited for industrial use, such as illumination of shopping malls.

Incandescant bulbs: much more heat than light

4-26 Batteries and Electric Cars

Many types of batteries for supplying or storing electrical energy are known. Batteries were invented, according to a popular theory, by the ancient Parthians somewhere around 235 B.C. when they occupied Baghdad. The apparatus, many examples of which have been found in Iraqi museums, had copper connections and a porous baked clay container. This container held a chemical complex of gold with cyanide ion, and sat in a second container filled with salt water. An object, such as a silver earring, was immersed into the gold solution, and connected by the copper to a piece of zinc in the salt solution. Electrochemical action guilded the silver. The evidence that the ancients had metallic zinc is weak. It seems very likely that the Baghdad batteries are of more recent origin.

There is no doubt that the Italian Volta devised a true battery and published his results in 1800. He employed a pair of metals, such as silver and zinc separated by cloth soaked in salt water or dilute sulfuric acid.

The energy density or capacity of modern batteries is measured in kilojoules per kilogram of the battery's mass, or watt-hours per kilogram (to convert the first to the second, divide by 3.6). Today's lead-acid and wet nickel-cadmium alkaline batteries typically can deliver at the most 125 to 145 kilojoules (35 to 40 watt-hours) of electrical energy per kilogram. Higher capacities than that will be necessary to make electric cars really acceptable. Chrysler and a Canadian company, Norvik Technologies, claim to have developed a new technique which can charge the batteries of an electric car within ten minutes, but this would require expensive changes in the electricity distribution system. If this is true, it could make electric vehicles more attractive, despite the extra wiring expense. Several electric cars are on the market today. The Japanese manufacture the IZA, a car with motors in all four wheels, a nickel-cadmium recyclable battery, and a range of 150 miles. Some electric minicars are imported from Europe. France has 3000 electric cars in circulation and is well ahead of any other country in this regard. Automobile heaters consume 1 to 5 kW, and compressor-type air conditioners run about 6 kW. Air conditioners which are heat pumps make much lower power demands. The best efficiency in electric vehicles is achieved by converting the direct current from batteries to alternating current for the motors; this step also permits faster acceleration. There can be a single motor or a separate motor for each wheel. Electricity-powered motors are not likely to replace all fuel-powered engines, for example in large trucks. Electric motorcycles, of trade name Lectra, are manufactured in northern California. Hybrid vehicles, with a small gasoline engine to charge a battery, are coming into higher demand.

The principal barrier to wide-spread public acceptance of electric vehicles has been lack of a battery with sufficient storage capacity. If this problem is solved satisfactorily, it will mean vast savings in petroleum imports. A barrel of oil refined into gasoline propels an average American automobile 620 miles. This same barrel of oil used to generate electricity efficiently could move an equivalent electric vehicle 1100 miles. Moreover, it would make other sources of electricity more available for transportation. Such steps would go a long way toward cleaning up urban air. One step which extends the range of electric vehicles is to use regenerative brakes, although this is an extra expense. Application of the brake pedal causes the motor to generate electricity, which is stored in the battery instead of being wasted as heat. This accomplishes an energy saving of approximately 15%.

What are really needed are some creative and ingenious ideas about batteries.

The classical automobile battery is of the lead-sulfuric acid type. Modifications of this kind by the Texas-based company Electrosource is said to improve the energy density significantly. Instead of heavy lead plates, the new battery uses lead threads woven into mesh grids supported on fiberglass. It is quick charging, and a bank of them can power an average car about 140 miles. A technique called impulse charging of lead storage batteries is several times faster than the ordinary method, and extends the life of the battery to the extent of about 50,000 miles for the vehicle. General Motors introduced its EV1 in the fall of 1996. This two-seat vehicle, priced at $34,000, uses lead-acid batteries and has a range of about 80 miles per charge, which is average for most electric vehicles today. In 1997 Honda introduced its EV Plus, which uses nickel-alloy-hydride batteries, but in 1999 the company withdrew from most electric vehicle production. Sales were just too slow.

Research in new types of batteries is underway in the USA, Europe, and Japan. The U.S. Advanced Battery Consortium was established in 1991 by the Department of Energy. One trend is to configure new types of batteries as a solid electrolyte made from a cross-linked polymer. Within a few years such rechargeable batteries might become available and be able to deliver 540 to 720 kilojoules (150 to 200 watt-hours) per kilogram; time will tell whether this is true. Nonrechargeable lithium batteries have been available for quite a long time, and rechargeable lithium batteries of several types have been on the market more recently. One kind uses a lithium cobalt oxide ($LiCoO_2$) as the cathode; a more recent one substitutes the corresponding lithium manganese oxide. Since manganese is more or less nontoxic and costs only about 1% as much as cobalt, this type is favored, but so far they cannot be recharged repeatedly. These batteries can deliver around 400 kilojoules (110 watt-hours) per kilogram. A promising new type of lithium battery consists of lithium hexafluoroarsenate in polyethylene oxide.

A high-wattage sodium-sulfur battery weighs 1200 pounds, and can store approximately 350 kilojoules (nearly 100 watt-hours) per kilogram, but it must be kept hot (350 °C), and could be dangerous in an accident. Ford's Ecostar uses such a battery imported from a Swedish firm; the British have also been very active in developing these batteries. Leakage of molten sulfur has been a problem. Use of numerous smaller batteries lowers the failure rate.

In 1993 a different type of aluminum-sulfur battery was announced at Clark University in Worcester, Massachusetts. It does not employ molten sulfur, but rather sulfur which has been made electrically conducting by treatment with a polysulfide solution, which is the electrolyte. The battery is said to have the prodigious energy density of 790 kilojoules (220 watt-hours) per kilogram, but there might be problems in recharging. It will require much more development before it is practical.

More good news is that a prototype of a satisfactory battery has recently been made. Under contract with the Advanced Battery Consortium, the Ovonic Battery Company has engineered a battery, invented by Ovshinsky, using an alloyed nickel hydride as the negative electrode and nickel oxohydroxide as the positive electrode. The negative electrode consists of an alloy of nickel, the main constituent, with titanium, zirconium, chromium, cobalt, iron, and manganese. These metals were carefully selected to improve hydrogen capacity and to catalyze charging and discharging or good performance. Supplies of nickel are adequate. The electrolyte is 30% aqueous potassium hydroxide, and the battery is sealed. Unlike lead and cadmium batteries, this new type contains no toxic metals, and its materials are easily recycled. A drawback is that the batteries are expensive.

This battery merits thorough testing.

The Ovonic battery has an energy capacity of up to 288 kilojoules (80 watt-hours) per kilogram, and is still being improved. Recharging up to 60% of capacity can be done in 15 minutes, and to 100% capacity in an hour; slower charging can use existing electric wiring. Tests in vehicles show a driving range of 265 miles for smaller cars and 140 miles for larger ones. The life of the battery covers a driving distance of at least 120,000 miles. This type of battery seems to be one of the most promising of all. Its main shortcomings are a high self-discharge rate (25-30% per month) and possible damage from overcharging. In 1994 General Motors Corporation agreed to provide financial and technical aid in perfecting the battery. A joint venture between Ovonic and GM planned to market electric vehicles after 1997, and Toyota and Honda announced a similar plan.

Batteries based on zinc and air have been used for years, and tiny ones are used to operate hearing aids. Recently a large rechargeable zinc-air battery has been developed. It has a graphite positive electrode and potassium hydroxide electrolyte. It needs a fan to blow air over the porous carbon, which has a catalyst, so that sufficient oxygen can be taken in to generate high power. On recharging, oxygen is evolved. One must cope with absorption of carbon dioxide from the air by the potassium hydroxide, but this can be managed. In1997 the German Post office began a test of zinc-air batteries, perhaps eventually involving 15,000 vehicles. The batteries are recyclable and do not contain toxic metals. They yield around 180 watt-hours (640 joules) per kilogram. The batteries are made by an Israeli company. During use, the batteries warm up to 70 °C, but operate satisfactorily at temperatures as low as minus 20 °C. It now appears as if these batteries might have problems in the recharging step, and more drastic, expensive measures will have to be taken.

The need for creative and ingenious new ideas for batteries was mentioned above. It just might be that the beginnings of several of these are in sight. The first began in 1994 when Japanese scientists devised an unprecedented kind of battery, namely a rechargeable organic cell. There are several modifications, some of which have already been manufactured to power portable devices such as laptop computers and cellular phones. The use of lithium makes light-weight batteries possible. There are two kinds of lithium batteries: those involving metallic lithium (in graphite), and those using lithium ions but no free metal. One Japanese version contains no free liquids, and has an exceptional capacity to store energy per unit weight. One such battery, in brief, contains a sheet of lithium and layers of two polymers which can be oxidized and reduced. One of the organic compounds is polyaniline; the other has one of those appalling names which only chemists can love, namely poly(disulfhydrylthiadiazole). Still another lithium battery developed in Japan employs amorphous tin dioxide (replacing graphite), a step which increased capacity by 50%. An American-British lithium battery, called Ultralife, uses polymers. It can be charged and discharged 1000 times with only a tiny loss of capacity. Another high energy density battery under development is constructed from alternate layers of lithium metal and permeable plastic. Still another recent advance employs a glassy (noncrystalline) form of carbon as a matrix for the lithium, and another modification was invented in Israel in 2000. It uses an anode made of magnesium metal, which is nontoxic. Lithium ion batteries contain a double oxide, such as lithium cobalt oxide ($LiCoO_2$), whose cobalt undergoes oxidation and reduction on charging and discharging. Such batteries produce about 3.7 volts, higher than average, and are widely used in cell phones, cameras, and other portable devices. The global market in lithium ion batteries is about $3 billion annually.

Still another promising new type of battery was invented at Johns Hopkins University in 1996. It is to be all plastic, and capable of being shaped in any useful manner, and its materials are nontoxic. The novel feature of the plastic battery is a polymer of an organic compound known as thiophene. Long chains of polythiophene molecules are linked as illustrated (each thiophene unit has a sulfur atom and four carbon atoms, not shown). As illustrated, the polymer is electrically nonconducting. But by adding a trace of a material such as silver perchlorate, the alternate single and double bonds are disturbed in a way which permits electrical conductivity. This means the polymer can serve as a cathode. Metallic lithium serves in a role similar to that of silver perchlorate. Another polymer, still anonymous because of an incomplete patent, serves as the anode. The experimental batteries give 2.9 volts and deliver 160 kilojoules (45 watt-hours) per kilogram.

Chemical structure of polythiophene

Aside from batteries, there is another way to store electrical energy, namely capacitors. A new type now under development, the ultracapacitor, holds electric charge much longer than earlier types. The units contain carbon and a liquid electrolyte and can be discharged slowly during use. An ultracapacitor can carry around 55 kilojoules per liter. Small models are already in use for calculators, watches, and electric razors.

Energy can also be saved in the form of compressed air. In France, a firm called Zero Pollution Motors has started producing a car which can travel 120 miles on one tank of compressed air. Finally, it might be mentioned that flywheels represent another means of storing energy. Energy is removed by magnets on the flywheel traversing surrounding wires, which generates a current. Several automobile companies are pursuing this concept. Chrysler Corp. has a 1994 model with several flywheels rotating at 200,000 revolutions per minute. They are mounted on magnetic bearings in vacuum chambers and these coast for six weeks when the power is turned off. Depleted uranium in metallic form, being about as dense as gold, is used in some flywheels. The energy-storage is around 540 kilojoules per kilogram, comparable to high-quality batteries. The range for autos is said to be as much as 300 miles before the flywheel must be accelerated freshly. Rosen Motors built experimental models of carbon-fiber flywheel-powered cars; in these the rate of rotation was up to 60,000 rpm. Flywheels must swivel during turns of the steering wheel to prevent gyroscopic forces from disturbing the handling of the vehicle. There is also fear of danger from energy-rich flywheels in the event of a crash.

Aside from electric vehicles, it might be a good idea to re-examine the concept of steam cars. They have many advantages, and perhaps modern redevelopment can produce a viable automobile.

4-27 Hydrogen as a Fuel

Aside from batteries, generation of hydrogen is another way to store energy. Excess energy from any source can be converted into electricity, and this, by electrolysis of water, produces both hydrogen and oxygen. Hydrogen burns cleanly in this oxygen; it also burns well in air, but in this case a little bit of oxides of nitrogen is also produced. Despite this, hydrogen is an excellent medium for energy storage, can be piped great distances, and can be stored under pressure (there are some safety concerns here). It is also suitable for internal combustion engines; in fact, BMW in Germany has made such experimental cars, the 7-Series, using the gas from a liquid-hydrogen reservoir. The Daimler-Benz firm as well is conducting research on the subject. Japanese companies also are tooling up for hydrogen-driven vehicles and planes. In 2001 Ford Motor Co. put the H_2ICE (hydrogen internal combustion engine) on the market. But the range of cars with its two tanks full of hydrogen is rather short. The Department of Energy spends only about $10 million yearly on hydrogen research.

A shortcoming of hydrogen is that it is explosive over a wide range of concentrations in air. An alloy of nickel and cerium or other rare-earth metals forms a hydride which readily dissociates into hydrogen, so when a tank is filled with a sponge of this alloy, a large quantity of hydrogen can be stored at relatively low pressure. This advance would permit thinner and lighter compression tanks, and can facilitate use of hydrogen in vehicles if the reservoir is not too heavy. Reports in 1996 and 1998 from Northeastern University in Boston describe preparation of a special, spongelike graphitic material which is alleged to be capable of absorbing up to 65% of its weight of hydrogen. Graphite consists of stacked layers of carbon atoms linked together into sheets of hexagons, like honeycomb. Exposed to hydrogen at moderately high pressure, the H_2 molecules penetrate the spaces between the carbon layers, causing the graphite to expand like an accordion. Another form of carbon, known as microtublar or nanotublar, is said to be capable of storing as much as 20% of its weight of hydrogen if it is first treated with lithium, or about 5% without lithium. Further development might permit fuel cells in automobiles to succeed in a competitive market.

Energy is consumed in producing hydrogen, so it will not be practical on a large scale soon. Another problem is that hydrogen leaked into the air destroys the ozone layer.

Fuel cells do not store energy as batteries do, but produce a direct current when the fuel (generally hydrogen) and an oxidizer (air or oxygen) are introduced into separate compartments. They were invented in England as early as the 1830s. One kind of fuel cell contains an ion-exchange resin in its hydrogen-ion form and electrodes made of a platinum catalyst. The adsorbed gases react on the metallic surface, resulting in electrons flowing from one electrode out and back to the other (that is, it functions as a cell). The water which is formed is removed from the bottom. One unit furnishes 0.8 to 1 volt. It is the platinum which runs up the cost of hydrogen fuel cells. In 1995 a catalyst containing ruthenium, iron, and phosphorus, as well as hydrocarbon radicals, was developed; it has the ability to play the same role as platinum when it reacts with hydrogen, and is much cheaper. Time will tell whether this is practical. An effective fuel cell using hydrogen was developed by NASA for the Gemini mission, and was then shelved. A Canadian company, Ballard Power Systems, uses this technology in manufacturing units which furnish enough power for cars. Daimler-Benz already manufactures a van, the Necar 2, powered by fuel cells, and in 1999 DaimlerChrysler began sales of Necar 4. Toyota has also made a fuel-cell vehicle. Experimental vehicles have been made by Chrysler in which gasoline is vaporized and partially oxidized yielding hydrogen, methane, and carbon monoxide, a process called reforming. This mixture is treated with steam and a catalyst when carbon monoxide and methane are converted into carbon dioxide, and this

Hydrogen certainly has its advantages, and might give us an important energy-storage means someday.

forms additional hydrogen. The hydrogen-rich gas is oxidized in a fuel cell, generating a current for motors and for charging a battery. The technique needs much development.

If ever fuel cells which consume hydrocarbons are developed, they would be of great service. Many experts think that fuel cells will play an important role in powering zero-emission vehicles during the 21st century, but engineering and economic obstacles will delay widespread use. Early in 2000 researchers in Canada announced a fuel cell which can use butane and other hydrocarbons as fuel. All attempts up till then suffered from carbon deposition on the nickel electrodes and consequent fouling of the cell, which stopped its operation. The new process avoids nickel and uses electrodes made of metal oxides supported on copper. An effective material for the anode was cerium dioxide/zirconium dioxide stabilized with samarium oxide, and for the cathode of porous zirconium dioxide stabilized with samarium oxide on lanthanum-manganese oxide. Air serves as the oxidizing agent. The advantage is that all the carbon from the hydrocarbon fuel is converted to carbon dioxide.

Methanol (CH_3OH) can also serve as fuel. It is fairly cheap to produce, can be easily stored, and is much safer than hydrogen. This prospect is being investigated at Jet Propulsion Laboratory and at DaimlerChrysler. A small fuel cell using methanol was recently patented by an American, Robert Hockaday. His model is said to power a mobile phone for 100 hours of conversation, compared with two hours for a classical nickel-cadmium battery. USC Nobel laureate George Olah, Surya Prakash, and their colleagues have gone a long way toward developing a fuel cell based on use of methanol.

A Saudi Arabian-German project called Hysolar has a 350-kilowatt photovoltaic generator which makes hydrogen by electrolysis of water. Researchers at the National Renewable Energy Laboratory in Golden, Colorado, developed a more efficient photo-electrolysis technique, announced in 1998. It uses a gallium indium phosphide photoelectric cell and a gallium arsenide photovoltaic cell, and has reached an efficiency of 12.4%.

Hydrogen can be made from water by reaction with coke or natural gas. Biomass can be cheaply converted to hydrogen by a gasification technique. Steam partially decomposes into hydrogen and oxygen at sufficiently high temperatures (above 2000°C, produced from solar energy), and theoretically separation can be accomplished at these temperatures. This technique requires much more research.

4-28 Standard Energy Sources

Energy from Petroleum and Natural Gas—Fossil fuels currently provide 90% of the world's total energy needs. About 740,000 barrels of oil are burned each day in the United States and this generates 4.3% of the nation's electricity. Imported oil, amounting to about 9 million barrels per day, contributes 45 to 50% of our foreign trade deficit. Additional costs are incurred by oil spills from tankers. In the U.S., nearly two-thirds of all petroleum is used for transportation, mostly in internal combustion engines. In generating electricity, liquid hydrocarbon fuel or natural gas is injected into a combustion chamber. The exhaust gases drive gas turbines and thus the generators. The surfaces of the combustion chamber and turbines are protected by a ceramic coating. The hot exhaust gases are used to produce steam for injection into the combustion chamber and for driving steam turbines and generators. This increases the mass of the gases turning turbines, and increases efficiency from 35% to around 50%.

Using natural gas, the production cost of electricity averages 4 to 6 cents per kilowatt-hour. Of course, a great deal of carbon dioxide is generated. Close to 27% of all the energy produced in the United States comes from natural gas. Using cogeneration techniques, such as using exhaust gases for industrial heating, efficiencies can be above 50%. About 9% of electricity in the U.S. is produced in this way. In principle, but not yet in practice, natural gas can also be used in fuel cells, generating electricity, and forming no nitrogen oxides. Compressed natural gas is also used in internal-combustion engines; some nitrogen oxides are formed. There are more than 30,000 vehicles in the United States using this fuel.

There are truly vast reserves of natural gas existing on ocean floors as crystalline methane hydrate. Estimates are that the amount of carbon in this form exceeds the total carbon in all coal and petroleum. It arises from the organic matter falling in from above. The problem is how to get it out without polluting the atmosphere with methane. In 1997 an astonishing discovery was made, namely that the mud filled with methane hydrate is swarming with pink worms an inch or two long. This colony was found in the Gulf of Mexico 150 miles off New Orleans at a depth of 2400 feet. It was in a mound that had recently been thrust upwards from the sea floor. The worms, a new species of polychaetes, live off the methane, courtesy of a bacterial intermediary.

Any high-temperature combustion process in air, such as fire or combustion in engines, inevitably produces some nitric oxide (formula: NO). This colorless gas in air is slowly oxidized to brown nitrogen dioxide, NO_2 (collectively, the oxides of nitrogen are NO_x). About half the nitric oxide in the USA is produced by automobiles, the other half arising from industrial processes. In some areas the biosphere becomes glutted with nitrogen compounds, stimulating algal blooms and causing other problems.

Sunlight decomposes nitrogen dioxide back to nitric oxide and atomic oxygen, which reacts with molecular oxygen (O_2) to form some ozone (O_3). Ozone is also produced by photochemical oxidation of hydrocarbon exhausts, forming smog. Ozone is aggressive, and rapidly attacks lungs and leaves. It affects the reproductive processes of trees, and in higher doses destroys foliage. The growth of agricultural crops declines significantly after one or two weeks exposure to 50 to 70 parts per billion of ozone. In some areas, ozone is a greater threat to forest health than acid rain.

Addiction to petroleum

Like it or not, the world's economy is currently addicted to petroleum. The United States pays dearly for its habit. Excessive use of internal combustion engines results in smog and other pollution, not only in our cities, but also increasingly in the open country, even in national parks such as the Grand Canyon. Currently, each American family of four uses approximately two tons of petroleum products per year. More and more development of alternative energy sources would yield cleaner and healthier air, and relieve us of too much dependence on natural resources.

Our Earth has at least a trillion barrels of known petroleum reserves, and more than half of this is in the Middle East. This estimate does not count vast oil and gas reserves in Siberia, the Canadian tar sands, Rocky Mountain oil shale, under-ocean deposits, or the heavy Orinoco Basin oils of Venezuela. The cost of petroleum crude in early 1993 was about $23 per 42-gallon barrel. Certain wells produce petroleum contaminated with radium and other radioactive elements. Regardless of how much petroleum there is, it is finite, and it behooves us to begin intensive conservation of this valuable resource. Petroleum is a treasure, and ideally should not be used as a fuel.

Energy from Coal—The electricity production cost using coal is 4 to 6 cents per kilowatt-hour. The overall efficiency is generally around 35%, not counting loss during transmission. Truly vast quantities of carbon dioxide are released into the atmosphere. Coal accounts for about a fourth of American energy generation. In 1990, coal production reached one billion tons. While more than half of the world's coal is in China, reserves in the United States amount to at least 268 billion tons. Mining coal underground is costly and dangerous; about 60% of American coal is now strip-mined. Various processes have been developed for direct liquefaction of coal, converting it to liquid hydrocarbon fuels.

Burning coal produces not only carbon dioxide, but also oxides of nitrogen and sulfur. Scrubbers containing a slurry of limestone can remove most of the last two, but also generate much sludge for disposal. A typical bituminous coal contains 2% sulfur and produces 9% of the starting weight as ash. The oxides of sulfur and nitrogen that escape the scrubbers are responsible for acid rain, which kill forests and aquatic life. Newer, but more expensive, scrubbers can remove 97% of the sulfur oxides. A catalytic reduction process using ammonia has been developed for destroying some of the nitrogen oxides, but it requires carefully controlled temperatures and might prove too costly. In late 1992 a new technique has proved successful on a pilot-plant basis. In it, the sulfur dioxide is adsorbed from the flue gases by a fluidized bed of "char" (partially burned coal). Heating the adsorbed sulfur dioxide with microwaves causes the char to reduce it to elemental sulfur and carbon oxides. The method is expected to cost about half as much as the older procedures. After that, in some cases the nitrogen oxides are decomposed into harmless oxygen and nitrogen using microwaves. Despite these improvements, more than 510,000 tons of nitrogen oxides are discharged into the atmosphere in the eastern midwest and are blown further east, causing extensive air pollution. The EPA in 1999 mandated expensive reductions, in conformity with the Clean Air Act of 1990. The use of ammonia to lower nitrogen oxide emissions by 85% is proving to be feasible

Cleaning up burning coal

A process called CanSolv, developed by Union Carbide company, shows great promise in more effectively removing sulfur dioxide from flue gases. The new technology employs scrubbers containing an organic amine which selectively removes more than 99% of the sulfur dioxide. The extractant is then transferred to a tower where it is heated, and this regenerates the amine as nearly pure sulfur dioxide is expelled. The amine is recycled over and over, and the sulfur dioxide is converted to sulfuric acid. Pilot plant studies using high-sulfur coal (3 to 4%) have been successful.

A process of removing sulfur from coal which depends on the use of bacterial action has been developed by the Institute of Gas Technology. Bacteria altered by gene engineering are given a diet free of sulfur, when they remove the sulfur they need from powdered coal and convert it to a soluble form, when it can be washed out.

The effects of sulfur dioxide on forests have been studied in detail. One effect is to lower the rate of photosynthesis, and thus lower the rate of carbon dioxide removal from the air. Temperate zone forests, as in the United States and Canada, normally remove 1 to 4 metric tonnes of carbon per acre each year. The forest ecosystems are also damaged by the heavy metals discharged as fine oxide dust from smokestacks, especially when the acidity of the soil is raised by sulfur dioxide and rain. Copper and zinc are essential trace elements, but the amounts are frequently high enough to prove toxic. Coal also contains mercury, and coal burning utilities are a primary source of this toxic metal. Investigations showed that coal-fired plants are the largest source of mercury emissions, discharging more than 100 tons annually. The United States produces about 150 tons of mercury each year, and it is used for thermometers, dental amalgams, and in various instruments.

Two improved coal utilization processes called Atmospheric Fluidized Bed Combustion and the Integrated Gasification Combined Cycle have been developed. These minimize the use of scrubbers, and the second reduces carbon dioxide emissions by more than 40% through greater efficiency. Conventional coal burning plants emit nearly 3 tons per 1000 megawatt-hours of electricity produced; the Integrated Gasification process drops this significantly. During 1995, American power companies reduced their output of sulfur dioxide by an amount nearly 40% more than government regulations required.

Coal usually contains traces of radioactive materials. American coal averages about 1.7 parts per million uranium. Nearly all (99%) of the light fly-ash from combustion of coal can be captured by electrostatic precipitation from the stacks.

A modification of the classical generation methods is called magnetohydrodynamics. In this approach, coal is burned at an unusually high temperature, high enough to create an electrically conducting plasma. The conductivity of the plasma is enhanced by injection of a potassium salt, which reacts with the sulfur oxides and precipitates out most of the sulfur pollutants. The charged plasma enters a magnetic field causing the charged particles to bend toward two conducting plates. This imparts a positive charge to one plate and a negative charge to the other. Connecting wires lead off a direct current of electric power. This is converted to alternating current. The exhaust gases are hot enough to produce steam for generating conventional turbine power. The result is electricity production with an overall efficiency of 50 to 60%. The process has not yet been fully perfected.

Hydroelectric Power—While water power, which is indirect solar power, is one of the cleanest ways to generate electricity, it often requires dams which have interfered in the normal life cycle of some peoples, as well as animals, especially fish. Another major problem is the gradual silting up of dammed lakes. Of America's total energy, 4.3% is generated by hydroelectric stations. Hydroelectric power usually costs about 2 cents per kilowatt-hour and is one of the least expensive sources.

A gigantic hydroelectric complex, which yields important lessons on several aspects of the matter, has been constructed near James Bay in Quebec. The network has a generating capacity of 24 gigawatts. Three great rivers were diverted to furnish sufficient water, and some 3900 square miles of land were flooded. An unexpected consequence has been that bacteria which decompose submerged vegetation generate chemical substances that dissolve mercury ore found there, forming methylmercury ion. This material, a neurotoxin, is soluble, and when ingested is about ten times as toxic as mercury metal. Fish tend to concentrate mercury in their bodies, and this circumstance is proving hazardous to the native Cree Indians, whose diet contains much fish. It is said to ravage the habitat of much wildlife. Some environmental groups

The negative side of hydroelectric power

have described the James Bay project as the worst ecological disaster ever in North America. Responding to these concerns, and to pressure from the Cree Indians, the Quebec government abandoned plans in 1994 to expand the power still further through a dam on the Great Whale River.

The amount of electricity produced is so great that consideration is now being given to electrolyzing water, and exporting the resulting hydrogen via pipeline. In recent years, evidence has come that the demand for all this electricity might have been overestimated. New York State now has an energy surplus, and no longer needs Quebec's electricity. The project is being scaled back.

The world's ten largest hydroelectric stations as of 1993 were:

James Bay, Quebec, Canada	24,000 megawatts
Grand Coulee, Washington	6,480 megawatts
Krasnoyarsk, Russia	6,096 megawatts
LaGrande 2, Canada	5,328 megawatts
Churchill Falls, Canada	5,225 megawatts
Bratsk, Russia	4,100 megawatts
Ust-Ilimsk, Russia	3,675 megawatts
Paulo Afonso, Brazil	3,409 megawatts
Brumley Gap, Virginia	3,200 megawatts
Ilha Soiteira, Brazil	3,200 megawatts

China announced a decision in 1992 to construct a huge dam on the Yangtze River, and work is now in an advanced stage. If completed as planned, it will flood the scenic Three Gorges and displace about a million people. The electric power will be 18,000 megawatts. Flood control is also a motive. The Export-Import Bank is being pressured to refuse participation in the dam on environmental grounds. The cost is estimated at $30 billion, and electricity production cost is estimated about 2.5 cents per kilowatt-hour.

Getting something for nothing—for a while

Geothermal Energy—The first geothermal source to be tapped for production of electricity was the Larderello hot springs in Tuscanny, Italy. It has been in operation since 1904. In some other regions of the Earth, such as Iceland and Rotarua in New Zealand, steam issues constantly from fissures in sufficient quantity and purity to permit generation of modest quantities of electricity. These are raw steam sources; most others are of the hot brine type. In most places where intense geothermal energy is available, it is deep underground, in water laden with dissolved salts and silica. These features of such brine have proven to be quite an obstacle to harnessing the energy, but in some cases the problems have finally been overcome.

The Geysers is a sprawling raw steam facility a hundred miles north of San Francisco. It has been producing 1350 megawatts of electric power for several decades at the low cost of 2 cents per kilowatt-hour. It is the world's largest such facility. But in recent times the available steam power has been dropping; during 1991 electricity production was down as much as 20%. Fearing the Geysers area is running dry, engineers have begun to pump the condensed water back into the source. Maybe geothermal sources have a limited lifetime for a sustainable level of power production.

In California's Imperial Valley there is another area with vast supplies of brine at around 315 °C (600 °F) and at depths of 3000 to 9000 feet. The Magma Power Company, cooperating with the Dow Chemical Company, solved the challenging technical problems a few years ago and now produces 126 megawatts of electricity. Other geothermal plants in California are in Mono-Long Valley and Cosco Hot Springs. About 6.5% of the state's electricity is generated geothermally. There are a few other promising areas in the country, including Hawaii. The underground steam just south of Hilo contains poisonous hydrogen sulfide. At this site, Puna Geothermal Venture experienced a blowout in 1991 after drilling 3475 feet. Sulfurous steam roared out for 30 hours before the well could be capped. A 25-megawatt plant is being constructed.

Not all geothermal ventures prove successful. In 1980 the Bottle Rock Geothermal Power Plant, a few miles northeast of The Geysers, was completed. At first it produced 55 megawatts of electricity, but the power gradually dropped, and by 1990 was only seven megawatts. It was closed down. A nearby sister plant, South Geysers Power, never opened. The financial loss will be about $450 million. Another source of geothermal energy is the hot brines which are situated along the Gulf Coast. In addition to their heat, they contain dissolved methane, which can be separated and used as fuel. The commercial feasibility of this procedure has been demonstrated, but not developed to its maximum capacity.

4-29 Renewable Energy Sources

During the Carter Administration, expenditures for research on renewable energy sources reached $708 million by 1980, but they were slashed by the Reagan and Bush Sr. authorities, and dropped to $157 million in 1990. The Department of Energy maintains the National Renewable Energy Laboratory near Golden, Colorado. Some of the studies described below were conducted there. The Center for Renewable Energy and Sustainable Technology is at website *<http://solstice.crest.org/>*. We should never lose sight of the fact that we have our Sun, a gigantic nuclear reactor of the fusion type a safe 93 million miles away. It will last billions of years.

Energy from Biomass—Maine generates about 20% of its electricity by burning wood chips. The McNeil Generating Station in Vermont generates 50 megawatts from wood, and is the world's largest of this type. Hawaii gets about a third of its electricity by burning sugarcane residues. In California's San Joaquin Valley, the Delano Energy Company burns 700 tons of prunings, fruit pits, and similar waste each day to generate enough electricity for 30,000 households. The cost is around 8 cents per kilowatt-hour. Bridgeport, Connecticut, burns municipal waste as fuel, making 10% of its electricity. Generally about 80% of such waste is combustible, but formation of toxic fumes has limited this fuel source. One of the worst toxic materials is mercury, which arises from some batteries or dry cells and other materials.

The question is: How feasible is it to generate really significant energy sources from biomass? This point has received a great deal of study and considerable experimental investigation by engineers. A recent investigation, one of a number, was a definitive study of the matter published in Science magazine in 1991. The general conclusion was that a cost-competitive process is now possible. It would comprise the following steps. First, suitable plants, such as shrubs, hemp, fast-growing hybrid trees, switch grass, sweet sorghum, alfalfa, etc., are grown on land of marginal agricultural value. Special varieties have been designed as energy sources. Perennial grasses can grow to a height of eight feet and yield five tons of dry biomass per acre annually. The bulk of such plants ("power crops") is cellulose, which consists of glucose molecules joined together. The harvested cellulosic biomass and similar waste material are hydrolyzed to glucose using enzymes. Fermentation yields ethanol (ethyl alcohol, C_2H_5OH), which is distilled off and used as a fuel for internal combustion vehicles. The unfermentable residues are used as fuel for processing (distillation, etc.). Ethanol is relatively clean-burning, and urban air quality would improve. There is no net contribution to the atmosphere's carbon dioxide content since as much is removed in growing the plants as is produced on combustion. Alternatively, heating the plant material in the absence of air produces crude oils and tars from which diesel fuel can be made. Biomass can also be converted to gas, which on combustion furnishes much more electricity than burning the biomass directly. If adopted, it would ease balance of trade deficits, and enhance energy self-sufficiency. The feasibility of economical ethanol production from biomass was furthered by gene engineering techniques. In 1992, two new genes were transferred to and encoded into the DNA of Escherichia coli and other bacteria, imparting to them the power to make enzymes which hydrolyze and then ferment cellulose directly. Thus cornstalks, corncobs, straw, sawdust, paper, etc., can be processed efficiently.

But growing such plants does wear out soil faster.

New studies suggest that biomass can also be converted into methanol (CH_3OH) instead of ethanol. This is accomplished by a gasification technique being investigated by the Department of Energy. It might be more efficient than ethanol production. Fuel cells can be developed which function on methanol, thus enabling electric cars to operate.

Present production of ethanol from starch crops is around 800 million gallons in the U.S. annually, and the cost is $1.25 per gallon. The practice in Brazil was for a time to use food-quality sugar or starch to make ethanol. The price could be much reduced by using cellulose. If a vigorous development program were undertaken, biomass would provide a viable energy source in the United States, probably within a decade. Sweden in 1991 approved expenditure of $180 million on cogeneration electricity plants using biomass as fuel. Methane resulting from the decay of waste organic matter in landfills or manure from cattle farms provides a small bonus. Vigorous development of some of these processes would be expected to furnish about half of current U.S. electricity or two-thirds of gasoline demand.

Coal and petroleum are ancient biomass products concentrated and processed by Mother Nature.

Brazil began its conversion to ethanol in 1975 in response to the oil crisis of that period. More than three-quarters of its cars operated on ethanol in 1985, but this proportion has been falling because of cheaper petroleum. In 1993, only one-third of the cars burned ethanol. A falling economy and inflation are forcing production of ethanol down. To burn ethanol, special adaptations must be carried out on automobiles. A motor running on ethanol discharges about 25% less carbon monoxide than one burning gasoline, and about 15% less nitrogen oxides. The sugar cane residues (bagasse) are used for fuel to generate electricity, and the ashes from this process make potassium-rich fertilizer. Combustion of ethanol yields 30 megajoules per kilogram, while for gasoline the figure is 42 megajoules.

The British are constructing a 600-kilowatt pilot plant which might be the most promising of all. It depends on using algae as diesel fuel. The type chosen is Chlorella, which has a very high photosynthetic efficiency in converting carbon dioxide into biomass. The nutrients for the algae, mostly nitrates and phosphates, derive from algal treatment of sewage. The fast-growing Chlorella is cultivated in coils of 1.5-inch transparent plastic tubing which are held in a framework for exposure to sunlight. Each coil has a unique self-cleaning device to prevent the green growing material from adhering to the inner walls. One of the best features of the system is that carbon dioxide from the diesel exhaust is dissolved in the nutrient solution, so that the carbon is recycled back into fuel. The algae mass is filtered off and dried using heat from the motors. The diesel engines are started with conventional fuel, and then a mixture of milled algae (95%) and diesel fuel (5%) is injected in. Residual water in the algae, on contacting the flame at 2000 °C in the cylinders, flash-evaporates and breaks the algae into minute particles, assuring rapid combustion. It is even possible to collect the oxygen evolved during photosynthesis and use it in the engines, thus avoiding production of nitrogen oxides. There are certain purple bacteria found in pond scum which might be even more efficient in absorbing light. Clearly, this integrated process has many attractive features.

When Rudolph Diesel unveiled his now-famous engine at the 1900 World Fair in Paris, he used peanut oil as fuel. The engines were later adapted to use petroleum fuel. In modern times, soy bean oil is being used, mostly in backup generators in hospitals. The vegetable oils, called biodiesel fuel, are forms of biomass.

Direct Solar Energy, Thermal—Solar thermal energy is inexhaustible and vastly cleaner than most other sources. Even the U.S. Postal Service has got into the action (Color Plate I, Fig. 4-29B). But there are several side effects, even in this case. First there is some unavoidable pollution during manufacture and transportation of the equipment. Second, the panels would take up a great deal of land space, but this is not a serious problem in the United States. Sunshine above the Earth's atmosphere has a power of 1370 watts per square meter; about half of this reaches the surface (more than half in deserts). Nevertheless, solar power has the promise of becoming greatly superior to nearly all other techniques.

In California's Mojave desert Luz International, the world's largest solar energy firm, built nine units, starting in the oil-shocked 1970s. The generating capacity totaled 275 megawatts. A series of long mirrors of parabolic cross section focused sunlight onto pipes containing a synthetic oil. The oil was heated to 370 °C (700 °F) and then pumped through a heat exchanger to boil water. The resulting steam powered turbines and a generator. Natural gas-powered generators were used at night. The capacity of the newer units was 80 megawatts. While successful, this mode of solar power is still somewhat more expensive than that burning coal. Such statements as this can be misleading. If the total social costs of the effects of sulfur dioxide in coal smoke, as well as the greenhouse-gas, carbon dioxide, are also taken into account, the opposite might be true.

Good ideas here, but watch the costs.

Solar plants initially cost more than fossil-fuel plants to build, increasing the cost of capitalization. The mirrors get dirty, and cleaning costs make maintenance expensive. In 1991, with dropping energy costs from petroleum and dwindling tax subsidies, Luz was teetering on the edge of bankruptcy. Toward the end of that year Luz and four subsidiaries had to file for bankruptcy. A private firm now operates the facilities.

But the Luz enterprise started again in Australia, where solar power has been unfolding since about 1992. The Israelis along with a Belgian company have built a power plant supplying as much as 300 megawatts of electricity. They replaced the heated oil with water, and generated superheated steam without use of pumps, and have made other innovations. The Australians have the world's largest dish reflector, 400 square meters, and also employ several new kinds of photovoltaic devices.

Solar I, an experimental power tower unit, was constructed in the California desert, and it produced electricity at the rate of 10 megawatts. The tower was surrounded by hundreds of mirrors, each with a mechanism to track the Sun and keep the reflected beam on target; these are known as heliostats. The production cost per watt was considerably higher than in the Luz method because of the heliostat costs.

A consortium of utilities in California in 1991 agreed to build a new solar generating facility in the Mojave desert, at a cost of around $40 million, about half of which was to come from the Department of Energy. It is to use a technique in which a low-melting salt (mixed sodium/potassium nitrates/nitrites) is the heat exchange medium. When melted by daytime sunshine, it continues to evolve heat on recrystallizing during the night, thus furnishing continuous power. The electric power is to be 10 megawatts; the cost is expected to be around 9 cents per kilowatt-hour. This development makes an important contribution to winning electric power from solar energy.

Direct Solar Energy, Photovoltaic—Photovoltaic cells generate electricity directly from sunlight. Small units are common, being used to recharge batteries in hand-held calculators, highway phones, etc. Some systems use mirrors or lenses to gather more light. The cells are made from elemental silicon, which is not difficult to prepare (except in high purity), and does not corrode. At present, most of the cells consist of layers of silicon (either crystalline or amorphous) with controlled concentrations of certain other elements ("dopants"); in sunlight they can produce electricity with an efficiency of up to 27%, but are generally 8 to 15% efficient. In a quiet revolution, recent advances in photovoltaic technology have created a rebirth in interest, and have brought the costs down.

The Southern California Edison Company and Texas Instruments have devised a different and less expensive means of manufacturing photovoltaic panels. Tiny beads of medium purity silicon are embedded into aluminum foil; there are about 1000 beads per square inch. The practicality of these panels is still to be proven in the marketplace. Since solar cells produce direct current, an inverter must also be used to change it to alternating current, except for those few cases where direct current is satisfactory. Fortunately, the cost of the inverter is only a small fraction of the photovoltaic costs. In 1996 an Australian utility company teamed up with New South Wales University to form Pacific Solar in a $50 million venture. They claim that their one-square-meter panels are 15% efficient and can produce photovoltaic current at 7.9 to 11.9 cents per kilowatt-hour.

Although solar-powered automobiles are not yet practical, a Swiss-made vehicle powered by solar cells raced across Australia in 1990, averaging 40 miles per hour. Its cells were 17% efficient, but were complicated and of unproven durability. In the fall of 1991 the Swiss announced a new type of solar cell, one which employs a titanium film thin enough to transmit light, and also a layer of light-absorbing dye. It is said to be inexpensive and to be relatively efficient. Honda Corporation's entry into the 1993 World Solar Challenge race in Australia achieved 52.8 miles per hour over the 1882 mile course, with a solar efficiency of more than 20%. American-made solar cars participated in 1995 in the cross-country "Sunrayce." The General Electric company has also made demonstration models of photoelectric cars, and some average more than 40 miles per hour. Photovoltaic materials other than silicon are also known. These include thin films of copper indium selenide with cadmium sulfide and related materials. An indium phosphide photovoltaic cell achieved 31.8% efficiency

A memorable advance was made late in 1992 when an array of thin-film photovoltaic modules was connected to the California power grid. Advanced Photovoltaic Systems of Princeton, New Jersey, built the power source, which is situated in the desert near the city of Davis. The assembly is constructed from 9600 units. Each consists of a thin film of amorphous silicon deposited on a glassy substrate of titanium dioxide. The array supplies 479 kilowatts.

By 1998 the outlook for photovoltaics began to brighten. World sales of units had increased significantly, reaching about $1 billion per year. U.S. capacity reached more than 140 megawatts. Electric companies founded the Utility Photo-Voltaic Group. The cost of construction dropped to around $5 per watt based on amorphous silicon of 8 to 10% efficiency. The Solarex company had annual sales of $60 million. Modules are sold for remote telecommunications applications, satellite uplinks, navigational aids, isolated ranches and medical clinics, certain road lights, boats, etc. There are still about two billion people in the world (nearly one-third of total) who have no electricity. A 50-watt photovoltaic unit could operate a radio, television, sewing machine, or battery charger. The Clinton administration pushed a program called its "million-solar-roof" initiative, with a $2000 tax credit; Vice President Gore regarded it as part of an anti-global warming step.

A process still in its infancy uses photoelectrochemical cells. Conceptually, these devices consist of a solid-state semiconductor immersed in an ionic solution. During operation, sunlight falls on the semiconductor, causing oxidation or reduction of ions. A metallic electrode of opposite electric charge is also in the solution, and an external circuit carries the current. Efficiency is around 15% in laboratory models.

Chemical Fuels from Sunlight—Another possible way to glean electricity from sunlight is the high-tech photolysis of water into hydrogen and oxygen. The two gases are then recombined in a fuel cell to produce an electric current. A 1999 publication from Korea showed that water can be decomposed by sunlight with a quantum yield up to 23% by using the mineral perovskite which has been activated with nickel. While partly successful on a laboratory scale, commercialization is a long way off. Still another technique for accomplishing the production of hydrogen from water, driven by sunlight, is through reactions with sulfur dioxide. Reaction of sulfur dioxide with iodine yields hydrogen iodide, which on thermal decomposition by sunlight forms hydrogen and iodine. The hydrogen is separated for use as a fuel, and the iodine is used over and over. Successful schemes of this are far into the future.

Energy from Wind—Many countries have installed wind-driven turbines to generate electricity. Most modern designs utilize bladed propellers. By regulating rotation speed, windsmiths have produced standard alternating current using synchronized induction generators. Older units produce 55 kilowatts, while newer ones generate 500 kilowatts or more, even as much as a megawatt. A new type of variable-speed turbines is now being developed. Solid-state AC-to-DC power inverters are used which remove frequency fluctuations arising from changes in wind speed. This modification results in higher efficiency and durability. Steel blades can interfere with television reception, but fiberglass blades do not, and are lighter and cheaper. The cost of producing energy from the wind dropped some 85% in the period 1983-1998. According to a 1998 report from The Institute for Energy and Environmental Research, located in Maryland, electricity from nuclear sources is about 40% more expensive than that from wind power. Another report from the Institute (1999), states that the cost of producing electricity from offshore wind is 5.5 cents per kilowatt hour, while that from reactors using mixed U-Pu oxides is 7.2 cents, and that from breeder reactors is 11.3 cents.

There's enormous public interest in this topic.

California produced 80% of the world's wind-generated electricity 12 years ago, but by 2001, other countries had surpassed the U.S., as the tabulation below shows:

- Germany 6,400 megawatts
- Spain 2,495 megawatts
- U.S. 2,495 megawatts
- Denmark 2,364 megawatts

California operates more than 17,000 units, generating 1646 megawatts at 5 or 6 cents per kilowatt-hour. The cost, already only a fifth of the cost in 1981, is still falling as better technologies emerge. The Lake Benton area of central Minnesota produces more than 100 megawatts. Currently, capital expenditure is about 80 cents per installed watt; the electricity costs about 4 cents per kilowatt-hour with wind averaging 15 miles per hour velocity. A minimum wind velocity of 12 miles per hour is necessary for good performance, and 30 miles per hour is optimum. At 50 mph turbines shut down automatically. From each square meter of area perpendicular to wind flow, perhaps 25 to 65 watts of electricity can be extracted, depending on wind velocity. Improved turbine blades can now capture 20% more energy from wind than earlier types. The United States, now generating

about 1% of its electricity from wind, could produce up to 25% (or perhaps more) of its electricity via wind turbines, according to one knowledgeable source. The cost has now fallen to 5 cents per kilowatt-hour, or even less. Like direct solar, power from wind is constricted by its low intensity, that is, it is spread out. But just the same there is massive potential for wind power in the Midwest. North Dakota alone could produce a large fraction of the electrical energy needs of the United States were wind power fully developed. Moreover, the value of ranchland rises when wind turbines and cattle co-exist. The trend at the end of the millennium was to construct much larger wind turbines and their towers: 300-foot heights and 76-foot, two-ton blades.

Since the energy crunch of 2000-2001, the costs of building facilities and generating electricity from wind power has been less than the corresponding costs of using natural gas. This is largely due to sharp rises in the price of the gas.

The Danes are enthusiastic about wind power and have pioneered in wind turbine technology. They raised their production to 500 megawatts by the end of 1993, and are considering another 1000 megawatts. Some of the turbines in Denmark have been installed off shore. The objective is to glean about half of the country's electrical power from the wind by year 2030. The European Community is now spending 10 times as much as the United States on research and development of wind energy. A recent study concluded that Scotland could produce 60 gigawatts, three-quarters of Britain's generating capacity. The Japanese plan to generate 300,000 kilowatts by 2010. Our world now has a theoretical capacity for making most of our electrical energy from wind. A remarkable young American, Peter Hayes, actually gained permission from the government of North Korea to construct a number of wind turbines for electricity generation for pumping water.

One drawback to wind turbines is that they kill quite a number of birds, especially when the towers are placed in bird migration paths. The latest turbines are designed to turn more slowly, minimizing loss of birds. There are also objections to their noise when near urban areas, but newer turbines are much quieter.

Energy from the Oceans—The tides of our restless oceans have attracted considerable attention as a power source. A successful French tidal power plant consists of a bay dammed off from the ocean. At high tide water flows into the bay, turning turbines. At low tides, the reverse process takes place. The Bay of Fundi in Nova Scotia has tidal level changes as high as 40 feet, and near Anchorage, Alaska, a height change of 25 feet has been reported. These sites could support economic generation of electricity, but in general, favorable sites are quite rare. The British have made a successful tidal turbine, a propeller some 11 meters long attached to a sturdy tower and immersed about 25 meters deep. The variable pitch of the blades permit a constant speed of 17 rpm, which is geared a generate 50-hertz current.

In 1997 an Australian oceanographer made a model of a parabolic wave-focusing device which can focus incoming ocean waves toward a point. The wide mouth of the funnel-shaped surface receives incoming waves, and these are channeled upward into a tapered vertical chamber. A turbine is situated at the far end of the chamber attached to a generator. Air in the chamber is compressed by the in-rushing water, driving the turbine. When the water falls back, the air is drawn back. A complicated gear system keeps the turbine turning in the same direction. Estimates have been made that up to a megawatt of electricity could be produced per 40 meters of shoreline. Several other techniques for harnessing the energy of the sleepless oceans have been newly announced. Great Britain has invested considerable sums into wave energy recently.

Another procedure, ocean thermal energy technology, relies on a temperature difference between surface layers of the ocean (warmed by sunlight) and colder depths. A volatile compound such as ammonia boils in tanks near the surface, the vapor turning turbines to generate electricity. Part of the electricity is used to pump cold water from a depth of 3000 feet to condense the ammonia vapor, which then enters the boiler again. The equipment is quite expensive and this technique shows little promise.

Power from ocean water is limited.

All marine equipment suffers from serious defects. Biofouling by algae, barnacles and other life forms reduce efficiency of the heat-transfer or smooth movement of water. It is expensive to maintain surfaces in good condition. Materials resistant to corrosion by salt water are costly. Large stretches of beaches devoted to machinery hardly seem to be the best use.

4-30 Human Use of Energy in Perspective

Consider the following comparisons: Sunshine reaches our Earth with a power of somewhat less than 180 billion megawatts, of which approximately 125 billion megawatts reaches the Earth's surface. Only a tiny share, 0.03% of solar radiation, is absorbed by green leaves in the process of photosynthesis. The entire human economy today runs on around 11 million megawatts (11 terawatts; tera = 10^{12}). About 85% of this energy is generated from fossil fuels. All human enterprise consumes approximately 0.008% of the energy falling on our Earth's surface from the Sun. Our energy use is trivial in the grand scheme of things. Nevertheless the heat balance of our planet is very delicate, and human activities just could affect the proportion of energy from sunlight which is retained by Earth. This point is discussed in the section on the greenhouse effect, below.

Our two intense sources of energy on Earth are fossil fuels and uranium. Most of the alternative energy sources discussed above could, with further development, supply important auxiliary amounts of energy, but they are inherently diffuse sources. With much development, coupled with conservation measures and efficient energy management, they might be expected to adequately support a growing, industrialized population, up to a point. They would certainly be sufficient in a world with a much lower population. A precautionary note is that enthusiasts for renewable energy often forget that it will take many decades to develop these sources to the degree that they play a really important role. Only about 0.24% of our electricity today comes from renewable sources, and most of that is geothermal. Prolonged experience might gradually improve matters.

4-31 The Greenhouse Effect

Aside from its global interest, a general understanding of the greenhouse effect is important in that nuclear energy might give us a means of avoiding or moderating its worst consequences (7-42).

Earth's Temperature—Over billions of years, our Earth has established a more or less steady state in regard to its temperature. This means that the energy it receives from the Sun is almost exactly balanced by the energy lost to outer space. Actually, additional energy from the interior of the Earth, arising from radioactive decay of uranium and thorium, supplies extra heat to the Earth's surface, and it is lost to outer space by radiation too. The equilibrium has been shifted somewhat now and then by natural fluctuations, resulting in ice ages, the last one starting approximately 18,000 years ago. It lasted about 7000 years. During that period the average global surface temperature was 10 °C (50 °F); it was the coldest climate humans have ever had to cope with. After warming, glaciers and much of the polar ice caps melted; sea level rose 400 feet.

Be thankful that you were not born during the last ice age.

An average global temperature takes into account daily, seasonal, and other variations, and is computed over a number of years. Shifts in air masses cause regional climatic changes and the extremes tend to cancel out on averaging. Average global temperature measurements of the atmosphere are measured nowadays using satellites and microwave radiometry. It is microwave emission from atmospheric oxygen which is recorded, and this depends on its temperature. The precision is high (0.01°C), and the method is far superior to reading thermometers distributed over the Earth. The two satellites now in use are in polar orbits, and each can measure temperatures at many altitudes, usually averaged over altitudes of 5000 to 30,000 feet covering an area of 780 square miles. The average temperature of the atmosphere (in degrees C), as measured by the microwave emission of oxygen, during the past few decades is as follows:

1950	*1960*	*1970*	*1971*	*1972*	*1973*	*1974*	*1975*	*1976*	*1977*	*1978*	*1979*	*1980*
14.86	14.98	15.04	14.89	14.93	15.19	14.93	14.95	14.79	15.16	15.09	15.15	15.28

1981	*1982*	*1983*	*1984*	*1985*	*1986*	*1987*	*1988*	*1989*	*1990*	*1991*	*1992*	*1993*
15.39	15.07	15.29	15.11	15.11	15.16	15.32	15.35	15.25	15.47	15.41	15.13	15.20

Note that the temperature rises and falls slightly with the years, but in general is creeping upward. The Earth has warmed by about 0.5 °C during the past century. In the time since the last ice age, the average global temperature rose slowly to 15.20 °C (59.4 °F) in 1998. The temperatures were so high that peat in the tundra began to release carbon dioxide; earlier, the peat would absorb CO_2. The Arctic warmed to the extent that the Greenland Ice Sheet melted at the rate of an average value of a meter per year. The Antarctic glaciers are also melting faster. Average Arctic temperatures have risen 6 °C (11 °F). Sonar data from submarines have shown that summer Arctic sea ice has declined from 10.2 feet to 5.9 feet during the period 1993–1997.

Essentially, the greenhouse effect is an influence in which solar heat as infrared which would normally reradiate out into space is instead absorbed by our atmosphere and retained, causing a rise in temperature. It can be divided into a natural component and a man-made component.

Minor changes occur frequently. For example, around the period 1300 to 1400, the average temperature dropped by 0.5 to 1 °C (0.9 to 1.8 °F). This small change was enough to force Norse farmers out of Greenland, and make the European climate extra cold for about 400 years (the "Little Ice Age"). By 1850, the average temperature had risen to its level of 500 years earlier. There is evidence that rising temperatures about 10,000 years ago came in quick jumps lasting decades.

The long-term history of Earth's climate has been determined by several techniques, of which bore holes in the icecaps of Greenland, Antarctica, and Tibet are most important. Core samples taken between 1960 and 1992 reach back as far as 250,000 years. Each year's deposit is a chemical archive of the time of its deposit. Imprisoned dust reveals much of the story. By measuring the ratio of oxygen-18 to oxygen-16 in the ice, the temperature at which it was formed is determined: the lower the temperature, the lower the concentration of the heavier isotope.

As described in section 4-29, the amount of energy flowing into the Earth is truly enormous. If it were not compensated by reradiation, Earth's temperature would rise to very high levels until a new steady state is attained. In the case of Venus, not only is it closer to the Sun, but also more heat is trapped than on Earth, so its temperature is quite high (approximately the melting point of zinc). A decrease of a fraction of a percent of the rate of loss of energy from our Earth would in time lead to raising the temperature noticeably; human enterprise might be sufficient to accomplish this.

Greenhouse Effect—As early as 1827 the French physicist Fourier wondered whether the Earth is kept warm because the atmosphere traps heat from the Sun, as if under a pane of glass (hence the idea of a greenhouse). During the following seven decades advances in spectroscopic research permitted Swedish chemist Arrhenius to speculate in 1896 that carbon dioxide in the air plays an important role in the heat balance. He wondered whether human activities might be important in this. This idea was reinforced in 1938 when British engineer Callendar suggested that the Earth was getting warmer because of all the carbon dioxide which industry was spewing forth. This was to become known as the greenhouse effect. Hardly anyone paid any attention to these ideas at that time.

Messing around with Earth's climate

To understand the greenhouse effect, it is first necessary to learn something of the rates at which energy streams in from the Sun, and the mechanism by which it is re-radiated. The first measurement of the sun's ultraviolet in outer space was made using a spectrometer in a captured German V2 rocket. Later, satellites carrying spectrographic equipment recorded the entire spectrum of sunlight. The results show that electromagnetic radiation is emitted continuously ranging all the way from the most energetic (gamma rays) to the least energetic (radio and power-line radiation); in between are X-rays, ultraviolet, visible light, infrared radiation, and microwaves. Each type of radiation is characterized by its wavelength. Convenient units of wavelength are the micrometer (μm, a millionth of a meter), and the nanometer (nm, a billionth of a meter). The wavelength ranges of the most important regions are:

— | — ultraviolet — | — visible — | — infrared — | —
20 nm 400 nm 750 nm 1,000,000 nm

The Sun's spectrum peaks in intensity in the visible range, being in the blue-green region (wavelength approximately 490 nm). About 95% of the Sun's radiation energy falls between 295 and 2500 nm. Precise satellite measurements of solar power have been made over the past 13 years, and these show that it is constant within 0.1%. The power of sunlight just above the atmosphere is 1370 watts per square meter. About half of the energy reaches the Earth's surface. As we move from the equator toward the poles, each square meter on the Earth's surface is of course illuminated by weaker and weaker light, so the polar regions are cooler.

Of the radiation reaching the Earth above the atmosphere (considering it on a 100% basis), the following prevails:

- reflected and scattered by clouds back into space: 24%
- reflected back by Earth's surface: 6%
- absorbed by clouds and atmosphere: 17%
- absorbed by Earth's surface (land and sea): 53%

Recent studies indicate that the percentage of solar energy absorbed by clouds might be somewhat higher than the 17% shown. To some degree, clouds act as Earth's window shades. The net effect of clouds may be either positive or negative, depending on their type. They are the largest single uncertainty in climate models.

What happens to the 70% of the radiant energy absorbed in the last two categories listed above? The answer is that it is converted into infrared radiation, and emitted back into space. The wavelength range of most of this infrared falls between 1000 and 7000 nanometers. This reradiation continues night and day from the entire surface of the Earth. But once released from the Earth's surface, some infrared is reabsorbed again by clouds and by certain gases of our atmosphere. Water vapor is the most important, and carbon dioxide is second. For thousands of years a more or less steady state in the energy balance of our Earth has prevailed, keeping the average temperature recently quite close to 15 °C (59 °F). But something has taken place during the past century or so. The large number of human beings on Earth, along with their industries, have steadily raised the concentration of carbon dioxide. Currently each year billions of tons of carbon (in the form of carbon dioxide) is discharged into our atmosphere. While this gas is a minor component of air, it absorbs infrared which was previously lost to outer space, and it could, just could, in time heat the Earth somewhat and cause changes in the climate: the greenhouse effect. Moreover, some other gaseous components in the atmosphere are also known to absorb infrared. The most important of these are methane (CH_4), nitrous oxide (N_2O), and chlorofluorocarbons (CFCs).

'hy our climate might change

There is evidence that the average global temperature has risen by 0.3 to 0.5 °C during the past century. One way to establish this is studying tree rings in a kind of tree known as Huon pines, which grow in northern Tasmania. The nature of the rings depend sensitively on their temperature during growth. The evidence is that atmospheric temperatures have risen more rapidly during the last 25 years than in any earlier period during the past 1000 years. Since for at least 11,000 years, natural fluctuations of about 2

°C have occurred, one cannot be sure that the change during the past century is really the beginnings of excessive greenhouse effect. Considerable evidence indicates that it is not. Studies of the rings of the second longest-lived trees, which are alerce trees of southern South America, show that above average temperatures prevailed from 80 BC to AD 160, and below average temperatures prevailed from AD 300 to 470 and from 1490 to 1700.

Absorption of Infrared—Why do some molecules absorb infrared while other types do not? For a molecule to absorb infrared, it must vibrate at very near the same frequency as the infrared, and also must have its electric charge distributed asymmetrically. It is this oscillating electric charge which actually interacts with the radiation, resulting in absorption. If the total electric charge is symmetrically distributed, no absorption takes place.

Consider oxygen and nitrogen molecules, O_2 and N_2. Since in each case the atoms in the pair are identical, no uneven electric charge distribution exists, even when the bond between the atoms is stretched by vibration. Therefore these gases, the major components of air, are transparent to infrared. But a molecule of water vapor is different. Unlike the oxygen molecule, different kinds of atoms are bonded together, and this results in a partial negative charge on the oxygen and a partial positive charge on each hydrogen. The molecule is V-shaped, like this:

Why some gases absorb infrared while others do not

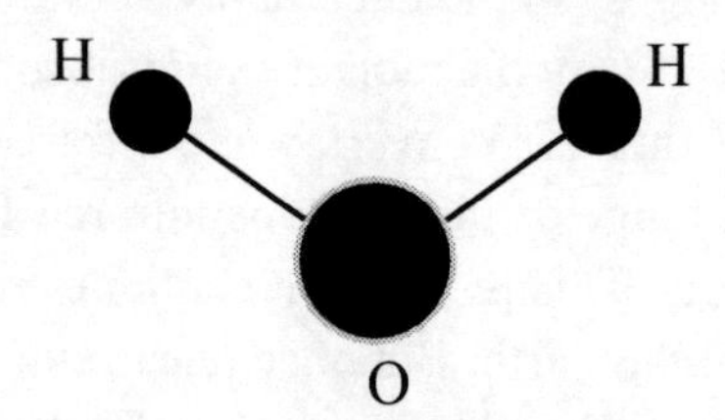

One mode of vibration is movement of the two hydrogen atoms toward and away from each other, like scissors; this corresponds to absorption of infrared of wavelength 6270 nanometers. Another vibrational mode is simultaneous stretching and contraction of the two H-O bonds; this causes absorption at 2740 nm. A third mode is stretching one bond while the other contracts; this causes absorption at 2560 nm. Considerable infrared of wavelength above and below these peak values is also absorbed.

The carbon dioxide molecule is linear, O=C=O, and partial electric charges are found on the atoms (positive on C, negative on each O). Symmetric vibration (the oxygen atoms moving away from the carbon atoms and back simultaneously) increases charge separation, but it is symmetrical all the time, and no infrared absorption occurs here. But when one O moves toward the C and the other moves away, asymmetrical charge separation does occur, and infrared absorption takes place (at 2350 nm). When the molecule bends, becoming momentarily V-shaped, absorption occurs at 15,000 nm. Methane, nitrous oxide and the CFCs absorb infrared similarly in nearby spectral regions.

Hydroxyl Radicals—When the water molecule pictured above absorbs ultraviolet light (much more energetic than infrared), the result is not a change in vibrational pattern, as in the case of infrared absorption, but the rupture of one of the H-to-O bonds. This produces H (a free hydrogen atom) and OH (known as the hydroxyl radical); neither has a net electric charge. These hydroxyl radicals are aggressive and powerful oxidizing agents and play many roles in atmospheric chemistry.

They are constantly formed at all altitudes whenever sunlight strikes the atmosphere. Their concentration, always minute, varies with sunshine intensity and other factors, and is somewhere around one molecule per ten trillion molecules of air, mostly nitrogen and oxygen. These concentrations are measured by absorption spectroscopy. By shining a laser beam of light about 12 miles through the atmosphere to a mirror, the light is reflected back to a detector near its source; alternatively, many mirrors can be used much closer together. A recent development by German researchers is called laser-induced fluorescence spectroscopy, and this relatively small instrument can analyze air for its hydroxyl concentration even aboard aircraft.

Trends in Carbon Dioxide Concentration—In Hawaii a monitoring station on a mountain top two miles high has been recording the carbon dioxide level of the pristine air since 1956. Reliable values were also obtained by ordinary chemical analysis in Europe and the United States from about 1880. Analysis of much earlier air trapped in Antarctic ice up to 160,000 years old has given additional data. The table below shows the levels of carbon dioxide, methane, nitrous oxide, and total chlorofluorocarbons in various years (ppm = parts per million). The first entry, 1750, applies to the time just before the industrial revolution began. Note that the carbon dioxide concentration rose an average of 0.1 ppm per year between 1750 and 1850, 0.25 ppm per year between 1850 and 1960, 0.7 ppm per year in the 1960s, 1.3 ppm per year during the 1970s, and 1.5 ppm per year after 1980. This correlates with the exponential growth in population. This new carbon dioxide is largely man-made, as has been shown by studies of its isotopic composition (fossil fuels have no carbon-14; see 6-6). The present carbon dioxide content, somewhat more than 360 ppm by volume, corresponds to about 540 ppm by weight.

Carbon dioxide is in Nature mainly a product of forest and grass fires, and decay (mostly of vegetable matter by microbes in soil). Animal respiration contributes some. Most dissolves in the oceans, especially the colder parts. Carbon dioxide is converted through photosynthesis by chlorophyll into biomass; oxygen is simultaneously released. The entire terrestrial ecosystem locks in close to 2 billion metric tonnes of carbon into biomass per year (carbon dioxide is 27.3% carbon and 72.7% oxygen by weight). Marine plankton removes it at about the same rate. About 700 billion metric tonnes of carbon is immobilized in peat bogs. For thousands of years, prior to industrialization, the entire atmosphere held around 580 billion metric tonnes of carbon (as the dioxide); today it contains 750 billion metric tonnes, and it is increasing. The increase comes from human use of fossil fuels. Annual emissions of carbon dioxide per capita in metric tonnes per year are approximately: in the United States, 20; in Germany, 12; in India, 1.

Green plants are the world's lungs.

Starting about 1994, the rate of increase of carbon dioxide in the air began to decline, and then the actual concentration dropped slightly. This occurred despite no decrease in the rate of release of the gas into the atmosphere. This change has confounded climatologists. The trends are shown in the table on the next page.

Changes in Concentrations of Greenhouse Gases in the Atmosphere

	carbon dioxide	methane	nitrous oxide	CFCs
1750	280 ppm	0.8 ppm	—	0
1850	290	—	—	0
1900	305	—	—	0
1940	312	1.1	—	—
1960	317	1.4	—	—
1970	325	—	—	—
1980	338	1.56	—	—
1990	353	1.70	—	—
1992	356	1.72	0.31 ppm	—
1994	360	1.74	0.31	0.0007 ppm

Currently, combustion of fuel puts 5 to 6 billion metric tonnes of carbon as its dioxide into the air yearly. Somewhat more than half of this is removed each year by terrestrial plants, the oceans, or in other ways. The 728 million forested acres in the United States remove some 1.7 billion tons of carbon dioxide per year. Destruction of forests decreases the rate of carbon dioxide removal, but increased farming for the growing population tends to increase the rate. Tropical forests are being cut at a rate of 40 to 50 million acres per year. Forests a century ago annually removed some 2 billion metric tonnes of carbon (as the dioxide) more than is the case today. Tropical countries with giant rain forests perform a great service to all of us by preserving these trees, and they should be paid for it. A 1998 study at New York University concluded that a tenfold increase in power by processes which to not emit carbon dioxide would be necessary to stabilize the level. Total rate of energy production in the world is now about 11 terawatts (tera = 10^{12}), and only 15% comes from non-fossil fuels.

Audit of CO_2

A suggestion has been made to fertilize ocean plants by adding iron, an element which accelerates their growth, thus causing absorption of more carbon dioxide. In addition this would raise the food supply for marine animals, causing much of their waste to carry carbon into the ocean depths, and thus sequester it harmlessly from the atmosphere. Indeed, a test of this idea was carried out during the summer of 1996 west of the Galapagos Islands. Three areas, each 60 square kilometers, were treated with a suitable chemical form of iron. This caused a massive bloom of phytoplankton, causing the ocean to change from clear blue to dark green. Each metric tonne of iron caused removal of 200 tonnes of carbon dioxide. If carried out on a massive scale, it might be possible to significantly lower the carbon dioxide content of the atmosphere.

Other Greenhouse Gases—Methane is released by soil bacteria, especially from agricultural areas such as rice paddies. It is also produced by digestion of cellulose. Each cow generates about 14 cubic feet of the gas per day. Termites scavenge cellulosic materials, and their ingestion of the fiber releases vast quantities of methane. Methane is eventually oxidized to carbon dioxide. Carbon dioxide from life forms does not truly represent additional amounts of the gas, however, because this same material was only shortly before removed from the atmosphere by plants. Some methane is destroyed in the troposphere, and the remainder eventually migrates into the stratosphere. In both regions it is oxidized by hydroxyl radicals (formula: OH), and in the stratosphere by ozone as well. A large fraction of methane is taken up and digested by soil microbes unrelated to those which produce it. The average life of methane in the air is about 12 years. It absorbs infrared 25 times more efficiently than carbon dioxide. Coal mines and natural gas systems are new sources of heat-trapping methane. Altogether, in the United States, about 624 million tons of methane are released annually.

Nitrous oxide (N_2O) is also generated by certain soil bacteria, especially after fertilizers have been applied. Its average life in the atmosphere is around 180 years. It is 200 times more effective than carbon dioxide as an infrared absorber. One estimate is that about 132 million tons of nitrous oxide finds its way into the air each year in the United States.

The chlorofluorocarbons are all artificial (see ozone layer, 4-32). They are 10,000 to 20,000 times more effective than carbon dioxide in absorbing infrared per molecule, so despite their exceedingly minute concentration, they make a significant contribution to the total greenhouse effect. They are inert chemically and so persist for a long time, but most are slowly destroyed by the traces of ozone and hydroxyl radicals in the air. The principal chlorofluorocarbon is dichlorodifluoromethane or CFC-12, (formula; CCl_2F_2), a common refrigerant. Another refrigerant is fluoroform, analogous to its chlorine equivalent, chloroform ($CHCl_3$).

The Total Effects—If we exclude water vapor, present-day contributions to the total greenhouse effect are approximately as follows: carbon dioxide, 55%; CFCs, 24%; methane, 15%; and nitrous oxide, 6%. Actually, water vapor and clouds introduce the greatest uncertainties in estimating greenhouse effects.

Much of the sulfur dioxide emissions from burning coal and from volcanoes is slowly oxidized and forms droplets of dilute sulfuric acid or sulfate aerosols. Lofted into the upper troposphere, these substances reflect a great deal of sunlight and thus diminish the greenhouse effect. It could be that air pollution has its benefits. The eruption of Mt. Pinatubo in the Philippines in 1991 injected some 30 million tons of sulfur dioxide into the stratosphere, causing the average temperature during 1992 to be 0.28 °C (0.50 °F) lower than in the preceding year. The cooling effect was rapid; it was measured by several satellites.

A natural greenhouse effect has prevailed for millions of years. If it did not exist, our Earth would have an average temperature below freezing, namely about minus 15 °C (5 °F). The water vapor and carbon dioxide trap enough heat to maintain it 30 °C warmer than that value, that is, at 15 °C (59 °F). Thus our concern is not the greenhouse effect itself, but only that fraction of it above the pre-industrial level. The contribution toward global warming caused by man-made gases is at an estimated rate of 2.5 watts per square meter.

Earth as a natural, controlled greenhouse

Climatology—Climatology is a struggling young science, regarded almost as an orphan by the mainstream scientific establishment. It has received little financial support, and deals with an enormous number of poorly understood variables which influence or control the world's climate. The advent of computers advanced it markedly, and observation via satellites greatly strengthened its dependability. Even so, it has a long way to go before genuinely reliable long-range predictions of climate patterns can be made. Numerous nuances of atmospheric behavior are too subtle as yet to quantify and include in computer programs. Experts studying climatology disagree among themselves; some even welcome a greenhouse effect. Theories of climatology available so far do not explain severe prehistoric climate changes.

One of the greatest advances in climatology has been a fuller understanding of feedback mechanisms in the climate. A feedback is a natural occurrence in Earth's climate which is activated by other components. There is a multitude of positive and negative feedbacks which influence the atmosphere's precarious balance. In the case of the greenhouse effect, a positive feedback is one which causes acceleration of global warming, and a negative feedback tends to lower the warming rate and stabilize the temperature. Examples of positive feedbacks are: (a) warming the upper layer of ocean water, which reduces the solubility of carbon dioxide, keeping it in the atmosphere, and (b) loss of polar ice which would cause less reflection of sunlight back into space. Examples of negative feedbacks are: (a) accelerated uptake of carbon dioxide (owing to its higher concentration) by green leaves and ocean plankton, and (b) formation of more clouds in a warming world, reflecting more sunlight. Which effects would dominate? There are great uncertainties in even the best theories. In addition, there are unpredictable factors, such as volcanic eruptions which spew massive amounts of dust and fumes into the atmosphere, or the influence of sunspots on the energy flux reaching the Earth. It is extremely difficult to distinguish between a genuine trend and a fluctuation.

Global warming would accelerate the decomposition of organic matter in the soil, releasing extra carbon dioxide, a positive feedback. Moreover, there has been some worry about release of greenhouse gases known to be in the tundra and permafrost if they melt from greenhouse heating. Methane exists in ocean sediments and as a crystalline hydrate (called a clathrate compound) in subsurface ice and under the seas. Recent studies have indicated that huge releases are unlikely.

NASA has launched several of a planned series of satellites in the Earth Observing System. These sophisticated probes are measuring climate parameters such as cloud radiation, concentrations of carbon monoxide, aerosol optical properties, atmospheric moisture, temperature gradients, sea surface temperature, and Earth's snow cover.

Consequences—If a serious and unmistakable greenhouse effect in excess of the natural level afflicts our Earth, there could be many repercussions. A doubling of the carbon dioxide concentration might cause a rise in average temperature of up to 4 °C (7 °F). While the total rainfall would be expected to rise, it would not be evenly distributed. Some areas would experience widespread drying of soil (the Colorado River flow rate might be cut in half, with corresponding loss of hydroelectric power). But Bangladesh would be flooded periodically, even worse than currently.

In some ways, our modern civilization is a giant experiment in climatology.

Heightened carbon dioxide levels would initially accelerate the growth of green plants, and also improve their ability to use water. This has been demonstrated many times, using air in glasshouses with 700 ppm carbon dioxide. But they exhaust soil nutrients more rapidly than before, and then grow at normal rates. Experiments show that such plants, if they are crops, are less nutritious and less palatable. Tundra plants do not respond to higher carbon dioxide levels.

Melting of polar ice and glaciers, accompanied by thermal expansion of ocean water, would raise the sea level, flooding low-lying coastal land and some islands, such as the Republic of Maldives and Tuvalu. Various measurements of the rise in sea level have been made. A careful series of tests to gauge the sea level was begun in 1950, and the results show that every year a rise of around 2 millimeters has taken place. Thus in 50 years the rise could be about 100 mm, or 4 inches. Other estimates indicate a rise of possibly 10 inches or more during the next century. The temperatures of the top layers of the Pacific Ocean have increased 0.8 °C (1.4 °F) during this time, and this alone has caused the water to expand, and raise the level about 0.9 mm. The sea level is known to have risen 100 to 200 mm (4 to 8 inches) higher during the past century. A U.S.-French satellite, Topex-Poseidon, observed sea levels in various oceans by using radar signals. The results revealed regional rises and falls caused by temperature changes. More water from the polar cap and glaciers might also disrupt the Gulf Stream.

Like that sinking feeling? Then move to Tuvalu.

If the average temperature rises by, say 4 °C, then tropical climates would shift northward and southward from their present limits. Deserts would expand in Africa and other lands. Food supplies would be drastically disrupted. Another consequence of this would be strong effects on the distribution and abundance of insects. Insect-borne diseases now associated with the tropics would expand to the southern reaches of the United States. These include mosquito-carried scourges such as malaria, encephalitis, yellow fever and dengue fever. Sand flies carry leishmaniasis, while a detestable little critter called the "kissing bug" carries dreaded Chagas disease (American trypanosomiasis). In 1996 a comprehensive study was completed which gave some disturbing results in connection with insects. A butterfly known as Edith's checkerspot lives along the American west coast from Baja California up into Canada. For years it has been known to be especially sensitive to subtle temperature changes. The study found that the butterfly has been leaving its southern habitat and flying to higher altitudes or north to escape the rising heat of the south. Antarctic krill, a major food for penguins, are declining in numbers. These changes are in harmony with, but not proof of, greenhouse heating.

In 1998 disturbing reports began to emerge from Kenya, South America, and New Guinea. The rising temperatures seem to have already caused mosquito-borne diseases such as malaria and dengue fever to spread to people who have no immunity to them.

A number of climatologists suspect that sufficient greenhouse effects have already developed to elevate the intensity of hurricanes by strengthening all the forces which shape them. Water vapor from the seas, rising and condensing with liberation of heat, is the engine which drives the storms; warmer oceans mean additional water vapor, and more energetic hurricanes. A recent spate of hurricanes might have strengthened this process. Similarly, the 1998 El Niño rains probably accelerated the greenhouse effect. Global warming means more evaporation and weather extremes, such as heavy snowfalls, torrential downpours with the consequent flooding, and droughts. A Norwegian study in 1995 of the Antarctic ice cap, using data from satellite-borne microwave sensors, indicate a significant decline of the ice over the past 20 years. It averages about 0.14% per year.

An International Panel on Climate Change was established by the United Nations in 1988. Its report in 1995 of the work of about 1000 scientists worldwide concluded that the Earth is now warmer than it has been in a million years, and the temperature has risen close to 0.56 °C (1 °F) during the past century alone. Moreover, all of the ten warmest years on record since 1860 have occurred during the past 15 years, despite the extensive cooling effect of the Mount Pinatubo eruption in 1991. Sea levels have risen four to ten inches as a result of expansion of the water caused by the global warming. Spring has been arriving earlier in the Northern Hemisphere, and the growing season is about a week longer an it was in 1975 and the amount of vegetation has increased nearly 20%. Floods and hurricanes have appeared more frequently. The South Pacific island nation of Tuvalu is so low lying that its government is considering evacuation of its population of 10,000, if they can find higher land somewhere. Maybe we should consider all these changes as much a global *warning* as a global *warming*. Many of the experts are convinced that the greenhouse effect is real and has arrived, but since climate changes are quite slow, perhaps one lifetime is insufficient to prove this. If it develops during the next century, the effects would by no means be uniform. Rainfall would increase in some areas, and deserts would form in others. Similarly, some areas would become much hotter, while others actually grow colder. A Panel of the United Nations meeting on global warming in 1997 in Kyoto, Japan, concluded that "there is no evidence that extreme weather events, or climate variability, has increased, in a global sense, through the 20th century." A report by the National Research Council concluded in early 2000 that the warming of the Earth's surface is "undoubtedly real," and is between 0.4 and 0.8 °C (0.7 to 1.4 °F).

Aside from climate, the Panel also considered the expected effects of global warming on human health. Many epidemics (cholera, dengue, hanta virus, lassa fever, ebola, plague) were closely associated with the temperature trend, as indicated earlier. This is worrisome.

Conclusions—Despite elevated temperatures, excessive floods, and unusual hurricanes during the 1990s, many climate experts caution that this is not yet proof of a real greenhouse effect. It is entirely possible that negative feedbacks will contain global warming which stems from greenhouse effects. It is also possible, but far less likely, that positive feedbacks will dominate, and a climatic debacle will take place. The chances of a runaway and catastrophic greenhouse effect are very slim. It might even be that the observed increase in carbon dioxide content of our atmosphere would have occurred independently of human activities. Nevertheless, it seems prudent to minimize fossil fuel consumption to prolong its availability for human use, to lessen pollution, and as insurance in case we unexpectedly do after all find ourselves in the grip of a merciless global hot house. Conservation steps were mentioned earlier (4-25). Worldwatch Institute calculations indicate that greater efficiency worldwide could lower carbon emissions as much as 3 billion metric tonnes per year. For many people it does not seem really warranted to undertake expensive social changes for the sole sake of avoiding a greenhouse effect, and yet we should not just depend on Mother Nature to save us from our own folly. The measures currently in progress to phase out CFCs are welcome, since these materials are both greenhouse gases and attack the ozone layer. Almost nothing is being done to address the problem of global warming so far as controlling the amount of carbon dioxide generated is concerned. This is because there is not yet much visceral feeling that something is wrong. One should be aware that entities such as the coal and oil

Common sense says be watchful and alert.

industries, as well as OPEC countries, finance challenges to theories of global warming, and downplay the significance of the whole idea. Incidentally, it might be that petroleum and gas will be mostly consumed before any drastic greenhouse effect appears.

While operating nuclear reactors do not emit carbon dioxide, they cannot be viewed as a panacea for global warming (see 7-42).

We should study the matter of our climate and learn as much as is practical. The real world is much more complicated than any computer models which predict global climate. Even though there is some doubt about the reality of global warming, there is enough to qualify it as a dangerous possibility. We buy life insurance and fire insurance. We should similarly take steps to reduce the threat of global warming as insurance for our future.

4-32 Our Fragile Ozone Layer

Ozone—The condition of Earth's ozone layer is a separate issue from the greenhouse effect, although there are some connections between them.

Oxygen—The oxygen we breathe has two atoms per molecule, O_2, but two other forms are also important. One consists of just single atoms, but it is not stable and cannot be isolated. Molecules of the other form, called ozone, consists of three oxygen atoms, O_3; it is rather unstable, but can be isolated. Ozone has a fierce odor. Both atomic oxygen and ozone are energy-rich relative to ordinary oxygen.

As explained in the section on the greenhouse effect, our Sun emits radiation in a continuous spectrum. The region of the spectrum most important in regard to ozone is the ultraviolet (UV) radiation of wavelength between about 175 and 400 nanometers. This is commonly divided into four segments: A, B, C, and "hard." The wavelength limits of these are: UV-A, 400 down to 320 nm; UV-B, 320 down to 280 nm; UV-C, 280 down to 260 nm; and hard UV, 260 down to around 175 nm, or even lower. The shorter the wavelength, the more energetic the radiation is.

Earth's sunscreen

Oxygen in the atmosphere absorbs hard ultraviolet radiation; in fact, nearly all the radiation of wavelength 242 nanometers and lower is absorbed. This process breaks the molecule into two single atoms of atomic oxygen. Almost all of this absorption takes place in the upper reaches of the stratosphere, so practically no hard UV reaches the Earth's surface. Some water molecules are also split (into H and OH fragments). Collision of atomic oxygen atoms (O) with ordinary oxygen molecules (O_2) produces ozone (O_3), which itself absorbs in the UV-A, UV-B, and UV-C regions. Altogether, about 99% of the ultraviolet has been absorbed by the time it reaches sea level. All radiation of wavelength below 330 nanometers is biologically deleterious. Filtering out the very energetic and destructive parts of the ultraviolet spectrum permitted higher forms of life to evolve. Scientists specializing in atmospheric chemistry believe that the ozone mantle built up over hundreds of thousands of years, and is constantly in a state of flux. It is being formed and destroyed constantly, and had achieved a more or less steady state up until recently. Sunspots cause some changes in its rate of formation. The ozone layer extends from about 9 miles to 25 miles above the Earth's surface, reaching a maximum concentration at approximately 15 miles.

Of course, most of the rarefied atmosphere at this height is still nitrogen and ordinary oxygen; of each million of all molecules, 10 are ozone. The concentration varies with time and place. The ozone layer serves as Earth's security blanket, and is quite fragile.

Nature's Balance—One natural way of destruction of ozone is diffusion of the oxides of nitrogen from lower down, enhanced by natural turbulence. These oxides of nitrogen result from several natural causes, such as lightning and some biological processes. Fires always produce a certain amount by combining the nitrogen and oxygen of the air. Nitrogen dioxide destroys ozone through a complicated but fairly well understood molecular mechanism, acting catalytically. Another important mechanism for destruction of ozone is reaction with methane which diffuses up from below. Substances containing chlorine are particularly effective in eliminating ozone. Volcanic gases, which often contain hydrogen chloride, destroy some ozone, but a relatively small amount because most of it is washed out by rain before reaching the stratosphere. Another natural material which contains chlorine is methyl chloride, traces of which result from rotting plants. Other volatile natural chlorine compounds, amounting to some five million tons per year, are released by fungi. All these slowly percolate upward and corrode the ozone layer. Most of these substances are oxidized by hydroxyl radicals in the troposphere, and the products are washed out.

Tampering with Nature—Human activities result in materials which diffuse upwards and accelerate the destruction of ozone. Fire and internal combustion engines produce oxides of nitrogen. Hydrogen and petroleum hydrocarbons play a role. But the most destructive agents are those which contain chlorine. Virtually all gaseous compounds containing chlorine eventually escape into the atmosphere.

How we thoughtlessly damage our ozone shield.

Chlorofluorocarbons (CFCs), such as Freon 12 and Freon 22, have many applications, the most important of which are as refrigerants and foaming agents in plastics. Their use as propellants in spray cans has been phased out already. Since they are excellent insulators, foam plastics blown with CFCs were selected for use in refrigerators. Many tons were used annually in cleaning circuit boards in the electronics industries, but the need for this has been greatly reduced through use of more efficient soldering in a controlled atmosphere and through other measures. Unfortunately, these chlorine-containing materials are especially effective in destroying ozone. This was discovered in 1974 by the American chemists Rowland and Molina (joint Nobel Prize in 1995) as a consequence of scientific curiosity about the fate of CFCs in the atmosphere. Starting in the 1930s, we have manufactured millions of tons of chlorofluorocarbons. About 33% went into air conditioners and refrigerators, 27% into foaming plastics, and 18% into aerosol propellants; today, nearly all of their use as propellants has been stopped. Released near the surface, they find their way into the stratosphere within about eight years. The chlorine from these substances, split off by ultraviolet radiation in the upper reaches of the stratosphere, works its way downward. During this time it is very effective in chewing away the ozone since a little bit goes a long way (one chlorine atom can wipe out 100,000 or more ozone molecules). The ozone is consumed by chlorine atoms, first forming chlorine monoxide (formula: ClO).

This material then destroys a second ozone molecule, forming free chlorine atoms again and ordinary O_2. Thus chlorine is a catalyst, and reacts in this way over and over. The concentration of chlorine in the stratosphere from man-made materials was approximately 4 parts per billion in 1994, 80 times the amount from natural sources. Chlorine atoms eventually react with methane diffusing up from below, and form hydrogen chloride. This substance, on reaching the troposphere, is finally washed out. In addition, ClO is destroyed by nitrogen oxides which diffuses up from below. Of course, CFCs are only one factor in the dynamics of the ozone layer, but the balance is delicate, and the CFCs have been devastating.

It is the chemical stability of the CFCs which makes them so useful, but this same property also causes them to survive until they reach the stratosphere. Until 1992 it was thought that there is no natural pathway for their decomposition except dissociation by ultraviolet, but American chemists have found that a few HCFCs are degraded by the same bacteria which oxidize methane. Perfluorocarbons, compounds which consist of carbon and fluorine only, have no effect on the ozone layer, but they are powerful greenhouse gases. Carbon tetrafluoride, for example, has a much more severe effect than carbon dioxide on the basis of equal weights, and it lasts thousands of years in the atmosphere. Halons are used as fire-extinguishing agents, especially on aircraft. Bromine, a heavier sibling of chlorine, is around 50 times more destructive to ozone than is chlorine. An intensive search for alternatives to halons is underway.

The five most important classes of compounds (collectively, the halocarbons) produced commercially and which are of interest in regard to the ozone layer are:

Chlorofluorocarbons or CFCs, containing only chlorine fluorine, and carbon
Hydrochlorofluorocarbons or HCFCs, containing hydrogen chlorine, fluorine, and carbon
Hydrofluorocarbons or HFCs, containing hydrogen, fluorine, and carbon
Fluorocarbons, containing only fluorine and carbon
Halons, containing bromine, fluorine, carbon, and sometimes hydrogen

The lists below characterize some of these substances.

Some Halocarbons Currently in Use

Code name	Formula
CFC-11	CCl_3F [Freon 11]
CFC-12	CCl_2F_2 [Freon 12]
CFC-113	$CClF_2CCl_2F$
CFC-114a	CF_3CCl_2F
CFC-115	$CClF_2CF_3$
Halon-1211	$CBrClF_2$
Halon-1301	$CBrF_3$

Some Halocarbons Less Damaging to Ozone

HCFC-22	$CHClF_2$ [Freon 22]
HCFC-123	$CHCl_2CF_3$
HFC-22	CH_2F_2
HFC-134a	CH_2FCF_3

There are many tons of CFCs in storage, so the problem of what to do with this inventory had to be faced. An economical solution was announced in 1996. All that is necessary is to pass the gases over solid sodium oxalate at 270° to 290 °C (518° to 554 °F), when carbon, carbon dioxide, and simple sodium salts result.

A voracious ozone eater is methyl bromide, an agricultural fumigant. Its major use is to sterilize soil before planting, killing nematodes, fungi, and weeds. Two of its other uses are to kill termites in houses and to fumigate fruit. Methyl bromide also is used to eradicate the Asian long-horned beetle from Chinese wood packaging materials being shipped to the United States. World production of methyl bromide was about 68,000 metric tonnes in 1996. Fortunately, aerobic soil bacteria rapidly destroy methyl bromide. Ocean-growing plants such as algae and phytoplankton release thousands of tons of methyl bromide into the atmosphere. Coastal salt marshes generate far more methyl bromide (and methyl chloride) than the same area of ocean; in fact, these marshes give off about 10% of the total. It has been recently discovered that a great deal of methyl bromide is released when biomass, especially that from marine origin, is burned, and rising plumes can carry some of it into the stratosphere. The residence time of the substance in the atmosphere is only about 9 or 10 months, so a very high percentage is degraded before reaching the stratosphere. Although only about 20 parts per trillion of bromine is present in the ozone layer, it is responsible for about 10% of the annual depletion of the ozone layer, but it seems to be removed from the upper atmosphere more quickly than chlorine. A recent advance made by the U.S. Department of Agriculture is that if soil is covered with manure and an impermeable plastic before injection of the methyl bromide, nearly all of the fumigant is eventually broken down into methanol and bromide ion. The extra addition to the ozone layer from agricultural use of methyl bromide is almost insignificant and halting worldwide use is of doubtful advantage.

Researchers have recently discovered that iodine, which is in the same chemical family as chlorine and bromine, also plays a minor role in nibbling at the ozone layer. Marine plants release methyl iodide, most of which is destroyed by sunlight, but some is carried into the stratosphere by huge tropical thunderclouds. Methyl iodide has been proven to be an ideal agriculture fumigant, but it is far more expensive than methyl bromide.

Sulfuryl fluoride (formula: SO_2F_2) is a safe fumigant for both residential and commercial structures. It cannot be used to treat food, grain, or plants. Phosphine (formula PH_3) has replaced methyl bromide to some degree in treating grain. A mixture of phosphine (2%) and carbon dioxide (98%) is not flammable, and is finding favor as a fumigant. Australian scientists have recently found that another chemical compound, carbonyl sulfide (formula O=C=S), is as effective as methyl bromide in fumigating soil, termites, fruit, etc., and has no effect on the ozone layer. Some carbonyl sulfide occurs naturally. So far, carbonyl sulfide has not found an American producer. Several other alternatives are known and some are being tested by growers. Both phosphine and carbonyl sulfide are toxic to human beings.

Another positive note is that mixtures of isobutane with propane or pentane ("Greenfreeze") are suitable as refrigerants, although redesign of the compressor and expansion assembly is required. These hydrocarbons are rapidly destroyed by hydroxyl radicals if released into the atmosphere. Indeed, refrigerators using these ozone-safe hydrocarbons are now

Not all news is bad.

being manufactured in Germany, and the DuPont Chemical company (manufacturer of the Freons) has also developed hydrocarbon refrigerants. Indeed, hydrocarbons are replacing all others, even in China. After 1998 replacement of automobile air conditioner refrigerants can only be done legally with ozone-safe materials.

Much evidence has accumulated showing that the ozone layer has been attenuated; over the United States, the loss had reached about 9% by 1991. It is today being destroyed at a much higher rate than first suspected. The peak summertime levels of ultraviolet radiation measured in New Zealand has increased about 12% over the past decade (1990-2000), and this is attributable to ozone depletion. Chlorofluorocarbons have been shown to have a lifetime in air of three centuries or so, and there is much of these materials yet to be disposed of. Fluorocarbons containing no hydrogen last more than 2000 years in air; while they do not affect ozone, they are greenhouse gases. If a new ice age threatens, there is the possibility of manufacturing massive amounts of fluorocarbons and deliberately releasing them into the atmosphere.

A Puncture in the Ozone Layer?—Curiously, measurements have revealed a hole in the ozone layer over Antarctica during part of the year. The ozone hole was discovered by the British in 1985. The next year atmospheric chemist Susan Soloman organized the National Ozone Expedition to Antarctica, which also performed measurements confirming that the ozone hole was real, that it was growing, and that made-made chemicals were responsible. It has been traced mostly to the action of chlorine. Chlorofluorocarbons are dissociated by ultraviolet into fragments, one of which is atoms of chlorine. Some of this chlorine reacts with water vapor to form hypochlorous acid (HOCl). These molecules are adsorbed on the surface of minute ice crystals in the stratosphere. At that altitude in winter, the temperature can be as low as minus 80 to 85°C, the same as dry ice. In springtime (late August and September), sunlight causes release of the chlorine, which acts catalytically in destroying ozone on a massive scale. Aerosol droplets of sulfuric acid can act in the same way as ice particles; one study indicates that the aerosol of sulfuric acid put into the troposphere by the eruption of Mount Pinatubo in the Philippines has accelerated ozone destruction. It is the low temperature rather than the nature of the particles which is important. The South Pole is the site of an ozone hole because the jet stream forms a circulating vortex. A drop in ozone concentration has been detected over the North Pole, and by 1995 the area had begun to resemble the hole at the South Pole, but is much smaller. This is true because the air is not quite as cold as over Antarctica owing to larger land masses in the Northern hemisphere, and because of different weather patterns. Nevertheless, the winter of 1994-95 was extraordinarily cold in the Arctic, and the result was that record ozone losses were observed. Decreases of 20 to 40% below normal were observed. Ozone levels plummeted to record lows over northern Europe during that winter, being some 30% below average values. This resulted in exposing the inhabitants to some of the highest ultraviolet intensities on record.

The ultraviolet pouring in through the southern ozone hole might be harming the plankton in the ocean, and the life chain depending on it, although this is not certain. The ozone loss is as much as 60 or 70% in the hole. UV-B penetrates ocean water at least 70 meters. The hole, at times four times as big as the United States, rotates once every two weeks. Thus it extends periodically over the southern tip of South America.

The world's southernmost city, Ushuaia, Argentina, experienced an increase of 50% in ultraviolet intensity at ground level during two Decembers (1990 and 1992). There have been reports of cataract-blinded sheep, as well as wild animals—even salmon—but proof that this is related to the ozone hole is as yet lacking. In fact, a study at Johns Hopkins University indicates that the animals were afflicted by an eye disease. Still, there has been more than the usual number of cataracts and conjunctivitis in animals; the matter is not yet settled. Shortly after the Antarctic springtime of September, 1992, the hole reached its maximum size to date, about nine million square miles. Ozone depletion will probably continue for at least another decade because time is required to convert to newer systems. Since attenuation of the ozone of the upper atmosphere has occurred, that region now absorbs less UV than before, and its temperature has dropped by about 0.56 °C (1 °F) during the last few decades.

A forewarning slips through the ozone hole.

Even outside the area near the South Pole, ultraviolet light has been increasing in intensity at sea level. At the latitude 55° N, it has been increasing by 6.8% per decade, and at 55° S, the increase has been 9.9% per decade. For one or two decades biologists have been aware that the world's frog and toad population has been dropping, and the rate is alarming. In 1994 this occurrence was traced to increased ultraviolet exposure of the amphibians' eggs. The declining populations were found even in national parks in the Pacific northwest, where the environment is fairly undisturbed. Frogs which lay their eggs in shallow water are most affected.

Keeping Tabs on Ozone—Ozone can be monitored by lofting analyzers into the stratosphere by plane or balloon (the results are radioed back to the surface). Even high-tech kites have been used to carry instruments, flying 1.5 miles high near southern Nova Scotia. In the National Ozone Expedition work, an airplane known as ER-2 flies 12 miles high, and enters the ozone hole to make instrumental analyses. These tests confirmed ozone destruction by chlorine beyond any reasonable doubt. Another ozone measuring instrument is the Total Ozone Mapping Spectrometer. One is carried by the satellite Nimbus 7. On August 15, 1991, the Soviet spacecraft Meteor-3 lifted off. It put a second American ozone mapping spectrometer into orbit, as well as three similar Soviet instruments. Sadly, budget restrictions might force shutting down the first Nimbus 7 instrument, as well as an Earth radiation satellite launched in 1984. In the spring of 1993 the Nimbus 7 satellites reported that the global average of ozone density was 2 or 3% lower than ever before, and that certain areas experienced a 12 to 15% drop owing to the Mt. Pinatubo eruption. By fall, this figure was revised to 18%. On May 7, 1993, the first Total Ozone Mapping Spectrometer failed. It had functioned more than seven times its expected life of two years. The second instrument, flying on the Russian satellite, recorded an increased ozone concentration in the summer of 1994, apparently in response to reduction in CFC emissions. But in the fall, a British station in Antartica observed the lowest ozone concentrations ever. Well, there is at least one advantage of this development: more ozone in the troposphere has generated more hydroxyl radicals from water vapor, resulting in lower carbon monoxide and methane levels (both of these gases are oxidized by OH radicals).

A plane carrying a resonance-fluorescence instrument records levels of chlorine monoxide. It found that 11 miles over Antarctica the chlorine monoxide concentration is 1.2 parts per billion. The Canadians have developed an ozone-measuring device, the light-radar system, in which strong laser beams are shot into the stratosphere. They are partially absorbed by ozone. By measuring the intensity of the light reflected back down, the ozone concentration may be measured.

Incidentally, a claim made by those who challenge a connection between ozone depletion and chlorofluorocarbons is that the ozone hole was discovered in 1958, well before CFCs were widely used. Thus, according to this idea, the synthetic gases cannot be responsible for ozone thinning. But the claim is false: Freons have been used in great quantity long before 1958. In addition, the 1958 study was based on an instrument now shown to be in error.

The main nexus between the greenhouse effect and depletion of the ozone layer is that both methane and the halocarbons are greenhouse gases as well as ozone destroyers.

First Endangered, then Rescued by Chemistry—Recognition of the ozone problem has stimulated international agreements on phasing CFCs out and replacing them with ozone-friendly materials. A great deal of research is now underway to identify suitable surrogate compounds, and a number have been found. These are mostly hydrochlorofluorocarbons (HCFCs) and hydrofluorocarbons (HFCs). These are at the very least suitable as interim compounds. In contrast to the much used CFCs, the hydrochlorofluorocarbons all have hydrogen bonded to carbon. To a large degree, they degrade in the lower atmosphere because the hydrogen atom is vulnerable to chemical attack by the traces of hydroxyl radicals found there (the troposphere). The products are washed out by rain. Thus only a fraction enters the stratosphere, where they still damage the ozone layer, but to only about 2% of the extent that CFCs do. The recognition of the ozone depletion problem and its solution is the first example of agreement by virtually every country. Extension of this type of action to other world problems would be welcome.

Anyone who is a chemist can't be all that bad.

The hydrofluorocarbons, being free of chlorine, have no effect at all on ozone. Perhaps the best of these is HFC-134a, since its global warming (greenhouse) contribution is far less than that of CFCs. It is already widely used. The task of replacing one giant industry with another is long and difficult, however, since many tests on physical properties, toxicity, flammability, cost, and environmental impact must be studied. World production is around a million tons per year, but this can be reduced by recycling and other measures. An Australian firm has developed an ozone-safe propellant for spray cans, namely tetrafluoroethane.

It is ultraviolet in the B region (280-320 nm) which is most dramatic in its adverse biological effects. Acute exposure causes sunburn. It has been estimated that in the United States ozone depletion can cause thousands of additional deaths from skin cancer over the next 50 years (see skin cancer and sunlight, 5-28). Skin cancer rates increased in the 1980s. In addition, increased ultraviolet intensity can cause cataracts, suppress the body's immune system, and damage plants and animals. A worst case would be a dramatic decrease in the world's food supply. Without doubt, news about the ozone layer will get worse before it gets better.

In 1993 Canadian scientists carried out meticulous research which gave compelling evidence that thinning of the ozone layer in the Northern Hemisphere has genuinely taken place, and that CFCs are the main culprits. This was done by employing a technique which distinguished between the absorption of ultraviolet by ozone and by other substances. A NASA satellite in late 1994 detected stratospheric fluorine, which does not occur there naturally, and must have come from CFCs. This fact and others demonstrate that CFCs are responsible for the excessive ozone loss, not some natural process.

The problem of the dissipation of our Earth's sunblock is one which is known to be very serious, but one whose remedy is also known. The answer lies in many steps. The simplest and least expensive is merely for people, especially those with fair skin, to reduce their exposure to sunlight by just using broad-brimmed hats and parasols. Long-term measures are: stop the production of ozone-eating chlorine- and bromine-containing gases and replace them with the newer, ozone-safe materials; increase the efficiency of insulation and energy production.

If you consider the term "straw hat" unacceptably low tech, just call yours an automatic, electronic, ultraviolet absorbing device (which it is, if the details of photon absorption are analyzed).

An international agreement known as the Montreal protocol was signed by 34 nations in 1987 to limit and then phase out the production of chlorofluorocarbons. The CFCs were scheduled to be banned by the year 1996 under the amended agreements. In fall 1992, in Copenhagen, 90 nations agreed on more steps to cut production of CFCs. The United States announced a ban on production of CFCs by the end of 1995; the European Community made a similar decision. The DuPont company, the world's biggest manufacturer of CFCs, began moving toward discontinuing production and manufacturing substitutes. If other producers follow suit, our sick skies can be cured. The protocol also calls for phasing out chlorine-rich solvents such as carbon tetrachloride and methyl chloroform, as well as the halons. If we are not willing to take these and similar steps, Nature will exact her price. By summer of 1993, the rate of growth of the CFCs in the upper atmosphere had slowed measurably, and indications are that about the year 2050, the levels will peak and begin to drop. There has not been a problem of excessive "essential use" exemptions. One such exemption is for metered-dose inhalers, which use CFCs to propel medication directly into the lungs of patients suffering from asthma. Regrettably, illegal CFCs are already being smuggled into the United States; the black market exceeded an estimated 10,000 to 22,000 tons in 1994. This unlawful CFC supply originates mostly in the seven remaining factories of Russia, though there are some in India and China. It is packaged in cylinders bearing the labels of legal CFCs. Moreover, the treaty allows American factories to manufacture 53,500 tons yearly of CFCs until 2005. In fall 1997, 110 governments agreed to curtail diverting CFCs to countries where they are banned. By 1999 enormous progress had been made in reducing CFC production, but there is still some danger of eroding the ozone layer further.

In 1995 evidence was collected showing that the Montreal agreement is working, despite the smuggled material. Measurements of the concentration of methyl chloroform in the atmosphere at five stations over the world showed a distinct decline; it fell from about 135 parts per trillion in 1992 to 120 parts per trillion in 1995. It turns out that the concentration of free hydroxyl radicals in the atmosphere is somewhat higher than previously thought, but it is still only about one part in 10 trillion. These hydroxyl radicals are a sort of chemical scavenger, cleaning out all kinds of oxidizable trash from our air, including carbon monoxide. As late as April 1996, there was evidence that the ozone layer was still shrinking. Global ozone was declining at the rate of about 4% per decade, in some areas even more. But somewhat later it appeared to be strengthening, and maybe the worst has passed. In 1998 the World Meteorological Organization and the United Nations Environmental Program prepared a report in which a prediction was made that if the Montreal Protocol is implemented fully, recovery of the ozone layer can begin about 2020, and approach completion about 2050.

A word of caution is introduced here. Recently a number of critics have sprung up who claim that the attenuation of the ozone layer is all a big hoax, inspired by chemical companies which want to make millions by manufacturing a whole new set of refrigerants, or by environmentalists who are opposed to "the American way of life." Other such critics even make the absurd claim that since CFCs are heavier than air, they do not rise into the stratosphere, or that volcanoes inject more chlorine into the stratosphere than comes from CFCs. These allegations are dead wrong. The governor of Arizona declared that depletion of ozone by CFCs is nonsense, and that they could be manufactured in his state (no such factories exist there). Some of these critics are right-wing zealots, such as Rush Limbaugh and Congressmen DeLay and Doolittle, who have not informed themselves about the intense research in the field over the last 20 years or so. Another source of disinformation is the Global Climate Coalition, a group supported by the coal, oil, utility, automobile, and chemical companies. Such efforts impede the steps required to set things right. Informed and disinterested critics are valuable, but those mentioned above can be ignored with profit.

Whereas the greenhouse effect may or may not be real, and may or may not be disastrous even if it is real, ozone depletion is certainly a potentially catastrophic problem, although its full dimensions are not yet apparent. Depletion of the ozone layer would also be of grave consequence in the event of nuclear war (10-III). In any case, the ozone layer protected the human race from its beginnings; now we can return the favor in our own self interest.

4-33 A Pointed Comment

A prevalent idea held by many people today is that the study of science is a cold and intellectual endeavor fit only for a few eggheads, and that nearly all of us can go on with our lives without bothering too much with eccentric scientists and their work. This concept had a certain validity until about a century ago, but today science is much too important to be left only to scientists.

Bibliography for Chapter 4: Nuclear Science, Radioactivity, and Energy

John J. Berger, *CHARGING AHEAD: THE BUSINESS OF RENEWABLE ENERGY AND WHAT IT MEANS FOR AMERICA*, Holt & Co., 1997.

Edgardo Browne and Richard B. Firestone, TABLE OF RADIOACTIVE ISOTOPES, Virginia S. Shirley, Ed., John Wiley & Sons, New York, NY, 1986.

G. R. Choppin and J. Rydberg, *NUCLEAR CHEMISTRY*, Pergamon, 1980.

Gale Christianson, *GREENHOUSE: THE 200-YEAR STORY OF GLOBAL WARMING*, Walker & Co., 1999.

W. N. Cottingham and D. A. Greenwood, *AN INTRODUCTION TO NUCLEAR PHYSICS*, Cambridge University Press, N. Y., 2001.

Farrington Daniels, *DIRECT USE OF THE SUN'S ENERGY*, Yale University Press, 1964.

Lydia Dotto and Harold Shift, *THE OZONE WAR*, Doubleday, 1978.

I. G. Draganic, Z. D. Draganic, and J. Adloff, *RADIATION AND RADIOACTIVITY ON EARTH AND BEYOND*, CRC Press, Inc., Boca Raton, FL, 1990.

David E. Fisher, *FIRE AND ICE: THE GREENHOUSE EFFECT, OZONE DEPLETION, AND NUCLEAR WINTER*, Harper & Row, 1990.

Jack Fishman and Robert Kalish, *GLOBAL ALERT: THE OZONE POLLUTION CRISIS*, Plenum, 1989.

G. Friedlander, J. Kennedy, E. Macias, and J. Miller, *NUCLEAR AND RADIOCHEMISTRY*, Wiley, 1981.

Paul Gipe, *WIND POWER FOR HOME AND BUSINESS*, Chelsea Green Publishing Co., Post Mills, VT, 1993.

Samuel Glasstone, *SOURCEBOOK ON ATOMIC ENERGY*, Van Nostrand Reinhold, 1967.

Dan Hirsch, Haley Mack, and Peter Tyler, editors, *NUCLEAR INFORMATION HANDBOOK*, Stevenson Program on Nuclear Policy, University of California, Santa Cruz, CA 95064.

John F. Hogerton et al., THE ATOMIC ENERGY DESKBOOK, Reinhold Publishing Corp., New York, NY, 1963.

Darleane C. Hoffman, Albert Ghiorso, & Glenn T. Seaborg, *THE TRANSURANIUM PEOPLE*, World Scientific Publishing & Imperial College Press, 1999.

Francesca Lyman et al., *THE GREENHOUSE TRAP*, World Beacon Press; also Resources Institute, Washington, DC 2006, 1991.

Arjun Makhijani and Kevin R. Gurney, *MENDING THE OZONE HOLE*, The MIT Press, 1995.

Michael Oppenheimer and Robert H. Boyle, *DEAD HEAT: THE RACE AGAINST THE GREENHOUSE EFFECT*, Basic Books, 1990.

Sharon L. Roan, *OZONE CRISIS: THE 15-YEAR EVOLUTION OF A SUDDEN GLOBAL EMERGENCY*, John Wiley & Sons, 1989.

Edward Teller with Judith Shoolery, *MEMOIRS: A TWENTIETH-CENTURY JOURNEY IN SCIENCE AND POLITICS*, Perseus Books, 2001.

Attila Vertes and Istvan Kiss, *NUCLEAR CHEMISTRY*, Elsevier, 1987.

Richard Wolfson, *NUCLEAR CHOICES: A CITIZEN'S GUIDE TO NUCLEAR TECHNOLOGY*, MIT Press, 1991.

Henry N. Wagner, Jr., and Linda E. Ketchum, *LIVING WITH RADIATION: THE RISK, THE PROMISE*, Johns Hopkins University Press, 1989.

Steven Weinberg, *THE DISCOVERY OF SUBATOMIC PARTICLES*, Scientific American Books, 1983.

Steven Weinberg, *THE FIRST THREE MINUTES*, Basic Books, 1988.

Ken Zweibel, *HARNESSING SOLAR POWER* (photovoltaics), Plenum, 1991.

Chapter 5: BIOLOGICAL EFFECTS OF IONIZING RADIATION

ABSTRACT—The mechanism by which powerful alpha, beta, gamma, neutron, and other rays form ions and free radicals in tissue is described. Damage to DNA is particularly important, but the body has some repair capacities. The various origins of cancerous growth and its inhibitions are outlined. The rem and sievert units of absorbed radiation by tissues are defined. The deadly effects of deliberate exposure in the past to radium and other dangerous radio-nuclides are recorded. The hazards of ever-present radon in the air and the radiation dose from the environment are detailed. Biological half-life is explained. Risk analysis, particularly in terms of radiation-induced cancer, is summarized. The intractable dilemma of low-dose irradiation and lethal doses is explained. Substances which partially protect against radiation damage are briefly reported. Some radiation accidents, deliberate release of radioactive iodine on the population, and unethical experiments on Americans are described. Finally, there is a brief report on skin cancer caused by sunlight.

5-1 Effects of Ionizing Rays on Living Tissue

How alpha particles mangle living cells

An adult human body consists of 30 trillion to 60 trillion marvelously functioning cells. Imagine a high-energy alpha particle arising from an atom of some radioactive substance like radium which is inside the living tissue. The particle plows through three or four cells, whose average diameter is around 20 micrometers, leaving a streak of havoc in its wake. Each alpha particle acts as an assassin at the cellular level. It strips electrons from atoms in its path, breaking chemical bonds between atoms and leaving them with positive charge (these are ions). The ion path of the particle resembles a thin column. When bonds between atoms are broken, the result is dislodged, energetic electrons and radiolytic products. In addition pairs of ions are formed, one from each bonded atom. Around 5000 ion pairs are formed per micrometer of tissue. Another result is formation of free radicals, which are energetic neutral fragments of molecules, and which have unpaired electrons. Some water molecules (HOH) are broken into H atoms and OH free radicals, both of which diffuse away and attack other cell components, a sort of secondary effect. Damage by free radicals is not as deep-seated as damage by direct radiation. Eventually the alpha particle transmits all its energy to the cells and after being spent in this way comes to rest. It finally picks up two electrons and becomes harmless helium. X-rays and gamma rays also form energetic electrons and free radicals; a certain fraction of the radiation passes entirely through the body without being absorbed. Every type of molecule in the cells is affected, but damage to the DNA (see below) has the most serious consequences.

Beta rays penetrate tissue as much as a thousand times as far as alpha particles, causing biological mayhem by breaking bonds and forming ions and free radicals. Beta particles, which are energetic free electrons, form only 5 to 10 ion pairs per micrometer of tissue. Despite its longer path length inside living matter, one beta particle does much less damage than one alpha particle. Depending on their energy, beta particles can penetrate 1 to 30 centimeters of soft tissue.

Gamma rays and X-rays are high-energy photons. When they are absorbed by matter, whether living or not, three kinds of interaction may take place: (1) Transmission of the energy to an orbiting electron in an atom, which rips it out and converts it to a beta particle; (2) Transmission of part of the energy successively to several electrons in several atoms, converting each into a low-energy beta particle; (3) Formation, near a nucleus, of a positive electron-negative electron pair; these are also beta particles. The energy of these various secondary electrons or beta particles is 15,000 to 20,000 times that required to break chemical bonds, and consequently these marauding electrons are responsible for the biological damage. Thus each gamma or X-ray photon absorbed acts as a microscopic grenade and causes a cascade of beta particles, which do the dirty work. These ionizing radiations (X- and gamma rays) and particles (alpha, beta, and neutrons) damage randomly, and at heavier dosages, the chances are good that cancer ultimately results.

Biological damage by gamma rays

The shower of electrons generated by X-rays or gamma rays lose energy by colliding with atoms in the tissues they are traveling through, leaving a trail of excited or ionized fragments. The electrons can travel a considerable distance between collisions. The two strands of DNA are about 3 nanometers apart, and it is possible for an electron to pass between the two strands without collision or damage. Each electron loses energy as it travels through protein, nerve tissue, fat, or water, in a manner described as linear energy transfer (LET). This is the amount of energy released or deposited by the particle or radiation per unit distance in the absorbing tissue. Its units are usually kiloelectron volts per micrometer. The concept applies to X-rays, gamma rays, and beta rays (low-LET radiation), and to alpha rays (high-LET radiation). Since all the photons or particles do not have the same energy, the LET values are really averages. They are closely related to the relative biological effectiveness (5-5). If the LET value is large, the ionizing particle is stopped in a short distance. If gamma rays are from decay of cobalt-60 (1.25 megaelectron volts), the LET value is about 0.3 kiloelectron volt per micrometer. Beta particles (electrons) are regarded as in the low-LET range, that is, the ionizing power is low. If the ionizing particle is a 2 megaelectron volt alpha particle, its ionizing power is 1000 times higher, and the alpha radiation is classified as high-LET helium nuclei.

Ordinarily, a person being exposed to gamma radiation is unable to detect it. But if the dose is extraordinarily high, a tingling and itching sensation is experienced. By then, the damage has been done.

When a medical X-ray image is made, absorption of some of the radiation by tissue means that those photons, having disappeared, cannot affect the film. The result is that the film is less affected than where the X-rays encounter only air, and a faint, shadowy outline of the tissue can be seen. If some of the tissue (such as bones or teeth) is dense, absorption of the X-rays is strong, and thus the shadows are readily visible after developing the film. The picture is a negative.

While neutrons are not at all like gamma rays, it turns out that their biological effects are similar in the case of low-energy neutrons. Depending on their energy and tissue type, neutrons inflict 20 or more times the degree of biological damage caused by gamma rays. The average path of neutrons in living tissues is around 20 centimeters, just the range which causes maximum damage. Extremely energetic neutrons are the most dangerous.

The extent of biological damage by radiation from radioactive materials depends on the type and energy of the radiation, the dose, and the kind of tissue affected. Biologists distinguish between somatic tissues, such as the liver, muscles, bone marrow, etc., which play no role in heredity, and genetic structures which carry the hereditary patterns. Both types of cells have chromosomes, but those in somatic tissues have no heritable characteristics. This genetic information is encoded in extended, double-helix molecules of deoxyribosenucleic acid (DNA) in the chromosomes of genetic tissues. These molecules (see Fig. 5-1, Color Plate I) have the shape of twisted, very long ladders whose rungs consist of what are called base pairs (thymine molecules hydrogen-bonded to adenine molecules and cytosine to guanine). The order of these base pairs (nucleotides) define the "letters" of the genetic "words." Each human cell has 46 chromosomes (23 from each parent), which contain most of the DNA; lesser amounts are in the mitochondria. Genes are sections of DNA strands with base-pair sequences strictly ordered in a highly specific way, and are strung out sort of like pearls. Most human genes are fragmented, that is, are divided into segments of DNA separated by a different kind of DNA whose base pairs are randomly arranged, or in some cases contain the remains of base pairs from ancient viruses. All this makes it extremely difficult to count the genes in the human genome.

Ribosenucleic acid (RNA) consists of single strands of base pairs. It is made by partial unzipping of DNA, one of whose strands acts as a template for synthesis of RNA. Short portions of RNA (microRNA) turn on genes, producing specialized cells. They cause identical cells to follow different paths in forming various tissues and play a role in stopping protein synthesis in tumors, controlling their growth..

The simplest microbe has 517 genes. The bacterium E. coli has around 4300 genes; and baker's yeast has about 6000 genes. The fruit fly genome has 13,601 genes. Each DNA molecule is a library of information and instructions necessary for life and reproduction. Each chromosome contains one extremely long DNA molecule, and these are copied during each cell division, one set going to each new cell. A human genome is a complete set of the body's genes in cell nuclei, that is, it does not include those in mitochondria; each cell nucleus contains such a set, though many of the genes are inactive. The number of genes in the human genome is not known; early estimates were between 50,000 and 100,000, but a modern estimate is lower, being around 34,000. Many human genes play several roles. Thus one gene can produce three to five different proteins, depending on other factors. The total number of base pairs is approximately 3.18 billion.

Radiation damage to somatic tissue has many consequences. Cell division is delayed, formation of essential metabolic materials is inhibited, enzymes are inactivated, and survival rate is diminished. Some cells are killed within hours.

Shuffling DNA molecules

Cells undergoing division, such as in an embryo, are much more sensitive to radiation than are adult cells. This is also true of most cancerous tissues, and accounts for the partial success of radiation therapy. Ionizing radiation damages chromosomes and their DNA molecules. The body does have the capacity to recover in part from radiation damage, and restore some degree of order to the system. Most damage, especially minor localized changes, is repaired by certain enzymes or p53 protein (see 5-4), but deep-seated, extensive injuries are not healed or are misrepaired. Ionizing radiation is thus a powerful mutagen. Low doses of radiation and certain chemical substances may break only one strand of the double-strand DNA molecule, and this type of damage can be and usually is repaired. The higher doses tend to break an increasing proportion of both strands, and this extensive damage is more likely to result in cancer or mutation. Reconstruction of injured DNA is thus more complete after low doses and low dose rates of irradiation. If the DNA is that in sperm or egg cells, it can lead to mutations in future generations, probably in part by forming proto-oncogenes (see below). If the radiation dose is heavy, the DNA and other molecules, such as those of enzymes, are so badly mangled that the cells die. Accumulation of defects in DNA is associated with accelerated aging. In general, the higher an organism is on the evolutionary scale, the more sensitive it is to radiogenic damage. Some consequences of radiation damage become apparent only months or years after exposure. Cosmic rays in outer space damage cosmonauts to some degree.

A strange response to radioactivity is that of the flowers of the spiderwort plant. The stamens change color on exposure, and this can be used to detect radiation. The new-year lily is a favored house plant during the Chinese New Year period. When the bulbs are treated with gamma rays (5 to 10 gray dose; see 4-23) and planted, the blooms look unchanged, but the foliage grows to only about three-fourths of the normal size.

Curiously, if a strong source of radioactivity is buried near the tunnel which ants burrow between their nest and the surface, the insects will construct a new pathway to avoid the radiation.

5-2 The Ways Cancers Arise

When one thinks of the effects of ionizing radiation on a human body, it is usually cancer which springs to mind first, although there are many other consequences. During the past generation an enormous body of information about cancer at the molecular biological level has been accumulated. A few high points of this incredibly convoluted topic are given in the next few sections. There are at least a hundred types of this disease, and nearly all types of tissue are susceptible. Despite these differences, the tumor-producing processes have features in common.

The great majority of cancers are generated by one of four agencies: genetic predisposition, certain viruses, ionizing radiation, or specific chemical substances. In the last category, tobacco is the most common. Tobacco smoke contains a mixture of carcinogenic substances which in time produce cancer of the lungs or other organs. Tobacco plants absorb enough alpha-active radioactive nuclides from the soil to give an appreciable radiation dose to the lungs when smoked. Even use of tobacco without burning (chewing or snuff) is similarly dangerous. Quite a number of other chemical materials, such as asbestos, are known which readily produce tumors, often cancerous.

Carcinomas, by far the most common form of cancer, originate in epithelial cells which line the body organs and skin. Cancers of the lung, pancreas, or colon are generally carcinomas. Other types are sarcomas (cancers of connective tissue) and gliomas (cancer of neuronal cells in the brain).

5-3 Most Cancers Are Based on Genetic Predisposition

Normally, cells of the body do not reproduce spontaneously. They duplicate themselves only when stimulated by chemical messengers from neighboring cells; likewise, they similarly regulate these nearby cells. This mutual control of growth plays a strong role in normal good health. But cancer cells disobey these neighborhood rules. Beginning with slight violations of the rules, they become more aggressive in time, growing malignant. The best evidence indicates that a single cell begins to act in this way. Not all of these variant cells survive; in fact, most die because of metabolic disadvantage. Five, ten, twenty, or even more years later, the growth can be felt as a lump or tumor. These cells inherited a specific class of genes (proto-oncogenes), and these accumulate a series of mutations, becoming true oncogenes, that is, genes which cause production of tumors. This can result in uncontrolled proliferation of the cells. A single cell holding such genes can be the point of origin; such genes are described as exhibiting genomic instability. A single gene of this type in the cell is probably not enough; several more are required. Not all cells with these faulty genes become cancerous.

The prefix* onco- *is from the Greek* onkos, *meaning* mass, *and was extended to mean tumor.

The full genetic set of genes is huge, and those which can produce cancer in time are but a tiny fraction of the total. There are also tumor-suppressor genes which inhibit wild proliferation of cells. Oncogenes are coded to synthesize protein and when deregulated, growth is stimulated. Neighboring cells also respond to signals arising from secretion of substances which accelerate growth. Cancer, manifested in runaway growth, results when the growth-repression is somehow curbed.

The pathways which stimulate or repress cell growth are controlled normally by a sort of clock, the cell cycle clock. When this clock, operating at the molecular level, goes out of order, unrestricted growth or runaway cell division takes place and the result is a tumor. A large body of detailed information about the mechanism of the clock is known. Increasing mutations in the oncogenes causes them to override all the control systems such as tumor-suppressor genes. Ionizing radiation is evidently one agent which is capable of activating oncogenes and/or deactivating tumor-suppressor genes. Cancer cells live and grow according to their own rules. When a woman inherits a breast-cancer gene, she does not develop cancer in every cell. An additional factor is required to make any cell become cancerous. One such co-factor is ionizing radiation.

Formerly it was believed that during therapy using ionizing radiation or chemotherapeutic compounds, malignant cells were killed directly by mangling their DNA. The new studies reveal that the actual damage to the DNA is not itself enough to kill the cell, but is enough to cause the affected cell to kill itself. This knowledge provides leads to the improvement of the effectiveness of radiation or chemotherapy. Cells have a mechanism built into their clocks which limits the number of times reproduction can occur. This is accomplished by a portion of DNA (telomeres) at the terminus of each DNA chain, part of which is lost during each division. Some specialists believe that ionizing radiation is more of a cancer promoter rather than a cancer initiator.

Genes are one of the most wonderful gifts from Mother Nature.

5-4 Tumor Development and the Body's Defenses

Let's examine how a carcinoma develops. Visualize a layer of epithelial cells; one cell has a few genetically mutated genes (proto-oncogenes). All the cells are normally at rest, but the one with the faulty genes divides more often than normal. The new cells appear to be normal under the ordinary microscope because genes cannot be seen in this way. The process producing the cluster of new cells is called hyperplasia. After several years or even decades, about one in a million of the new cells undergoes a second mutation (dysplasia). These cells divide excessively and have a shape different than those from which they sprang. While difficult to find in the small growth, they can be recognized under the microscope as malignant. The three main types of cell aberrations are: (a) having the wrong number of chromosomes; (b) failure to be copied with all the normal DNA segments, that is, deletions; and (c) containing extra copies of DNA segments. Even a minor error in a DNA strand can lead to serious biological consequences.

The relentless advance of cancer

In due time still another rare mutation occurs in the malignant cells. Growth accelerates and the new renegade cells are still more aberrant. At this stage the tumor can be considered to be a cancer. In most cases, the collection of cells remains dormant for years, but eventually still further mutations are caused by the faulty genes (oncogenes). The most recently mutated cells are the most aggressive. Sooner or later the growing mass begins to invade neighboring tissues, and is strongly malignant. Breaking through the walls of blood vessels, a few malignant cells may become detached and are carried to new sites in the body where colonies, that is, new malignant tumors, are established. This process is called metastasis. Something similar takes place if the parent tumor intrudes into the lymph system. Finally, if untreated, a vital organ is attacked and death from cancer results. To make matters worse, each cancer has certain unique qualities, meaning that in various patients a given type of cancer may respond differently to the same treatment. For these and other reasons, the newer types of therapy for patients suffering from cancer might well involve cutting off the blood supply to malignant tumors, causing them to shrink or even disappear. Such research is now being carried out, employing drugs such as angiostatin and endostatin. Angiostatin is a fragment of a blood-clotting protein found naturally in the body. A study in 1998 at the University of Chicago showed that a combination of treatment of cancer with angiostatin and an external radiation source is far more effective than either treatment alone.

In Western nations, and probably in some others, somewhere between 19 and 22% of all deaths are attributed to one form of cancer or another. Most of these are of genetic origin or predisposition, as described above.

In 1979 a protein, known as p53, was discovered which turned out to play an extraordinary role in the majority, perhaps 60%, of human cancers. A few years later the gene which forms this protein (that is, gene *p53*) was identified; it dwells on the short arm of chromosome 17. The "p" in p53 identifies the substance as a protein, and the "53" indicates its approximate molecular weight as 53,000. Concerning the term *p53*, it is generally italicized when referring to the gene which codes for the protein, but not when referring to the protein itself.

Police at the cellular level

Gene *p53* in healthy cells constantly generates and degrades protein p53 molecules, and thus a supply is always available. The genes act as the cell's damage control. If the cell's DNA is injured by ionizing radiation or a carcinogen like benzopyrene from tobacco smoke, or some other factor, then gene *p53* stops the degradation of protein p53 and the supply of the protein rises.

Smoking by itself does not induce cancer, but one or two other factors are generally available, and concerted action is carcinogenic. Smoking in the U.S. has declined during the last couple of decades, but has tended to level off recently. Molecules of protein p53 consist of clusters of long ribbons and these become intertwined with the base pairs of the DNA. By repairing the error in the base-pair sequence, the further manufacture of the wrong kind of protein is reduced or prevented. Any nascent tumor is stopped dead. In case of extreme damage to the DNA, protein p53 can cause the whole cell to commit suicide, thus arresting wild growth of tumor tissue. This protein, which barely has a name, plays such a vital a role that it really deserves a more imposing appellation.

Even gene *p53* can be damaged or undergo mutation, and as a result can be instrumental in many kinds of common cancer, such as of the colon, breast, lung, liver, prostate, cervix, etc. A *p53* gene with garbled base-pairs assembles faulty p53 protein molecules which have no tumor-suppressing capacities. In some types of cancer the p53 protein appears to be normal, but somehow ineffective (at least this appeared to be the case as of 1998; with advancing research, the picture might well change).

Research on protein p53 and gene *p53* has forced a change in the long-established belief that ionizing radiation kills cells by seriously scrambling their DNA. In cancer therapy using X-rays, the radiation does not actually kill malignant cells directly, but rather activates healthy *p53* genes to build more p53 protein, which is the tumor-arresting agent. If no healthy *p53* genes were present, the radiation would do more harm than good. Some chemotherapeutic agents, such as taxol or tamoxifen, also activate *p53* genes. Gene therapy studies are underway which insert healthy *p53* genes into tumor cells which don't have them. This might be possible using a retrovirus, modified so it can't replicate, to ferry the genes into target cells. These types of studies are still in their infancy.

A collaborative group at the Whitehead Institute for Biomedical Research in Massachusetts reported in 1999 that transformation of four particular genes, one never suspected before, play a dominant role in cancer growth. The newly-implicated gene normally governs repairs of telomeres, which are short, repetitive strands of DNA on the ends of chromosomes. Since each cell division shortens the telomeres, they eventually stop replication of the cells. The new discovery demonstrated that the altered gene begins to synthesize more telomere strands and thus the cells keep dividing: uncontrolled cancerous growth.

High-energy radiation causes both ionization and formation of free radicals. Some water molecules are ionized (forming H_2O^+) and others are split into H and OH radicals, which are neutral and thus are not ions. The details of how the hydroxyl radical (OH) can cause mutations was recently made clear by Harvard researchers. The energetic radical readily attacks guanine in DNA molecules, forming the derivative 8-oxoguanine. This aberrant base no longer forms hydrogen bonds to cytosine, and this difference causes mutations in DNA replication. A mammalian gene in chromosome 3 produces an enzyme which cuts out the faulty oxoguanine and corrects the damage. This type of enzyme seems to "proofread" DNA strands and repair any errors found. It is known today that DNA is in constant flux. Bonds between base pairs are being constantly broken, and natural oxidizing agents constantly alter the structure of the bases. Errors occur in replication of the DNA chains. The mismatches and other faults are being constantly repaired by the protein p53 and in other ways. Only one of the two strands of DNA might be damaged, when repair enzymes can remove injured segments and rebuild the correct strand using the other strand as a template. Genetic diseases in human beings involves errors in assembling base pairs in DNA which have errors in which an extra base pair is inserted, or a base pair is deleted, or their order is incorrect. For example, one type of hemophilia involves a deletion.

In early 1998, research at the University of Washington in Seattle by a group of biochemists uncovered some amazing details of how enzymes and other proteins are able to perform their tasks. Working with the critically important enzyme called human topoisomerase I, their structural studies demonstrated that the enzyme molecule is shaped something like a hinge which can open and close. Normally, the DNA strands separate momentarily to permit their patterns to be replicated (acting as templates), and they become twisted during the process. The enzyme relieves this strain. When open, the inner surface of the enzyme has a positive electric charge, and this enables it to attract and hold a DNA helix which bears a negative charge. This permits the enzyme to envelope a section of the DNA and cut one of the two strands of DNA. One free end is held by clamplike action and the other is twisted in the direction which relieves stress. The strand is rejoined and the enzyme departs to work on another DNA segment.

Damage to DNA by free radicals is different from damage by ionizing radiation. The latter (especially alpha particles) usually causes more deep-seated damage that is more difficult for enzymes to repair. DNA which is misrepaired is at least as bad as unreconstructed, injured DNA.

During every 24-hour period, several thousand repairs are made in every cell. We need to know much more about repair mechanisms of DNA before putting too much faith in their ability to cope adequately with damage from even small amounts of ionizing radiation and carcinogens.

The researchers who contributed most heavily to the nature and limits of gene repair are M.M. Elkind and H.R. Withers.

5-5 The Rem and Sievert Units

We have seen (4-23) that rads and grays are units of absorbed radiation by matter. These units hold true for all matter, whether living or not, but it is more meaningful to modify them when speaking of animal and human tissues. Since alpha radiation is much more destructive than X-, gamma, or beta radiation, one rad of alpha radiation has more effect than one rad of the others. This difference has caused the introduction of the unit "roentgen equivalent, man" (or *rem* unit). A standard is needed as a base in order to make quantitative comparisons. The most common standard ionizing radiation is medium-voltage X-rays (180 to 200 kilovolts). A rem is the quantity of radiation in rads which produces the same biological damage in human tissue as that resulting from the absorption of one rad of X-rays. For gamma and beta rays, the rem and rad values are roughly the same, but for alpha radiation one rad is equivalent to 20 to 30 rems, depending on the tissue and alpha particle energy. The number of times alpha particles are more damaging than X- rays is called the relative biological effectiveness (RBE). Thus:

Dose in rems = Dose in rads x RBE

Actually, one rad of medium-voltage X-rays is somewhat more damaging to human tissues than one rad of gamma rays. For slow neutrons, the RBE varies with the type of tissue affected: for neutrons from nuclear bursts, it is 1or 2 for most tissues, but for the eyes, bone marrow, and genetic tissue, it is 4 to 20. Fast neutrons, as those directly from fission, are characterized by a RBE factor as high as 30. The RBE factor for alpha particles is variable, but is always more than 12, and usually 20 to 30. For tritium, there is considerable controversy, but the RBE factor is probably 3 to 5. Clearly, RBE factors are complex.

The number of rems equal to one rad must be determined by observation. Dosage in rads is directly measurable; dosage in rems is inferred from this. Human tissues which are especially sensitive to radiation, listed in order of susceptibility, are lymphoid tissue, bone marrow, the reproductive organs, intestines, eyes, skin, liver, nervous system, and adult bones. The lenses of the eyes are also very sensitive, and radiation tends to make them opaque through cataract formation. Two years after Hiroshima was bombed, cataracts began to appear, and were exceedingly common.

Ultraviolet also causes cataracts, and practically everyone gets them if they live long enough.

If a person swallows 1000 aspirin tablets (standard size 325 mg) within a short time, the result is death. But if the same amount is taken at the rate of one tablet per day for 1000 days, the effect on health is a small increase in the chance of a hemorrhagic stroke, as well as some beneficial factors. Similarly, a whole-body radiation dose of 500 rems over a short period of time, a few hours, say, results in death within less than a month. But if the same dose is spread over several years, the body has time to repair itself partially and there is less damaging injury. Repair of radiation damage is never complete.

For a given radiation dose, acute exposure is worse than chronic exposure.

Just as 100 rads is 1 gray unit (Gy) of absorbed radiation, so also 100 rems is 1 *sievert* unit (Sv). This unit is gradually coming into use. One rem is 1 centisievert. The following equations relate rads to grays and rems to sieverts, and their multiples:

100,000 millirads = 100 rads = 1 gray = 100 centigrays = 1000 milligrays

100,000 millirems = 100 rems = 1 sievert = 100 centisieverts = 1000 millisieverts

Rolf M. Sievert (1897–1967), Swedish physicist. A specialist in radiation biology, he established procedures to standardize radiation doses administered in hospitals and all aspects of medical radiology. The unit is now in use all over the world.

Radiation damage to living tissue is silent, stealthy, and, if the level is less than a few hundred rads, painless (although severe damage is done). It is invisible, tasteless, and without odor. Doses above about 10 rads, far below lethal, certainly can cause cancer, with increasing probability as the dose increases. Ionizing radiation is known to induce birth defects and other damage. These factors conspire to generate demoralizing anxiety in potential victims.

5-6 Three Notorious Fission Products

Suppose you were asked to describe the combination of properties a fission product must have for it to be especially damaging to human health. Your list would be something like the following. Such a dangerous fission product would enter the food chain, be taken up by the human body (particularly by a specific organ), have a half-life long enough to survive a considerable time and thus be able to inflict significant damage, and be formed in high fission yield. Three fission products fill the bill: strontium-90, cesium-137 and iodine-131. Strontium-89 might be included in this list, but most decays before it can be assimilated.

Chemically speaking, strontium mimics calcium, while cesium mimics potassium; calcium and potassium are elements which all living things must have. All of these elements are absorbed by plants. Strontium, being an impostor of calcium, enters the food chain and lodges in the bones and teeth of mammals. Cesium-137 accumulates in muscle and other soft tissues, where it tends to induce malignant cancers, namely sarcomas. The half-life of strontium-90 is 28.5 years, and that of cesium-137 is 30.0 years, both being not too short and not too long from the standpoint of tissue damage. Finally both are formed in relatively high fission yields: 5.9% for strontium-90 and 6.3% for cesium-137. Cesium-137 is slowly lost from the human body in urine and sweat (biological half-life, 80 days; see 5-11); strontium-90 is retained more tenaciously (biological half-life, 18 years).

There is another pernicious feature of these two radionuclides. DNA, that ultra-miniaturized information-storage molecule, is known to bond chemically to calcium and magnesium. Strontium, barium, and radium, being in the same chemical family as these two elements, similarly bond to DNA. These five elements also link to certain enzymes. Therefore, when strontium-90 is attached chemically to DNA or an enzyme molecule, it is fixed in close proximity and the beta particle erupting from it on radioactive decay is especially injurious. This is true for strontium-89 too. Neither strontium isotope emits a gamma ray. Something similar occurs in the case of cesium-137. An atom of cesium-137, on emission of a beta particle, does not go directly to stable barium-137; instead it goes to an excited form of barium, labeled barium-137m. This has a half-life of just under three minutes. This activated atom, which chemically resembles strontium, calcium and magnesium, can bond to DNA and to enzymes and then eject a gamma ray photon. It is this tendency of strontium, and also cesium (or rather the excited barium from it) to specifically target essential molecules which makes them especially damaging.

The third insidious fission product, iodine-131, is formed in a fission yield of roughly 0.5%. The free element is easily vaporized, and thus can be inhaled. As solid iodides from nuclear bomb fallout or nuclear reactor debris, it also is readily absorbed by plants and quickly enters the food supply, especially milk. Inside the bodies of mammals, it is soon incorporated into the extremely important hormone, thyroxine, and thus undergoes a second concentration step. The result is internal irradiation of the thyroid gland. The effective half-life (5-11) of iodine-131 is only about a week, but that is long enough for it to be fearfully dangerous.

5-7 Health, Ignorance, and Radioactivity

Whenever scientific advances catch the public fancy, cultlike enterprises often spring up which promise either outlandish benefits or unsurpassed hazards from them. This has happened in the cases of electricity, radios, X-rays, radioactivity, fluoridation of water, food irradiation (6-29A), and others.

After physicians demonstrated that X-radiation and rays from radioactive substances could be used to treat many tumors, including cancer, there was a great deal of publicity on these topics. Thus it seemed logical that drinking water containing radium or other radioactive elements might destroy cancer cells in the stomach and intestines. After 1900, spas began to become popular for their radium water for drinking or bathing. Old uranium mines were used to relieve the ailments of humanity; patients would sit inside and breathe the air containing radon. Devices called "emanators" were sold by the tens of thousands. They produced water containing traces of dissolved radon. They were supposed to cure everything from halitosis to blindness.

Radium causes certain substances (phosphors) to become luminous, and watch dials which could be read in the dark became popular. Starting in 1917 about 2000 young women were employed in New Jersey to paint the hands and faces of watches with the glowing paint. The workers who applied the luminous material would form a point on the tips of their brushes by licking them, and thus inadvertently ingested radium. By 1924 local dentists were finding "jaw rot," and within a few years it was proven to be a consequence of the radium. Nearly all of the women became anemic and eventually died of bone cancer or leukemia. Nevertheless, the magic allure of radium was so strong that it continued to appear in hair tonics, skin creams, toothpaste, and even chocolate. Certain French wines included the radium concentration on their labels.

One William Bailey purveyed "Radithor," a tonic containing rather high levels of radium (about 0.1 microcuries each of Ra-226 and Ra-228 per bottle). A wealthy customer, Eben Byers, drank one or more bottles every day from December, 1927, for three years. In March, 1932, he expired in a gruesome death from cancer of the jaw and related disorders. Byers, formerly a robust and athletic man, had shriveled to 92 pounds. His bones contained enough radium to easily give autoradiographs. Later estimates disclosed that Byers had consumed perhaps a total of 1 to 1.5 millicuries each of radium-226 (the common isotope) and radium-228 (a decay product of thorium; half-life 5.76 years). His skeletal system sustained a dose of approximately 1800 rads.

Byers' demise went a long way toward arresting the fad. But injections of a suspension of thorium dioxide, "Thorotrast," used to enhance contrast in X-ray photos, continued as late as 1975. Internal exposure, mostly to the liver, was around 25 rads per year; altogether, nearly 10,000 people died from this cause. Incredibly, radon spas are still operating in the United States and Europe.

As late as 1951, 2000 German patients with tuberculosis were injected with radium-224 (a member of the thorium series); twenty years later bone cancers began to appear. These and other events contributed to deep public fears of all radioactive materials, while death and injury from smoking, handguns, and auto accidents seem to cause less concern.

5-8 Radon: a Real Hazard

Referring back to the uranium series (figure, section 4-9), we see that radium-226 is one of the decay products or progeny of uranium-238. Radium decays by alpha emission, and its decay produces radon-222. All uranium ores contain a certain amount of radon. Radon is a colorless, odorless, chemically inert gas. Some of it, those atoms very near the surface of the grains of ore or rock in which it occurs, is ejected by recoil out into the porous space between grains when it is formed by alpha decay of radium. It then diffuses outward, rapidly in dry soil, more slowly if moist, and enters the atmosphere. It becomes a minor constituent of air, and wind currents tend to make it more or less uniform. Each year there is an estimated 2.4 billion curies of radon in soil and ocean water released into the atmosphere worldwide. Radon is alpha active, with the rather short half-life of 3.8 days. It successively yields polonium-218, lead-214, bismuth-214, and polonium-214, among other products. Each of these last four nuclides has a half-life of less than 30 minutes, and each is a solid, not a gas.

The minute traces of radon give outdoor air a low level of radioactivity, namely about 0.5 picocurie per liter. This value varies somewhat from place to place and from week to week. A picocurie is a trillionth (10^{-12}) of a curie. The low level quoted figures out to be 1 atom of radon per liter of air emitting an alpha particle each minute. This doesn't seem significant, but remember that we breathe all the time. Moreover, the radiological properties of radon and its descendants are all dangerous biologically, having short half-lives. We get a good fraction of the natural background exposure to radioactivity from this source. It is not entirely natural in that human intervention plays a role: selection of a house site and design are important in indoor radon concentration.

No place to hide

As early as 1546 it was realized that silver miners in Czechoslovakia suffered from lung disease (now known to have been cancer) at a high rate. Later uranium ore was removed from the same mines to be used as a pigment to color glass. It was not until 1932 that the carcinogenic effect was traced to the radon-222 in the decay series of uranium.

It isn't the radon itself which is responsible for inducing cancer of lung tissue; it is breathed in and out too fast to be of much consequence. Rather, this short-lived gaseous alpha emitter deposits its solid decay products (radioactive isotopes of polonium, lead, and bismuth, all born as ions) everywhere, and these adhere to dust or to droplets of moisture or oil. A fraction of these get stuck inside the lungs and throat, especially in the upper regions. Their alpha particles penetrate tissue only about 70 micrometers, but the epithelium where what are called stem cells are located is only around 40 micrometers thick. Stem cells earned their name from the fact that specialized cells stem from them. These stem cells of the lung readily become cancerous on irradiation by alpha particles.

Tobacco smoke deposits substances in the respiratory system which readily capture the dangerous decay products. British studies have indicated that stem cells exposed to but not killed by alpha particles exhibit radiation damage after several cell divisions. Radon is believed to rate second—a distant second—as a cause of lung cancer, first prize being awarded to smoking itself. Moreover, the effects of radon and smoking are synergistic, each reinforcing the other. A 1995 study disclosed that around 30% of lung cancers in people who have never smoked may be caused by radon. Cigarette smoking causes about 85% of lung cancers. A National Research Council report in 1998 presented evidence that about 21,800 American lung cancer fatalities occur annually, with most sufferers being smokers. Additional data published in 1998 suggest the number of deaths of nonsmoking Americans is about 2500 per year, most of these being attributed to radon.

A large-scale, five-year epidemiological study was carried out by the University of Iowa on cancer caused by residential radon in women; this Radon Lung Cancer Study was published in June, 2000. Women were chosen because they historically spend more time in the home than men do, and also they typically have less occupational exposures to other substances which cause lung cancer. The study showed that residential radon exposure is definitely a significant cause of lung cancer. Iowa has the highest average radon concentrations in its buildings than any other state in the United States. This is because of the uranium in the glacial deposits of its soil.

The Environmental Protection Agency has established an alert or action level of 4 picocuries of radon per liter for indoor air; Canada and European countries have limits 20 times higher. These countries generally measure the radioactivity levels in becquerels per cubic meter. To convert picocuries per liter to becquerels per cubic meter, multiply by 37.

Although the radioactive gas radon was recognized as a major indoor pollutant in Canada and Sweden in the 1970s, little attention was paid to it in the United States until 1984. At this time nuclear engineer Stanley Watras in Pennsylvania set off a radiation alarm at the Limerick Generating Station as he was entering the plant, not exiting. Investigation of this puzzling event disclosed that his home was situated on uranium-bearing land and that radon had been seeping inside in harmful concentrations. The Watras house was found to contain radon at a whopping 2700 picocuries per liter in the basement. Media attention turned this discovery into a watershed event.

Subsequently radon has been found to be a serious contaminant in millions of American homes. It arises almost entirely from radium in the soil below the structures; recall that radium and radon are generated from the stepwise decay of uranium. A heated house behaves something like a chimney: warm air rises inside and some escapes, drawing any radon upward into the inside. Well-insulated houses retain radon much longer than more open buildings. A number of houses have inadvertently been constructed on areas where human enterprise has loosened uranium ores. Examples are on old uranium mines or tailings from them; several of these are found in Colorado. Abandoned radium-processing facilities in New Jersey are another. But the great majority of cases involve just the natural, high-uranium level of the soil.

Danger at home from radon

Radon dissolved in water also presents some hazard. There is almost none in most city municipal water supplies, but water from wells frequently contains as much as 1000 to 3000 picocuries per liter. Dissolved, radon presents little danger, but it becomes airborne when the water is used in showers, baths, laundry, etc. On moving from water to the air, the radon is diluted enormously. Municipal water typically has a level of alpha activity of around 15 picocuries per liter, one third of which is due to radium.

Aside from the Pennsylvania area mentioned above, quite a number of other sites in the United States are known where houses accumulate radon above the EPA action level. Some of these are in Iowa, North Dakota, Wyoming, Utah, and Nevada. But other cases occur where they would not be expected. Recently 70 homes were found near Santa Barbara, California, which had dangerous radon levels, some as high as 20 picocuries per liter. About 14% of the homes 20 to 30 miles northwest of Los Angeles have been found to hold excessive radon. Many schools in the United States were found in 1993 to have radon levels somewhat higher than EPA standards permit. Generally, radon abatement steps can be taken to remedy the trouble. Prospective home buyers would be well advised to have radon levels measured before purchasing, especially if there is a basement. Radon levels are higher in dwellings during winter than summer, and are not related to the age of the house. While vast numbers of Americans profess to be horrified by the thought of being exposed to excessive radioactivity, only 2 or 3% have bothered to have their homes tested for radon.

Have you had your home tested for radon?

There are several methods of measuring the radon concentration in homes. A common method consists of allowing about an ounce of activated charcoal to stand in the house for several days, when it adsorbs radon and its decay products. Gamma rays from the charcoal are measured directly. From calibrations using known radon concentrations, the level inside the structure can be calculated. Another technique uses a piece of special polymer film on which alpha particles make a track. After an exposure of 3 to12 months, the film is etched chemically and the alpha tracks are counted optically or electronically. This permits the radon concentration to be calculated. Plastic lenses from eyeglasses also serve this purpose. A qualitative procedure is to let a television set run for a few hours, when the screen becomes negatively charged and attracts the positively-charged ions arising from radon disintegration. Then the screen is wiped with a moist tissue and tested with a counter sensitive to alpha particles. In still another procedure, developed in Sweden, a glass object which has been inside the house for at least a year, such as a window pane or mirror, is removed and its lead-210 content is measured with a sophisticated radiation counter. This reveals the long-term radon history of the dwelling. A quicker method uses a chamber with an electrically-charged Teflon disk. The radon in a filtered air sample inside ionizes the air, permitting the charge to leak off. Simple measurement of the drop in voltage reveals the radon concentration. Finally, a very sensitive procedure measures the three alpha and two beta particles in the decay sequence of radon using a scintillation counter; the radon is adsorbed from the air on a few grams of activated charcoal.

Since radon is natural (a word most people like), it does not seem threatening in the home, where most folks feel safe. Thus there is little suspicion of capricious manipulation by authorities, as might be the case when man-made radiation is involved. Some can become alarmed at a nuclear waste repository, but ignore danger from radon 100 times as great.

5-9 Radiation Dose from the Environment

All of us are exposed to a minute but steady radiation dose from natural and artificial sources. The dose varies greatly from person to person, depending on such factors as the altitude of dwelling place, occupation, and type and location of home. People living in high mountain areas receive more cosmic radiation than those at sea level because the thinner air attenuates the rays less than lower, denser air. Similarly, certain crews in aircraft receive more radiation than workers in nuclear reactors. Some individuals receive much more medical X-ray exposure than others. Approximately 300 cosmic ray high-energy photons pass through each of our bodies each second.

Rough estimates of the average environmental radiation dose are given in the table below (whole-body values for one person in the United States in one year). The data are mostly from the Nuclear Regulatory Commission, measured in 1987-88. The range of doses and a most probable value are given.

Annual Whole-Body Radiation Dose Per Person in Millirads

	Range	Probable value
Cosmic radiation	25–50	29
Radiation from the Earth	10–250	25
Internal radiation, total	–	40
Potassium-40	–	15
Radium in food and water	–	5
Carbon-14, others	–	20
X-rays (medical)	0–200	40 to 100 (see text below)
Nuclear bomb tests	–	less than 1
Nuclear medicine	0–50	14
Nuclear industry (reactors)	0–0.4	less than 0.2
Consumer products	0–20	11
Other sources	0–5	less than 3

The entry for medical X-rays in the table above is an estimate; the true value is not known. This is because the doses from X-ray images in physicians' offices are usually not recorded, and because a fair amount of fluoroscopy is carried out (such as in guiding catheters, etc.), when exposures can be above even 100 millirads. The National Council on Radiation Protection records, for example, bone marrow doses from diagnostic radiology of 115 millirads. The total whole-body background exposure from natural sources (the first three entries above) total 94 millirads per year, and the three largest contributions from man-made sources total another 65 to 125, making 159 to 219 millirads per year.

Note that the important contribution by radon is not included in the table above. This is because the dosage inflicted by the disintegration products of radon affect the lungs and nearby respiratory tissues only, and thus this part is not whole-body exposure. The exposure by radon is shown on the next page:

Annual Radiation Dose to the Lungs by Radon, in Millirads

	Range	Probable Value
Radon from the air, total	–	198
Outdoors	18–22	20
Indoors	70–260	178

Since the decay products of radon are mostly alpha emitters, the numbers of millirads must be multiplied by a relative biological effectiveness factor of at least 20 to convert them to millirems. Smokers are exposed to an extra dose of radiation from the alpha emitters in tobacco, radium-226 and polonium-210. In order to normalize the dose from radon to a whole-body dose, it must be multiplied by a weighting factor which reflects the much lower mass of the respiratory system compared to that of the whole body. In this case, the weighting factor is close to 0.08, and thus the dose equivalent from radon based on the whole body is 198 x 0.08 = 16 millirads. Therefore a reasonable estimate of an average whole-body dose is the range 159 to 219, plus this additional 16, making 175 to 235 millirads per year.

The first contribution to whole-body dose, 159 to 219 millirads per year, is mostly from radiation with relative biological factors near unity, so these numbers are approximately the same as the numbers of millirems. The second contribution, that from radon, is from alpha activity and so the relative biological factor is perhaps 20. This means that the 16 millirads calculated above is around 320 millirems. Thus the total of the two is at least 479 millirems per year, but there is quite a large spread. The dose to each human body from natural sources is generally taken as 365 to 500 millirems per year. A bit more than a millirem per day is a useful rule of thumb.

Except for the last few entries in the first list, the human race has been exposed to this level of radiation or higher during its entire evolution, so we know our species can survive with this dosage, but that is not to say it is harmless. After all, we human beings have been afflicted by cancer from our start. About 20% of cancers arise spontaneously, and it could well be that the natural background of radioactivity plays a role in this. Other factors, such as diet, health care, smoking, and life style in general are much more important, so higher cancer rates are not found in areas with somewhat elevated background radiation; any small increase is submerged by the much larger natural rate. In Colorado, which experiences about 75% higher natural background than the national average, the cancer rate is some 35% lower than the national average because of healthier lifestyles.

The high radiation levels of two or three billion years ago probably accelerated evolution.

In that much of Earth's natural radioactivity has decayed away during the past, we see that life originated and evolved in a radiation background several times as intense as present levels. If a supernova explosion occurred within 30 light-years, the cosmic ray contribution listed above could increase a thousandfold for a while. This would have significant effects on Earth's life, but would not wipe it out.

Certain people are exposed to higher background doses. Some 100,000 people live in coastal southwest India (Kerala), in an area rich in monazite, a mineral with high thorium and uranium content. On the average they absorb 0.5 to 0.6 rads per year, which is around 3 times the natural background (excluding radon and its progeny). Large numbers receive a dose of around 1.3 rads per year, and some get 3.25 rads. There are approximately 100 inhabitants who receive as much as 12 rads per year each. There are stories that these higher irradiation levels cause an elevated rate of Down syndrome in children born in Kerala, but additional studies are needed. The Brazilian coast near Espirito Santo also has monazite, and ignorant visitors lie in the black sand, thinking radioactivity is healthy (see 5-7). A dose of 5 millirads per hour during such self-exposure is not unusual. Another highly radioactive site in Brazil is in the state of Minas Gerais. Plants growing in Morro do Ferro in this area contain so much radium (from the decay of both thorium and uranium) that they can be autoradiographed; merely holding the leaves against a photographic film in a dark room exposes the film and gives a picture. An area in China, Guandong Province, has a high background, giving an extra dose of about 0.35 rem per year. A similar area is near Ramsar, on the Caspian Sea in Iran. Few scientific investigations seem to have been carried out to determine the health effects of these elevated radiation backgrounds, but there is nothing obvious to the casual visitor. No increase in the frequency of cancer in these regions has been documented, but that means little: no thorough investigation has been carried out. In these areas of high background, an increased frequency of chromosome abnormalities has been observed.

The drinking water in a typical American coastal city contains the following maximum levels of radioactive substances (all in picocuries per liter):

radium	5
uranium	20
other alpha emitters	10
strontium-90	8
tritium	20,000

Brazilians who love both radiation exposure and tobacco should be happy with the cigarettes made in their country. A recent study at the University of Sao Paulo found 12 times as much uranium in some Brazilian tobacco as in the U.S. or European product. Brazilian tobacco averages 0.28 ppm (parts per million) uranium, with a worst-case level of 0.88 ppm. U.S. and European brands average 0.07 ppm. The excess uranium arises from the fertilizer prepared from phosphate rock, which contains considerable uranium. Moreover, any product containing uranium also contains its decay products, including radium-226 and polonium-210, both known carcinogens.

Nevertheless, there is no absolutely safe level of radiation exposure, and no threshold dose is so low that the risk is zero. It is just that the body is able to repair most damage from low-level doses, but at a cost. It might be that low dose levels are actually more dangerous than higher, in that cells are not killed, but only damaged, permitting cancer-prone and mutated cells to survive. While the effects of minute radiation doses on our health are not very well understood, and are controversial in the extreme, there is general agreement that they can cause cancer in time. Examination of 8,318 employees at Oak Ridge over 40 years disclosed leukemia rates ten times that of Hiroshima survivors. The data in BEIR VI (see 5-14), which includes the 1990 report on radiation-exposed on the Hiroshima population, are not in contradiction to the low-level radiation effects of ionizing radiation as a linear, nonthreshold function of the dose.

For personnel who work in the field of radioactive materials and X-rays, occupational exposure limits are higher than the average levels. Examples are, in rems per year: skin, 9 to 15; bone, 15 to 30; and hands, 15 to 75. The Department of Energy amended the regulations in 1994 for whole-body dosage, making it 5 rems per year for occupational workers. The standards cannot be based on scientific certainty; judgment, emotion, and compromise play roles. There is room for differing interpretations and arguments, leaving benefits to be weighed against hazards. This allows considerable latitude for personal opinions and preferences. There is also the factor that authorities in nuclear businesses have a vested interest in seeing that limits are not set too low. But the trend in regulations reflects that we are more vulnerable to ionizing radiation than previously thought.

Another contributor to radiation damage to all living things is carbon-14. It is formed naturally in the upper atmosphere and diffuses downward, where it enters the food chain. Becoming part of our bodies, some radiation damage is done as it slowly decays. The amount of carbon-14 has been significantly increased by nuclear explosions in the atmosphere (see Chapter 9). Each of us also contains a great deal of the necessary element potassium, namely about one gram per pound body weight. Ordinary potassium is 0.0117% potassium-40, which is weakly beta and gamma active. Each of our bodies holds about 0.11 microcuries of this nuclide.

There's no way to escape this exposure.

Our atmosphere largely protects us from cosmic rays. The thinner air at high altitudes affords less shielding, so radiation doses from this source are higher. There could be a serious problem in prolonged exposure of cosmonauts during 15-months of travel on a round-trip to Mars. Cosmic rays readily penetrate the thin walls of spacecraft. Massive shielding is too heavy to launch. NASA has a study of the matter underway.

5-10 Plutonium and Health

Plutonium is of course a substance dangerous to health, but it is not the most toxic substance known or the ultimate poison. Its reputation in this regard is overblown. Like radium, it is a hazardous element which is among many dangerous materials that must be handled with caution. Apparently plutonium, deposited in soil or water, does not concentrate in the food chain as is the case with some fission products and some nonradioactive toxic elements, such as mercury.

Plutonium can enter the human body by inhalation of its oxide as dust, by ingestion in food, or even by absorption through wounds. Prior to 1963, at least 10,000 pounds of plutonium had been dispersed in the world environment via testing of weapons in the atmosphere. The metal is converted to plutonium dioxide dust so fine that it takes decades to settle. Inhalation of this dust is the route of exposure of greatest concern. It is the smallest particles (around 1 micrometer) which are most dangerous, since the larger particles are mostly trapped in the upper respiratory tract and are eventually expelled as in the case of the disintegration products of radon (5-8). In the case of exposure of the lungs, the dose is best expressed in rems, not rads, because plutonium is an alpha emitter, and alpha particles inflict many times as much damage to tissues as beta particles or gamma rays do. Reports from the International Commission on Radiological Protection show that the lining of the gastrointestinal tract is quite an effective barrier to plutonium. Plutonium dioxide is so insoluble and inert chemically that only the smallest fraction dissolves and enters the blood stream. Nevertheless, the cells of the intestinal tract on the surface could get a sizable dose from the plutonium alpha activity. In the case of the dioxide absorption is as low as 0.001%, while for soluble compounds, as plutonium nitrate, absorption is about 0.1%. Complexes of plutonium, such as the citrate, are absorbed to the extent of about 0.02%. Once in the blood, 90% or so is taken up by the bones and liver. In bones, it concentrates in the marrow and outer surfaces. Soluble forms of plutonium, as well as of americium and curium, can be partially cleared from the human body through the use of chelating agents.

A group of men were assigned to the "Recovery Group" in 1944 at Los Alamos. Their job was to clean all traces of precious plutonium from glassware, working surfaces, tiles, fume hoods, and accumulated waste liquids. They wore respirators and changed clothes twice a day. Starting in 1951 a study of the men, now civilians, was begun. They all had appreciable burdens of plutonium in their bodies and traces of it were being slowly excreted. By the early 1990s seven of the 26 men had died, three of them from cancer, one of which was osteosarcoma. This number is lower than that expected from cancer statistics; they were healthy young men at the start. Still, we can come to no conclusion from the incident since the study was weak in several respects.

Two British scientists volunteered to be injected with traces of plutonium-237 citrate, a soluble form. This plutonium isotope has a half-life of only 45.2 days and thus after one year, 8 half-lives had passed and most radioactivity had decayed away. Plutonium-237 undergoes decay via several processes, the main one, more than 99%, being accompanied by gamma rays and so it was easy to follow in the body. The results showed excretion in the urine and feces, some uptake by the bones and liver, but no excretion in the sweat or saliva. The radiation dose in the subjects was low.

Volunteering for a nice shot of plutonium

Purified uranium (that is, not an ore with accumulated decay products) is far less damaging than plutonium. The two common isotopes, U-235 and U-238, have half-lives of hundreds of millions of years, and therefore are capable of giving radiation doses much lower than those from plutonium if the same exposure times and weights are involved. One microgram of plutonium-239 emits about the same number of alpha particles per second as 185,000 micrograms (which is 185 milligrams) of uranium-238. Moreover, one must consider that as uranium ages, its daughter products (thorium-234, radium-226, radon-222, polonium-138, etc.) accumulate, raising the exposure level. Uranyl salts are soluble, and if ingested can cause nephritis (kidney damage); this is from chemical poisoning and radioactivity combined.

The Cassini space probe (6-37B) carries 32 kilograms of the dioxide of plutonium-238 (half-life 87.7 years). The whole mission was opposed by some people, a few of whom made the argument that if it had exploded on launch or in the upper atmosphere, the amount of plutonium could kill millions or even billions of Earth's population if the dioxide dust were all inhaled. That is a colossal ***if***. The matter deserves careful evaluation since plutonium-238 is inherently a very dangerous substance. But still, considering the elaborate precautions, the alleged danger is exaggerated. It's something like saying that if all the radium in the oceans (a billion curies) were distributed evenly among the whole population of the Earth, it would kill off the human race, which is true (each person would receive about 180 millicuries of radium, far more than the lethal amount). This could be said about poisoning by arsenic, lead, cadmium, etc. The point is that this sort of event simply does not take place.

5-11 Biological Half-Lives and Effective Half-Lives

If a person ingests a compound of a chemical element mixed with food, or by inhaling vapors or dust, or by injection, the material stays a certain time inside the body before being largely excreted. Each element, as a specified compound, transported to a specified type of tissue (or the whole body), is characterized by a *biological half-life*, the time required for half of it to be eliminated from the body. Let's use iodine as an example. The rate of excretion does not depend on whether it is a radioactive form or not, but if we choose a long-lived radioactive isotope as a tracer, we can follow it easily. Studies show that it takes about 138 days for half of ingested iodine (as potassium iodide) to be excreted from the whole body. Actually not quite all of the iodine is excreted at this rate. The thyroid gland, which takes iodine from the blood to make the hormone thyroxine, retains iodine longer. This was determined using iodine-129, whose half-life is 15.7 million years, so only the merest trace decays during the experiment.

If we had chosen iodine-131, with an ordinary radioactive decay half-life (also known as the *physical half-life*) of only 8 days, the result is that the *effective half-life*, which takes both the physical half-life and biological half-life into account, is shorter than either of the other half-lives alone. This is because both processes are working simultaneously. If the physical and biological half-lives are quite different, the effective half-life tends to be the same as the shorter one. The table below summarizes these properties for a few nuclides.

Nuclide	Effect On:	Physical Half-Life	Biological Half-Life	Effective Half-Life
Tritium	whole body	12.3 years	4 to 18 days	4 to 18 days
Phosphorus-32	bone	14.2 days	1155 days	14.1 days
Chromium-51	whole body	27.7 days	616 days	26.5 days
Cobalt-60	whole body	5.27 years	7 days[a]	7 days[a]
Strontium-90	bone	28.5 years	50 years[b]	18 years[b]
Iodine-131	thyroid	8.04 days	138 days	7.6 days
Cesium-137	whole body	30.0 years	50 to 150 days	50 to 150 days
Plutonium-239	bone	24100 years	100 years	100 years
Plutonium-239	liver	24100 years	40 years	40 years
Plutonium-239	lung	24100 years	500 days	500 days

a. Additional components of 60 and 800 days. b. Values very rough; behavior is complex

The values of the biological and effective half-lives above are not exact since their values vary somewhat with the chemical form of the specified radionuclides. Whether the term biological half-life applies to the whole body or to one organ should also be specified.

5-12 Hazardous Life

In the popular press, one reads about a property of a dangerous radioactive nuclide in terms of "hazardous life," "hazardous lifetime," "dangerous life," "decay life," or some similar term. The time spans and their danger levels referred to are loose expressions which are composed principally in some undefined way of:

a. The physical half-life of the radionuclide;
b. The chemical form of the nuclide;
c. The number of curies of this isotope involved at the start;
d. The type and energy of its radiation;
e. Whether the exposure is external or internal;
f. The length of exposure;
g. The degree of shielding and quality of containers or packaging;
h. The biochemical properties of the radionuclide, in particular, whether it is selectively absorbed by any particular organ (see biological half-life, 5-11).

5-13 Calculation of Radiation Dose

Here we calculate the radiation dose imparted to a person's body by a radioactive substance. Let's say the body weight is 150 pounds (68 kilograms). Let's choose strontium-90 as the radionuclide since its radioactivity is by pure beta decay, that is, there are no gamma rays to complicate matters. The subject drinks a solution containing one microgram of strontium-90 as its chloride; this is 140 microcuries. This radionuclide has a physical half-life of 28.5 years, a biological half-life of 50 years, and an effective half-life in the body of 18 years (5-11). Our objective is to estimate the radiation dose to the subject during the course of the first year.

First let's calculate the amount of Sr-90 left after each step of decay or excretion. Using the exponential law of radioactive decay (Appendix IV), it can be shown that at the end of one year and considering radioactivity decay only, of the original 1.000 microgram (μg) of Sr-90, 0.976 μg remains unchanged and will continue to decay and expose the host during the following years. The amount which decayed was 1 - 0.976 = 0.024 μg. Similarly, application of the same law to excretion of Sr-90 (biological half-life 50 years), we calculate that 0.986 μg is retained and 0.014 μg is excreted. The amount lost (via decay and excretion together) is 0.024 + 0.014 = 0.038 μg. Second, we'll repeat the calculation for the two ways of loss of Sr-90 together: we use the effective half-life of 18 years mentioned above, then we find that in one year, 0.962 μg is retained and thus 0.038 μg is lost (decay and excretion combined), agreeing with the sum above.

To estimate the *maximum* radiation dose for the first year, we need consider only the 0.024 μg of Sr-90 which has decayed since this is the only process causing a radiation dose. Each atom of Sr-90 on decay emits one beta particle. Laboratory measurements of the energy of these betas show that they have an average energy level of 0.546 megaelectron volt (MeV). First we consider the number of atoms which were in the 0.024 μg of Sr-90 which decayed, since this is also the number of beta particles (Avogadro's number gives the number of atoms in one mole; see 4-10):

$$0.024\ \mu g \times \frac{1g}{10^6\mu g} \times \frac{1\ mole}{90g} \times \frac{6.022 \times 10^{23}\ atoms}{1\ mole} = 1.61 \times 10^{14}\ \text{atoms of Sr-90}$$

This is also the number of betas emitted. We also need the relation between MeV and joules, which is 1 J = 6.24 x 10^{12} MeV (Appendix IV). Then:

$$1.61 \times 10^{14}\ \text{betas} \times \frac{0.546\ MeV}{1\ beta} \times \frac{1J}{6.24 \times 10^{12}\ MeV} = 14.1\ J$$

This 14.1 joules of energy is absorbed by the 68-kilogram body, so the dose per kilogram amounts to:

$$\frac{14.1J}{68\ kg} = 0.207\ J/kg$$

Since 1 J/kg is also 1 gray unit (Gy; see 4-23), the whole-body dose is 0.207 Gy. Moreover, each gray is 100 rads, so the maximum dose based on the whole body is 20.7 rads. We are dealing with beta particles, not alpha, so the relative biological effectiveness (5-5) is about unity, and the dose is also close to 20.7 rems. Since strontium tends to be concentrated on bone surfaces and in the bone marrow, these organs, having a much smaller mass, receive a much higher dose.

It is astounding that one microgram of strontium-90, a mere speck, can deliver to one's body a radiation dose as high as 20 rads in one year. After all, the environmental radiation dose (5-9), mostly from natural sources, amounts to only about 0.2 rads per year (normalized to the whole body). The Nuclear Regulatory Commission's "Annual Limits on Intake" (1996) specifies a limit of 30 microcuries of strontium-90, which is 0.214 micrograms. This amount would be expected to give the body a maximum dose of around 4.4 rads during the first year.

5-14 Risk Analysis of Radiation-Induced Effects

Sources of Data—The only known way to reliably determine the number of cancers (or birth defects, mutations, etc.) which arise from ionizing radiation absorbed by a population is based on experience. This means that the radiation doses of large numbers of people are determined and the numbers of cancers are determined over time. To be meaningful, it must be compared to large numbers of the same kind of population who have not been exposed; these serve as controls. The observations are known as a database. Using this information, one can calculate the probability that any one person (or the number per 1000, or 100,000, etc.) will contract the disease if reliable estimates of the radiation doses are known. These studies are difficult and errors may arise from several sources. Low-dose calculations are especially challenging.

Data are derived from study of wartime exposure at Hiroshima and Nagasaki and of gigantic accidents (such as the one at Chernobyl), X-ray therapy, many individual accidents, experiments with animals, and a few other ways. The primary series of these studies, sponsored by the National Research Council, is called Biological Effects of Ionizing Radiation, or BEIR. The last report, BEIR VI, is dated 1998. Another important data source was published by the United Nations Scientific Committee on Effects of Atomic Radiation, or UNSCEAR.

It is of the utmost importance that the database be as accurate as possible; otherwise, the results are not scientifically credible. It is not easy to meet these criteria. If the exposure of one group is low, then the difference from the control group is small, and the study has higher uncertainties. An appreciable difference in exposure between the control and affected groups makes the study more dependable. Reconstruction of doses of ionizing radiation is tedious and sometimes based on incorrect data. Biological dosimetry, often based on measurement of chromosome injuries, is objective and believed to be reliable. The analysts who carry out the studies to build data-bases to access cancer rates are just as human as the rest of us, and therefore are liable to let knowledge of radiation exposure influence conclusions. For that reason, one who examines chromosomes for radiation damage must not be allowed to know anything about the person involved (such as where he or she was at the time of accident or explosion). The analysts are said to be "blinded." Those who determine the health response to the radiation dose (detection of cancer, etc.) must also work "blind," that is, not know anything about the radiation dose itself. This technique, the best known for reliable data, is called double blinding.

When being blinded is an advantage

Person-Rems—A term often used in radiation epidemiology is the person-rem. If each of one million people is subjected to a radiation dose of 1 rem, the total dose is 1 million persons times 1 rem, which is 1 million person-rems. If half a million people absorb 2 rems each, the total number of person-rems is still 1 million (½ million persons times 2 rems). If 1000 people are exposed to 3 rems each and 2000 people to 2 rems each, then the 3000 people have a total exposure of 7000 person-rems. Suppose experience shows that a dose of 10 rems to each of a large group of people, causes 1 chance in 10,000 of getting cancer over and above a like control group who get no extra exposure. Then, if each of 500,000 people receives 10 rems, we would expect the total number of excess cancers to result to be 500,000/10,000, that is, 50 extra cancers in the group. The size of a radiation risk is tied to the amount of the accumulated dose and the number of people who receive it.

We do not know how many will develop cancer or die altogether, but there will be an increase over the natural rate, which is more than 20% of deaths resulting from cancer (it was 23.4% in 1993). Consider a radiation exposure of 10,000 person-rems. How many deaths result from cancer over the natural rate (the risk factor) result? A benchmark figure used by the International Atomic Energy Agency since 1977 is 1 fatal cancer. The Environmental Protection Agency uses a figure of 2, while the Department of Energy asserts that 2.3 deaths per 10,000 person-rem exposure is more realistic (this is the same as 23 deaths per 100,000 person-rems). All of these agencies, sadly enough, are essentially political in nature, and all have an interest in minimizing the number of cancers caused. The true figures are not known, but could well be higher; estimates as high as 25 cancers per 10,000 person-rems have been made.

Estimating the Damage—Radiological health studies are conducted to determine the kind and degree of harm done to any exposed population. In epidemiological studies, the aim is to determine the degree of radiation injuries and/or disease of a given population, as compared to a similar number of people with the same life style who have not been exposed. An important complication is the role of toxic, nonradioactive substances. In radiation dose reconstruction studies, attempts are made to determine the dose inflicted on a defined population. The aim of dose reconstruction is to estimate the average number of rems per person, as well as the range; the number of person-rems can also be calculated. In both cases one must cope with the lack of reliable data.

In carrying out both types of study, the expression "source term" means the source and amount of harmful radionuclides released from a facility or during an accident.

A branch of statistics still undergoing development is risk analysis. It plays a role in fixing public policies. This discipline attempts to quantify hazards which stem from substances or processes which affect the populace or the environment. Costs to an insurance company from a particular cause, such as automobile accidents or earthquake damage to homes, consist of two factors: the number of cases and the average amount of insurance per case. Risk (monetary costs in this case) is the product of the two terms. In general, risk is the product of probability of occurrence and the magnitude of the consequences.

The term risk in this sense comes to us from the insurance industry.

It is experience which teaches the magnitude of hazard. If a new chemical substance is put on the market, we would like as much information as possible about its acute toxicity and the consequences of prolonged exposure. To analyze risk from use of the material, the exposure levels (dose) must be known. The same concepts are extended to estimate risks from radioactive materials. Exposure meters in the facilities and badges worn by workers aid in measuring or reconstructing dose levels. Relative risk is the ratio of incidence of an exposed population (to contract some specified disorder such as cancer) to the incidence of a comparable or control group which is not exposed.

Science *vs.* Folklore in Statistics—Most of our population is not trained in risk evaluation, and therefore tends to have unreal perceptions of many risks. For example, a risk taken voluntarily is more acceptable than one imposed by a regulation; moreover, a risk tends to be downplayed if it gives pleasure. Thus, while smoking is responsible for far more deaths per year in the United States than nuclear reactors, surveys of public opinion show the reverse order. Nevertheless, our citizens do learn to be quite sensible about risks. Thus smoking is less and less socially acceptable, and the trend in diet, admittedly weaker, is towards low-fat, high-fiber foods.

Unscientific predictions are appealing to many because they are based on intuition, faith, compelling anecdote, or a personal experience. Predictions of risk of this type are little better than guesses, and everyone is tempted to fall into the trap. Scientific predictions of risk are derived from probabilities based on objective evidence. While quite accurate when an extensive database is available, to the general public they often seem remote, burdened with qualifications, and sometimes even wrong. Drinking alcoholic beverages, eating an unbalanced diet, and driving are considerably more dangerous than most exposures to radioactivity.

Estimating Numbers of Cancers from Radiation Dose—Very rough risk estimates for fatal cancer of various types, caused by a total or collective dose of one million rems (in some specified large number of people, that is, one million person-rems), are given below. The data are from BEIR and UNSCEAR reports.

Type or site of fatal cancer	*Risk per 1,000 000 rems*
leukemia	20
thyroid	5
breast	25
bone	5
liver	10
skin	1
other tissues	34
Total	approximately 100

To illustrate the above figures, consider 1,000,000 people who collectively receive 1,000,000 rems. Thus the average dose is 1,000,000 rems/1,000,000 persons, or 1 rem per person. The number of person-rems is 1,000,000 persons x 1 rem or 1,000,000 person-rems. According to the table, the risk of the 1,000,000 rems is to cause 100 excess fatal cancers, or 100/1,000,000 = 1 cancer per 10,000 persons. Of these 100 fatal cancers, 20 are leukemia, 5 are cancer of the thyroid, etc., as shown in the table. Of course, there are statistical fluctuations.

Consider next the case if there are only 10,000 persons. Here the average dose is 1,000,000 rems/10,000 persons, or 100 rems per person, much higher than in the case of 1,000,000 persons. The number of person-rems is 10,000 persons x 100 rems or 1,000,000 person-rems, as before. The total number of excess fatal cancers is still 100 (distributed among the various types), which is 100 cancers/10,000 persons, or 1 cancer per 100 persons. This higher rate is to be expected at the higher average dose. If the number of persons is reduced again, this time to a quite low number, the calculations tend to break down because few people get enormous, fatal doses. It should be emphasized that the calculations are approximate, but they do indicate trends and have value.

Of course, the above calculations assume the validity of the premise, namely that 100 cancers result from a collective dose of 1,000,000 rems. The true number might well be higher, as indicated in earlier discussions.

5-15 Radiation-Induced Cancer and Other Disorders

We have seen that early on, before the hazards were known, exposure to radium frequently led to cancer. Moreover, before about 1920, a hundred or so radiologists had died from cancer induced by their X-rays. The earliest studies showed that young, growing cells, such as in an embryo, are particularly sensitive to ionizing radiation. After Hiroshima was bombed, President Truman ordered a long-range, continuing study of the biological and medical effects of ionizing radiation on humans. Many survivors of the Hiroshima explosion who received 150 to 200 rads of gamma radiation eventually developed cancer, frequently leukemia. The maximum in leukemia incidence occurred five to seven years after exposure; this latent period in some cases was as short as two years, or as long as 20 years. Survivors in Hiroshima have a

Cells which are growing are most sensitive.

29% greater chance of dying of cancer than unexposed people. Examinations of 72,216 children who had been conceived after the time of their parents irradiation have disclosed no increase in birth defects, incidence of cancer, or abnormalities in white blood cells. Apparently, while Hiroshima survivors and their offspring do have certain new genetic markers, these are not harmful. According to a study concluded in 2002, similar results occur in the irradiated populations of Kazakhstan, where markers were found in certain satellite regions of the genome. They do not appear to be damaging.

The Marshallese people who were exposed to radioactive fallout from American hydrogen bomb tests in 1954 received external doses of up to 175 rads; they also inhaled or ingested radioactive iodine. Cancer of the thyroid gland induced by uptake of this iodine is well documented. Of course, cancer has many causes, only one of which is ionizing radiation, but cancer of the thyroid gland in the absence of irradiation is extremely rare. Ionizing radiation has both immediate and delayed effects. Cancer is the most serious somatic consequence, while mutations are the most serious genetic result. Cancers caused by ionizing radiation have no distinguishing characteristics which permit distinguishing them from cancers of the same type which occur spontaneously.

Irradiation experiments on mice have revealed a great deal of information about inheritable mutations caused by ionizing radiation. If we extrapolate from mouse to human beings, the result is that an estimated radiation dose of 100 rads is required to double the natural mutation rate. Another study, published in 1990, gives 200 rads as the dose required to double the human mutation rate. These doses seem surprisingly large. Extrapolations from one species to another are generally unreliable, but the process is about the best available. No statistically valid, quantified increase of important human genetic effects traceable to radiation has been proven. One must beware of mistaking congenital defects, such as missing digits, deafness at birth, etc., for hereditary imperfections.

The Nuclear Regulatory Commission, using data from a 1950 study of 80,000 survivors of the Hiroshima blast, specifies the maximum permissible whole-body dose per year as 5 rems for workers in the field and one-tenth that level for the general public. Many feel that these limits are too high, particularly after a 1987 study showed that gamma ray exposure is about twice as likely to cause cancer as previously thought. Since there is no level of radiation which is completely safe, setting standards is as much political as scientific, and represents a compromise between harmful effects and social benefits, as in all other human endeavors.

The incidence of cancer mentioned above is not especially high, considering that around 20% of all deaths are from cancer anyway. Prediction of the numbers of deaths from excess cancer from a specified dose of radiation is inexact. Currently, physicians specializing in radiogenic disorders still disagree among themselves on the rates at which cancer is induced by exposure, as for example at Chernobyl. Although there is room for honest disagreement, the arguments are at times heated, one group accusing the other of either exaggerating or downplaying the dangers.

The number of cancers from radiation depends primarily on the dose. The number of cancers in these studies means the number in excess of those which arise spontaneously. If the radiation dose is not acute, but accumulated in small amounts over several weeks or months, then the excess cancer incidence is smaller; this is because the body has an opportunity to repair itself to a greater degree than in the case of the acute irradiation.

Doses to breast tissue caused by modern mammograms (two-view, that is, two exposures of each breast) have been greatly reduced during the past generation. It is now generally below 200 millirems, sometimes as low as 100 millirems, although in a few facilities it can be considerably higher than 200 millirems. The dosage accumulates over the years. There is no doubt that there is a long latency period between exposure and occurrence of cancer.

Studies of the children of women who experienced ionizing radiation during pregnancy has shown that exposure of the embryo at 8 to 15 weeks of gestational age results in a definite increase in rates of mental retardation in the offspring. This dreadful effect held true with those exposed in Hiroshima and Nagasaki, as well as with women exposed to fallout in Soviet tests in Kazakhstan (1949 and following). The evidence is that the risk of such mental retardation is approximately a 4% increase per 10 rem exposure. It seems probable that in such cases, a small exposure almost inescapably results in a small decrease in mental function. Exposure at 16 to 25 weeks was less dangerous, and was much less if exposure occurred before 8 weeks or later than 25 weeks. Another effect was microcephaly, abnormally small heads often associated with mental retardation. Cases of microcephaly are known from other causes than ionizing radiation. Teratology is the study of monstrous deformities in newborn, small numbers of which have been known for centuries. Evidence is lacking of such instances resulting from ionizing radiation. Just under 1% of live births involve severe birth defects such as cleft palate or lip, club foot, polydactyly, or congenital heart disease; apparently ionizing radiation does not increase the numbers of such cases.

A couple of the more appalling effects of nuclear bombing

In 1990, a British study revealed an apparent connection between radiation exposure to men and their children born during the years afterward who developed leukemia. The men were workers at the Sellafield nuclear plant. At the time it was thought that there was "overwhelming" evidence that the children suffered an incidence at about twice the rate of children whose parents were not exposed. But in 1997 a more detailed analysis of the data proved that there was no direct connection between the dose of the workers and the leukemia incidence in the 36,000 children; indeed, the highest rate of leukemia correlated with the fathers of lowest exposure. Some other factor was probably responsible, such as a cancer-triggering virus or maybe internal exposure by alpha particles (which were not registered by the film badges the men wore).

During all of the Cold War, the U.S. government claimed that the radiation to the bodies of workers in nuclear-bomb facilities were low enough to be harmless. In January 2000, the evidence that this is not true was acknowledged for the first time. The evidence of cancer and other disorders in workers at 14 plants was so decisive that it finally had to be conceded. The reports indicated that 22 categories of cancer were found among workers in the nuclear-weapons complex. Thus, the U.S. government finally recognized that large numbers of workers in the nuclear weapons efforts had genuinely been severely injured by radiation. Earlier, those who complained about the dangers were dismissed as troublemakers or unpatriotic. An invitation to a meeting at the Hanford site attracted hundreds of personnel who thought their illness was the result of their work. Studies indicated that these might number as many as 600,000 at all of the sites. Their histories revealed cancers of the thyroid gland, lungs, skin, as well as leukemia and lymphoma.

A few were found to be suffering not from radiation, but exposure to beryllium, a carcinogenic and extremely toxic metal. The survivors in this tragedy are eligible for compensation.

5-16 Studying the Hiroshima Explosion

More than $100 million have been spent on studies of the Hiroshima bomb aftermath. Exposures by the blast are complicated by its particular nature: it was a uranium-235 bomb, and these emit many more neutrons that plutonium bombs do. To learn more about the behavior of neutrons in air, in the early 1960s a nuclear reactor without shielding (Bare Reactor Experiment) was hoisted up to the top of a 1527-foot steel tower in the Nevada desert, a height only about 375 feet lower than the Hiroshima explosion. Neutrons from the reactor were studied at various points on the ground. A simulated Japanese village was constructed nearby so that the effects and doses of neutrons could be determined. But the comparison was flawed in that the bomb circumstances (especially the steel tamper) were quite different from those of a reactor. Nevertheless, much valuable data were collected. Another experiment was conducted near Los Alamos in which a replica of the Hiroshima bomb was constructed. By slowly moving the projectile into the rings (see 9-2), the assembly was brought just up to the point of criticality, and studies were made of the gamma rays and neutrons emitted.

There is increasing evidence that low radiation doses (maybe 10 or 20 rems), once thought to be without noticeable aftereffects, do in time lead to cancer. Indeed, a recent set of studies of Hiroshima bombing victims (1987) indicate that the subsequent leukemia and carcinoma rates are higher than first suspected. But the matter was again questioned in 1992 in a Livermore investigation carried out by biophysicist Tore Straume and coworkers. Their technique depends on the capture of slow neutrons by ordinary chlorine-35, which is present to some extent in nearly all construction materials. This forms chlorine-36, a radioactive material with a half-life of 300,000 years. Samples were isolated from various sites in Hiroshima, such as roof tiles and concrete, and analyzed for chlorine-36 using an accelerator mass spectrometer (6-6). Thus the neutron flux at the time of the explosion could be ascertained. The results differ significantly from the earlier data, generally requiring a shift of permissible radiation exposures back toward the pre-1980 values. The discrepancies are yet to be ironed out.

There are five other areas over the world where large numbers of people have been exposed to radionuclides and gamma rays. These are: Nagasaki, Kazakhstan (9-25C); Bikini/Marshall Islands (9-19); Nevada, Utah, and other parts of the American west (9-31); and Chernobyl (7-25).

5-17 The Dilemma of Low-Dose Ionizing Radiation

A century after the initial studies of ionizing radiation and its effects on humans, there are still some aspects which remain controversial. We are interested here in estimating the effect or response (say the cancer deaths per 10,000 exposed persons over and above the controls) to specified dosages in rems. If the dose is zero, there can be no effect; if the dose is large, say 450 rems, it is the semi-lethal dose (5-19).

The A-Bomb Study reporting the data was prepared by the Radiation Effects Research Foundation (RERF, formerly the Atomic Bomb Casualty Commission) cosponsored by Japanese and American agencies. The actual Hiroshima data extend from 1950 to 1982 and cover 91,231 survivors; data pertaining to leukemia were not included. They are plotted in two ways (next page), Graph A and Graph B; both are from Gofman's 1990 work (see Bibliography). In both, the response axis starts at 650 cancers per 10,000 persons because this figure represents the control group. Graph A represents the data according to the linear model and shows that the actual response is somewhat above the value expected for this model. Graph B has a curve drawn which comes closest to fitting the observed data and is therefore to be preferred. The evidence from Graph B indicates even more strongly that there is no threshold dose below which there is no biological damage. It is the low-dose part of the curve which is most difficult to investigate by observation. This is because there is already a rather high background, namely the cancer death rate of the unexposed control group, and a few extra cancer deaths tend to be submerged. Indeed, quite a number of experts in the field believe that a threshold dose exists. There is probably no topic in radiobiology more emotionally charged than the no-threshold hypothesis. The Health Physics Society in 1966 adopted a position stating that annual doses below 5 rems, or 10 rems during a lifetime (each above background) cause health effects too small to be observed or are non-existent, and should not be quantified. This view is in harmony with the existence of a threshold.

But there is considerable evidence that a dose of 10 rems does have an observable effect. This is seen in Graph B at the 10 rem point, where the cancer death rate is more than 50 above the level of the control group. Moreover, a cell goes through several transitions to become cancerous, as described earlier (5-2, 5-3, 5-4). These steps are delicate, and it does not seem reasonable that 5 or 10 rems would be without effect. Perhaps the most compelling evidence that low-dose ionizing radiation is actually dangerous is afforded by the investigations of Dr. Alice Stewart. This remarkable English physician (1906-2002) was still going strongly well into her nineties, and was a radiation epidemiologist. She has been bringing the message that ionizing radiation is considerably more dangerous than most leaders in the X-ray, nuclear, and medical establishments have realized or been willing to admit. In the 1950s she demonstrated that children who had undergone even a single X-ray exam prenatally (about 0.5 rad) were twice as likely to develop leukemia and other cancers as non-exposed children. Later studies in the U.S. confirmed these observations.

The epidemiologist Jay Gould has suggested (1997) that the slightly elevated dose of ionizing radiation of millions of Americans born since 1945 has weakened our immune systems, and that this plays a role in immune-deficiency diseases such as AIDS. The assertion is highly controversial. In 1997 researchers in Scotland demonstrated that alpha radiation from traces of plutonium causes cancer in human thyroid cells. Roughly two-thirds of mice, injected with irradiated cells, developed thyroid cancer within 125 days. When the dose corresponded to two alpha particles passing through each cell nucleus, the cancer rate was as high as cases in which higher doses were employed. This is experimental evidence that extremely low doses can be carcinogenic.

We can use the linear no-threshold model to make a first estimate of the risk of cancer for a given dose of a specified form of tissue. This means that the risk is directly proportional to the dose. If for a large number of persons the dose is doubled, the number of cancers generated from it also doubles, at least.

An equation approximately relating lethality R and dose D for low-LET radiations often has the form below:

$$R = \alpha D + \beta D^2$$

If the lethality R is 1, all cells are killed; survival is 1 - R. The first term to the right of the equality sign is linear and the second term is quadratic. These two contribute differently, depending on the radiation and type of tissue. At low doses and low dose rates, primary events predominate and the first term is most important. At higher doses, secondary events begin to play a more important role, and the quadratic term becomes more prominent.

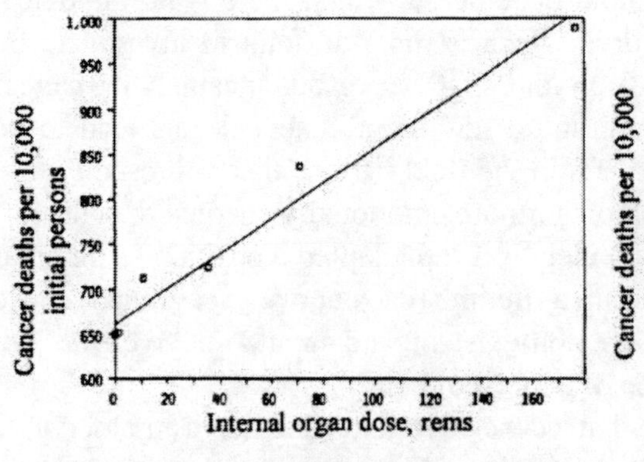

Graph A: Linear dose-reponse plot of the Hiroshima data

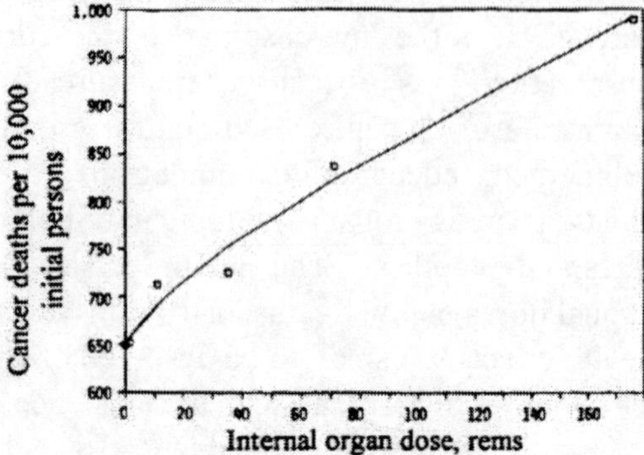

Graph B: Supra-Linear dose-response plot of the Hiroshima data

5-18 Hormesis

Another development has emerged concerning the presence or absence of effects by low-level doses of ionizing radiation. Homeopathy is a practice for treating a disorder in which minute amounts of a substance are administered, this substance being known to induce in healthy persons symptoms similar to those from the disorder. Extension of this concept by pharmacologists gave rise to the word hormesis, today meaning a stimulatory effect of a low dose of a toxic substance or ionization radiation which produces a net benefit. There are no studies of human populations exposed to low-level radiation which have demonstrated beneficial effects. Essentially, the alleged phenomenon of hormesis is speculation and deserves to be rejected in the absence of reliable supporting evidence.

5-19 Mutations

Genes, which are specific segments of DNA molecules and embody the genetic code, enable each species to reproduce and pass its own characteristics on to future generations. Several factors can alter genes and cause them to transmit an abnormal feature; the new offspring are mutants. The mutant gene is permanent. One of the most significant agents which can cause the formation of mutant genes is ionizing radiation: alpha,

Mutation and fear of it can be scarry

beta, gamma, or X-rays. All of these can arise from the radioactive decay of ingested radionuclides. The more penetrating gamma and X-rays might enter from the outside as well. Certain chemical substances are also mutagens. Mutations also arise naturally during chromosome rearrangements. Depending on the site and kind of change in the DNA molecule, a mutant gene might be benign or might be harmful. The majority of mutant genes are not particularly injurious. In by far most cases, heavily damaged genes result in offspring which are not viable. A minuscule fraction of mutants have qualities superior to those of their parents; indeed, this is a mechanism or engine of the slow process of evolution. (The effects of radiation on human genetics is discussed further in section 10-63).

A great deal was learned about mutations from X-rays using fruit flies. These insects' life cycle is only a short nine days, so many generations can be studied in a reasonable time. After exposure to radiation, their offspring are examined for mutations. For example, some insects grow a second set of wings.

In 1948 the famous British biologist J. B. S. Haldane proposed that it is the natural radiation background which is responsible for a significant fraction, maybe one-fourth, of human mutations. Keeping in mind that, as one generation follows another over millennia and errors in germ cells accumulate, this idea seems credible, and today there is some evidence to support it. Any suggestion that we can dispose of radioactive waste in a fashion which might double the background of ionizing radiation is wholly irresponsible.

5-20 Lethal Dose of Radiation

We have seen that ionizing radiation, from either an external or internal source, causes considerable damage to tissues. There must be a certain dose which results in the death of the organism. If exposure is over a long period of time, the living organism can repair itself to some degree, and can thus withstand a higher total radiation dose than in the case of acute exposure. In all organisms there is a spectrum of weak to strong individuals. For this reason we should speak not of one individual, but of a statistical number (say 1000 or more), and use average values. We will define the semilethal dose (also called the median lethal dose) as the number of rads or rems absorbed in a short time (say one day or less) which results in death within 30 days of half of a large number of individuals.

Below is a list of semilethal doses for a few species. Note that the first entry (the amoeba) has what appears to be an extremely high semilethal dose, 100,000 rads. But we must remember that the rad unit is based on one kilogram, and one kilogram of amoebas is around one trillion of the little beasties.

Species	*Semilethal Dose*
Amoeba	100,000 rads
Fruit fly	60,000 rads
Shellfish	20,000 rads
Goldfish	2,300 rads
Poultry	800 to 900 rads
Rabbit	800 rads
Human	450 rads

All the doses in the list are in rads, and are thus normalized to a basis of one kilogram, and therefore can be compared. The amoeba is exceedingly resistant. Another kind of microbe, a bacterium called *Deinococcus radiodurans,* was found recently to be still more resistant. It can withstand a dose of 1,000,000 to 1,500,000 rads, thousands of times the semilethal dosage for humans. Ordinary bacteria die if their DNA molecules suffer only two or three breaks in both strands. *D. radiodurans* requires around 120 such breaks to prove lethal. This is because of its peculiar double-ring DNA pattern and efficient repair enzymes. Consideration has been given to putting these bacteria to work in breaking down toxic chemicals in radioactive waste. In fact, a modified form of this bacterium has been made by introducing genes encoding an enzyme that reduces mercuric ion to metallic mercury, greatly reducing the toxicity of certain wastes.

In the case of human beings, the semilethal dose is not known precisely. From data on victims of the Hiroshima and Nagasaki nuclear explosions, it was at first concluded that the semilethal whole-body dose was 450 rads (about the same as 450 rems), but recent evidence has shown that it might be closer to a value between 250 and 300. Cavalier statements such as "you can afford a couple of hundred rads without getting sick" (Deputy Undersecretary of Defense T. K. Jones, 1981) are simply appalling. The reasons that the lower level of 250 rads might be closer to the true semilethal dose are: the biological damage associated with gamma radiation and burns mutually reinforce the physical and psychological trauma; radiation effects suppress the immune functions, resulting in a condition which predisposes the victims to disease; and in a war there would be only the most limited supply of antibiotics and other medicinals. Thus the combined or synergistic consequences are deadly. Joseph Rotblat reported in 1985 that his reanalysis of the data on Japanese survivors of Hiroshima and Nagasaki caused him to conclude that the semilethal dose is closer to154 rads.

A dose (an overdose, really) somewhat above lethal is followed by symptoms of radiation sickness (acute nausea, intractable diarrhea, easy bruising), after which the symptoms disappear for about two weeks; but then a high fever sets in, followed by death. With excellent medical care, some healthy human beings can live through acute exposure to considerably more than 450 rads. Recently, through genetic engineering, a hormone has been manufactured which stimulates bone marrow cell division and this aids in recovery from radiation exposure. The hormone tentatively has the imposing name granulocyte-macrophage colony stimulating factor. There are biochemical tests of red or white blood cells which reveal approximately how many rads a person has been subjected to. After the accident in Japan in 1999 (7-16B), a worker received a high radiation dose, estimated at 1700 rems. His treatment included transfusions of bone marrow cells, of blood cells from the umbilical cord of a newborn, and of stem cells. In spite of the heroic therapy, the exposed worker died in 82 days.

The American people, having on the average a low level of education in science, are irrationally fearful of radioactivity (and other hazards, such as the disease AIDS). It is good to have knowledgeable consideration for these dangers, but not to lose one's perspective. Physicians have dropped the word nuclear from the term nuclear magnetic resonance imaging, although radioactivity is not involved at all.

5-21 Radioprotectors

A number of substances have been developed which increase survival chances in case of heavy exposure to ionizing radiation. These radioprotectors contain the sulfhydryl chemical linkage (—SH) or its derivatives. They were developed by both the American and Soviet military establishments during the Cold War. The most effective such preventive, known by its code number WR2721, has the formula $NH_2CH_2CH_2CH_2NHCH_2CH_2SPO_3H$. These substances must be ingested or injected before exposure to the radiation or very quickly afterwards. They act by scavenging the free radicals formed by radiolysis. If a certain radiation dose causes a given level of mortality, the administration of WR2721 permits absorbing a dose up to 1.8 times as high without increasing the mortality rate. The drugs find a limited use in radiotherapy. The patient is injected just before irradiation, and the whole body becomes flooded with the drug, except the tumor to be treated. Thus a higher radiation dose can be given and normal tissues have some protection.

5-22 Exposure to Radiation

Dramatic accidents

Some Radiation Accidents—A group of physicists was working with the core of a plutonium bomb in a canyon laboratory four miles from Los Alamos. This was May 21, 1946. They were gathering data linked to the warheads for the upcoming tests in the Marshall Islands. Dr. Louis Slotin, who was leader of the Critical Assemblies Group, was using a screwdriver to lower one hemisphere of beryllium-coated plutonium onto another, a type of experiment known as tickling the dragon's tail. Through some mishap, the upper metallic mass fell onto the lower, and the assembly suddenly went supercritical. A blue glow engulfed the room. Slotin received a gamma ray and neutron radiation dose later estimated to be 880 rads. Within 12 hours he became nauseous and his blood white count soon dropped to almost nothing. He died a few days later. Another member of the group, Allan Kline, only 26 years old, received approximately 100 rads, a nonlethal dose. Kline became the victim of callous bureaucratic treatment. After two weeks in a hospital he was fired. He was sterile for two years, and suffered the debilitating effects of radiation exposure. He was denied his medical files, and later there was conclusive proof that Atomic Energy Agency officials had lied to him about the existence of many records.

Ionizing radiation of adult human ovaries or testes causes sterility. The dose for ovaries which causes permanent sterility is the rather high value of 250 to 600 rems. The corresponding dose for testes is about 350 rems administered as a single dose. A smaller dose, 15 rems, results in temporary sterility. One should keep in mind that the rem unit is based on one kilogram of tissue, and that the above cases are not whole-body doses.

In 1958 at Los Alamos, a solution containing plutonium salts was accidentally mixed with plutonium-rich solids, resulting in a supercritical mass. There was a blue flash, and one worker, Cecil Kelley, received a whole body dose somewhere between 6,000 and 18,000 rads. He died within 35 hours. In an autopsy, nearly nine pounds of tissues was removed from his body, causing distress to his family when they discovered this in 1996. A criticality accident took place in 1997 in Russia at the Arzamas-16 plant, killing one researcher. At least 60 criticality accidents have occurred worldwide. An acute dose of 8000 rads causes immediate incapacitation. Cases of unintended criticality with aqueous solutions easily give a fatal dose of radiation, but the events can hardly be classified as explosions; the word eruptions would be more accurate.

Exposure to a dose of 700 rads (whole body) results in lingering death generally in less than ten days, with indescribable suffering. With the breakdown of the body's defenses, the herpes simplex virus (which most of us harbor in dormant form, and which like all viruses is surpassingly resistant to radiation) breaks out into ugly ulcers in and near the mouth. Actual death is generally caused by multiple infections.

On April 17, 1962, in the Z-Plant at Hanford Nuclear Reservation another criticality accident occurred. A malfunctioning valve allowed a plutonium solution to be sucked into a five-gallon glass vessel which already held plutonium. One worker, Harold Aardal, saw the blue flash and feared for the worst. Neutron activation of all the metals nearby caused them to become radioactive. This included the metal buttons on his coveralls, keys, rings, watch, and even fillings in his teeth. Later measurements revealed that Aardal received a whole-body dose of around 115 rems, but his eyes absorbed four or five times more than that figure. After suffering for a couple of years with anemia, he recovered to a large degree.

In the cases described above, the exposures were in a short time. One incident provides data on heavy exposure spread over a longer time. In 1962 a boy in Mexico found a radiographic source of iridium-192 which had evidently been negligently left near a construction site. It might have been around 10 curies. He innocently took it home, where he, his mother, sister, and grandmother all received fatal doses of gamma rays. His father, who was home only for short periods, was exposed to approximately 1000 rads (whole body) over 15 weeks. His immune system was impaired, and he showed signs of anemia, but he apparently recovered his health and lived at least nine more years, when authorities lost track of his whereabouts.

It should be emphasized again that when speaking of dosage in number of rads or rems, it should be made clear whether exposure is whole body or to some localized organ or part. In radiation treatment for cancer, an organ might be given a dose of as much as 6000 rads, but this is not fatal because it is limited to a fraction of the total body.

One should note that when a person receives a whole-body dose of 250 rads, the energy absorbed, if it were converted entirely into the form of heat, would raise the body temperature by less than 0.01 degree. Such a small temperature increase is easily tolerated. The deadly effects of ionizing radiation are not thermal, but interruption of essential metabolic processes.

Radiation and Plants—Various kinds of plants differ radically in their resistance to ionizing radiation. Onions and wheat are very sensitive, but rice is resistant. It takes around 1000 rads to kill half of young rice seedlings, and the semilethal dose for more mature rice is as much as 15,000 rads. Evergreens are much more sensitive than deciduous trees, which require several thousand rads to kill. The effects of gamma rays on a forest were studied at Brookhaven National Laboratory, Long Island, NY, in the 1960s and 1970s. The source of gamma rays was cesium-137 suspended from a pole and the exposure was for about ten years. Near the source, the trees were slowly killed, with the

How about plants?

fraction which survived increasing radially. Scarlet oaks proved to be the hardiest trees. The dead forest today is an eerie, mournful sight.

5-23 Release of Iodine-131 at Hanford

In 1944 at the Hanford nuclear site, iodine-131 had accumulated, and a decision had to be made concerning its disposal. The material has a half-life of 8 days, and was well known to be dangerous to human beings and other mammals. What should have been done was to store the material at least 10 half-lives, when 99.9% of it would have decayed (4-6B). But what was actually done, through either the emergency of war or some grotesque error of judgment, was to release the vapors into the air, and thus expose the surrounding population. Releases occurred on a dozen occasions between 1944 and 1956; the total iodine amounted to 530,000 curies. In a single episode in 1945, about 340,000 curies of iodine were released; this is an enormous quantity. During the infamous1949 release, the weather pattern shifted and the vapors fell to the ground over a small area, giving heavy exposures to a few people. Before diffusion of iodine vapor into the air, clouds of the element in gaseous form are about nine times as dense as air and thus tend to sink to ground level before diffusion can spread it out evenly. It became trapped in basins and other low-lying areas. The iodine was absorbed by the thyroid glands of the nearby citizens, and in some cases their glands received as much as 1175 rads of exposure. Additional exposure resulted from food grown in contaminated soil. Information pried loose from the Department of Energy in 1990 revealed that around 13,500 residents were exposed. The releases continued ten years after the war ended. The fiercely patriotic populace just couldn't believe that their government would dare to do such a thing, and that the government had lied to them about the matter. Claims have been made that the radio-iodine releases were made to complement studies in radiological warfare.

This outrage was not an accident.

Hyperthyroidism is treated medically by injections of iodine-131 (as potassium iodide), which virtually destroys the thyroid gland. The dose to the thyroid gland is commonly between 3000 and 25,000 rads, and the result is hypothyroidism; there is also a certain chance of thyroid cancer years later. Hypothyroidism is managed by taking thyroxine orally. Doses to the thyroid of several hundred or a thousand rads can take up to 14 years to induce hypothryoidism.

In early 1999 results of a study of the health effects of the iodine releases by the U. S. Centers for Disease Control and Prevention were announced. The claim was that there was no link between the radiation releases and thyroid diseases of those studied. The study covered 3441 people born in eastern Washington between 1940 and 1946. But the first substantial release of iodine did not occur until 1944, and they continued until 1956, meaning that those born in the first three or four years of the period had no exposure, and those suffering the heavy exposures from 1947 to 1956 were excluded. The affected people just could not accept the results of the study. After all, similar exposure of the inhabitants of Rongelap Atoll in 1954 from hydrogen-bomb fallout caused numerous cases of hypothyroidism, as well as cancers and other tumors (9-19). There is abundant other evidence on this point. The study, or at least its form of presentation, seems to be seriously flawed. One analyst interpreted the report to mean a 20% higher death rate than expected.

Considering the iodine-131 and other releases at Hanford, the endangerment of uranium miners, the exposure of citizens downwind from nuclear tests in Nevada, and other instances, Dr. John W. Gofman wrote: "Trust in the government and science has been a casualty for these people. A terrible political betrayal has taken place. Increased disease will occur because of it." Gofman is a respected expert in effects of radiation on health, an emeritus professor at the University of California, Berkeley, and today is a compelling critic of the nuclear complex.

5-24 X-Rays, Breast Cancer, and Heart Disease

In a detailed evaluation of breast cancer in American women, Gofman (see Bibliography, 1990, 1995, 1999) has concluded that X-ray doses received nationwide are sufficient to account for up to 75% of the incidence of breast cancer, a result which is not accepted by many physicians. Of course he is aware of the contribution of heredity and other factors, and does not advocate halting all X-rays for diagnosis. But look at the figures for the United States (derived by the American Cancer Society):

In 1970, 68,000 cases diagnosed, which is	65 cases per 100,000
In 1975, 88,000	80
In 1980, 108,000	93
In 1985, 119,000	97
In 1990, 150,000	117
In 1994, 182,000	137

The Hiroshima data likewise gave evidence of increased breast cancer from ionizing radiation. Actually, making mammograms using X-rays is a rather primitive and crude technique for detection of tumors. A high percentage of tumors, perhaps 10%, is missed. The accuracy in distinguishing malignant from benign tumors is only 20 to 50%, so there are many false positives. Since film X-rays disclose only gross variations in the density of breast tissues, a newer procedure using digital techniques has been developed in Canada. Such images can be manipulated to highlight any suspicious regions. Also, imaging techniques using non-ionizing radiation are being developed (below and 6-39D). Recent advances in thermography have greatly enhanced its sensitivity. Tumors are detected, but not imaged, by using pads full of heat-sensor dots over suspected cancers. These dots change color from blue to pink when the skin is a few degrees above normal, disclosing elevated metabolism due to a tumor. Increased attention to breast cancer is being boosted by a United Sates Postage stamp (Fig. 5-24, Color Plate I).

In addition, Gofman carried out analyses of statistical data from many sources, including the American censuses from 1940 to 1990, and has given strong evidence that medical X-ray exposure is an important component in causing more than half of cancer (all types, not just breast cancer) and coronary heart disease cases. That X-rays play such a role in heart disease comes as a genuine surprise. Coronary disease, more accurately known as ischemic heart disease, results from localized anemia of heart muscle from obstruction of the inflow of arterial blood. Gofman's hypothesis is that the coronary arteries are particularly sensitive to X-rays, which produce abundant mini-tumors in smooth muscle cells.

Are we to conclude that the medical profession should give up use of X-rays? No, not at all; imaging by X-rays is simply too valuable for that. What should be done then? There are three steps which are recommended:

1. The most urgent measure is to start reducing the radiation dose in making medical images. Radiologists have shown how to cut exposure dosage by at least 50%, and in many cases much more, without losing quality. The techniques involve improved X-ray beam collimation, use of rare-earth screens and filters, use of carbon-fiber materials, and more frequent shielding of tissues which are not to be imaged. Capturing images by digital radiography, using pulsed X-rays, reduces not only dose, but also reduces labor (for example, no film is used, eliminating development, simplifying storage, etc.).
2. Development of smaller magnetic resonance imaging (6-39B) units for medical office use. This would require much research in perfecting strong permanent magnets, such as those based on rare-earth alloys, and accompanying electronics adapted to magnetic fields weaker than those made using liquid helium and superconducting coils. They would be too small to be used for whole body imaging, only for organs such as the human head or those which are smaller. There would be no ionizing radiation.
3. Imaging using terahertz radiation (6-39D). This technique, also employing non-ionizing radiation, has already been demonstrated to be suitable, but more development is required to build units compatible with medical use.

5-25 Effects of Increasing Acute Doses

Experience from the Hiroshima and Nagasaki explosions, as well as various accidents worldwide, are summarized in the table below (adapted and abbreviated from the data of Glasstone and Dolan, 1977; see Bibliography). The whole-body doses are given in rems, but if little alpha irradiation is involved (as is usually the case), rems and rads are approximately equal. The semilethal dose for human beings is generally considered to be 450 rems.

Clinical Effects of Acute Doses of Ionizing Radiation

Whole-body dose (rems)	0-100	100-200	200-600	600-1000	1000-5000	over 5000
Incidence of vomiting	none	5–50%	300 rem,100%	100%	100%	100%
Time of onset	—	3–6 hr.	½–6 hr.	15–30 min.	5–30 min.	a few min.
Symptoms	none	some loss of white blood cells	more loss of white blood cells	severe loss of white cells; infection	diarrhea; fever	convulsions; tremor
Prognosis	excellent	good	fair	poor	hopeless	hopeless
Incidence of death	—	very low	up to 80%	80–100%	90–100%	90-100%
Death within	—	—	3 months	1–6 weeks	2–14 days	2 days

5-26 Accidental Exposures from Medical Electron Accelerators

Radiation to treat tumors arises from radioactive nuclides or is generated as X-rays or high-energy electrons using medical linear accelerators. The instrument known as Therac-25 is a recent model accelerator. It produces a stream of electrons of energy up to 25 megaelectron volts, and also has the capacity to generate X-rays from the electron beam. In the period 1985–1987 there were six accidents in the United States or Canada involving massive overdoses of radiation by Therac-25 units, resulting in deaths or serious injuries.

A single therapeutic dose to an organ is generally around 200 rads (rads and rems are approximately equivalent in these cases). Owing to errors in software and other sources one patient received between 13,000 and 17,000 rads, and died a few months later. In another case, a patient whose radiation prescription was for 180 rads in an electron beam directed to a spot on his upper back actually received between 16,500 and 25,000 rads in a small area. He passed away five months later. The evidence from these and other cases emphasizes that while the semilethal dose for whole-body exposure is approximately 450 rads, death can result from exposure of limited areas or a single organ if the dose is exceedingly high.

5-27 Unethical Radiation Experiments

Late in World War II, rumors began to emerge that human beings were being used as guinea pigs in testing ionizing radiation in a number of facilities scattered over the United States. In 1993 Energy Secretary Hazel O'Leary, in an American type of *glasnost,* blew the cover from government secrecy and publicly acknowledged that indeed a series of such tests had been carried out up to 1974, and that many if not most of these were illegal. O'Leary was "appalled, shocked, and deeply saddened," she said. Her revelation was a welcome and rare instance of government candor.

While some records have been destroyed, at least 800 people were used in experiments in which potentially harmful amounts of radioactive materials were injected into their bodies, or they were exposed to harmful doses of X-rays. In addition, around 8000 American military personnel were exposed to fallout during nuclear bomb tests, and others suffered radiation injury in cleanup operations of battleships contaminated with fallout.

The "patients" selected were not a representative cross-section of the American people: they were mostly prisoners, poor and pregnant women, the elderly, disadvantaged people of color, and some who were believed to be mentally retarded. In many, perhaps most, cases the consent of the persons affected was not obtained, and little or no explanation was given. In one of the earliest experiments (April 1945 - to July 1947), 18 unwitting Americans were injected with soluble plutonium compounds. Seventeen of them died slowly and painfully. In the end, there was no admission of responsibility by the government, no compensation, and no apology. In 1946-47, a study at the University of Rochester involved injecting six patients with increasing doses of uranium to induce renal damage. The object was to determine what level of radiation and/or chemical toxicity would cause a given level of damage to the kidneys. The patients included a homeless person and alcoholics. In 1948, 751 women sought care at the prenatal clinic of Vanderbilt University. They were treated with low doses of radioactive iron (Fe-59), producing a level of radiation about 30 times background, which was considered safe at the time. Three of the children born later died, and the radiation probably played a role in this. Between 1960 and 1972 at Cincinnati general Hospital, at least 82 charity cancer patients (61 of them African American) received whole-body X-irradiation. The maximum dose was 200 rads. According to the physician in charge, the intent was to give relief from pain and to cause the cancers to shrink, but there is documentary evidence that the study was also designed to gauge the level of radiation exposure to soldiers on the battlefield. Moreover, the Department of Defense paid $651,000 to support the experiments. The Pentagon sent copies of the report on the radiation experiments to numerous weapons testers, but not to a single civilian cancer researcher, so one can see where the priorities lay. The 200-rad dose was known to be unsafe; indeed, 25 of the patients (about 30%) died within 60 days. In 1999 the families of the victims were awarded $4.6 million in compensation.

Shortly after the war, there was curiosity and an alleged need to know how and at what rate the body eliminated plutonium. At the Manhattan District Hospital at Oak Ridge and at other sites, 18 seriously ill patients were given injections of soluble plutonium salts. Their excreta were monitored for periods up to about 135 days. Five of the 18 subjects were still alive in 1974, when they were informed of the nature of the experiments. The plutonium could hardly have contributed to improved health of the patients, but most were so sick that they probably would have died regardless of the plutonium. In 1961 two small nodes were found under Woodrow Litton's arm, and cancer was suspected. He died in 1965 at the Oak Ridge Institute of Nuclear Studies hospital. His son tried to get the medical records, but was told they were "classified." They were not released until 1994, when his son described his father "was part of one of the most horrifying radiation experiments by the U.S. Government," and that his father had been "used like an animal for experimental purposes." The records revealed that Woodrow Litton had been given lanthanum-140, iodine-123 and -131, and iron-59. He received a dose of 4500 rads of gamma rays from cobalt-60 and 150 rads from cesium-137. There was a statement that "Mr. Litton is not responding to radiation by cobalt-60 or cesium-137." But nevertheless, the next day he received an additional dose of 220 rads from cobalt-60. There is no way in which even the Cold War could justify such acts.

Again, these outrages were not accidents.

President Clinton set up an advisory committee to study the matter, offer an official apology, and arrange financial compensation. He said the experiments "were unethical not only by today's standards but by the standards of the time." A payment of $6.5 million was made to the families of 16 of the 18 the victims who were injected with plutonium or uranium; the remaining cases are yet to be settled.

It is self-evident that each of us has the fundamental right not to be used involuntarily or unknowingly as subjects in experiments on our bodies.

5-28 Skin Cancer and Radiation from the Sun

It is ultraviolet radiation (UV) in the B region (280-320 nm wavelength) which is most dramatic in its adverse biological effects (see the ozone layer, 4-31). Acute exposure causes sunburn. UV can penetrate well below the surface of skin. Human skin reacts to steady doses of UV-B by thickening and producing more of the UV-absorbing pigment melanin, that is, a tan. Light-skinned individuals burn easily and tan with difficulty. Recent evidence suggests that UV-A (wavelength 400 down to 320 nanometers) is also capable of inducing skin cancer. Exposure to sunlight is a major cause of wrinkles. It is amazing how our youth can fear radiation, and yet bask in the Sun, absorbing much ultraviolet radiation to the great detriment of the health of their skin in the future. About 90% of skin cancers are a consequence of excessive exposure to the Sun. They are found in three types. Two of these, basal cell and squamous cell carcinomas, arise from long-time exposure. Being readily curable, they are rarely fatal, but can be disfiguring. Continued exposure leads later to lesions called actinic keratoses, which if untreated can lead to skin cancer (mostly squamous cell type), although the probability is low. Considerable information about the mechanism by which ultraviolet light induces cancer has recently become available. The ultraviolet causes a mutation in a tumor-suppressing gene identified as *p53* (5-4). The third type is malignant melanoma which, although constituting only about 4% of skin cancers, is often deadly; early detection and treatment are often successful. Such cancers metastasize readily, especially to the eye or brain. A recently developed treatment for melanoma which is still experimental but seems to be really promising consists of injecting attenuated melanoma cells. The cells are grown in the laboratory and irradiated with X-rays to disable their ability to proliferate, similar to the way some vaccines are prepared. Advanced melanoma is incurable. Numerous studies have linked the use of tanning salons to melanoma.

Skin cancer

There must be important factors in addition to sunlight which contribute to causing melanoma, since the lesions sometimes form on protected areas, such as the soles of the feet. It has been estimated that in the United States ozone layer depletion can cause thousands of additional deaths from skin cancer over the next 50 years. Skin cancer rates greatly increased in the 1980s. About 53,600 cases of skin melanoma and 7,400 deaths are expected in the United States yearly. So many young people nowadays are contracting skin cancer that one must conclude that they are simply not getting the message about the dangers of excessive exposure to sunshine.

Bibliography for Chapter 5: Biological Effects of Radiation

David J. Brenner, *RADON: RISK AND REMEDY*, Freeman, 1989.

Leonard A. Cole, *ELEMENTS OF RISK: THE POLITICS OF RADON*, AAAS Press, 1993.

John W. Gofman, *RADIATION AND HUMAN HEALTH*, Sierra Club Books, 1981.

John W. Gofman, a series of three books available from the Committee for Nuclear Responsibility, Inc., P.O. Box 421993, San Francisco, CA 94142; 1. *RADIATION-INDUCED CANCER FROM LOW LOW-DOSE EXPOSURE*, 1990; 2. *PREVENTING BREAST CANCER*, 1995; 3. *RADIATION FROM MEDICAL PROCEDURES IN THE PATHOGENESIS OF CANCER AND ISCHEMIC HEART DISEASE*, 1999.

Institute of Medicine/National Academy of Sciences, *THE MEDICAL IMPLICATIONS OF NUCLEAR WAR*, National Academy Press, 1986.

S. K. Majumdar, R. F. Schmalz, and E. W. Miller, *ENVIRONMENTAL RADON: OCCURRENCE, CONTROL AND HEALTH HAZARDS*, Pensylvannia Academy of Sciences, Lafayette College, Easton, PA 18042, 1991.

Jonathan D. Moreno, *UNDUE RISK: SECRET STATE EXPERIMENTS ON HUMANS*, W. H. Freeman, 1999.

Karl Z. Morgan and Ken M. Peterson, *THE ANGRY GENIE: ONE MAN'S WALK THROUGH THE NUCLEAR AGE*, University of Oklahoma Press, 1999.

John V. Neal and William J. Schull, *THE CHILDREN OF ATOMIC BOMB SURVIVORS: A GENETIC STUDY*, National Academy Press, Washington, DC,1991.

Anthony Robbins, director, *RADIOACTIVE HEAVEN & EARTH: HEALTH & ENVIRONMENTAL EFFECTS OF NUCLEAR TESTING IN, ON & ABOVE THE EARTH*, International Physicians for Prevention of Nuclear War, 126 Rogers St., Cambridge, MA 02142-1096, The Apex Press, New York, NY, 1991.

W. J. Schull, *EFFECTS OF ATOMIC RADIATION: A HALF-CENTURY OF STUDIES FROM HIROSHIMA AND NAGASAKI*,, Wiley, NY, 1995.

Fredric Soloman and Robert Q. Marston, eds., *THE MEDICAL IMPLICATIONS OF NUCLEAR WAR*, National Academy Press, 1986.

J. Newel Stannard, *RADIOACTIVITY AND HEALTH, A HISTORY*, Vol. 1, Laboratory Research; Vol. 2, Environmental Aspects; Vol. 3, Applied Aspects; Pacific Northwest Laboratory, Battelle Memorial Institute. Available from National Technical Information Service, 5285 Port Royal Road, Springfield, VA 22161.

Manuel Tubis and Walter Wolf, *RADIOPHARMACY*, Wiley Interscience, N.Y., 1976.

United Nations Scientific Committee on the Effects of Ionizing Radiation (UNSCEAR), *SOURCES AND EFFECTS OF IONIZING RADIATION*, United Nations Publications, Room DC2-0853, Dept. 141, New York, NY, 10017. Vol. 1 *SOURCES*; Vol. 2, *EFFECTS*, 2000. *HEREDITARY EFFECTS OF RADIATION*, 2001.

U.S. Department of Health, Education and Welfare, *RADIOLOGICAL HEALTH HANDBOOK*, 1970.

U.S. Office of Technology Assessment, *THE EFFECTS OF NUCLEAR WAR*, Washington, DC, 1979.

Eileen Welsome, *THE PLUTONIUM FILES* (experiments on human beings with plutonium), The Dial Press, 1999.

James N. Yamasaki with Louis B. Flemming, *CHILDREN OF THE ATOMIC BOMB*, Duke University Press, 1995.

Chapter 6: RADIOACTIVITY IN HUMAN SERVICE

ABSTRACT—While the peacetime applications of radioactive materials are not as extensive as those of electricity, they are growing every year. Nuclear reactors, aside from furnishing energy to generate electricity for our citizens, also power ships, buoys, spacecraft, generate radioisotopes for nuclear medicine, and the like. Underground explosions form cavities in which natural gas can be stored. Determination of the age of our Earth, of paintings, and of archaeological objects is made possible by radioactivity measurements. Temperatures which prevailed millions of years ago can be determined. Use of radioactive isotopes to trace a chemical element through reactions in plants, animals, and nonliving systems has given priceless information. Some of the more important developments are analysis by neutron activation, selective control of insects by sterilizing their eggs with gamma rays, preservation of food and disinfestation of fruit by irradiation, thermoelectric generators, magnetic resonance imaging, nuclear magnetic spectra, moisture meters for use by farmers, and incredibly accurate atomic clocks. But it is probably the development of nuclear medicine which is most significant in raising the quality of human life. This comprises radiotherapy (including particle beams), and especially imaging the organs of the living body, studying thought processes, brain disorders, speech and its disorders, human emotions, and many other functions.

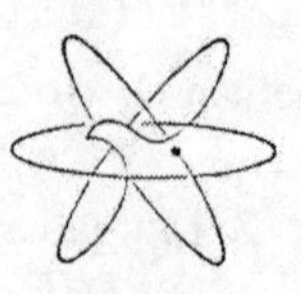

6-1 Introduction

In the grand scheme of things, radioactivity and related phenomena are new in human history. While THE BOMB has been overshadowing all else, the next most important development (electricity-producing nuclear reactors) is primarily nonmilitary. Nuclear reactors are used to power many submarines and aircraft carriers, and these are military uses, but they are also used to power civilian ships. For example, by 1964 the Soviets had built the icebreaker, the Lenin, and the U.S. had built the freight vessel, the Savannah. It is the applications of isotopes, both radioactive and stable, which probably have brought more benefits to humankind than all other nuclear developments. While the peacetime applications discussed in this chapter deal mostly with radioactive isotopes, many topics involve stable, nonradioactive isotopes.

The following anecdote describes the most trivial use of uranium metal. The incident dates from Manhattan Project days, being January 1943. The author and two companions, Dr. A. S. Newton and Dr. Adolf Voigt, were driving a station wagon from the first nuclear reactor, the historic original one at the University of Chicago, to our laboratory at Iowa State University, in Ames. Our cargo was a lead box of uranium ingots from the reactor, and they were fairly radioactive because of the fission products. Snow covered the landscape. About three o'clock in the morning we had a flat in the lonely Iowa prairie, and were dismayed to find that the jack was faulty. It had a lifting span of only three or four inches. Driven by desperation,

Well, at least uranium is good for holding up cars.

we devised a system in which, using radiation-protection gear, we jacked up the axle enough to slide a stack of the uranium ingots underneath, lowered the car, and used the jack another time when it too rested on a stack of uranium ingots. In this way, alternately putting uranium ingots under the axle and jack, we managed to raise the car by notches enough to change the wheel.

6-2 Nonmilitary Nuclear Explosions

Consider the cost of energy produced by a high-yield thermonuclear explosion (described in Chapter 9). Counting the dollars per bomb and the amount of energy released (ignoring the destructive effects), the price per joule (or billion joules, or calories, or whatever unit) is the lowest of all known intense energy sources. Solar energy is cheaper, but it is spread out, not concentrated, and is less favorable to harness efficiently. Thermonuclear explosions provide the most intense or concentrated energy source known. The cost of TNT itself per ton is around 330 times more than the equivalent of TNT per ton from a 2 megaton bomb; when the bomb is as small as 10 kilotons, real TNT still costs 100 times per ton more than its equivalent in nuclear explosive power.

At one time there were rosy dreams of using nuclear explosions to "unlock a treasure chest of Arctic oil, dig open an Alaskan harbor, open the spigot for Colorado's shale," and to construct a sea-level Panama Canal. In 1957-58 an operation called Project Chariot was promoted to dig a harbor or channel at Cape Thompson on Alaska's northwestern coast using six nuclear explosions. None of these schemes ever materialized.

About the only decent use of nuclear explosions is to make underground cavities to store natural gas.

A fair number of tests have been carried out to put nuclear explosions to nonmilitary and scientific use. The Soviets took the lead in this work. Approximately 17% of their tests, numbering 124, are classified as peaceful nuclear explosions; only 3% of American tests fall into this category. The Soviets blasted a cavity for a lake in Kazakhstan in 1965 (9-25I) but the water was too radioactive for many years to be very useful. To this day it remains contaminated with tritium and lesser amounts of other radionuclides. Twenty-one underground explosions were made in Russian territory in connection with oil and gas extraction. Another objective of nonmilitary Soviet tests was to create underground cavities for storage of natural gas, and 19 more explosions were made for this purpose, mostly in the Astrakhan gas field not far from the point where the Volga runs into the Caspian Sea. At least one cavity in that area was blasted in a giant salt deposit, with the intention of using it to store oil. The cavities have also been used to dump waste brine produced by oil fields. But some of the sites were poorly chosen and the cavities filled with water. Only about half of them are still in use today. In addition, five tests were made to extinguish oil-well fires by nuclear explosions. At least 39 underground nuclear explosions were made to create shock waves in seismological research. The purpose was to study the deep structure of the earth. The resulting data permitted more accurate measurements of the depth of magma and tectonic plates. Still others were stated to be for the purpose of canal construction to change the course of rivers, mining, and excavation of water reservoirs, but too much radioactivity was released to make these projects feasible. Four explosions were conducted on the Kola

Peninsula for mining purposes. The American Plowshare program included tests to break up hard rock to permit the flow of natural gas. A few American experimental explosions were to test neutron sources and theories in basic physics not related to weapons. Seismic studies were also made using nuclear explosions. In general, the results of the tests have been disappointing because of the high levels of radioactivity released. Water in particular becomes too contaminated. Even the natural gas tapped cannot be safely used. It might be that after several decades the underground cavities will permit safe storage of gas. There is the possibility of using blast cavities deep underground as dumps for radioactive and other waste (8-34E). These appear to be about the only practical constructive use of nuclear explosions in the foreseeable future.

In 1993 American and Canadian geologists published a report concerning a new technique of studying the interior of the Earth. They took advantage of a 600-kiloton hydrogen bomb detonated 1 kilometer underground in China in May,1992. The tremendous shock wave grazed the core-mantle boundary 1500 miles deep and was reflected upward. The high-frequency signals were picked up by a network of 1062 seismometers in North America and synthesized into images by computer. The resolution was about ten times better than previously possible. Relatively sharp images of "islands" about 60 miles across were detected atop the molten iron-nickel core, and other still larger structures also were found. The nature of these features is unknown.

6-3 How Old Is Our Earth?

The age of our Earth is a topic which has intrigued philosophers and religious leaders since prehistoric times. By about1875 geologists had evidence that the Earth is at least several million years old. It was recognized quite early in the study of radioactivity that a new and dependable way to measure the age of the Earth was at hand. As early as 1906 Rutherford demonstrated that the age must be more than 400 million years. The next year the American physicist Boltwood, studying the radioactive decay of uranium, showed that the age of the mineral which contained the uranium was at least 2.2 billion years. By the 1980s, the use of radioactivity to determine cosmic, geologic, and anthropological age was well advanced; the discipline is called geochronology. Much more sensitive instruments became available, and a dozen or so techniques were developed to read these nuclear clocks. The more important methods are described below.

Cosmic clocks

The Uranium/Lead Method—The most abundant isotope of uranium, U-238, has a half-life of 4.468 billion years (this and other long half-lives can be determined by measuring the activity of small, pure samples). It decays through 8 alpha and 7 beta emissions through various intermediate nuclides (with some complications; see uranium series, 4-8), and ends up as stable lead-206. The more lead-206 present in a uranium-bearing mineral, the older it must be. To determine the age of a mineral, the isotopic abundances of the uranium-238 and lead-206 are determined using a mass spectrometer. Knowing the half-life of the uranium, the age of the mineral can be calculated. One difficulty is that one of the intermediates in the decay of both isotopes of uranium to lead is radon, a gas, and this might diffuse out somewhat, making the age determined appear to be lower than the true age. Choosing uranium imprisoned in impervious crystals of zircon helps insure no loss of radon.

The technique just described is well suited to determining the age of diamonds. It is known that diamonds are formed from the less dense form of carbon, graphite, at the temperatures and pressures existing about 125 miles deep in the earth. In some cases a trace of uranium is held captive inside the newly formed crystal. After millions of years, geological processes bring the diamonds up to or near the surface where they can be mined. The ratio of uranium-238 to lead-206 is determined spectrographically, and since the half-life of the uranium is known, the age of the diamond host can be computed. Most diamonds prove to be 2.4 billion to 3.2 billion years old; the youngest found so far, from Zaire (Belgium Congo) , is a mere 628 million years old.

The general procedure can be summarized: If a radioactive element of known decay sequence is locked in a structure when it is formed, and the decay products also remain secured in the structure (sometimes not the case), then by determining the amount of decay product relative to the parent element, one can compute the age.

The Lead-206/Lead-207 Ratio Method—The two major isotopes of uranium, U-238 and U-235, always occur together. While uranium-238, in a series of steps, ends up as stable lead-206, uranium-235 ends as stable lead-207. Therefore if the ratio of these two isotopes is determined, the age of the specimen can be calculated, since the half-lives of both isotopes of uranium are known. The lower the lead-206/lead-207 ratio, the older the sample must be. This technique is considered more reliable than the first.

The Rubidium-87/Strontium-87 Ratio Method—One of the two natural isotopes of rubidium is beta active, but its half-life is exceedingly long (48.0 billion years). It decays to stable strontium-87. If the ratio of these two nuclides is determined, the age of the specimen can be determined. This method is widely used, and is one of the most reliable. We must keep in mind that all these atomic clocks are set at zero on the formation of the specimen, whether by crystallization from a melt, precipitation, or otherwise.

The Argon-39/Argon-40 Ratio Method—A minor isotope of potassium (mass number 40) decays in two ways: by electron capture forming argon-40, and by beta decay forming calcium-40. By measuring the ratio of the potassium and argon nuclides, the age of rocks may be computed. This is the potassium-40/argon-40 technique, which has been largely replaced by its derivative, the newer, more accurate procedure, the argon-39/argon-40 method, and it is truly elegant. One could say the technique makes the silent stones speak. In the argon-39/argon-40 method, the specimen of rock is first exposed to neutrons in a nuclear reactor. Energetic neutrons interact with some of the abundant potassium-39 nuclei, forming argon-39 and protons. Since argon-39 is radioactive (half-life 269 years), none exists in the ancient rock specimens before neutron bombardment. By now removing the argon (both the newly formed argon-39 and the stable argon-40 which arose from potassium-40 decay), and measuring their ratio by mass spectrometry, the age of the sample can be computed. A further refinement, recently developed, consists of heating the grain of rock by a laser beam to drive out the argon. By successive exposures, argon from deeper and deeper in the grain is removed for analysis in an accelerator mass spectrometer (6-6). The most reliable results derive from use of a single crystal, as found in volcanic dust. The error in age determination is only 0.1%.

An example of using the argon-39/argon-40 procedure is work done at the Institute of Human Origins, Berkeley, California. In 1994 a team of researchers from this laboratory examined the famous fossils discovered in 1936 near Mojokerto, Java. The results disclosed the age of the *homo erectus* hominids to be 1.81 million years. This indicates that these beings, who were athletic and humanlike, migrated out of their African homeland much earlier than previously thought. This might be an important link in the evolution of the races of mankind. The technique was also employed in establishing the date at which an asteroid fell onto the Earth 65 million years ago, hastening the extinction of dinosaurs (10-60).

Other Methods—The samarium-147/neodymium-147 ratio technique is analogous to the above, and is increasingly used. A different approach employs analysis for special nuclides which arose from ancient radioactive decay processes. An example is iodine-129, now extinct; it decays to xenon-129. Many meteorites have an abnormally high xenon-129 content, and by measuring its abundance, and using the known half-life of iodine-129, their ages can be calculated. Another example is based on the spontaneous fission of primordial plutonium-244.

The Earth's crust is active geologically: the continents are shifting, there is volcanism, erosion, sedimentation, metamorphic processes, and other changes. The uranium/lead method shows ages of several billion years for various minerals. The lead-206/lead-207 method gives essentially the same results with the same specimens. When this method was applied to the lead found in ocean sediments, the age came out to be 4.57 billion years. Meteorites were dated as being 4.55 billion years old; the rubidium/strontium technique gave 4.6 billion years. Many analyses, using several of the procedures outlined above, of hundreds of meteorites, and also of minerals and obsidian-like glass brought back from the Moon by the Apollo astronauts, disclosed them to be 4.5 to 4.6 billion years old. Thus the results of the various measurements are surprisingly consistent.

Our earth and solar system are 4,600,000,000 years old.

When various minerals crystallized, any magnetic components align themselves with the Earth's magnetic field. By determining the direction of the mineral's magnetic pole, and knowing the sites of the Earth's magnetic poles, studies coupled with dating techniques based on radioactivity have permitted finding out the earliest history of the Earth's continents and their movement on tectonic plates. For example, the continent of Africa about 3.5 billion years ago was up near the North Pole, and 300 million years later was on the equator, but rotated 90° relative to its present site. Continental drift carried it northward 1800 miles again (2.9 billion years ago), and after another 200 million years it was back on the equator and rotated oppositely relative to the previous orientation. After considerable more wandering, Africa arrived at its present site, but is still migrating at a rate of around 1.5 centimeters per year.

Americans like to put messages on bumper stickers. A USC geology student made one reading "STOP CONTINENTAL DRIFT!"

Conclusions—The conclusions are inescapable: the genesis of our Earth and solar system was approximately 4.6 billion years ago; the uncertainty is about 70 million years. The reason many rocks are younger (ages up to 4.3 billion years) is that their matter was recycled, and the age determined shows only when they crystallized last. This does not apply to the lead-206/lead-207 technique; employed using ocean sediments; the age determined, 4.6 billion years, is the directly determined age of the Earth. In 1991, a painstaking investigation of a well-studied meteorite by this technique disclosed an age of 4.566 ± 0.002 billion years. Samples of volcanic basalt from the Moon proved to be 3.6 to 4.2 billion years old, showing that they crystallized from lava which was forced out during the Moon's first billion years. The oldest mineral found on Earth so far consists of crystals from the Jack Hills, western Australia, of age 4.3 billion years. Specimens of the mineral zircon from Canada have proven to be 4.0 billion years old. The immense span of time which is the age of our Earth, 4.6 billion years, is hundreds of thousands of times longer than that suggested in various sacred scriptures.

6-4 How to Detect Forgery in Paintings

The principal pigment in nearly all paint used by classical artists was white lead, a basic carbonate of that metal. About 24% of ordinary lead is lead-206, the final product in the uranium-238 decay series discussed above and in section 4-8. One of the intermediates is beta-active lead-210, which has a half-life of 22.3 years. When lead ore is processed to make white lead, traces of lead-210 are always incorporated in it, as well as small amounts of radium. By measuring the radioactivity of the lead-210 (there are various corrections and complications not presented here), it is possible to determine the age of the white lead in a given painting. The technique has been verified by comparing with the age of paintings whose dates of creation are known without doubt. In this way some paintings alleged to have been made by the Dutch master Vermeer van Delft in the 17th century were shown in 1968 to have actually been counterfeited during the period 1930-40. The forgeries, by one van Meegeren, were of such high talent that they are now valuable on their own merits.

If you intend to fake a painting, mind the isotopic composition of its lead.

6-5 Dating Using Fission Tracks or Thermoluminescence

Most rocks and minerals contain at least trace amounts of uranium. The principal isotope, uranium-238, is known to undergo spontaneous fission with a half-life of 8 million billion years, which is the same as 25 atoms experiencing fission every hour per gram of uranium. The two fission products plow in opposite directions from their source, penetrating the solid matrix some 10 to 20 micrometers, depending on the mineral. In these energetic disintegrations, the atoms of the host material are displaced, and fission tracks remain permanently and accumulate over the centuries.

If a mineral specimen is sliced and examined using an electron microscope, the tracks are visible; if the surface is etched chemically, they can often be seen by using an ordinary optical microscope. Now, if we count the tracks within a certain area, and analyze the specimen for total uranium, its age can be computed; the more tracks per unit of uranium, the older the specimen is. In this way the uranium ores at Oklo (7-18) were found to be 1.74 billion years old. If a specimen is heated strongly, the material anneals and the tracks disappear. Thus if we examine pottery, the date at which it was made can be determined, for the nuclear clock was reset to zero on firing. In this way certain Japanese ceramics were dated at 300 BC; others were found to be only 700 years old.

Most minerals have absorbed energy from the fission or radioactivity of uranium, thorium, potassium-40, etc., some of which is generally present. Over the eons this energy, resulting in fission tracks or similar displacements, accumulates and might be around 0.1 to 1 rad each year. The energy actually is stored by electrons which have been forced into high-energy states. When heated to 500 °C, a temperature just below that at which a red glow begins, the electrons fall back to more stable low-energy states and the accumulated energy is released as light (thermoluminescence). If the intensity of this light and the radioactivity of the sample are measured, the age can be calculated. Here too the clock is reset to zero by firing; unfired clay cannot be used. Errors in age determination are rather large, being 25 to 33%; nevertheless, the method is suitable for authenticity dating. This technique has become standard among archaeologists. Using it, Chinese porcelains from Western museums were dated at approximately 1500 years, proving them to be authentic 6th dynasty pieces. But many other specimens, identical in appearance, proved to have been made about the year 1900, and were thus forgeries. A skilled Mexican ceramist, Brigido Lara, made copies of pre-Columbian art of the Veracruz style. They were so nearly perfect that several museums exhibited them as bona fide pieces until thermoluminescence testing revealed their recent origin. Curiously, fossil bones over extended time accumulate uranium from the surrounding soil, often becoming 100 times richer in the radioactive element than the soil. A Los Alamos team took advantage of this observation and, using a sensitive gamma-ray spectrometer, explored areas of New Mexico. Fossilized dinosaur bones, evidently from a sauropod, were detected near the surface. The technique is in its infancy.

If you make facsimilies, label them as replicas, not authentic originals.

6-6 Dating Using Carbon-14

Cosmic rays interact with the upper reaches of the atmosphere, releasing free neutrons with a spectrum of energy levels. Slower neutrons convert some of the abundant nitrogen-14 to radioactive carbon-14, which has been forming (and decaying away) in trace amounts since the Earth was born. This isotope was discovered in 1940 by Martin Kamen, who later became a professor at USC. It made possible the determination of the ages of thousands of archeological specimens, described below. Kamen worked on the Manhattan Project, but after helping a Soviet consul get access to some radioactive phosphorus to treat his leukemia, he was removed on the groundless charge that he gave the Russians atomic secrets.

The carbon-14, as carbon dioxide, diffuses downward within a few years. Green plants take up and assimilate both ordinary carbon-12 dioxide and the carbon-14 dioxide. Thus some carbon-14 becomes incorporated into plant components such as cellulose, sugars, etc. When the plants are eaten by animals, the carbon-14 finds its way into bone, muscle, fat, and other tissues. At the death of the plant or animal, assimilation of fresh carbon-14 ceases. It occurred to the chemist Willard Libby that these processes afford a means of determining the age of ancient biological specimens from Nature's scrapbook. Development of the technique began in the early 1940s.

Willard F. Libby (1908–1980), American chemist. Professor at the University of Chicago's Institute of Nuclear Studies and at UCLA. Nobel Prize in chemistry, 1960. Developed dating technique using carbon-14.

Carbon-14 decays by beta emission with a half-life of 5730 years; no gamma ray is released. Suppose we take many biological specimens which are of recent origin (but which lived before nuclear explosions in the atmosphere added a great deal of carbon-14; see 6-6). These are burned in oxygen and the radioactivity of the carbon dioxide is measured. The result is that the concentration of carbon-14 is such that an average of 15.2 beta particles are emitted each minute for every gram of carbon. This holds for all contemporary specimens. This trifling level of radioactivity corresponds to one atom of carbon-14 in every 765 billion atoms of carbon-12. Each beta particle comes from disintegration of one carbon-14 atom, and the observed rate of radioactive decay is 15.2 disintegrations per minute per gram of carbon, as mentioned. This unit is abbreviated as dpm/g; it can also be expressed as 15.2/60 = 0.25 becquerel (Bq) per gram of carbon, or as 1 disintegration every 4 seconds. A fraction of the plant or animal substance eventually becomes fossils. The tiny amount of carbon-14 becomes even smaller as radioactivity claims its toll. After one half-life (5730 years), the activity will drop to 7.6 dpm/g; after a second half-life, it will be down to 3.8 dpm/g. If the logarithm of the radioactivity is plotted against time, we get a straight line (see 4-5 and figure below).

All living things are slightly radioactive.

What if the specimen was from an organism which lived 5730 years ago? Its activity today would be 7.6 dpm/g. The experiment is the same as the one described above, except that it started 5730 years earlier. It is clear that we can take any specimen of biological origin from antiquity, measure its carbon-14 content via radioactivity, and at once learn its age, provided it is not so old that the radioactivity has nearly died out. Carbon-14 dating has proved to be a powerful tool for archaeologists, anthropologists and geologists (see sketch below). Its limit is about 10 half-lives (57,300 years), when the weak radioactivity is overwhelmed by background from cosmic rays and other sources.

But what if the intensity of cosmic rays, and thus the rate of formation of carbon-14, has not been constant over the millennia? This point is addressed in several ways. If we cut ancient trees, such as the sequoia or the even older bristlecone pine (8000 years), we can count the rings and establish the age of the wood in each ring. Each wood sample is dated by carbon-14. The results show that cosmic rays have not been constant, but vary as much as 10%. It is easy to make appropriate corrections. A way to test the method is to date an object whose authentic age is known from history. A wooden coffin from the Ptolemaic period of Egypt for example, was known to be 2280 years old in 1980. The carbon-14 method showed 2190 years (a 90 year error, fortuitously less than the uncertainty range of about 400 years).

Carbon-14 dating has presented us with some interesting and valuable conclusions. One of the earliest was in 1953 when scientists Oakley, Weiner, and Clark used the newly-developed technique to examine the skull and jawbone of the Piltdown man, unearthed in England in 1912 and alleged to be from a sort of missing link in human evolution. The measurements proved conclusively that the so-called fossils were of modern origin. The jawbone was that of an orangutan. The whole matter was a hoax. Wooden artifacts made by Mayan Indians at Tikal, Guatemala, were shown to be 1513 years of age.

The matter of when the first human beings entered the new world is still not settled, but is a topic of enduring interest. Leather from caves in Oregon was found to be approximately 9000 years old. The data substantiate human (Paleoindian) habitation at Clovis, New Mexico, at least 13,600 years ago. A striking case is that of the Monte Verde site in southern Chili. Carbon dating in 1997 established the age of charcoal, wooden tools, and bone there at 12,500 years. Mineralized bones of now extinct animals associated with human activity at three sites in Columbia were found to be nearly as old. Native American artifacts which are still older have been found in South Carolina (stone blade and wooden handle, 12,000 years) and in Pennsylvania (stone tools, woven material, 14,000 years). Sea level has risen about 300 feet since those times, probably obliterating many coastal settlements. Bones of mastodons which were killed by Native Americans in Taima-Taima in Venezuela were carbon dated at 13,000 years. Stone tools and bones from the site of a mastodon barbecue at Saltvillle Valley in Virginia dated at 14,000 years. There are a number of a sites in the Americas in which artifacts thought to be much older have been found. These places include the Bluefish Caves and Old Crow Basin in Alaska, Orogrande Cave in New Mexico, and Pedra Furada in Brazil, all of which might be 15,000 years old or more. But reliable radiological dating of these sites seems to be lacking so far. There is some evidence that certain of the earliest peoples were related to the Ainu of Japan.

Dating an older person

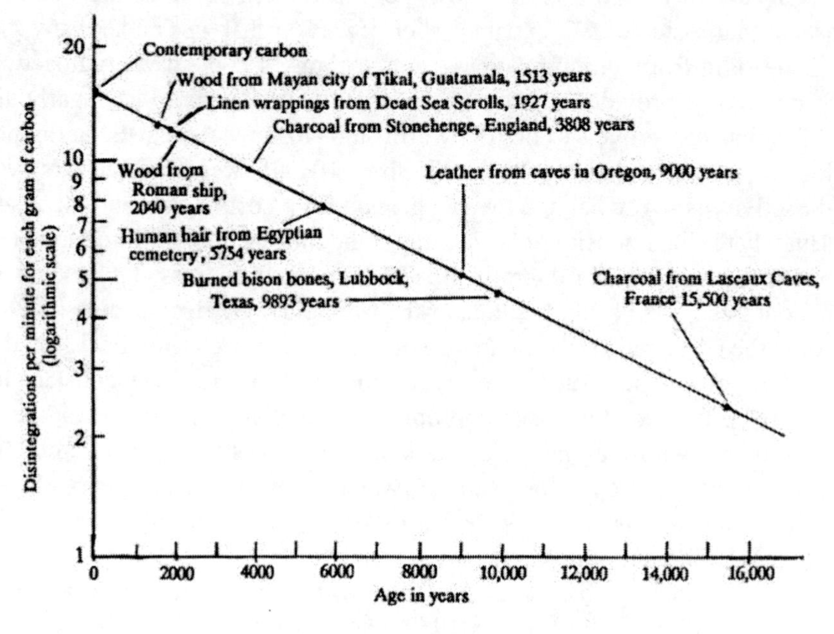

Radiocarbon dating

Data gained using the carbon-14 technique have shown that the Dead Sea scrolls were written over a period starting about 100 B.C. and ending about A.D. 68. Charcoal from the Lascaux caves in France, site of a prehistoric people, was found to be about 15,500 years old, while that from the Stonehenge area of Great Britain checked out at 3800 years. The Shroud of Turin was dated in 1988, and found to derive from a time (1260-1390) during the Middle Ages, not the time of Christ. In 1995 a claim was made that the cloth had been exposed to smoke during a fire about 500 years ago, and that the newer carbon caused an error in the 1988 tests; this allegation remains unproven. In 1991 the frozen body of a prehistoric man was found in the Alps near the Italian-Austrian border. Carbon-14 dating revealed it to be between 5000 and 5500 years old. This means that the man lived during the Copper Age, which was 4000 to 2200 B.C. in Europe.

Every year many new archaeological dates are reported. A recent example (1995) is that radioisotopic dating of Neanderthal fossils from Zafarraya Cave in southern Spain revealed that these beings survived for 10,000 years longer than had been thought earlier. The tests demonstrated that the Neanderthals did not become extinct until at least 33,400 years ago. Another example concerns a bone on which a sketch of a horse had been made, supposedly discovered by schoolboys in England in 1911 and asserted to be of caveman origin.

Talking about old money . . .

Carbon-14 dating in 1995 proved that the bone cannot be more than 600 years old, and thus the carving is a fake. Carbon isotopic techniques are used to establish the age of prize wines; the information can also be used to fix the area where the grapes were grown. This second feature depends on the carbon-12 to carbon-13 ratio. Similarly, the U.S. Secret service uses the technique to determine the age and place of origin of paper money which is suspected of being counterfeit. This is possible because the main ingredient of paper currency is cotton from rags. The presence of carbon-14 in the air from nuclear bomb tests in the atmosphere in the 1950s was taken up by the growing cotton. A reference set of analyses is made of cotton from wherever it is grown, and this information helps track down and convict counterfeiters. In 1994 carbon-14 was detected in space through spectral emissions of its monoxide. This was in the gas surrounding a red giant star known as CW Leonis, which is about 600 light-years away. Since the half-life of carbon-14 is a mere 5730 years, it must have been formed comparatively recently. It appears as if it was synthesized from helium nuclei inside the star and then ejected during a Sun spot episode into the surrounding gas. All types of steel contain carbon. After burning small samples in oxygen to form carbon dioxide, measuring the radioactivity of the carbon dioxide has been used to date the steel.

Determination of the age of objects from antiquity depends on measuring the carbon-14 content in the present, but radioactivity measurements are not the only way to carry out the analysis. About 1984, British, Canadian and American scientists made new advances in an older technique, the accelerator mass spectrometer. This sophisticated instrument, which is much more sensitive than weak radioactivity measurements, uses samples a thousand times smaller, has half the error, and can reach further back in time (to 75,000 years). It is also free from interference by "new" carbon, material which might have contaminated an ancient specimen by much later bacterial growth or other ways. Radioactivity measurements require up to 5 grams of carbon for older specimens;

the new method needs only 0.1 to 5 milligrams. The great sensitivity of the accelerator mass spectrometric method derives from the fact that it counts all the carbon-14, not just the minuscule fraction of it which disintegrates per minute, emiting beta particles. The instrument can also be used with chlorine-36, tritium, etc.

Sample decontamination is accomplished by extracting only those molecules which contain the ancient carbon. For example, if the sample is a fossil bone, the protein remaining in the bone (collagen) is extracted and purified, and only particular amino acids from the protein are used.

Since the accelerator mass spectrometer technique for radiocarbon dating requires only a tenth of a milligram for analysis, it can even be used to date petrographs, which contain traces of organic matter. Thus the rock paintings in the Petrified Forest of Arizona proved to be 1000 years old. Pictures of three bison painted in a cave in northern Spain were shown in 1993 to have been made at three different times: 13,570, 13,940, and 14,330 years ago.

Analogous methods using other elements have been developed. Minute traces of beryllium-10 (half-life 1.6 million years) are formed by the action of cosmic rays on atmospheric oxygen. When washed out by rain, it is incorporated into sediments on the top of tectonic plates. These plates are eventually subducted in movement of continental masses, typically to a depth of 150 kilometers. After collecting samples of volcanic magma arising from this material, the beryllium-10 content can be measured using an accelerator mass spectrometer. The results permit calculation of the age of the tectonic plate.

A new technique in geochronology detects thorium-230 instead of carbon-14. Traces of uranium, 99.3% of which is U-238, are frequently found in rocks, minerals, and fossils. The first few steps of uranium-238 decay are: U-238 => Th-234 => Pa-234 => U-234 => Th-230 (see 4-9). Analysis for traces of U-238, U-234, and Th-230 is done using an accelerator mass spectrometer. Since the half-lives of these three nuclides are known accurately, the age of the specimen can be reliably computed. For example, coral picks up minute amounts of uranium from the ocean water, and the ages of specimens can be established. The higher the ratio of Th-230 to U-238, the older the specimen is. Coral reefs near Barbados were dated at 122,000 to 130,000 years.

Fossils of a hominid species, Homo erectus or "Peking man," were discovered in limestone at Zhoukoudian, China, during the 1920s. Remains of at least 40 individuals have been found. These beings used fire and made stone tools. They were at first dated in the range 200,000 to 300,000 years. A much more accurate measurement of the time when Homo erectus lived was made in 1996 in which an accelerator mass spectrometer was employed. The limestone contains traces of uranium and the ratios of the three nuclides (U-238, U-234, Th-230) were determined. The data collected revealed that Homo erectus lived close to 400,000 years ago. This observation was an important step in the on-going study of human evolution.

There is one other role which carbon-14 plays in dating certain paper manuscripts, and that is beta radiography. It can best be illustrated through an example. English poet John Donne (1572-1631) wrote some 76 volumes, but most of it was published after his death. Measuring the age of the paper used by regular carbon-14 dating techniques suffers from rather large uncertainties, but in this case an alternative is available. European paper mills in this period would impress their products with watermarks showing some emblem such as a shield or hunting horns. The molds for producing these watermarks would last only for about six months, when others had to be made. Each mold had its own characteristics, like fingerprints. In beta radiography, the manuscript to be examined is sandwiched between a plastic sheet containing carbon-14 and an X-ray film. After a ten-minute exposure, development of the film clearly reveals even the finest details of the watermarks, and from it the date can be determined within six months. There is no effect on the paper, and the inked portions do not show up. American Prof. T. L. Pebworth has used the procedure successfully to date about one-third of Donne's work.

6-7 Isotopic Tracers

Every element has several isotopes, all with essentially the same chemical properties, even though some isotopes are radioactive and others are not. Suppose we wish to study the process of photosynthesis, which is the production of simple sugars such as glucose from atmospheric carbon dioxide and water in green plants by the action of sunlight. When glucose is produced, free oxygen is also released; indeed, the oxygen of our atmosphere is of photosynthetic origin. The process is complicated, but the use of isotopic tracers has led to a much deeper understanding of the mechanism. For example, if an experiment is carried out using ordinary carbon (C-12) dioxide and water which is rich in oxygen-18, rather than ordinary O-16, it is found that all the gaseous oxygen produced comes from the water, not the carbon dioxide. If carbon dioxide containing O-18 is employed, along with ordinary water, then the oxygen produced is all O-16, and the O-18 appears in the glucose. It only requires a percent or so of oxygen-18 to serve as a tracer. Further studies use carbon containing traces of carbon-14, whose faint radioactivity serves to follow the carbon wherever it goes in photosynthesis. The carbon has been tagged, or labeled. Many of the innermost secrets of photosynthesis have been ferreted out using these techniques. When the Viking rockets set down gently on the surface of Mars in 1976, each carried instrument packages to detect any microbial life in the soil (the author participated in this research at Jet Propulsion Laboratory). Samples of soil were treated with carbon dioxide labeled with carbon-14. Wet, dry, warm, cold, light and dark conditions were employed in various runs. The idea was that any living organisms would assimilate carbon dioxide (with C-14), since the native atmosphere of Mars is largely this gas. Then the excess carbon dioxide was flushed out and the soil sample decomposed with heat. If carbon-14 appeared in the gases evolved, it could only have come from something alive. The results all proved negative.

Tracers may be radioactive or simply heavy or light nuclides which are stable.

The first tracer experiment was performed in 1913 using naturally occurring lead-210, which is one of the intermediates in the uranium-238 decay series. The objective was to measure the minute solubility of lead chromate in water. Lead chromate is normally considered "insoluble," but nevertheless an amount so tiny that it is difficult to weigh does dissolve. A trace of lead-210 was mixed with ordinary lead in the form of a soluble salt. Some potassium chromate was added, which caused bright yellow lead chromate to precipitate. This solid was filtered off, washed, and divided into two

How to determine the weight of a mere speck

parts. One part was dried, and the radioactivity of exactly 1 milligram was measured. The other part was shaken with water until a saturated solution resulted. A known volume of this solution was evaporated to dryness and the weak radioactivity of the minute residue was measured. Calculation by simple proportion gave the weight of residue and thus the almost imperceptible solubility of the lead chromate. The number of isotopic tracer studies which have been carried out since that time is so large that only a mention of the more important techniques can be made.

Radiometric Analysis—This topic has many modifications, but the principle can be illustrated by an example. Suppose we need to analyze an alloy for zinc. We dissolve a weighed sample and add an excess of ammonium phosphate which has a measured amount of phosphorus-32, a beta emitter with a half-life of 14.3 days. All of the zinc is precipitated as zinc ammonium phosphate, which is centrifuged and washed. By measuring the radioactivity of this compound, the total zinc can be calculated. The precipitate need not be dry. The method is fast and quite accurate.

Isotopic Dilution—Here is a procedure for analyzing for one component in a hopelessly complex mixture, such as coal tar or some biological fluid. While we can separate some of the material to be determined, we cannot remove all of it. Take the example of determining naphthalene in tar. Naphthalene, from which mothballs were formerly made, is a crystalline hydrocarbon. We need a sample of naphthalene which contains a little carbon-14; this is made synthetically. A known amount of this radioactive naphthalene is added to a weighed sample of the tar. After mixing thoroughly, a part of the naphthalene is isolated from the tar, and its activity per gram is measured. If this activity turns out to be half that in the synthetic naphthalene added, then the unknown amount in the tar must have been equal to the amount added. In short, the more the dilution, that is, the lower the activity, the more naphthalene there is in the tar. It is not necessary that the synthetic naphthalene be radioactive from carbon-14; if it is prepared using stable carbon-13, this can be detected using a mass spectrometer, giving the same result.

Surface Studies—To study the behavior of silver, its isotope silver-110m is generally used. Suppose we put some metallic silver into a solution containing radioactive silver nitrate; this solution contains silver ions, that is, silver atoms lacking one electron each (Ag^{+}). Rather surprisingly, it is found that the surface atoms of silver metal exchange with the ions in solution, so that radioactive silver atoms are deposited on the surface. And then these radioactive atoms diffuse into the interior several hundred atoms deep. Use of isotopes is the only known way of studying such diffusion.

Use of tracers is the only way to investigate diffusion of an element into itself.

Other Studies—Active isotopes permit investigation of chemical equilibrium, rates of reactions, adsorption, colloids, crystallization, electrochemistry, extraction, chromatography, and many, many other subjects. Radioisotopes are routinely used in industry to monitor production of metals, plastics, pharmaceuticals, textiles, and any continuous process. They make it possible to determine when mixing two or more components is complete; insufficient mixing results in a flawed product. Copper ores and the metal made from them contain traces of lead. By determining the ratios of lead isotopes in ancient bronze and all Mediterranean ore deposits, it has proven possible to find where each Near Eastern culture mined its copper during the Bronze Age. Miscellaneous studies include: rate of diffusion of carbon or chromium into iron, or of fungicides into wood, or of sulfur into rubber. Efficiency of washing of fabrics; testing for leaks in hermetically sealed units; abrasion and wear of metal parts such as piston rings; and contamination of lubricating oil, all these have been valuable subjects for research.

6-8 Temperatures During the Geologic Past

It seems almost incredible that lake, ocean and bone temperatures which prevailed millions of years ago (paleotemperatures) can be determined today, yet this is the case. Natural oxygen consists mostly of oxygen-16, but there is 0.204% oxygen-18. Isotopic studies have revealed that carbon dioxide and carbonates in water tend to be slightly richer in the heavier isotope of oxygen than the water itself, and that the degree of enrichment is temperature-dependent. When the carbonate of natural water is taken out as a sea shell (which consists largely of calcium carbonate, $CaCO_3$), the ratio of oxygen-16 to oxygen-18 is fixed at a value which depends on the temperature. The lower the temperature, the more oxygen-18 is fixed as carbonate. In one case a shell from the Jurassic geologic period was chosen. This period was the great age of the dinosaurs, when mammals and birds were just getting started, 130 to160 million years ago. Starting at the center, a bit of shell was drilled from each annual layer of shell. The oxygen-16/ oxygen-18 ratio was determined for each, using a mass spectrometer. The results showed a periodic rise and fall of temperature, corresponding to the seasons of the years. The summer temperature was 23.5 °C (74 °F) and the winter temperature was 18 °C (52 °F). If the water is salty, different ratios of the two isotopes prevail, but nevertheless, ancient temperatures can be determined. Studies in 1996 revealed that the temperature of tropical ocean water at the surface 66 million years ago, during the Cretaceous period, was 20 to 21 °C. This is well below the present temperature of 27.5 °C.

Another factor which affects the ratio of oxygen-16 to oxygen-18 is the pressure at which a mineral is formed. Each deposit of marble, for instance, has a characteristic ratio of the two isotopes (marble is also calcium carbonate). Then, by generating a data base of many sources of marble, it is possible to determine where marble in artifacts, such as statues, came from. Similarly, gemstones which contain oxygen, such as emerald, can be traced. A tiny bit of the surface is bombarded with an electron beam, which frees oxygen ions into a mass spectrometer. The technique is called ion microprobe analysis. It unerringly reveals the origins of various emeralds. Before discovery of rich emerald mines in the New World (mostly in Columbia), emeralds had been mined in Egypt, Pakistan, Afghanistan, and Austria. A large emerald in the princely coffers of the Nizam of Hyderabad in India was found to have come from Afghanistan, while the one in the Holy Crown of France came from Austria. An emerald recovered from a Spanish treasure galleon, which sank off Florida in 1622, proved to have come from Columbia.

In 1996 a discovery was made through study of a meteorite which had been blasted off Mars by an incoming meteor. It had landed on our Earth in Antartica about 13,000 years ago, and had thus been preserved in ice. The amazing feature was that the interior of this chunk contained what appeared to be evidence that microbial life had once been there. The evidence that the meteor, as well a limited number of others, really came from Mars is varied, but one of the most important points is derived from its ratio of oxygen-17 to oxygen-18. The evidence of early life on Mars is subject to various interpretations, and life probably never has existed there. The latest study strongly indicates that no life form ever was on the meteorite either.

The same principals apply to calcium phosphate in bones as to calcium carbonate in shells. The technique has been employed to estimate the body temperatures of long-extinct dinosaurs. It was tested using the bones of a recently deceased specimen of a reptile, a giant, carnivorous lizard from the island of Komodo, Indonesia. The results showed that its ribs and vertebrae were 2° to 9 °C warmer than the tail bones, indicating some self-heating. In the case of mammals, all bones register the same temperature when analyzed by the O-16/O-18 ratio technique. Analyzing bones of two small herbivorous dinosaurs, an Orodromeus and a Ceratopsian, species known to have led active lives, revealed that the body bones had grown at temperatures 3 ° or 4 °C higher those in the extremities. Testing bones of a Camarasaurus, researchers found that while young it had been warm-blooded, but as it grew older, it became more cold-blooded. Similar work with a well-preserved skeleton of a Tyrannosaurus rex disclosed that the extremities were only a little cooler than the ribs, suggesting an active life, much like mammals.

A similar situation prevails with the two common isotopes of hydrogen, hydrogen-1 and hydrogen-2 (deuterium). By determining the ratio in the rings of the bristlecone pine from California, it has been shown that the average temperature in that area has declined about 5 °C over the past 6800 years.

Proportions of stable isotopes also vary in the cellulose of trees depending on the abundance of water when growing. Cellulose from trees growing under dry conditions has higher concentrations of oxygen-18 and carbon-13 than cellulose grown under wetter conditions. Advantage was taken of this information in studying the mountain citadel of Masada, on the shores of the Dead Sea. The mountain has a flat top and rainfall was sufficient to permit agriculture in early times. The Romans cut local tamarisk trees to build a ramp up to the fortress, and succeeded in conquering the Hebrew defenders. Analysis of samples of both the ancient and modern wood for isotopes of carbon and oxygen showed that the old tamarisk trees grew under milder circumstances than exist today.

6-9 Radioautography

Self-portrait

When Becquerel first discovered radioactivity, he placed a uranium sample on a photographic film; the film was protected from light by black paper. After some time development of the film showed the image of the sample, which had in a sense taken its own photograph: a radioautograph. Suppose we use this technique in a somewhat different way. Phosphorus is an essential element for plants, and phosphates in the soil are taken up by the roots. If we put a phosphate containing radiophosphorus (P-32, half-life, 14.3 days) in the soil, and wait until it is absorbed into the plant, we can learn the distribution of this element by pressing a leaf or a slice from a stalk against film, working in the dark. After exposure of the film by the beta particles, development of the film shows that the phosphorus tends to accumulate in the veins and stems of mature leaves and throughout young, growing tissue (see figure). The same procedure can be used by allowing the leaf to photosynthesize carbon-14 as carbon dioxide This methodology has become a valuable tool in biological research. For example, if the RNA base cytidine is labeled with tritium (hydrogen-3), and then injected into a rat, after only five hours liver cells show by radioautography that the cytidine is concentrated in each nucleolus (an active site within each cell nucleus).

Radioautograph of a leaf of a bean plant containing phosphorus-32

Biologists have fed animals diets containing carbon-14, which becomes incorporated in the tissues. If the animal is sacrificed and frozen tissue slices made, such as brain tissue, radioautographs can then be made. When a rock such as granite is sliced and polished, and then washed in a solution containing a radioactive compound, certain mineral constituents in the rock adsorb some of the active substance. This prepares the surface for its radioautograph.

In a sophisticated procedure in which tests are made for defective genes, such as those which give rise to cystic fibrosis, Huntington's disease, and other disorders, DNA is taken from white blood cells. It is processed using enzymes and the two strands are unraveled into single strands. A genetic probe, consisting of a single strand of DNA labeled with radioactive markers, is seen under scrutiny to match the DNA. If the suspected gene is present, the probe will bond to the specimen tested. Placed next to photographic film, the resulting radioautograph discloses any defective site as a dark band; if no match for the pattern is found, no radioactive DNA is bound, and no dark band appears.

6-10 Neutron Activation Analysis

In 1936, a few years after neutrons were discovered, scientists realized that the majority of elements, when exposed to neutrons, are converted into radioactive nuclides. The mass number of each atom, on absorbing one neutron of suitable energy, increases by one unit; most such nuclides are activated, that is, become beta active, and many emit gamma rays as well. This behavior has led to a marvelous analytical technique for qualitative and quantitative analysis: neutron activation analysis. It reveals elemental composition without destroying the material analyzed, and is amazingly sensitive. Each new nuclide has its own characteristic half-life and beta or gamma energy, which uniquely identifies the element. The principal drawbacks are that a strong neutron source is needed (generally a nuclear reactor), and that expensive, sophisticated instrumentation is required.

In practice, a standard sample of known composition is prepared; it should resemble the unknown to be analyzed so far as possible. The standard and unknown are irradiated and later counted simultaneously and identically. Advanced multi-channel gamma ray spectrometers are used as analyzers, and the gamma ray spectra are recorded for both samples. In some cases beta ray spectra are registered. Each nuclide shows up as a peak, and is identified by its energy and the rate at which it decays. Comparison with the standard tells the analyst the quantity. The method is sensitive to a millionth, sometimes a billionth, of a gram. Lighter elements, such as oxygen and nitrogen, must be activated with fast neutrons.

The benefits from neutron activation analysis are growing constantly.

Here are some results of neutron activation analysis. Seawater contains, aside from lots of salt and many common elements, minute traces of nearly all the other elements on our planet. A sample was neutron-activated and counted. More than a dozen trace elements were determined; for example, mercury registered at 100 parts per billion, and copper at 500 parts per billion. In view of the extreme sensitivity of the method, it is employed in analysis of moderators for nuclear reactors and electronic materials, such as silicon for transistors. Prehistoric trade routes have been mapped by analyzing ceramic materials for trace elements; each clay deposit has identifying trace metal components, which serve as fingerprints. An unanswered question in nutrition is whether ultra-trace amounts of arsenic are necessary in human diet; maybe neutron activation analysis can provide the facts. Of course, the authenticity of objets d'art have been investigated. Pigments from several paintings, claimed to date from the 16th and 17th century Dutch masters, were shown to contain only about 7 parts per million of arsenic and 1.3 parts per million of antimony, and were thus fraudulent; the genuine paint has up to 1000 and 230 parts per million of these elements respectively.

Forensic science employs neutron activation analysis extensively. Human hair normally has traces of copper, sodium, cerium, and other elements, each person having a unique pattern which serves for identification. Analysis of hair has provided vital information in several investigations of crime. Swedish King Eric XIV died suddenly in 1577 after a meal of pea soup. A sample of his hair, preserved by his family, was shown by neutron activation analysis to be rich in arsenic; foul play is indicated. Human hair normally contains about 1 part per million of arsenic; in the case of people who live amidst industrial smoke, the arsenic content of hair can be as high as 3 ppm. American President Zachary Taylor passed away in 1850, and an American writer in 1991 suspected that he had been poisoned with arsenic. His body was exhumed and hair, fingernails, and bone scrapings were analyzed for arsenic by neutron activation analysis at Oak Ridge National Laboratory; the results were confirmed spectrometrically. The outcome revealed the normal amounts of arsenic in the tissues. Taylor had not been poisoned. A related technique called radioimmunoassay proved that the body of English poet John Keats, who died in 1821, contained much morphine. He was known to use opium.

Nuclear detective

Each plant picks up trace elements from its soil, and the pattern of these elements provides a means of identifying the area where it was grown. This is helpful in running down sources of marijuana and opium. Mud from a truck in New York was shown to be identical with a sample from Georgia, which led to a conviction. Each batch of crude oil similarly has a characteristic fingerprint of trace chromium, vanadium, and iron content. This fact has been employed in identifying the source of illegal crude oil flushings dumped at sea. Many other cases of environmental pollution have also benefited from the results of nuclear activation analysis.

Small neutron-activation units have been built to use outside the laboratory. Lowered into the boreholes of oil wells, they test for oil and other valuable minerals. They are used for underwater exploration, ore grading, to measure the sulfur content of coal on a conveyor belt, to analyze steel for manganese as it comes from the furnace, and to control the calcium content of cement, to give a few examples. The neutron-activation is also employed in detecting explosives (6-38, page 282).

6-11 Saga of the Screw-Worm Fly

In the islands of the Caribbean and mainland stretching from South America to the southern United States, a vicious little fly, one of Nature's most unlovable creatures, has been endemic for centuries (see sketch). Its name, the screw-worm fly, derives from a prominent spiral down the length of the worm or larva stage. This pestilent insect looks something like an over-sized common housefly, but has breeding habits deadly to domestic and wild animals alike. The female lays 200 to 300 eggs inside any cut, abrasion, tick bite, or infection on an animal, or in the navel or nostrils of the newborn. Maggots hatch within 24 hours and feed in the wound. The larvae gorge on the flesh of the host, causing grievous distress. A discharge flows from the wound; this attracts more flies, and soon there are thousands of maggots. Agonizing death is certain for the host unless the animal is treated. In five days the maggots are grown and fall to the ground, where they burrow under and pupate. After about eight days the adults emerge, and live for several weeks while migrating in search of food. During this time mating occurs, and in four days the female seeks out a suitable host for the next generation. Where it is warm enough for year-round survival, there might be 10 or 12 generations per season.

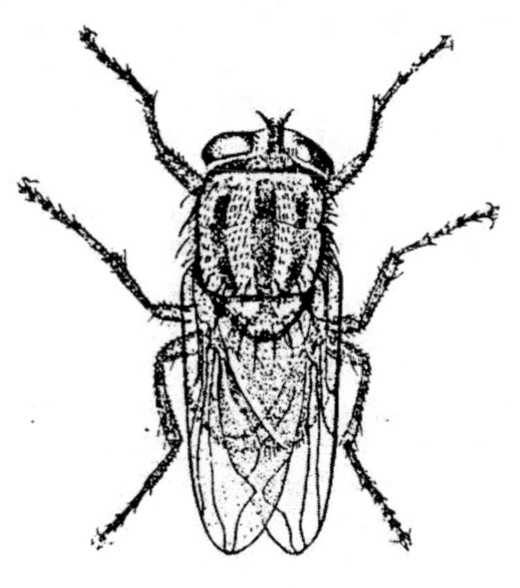

Screw-worm fly

In 1937 an American entomologist, E. F. Knipling, had a brilliant idea for controlling the screw-worm fly by a fundamentally new method. It had been shown as early as 1916 that cigarette beetles produce infertile eggs after exposure to X-rays. Why not take advantage of this, thought Knipling, in the following way. First raise the insects in cages by the millions, sterilize them with radiation, and release them into the countryside. When the wild females breed with the sterile males, the resulting eggs are infertile, and so the population of screw-worm flies drops. Repeat this over and over, until they are under control, or even eradicated. Bugs soon become resistant to insecticides, but they can't adapt to being deprived of their reproductive capacity. And not only that, whatever pest one wants to control can be targeted selectively. This kind of warfare on insects might seem a bit unfair, but consider the tactics of the enemy. Tests of the proposed technique became feasible with the advent of nuclear reactors.

Screw-worm flies were reared in air-conditioned cages with controlled humidity. The flies were fed well and received the best of care. They laid their eggs in ground meat and carrion which was kept at the body temperature of cattle. The pupae grew in sand, and were screened out. On the sixth day the pupae were exposed to a dose of 8000 rads of gamma rays from cobalt-60 sources. This insured sterility of both male- and female-producing eggs.

The first test was made on Sanibel Island, off the Florida coast. For each of the island's 15 square miles, 100 irradiated males (with a like number of females) were released each week for three months. Within two months, 80% of the egg masses were sterile. By the end of the third month, the natural insect population had vanished. A more ambitious test was carried out in 1954 on the island of Curaçao in the Netherlands Antilles. Its 170 square miles were populated at the rate of 400 sterile flies per square mile per week. By the fourth generation, all screw-worm flies had been eradicated from Curaçao. This procedure is often called autocide.

What an elegant way to exterminate a noxious insect!

The next step was to treat the entire state of Florida, as well as southern Georgia and Alabama. This required a massive breeding program; more than two billion flies were released over 18 months. There were about nine sterile males for each fertile male, so the vast majority of females mated with sterile males. Puerto Rico was treated in 1975. The programs were completely successful. The cost was $8,000,000, but the savings were in excess of $20,000,000. By1980, savings had accrued to billions of dollars. But more flies keep coming in from further west, sometimes carried by infested cattle. The goal of a Mexico-U.S. program is to establish and maintain a barrier of sterile flies across Central America. By 1991 efforts were underway to push the fly-free line as far south as Belize and Guatemala. An infestation of the screw-worm fly broke out in north Africa in the summer of 1988. A shipment of infested cattle had been shipped in from South America. The United Nations Food and Agriculture Organization organized a drive to eradicate the pest. Over a period of six months, weekly flights brought in 40 million sterile flies from insectaries in Mexico, and these were released from low-flying aircraft, mostly over Libya. About 16,000 square miles were covered. By April 1991 no more fertile screw-worm flies could be found, and by fall there was confidence that elimination was complete.

6-12 Control of Other Insects by Irradiation

The spectacular success of the screw-worm fly eradication program focused attention on similar technology with other pests. While the screw-worm fly is the case best adapted to the sterile insect release (autocidal) method, other insects have been targeted. Only certain insects are susceptible to the method because of their biology and behavior, but it is not necessary that monogamous mating habits prevail. Incidentally, introduction of genetically-engineered defects into the genes of pests is an alternative approach.

The melon fly, a kind of fruit fly, was caused to breed itself out of existence on the Pacific island of Rota, and the oriental fruit fly was wiped out on the island of Guam. The technique is now standard practice in combating various fruit flies, but the costs are high. The Mediterranean fruit fly, which preys on more than 200 types of produce, invades California repeatedly. The 1981–82 eradication project cost $100 million, but without it growers would have lost still more in fruit sales because of quarantine. The areas are simply too big to use the sterile insect procedure successfully, although they are locally of great help. Sterile flies are dyed red or orange so that those captured in traps can be distinguished from fertile flies. Spraying with Malathion and use of sticky traps with lures, combined with sterile insect release, is widely practiced. Two fruitfly nurseries in Hawaii produce 650 million sterile flies per week. Others are in Mexico and Guatemala. After irradiation, the flies are stored at a temperature a few degrees above freezing (38 °F) until release.

Ideally, the sterile-insect procedure would be most effective if only sterile males were released, since the absence of sterile females would mean no wasted breeding. It is no easy task to separate the sexes when millions of insects are involved, but ways are being sought to accomplish this with fruit flies through genetic engineering and the use of pheromones. More than 500 species of insects attack cotton. Some of the worst of these are the common bollworm, the pink bollworm, the boll weevil, and the cotton aphid. The pink bollworm alone often causes losses of 25% of the crop. The larvae chew their way out of the cotton boll and drop to the ground to pupate. By using boll weevils and cotton bolls in a box equipped with sensitive acoustic sensors, the worms can be heard as they feast noisily. The pink bollworm was targeted for control by the sterilization method in1961. Only partial success has been achieved. Much higher doses of radiation are required (20,000 to 40,000 rads). It seems that this heavy irradiation causes a number of effects which combine to lower effectiveness of the procedure. The males seem to become less competitive sexually than wild males. To some extent, scales fall from the mature moth, interfering with flight and finding mates. Even when mating takes place, sterile egg production is reduced. By tagging some of the sterile males with a substance containing radioactive phosphorus, they could be followed and monitored in the field. It might be that irradiation with neutrons instead of gamma rays will be more effective. By 1997, a type of cotton containing genes from a bacterium was being planted. The foreign genes make a kind of protein which controls bollworms to a large degree. It is clear that more work on the matter is in order; current procedures do not offer full solutions.

More research is needed to control tough bollworms.

The Department of Agriculture is conducting work on control of the gypsy moth by the irradiation-sterilization technique. It has proved successful in limited areas in several states, but the work is difficult and expensive. The gypsy moth is widespread, and it is impractical to swamp the entire country with sterile insects. Control of the codling moth seems to be promising. Efforts to control the Colorado potato beetle have taken a different turn. Irradiation is employed in conjunction with parasitism of their eggs by a wasp.

Work is continuing to control mosquitoes, but it is not encouraging, except for perhaps a few species. In this case, the sexes must be separated and only sterile males released. This and other factors make the costs very high, and fresh mosquitoes keep re-infesting a given area. A field evaluation was carried out in El Salvador in the early 1970s. The insects were sterilized chemically, not with radiation. Mosquito populations dropped by 99%, but soon rose back to normal levels. By 2001, however, a new breakthrough seemed probable. Through gene engineering, a strain of mosquitoes has been made which is incapable of transmitting malaria. The idea is to release them into the wild, where they interbreed with their evil cousins, transmitting this new quality to their offspring.

The horn fly of cattle can probably be suppressed or even eliminated by the autocidal technique. It causes at least $200 million in losses each year. Tests have shown that overflooding an area with ten sterile flies to one natural insect is effective. The stable fly, which is not particular about the kind of animal it bites, is also a good candidate for control.

Another nominee for irradiation-sterilization control is the tsetse fly of Africa. Their bites infect humans and swine with two types of microbes (trypanosomes) which cause two corresponding types of sleeping sickness. Cattle carry the trypanosome which causes the disease in humans. A related kind of microbe in cattle is responsible for a disease called nagana. Twenty-two species of tsetse fly are on the African mainland, vastly complicating complete control. Wild animals are infected but show no symptoms. To control the tsetse fly, their population would have to be reduced first using insecticides, and then releasing sterile insects. Tsetse larvae develop mostly within the female's body, and when hatched at once burrow into the ground to pupate. This behavior makes the fly very resistant to insecticides. In 1997 all tsetse flies were eradicated from Zanzibar, an island off Tanzania's coast, using the sterilization technique. The task was facilitated by the fact that only one species of tsetse lived there.

Solving one problem creates another.

Moreover, tsetse flies exhibit a fearsome adaptivity. The fly is a slow breeder, making rearing of insects to sterilize by gamma rays expensive. In 1993 a new technique for controlling the tsetse fly was developed. It consists of using a substance called pyriproxyfen, which attracts the insects and also renders them sterile. Samples of the substance made with radioactive isotopes revealed that it lasts more than nine months. There is a negative side to eradication of the tsetse fly. It is this insect and the diseases it carries which have kept large human populations at a minimum in extensive areas of central Africa, so if the fly is eliminated, people and cattle will begin to encroach on and displace wildlife more vigorously. Such steps compel us to reflect on what kind of world we want.

In 1991 there was a serious infestation in winter agricultural areas in southern California by the poinsettia whitefly, discovered in 1986. This bug, which some entomologists believe is a new species (the silverleaf whitefly), was first thought to be a new variety (strain B) of the sweet potato whitefly. This tiny but voracious insect attacks a wide variety of vegetables, and even cotton. Swarms of whiteflies look like miniature blizzards. They seem to be quite resistant to insecticides. Losses in the Imperial Valley have exceeded $500,000 in two years. By 1992, the flies had invaded the San Joaquin Valley, much farther north. One factor favoring such infestations is the tendency of modern agriculture to plant a single strain of crops; a second factor is excessive use of insecticides, which kills off natural predators. It remains to be seen whether the gamma ray-sterilization technique can control this scourge. Other candidates to be considered for control are killer bees and fire ants.

During the late 1990s, impoverished Russia needed to export logs, cut from their abundant timber, to the United States and other countries. But much of the wood was infested internally with insects which could not be eradicated using insecticides. By employing their idle nuclear experts, the Russians developed a means of killing all insects in logs for export. This technique uses gamma rays, much as is done in disinfestation of fruit, but in massive radiation doses.

6-13 Mutated Plants

Irradiation of plant seeds with controlled doses of gamma rays subtly alters the DNA sequences to an extent depending on dose. Treating tens of thousands of seeds in this way, and then allowing them to germinate and grow, produces some mutations. For every mutation which represents an improvement there are approximately 1000 which are disadvantaged. By selecting only the upgraded plants, strains with higher yields and improved resistance to cold, insects, fungus, and virus diseases have been developed. Most of the grain grown in northern climates today are these radiation-induced varieties. New strains of rice have yields 45 to 55% higher than the older varieties. A strain of navy bean was made using radiation, and it yields 30% higher yields than the parent. Most peanuts grown in the U.S. today stem from radiation alterations, and have a flavor superior to the older varieties. In the late 1950s a strong cobalt-60 source of gamma rays was sunk in the center of a plot of land contoured something like a bowl. By remote control it could be raised to any desired height above ground. The terraced land around the center was planted with many kinds of plants for study. The cobalt-60 was raised for controlled lengths of time to irradiate the plants. Of course, the area was dubbed "Gamma Garden." Formation of mutations by radiation is one of the ways Nature induces evolution, so the use of heavier radiation doses is really an extension of a natural process. The "green revolution" which elevated the world's food supply depended largely on these better strains of corn, wheat, oats, and rice. But it is not all gain. Any crop which gives higher yields than its antecedents also drains soil fertility faster. Moreover, more abundant food eventually adds to human population pressures, especially in third world countries.

Here too the solution aggrevates the problem

6-14 Other Uses of Gamma Irradiation

Since gamma rays in sufficient doses sterilize everything they penetrate, it is not surprising to learn that equipment for surgery is irradiated. This includes sterilizing packaged bandages, sutures, rubber gloves, catheters, and other equipment. The process serves as an alternative to autoclaving. Sterilization by irradiation is suitable for samples which are altered or destroyed by heat, such as biological specimens and heat-sensitive pharmaceuticals, including ointments. Other items commonly sterilized by gamma rays include medical supplies, nipples for baby bottles, milk cartons, and cosmetics. Wool suspected of carrying the anthrax bacteria is similarly exposed. The two common sources of gamma rays for commercial irradiators are cobalt-60 and cesium-137 (as the chloride). The apparatus somewhat resembles that for food irradiation (6-29).

There have been accidents at these installations where high levels of radioactivity are used. One of these incidents occurred in 1977 when an employee of the Radiation Technology Inc. plant in New Jersey was exposed to 150 to 300 rads in about 15 seconds. The second was in 1982 at the Institute for Energy Technology; a technician inexplicably entered the radiation cell which contained 650,000 curies of cobalt-60. He received a dose of 1000 rads and died in 13 days. Another irradiator is located in Decatur, Georgia. It holds more than 12 million curies of cesium-137 chloride. An accident there in May

1988 was caused by failure of a doubly encapsulated cesium-137 chloride unit, resulting in contamination of the area. Cleanup costs were estimated at $32 million. In 1989 in El Salvador, a similar installation used 17,000 curies of cobalt-60 in a medical sterilizer. One cobalt unit had fallen out of the source rack and caused three workers to be exposed to 400 to 600 rads. The radiation monitors had been disabled. As of summer 1998, the world had 196 commercial gamma irradiators, of which 56 are in the U.S.

Another application of irradiation is introducing crosslinkages and stresses into plastics. This is done either with gamma rays or electron beams. Imagine some tubing made of polyethylene, PVC, Teflon, or other plastic. If it is irradiated strongly with gamma rays, stresses are created, although to outward appearances no change is visible. But if the treated tubing is heated, either with a hot air gun (resembling a high-wattage hair drier) or a soft flame, the tubing shrinks to about half its original diameter. Thus, if a soldered electric connection is covered with shrink tubing and then heated, the tubing collapses down on the bare metal and forms an excellent insulation. Bundles of wires can be bound together in this way. Weld lines of joined pipes are protected from corrosion. All kinds of retail items, from foodstuffs to hardware goods, are routinely wrapped in irradiated plastic and then shrunk down with heat. Gamma rays are employed to cure plastic polymers. The uses are endless.

Splendid uses of shrink tubing abound.

Since gamma rays from cesium-137 have become available at a moderate cost, another use has opened up, namely the irradiation of sewage sludge. Why in the world would anyone want to irradiate sewage sludge? There are several reasons. There is an endless supply of sewage sludge, and its disposal presents a challenging problem. Since it is rich in organic matter, it would be an excellent agricultural fertilizer except that it is loaded with pathogenic microorganisms and has a disgustingly foul stench. If an economical way could be found to destroy these bacteria and viruses, it would be a notable attainment. Since a reliable supply of cesium-137 is available in quantity, irradiation experiments are underway. Alternatively, spent fuel rods from nuclear reactors can serve directly as a source of ionizing radiation. The product is without rank odor. One difficulty in the case of certain municipal sewage treatment facilities is that the sludge contains too much heavy metals, such as chromium, to be used as fertilizer; the contamination results from illegal dumping in sewers. The Canadians are constructing a sewage irradiation plant in Edmonton, Alberta.

A proposal has been made to employ gamma rays from spent fuel rods to irradiate agricultural fields to kill nematodes, which are microscopic worms which live in soil and reduce crop yields. Another idea is to irradiate fertilizer to eliminate virulent strains of E. coli, which infest produce.

6-15 Radiotherapy

It wasn't long after the discovery of X-rays and radioactivity that their damage to living tissues was recognized. Medium exposure to the various radiations was observed to increase chances of cancer, while higher doses were found to kill all living tissues, including cancer. The rate of cell reproduction in cancerous tissue is higher than in normal tissue, and the abnormal tissue is therefore more susceptible to ionizing radiation.With more radiological experience, physicians gradually learned how to use both X-rays and radioactive substances to treat cancer.

The basic idea is to irradiate the cancerous tissue with X-rays, beta rays, or gamma rays to the extent that the carcinoma is destroyed and resorbed; healthy tissue is unavoidably exposed and becomes more prone to cancer, but that takes time. Different forms of cancer were found to respond to different doses. Surgical procedures are not suitable for treatment of many cancers. In some of these cases, small amounts of radioactive substances, enclosed in tiny cylinders or needles, can be implanted into the diseased area. The material might be cobalt-60 encased in silver or gold; the heavy metals filter out most of the beta rays, allowing only the gamma radiation to emerge. Other nuclides useful for implants are gold-198 (half-life 2.69 days), iodine-131 (half-life 8.04 days), iodine-132 (half-life 2.28 hours), radon-222 (half-life 3.83 days), and californium-252 (half-life 2.64 years). Such implants are common for treatment of cancer of the prostate, cervix, breast, etc. Iridium-192 irradiation in this fashion has been recently shown to be as effective in arresting cancer of the breast as mastectomy. The local dose might be several thousand rads.

Cancer of the liver is usually not effectively treated by irradiation, but in 1991 an advance was made in Michigan which shows considerable promise. Yttrium-90, with half-life 64.1 hours, is prepared as microspheres of glass. These are introduced into the hepatic artery and they lodge in the peripheral branches of the blood vessels. Of 24 patients with inoperable liver cancer, 16 showed marked benefit. In 1937 the first application of a radionuclide was made to treat a disease by internal radiation from a substance which on injection seeks out and is absorbed by the target tissue. To treat leukemia, a phosphate made from phosphorus-32 (half-life 14.3 days) was injected into a patient. The phosphate was adsorbed by the bone marrow, where white blood cells are made, in an attempt to lower production of these cells. A later and less dangerous method involves pumping blood out of the patient through tubing which leads through a few curies of a gamma ray source. This destroys the sensitive white cells, and the blood is returned to the patient. Neither procedure was fully successful. Phosphorus-32 is still employed to treat *polycythemia vera*, a condition in which there is overproduction of red blood cells.

Implants of radioactive nuclides have extended many lives.

Iodine is taken up from the blood by the thyroid gland with extremely high selectivity, and this permits diagnosis of the gland for over- or underactivity. Iodine-123 is generally preferred for this purpose. It decays by orbital electron capture with a half-life of 13.2 hours. To treat an enlarged or tumorous thyroid gland (and its accompanying hyperthyroidism), iodine-131 is administered to the patient. The amount of this radio-iodine must be enough to irradiate the thyroid gland with a heavy dose of beta and gamma rays, maybe several thousand rads. This generally requires 5 to 60 millicuries, much of which is excreted before it decays. This method of treatment is generally preferred over surgery, one reason being that there is less danger to the four tiny parathyroid glands, whose hormone regulates calcium metabolism. Radio-iodine therapy is not without its dangers: it increases the chances somewhat of coming down with leukemia. Radio-iodine is also employed to treat adults for Graves' disease, and is generally considered safe and effective. President Bush (the elder) and his wife both underwent treatment with iodine-

131 for Graves' disease. Millions of patients have been treated by radiotherapy, and many of them are alive today who would have died without this diagnosis and treatment. Iodine-131 is also used to irradiate certain classes of tumors such as neuroblastomas, namely those which readily absorb the chemical compound meta-iodobenzylguanidine (the iodine being I-131), which is easily synthesized. Since the gamma rays from iodine-131 have an energy level of 364 kiloelectron volts, it is not the best for imaging, but can be used. If an image is needed, the same material containing iodine-123 is superior (gamma energy 159 kiloelectron volts, half-life 13.2 hours). About 8% of childhood cancers are of the neuroblastoma type.

Since calcium and strontium have similar chemical properties, both are absorbed from the blood into bones, especially the marrow. Cancer often metastasizes to the bone marrow, and the incipient cancers resulting are especially painful. Recent studies have shown that if strontium-89 (half-life 50.6 days) as the chloride is injected, it subdues the cancers for some months. The treatment is largely effective in about 80% of the patients and completely effective in 10%. The amount of strontium-89 per injection is typically 40 microcuries per kilogram of body weight.

How to make a cat feel important

The citizens of Los Alamos County, NM, are perhaps a bit more alert to matters involving radioactivity than most others. In 1994 a garbage truck set off alarms at a city dump. The response was massive: Fire Department, ambulances, hazardous-material unit, the works. The source of the gamma rays was traced to cat litter; a cat had been undergoing iodine-131 treatment for hyperthyroidism or cancer.

6-16 Therapy Using X-Rays and Gamma Rays

X-rays have the advantage that their energy can be controlled, and the machine producing them can be turned on and off. Gamma rays have the advantage of being more penetrating. The two most common gamma ray sources for therapy are cobalt-60 (half-life 5.27 years) and cesium-137 (half-life 30.0 years). Gamma rays from cobalt are more energetic and more penetrating than those from cesium. In either case, a heavy lead cylinder with a cavity holds the radioactive material; the beam of gamma rays shines out through a series of holes, forming a pencil of parallel rays, which are directed by the radiologist at the target. As in the case of X-rays, accidental overexposures do sometimes take place. In 1992, a patient in New Jersey received a dose of 400 rads from a unit containing 3.5 million curies of cobalt-60. A specialized type of gamma ray therapy was developed in Sweden. By employing CAT or MRI scanning in conjunction, small cancers of the brain can be treated and often eradicated with gamma rays from cobalt-60. The technique, called stereotactic radiosurgery, requires immobilizing the patient's head and directing a number of narrow beams of gamma rays into the cancer, where the several beams intersect. This gives a high dose to the tumor but low dose to the other tissues.

Radiation therapy requires the presence of oxygen at the target site to be effective. To promote oxygenation of solid tumors, chemically modified hemoglobin is sometimes used. This is hemoglobin bonded to a synthetic material called polyethylene glycol, which carries it abundantly, and can penetrate tumors more quickly than normal red cells.

Another recent invention has promise of advancement in radiotherapy using X-rays. This is the Kumakhov lens. Kumakhov is a Russian physicist who devised a bundle of capillaries which actually reflect X-rays, without much loss of intensity, from their internal tubular surface. This permits construction of a conduit resembling fiber optics which can lead X-rays directly to a tumor to be irradiated. Aside from medical applications, the device might be used to stencil designs on electronic chips. The Kumakhov lens also works, it is claimed, with neutrons, and might succeed with gamma rays.

The Leksell gamma knife employs radiation from cobalt-60 to treat an inoperable brain condition known as arteriovenous malformations. In this disorder, there is a tangle of dilated blood vessels, often deep inside the brain. Both benign and malignant tumors, as well as some cases of epilepsy, can also be managed. The gamma knife has also proved effective in treating, sometimes curing, cancer of the pituitary gland, which if uncontrolled puts pressure on the optic nerve, causing blindness in one or both eyes. It can also compress the carotid artery. The "knife" has no blade, and so no tissue is removed; the procedure is non-invasive. The instrument has about 26 grams of cobalt-60 housed in 2.5 tons of lead. The cobalt-60 is divided into several portions, and these are arranged so all their gamma rays converge on the target, in a conelike pattern. The afflicted area is first imaged using magnetic resonance or some other technique, and the patient's head is fitted with a coordinate frame to fix the exact site of the gamma ray beams. Only a local anesthetic is employed. A high dose of precisely focused radiation is administered to the selected area. Up to four shots of five to ten minutes generally suffice. The patient typically spends only one night in the hospital.

Macular degeneration is a leading cause of defective vision or blindness in people more than 60 years of age. The type referred to as "wet" macular degeneration occurs when tiny vessels leak blood and fluid behind the macula of the retina, resulting in loss of vision just in the spot where it is most important; peripheral vision is almost unaffected. Radiation therapy was found in 1999 to delay or even prevent further deterioration of vision. Treatment of the retina with low-dose gamma radiation (6 MeV) once a day for ten to fourteen days is performed. Such gamma rays are sometimes generated using a small electron linear accelerator.

6-17 Hazardous Junk

In 1983 a truck delivered some steel rods for making reinforced concrete to Los Alamos National Laboratory. An automatic radioactivity detector was triggered, causing a photo of the truck to be made. Tracing the license number, an investigation finally revealed the story. A hospital in Lubbock, Texas, had an aged cobalt-60 unit and its shielding, and sold it. The 46-pound unit found its way into a Mexican junkyard. It contained about 6000 pellets of metallic cobalt, each a millimeter or so in size. In the 20 years since the radiation unit was purchased, more than three-quarters of the cobalt-60 had decayed to nickel, but the remaining one-quarter was still lethal.

Evidently someone had punctured a hole through the thin stainless steel which covered the opening, and the pellets began to fall out into the bed of the pickup truck used. The truck was parked on a Juarez street for seven weeks. There was an estimated exposure of 50 rads per hour near the driver's seat. A mouse seeking shade under the truck was killed by the gamma rays. Finally, in the junkyard, pellets were scattered everywhere. Since both cobalt and nickel are magnetic, they were picked up by the magnetic crane and mixed with scrap iron. This iron was sold to two foundries, one making reinforcing rods, the other ornamental table legs. It took months to run down all the steel rods and 2500 sets of table legs all over the U.S. and Mexico. While no one was killed at once, one worker in the scrap yard, Benjamin de la Rosa, died eight years later of bone cancer. Quite a number of other persons received large radiation doses, and two young men were sterilized.

Recycled danger

A radiation disaster began to unfold in September, 1987. A clinic in Goiania, Brazil, used a radiotherapy unit containing cesium-137, but on moving to a new location, the staff negligently abandoned the 220-pound, 16-inch cylinder in the old building. Two years later scavengers entered the doorless facility and carted off the heavy instrument. They sold it to a junk dealer, who valued it for its lead shielding. Having no idea of what he was dealing with, an employee of the junkyard removed a platinum cylinder inside which was about an inch in diameter. Moved by curiosity, he opened it up, finding a white solid, which was actually 1375 curies of cesium-137 in the chemical form of the chloride. In the humid atmosphere, the solid soon broke into a coarse powder, but strangely it glittered with a blue color (arising from the ionization of the air by the intense gamma rays). The junkman took it home, where his young niece began to play with the material, enchanted by its sparkle. She and her friends rubbed it on their bodies, beguiled by its unearthly glow. The powder was circulated widely, and 244 people were exposed.

The junkman's niece had apparently swallowed some of the material with a sandwich she was munching. Signs of radiation sickness soon appeared. When a week later it was realized what had happened, the Brazilian government, using the facilities of the International Atomic Energy Agency, called in expert medical help from the U.S., the USSR, and West Germany. In the end, four persons died, including the little girl. Absorbed whole-body doses were estimated to range up to 800 rads. One method of treatment was administration of Prussian blue, a material containing potassium which is exchanged for cesium; this accelerates excretion of the harmful radioactive ion. The survivors soon found themselves treated as pariahs, their ignorant countrymen thinking it was some sort of infectious disease. A national trade fair in Rio de Janeiro refused to accept an exhibition from the state where Goiania is situated. The incident has caused reforming and enforcing the safety regulations set up by Brazil's National Commission on Nuclear Energy.

When ignorance is not bliss

6-18 Therapy Using Particle Beams

Proton Beams—Ways are constantly being discovered to refine radiotherapeutics. A technique for increasing the destruction of tumorous tissue with minimal destruction of healthy tissue was developed in 1990. It has been known since 1946 that proton beams destroy tissue effectively. A small, inexpensive ion accelerator was developed which produces a beam of helium-3 ions of energy 800 kiloelectron volts. These travel along an evacuated steel tube and strike a target of deuterium, held as solid titanium deuteride. The nuclear reaction produces a stream of protons of energy 13.6 megaelectron volts.

Protons of this energy penetrate tissue precisely 2.2 millimeters. By positioning the end of the steel tube near the boundary of the tumor, even resistant ones can be destroyed with little damage to healthy tissues. Proton beams are also generated by small synchrotrons, sometimes with energies up to 250 MeV. Proton therapy is becoming more common. More than 20,000 patients have been treated, many of these at Loma Linda University Medical Center in California. Prostate cancer, ocular melanoma, and macular degeneration are often treated in this way.

Heavy-Metal Ion Beams—German scientists at the Heavy-Ion Research Laboratory in Darmstadt are conducting studies in which cancerous tissue is irradiated with ions of very heavy metals. The advantages of heavy ions are that they experience low lateral and angular scattering, and that they travel in straight lines and stop at a specific penetration depth. German researchers have developed a new beam-steering system. It divides the target tumor into layers and scans each layer, starting with the deepest. Combining this technique with varying the energy of the incoming ions, it is quite promising.

Carbon Ion Beams—Japan has taken a commanding position in the use of heavy ions for treating cancer. In Chiba an apparatus was constructed in which carbon vapor (from heated graphite) is ionized by an electric arc in vacuum and then fed into a linear accelerator. This apparatus uses pulsating electric fields to energize the ions to the point where they can go through a metal foil, which removes the remaining electrons. The result is a beam of carbon nuclei, each with a +6 charge. These nuclei enter one of two synchrotrons, which are huge, circular accelerators which raise the particles' energy and speed (corresponding to about two-thirds the speed of light). This amounts to about 800,000 revolutions per second. One synchrotron produces a horizontal beam of carbon nuclei, and the other a vertical beam. The heavy nuclei are directed into a tumor. They do minimal damage to healthy tissue, but are able to destroy or at least arrest growth in most of a tumor mass. Quite a number of patients have been treated with no recurrence of the tumor in a year or so. If the tumor has metastasized, the technique cannot be used.

Boron-Neutron Capture Therapy—Another technique for manipulating irradiation to slay tumorous cells with minimum effect on healthy tissue is boron-neutron capture therapy. This promising method was originally researched primarily by American scientists. The idea is hardly new, having been proposed in 1936, but means to accomplish it have only recently been available. It is based on the enormous neutron capture cross section of boron-10, one of the two common isotopes of this element, for thermal neutrons (4-15). When a neutron strikes the nucleus of boron-10, it causes it to split into an energetic alpha particle (helium nucleus) and a lithium-7 nucleus, and also to release a gamma ray. These heavy particles carry 2.79 MeV of energy. The alpha particles have a path length of about 0.01 millimeter within tissue. The nuclear reaction is:

$$^{10}_{5}\mathrm{B} + ^{1}_{0}\mathrm{n} \Rightarrow ^{4}_{2}\mathrm{He} + ^{7}_{3}\mathrm{Li} + \text{gamma}$$

The reaction products are extremely energetic and all participate in killing malignant cells.

The low-energy neutrons have a small but tolerable effect on tissues, and penetrate considerable distances. Therefore if a way could be found to induce tumors to take up boron which is injected into the blood stream, exposure to neutrons would then cause generation of alpha particles at the precise sites where they are needed. Development of a boron compound which is so selectively adsorbed on tumorous tissue proved to be a difficult task. This part is analogous to the substances used in gamma-ray imaging (6-22 ff.). But a number of materials have been developed, including monoclonal antibodies (those produced or derived from a single cell), amino acid derivatives, and other materials, each chemically bonded to boron atoms in the laboratory (see also radioimmunotherapy, below). One effective type has a sulfur-to-hydrogen linkage (sulfhydryl, —SH), causing it to mimic materials rapidly taken up by tumors. As developed by Japanese chemists, the sulfur atom is bonded to boron in a substance which was just a curiosity to inorganic chemists a few years ago, namely an ion with 12 boron atoms which form a polyhedron. Chemists at UCLA in 1998 synthesized such a complex which has five such polyhedra, each with nine boron-10 atoms (and two carbon atoms, known as carboranes). Each such unit is bonded to a phosphate ester on one end and a fluorescent dye at the other. This material is selectively adsorbed by the nuclei of cancerous cells. This approach is at the threshold of entering mainstream medicine. It has minimal effect on normal tissues since it selectively targets tumors. It is not very effective with hard tumors. The antibodies are produced in mice or rats which have had human genes inserted at appropriate sites; they are also obtained from human lymphocytes. Molecules rich in boron which are attracted to fatty tissues are useful in targeting tissues containing lipoproteins. Researchers at the University of California at San Francisco have employed large flat molecules of porphyrin (its derivatives occur naturally in many living cells) as a sort of scaffold on which to bond glucose molecules which are in turn linked to many carborane units. This procedure can put perhaps 200 boron atoms into one molecule. This means lower radiation doses to patients and fewer side effects.

A sort of nuclear howitzer

To be effective, around a billion boron atoms per cell of cancerous tissue are required. A quite high neutron flux is necessary. A nuclear reactor is one neutron source, but these are usually unavailable. Californium-252 (6-35F) can be used, and small proton accelerators are being built which form neutrons when lithium targets are bombarded.

A few clinical tests have been carried out. An aggressive type of brain cancer called glioblastoma multiforme, always fatal earlier, has been treated in Japan. After surgical removal of most of the cancer, boron neutron capture therapy was employed. Only one of 100 patients experienced damage to healthy brain cells. Several patients have survived for years, and some even appear to be cured. Moreover, by using pure boron-10 bonded to an amino acid (dihydroxyborophenylalanine), successful treatment of deadly skin melanoma was accomplished.

This line of medical research has been continued at Brookhaven National Laboratory on Long Island, New York. Started during the 1950s, several patients died, and the work was discontinued until 1994. The updated research involved 15 patients and the results were much more promising. The brain is exposed to neutrons from both sides to deliver a higher neutron dose.

Working at the Garching research nuclear reactor near Munich, German scientists have also explored boron-neutron capture therapy. They use fast fission neutrons directly. Part of the dose arises from the neutrons themselves, the rest from the neutron-boron-10 interaction. Both the helium nucleus and the lithium nucleus formed contribute to the energy absorbed by the tumorous tissue. A single such energetic particle can break both strands of DNA in the tumor, greatly lessening its chances of being repaired by enzymes, and thus causing the tumor to shrink. The procedure is employed mostly in treating surface cancers, near-surface cancers such as of the salivary glands, and malignant melanomas. In addition, glioblastoma multiforme, the lethal brain cancer, is also treated. Normally, the tumor prevents the boron-rich compound from entering the brain, but the cancer breaks down this barrier, so the boron can enter just the region where it is needed. A great deal more research must be carried out in this auspicious field.

6-19 Radioimmunotherapy

The type of radiotherapy in which a radioactive atom is bonded to an antibody is radioimmunotherapy. The earliest trials were made in the 1950s, but were disappointing. In 1990 beta-active yttrium-90, with half-life 64 hours, was bonded to a monoclonal antibody which homes in on an aggressive cancer causing adult T-cell leukemia. As many as 10 of 14 patients experienced at least 95% reduction in cancer cells, and three appear to have been cured. But yttrium bonds rather weakly to the antibody, and some dissociates, finding its way to bone tissue. Therefore another isotope is under study, namely bismuth-212. This nuclide undergoes both beta and alpha decay, and thus delivers an enhanced therapeutic punch.

In 1992 a remarkable advance in radioimmunotherapy was made by incorporating rhenium-188 as a "warhead" into an antibody which homes in on certain types of cancer that resist older methods. Rhenium-188, with a half-life of 17 hours, emits beta particles which penetrate about 8 millimeters into the tumorous tissue. Tests in which rather large colorectal cancers have been treated have proven very promising. In 1993, the Dutch advanced the technique by using what is called an oligonucleotide conjugate, which carries a radionuclide. Its antibody binds to the tumor antigen, directing the radioactive material to the tumor with minimum exposure of normal tissue. In 1994, two California companies, GenPharm International and Cell Genesys, Inc., began to produce human monoclonal antibodies. This was accomplished by genetically engineering mice to produce the antibodies, and the mice cells were then grown in vats to yield the antibodies in quantity. This technique could serve to make radioimmunotherapy accessible to many more patients.

We will hear much more about this technique in the coming years.

Radionuclides bonded to antibodies, aside from rhenium-188, include rhenium-186, iodine-131, and yttrium-90. The beta particles from their decay while concentrated on the tumor site can penetrate a distance of 100 to 300 cells, and thus every single tumor cell need not be targeted. There are numerous modifications of the technique. A drawback of antibody use is that they bond strongly to the target tissue and therefore are cleared out only slowly. Thus there can be over-irradiation of the tissues near the tumor and also any other organ which adsorbs the antibody. Experimental carriers for the radionuclides include biotin (a vitamin in the B complex) and streptavidin (a protein).

Clearly, any technique which can cause a tumor to selectively adsorb a radionuclide for the purpose of therapy would also be of great interest in imaging. The two objectives, therapy and imaging, are the two faces of the same coin. Fig. 6-19-1 on Color Plate I shows an image (procedures described more fully in 6-24) of the cranium of a patient suffering from parietal (that is, attached to a cavity wall) glioma, a dangerous condition, to put it mildly. The image was made using a three-step procedure, namely (a) pretargeting with a monoclonal antibody, (b) followed by streptavidin, and then (c) injection of technetium-99m-biotin. The cancer is clearly visible.

The advantages of the three-step procedure are illustrated sharply in Fig. 6-19-2 on Color Plate I. An X-ray photo disclosed a melanoma in the left eye of a patient (part B, arrow). The image in part A on the left was made using technetium-99m carried by a monoclonal antibody. The bright areas are distributed over much of the brain. In contrast, the image on the right, made using the three-step method, locates the melanoma precisely, and enables more effective treatment to be carried out.

Researchers at Duke University Medical Center in 1998 used iodine-131 bonded to an antibody (identified by the term 81C6) to treat the deadly brain cancer, glioblastoma multiforme. This affliction strikes approximately 12,000 people per year in the U.S. While the procedure effects no cures, it has extended the lives of patients significantly. The main tumor mass is first removed surgically, minding the danger to areas controlling motor or speech areas. About 100 millicuries of iodine-131 was used. Another radionuclide used in the same way was astatine-211, an alpha-active isotope with half-life 7.2 hours. Only about two iodine-131 atoms can kill a cancerous cell. This procedure shows great promise.

Most biomedical research employs radioactive nuclides at one stage or another. More than 95% of new prescription medicinals were initially tested using radioactive tracers. While most radioisotopes used in medical work have relatively short half-lives and decay to almost nothing on storage a couple of months, there are some longer-lived residues from this work and they fall into the low-level waste category.

Like treatment of cancer by surgery, radiation therapy must be considered basically as brutal; but it is sometimes the best treatment available. Chemotherapy for cancer treatment is similarly primitive, but has the promise of becoming highly refined during the next few centuries.

6-20 Radiodiagnostics

The use of radioactive nuclides in diagnosis of a multitude of disorders is one of the great triumphs of modern medicine and nuclear chemistry. The general idea is to inject the patient with a tiny amount of a selected radioactive substance, and detect the gamma rays it emits from various organs. More than a hundred years ago biologists began using stains to dye tissue specimens for examination under the microscope. They found that certain types of tissue would selectively adsorb different stains, greatly improving contrast. This property also prevails in use of radiopharmaceuticals used in nuclear medicine. By judicious choice of radioactive material, most organs of the body can be examined and tested. The procedure can also be used with animals. Nearly 10% of hospital patients today undergo some tests using radionuclides. There are two general techniques, those which do not involve images, and those which do. These are discussed in the sections following. Much additional information on nuclear medicine is available at the website *www.nucmednet.com.*

One of the earliest uses of a radioactive material to study blood circulation involved bismuth-214 (half-life about 20 minutes). This was in the period 1927-29, and was carried out by physicians Blumbart and Weiss in Massachusetts.

Patients are of course concerned that being injected with a radioactive material might endanger their health. As is so often the case, there is a trade-off. Physicians agree that the danger from radiodiagnosis is minimal. Generally a short-lived nuclide (half-life less than 10 days, sometimes a month) is employed, and even if all of it decays inside the body, the whole-body absorbed dose of radiation is only 0.01 to 0.05 rads, which is 10 to 50 millirads, about the same as from a medical X-ray. Targeted organs receive a higher dose than others.

The procedures give a radiation dose about equal to that of a chest X-ray.

6-21 Nonimaging Radiodiagnostics

Nuclear medicine which does not involve imaging divides into two main categories: evaluation of physiologic functions and radioimmunoassay. The first category, evaluation of body functions, is used in measuring fat absorption, bile acid processing, blood volume, and many others. Radioimmunoassay is employed to determine biologically important materials in body fluids quantitatively.

Suppose we have a container whose volume we want to know, but it is so irregular in shape that we cannot measure its dimensions and compute the volume. A good way to find out the volume is the isotope dilution procedure. First we put in a known amount of radioactive material and fill the container with water. After mixing, a measured sample is withdrawn and its radioactivity is measured. The unknown volume is now easily calculated. This approach is used to determine the blood volume of human beings. Actually, the two main components of blood, serum and red blood cells, are determined separately; their sum is the blood volume. This knowledge is important in managing certain endocrine disorders and in guiding blood transfusion therapy, especially in major surgery. It is said that the first blood volume measurement occurred during the French Revolution, when a physician drained the bodies of guillotined subjects into a measuring glass. It seems safe to say that most patients today would prefer the radioactivity-dilution method.

The measurement of blood volume requires two radioactive materials, one for the plasma and one for the red blood cells. Albumin from human blood is labeled with iodine-125 (half-life 60.1 days). A small amount of blood from the patient is withdrawn and red blood cells are separated by centrifuging. Treatment with sodium chromate made with chromium-51 (half-life 27.7 days) labels the cells. The radioactive albumin and red blood cells are injected together into the patient. After circulation has mixed the blood until it is more or less uniform (about half an hour), a small sample of the blood is withdrawn and the levels of activity of the iodine-125 and of the chromium-51 are measured. These results permit the plasma and red cell volumes to be calculated. Another technique uses technetium-99m.

Similar techniques permit following the metabolism of a fat labeled with carbon-14, or the course of iron-59 as it travels from the intestines to the blood, bone marrow, and finally

These techniques were developed by biologists cooperating with radiochemists.

Rosalyn S. Yalow received the Nobel Prize in 1977 largely for developing radioimmunoassay techniques.

appears in red blood cells. Another procedure allows determination of bone density, and others test iodine uptake by the thyroid gland. Radioimmunoassay (RIA) is a general analytical technique for the determination of a wide variety of substances in biological systems. It depends for its success on the formation of antibodies by a human or animal body to biologically active materials (called antigens) such as hormones and drugs. Antigens react with and are bound by antibodies in a unique and specific manner. The test employs labeled antigen, that is, antigen which is prepared and labeled with a radioactive isotope such as iodine-131 or tritium.

Blood serum containing an unknown amount of antigen is mixed with the radioactive antigen; the total of the two antigens is in excess over the antibody. A competition between the two antigens for the antibody reaches equilibrium during an incubation period. Then the excess free antigen (both forms, radioactive or not) and the antigen-antibody complex (both forms) are separated by an adsorption process. Measurement of the gamma-ray activity of the two fractions and comparison to a calibration curve gives the result. Radioimmunoassay is easily automated so that thousands of clinical analyses can be carried out per day. It is exceedingly sensitive. Typical analyses include determination of growth hormone, thyroxine, steroids, cocaine, and morphine in human bodies.

6-22 Imaging Radiodiagnostics

X-Rays have been used since their discovery by Roentgen in 1895 to cast shadows of portions of the human body onto photographic film. The use of X-rays in medical practice quickly spread over the world. The outlines of bones and other tissues were not sharp because the X-rays ionized atoms in tissues and this gave rise to secondary rays, resulting in fuzzy images. Estimates were made that more than half, maybe three-fourths, of the radiation received by the film was that causing blurring. Today we see sharp images from X-rays, and from gamma rays coming from the radioactive decay of injected substances, and from use of other techniques. Here is a brief account of how we arrived at this point.

In 1913 Gustav Bucky in Berlin contributed to the solution of the problem of blurred X-ray images by placing one metal grid (like a heavy screen made from small bars of iron) in front of the patient, and a second grid between the film and the patient. By positioning the grids correctly, the secondary rays were mostly blocked by the second metal grid. This process made the rays striking the film parallel, that is, they were collimated. While the grids did improve the quality of X-ray images, they also imposed annoying shadows of the grid. American inventor Potter improved on Bucky's technique by making the grids moveable. This eliminated the grid image itself, and greatly improved the clarity of images. Radiographers soon learned that moving the X-ray source and the film in parallel planes but in opposite directions, while maintaining the beam passing through, say, a patient's heart, the images of the ribs could be made faint and blurry, but the image of the heart was fairly sharp. Such images appeared to be a two-dimensional slice through the target organ. The ideas behind these techniques occurred to a number of researchers. A Polish physician made a planar-slice image as early as 1914. Three Frenchmen separately thought of the idea in the 1920s. In 1930 the Italian Vallebona built a machine to get planar-slice X-ray images. Jean Kieffer, a poorly educated French immigrant in Connecticut, devised a system in 1928 in which the X-ray tube could move any direction in a given plane, while the film moved in synchrony in a plane in the opposite direction, with the target organ in between. Physically, it resembled a lever with the X-ray tube on one end and the film on the other, with the target to be imaged as the fulcrum. This yielded a quite clear planar-slice image of the area of interest, with bony structures blurred out. Poor Kieffer. No X-ray company or other manufacturer showed any interest in his invention (but a few years later he did profit to some degree). By 1936 two Americans, Andrews and Stava, had constructed a model of a device that gave "body-section" X-ray pictures. The planar-slice or body-section images are today called tomographs. The word tomography literally means making a section or cross section (from the Greek *tomos*, cutting or dividing, the same root from which the word atom is derived).

But one person did realize the promise of the ideas of these visionaries. He was the director of the Mallinckrodt Institute of Radiology at Washington University in St. Louis. He consulted with Kieffer, Andrews, and Stava and had a prototype instrument built. In 1937 this instrument made clear planar-slice images of soft tissue (actually, an aneurism in this instance), a task never before accomplished. By moving the X-ray tube/film focus a bit, a series of images could be generated, each a slice through the target tissue. Many improvements were made in the following years.

Throughout the world, use of radioactive nuclides in conjunction with computers to image human organs has effected a revolution in medical diagnosis during the past 30 years. The full name of the procedure is *radionuclide emission computed tomography*. There are several imaging techniques aside from the one using gamma rays from radioactivity; others are computed tomography (CT), which employs X-rays (and is sometimes called computer axial tomography, or CAT), magnetic resonance imaging (generally abbreviated as MRI; see section 6-39B), electrical impedance tomography, and sonography. Two men who contributed heavily to making these forms of imagines were Allan Cormack, an American physicist, and Godfrey Hounsfield, a British engineer. They received the Nobel Prize in 1979.

A selected plane through the patient's body is recorded. In making images using radioactive substances injected into the patient, gamma rays emitted from the decaying nuclide adsorbed on a targeted organ, such as the heart, travel through the patient's body and out in all directions, giving a sort of inside-out X-ray. These gamma rays make the image possible through use of a scintillation camera, which consists of a detector head connected to the television electronics. The scintillation camera, first designed at the University of California at Berkeley by American physicist Hal O. Anger in 1957, contains a screen which emits a scintillation when struck by each gamma ray photon. The screen referred to was actually a sodium iodide crystal containing some thallium iodide impurity which emitted scintillations when struck by gamma photons. The first camera had a 4-inch crystal and a single pinhole collimator. In later versions a slit or holes admits a fraction of the gamma rays to the scintillation screen. The flashes are proportional in brightness to the gamma ray energy or dose absorbed. An array of photomultiplier

Marvelous technology goes into the gamma-ray camera/TV.

vacuum tubes converts the flashes into electronic pulses. These serve as input to the computer. The pulses are translated into voltages applied to horizontal and vertical plates at the back of the cathode-ray (television) tube. This process directs tiny beams of electrons at the proper locations on the screen. This procedure became available in 1964 and in the 1970s was highly refined. Modern tomographs appear with breathless clarity.

The television screen on which tomographic images are projected hold a large number of adjacent squares, each of which is struck by a stream of electrons which excite a substance (a phosphor) on the screen, causing it to emit light. When the number of squares becomes large and each square is thus small, they cannot be perceived individually by the human eye. Squares are called pixels (for picture elements), and the brightness of each is governed by the number of electrons striking them. The image is represented by a long series of digital numbers which can be stored on a disk, the array of binary numbers corresponding to the pixels. The computer composes the images through use of a mathematical tool called Fourier transforms. Imaging in nuclear medicine partakes of many disciplines: medicine, physics, chemistry, biochemistry, mathematics, digital photography, and others.

In tomography, the image can be changed by manipulating the numbers using a computer program. A sophisticated computer can smooth images and filter out selected frequencies. This increases contrast. Scanners feed the computer with millions of numbers representing coordinates and density measurements of radiation which passed through the patient, calculating a new list of numbers corresponding to the pixels. Measurements can be confined to a plane perpendicular to the patient's head-to-toe axis, thus showing the reconstructed cross section on the screen. If an image of a lung is being made, proper adjustment can subtract images of ribs so that pulmonary blood vessels alone can be viewed. If kidneys are to be inspected, overlying soft tissue is visible, but these images can be removed.

Peering into a living body, layer by layer, inspecting slice by slice

Each pixel may be illuminated in 16 different shades of gray, but most modern tomographic screens are in color. This is accomplished by having each of the 16 shades of gray or intensities coded to a different color across the spectrum. The colors make viewing easier, but have no relation to the actual color of the organs. To image a beating heart, the exposure is limited to a fixed instant during each stroke. This is accomplished by closing a sort of gate to stop the gamma rays except during the instant of exposure, the process being called "gating." The process is analogous to the principle of a stroboscope. It is also possible to make movies of organs in motion, such as a throbbing heart.

The advent of nuclear imaging techniques has greatly reduced the need for exploratory surgery. The techniques are well suited to test the functioning of the various organs.

A new development for imaging was announced in preliminary form in 1996. It forms three-dimensional images in a cube made of laminated glass containing rare-earth oxides. The inventors, at Stanford University, excite pixels inside the glass using beams of infrared radiation. The pixel where the beams intersect causes that area to glow in various colors. The technique will not be ready for a number of years.

An important improvement in nuclear imaging took place in 1997 when a solid-state digital camera was announced. This was by the DigiRad Corp. of San Diego. The vacuum tubes used by bulky scintillation photomultiplier devices are being replaced by the much smaller, portable cameras. A key component of the new camera is the crystals, cadmium zinc sulfide, used to detect the gamma-ray photons. Electric current is produced directly on absorption of the gamma rays. Being portable, the apparatus can be wheeled into any hospital room and the digitized images can be fed directly into the hospital's information system. The resolution of the new system is somewhat superior to that of the older cameras, but the price is about the same. As of the late 1990s, about 12 million nuclear medicine procedures were being carried out each year in the United States. A useful website for nuclear medical information and images is *www.nuc.berkeley.edu/neutronics/todd/frame.* Today the field of nuclear medicine is bubbling over with energy and enthusiasm. International conferences are held in Los Angeles, Barcelona, Vancouver, Philadelphia, Sapporo (Japan), Rome, and elsewhere, and job opportunities abound.

6-23 Radiopharmaceuticals

While there are several dozen radionuclides currently used in nuclear medicine, one, technetium-99m, is a radiochemical virtuoso. This synthetic element seems to have just the right radiological properties. The half-life (6 hours) is not too short or too long, the gamma ray has the correct energy (125 kiloelectron volts) for maximum detection efficiency and it is not accompanied by a beta particle. Technetium-99m has become the workhorse of nuclear medicine. Each day in the United States, close to 36,000 medical imaging procedures are carried out. Technetium was discovered by C. Perrier and E. Segrè in Italy in 1937, and Glenn Seaborg and Segrè made the isotope technetium-99m two years later.

The name technetium comes from the Greek word for artificial.

Technetium-99m is made by putting ordinary molybdenum inside a nuclear reactor, when its isotope molybdenum-98 absorbs neutrons and becomes molybdenum-99. This nuclide has a half-life of 66 hours, decaying by beta emission not to technetium-99 in its low-energy (ground) state, but to metastable technetium-99m. Metastable refers to a tendency to be stable, that is, any change is suspended or altered for a while. The two isotopes, Tc-99m and Tc-99, are referred to as *nuclear isomers*. Thus technetium-99m exists for some time before going on to the more stable (longer half-life) technetium-99. Thus the metastable nuclide is the useful material. With a half-life of 6 hours, technetium-99m emits a gamma ray photon with energy very suitable for imaging and forms technetium-99, a material with a quite long half-life, 213 thousand years. The chemical form of molybdenum irradiated in the reactor is molybdic acid, which is sent to hospitals in lead containers in quantities of about 2 curies. Technetium-99m is extracted periodically as the pertechnetate ion with a mildly acidic solution. This pretty, symmetrical ion, TcO_4^-, is analogous to the permanganate ion, and is shaped like a tetrahedron with the technetium atom in the center and the four oxygen atoms on the corners. This ion itself may be injected intravenously into the patient, or it may be converted to one of several technetium derivatives. The amount administered is generally 10 to 20 millicuries.

Aside from the pertechnetate ion, technetium-99m is converted to other chemical forms which are absorbed selectively from the blood by various organs. Technetium forms many compounds whose molecules have unique architecture. The chemistry of its compounds is fickle and murky even to chemists. Some of these compounds of interest in nuclear medicine are:

technetium phosphates, diphosphates, and phosphonates
technetium sulfide carried by colloidal sulfur
technetium glucoheptonate
technetium complexes with chelating agents, such as iminodiacetic acid (IDA), or
dimercaptosuccinic acid (DMSA), or
diethylenetriaminepentaacetic acid (DTPA)
a reduced technetium isonitrile complex (sestamibi; trade name Cardiolite)
technetium-blood albumin complex
technetium-red blood cell complex (fixed using a tin salt, stannous chloride)

Probably the best agent for examining the heart for muscle function and blood supply employs the technetium-isonitrile radiopharmaceutical mentioned above, and it is replacing an earlier nuclide, thallium-201. The chemical structure of this technetium-99m complex is illustrated. Note that the geometry of this shapely molecule is that of an octahedron with the metal atom in the center. Each of the six corners is embellished with a molecule of the isonitrile component, represented by an R. Six bonds radiate out from the technetium atom to the six corners where isonitrile groups lie. In medicine, the compound is commonly known as sestamibi, (two trade names are Cardiolite and Miraluma). One molecule bears a positive electric charge. It is also used in mammography.

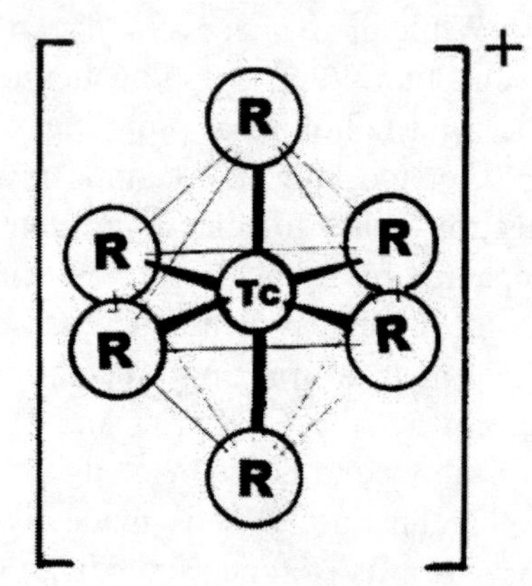

$$R = -C \equiv N - CH_2 - \underset{CH_3}{\overset{CH_3}{C}} - O - CH_3$$

Cardiolite

Another new imaging agent is known as CardioTec, a technetium complex containing carbon, nitrogen, oxygen, boron, and chlorine. It differs somewhat from sestamibi in that the two have different transport and retention characteristics in tissues. By comparison, sestamibi is retained longer by heart muscle. Imaging of the heart has made it possible to determine whether a patient brought into the emergency room is suffering a genuine heart attack or whether the disorder is of some other type.

Two very recent radiopharmaceuticals containing technetium-99m have the impossible names arcitumomab and nofetumomab merpentan. The first is a monoclonal antibody fragment. It recognizes a specific target site of any antigen (substance inducing an immune system response) and is absorbed there. The antigens in this case are those associated with cancers of the gastrointestinal tract, breast, or lung. Thus these are set up to be imaged. The second, nofetumomab merpentan, has proved especially suitable for imaging small-cell lung carcinoma; 30,000 patients are diagnosed in the U.S. each year with this disease.

In addition to technetium-99m, other useful radionuclides include the following: iodine-123, -125, and -131 for imaging thyroid and renal glands; indium-111 and -113 for imaging spinal and cranial fluid and lungs; mercury-203 for renograms (images of the kidneys); gallium-67 for tumor localization, especially lymphoma; thallium-201 and rubidium-81 for myocardial imaging; platinum-195 for cancer imaging; and xenon-133 for lung ventilation.

Thallium-201 chloride is taken up by heart muscle and its clearance is rapid. Thus imaging with this isotope pinpoints damage from a heart attack or other causes. Incidentally, on two occasions radiation detectors were set off by patients who had recently had this test, and were about to begin a group tour of the White House; the guards were not amused. The technetium isonitrile complex sestamibi is replacing thallium-201, in part because the gamma ray energy from thallium is a bit too low (around 75 kiloelectron volts) and its half-life (73 hours) is a bit too long. Indium-111 bonded to a monoclonal antibody (capromab pendetide) is a new radiopharmaceutical which has proved successful in imaging of the prostate gland and detecting metastatic prostate cancer. The gastrointestinal tract is also imaged using technetium-99m. The patient eats a solid meal specially prepared for the tests; it contains the radiotracer. What might be called a rather specialized branch of the culinary arts has been developed. The framed recipe, credited to J. H. Meyer et al., 1976, is one example. Now, dear reader, keep a straight face; this is serious business.

Recipe for in vivo chicken liver meat

1. Obtain live chicken. Subdue without anesthesia by stroking its gullet.
2. Locate wing vein and inject 500 μCi ^{99m}Tc-sulfur colloid intraveniously.
3. After 30 minutes, kill the chicken and remove the liver.
4. Dice the liver into cubes and cook (microwave oven or toaster oven) to a rubbery consistency.
5. Combine cooked liver cubes with the contents of a can of beef stew.

An ingenious dual isotope technique for imaging the parathyroid gland has been developed. The parathyroid gland, imbedded in the outside regions of the thyroid gland itself, secretes a hormone which regulates the metabolism of calcium and phosphorus in the body. Disorders in this endocrine gland may lead to hypercalcemia, an excess of calcium in the blood. The thyroid gland can be imaged using technetium-99m or thallium-201, but the tiny parathyroid gland is obscured. In order to reveal the parathyroid gland, images are made using both Tc-99m and Tl-201, and then the density of second image is adjusted (normalized) to that of the first via computer. Once this is accomplished, computer subtraction of the technetium image from the thallium image cancels out the thyroid gland, leaving the parathyroid gland plainly visible. These steps are illustrated in Fig. 6-23, a tomograph on Color Plate II.

6-24 Use of Technetium-99m and Other Radionuclides in Imaging

Made using technetium-99m, pertechnetate ion (TcO_4^-), is selectively absorbed by the thyroid gland and, less efficiently, by the salivary glands. The two lobes of the thyroid gland are clearly revealed, one on each side of the trachea. Pertechnetate is also used to study the stomach lining. It gives good results in imaging the scrotum, and can inform the physician whether surgery is required in case of certain problems.

In imaging the brain, technetium-99m glucoheptonate is frequently used. It is carried by the blood over the body and an image of the brain is recorded every 2 seconds. This provides an angiogram (blood vessel image) which reveals any lesions as regions of increased activity. Brain tumors are difficult to diagnose by classical techniques, but the methods based on radionuclides have proven very successful. Tumors can even be distinguished from old scar tissue from a concussion. Strokes can be diagnosed as well. In examining bones, technetium-99m phosphates are employed. They are selectively absorbed and disclose diseases such as cancer. Bone marrow is imaged using technetium-99m sulfide on colloidal sulfur; this material also is used to see the liver and spleen. The figure below shows front and side views of the spleen of a boy who had been struck by a car. Clearly the spleen had been fragmented, and this image was of great help in the surgery.

If you've ever known anyone with a brain tumor, you'll appreciate this.

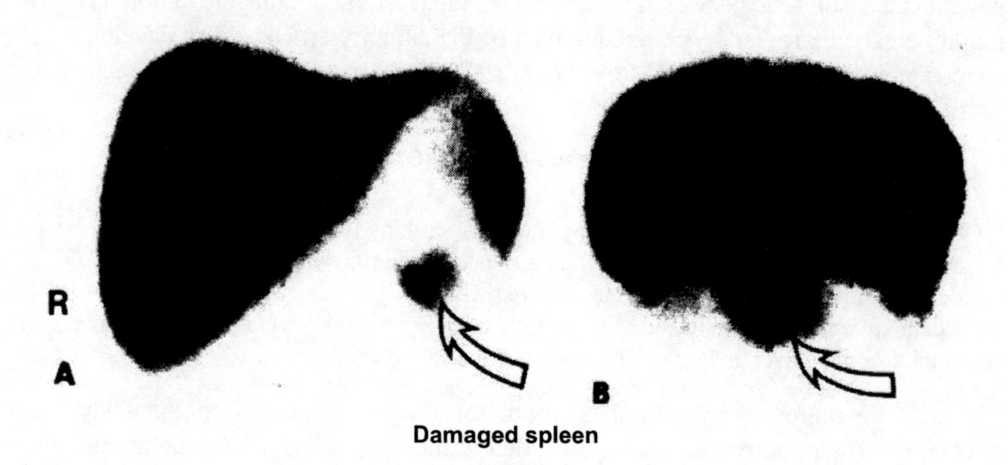

Damaged spleen

To scan the lungs, the technetium-99m is converted to its complex with blood albumin; any blockage of the capillaries, embolism, or tumor can be detected. There are several complexes of technetium, such as the DMSA derivative, useful in examining the kidneys, ureters, and bladder. Comparison of the images of both kidneys tells whether one is relatively impaired. The DTPA complex is also used in imaging the bladder and kidneys. Using 1.0 millicurie of technetium-99m, the total body dose is 7.5 millirads during a 2.5 hour exposure; a little more internal irradiation takes place during elimination of the technetium.

In other scans, up to 10 millicuries of technetium-99m might be employed. Technetium-99m IDA is rapidly taken up by the liver and transported into the gall bladder, making it possible to visualize the pathway of bile flow. Any obstruction is readily seen. Use of red blood cells labeled with technetium-99m discloses whether blood is circulating to a foot in a wounded area, such as a broken leg. In 1994 a procedure, called scintimammography, for improved diagnosis of breast cancer, was announced. Some of the pharmaceuticals used to image the heart are also taken up by malignancies in the breast, permitting a diagnosis without biopsy. Tests indicated about 90% accuracy, much higher than in classical mammography. The cost of the new test is about $600, about one fourth of that of a biopsy, and is also painless.

Lymphoma is one of the more dreaded forms of cancer. Lymph glands (nodes) have several functions, including clearing the body of foreign particles such as bacteria. They also trap cancer cells released by any cancer in other parts of the body, and thus themselves become cancerous (metastasis). Hodgkin's disease is a common type of cancer of the lymph system. About 8000 Americans are diagnosed and found positive for this disease every year, and about two-thirds are cured with chemotherapy and radiation. Up until recently tests were made by removing a lymph node, or in some cases making a biopsy, and examining the tissue microscopically. This procedure has been displaced by a process called lymphoscintiography. Colloidal sulfur containing technetium-99m sulfide is injected around the tumor site and then an imaging procedure is carried out. The path of lymph flow is revealed. Closely related techniques are employed in the cases of melanoma and breast cancer.

A technique for effective treatment in many cases of Hodgkin's disease has been developed at Arlington Cancer Center in Texas. It consists of first isolating yttrium-90 (half-life 64 hours) and bonding it to a type of immunoglobin called IGG, and introducing it intravenously. Specific absorption at the cancer site subjects the diseased tissue to beta bombardment. The energetic beta particles (2.3 MeV) penetrate 5 to 10 millimeters, so every tumorous cell need not receive an yttrium-90 atom. The procedure is successful in about half of the cases treated. The yttrium-90 is the decay product of strontium-90, of which there is a huge quantity in high-level nuclear waste.

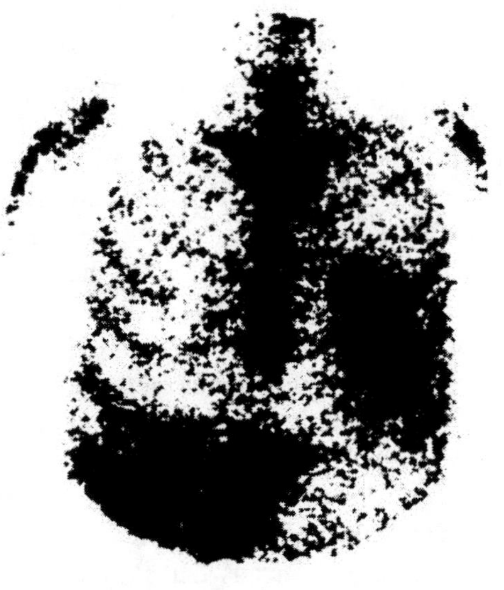

Gallium-67 image showing cancer of the lung (Dark area on the right)

Gallium-67 as the citrate is selectively picked up by cancerous tissue in the lungs. Imaging thus permits diagnosis of this serious condition. The figure indicates a cancerous growth in the left lung of a patient (this is a front view). Gallium-67 citrate accumulates in many normal and abnormal tissues, including infections. It is useful in general diagnosis.

Ventilation imaging is the term given to examining the lungs via a radionuclide which is breathed in by the patient. A radioactive noble gas such as krypton-81m (half-life 13 seconds) or xenon-133 (half-life 5.24 days), or an aerosol containing technetium-

99m DTPA is employed. Lung function and disease are shown. Since the half-life of krypton-81m is so short, it must be collected from its parent, rubidium-81, just before use. Instead of breathing in the gases, they may be dissolved in normal saline and administered intravenously.

Iodine-131, if substituted into molecules of hippuric acid, enables imaging of the kidneys and also the testicles, permitting any disorders to be quickly discovered. A new copper-67 complex of porphyrin serves to monitor lymph nodes following cancer treatment. Osteoporosis is a bone-crippling, painful disease afflicting millions of the elderly, especially women. It may be diagnosed early using a radiopharmaceutical containing gadolinium-153.

Monoclonal antibodies described earlier (6-18D, 6-19) in connection with treating tumors, are also used to carry radionuclides to target organs or tumors for the purpose of imaging, as mentioned earlier. The first commercially available such imaging agent has the trade name OncoScint CR/OV, and is made by the CYTOGEN Corp., Princeton, NJ.

A way of evaluating the functioning of transplanted organs is imaging using radioactive isotopes.

6-25 Positron Emission Tomography (PET)

Positron Emission Tomography—We have learned (4-3) that certain nuclides undergo beta decay by emitting positively-charged electrons (positrons) rather than ordinary negatively-charged electrons. What happens to these positrons? First they are slowed down by being scattered by atomic electrons (which are everywhere), and once slowed, they don't last long. This is because they can then interact with the negative electrons. What happens is that the positive and negative charges neutralize each other, the matter-antimatter pair annihilate each other, and the two electron masses become their equal in radiative energy (4-13). This radiation is two gamma ray photons, and they recoil exactly away from each other in opposite directions. The detectors consists of a ring of photomultiplier tubes connected to a computer.

A positron-emitting nuclide chemically bonded to glucose is injected into the patient, when it is absorbed by any organ consuming glucose. In this case it is brain activity to be examined; brains consume considerable glucose. The patient's head is inside the ring of detectors. If two photons are detected simultaneously on opposite sides (coincidence), it means that they came from the same electron-positron annihilation. These gamma rays are thus used in the technique of tomographic imaging, in this case being *positron emission tomography* (PET). Essentially, the scans reveal which parts of the brain are active (and consuming glucose) at the time of the scan. Modern techniques can produce the images in color (really false color). The technique started to evolve in 1951 from the work of Benedict Cassen at UCLA and was perfected by the seminal contributions of Michael E. Phelps (Fermi Award 1998). It became satisfactorily operational in 1973 when the first hospital-based cyclotron was installed. It is now used in many facilities worldwide.

Four radionuclides are commonly employed in positron emission tomography: carbon-11 (half-life 20.4 minutes), nitrogen-13 (half-life 10 minutes), oxygen-15 (half-life 2 minutes), and fluorine-18 (half-life 110 minutes). These short half-lives mean that the nuclides must be generated in a cyclotron or particle accelerator on site, which increases the expense of PET research. Another limitation is that after a positron is ejected from a nucleus, it travels a short distance before it collides with an electron and annihilation producing gamma rays takes place. This means that a built-in uncertainty diminishes resolution somewhat, but this limitation is not serious. By 1993 a more cost-effective accelerator had been invented at Washington University Medical Center in St. Louis. While a medical cyclotron costs $1.5 million, this new instrument, called a Tandem Cascade Accelerator, costs half as much and weighs only one ton (medical cyclotrons weigh 30 tons). The new procedure promises to reduce the cost of each PET imaging procedure down from the previous price of about $2000. PET does not generate the same type of images in the same way most other imaging systems do, but rather registers a metabolic function.

Through PET, brain functions have been elucidated in ways never before possible using living subjects, a sort of window on the soul. The subtlety of thought processes makes it all the more remarkable that anything at all can be seen. The cartography of this three-pound marvel, the human brain (see sketch below and Fig. 6-25A on Color Plate II), is being clarified as never before. Areas specializing in languages, emotions, forethought, cognition, and other lofty capabilities are clearly recognizable. PET catches the brain in the very act of thinking or feeling. These techniques enrich our capacity for wonderment.

Fragments of memory are scattered throughout the brain to some degree, but most knowledge is accumulated in certain specialized areas. In making PET images of the brain, the subject is first asked to look at a blank screen, and the background impulses are recorded. These marginal stimuli are then subtracted by the computer during a normal scan.

Carbon monoxide when inhaled bonds tightly to the hemoglobin of red blood cells. If traces of carbon monoxide containing carbon-11 are prepared and breathed in, flow of blood through the brain or other organ can be followed. Obstructions in blood flow, as from a stroke, may be kept under surveillance. Carbon-11 may also be administered as an amino acid or a fat; nitrogen-13 may also be incorporated into amino acid. Tomographic techniques are employed. Hundreds of radiation detectors in multiple rings encircle the subject's body and record millions of gamma photons for each image.

The vehicle of most energy of the body is glucose, $C_6H_{12}O_6$. Each molecule has five hydroxyl (-OH) groups. Suppose we prepare some glucose with one of the hydroxyl groups replaced by a fluorine-18 atom, or one ordinary oxygen atom replaced by an oxygen-15 (F-18 and O-15 are beta active by positron emission). When this fluorodeoxyglucose or O-15 glucose is metabolized in the brain, it mimics true glucose in the first step or two, and then gets trapped in the cells (after all, it is not true glucose). The rate of trapping is a measure of the brain's activity. Tests showed that when a subject was blindfolded, the part of the brain which processes vision (now inactivated by the blindfold) consumed 23% less glucose. Hyperactivity in children and adults has also been subjected to investigation by PET. The results indicate that about 8% less glucose,

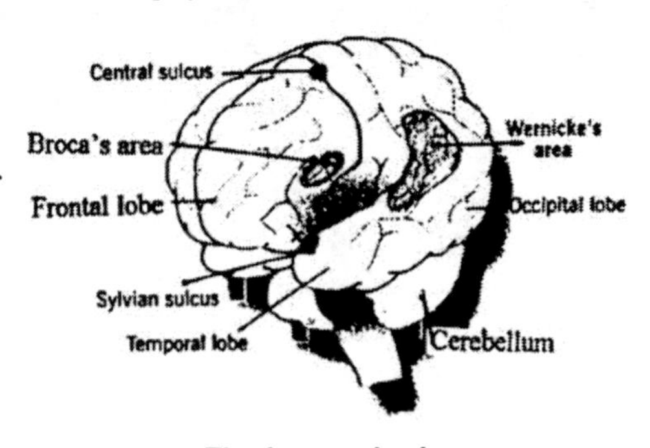

The human brain

PET allows mapping the brain for various thought processes.

compared to the controls, is consumed in the pre-motor cortex and prefrontal cortex areas of the brain. It is known that these regions control attention and motor activity, so lower neural metabolism here would result in less volition. Evidently, hyperactivity has no relation to consumption of food additives or sugar; there might be a genetic contribution.

In an alternative technique in which the metabolism of glucose in the brain is monitored using PET, water (rather than glucose) labeled with oxygen-15 is injected. Any area which uses glucose is at once seen in the scan. When a subject is trying to memorize words, PET discloses that it is the hippocampus structure deep within the brain which plays the dominate role. It is this area which is important in long-term memory and spatial relationships. But when a person attempts to recall specific words, the frontal cortex of the brain is involved. When subjects were asked to say the first words that came to mind, the rear parts of the brain became active. In all cases, less glucose and less energy were expended with successive efforts. It is as if the learning process etches a channel in the cortex. The human brain is exceedingly nimble in concocting new integrated circuitry.

Early Applications of PET—Before PET research on the brain, the common belief was that the brain activity of brilliant people was more intense than in the case of average or dull people. But research at UCLA has revealed that the opposite is true. Those who scored higher on IQ tests displayed on the average a lower degree of glucose metabolism, according to PET scans. The brains of the less intellectually gifted showed stronger activity, that is, they had to work harder to accomplish tasks which the precocious easily mastered. Persons involved in the study, analysis, and appreciation of music were shown through PET studies to undergo a shift toward the left hemisphere in brain activity. The PET technique has also been employed to determine which regions of the brain process phonetic and pitch discrimination during speech. In processing words, the central rear portion of the brain is used in hearing, the very back portions in reading, the upper central portions in speaking, and the lower front areas in generating words.

The dreaded mental illness schizophrenia afflicts more than two million Americans. In 1995 American and English investigations of the disorder used a modified, faster PET technique which responds in a matter of seconds. The results were revelation of some astonishing facts gained by testing volunteers. The subjects during the time of study were instructed to alert the operators when hallucinations were seen or heard in their minds. The area of the brain where the hallucinations were generated lighted up and could be clearly mapped. In normal brains, the prefrontal lobe monitors thoughts and actions, and serves as a sort of reality check. This function doesn't sort out sensory information in schizophrenics. Bizarre images go on uncontrolled. The brain's wiring seems to be confused.

Investigations using PET to study patients with Parkinson's disease have made impressive progress in recent years. Approximately 1% of Americans over 60 live with the disease. Roughly 10% of the cases seem to be hereditary. It is found in every country. In a normally functioning brain, a structure called the substantia nigra generates the neurotransmitter dopamine and a great deal of research in PET concerns dopamine and its derivatives. This substance is supplied in a steady stream to an adjacent area known as the striatum; this process is necessary for controlling bodily movements. In parkinsonism, insufficient dopamine is generated; the deficiency can be as much as 85%. The most effective treatment so far is regular doses of the medicinal L-dopa, which is converted into dopamine inside the brain; its effectiveness, however, falls off within a few years, and there are side effects. Various newer medicinals (bromocriptine, diprenyl, and related materials) are also employed, but they too have a limited useful lifetime. In 1995 a way was found to bond technetium-99m to dopamine and this has permitted imaging the transport of the essential material inside the brain.

Another window on parkinsonism

PET scans of this neurotransmitter system in action employ L-dopa tagged with an atom of fluorine-18, which acts as a beacon in the obscure corners of the brain under investigation. The topographic images clearly reveal the differences between normal and L-dopa-deficient brain tissue. In 1992, primates with artificially-induced parkinsonism were treated with a substance called GM1 ganglioside and this was found to effect remarkable recovery of motor and cognitive functions. The results permitted some important conclusions. The striatum consists of two parts, the caudate nucleus and the putamen. L-dopa labeled with fluorine-18, using PET, shows that when Parkinson's disease starts, it is the putamen which undergoes deterioration first, and the caudate nucleus remains undamaged until late in the disease. This strongly suggests that neural grafts might be much more effective directly in the putamen rather than in the substantia nigra. Fetal cell transplants into the putamens of patients with parkinsonism have shown modest improvements in most cases, dramatic improvements in others. PET studies disclosed that, in the early studies, only 5 to 10% of these cells survived 34 months. Improved surgical techniques have decidedly increased the percentage of thriving cells. During the past few years, at least a hundred Parkinson's patients have regained control of their bodies after fetal-cell transplants. Cultivation of stem cells outside the human body has promise of supplying enough L-dopa to meet the demand. Surgical procedures such as pallidotomy also provides relief from the ravages of parkinsonism in some cases. More research is clearly needed.

The author's brother died of Parkinson's disease; it is a dreadful disorder.

PET scans of the living brain enables observing directly the effects of medications, and so have considerable promise for the treatment of Alzheimer's disease, epilepsy, and other disorders. In 1995 measuring the brain's metabolic activity using PET at Duke University proved to be a means of predicting Alzheimer's disease before any outward symptoms appeared. Indeed, work a year later disclosed definite damage to areas of the brain that are known to develop into Alzheimer's, which occurs in patients carrying copies of a gene called Apo-E4. In most cases of mental illness, no abnormalities can be detected in post mortem examinations of brain tissue, except in cases of Alzheimer's disease.

How the Brain Processes Words and Some Disorders Therein—PET studies at several American universities gave a certain degree of insight into the process the human brain employs to find and use words. The soft furrows and corrugated folds of this marvelous nerve tissue retrieves words stimulated by objects or photos by rapidly assembling impulses from many areas, not just a limited region. There is no central dictionary, but there seems to be a sort of mental thesaurus in the left hemisphere. Patterns of what might be called mental sound are reconstructed using even the smallest of phonetic units of language. People born blind who learn Braille use the same areas of the brain to "see" any object mentioned orally. Similarly, those born deaf learn sign language, and use the same areas to process the information which hearing people do for the same words or ideas.

Evolution has tailored communication through speech, and reading is learned later. PET scans have demonstrated that reading silently and reading aloud activate different areas of the brain. The studies promise to spawn new techniques and neurological insights for teaching reading, especially to those for whom reading does not come easily.

Learning one's first language is a natural process; learning to read is not. Quite a large number of people simply cannot learn to associate printed words with their spoken form. This is called dyslexia. In 1996 British scientists made a study of dyslexia using PET techniques. The scans revealed differences between dyslexics and nondyslexics in those parts of the brain called the left perisylvian areas, just above the ears. In these regions lie Broca's areas and Wernicke's areas, which function to process words. They are separated by tissue known as the insula whose function was unknown until this PET study. Evidently, recognition of complete written words takes place in Wernicke's areas, while Broca's areas break the same words down into segments while creating a mental representation of the sound. The insula forms a bridge between the two areas. Injuries to Broca's areas results in inability to speak fluently, but seems not to cause interference with understanding. Conversely, people with injuries to Wernicke's areas can speak easily, but what they say has little meaning. The location of language functions in the brain varies from one person to the next by as much as 3 or 4 centimeters, or more.

A cluster of cells called the angular gyrus, in the back part of the brain, links letters with sounds, and the striate cortex behind it determines the meaning of the words. In nondyslexics, both language areas and the insula undergo intense activity during reading, according to the PET investigation, while with dyslexics, the insula was inert, leaving the language areas to struggle in isolation. Dyslexia in Japan and China is much less common than in the West because words are written with a single kanji character, or sometimes two or three, and need not be broken down into segments. Moreover, dyslexia is considerably less common among speakers of Italian and Spanish, in which words are spelled quite phonetically, than in French or English, in which various sounds are represented by several letters or groups of letters (more on dyslexia in 6-39B).

Epilepsy and Depression—About half of the people suffering from epilepsy (electrical storms in the brain) hardly respond to standard drug treatment. PET or SPECT (next section) scans reveal abnormalities in blood flow around the areas of the brain where the seizures originate. Brain tumors are readily revealed. The British have even made a PET scanner suitable for use with mice and rats as laboratory animals.

PET imaging of the brain has also been employed to study depression. In the type of depression which is severe and prolonged, and is perhaps hereditary, the results show that the caudate nucleus is markedly underactive. This part of the brain is known to be important in experiencing emotion. It is not known whether the lowered caudate nucleus activity is a symptom or a cause of depression. An estimated 5.4 million Americans are afflicted by depression, and their primary physicians can misdiagnose half of the cases.

Several million people suffer from obsessive-compulsive disorder, manifested by such irrational acts as washing one's hands 40 or 50 times per day, or checking six or eight times that an appliance has been turned off. Most cases can be treated more or less successfully with Prozac. Psychiatrists have developed techniques for modifying behavior and cognition for coping with the disorder. PET examination in 1996 of patients' brains after such psychotherapy revealed markedly decreased activity in the caudate nucleus, indicating that the mind itself is capable of altering thought patterns.

Tinnitus—This disorder is a constant and debilitating ringing in the ears which afflicts millions of Americans. The sensation is manifested by sensations of buzzing, whistling, hissing or other sounds. Treatments are rarely satisfactory. They consist of using hearing aids which amplify normal sounds to overcome or mask the ringing. Tinnitus seems to result from frequent loud sounds, certain medications (especially high doses of aspirin), ear or sinus infections, head trauma, and other causes.

Maddening noiseless sound

A giant step in finding the source of tinnitus was made in 1997 using PET. The studies revealed that the sound does not originate in the ear at all, as formerly thought, but rather in the temporal lobes of the brain, one opposite each ear. When the ear is damaged, the brain starts to rewire itself within these temporal lobes, and this activity results in the constant illusory sound sensations. This phenomenon is akin to the phantom pain which many amputees feel when the brain repairs its connections formerly used to control the lost limb. The discovery of activity in the temporal lobes of the brain might open the door to new directions of research, for example with neurotransmitters in the affected areas.

Other Studies Using PET—Inherent differences in the brain functioning of men and women have been recently revealed by PET. Different neuron pathways are used by the two sexes both when their brains are "on idle" and when the subjects are reading. A primitive brain area called the temporal-limbic system, controlling emotions such as those evoked by fighting, was much more active in men, while in women activity in the posterior cingulate gyrus dominated. Women seem to be more proficient in language because they utilize the right hemisphere (seat of most emotions) as well as the left hemisphere (where most reasoning takes place). PET scans disclosed that the limbic system of women's brains could more easily judge emotion in others than is the case with men.

A study in 1997 was made using PET of the brain activity of very young children. The results further confirmed what had long been known with fair certainty, namely that compassionate attention involving singing, stories, reading, etc., causes growth of trillions of neural connections in the brain and an actual increase in intelligence. This amplification of cognitive gifts amounts to turning on or turning up certain genes. Children deprived of such stimulation, such as some of those unfortunates from Romanian orphanages, lacked this neuron development. Over-stimulation or excessive demands were found to retard development. There seems little doubt that motherly love, expressed in many ways, but especially touching and stroking plays a most important role in rearing balanced and intelligent children. Two PET images from this study are reproduced in Fig. 6-25F, Color Plate II. A scan of a normal, fully functional brain is on the left, while that of one of the deprived Romanian orphans, on the right, distinctly reveals extreme underdevelopment of the temporal lobes. It seems fair to say that such studies provide an opportunity to guide us in creating a more gracious world, if we will act on our new knowledge.

Studies of psychostimulants, such as cocaine, have also been made using PET. This work might reveal the molecular roots of addiction. Cocaine blocks uptake of dopamine in synapses, causing them to become flooded with the neurotransimtter. Studies at Brookhaven National Laboratory demonstrated that the action of a drug used in Europe to treat epilepsy, Vigabatrin, depends on its adsorption at nerve synapses, and that this prevents adsorption of cocaine. Studies are continuing to see how successfully addiction can be treated using this epilepsy drug. PET examination of alcoholics show that the subjects have decreased whole-brain metabolic activity, as much as 20 or 30%. Clearly, brain research using PET is still in its infancy.

A comparative PET study of the brains of 41 murderers and 41 normal people of similar age was carried out by Adrian Raine of the University of Southern California. This revealed that the murderers have a lower glucose metabolism in the prefrontal cortex, a sign that this region was not functioning as it should to inhibit aggressive impulses.

The second most common cause of absenteeism from work is irritable bowel syndrome (the common cold rates number one). The disorder is characterized by abdominal pain and discomfort, bloating, diarrhea, and other such annoyances.

Exalted proctology?

Examinations of the colon by X-rays or other imaging techniques disclose no abnormalities, leading many physicians to suspect the disorder is psychological. In studies of irritable bowel syndrome at UCLA using PET, balloons were inserted into the rectums of both healthy and afflicted volunteers. While the subjects were being examined by PET, the balloons were inflated. In both groups, the brain's anterior cingulate in the frontal cortex was activated, but in persons with the disorder, a much lower balloon pressure caused the brain areas to light up, and to extend over a larger area. Moreover, the part of the brain which filters out sensations from the intestines is activated in healthy individuals, but not in patients with the syndrome. It appears that irritable bowel disorder arises from a greater sensitivity to bowel pain. Certain drugs afford some relief.

It had been thought by physicians that the human brain developed into maturity by age ten, approximately, but modern PET investigations showed that the maturation process continues until the early twenties. Thus the often bizarre behavior of adolescents is not simply hormonal overdrive, but prematurity. The frontal lobes, responsible for "executive" functions, as self-control, judgment, and planning, are not fully developed in adolescents.

PET is also employed to diagnose breast cancer. The patient is injected with an estrogen labeled with fluorine-18. Tomographic imaging clearly reveals any cancer, including metastasized new growths. The liver also shows up in the image because it clears the tracer from the body.

A controversial use of PET technology is in connection with criminal trials. Irregularities in PET scans confirmed defects in cerebral function in the cases of several men addicted to senseless violence, although CT scans of their brains disclosed nothing unusual. Attempts are made to prove innocence or guilt. The Society of Nuclear Medicine was so uneasy about possible misuse of PET in this connection that it set up a committee to establish guidelines. Research in 2001 at the University of Pennsylvania have found that a modified imaging technique called functional MRI imaging (6-39B) discloses whether a subject is lying or telling the truth. The brain requires more energy to lie convincingly than to merely say what is true.

Rubidium-82 is a positron emitter with a 76 second half-life, and it is used in PET imaging the heart. It result from the decay of strontium-82 (by electron capture, half-life 25.6 days) and is collected as needed. The United States buys much of its strontium-82 from Russia. Heart muscle needs a great deal of potassium, which rubidium mimics, and so it concentrates in the heart tissues.

Brain studies are supplemented by other imaging techniques, such as imaging via nuclear magnetic resonance (6-39B) and through use of a superconducting quantum interference device (SQUID, not discussed here).

6-26 Single-Photon Emission Computed Tomography (SPECT)

Another form of radioactive decay mentioned earlier (4-5) is capture of an orbital electron by the nucleus of an atom. This process emits a single gamma-ray photon, unlike the pair of photons in positron-electron annihilation. Using such materials in imaging is called single-photon emission computed tomography (SPECT). The advantage of SPECT is that longer-lived radionuclides can be employed, avoiding the cost of cyclotrons or accelerators. The disadvantage of SPECT is that it is less clear and accurate than PET.

An agent used to spy on the brain using SPECT is an amphetamine derivative. This radiopharmaceutical is prepared by bonding amphetamine to iodine-123, a nuclide which decays by electron capture with a 13 hour half-life. This substance is retained by the brain. Abnormalities not shown by other techniques are revealed. It offers great promise in research in epilepsy, stroke, Parkinson's disease, and Alzheimer's disease. In Great Britain, studies by SPECT of schizophrenia using a radio-iodine compound (Epidepride) pinpointed the receptor sites of nerve cells whose loss of function causes Alzheimer's. The two technologies, PET and SPECT, in conjunction can determine brain death.

The causes of stuttering have been studied long and hard by speech specialists. Connections to losses in hearing, deficiencies in the areas of the brain which govern motor functions of speech, as well as other suspected sources have been made. SPECT has been employed to study brain activity of persons who stutter, or experience the less common speech disorder called spasmodic dysphonia. The results so far indicate that stuttering might have a biochemical or faulty wiring in some area of the brain rather than an emotional origin. A 1996 study using PET to investigate ten chronic stutterers compared with ten normal speakers disclosed that in the brains of the stutterers there was twice the activity in the motor areas of the cerebellum as in the normal speakers. This might be due to a failure in "planning" speech. This means that there is difficulty in communicating the intended instructions to the muscles which control speech. Many stutterers are completely fluent when they recite or sing in chorus. PET shows that in these cases, the previously inactive areas of the brain had been turned on. When a stutterer stumbles over words, regions of the brain switch on which are supposed to be dormant, and other connections appear. In speakers without a stutter, the brain activity during speech is in the left hemisphere, whereas with stutterers the activity is in the right side.

Additional PET studies use an additional tool, namely transcranial magnetic stimulation in which short pulses of a magnetic field are aimed at carefully selected sites in the brain, sites located via PET. This procedure has the effect of turning that portion of the brain off for a short time. It might enable neuroscientists to interrupt the faulty circuitry surgically. Incidentally, a new treatment for stuttering involves injecting the vocal cords with tiny amounts of botulinum toxin, which causes the muscles to relax somewhat. About 2.5 million Americans stutter to some extent.

A disorder difficult to pin down is now called chronic fatigue immune dysfunction syndrome. Its symptoms include extreme and chronic fatigue, tender lymph nodes, headaches, joint pain, night sweats, and other signs that something is very wrong.

How would YOU diagnose this disorder?

A diagnosis occurs when almost everything else has been ruled out. Examination of patients' brains via SPECT at Harbor UCLA Medical Center disclosed abnormally low blood flow to one of the two temporal lobes. The affliction probably involves an immune-system failure or a virus infection or both. It is still under study.

In some cases superposition of a SPECT image of a brain, for example, on a CT image of the same brain and adjusted to the same size helps in analysis of abnormalities such as Alzheimer-type dementia. Such double images are referred to as "fusion" images.

The ultimate impact of PET, SPECT, and similar studies of the brain on human society might be tremendous. For the first time the biochemistry of the innermost reaches of the living brain might be clarified to a far higher degree than ever before. A better understanding of thinking, learning, forgetting, compassion, insanity, tendency toward violence, aggression, instincts, and passions—in short, human consciousness—might be within our grasp by watching the brain in action. A sort of window opening onto the human psyche has been found. Of course, these are not the only techniques possible. Incidentally, in nearly all of the processes described above, the amounts of radioactive substances administered are quite small, and their half-lives are short. Therefore, during storage on site for a couple of months, the materials decay down to practically no radioactivity, and no waste problem arises. But in the synthesis and handling of the materials and the substances from which they are made, a certain amount of low-level radioactive medical waste is unavoidably generated, and this requires proper disposal. Those who, in their in-depth ignorance, clamor for a halt to production of all radioactive substances are also demanding that we give up the marvelous medical advances described.

Images made by various nuclear techniques are available on the web at:

www.weber.edu/todaytext/, sites 10.1> ff, and
www.nuc.berkeley.edu/neutronics/todd/frame

6-27 Imaging Using Nonradioactive Materials

Several factors have spurred research with the objective of developing techniques to conduct medical examinations using stable nuclides only. Foremost of these factors is the problem of disposing of radioactive waste, especially carcasses of experimental animals. One procedure is to inject minute spheres of blood albumin into the artery of the organ being examined and to visualize them using X-rays, CT scans, or MRI. The microspheres contain contrast agents which make this possible. Some spheres, about 15 micrometers in diameter, are slightly larger than red cells of blood and so become lodged. The albumin spheres slowly dissolve. Other microspheres (usually 3 to 5 micrometers in size) are smaller than blood cells and enter general circulation. They are detected using ultrasound techniques. The use of microspheres, pioneered by Medical Technologies Ltd. in Los Angeles, appears to be quite promising as an alternative medical technique.

Another means of avoiding radioactive labels is to craft experimental drugs into a fluorescent form, and follow the path of the materials using ultraviolet light. In other cases, staining tissues with fluorescent dyes is sufficient.

Still another technique of imaging without using radioactive materials, developed in the late 1990s, employs what are called hyperpolarized gases. This procedure is a great improvement over imaging of the lungs made using radioisotopes, which are not very clear because the tissue mass and water content in lungs is small, and the uptake of gamma-emitting radiopharmaceutical is necessarily small; after all, the volume of space in the lungs is mostly air. In the years following 1960 it was discovered that certain gases, namely those whose nuclei have a magnetic moment, can have their spins oriented in the same direction in a magnetic field, and maintain this condition for hours. For generating images in a living subject, a noble gas (helium, neon, argon, krypton, xenon; see periodic table) is best. Of these, helium-3 and xenon-129 qualify. When inhaled while the patient lies in a magnetic field, a second magnetic field at right angles to the first is imposed and made to oscillate in polarity. This makes the atomic nuclei of the polarized gas atoms emit radiation, which permits making an image. Helium-3 is formed from radioactive decay of tritium (4-6B). Most helium-3 is purchased from Russia; it costs several hundred dollars per liter. Xenon, occurring in trace quantities in the atmosphere, contains 26% of the isotope Xe-129. To polarize the gases, they are heated with rubidium vapor and exposed to circularly polarized laser light; the rubidium atoms are easily polarized. The rubidium atoms then transfer their quantized spin to the noble gas atoms.

The signals from helium-3 and xenon-129 are strong, permitting excellent images to be made of the lungs even with weak magnetic fields, as low as a thousandth of the strength of the fields used in magnetic resonance imaging, and this helps to lower costs. Even the tiny air sacs in the lungs become visible. Aside from examining lungs for cancer, the areas of lung tissue which are afflicted with emphysema are readily identified, enabling their surgical removal to be more precise. Helium is almost insoluble in blood, but xenon dissolves to some extent. This property promises to permit imaging of other organs possible, such as the colon.

6-28 Stomach Ulcers

Bleeding, painful ulcers of the stomach and duodenum have plagued humankind for centuries. Formerly, ulcers were ascribed to high living, consumption of excessive rich food and spices, or to stress. Around 1979, evidence began to seep in that a spiral bacterium, *Helicobacter pylori*, might be the culprit in most cases of peptic ulcer and gastritis. The evidence is now incontrovertible that *H. pylori* causes most, but not all, peptic ulcers. Approximately 75 million Americans harbor the bacterium but only a small fraction of these suffer from peptic ulcers.

This remarkable bacterium survives in the acidic conditions of the stomach and upper duodenum, a hostile habitat. It can do this in part because it lives in the mucus of the stomach lining and thus avoids much acidity. Additionally, the bacterium is able to decompose the urea which is found in all body fluids (most urea is excreted in the urine). *H. pylori* manufactures a type of urease, a class of enzymes which decompose urea into carbon dioxide and ammonia. The ammonia neutralizes that small amount of hydrochloric acid formed in the stomach which diffuses through the mucous layer. This process permits the clever freeloading bacterium to create its own chemically favorable environment. The type of urease which the bacterium makes is many times more active than other bacterial ureases. The carbon dioxide generated dissolves in the blood stream and is finally exhaled. More than 95% of patients with ulcers carry these bacteria. Treatment consists of taking a bismuth basic salicylate drug along with antibiotics.

There is some evidence that H. pylorli evolved from a type of E. coli.

Four strains of the bacterium have been identified, corresponding to human sources from Europe, China, Japan, and New Zealand. The slight differences in their DNA are consistent with patterns of human migrations which began more than 100,000 years ago, suggesting that people have been coping with the bug for at least this long.

It is the release of carbon dioxide from urea which gives clinicians a means of performing an accurate diagnosis for the presence of the bacteria. Ordinary carbon consists of 1.1% carbon-13, the rest being carbon-12. Neither is radioactive. Carbon highly enriched in the isotope of mass number 13 is available on the market, and so is urea synthesized using it. To carry out the test, the patient drinks a harmless solution of urea made from carbon-13. After 20 to 40 minutes the carbon dioxide in the air exhaled is captured chemically, and it is analyzed for carbon-13 using a mass spectrometer. If the carbon-13 registers above 1.1%, it is evidence for an ulcer or gastritis. In 1994 the British devised a carbon-dioxide laser which can perform the analysis much more cheaply than a mass spectrometer can. There is the promise of using the technique with glucose for liver tests or, say, to study the metabolism of caffeine.

If the patient is uncomfortable with the name urea, simply call it by its true chemical name: carbamide.

A vaccine against the strain of *Helicobacter pylori* which is apparently responsible for most ulcers was announced in 1995. It was developed by Italian scientist Marta Marchetti and her group. Evidently the bacterium is developing resistance to the drugs used to eradicate them. There is suspicion that it can also cause stroke. The germ is spread by houseflies.

Just as a point of interest, the complete gene sequence in *H. pylori* was worked out in 1997. The bacterium has 1590 genes on a single, circular chromosome.

6-29 Irradiation of Food

In 1896, one year after Roentgen discovered X-rays, a suggestion was made to use this new energy form to kill microbes in food. In 1905 the first patent application was filed. As early as 1916 strawberries were irradiated in Sweden. The first patent on preservation of foodstuffs, as well as a variety of other organic products, was issued in 1918.

Food Irradiation—Up to one-third of the world's food is lost owing to spoilage; in developing countries, with a minimum of refrigeration, up to one half is lost. Classical means of preservation of food are: drying, especially in sunlight where ultraviolet irradiates and kills bacteria; smoking; salting; mixing with spices; canning; and freezing. Some foods which perish quickly, such as ocean fish, are only available in coastal areas of developing countries, where preservation by canning or freezing is too expensive. Irradiation of foodstuffs could help overcome these difficulties, not as a substitute for refrigeration, but as a supplement.

Deep-penetrating ionizing radiation (gamma rays, X-rays, high-energy electrons) kills microorganisms by fracturing their genetic material and cell walls. If food is packaged in germ-tight containers or wrappings, and then treated by irradiation, the process is an alternative to canning, drying, smoking, salting, or freezing. In most cases, the original flavor, texture, and nutrient value of food preserved by irradiation are retained to a higher degree than with other methods. Ultraviolet radiation is also ionizing, but does not penetrate nearly as far as the other types mentioned, and is strongly attenuated by most plastic wrappings.

Microorganisms are killed by ionizing radiation through several different mechanisms. One is the disruption of their DNA directly. Another, less powerful but still important, is by free radicals generated by irradiation, especially hydroxyl radicals (neutral OH groups). These energy-rich radicals attack and deactivate essential enzymes, among other processes.

Two main classes of microbes in meat are encountered, the first causing spoilage, the second causing foodborne illness among consumers. Risks from salmonella bacteria can be lessened by dipping chicken carcasses in a solution of trisodium phosphate or treatment with ozone, but this process destroys surface bacteria only. Trichinosis is rather rare, but really serious. It is not necessary to kill the trichina larvae lurking in pork by radiation because low-dose radiation is sufficient to prevent them from reproducing in human intestines. The microbes which cause botulism form radiation-resistant spores, and their complete control via irradiation requires a radiation dose higher than average. Recently, a long-known chemical compound, 3,4-diaminopyridine, has been found to give immediate relief from botulism, and might effect a cure in some cases. From the standpoint of just the number of cases, botulism is not very important. A particularly virulent strain of the bacterium *Escherichia coli* (strain O157:H7), diagnosed as a human pathogen in 1982, sometimes contaminates beef and other foodstuffs. As few as 10 cells can cause illness. The cells survive for months in mildly acidic foods. Outbreaks of sickness caused by this pathogen started in 1982 and have caused much sickness and quite a number of deaths. The beef in the first case was traced to a farm where cattle had been treated with low doses of penicillin and tetracycline, conditions which promote development of drug-resistant bacteria. The complete genetic blueprint of *E. coli* was determined in 2001.

More than 9,000 people in the USA die each year from food poisoning.

Another serious disease which can be prevented by meat irradiation is cysticercosis. It is caused by a tapeworm and is transmitted by consuming undercooked pork. The cysts lodge throughout the body, and those in the brain can cause seizures, dementia and death, especially in children. Another form of food poisoning is listeriosis, caused by listeria bacteria in cheeses, especially those of the soft sort. This can be prevented by irradiation.

Diseases caused by foodborne pathogens are much more common than generally believed. The most common disorders are food poisoning (gastroenteritis), the results of salmonellosis and infections by Campylobacter or Staphylococcus aureus. The Centers for Disease Control of the Public Health Service has made informed estimates of the number of cases and their consequences. The data for the United States annually are summarized in the table below. The annual number of fatalities from foodborne diseases in the United States, according to the older data is approximately 6000, and this is the conservative figure given in the table. But recent data from the Centers for Disease Control is closer to 9000. Much of the increase arises from imported food. As many as 76 million people become ill from foodborne infection. These disorders are largely preventable. Irradiation is not effective in controlling viruses, such as Norwalk-like viruses, which are rare but can cause food poisoning.

FOODBORNE DISEASES IN THE USA*

Organism	Disease	Primary food	Annual deaths	Number of cases	Cost per year	Symptoms
Salmonella	Salmonellosis	Chicken	2000	2,000,000	$1,400,000,000	Fever, diarrhea, dehydration, death
E. coli 0157:H7	Hemolytic uremic syndrome	Beef	100	50,000	$60,000,000	Blood disease, kidney failure, death
Staphylococcus aureus	Infections	Chicken	1210	1,513,000	$908,000,000	Blood, heart, lung disease, death
Campylobacter	Infections	Chicken	2,100	2,100,000	$1,470,000,000	Meningitis, diarrhea, death
Listeria monecytogenes	Listeriosis	Cheese, fruit, vegetables	510	1,860	$ 231,000,000	Meningitis in newborn, death
Shigella	Shigellosis	Meat, vegetables	180	90,000	$108,000,000	Dysentery, death
Taenia solium	Cysticercosis	Beef, pork	66	1,104	$7,800,000	Tapeworm, seizures dementia
Taenia saginata	Gastroenteritis	Beef, pork				
Trichinella spiralis	Trichinosis	Pork	3	131	$698,000	Larvae infection, muscle pain, death

*The total deaths each year exceed 6000, the number of cases is more than 5,560,000 and the total cost approximately $4.2 billion. Botulism is not included. Another disease, toxoplasmosis, is caused by Toxoplasma gondii, and affects more than 4000 persons, generally children. While fewer than 100 die, the cost is tremendous, being millions of dollars per year. This is because one effect is severe mental retardation, requiring lifetime care.

Equipment and Procedure—Less expensive gamma ray sources became available with the development of nuclear reactors. The only nuclide used at present is cobalt-60, but this might change within a few years. Most cobalt-60 is produced in Canada in nuclear reactors (CANDU type) moderated with heavy water. Natural cobalt, consisting only of cobalt-59, is exposed to neutrons inside the reactor for a year, when a good fraction of it is converted to cobalt-60. The half-life of this nuclide, 5.27 years, figures out to correspond to 1.0% of it decaying each month. It is shaped into small cylinders about 1 inch long, which are nickel plated. These are loaded into thin-wall stainless steel tubing, forming "pencils" 18 inches long. During transport, the pencils are enclosed in sturdy casks (Type

B). To date several accidents have taken place, but in no case has failure of the integrity of the cobalt-60 encased in these casks occurred (the old hospital-type in the 1983 accident was not in a cask; see 6-17).

When irradiation plants began, a different radionuclide was used in some installations. This was cesium-137 (half-life 30 years), which was recovered from the fission products from nuclear reactors. It was prepared as cesium chloride (a white solid), and sealed in capsules made of stainless steel or other inert metal. Cesium-137 was suspended for food irradiation, but it has many advantages and plans are afoot to start using it again (next page). The gamma rays emitted by both cobalt and cesium are both less than 1.5 megaelectron volts in energy, a value far below that required to induce nuclear reactions and thus no artificial radioactivity can be created on irradiation.

Typically, an irradiator might contain approximately three million curies of cobalt-60. In air, these metal ingots self-heat and can reach a temperature higher than the boiling point of water. The packaged foodstuff units on conveyor belts are moved on overhead tracks, and are lifted at a predetermined rate inside, so that the irradiation occurs as uniformly as practical. Dosimeters record the degree of exposure. The intense gamma rays convert some oxygen in the air to ozone and nitrogen oxides, so ventilation must be supplied. When not in use, the radiation source is immersed in water to permit the loading and unloading. The gamma rays, interacting with water, produce a blue glow (the Cherenkov effect; see page 103). The irradiation facility of the firm MDS Nordion, headquartered in Ontario, Canada, is illustrated (next page).

The gamma rays, of less than 1.5 megaelectron volts energy, are incapable of nuclear reactions here, and thus produce no radioactivity.

Another plant is that of Food Technology Service, Inc. in Florida, opened in 1992. Its irradiation cell has six-foot-thick, steel-reinforced concrete walls. The racks of cobalt-60 are drawn up hydraulically out of the pool into the irradiation cell. Carriers, laden with packaged food, move slowly around the gamma-ray source, stopping briefly at eight positions to expose both sides. Exposure times vary, depending the number of curies of cobalt-60 used, the type of foodstuff (and thus the dose), and other variables. Another facility is Sterigenics, Inc., and still another is SureBeam; both of these are in southern California. SureBeam closed its California facility in 2003, but has another in Sioux City, Iowa. The Belgium-based company, Ion Beam Applications, has a facility in Memphis Tennessee.

Other irradiation facilities (not treating foodstuffs) now operate in New Jersey, Virginia, North Carolina, Arkansas, Georgia, and California. The great majority of irradiators in the United States are not for food processing, but for sterilizing medical supplies and a wide variety of other items (6-14). There are more than 50 facilities at present in the U.S. and about 170 in the world.

Dosages in food irradiation are generally in the thousands of rads, and therefore the more convenient unit, the gray, is increasingly used (see 4-22). One gray is 100 rads. Three dose levels are generally employed, as below. The irradiation costs are a few cents per pound, the exact amount being very dependent on production volume. Except for the highest doses, irradiation does not completely sterilize the food, and hence it must be refrigerated. In any case, its shelf life is greatly extended. Typical dose levels are tabulated below.

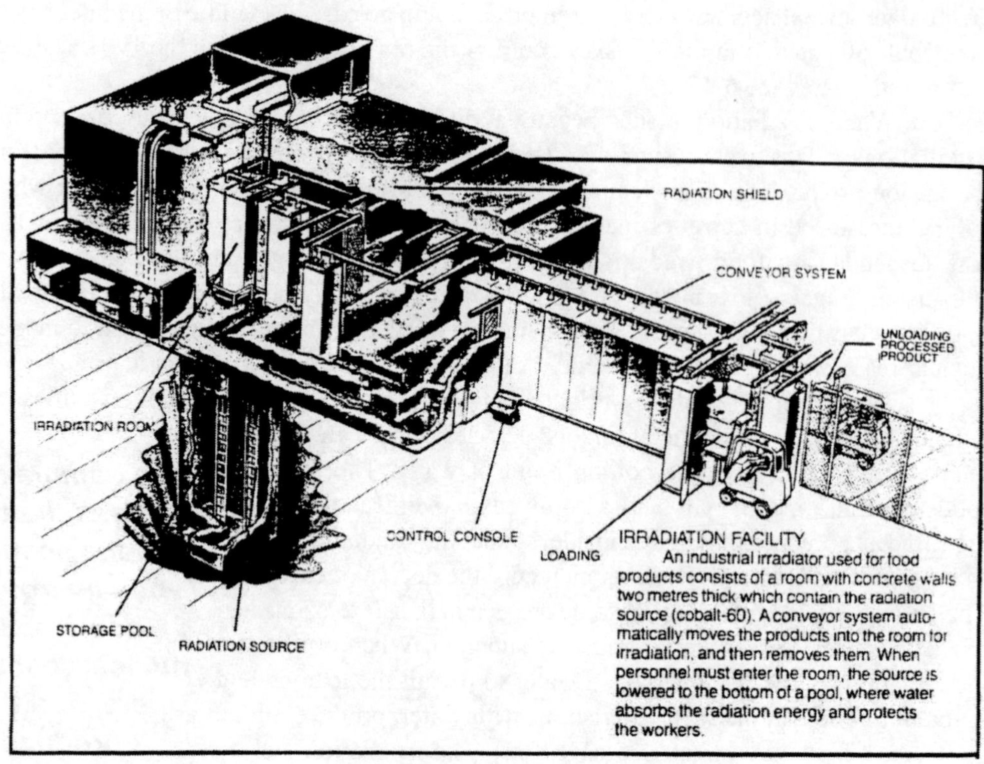

Facility for industrial irradiation of food

Dose Level	Typical Applications
Low dose (Up to 1,000 grays)	Inhibition of sprouting in potatoes and onions. Elimination of insect infestation in wheat and flour. Control of trichina parasite in fresh pork. Extending shelf life of fruits, vegetables, and mushrooms. Disinfestation of fruits and nuts. Killing all insects.
Medium dose (1,000 to 10,000 grays)	Control of salmonella bacillus. and other pathogenic microbes.
High dose (over 10,000 grays)	Microbial reduction in dry foodstuffs, as spices, herbs, and tea.

The medium-dose treatment is sometimes referred to as pasteurization. To achieve sterilization requires doses of 25,000 grays or above.

Renaissance in the Use of Cesium-137 for Food Irradiation—One advantage of cesium-137 is that extremely large amounts of it are available in nuclear waste. Its cost is mainly that of extracting it from all the other waste, but there are several processes for this which function satisfactorily. Some in the anti-irradiation community seem to think that just because the radiocesium is a waste product it should therefore not be employed for anything useful; just why this should be so is not made clear.

To see the advantages which cesium-137 has over cobalt-60 for use in irradiators, compare their radiological properties (based on pure materials):

	Cobalt-60	Cesium-137
Half-life, years	5.27	30.17
Specific activity, curies per gram	1,130	87.0
Thermal energy released, watts/gram	174	0.0878 (elemental Cs) or 0.0698 (cesium chloride)
Percentage which decays in one year	12.32%	2.27%

These figures show that the more rapidly decaying cobalt-60 must be replaced more frequently than cesium-137, and that the cobalt generates more heat per gram. The result is that the cobalt must be stored under water, while the cesium can be stored with air cooling alone. The gamma rays from cobalt are more energetic than those from cesium and thus require more massive shielding. In the case of each radionuclide, after one half-life, the activity or thermal energy released is half the value in the table. The cesium-137 isolated from nuclear waste actually contains other radio-isotopes of cesium and the specific activity is considerably lower than the figures in the table above. About 5 curies of cesium is required to give the same irradiation dose as 1 curie of cobalt. It has been estimated that all the spent cobalt-60 in North America could be stored in a space of 1.25 cubic meters, about the size of a small desk.

These and other properties enabled a new company, Gray*Star, headquartered in New Jersey, to invent and design an irradiator which is prefabricated from steel. It consists of two parts, a lower component weighing 165 tons and an upper component weighing 37 tons. Both units are portable by rail, truck, or ship. The lower section contains 2.8 million curies of cesium-137 as the chloride, and it is air-cooled; no water pool is required. The walls are 16-inch steel, which absorbs practically all of the gamma rays. The cesium chloride is loaded and its security shield is welded shut. The irradiator is built to accept the standard pallet (40 by 48 inches) of food packages to be treated, thus avoiding expensive handling. The units can be shipped to existing central food-packing houses and installed in only a day or so.

A safe, radioactive safe

In use, pallets with packaged foodstuffs are rolled into position. The cesium chloride unit is raised and gamma ray exposure takes place from all sides. An ingenious device distributing radiation insures that exposure and dosage are at the specified levels. A real time dosimetry system employing an array of ion chambers insures proper exposure of the foodstuffs. All operations are automatic, including dose adjustments which compensate for varying food densities, the fraction of cesium which has decayed, etc. Irradiation costs are estimated to be approximately 2 cents per pound. Eventually (after about one half-life, 30 years), the cesium-137 must be replaced for food-irradiation units, but those used to sterilize medical devices, milk cartons, etc., last much longer. The exhausted units are easily processed: cesium-137 decays to stable barium-137, and this is separated from the cesium. The units are inherently safe: one cannot cause an "accident" even intentionally. The Gray*Star units are equipped with satellite communication facilities so that regulatory agencies can monitor operations. Each Gray*Star assembly costs around $1.5 million, not counting installation. In 1999, a prototype is scheduled to undergo tests by the Department of Agriculture under the direction of Donald Thayer, a respected expert in the field.

Preservation of Meat—The idea is to wrap the product in plastic (several types have been approved, different for poultry and red meat) and seal it hermetically. It is then (after pretreatment described below) subjected to sufficient ionizing radiation to destroy nearly all microorganisms. Suitable wrapping materials are special types of polyethylene and other plastic films. The wrapping materials are required to allow oxygen, but not moisture or microorganisms, to enter or leave the package. This is to prevent botulism from any spores surviving the irradiation. The energy requirement is only about 2% of that necessary for sterilization by heat, and therefore the natural character of the food is hardly changed. When meat absorbs a radiation dose of 10,000 grays, its temperature rises by 2.4 °C (4.3 °F).

In the pretreatment step, meat destined for sterilization is first heated briefly to a temperature between 73 and 80 °C (163 to 176 °F) in order to deactivate all enzymes present. Then the irradiation is carried out with the meat packaged in vacuum. It is either refrigerated to a few degrees above freezing (about 41 °F) or is chilled to minus 30 °C (minus 22 °F). The temperature of the food during irradiation is quite important. Bacteria become more resistant to gamma rays at lower temperatures. The product is free of objectionable odor and taste on warming, even after long storage at room temperature. High-fat meats develop some objectionable odor. X-rays serve about as well as gamma rays to sterilize foodstuffs. When X-rays or gamma rays are absorbed, energetic electrons are generated which sterilize the foodstuff. An economical means of generating energetic electrons directly is the use of a linear accelerator. Unlike radioactive sources, these machines can be turned on and off. A demonstration unit for irradiating meat and other foodstuffs, which is rather small (power level 20 kilowatts) was built in 1992 at Iowa State University at Ames. One of its main purposes was to encourage increasing export of Iowa meat products. The Titan Corporation of California in 2000 began building a processing facility in Sioux City, Iowa, for electron irradiation of poultry.

In the spring of 1990, the Food and Drug Administration approved irradiating chicken up to 3000 grays. Other foods well suited to preservation via irradiation include other poultry, spices, powdered dried eggs, rice, and Camembert cheese. By 1996 irradiation of domestic fresh fruits and vegetables was authorized to delay sprouting, kill insects, and retard ripening.

6-30 Are Irradiated Foods Safe?

At this point we venture forth into a spirited controversy. When you start tinkering with anyone's food, it arouses an intense emotional response, the same as with topics such as medical practices, fashions, religions, or homes. Strong objections to food irradiation have been registered by many critics, whose spectrum ranges from competent and fair-minded to the uninformed and outright crackpot. An example of the latter is the author of an article in Harrowsmith magazine in 1986, whose Olympian fulminations claimed that "Simply put, the proposal to establish an irradiation industry [in] the industrial world and developing nations poses the greatest single technological threat to the health and welfare of the planet next to actual nuclear war." An extremist organization called Food & Water, Inc. specializes in scare tactics, harassment, and misleading ads concerning food irradiation. But most activists now agree that irradiated food is safe. In general the anti-irradiation community panders to the visceral fear of Americans of radiation, a fear that began with Hiroshima and was fertilized by Chernobyl. Emotions and ignorance also play strong roles in similar controversies over foods altered by genetic engineering. Nevertheless, there is virtual consensus among food scientists and other experts that irradiated foods are safe. In fact, irradiation is the most studied food preservation technique in history. After all, the topic has been researched more than 60 years, and the investigators are highly competent scientists. There are a few fringe scientists, who are not specialists in the topic, who claim such foodstuffs are unsafe.

In our pluralistic society, all opinions are welcome, the more competently informed, the better.

The more rational complaints deserve careful consideration. After all, the Department of Agriculture is charged with the responsibility of assuring consumers that foodstuffs are "safe, wholesome, and accurately labeled." This means that in irradiated food pathogenic microorganisms must be controlled, there cannot be excessive loss of nutrients, and toxic products must not be formed, or if formed, they must disappear before consumption. Spoiled food cannot be disguised by irradiation.

Whenever a new technique appears, there are always a few people who oppose it with incredible determination. Many are simply opposed to change. This happened with the introduction of electricity, with vaccination, and with water chlorination or fluoridation. When the changes concern food, the matter is even more emotional. When canned food appeared on the market a century and a half ago, it met a certain resistance. Before 1920 thousands of babies died annually from drinking contaminated milk. The solution to the problem was not more government regulation, but the technology of pasteurization. When pasteurization of milk was introduced, some farmers objected from fear of loss of markets. A few consumer groups claimed loss of nutritional value in the milk. In some places, laws prohibiting the sale of pasteurized milk were passed. Believe it or not, there are still some folks who will not eat food which has been frozen. There are still others who refuse to use microwave ovens. Curiously, the irradiation of meat by electron beams, as in the Iowa State University unit, has escaped nearly all criticism by the anti-irradiation community. This is probably because the energy source is electricity, not radioactivity. But the ionization effects on the product are essentially identical to that of gamma rays. Energetic electrons cannot penetrate meat more than about 3½ inches, considerably shorter than in the case of gamma rays.

Nutritional Value of Irradiated Foodstuffs—Proteins consist of amino acid units bonded together in long spiraled chains. Human beings require 20 kinds of amino acids (possibly 21 if the newly discovered selenocysteine is included). Of these, 12 can be synthesized inside the human body. Gamma ray irradiation destroys only the tiniest fraction of amino acids. No significant changes occur in the quantities of carbohydrates, although some hydrolysis of starch to glucose takes place. Mineral constituents, such as calcium, magnesium, iron, etc., are not affected at all. A small quantity of certain fats is altered (see below).

Vitamins—Like all other food processing or preparation methods, irradiation results in some loss of nutrients. Two water-soluble vitamins are affected by irradiation, thiamine (vitamin B_1) and ascorbic acid (vitamin C). A fraction (one-tenth to one-fourth) of the thiamine is destroyed on irradiation. A larger fraction (one-third) of this vitamin is destroyed on cooking. Cooked irradiated meat therefore does contain less thiamine than cooked unirradiated meat. The other water-soluble vitamin, ascorbic acid (vitamin C), is changed. Radiation does cause dehydrogenation of a fraction of this vitamin, but during digestion it is converted back to ascorbic acid. The important fat-soluble vitamins are vitamin A, vitamin D, vitamin E, and vitamin K. They are sensitive to radiation and a third to a half might be lost. Vitamins B_2, B_3 and B_5 in food are not destroyed appreciably. The radiation dosage and temperature determine the degree of vitamin loss. Opponents of irradiation have overstated vitamin losses because they focused on results of extreme, experimental conditions. Recent German tests have shown that vitamin losses through irradiation are generally much less that in cooking.

In some early studies, rats fed highly irradiated foods died from internal bleeding. This effect was traced to destruction of vitamin K in their diet. Adding some of this vitamin, or incorporation of fresh food, corrected the problem. The problem does not arise in food for humans because our bodies can synthesize vitamin K.

Are Harmful Substances Formed in Foods by Irradiation?—The first point to make is this: No radioactivity is introduced into food which has been irradiated, just as a patient does not become radioactive when a medical or dental X-ray photograph is made.

Irradiation of foodstuffs breaks chemical bonds (radiolysis) to an extent depending on dose. Each single bond between atoms involves a pair of electrons. If both electrons stay on one molecular fragment, two electrically-charged (positive and negative) ions result; if one electron stays on each fragment, the two fragments are neutral, and are called free radicals. High-energy irradiation also strips electrons from molecules, leaving positively-charged ions. Both ions and free radicals are unstable and reactive. Tests on irradiated foodstuffs have shown that the free radicals slowly recombine even at cryogenic temperatures, and on warming, they disappear rapidly. By the time the temperature rises to the melting point of water nearly all are gone, and on thawing essentially none survives. This applies, for example, to fragments from water molecules, namely free hydrogen atoms (H) and hydroxyl radicals (OH). In dry materials, such as spices and wheat, free radicals survive longer, but when wet, they disappear quickly. Free radicals do remain for some time in bone. Radiolytic ions disappear about as fast as free radicals.

Radiolytic free radicals and ions disappear on warming to room temparature.

Radiolytic breaking of chemical bonds also forms a variety of other substances in trace amounts (about 30 parts per million for each 1000 gray dose), and these have been carefully studied. For example fats are converted into long-chain hydrocarbons in trace amounts. These hydrocarbons are also found in unirradiated apples, pears, and berries, and are not harmful. Another class of radiolytic products is the peroxides, an unstable class of substances. Peroxides are also found in non-irradiated foods. Peroxides have been shown not to cause cancer. In any case they are rapidly decomposed into oxygen and water by enzymes and by natural antioxidants. Vitamin E is one anti-oxidant which destroys peroxides. Unsaturated fats such as fish oil, in the presence of air, form considerable amounts of peroxides, but this is avoided by irradiation in sealed containers or under vacuum. Additionally, it should be noted, all peroxides are decomposed on cooking.

Most (more than 90%) radiolytic products are known to occur naturally in nonirradiated, cooked foodstuffs. For example an unirradiated boiled egg contains 2000 times as much benzene as an irradiated, unboiled egg. Those who shudder at the thought of what irradiation does to food should contemplate what cooking does. Not only are chemical changes induced throughout the food on cooking, changing its texture, taste, odor, and appearance, but also most of the same products—hydrocarbons, aldehydes, ketones, etc.—are formed on cooking and in greater quantities. But on digestion, the same amino acid subunits, etc., are formed, and in general normal processes are restored. American consumers today take in chemical food preservatives and additives to the extent of about a million times the amount of radiolytic products they would consume if they ate irradiated food. Sometimes the substances formed on irradiation are called unique radiolytic products, but this name is inappropriate because they are not unique. Digestion of these compounds by digestive enzymes is expected to yield the normal substances which would be the same as those resulting from the original molecules.

To test a food preservative by use of animals, it can be added in high concentrations to their diet. This is not feasible in the case of irradiated foods, because the traces of radiolytic products cannot be easily removed and concentrated. Early feeding studies were marred by unbalanced diets, and any effects of radiolytic products could not be determined. We may never know whether irradiated foods are perfectly safe, just as we don't know whether non-irradiated foods are perfectly safe from the standpoint of causing delayed cancer, for example. About 20% of deaths naturally result from cancer; how many of these arise from diet? Seemingly healthy foods such as alfalfa sprouts or barbecued fish have many carcinogenic substances. That doesn't mean we should avoid all such foods because our bodies have evolved with these carcinogens and thus self-protective processes are built into our alimentary canals (sloughing off of cells from intestine lining). Of course, one should use common sense and not live off of alfalfa sprouts and barbecued fish. Nearly all vegetables contain natural insecticides in trace quantities. Our bodies are marvelously adept at coping with these substances, and radiolytic products are not expected to behave much differently.

Mutation of Microorganisms—Some worry that extensive irradiation of foodstuffs will not kill all microorganisms, but will cause some to mutate into much more dangerous forms. With a large population of organisms, some mutants would likely result. The problem has been investigated by a number of microbiologists. Although radiation-resistant bacteria have evolved, in no case has any mutant colony been able to compete with the tough normal organisms. The problem is not one of great concern.

Feeding Studies—Many investigations have been conducted to test the wholesomeness of irradiated foods. Tests were designed to provide data on toxicity and cancer-causing substances. In general, the studies which were carefully designed and statistically sound have revealed no adverse effects. There have been some disturbing results, but these have proven to be the consequence of poorly conducted and irreproducible tests. For

Irradiated foods should not be held to higher safety standards than non-irradiated foods.

example, in 1975 children fed bread made from freshly irradiated wheat in India were reported to have shown slight chromosomal changes (polyploidy) in white blood cells. But a committee of Indian scientists ten years later critically examined the procedures, data, and interpretations of these tests and concluded there was no increase in chromosomal abnormalities. Chinese human-feeding studies came to the conclusion that irradiated food had little if any effect on chromosomes, within the statistical uncertainty. In this test, more than 400 volunteers consumed a variety of irradiated foods over a period of 7 to 15 weeks. Separate investigations in the United States, Canada, Denmark, France, and Great Britain concluded that no chromosome abnormalities resulted.

Foods irradiated at high doses have been fed to mice, rats, dogs, monkeys, and other animals over a number of generations, and no excess cancers were detected. Worldwide tests over 45 years have failed to show any dangers in excess of those from unirradiated food. The U.S. Army undertook studies of food irradiation and feeding tests; later the program was transferred to the Department of Agriculture. Feeding experiments were carried out using dogs, mice, rats, and other animals, covering many generations. The conclusion was that irradiated food, even that exposed to a dose of tens of thousands of grays, is safe. Irradiated food has been consumed in quantity by soldiers, astronauts on the Apollo voyages to the Moon, and by volunteers over many years. No deleterious effects have been found. One special use of irradiated foods is for patients with defective immune systems who must have a strictly sterile diet. Another instance is cancer patients recovering from bone-marrow implants.

Individuals with defective immune systems have for years consumed food sterilized by irradiation with no obvious harm.

Tests of Foods for Irradiation—Suppose someone tries to sell irradiated food as unirradiated, how could we tell? Since the texture and taste are virtually unchanged, one must rely on chemical tests. The hydroxyl radicals formed during irradiation attack other molecules, including the amino acids phenylalanine and tyrosine. This produces new materials in trace amounts which can be detected chemically. The concentration of the new material also depends on radiation dosage, and so the number of rads or grays can be estimated. Another test, suitable for meat products, depends on detecting the rather long-lived free radicals inside bone using a technique known as electron paramagnetic resonance.

In the case of foodstuffs which contain any residual stony material such as bits of gravel, a new procedure developed in Scotland has proven to be reliable. A variety of foods are in this class, such as spices and many vegetables, but not meat. The residual material is mostly in the chemical form of silicates, which are crystalline. On irradiation, they absorb energy which is later emitted as light on warming (see thermoluminescence, 4-23 and 6-5). The light is monitored and compared to that from calibrated samples.

By 1994 a technique had been perfected which inexpensively and accurately permits determination of irradiation dose. The National Institute of Standards and Technology has sponsored development of a simple dosimeter. Crystals of the amino acid alanine are compounded with a polymeric binder and mixed to a consistency like that of pasta. Little buttons of this material, after hardening, are packaged with foodstuffs, medical supplies or other goods, and are irradiated along with the main contents. Each tiny unit costs only about 20 cents. Irradiation forms free radicals from alanine, and measurement of their concentration using electron spin resonance reveals the radiation dosage.

A new, rapid, and inexpensive testing method was developed by the North Ireland Department of Agriculture, and one more, based on the level of enzyme activity, has been developed by the International Atomic Energy Agency. The problem is difficult because so little change occur in foods on irradiation. The method discovered in North Ireland is a test for materials formed from fats by gamma rays, namely cyclobutanone derivatives, and is a color test which provides a telltale fingerprint of irradiation which is absolutely reliable.

Conclusions—In view of the favorable results of irradiation studies, the government has approved irradiation of wheat, spices, pork, beef, lamb, fruits, and vegetables. Only low-dose treatment of pork (300 to 1000 grays to control trichina parasites) is allowed so far. Its market share might remain low in any case because pork certified to be trichina-free is now available. This is made possible by a new, quick serological test. In 1992 the Department of Agriculture approved gamma irradiation of poultry, estimating that 40% of the current American product is contaminated with salmonella. Strain DT104 of this bacterium has grown extremely resistant to antibiotics. After irradiation, any surviving bacteria are extremely sensitive to heat. Irradiation of red meat, namely beef, pork, and lamb, has also been recently approved. Tasting tests of poultry show that consumers prefer the irradiated product, and this is probably because it tastes fresher.

The Bhabha Atomic Research Centre near Bombay in India has been increasingly active in food irradiation research. The most important foodstuffs treated are grain, spices, onions, potatoes, and fish. It has been found that irradiation of iced fresh fish, rather than the less expensive frozen fish, extends marketability about two weeks. The government has made attempts to elevate Indian public awareness and knowledge of the subject, but some opposition groups persist.

Irradiated foods are required to carry the international logo ("radura") shown, generally colored green, as well as printed words which notify consumers that the food has been treated with ionizing radiation. People who object to consuming irradiated food have the right to be informed clearly on the status of food they consider buying, but hardly have the right to deny irradiated food to those who consider it safe. Foods which contain only a minor ingredient which has been irradiated need not bear the logo. Opponents of irradiation believe that the benefits do not justify the alleged risks. It is estimated that in any case irradiated food would rarely exceed 10% of the diet.

Logo for irradiated food

The trend today is toward expanded irradiation of foodstuffs; the technology is at a turning point. The process has been approved by many American and international agencies. These include the American Medical Association, the Canadian Medical Association, the World

Health Organization, the U.S. Public Health Service, the Institute of Food Technologists, the United Nations Food and Agricultural Organization, the Health Physics Society, the Council for Agricultural Science and Technology, the US Food and Drug Association, the American Gastroenterological Association, and many other professional groups. WHO scientists convened to evaluate popular objections to the technology, and in June 1992, after extensive review, labeled it a "perfectly sound food preservation technology." In particular, the panel addressed the issue that new strains of dangerous bacteria are being generated by the survival of a few organisms after irradiation, and found the risk very small. Actually, the safety of food irradiation has been comprehensively evaluated to a degree higher than any other food technology, without finding any important failing. About 38 countries approve limited sale of irradiated foods. Multigeneration studies with animals have shown complete safety and no adverse effects. After all, there comes a point when a decision has to be made, even before every last, trivial objection is overcome. Polls in the 1980s indicated that about one-quarter of the American public would buy irradiated products, and a 2001 study by the Food Marketing Institute found that 57% of consumers reacted positively. Three test marketing occasions in 1992-3 revealed that more than half of American consumers bought irradiated strawberries, mangoes, and papayas. Public acceptance will grow slowly, especially when it is realized that irradiation eliminates use of fumigants and food additives. Outbreaks of foodborne illness recently have accelerated acceptance of irradiation, and this played a role in the Food and Drug Administration's approval of beef and lamb irradiation in late 1997. Another factor was the recall and destruction of 25 million pounds of tainted beef in 1997 by Hudson Foods, in Nebraska. Still, as of the end of the millennium, few food outlets offer irradiated food for sale. There doesn't seem to be many markets which want to be first to promote irradiated food, but there might be many who want to be second.

The Pope has endorsed irradiation of foodstuffs, as has the Islamic Food and Nutrition Council of America. Acceptance of irradiated foods was enhanced by the endorsement by the renowned culinary expert, Julia Child. Another factor which contributed to softening of attitudes toward irradiation was its use by the U. S. Postal Service to sanitize mail suspected of being contaminated by anthrax spores; this occurred in the aftermath of the terrorist attacks on the World Trade Center and other buildings on September 11, 2001.

In short, it is not known for certain that irradiated foods are completely safe, no more than is the case with non-irradiated foods. But basic rights are to be informed whether a foodstuff has been irradiated and to get unbiased information about the subject. Then one can make an informed choice, just as is the case with untreated foods. The last word on food irradiation has not been said; we still have much to learn about it. The dangers associated with use of alcohol and tobacco are well documented, and millions accept the risk; these hazards are much higher than those which might arise from a few parts per million of radiolytic products.

Aspects not addressed in detail here include: health and safety of workers in the irradiation facilities; the economics of food irradiation; and problems of international trade in irradiated food.

Alternative Processes—A recent means of food preservation utilizes application of very high pressure to pasteurize fruits, jam, berries, fish, and meats. The discovery that such intense pressure (50,000 to 100,000 pounds/square inch) kills microorganisms was made by an American, Bert Hite, as early as 1899, but the Japanese have now developed it into a commercially successful business. American firms are just getting started. Foodstuffs so pressurized in packages keep well, and have a fresh, natural taste and texture, and suffer no loss in nutrients. It might well be that this new, high-pressure (hyperbaric) procedure will become a prime means of preserving food. Bacteria such as *E. coli* are easily killed by pressure (by disrupting their membranes), but spore-forming bacteria, such as *Clostridium botulinum*, are more resistant.

The Food and Drug Administration has recently approved a product called PreEmpt which prevents infection by salmonella, *E. coli,* and other pathogens. It is a spray which, applied to chicks, introduces many kinds of benign bacteria, which fill the intestinal tracts of the poultry, thus preventing growth of dangerous microbes.

A new process which has some similarities to irradiation is to subject meat to intense electric shocks. The meat is chilled until it is nearly as cold as dry ice and then exposed to high-voltage shocks. This kills or stunts bacteria to the degree that shelf life is extended for about two weeks.

A great deal of information on this topic is available from the International Consultative Group on Food Irradiation at the website:

www.iaea.org/worldatom/Press/Booklets/foodirradiation.pdf

A Possible Anti-Terrorism Tool?— In September 2001, a terrorists hijacked four civilian aircraft and ravaged the World Trade Center towers in New York City, a side of the Pentagon, and crashed the fourth plane. A few weeks later, the spores of anthrax bacteria were sent through the mail to a variety of potential victims. This resulted in a sort of national frenzy in which citizens were finding white powder everywhere, mistaking it for anthrax spores. Suggestions were made to install irradiation units similar to those employed in irradiating foodstuffs, in order to sterilize all mail. If adopted, it would add a bit to the cost of postal stamps. No final decision on this point had been made at the time of this publication.

6-31 Ultraviolet Irradiation of Milk

A process for pasteurizing milk has been developed which is rigorous enough to cause sterilization. The milk is heated to a much higher temperature than for normal pasteurization, but only for a short time. During this transient period, it is irradiated with strong ultraviolet, and packaged in paraffinized cartons sterilized using electron beams or gamma rays. Such milk keeps well without refrigeration for at least six months (often a couple of years), and has a normal taste. It is sold in some European countries. Properly applied, the thermal process alone is sufficient to sterilize milk, and this simpler process has caused use of most ultraviolet irradiation to be abandoned.

Objections have been raised to irradiation of food on the grounds that producers will become less vigilant in regard to cleanliness. The same objection was raised to pasteurization of milk. The actual result was just the opposite: dairies became more careful. A sloppy business will fail.

6-32 Disinfestation of Food

We have seen that irradiation can be used to control or eradicate certain insects such as the screw-worm fly, and to pasteurize sealed meat. As early as 1956 a suggestion was made to irradiate fruits and vegetables to eliminate infestation by various flies, moths, and other pests. This was proposed as an alternative to the use of fumigating agents.

In recent years there has been growing demand in the Pacific Rim countries for American deciduous fruits, nuts, and other commodities. Fruits from Hawaii, California, Oregon, Washington, and Florida have faced import quarantine regulations owing to insect infestation. Irradiation is a promising means of overcoming these barriers in certain cases. Reference has already been made to irradiation of spices. Black pepper, caraway, coriander, and others are generally highly contaminated with bacteria and fungi. The irradiation of bulk spices with high doses of gamma radiation is being carried out routinely in the U.S.; annually, about 25,000 metric tonnes of spices and seasonings are irradiated. India is the world's leader in spice irradiation. Wheat is irradiated in some countries. A new Danish process sterilizes spices by first coating them with a beef protein to lessen loss of flavoring ingredients, and then subjecting them to a thermal treatment.

Some Insects Infesting Fruits and Vegetables—Several species of fruit fly are among the most common which ruin many kinds of fruit. Control by the sterile insect release technique is successful, but expensive and temporary. Three fruit fly species in Hawaii pose a continuous threat to fruit production on the mainland. The codling moth is a small, hardy insect whose larvae devour apples, pears, walnuts, and many other crops. There are also various weevils, in particular those specializing in mangoes. Spider mites, citrus red mites, aphids, and a few other nuisances also claim a share.

We'll be fighting these bugs for centuries.

Fumigation—The standard means of controlling infestation in horticultural commodities has been the use of fumigating agents, which are either gases or vapors of liquids. Adult insects are rather susceptible, but eggs, larvae, and pupae are resistant. The most common fumigants are:

Sulfur Dioxide. This gas is the old standby for fumigating grapes and dried fruit. It produces sulfites, to which some people are allergic.

Ethylene Dibromide. Normally a liquid, ethylene dibromide vaporizes easily inside containers of fruit and is highly effective in killing off most pests in all stages. Curiously, codling moths, except for those at the adult stage, are not killed. The objection to ethylene dibromide is that it is absorbed deeply by fruit, and diffuses out slowly. Fruit aired for as long as 25 days still retains detectable fumigant. Since ethylene dibromide has been proven to cause cancer, its use was prohibited by the Environmental Protection Agency in 1984.

Methyl Bromide. This compound is a gas whose action resembles that of ethylene dibromide. It does kill the codling moth in all stages. There is little hard evidence concerning its carcinogenic tendencies or other such effects, but suspicions run deep. It also contributes to the destruction of the ozone layer (4-31).

Carbonyl Sulfide. Australian scientists have recently found that another chemical compound, carbonyl sulfide (formula O=C=S), is as effective as methyl bromide in fumigating soil, termites, fruit, etc., and it has no effect on the ozone layer. Some carbonyl sulfide occurs naturally. It might be that this substance will earn a valuable place in control of insects in fruits and vegetables..

Other Fumigants. Phosphine (PH_3) is a gas made by the action of moisture on aluminum phosphide. It is sometimes used to fumigate fruits and grains, but does not destroy eggs inside grain kernels. The gas has a horrid odor, and is a fire and explosion hazard. Quite a number of deaths have occurred among Indian farmers from indiscriminate use of aluminum phosphide. The rather harmless compound acetaldehyde is effective against aphids. Ethylene oxide and propylene oxide are slow-acting agents which control molds and yeasts.

Irradiation of Fruits and Vegetables—Experience has shown that irradiation treatment is suitable for disinfestation of certain fruits and vegetables. In no case, however, can irradiation be employed to kill off fungi and their spores. They are very resistant to irradiation, and any treatment sufficient to sterilize the fungi spores would overexpose and ruin any fruit. Florida exports more than $35 million worth of citrus fruit to Japan each year, commerce which might stop if fumigants are banned. If irradiated fruit is acceptable, exports can continue. Experiments by the Department of Agriculture and others have shown that in the case of grapefruit, doses of 100 to 300 grays inactivates nearly all fruit fly eggs and larvae; those few which hatch do not produce viable insects. Yet, the damage to fruit is minimal. The higher dose of 600 to 900 grays causes unacceptable damage to the rinds. Other fruit for which irradiation seems promising are papayas, mangoes, and strawberries.

Execution of insects by gas, freezing, or irradiation.

An alternative means of decontaminating citrus fruit without irradiation or fumigants is storage for seven days at 60 °F followed by 19 days at 34 °F. This could be done on shipboard. Japan has accepted the procedure as effective. A Canadian process preserves berries by packaging them in a modified atmosphere. Grain can be disinfested by microwave heating.

Codling moths are not found in Japan, Korea, and Taiwan, and strict quarantine measures are in effect. Only shelled nuts fumigated with methyl bromide are currently imported, but use of this gas might soon be restricted because of its ozone-destroying potential (4-31). Irradiation tests show that the medium dose of 160 grays suffices to inactivate the larvae. Codling moths sometimes form cocoons inside unshelled walnuts, and higher doses are required.

Toxicity—The story here parallels that of sterilization of meat and other foodstuffs, raising the question: Does irradiation at the disinfestation level form appreciable toxic substances? The question has been studied more than 35 years. Quarantine treatments use doses of less than 1000 grays, which is less than the sterilization doses. While there is sometimes damage to fruit, no significant danger to consumer health has been found.

In summary, disinfestation of a variety of fruits and nuts using gamma irradiation has a promising future.

6-33 Prolonging Shelf Life of Fruits and Vegetables

In principle, irradiation can prolong the storage life of fruits and vegetables by preventing their sprouting and other changes. Early experience suggested that these expectations were mostly disappointing. But more recent research has revealed techniques to treat many fruits and vegetables to extend shelf or market life.

One application which has met with success is irradiation of onions and white potatoes to prevent sprouting on storage. Potatoes, irradiated at a dose of 50 to 150 grays, keep for months without sprouting. The process also destroys tuber moths. Treated potatoes have proven to be popular in Japan, and while permitted in the U.S., are not yet common. Irradiation to delay sprouting of onions has proven extremely important in India, which is the world's second largest producer. Garlic, yams, and ginger also respond well. Another crop which can be irradiated successfully is mushrooms. It greatly retards aging after harvesting. Cherries and strawberries also may be irradiated with benefit. Irradiation of bananas delays ripening and thus extends shelf life. Low-dose irradiation of mangoes not only extends shelf- life, but wipes out weevils. Irradiated mangoes from Puerto Rico sold well in a test case in Miami. The Florida Department of Citrus had recently approved disinfestation using irradiation, and irradiated fruit was marketed to a small extent in 1991.

6-34 Recent Trends in Public Acceptance of Irradiated Food

There are clear signs that during the 1990s public understanding and acceptance of food irradiation was growing, and that entrenched resistance is dissipating. Those consumers who learn the basic facts about the process purchase irradiated products repeatedly if given the opportunity.

A survey by the University of Georgia revealed that consumer awareness of irradiated foods was up from 23% in 1984 to 70% in 1993. Asked whether they would buy properly labeled, irradiated food, 45% answered yes, and 17% answered no. A Gallup poll in late 1993 confirmed that the more shoppers knew about irradiated food, the more likely they were to buy it. Some said they would be willing to pay a 5% premium for irradiated hamburger. Public attitudes toward the subject have not been exhaustively determined yet.

6-35 Radiography

Since ionizing radiation of all types affects photographic film, a valuable supplement to ordinary photography is available. Radiography employs penetrating radiation to pry into opaque objects. Besides X-rays, the following are employed:

beta rays, gamma rays, and neutrons. Medical X-ray photography has already been briefly described (5-1). Beta rays are not widely used in radiography because their low penetrating power limits them to thin materials, such as a coat of paint.

Gamma ray radiography generally utilizes cobalt-60; in some facilities, cesium-137 or iridium-192 is used as a source. The dangerous materials are kept in massive lead housings. The object to be radiographed is positioned about a meter away, with a cassette holding film behind it. Exposure is made by uncovering the gamma ray source for a time. In this way defects in brass or steel valves can be detected, the number of steel rods in a concrete wall can be counted, cracks or cavities in castings are revealed, or welded joints are inspected, to mention a few applications. The common radiographic instrument for field use contains iridium-192 (half-life 74 days). Being relatively small, the apparatus is easily portable. To inspect a pipeline weld, the seam is wrapped with protected film, and the gamma ray source is positioned inside for the exposure. Misuse of these instruments has caused many radiation accidents (6-17).

Looking through concrete

Gamma rays are most strongly absorbed by elements of high atomic number, while with neutrons the opposite is true. A parallel beam of neutrons from a nuclear reactor or a portable neutron source (californium-252; see 6-38G) is allowed to shine on the object to be radiographed. Greater film sensitivity is achieved by surrounding it with a gadolinium transfer screen; the gadolinium readily absorbs neutrons, releasing gamma rays, which act upon the film. Neutron radiograms clearly show materials made of light materials, such as rubber gaskets or lubricants, even if they are behind several inches of steel. An imaging probe of neutrons, generated by a small cyclotron, has been devised to study streams of cooling water in engines. Another use is to inspect fatigue cracks in the aluminum around the fastener holes in aircraft, particularly the bottom skins of the wings, which flex in flight. Neutrons see where X-rays can't.

6-36 Coloring Gemstones

The colors of natural gemstones span the spectrum, and can be traced to the preferential absorption of certain wavelengths of visible light by atoms of impurities or ions or crystal defects inside the stones. In some cases these color centers, as they are called, are vacancies, that is, holes from missing atoms.

Gemstones in Nature which contain radioactive elements change color through eons of internal irradiation. For example, zircon which contains uranium may change from colorless to red as the alpha particles from uranium cause a change in the charge of impurity niobium ions, which act as color centers. Pure beryl is colorless, but if the carbonate ion is present, prolonged irradiation produces a blue color. Certain rare diamonds appear green because of surface irradiation by nearby radioactive minerals.

A few years after the discovery of radioactivity and X-rays, the first reports of changing the color of gemstones artificially began to appear. Commercial irradiation to alter color began in the late 1940s, and today approximately 6,000 kilograms (30 million carats) of topaz are irradiated worldwide annually.

Gamma rays from cobalt-60 or cesium-137 are employed to administer heavy doses to stones such as topaz, quartz, or tourmaline. Topaz, often yellowish, subjected to several megagrays becomes blue (one megagray is a hundred million rads). Quartz containing some iron impurity becomes amethyst-colored; subsequent heat treatment causes it to become lemon yellow. Colorless tourmaline receiving a dose of two megagrays is transformed into a pink or red stone.

Beta rays from natural elements generally are not energetic enough to cause significant color changes. Therefore heavy doses (10 to 100 megagrays) are delivered using high energy electrons (10-15 megaelectron volts) from a linear accelerator. The most prized blue topaz is subjected to both gamma ray and electron bombardment.

Nuclear reactors afford both gamma rays and neutrons. Fast neutrons produce colors in gemstones more appealing to jewelry fanciers than do slow neutrons, so the stones are placed in containers lined with boron or cadmium compounds. Inside the reactor, slow neutrons are absorbed by the boron or cadmium, permitting the resulting fast neutrons to bombard the stone. Alternatively, the container is lined with uranium, and fission of the U-235 releases fast neutrons to achieve the same end.

The process is complicated by the formation of radioactive nuclides when impurities are activated by neutron absorption. Consider topaz, for example. Chemically, this stone is an aluminum silicate with hydroxide and fluoride ions, and if pure, it is colorless. Neutron bombardment produces some beta-active aluminum, oxygen, fluorine, and perhaps silicon, but all half-lives are short, being seconds, minutes, or hours. After storage for a day or so essentially all radioactivity dies out. But various trace-metal impurities are almost always present in topaz, and so additional radioactive materials result. Tantalum is such an impurity in topaz. It consists almost entirely of tantalum-181; neutron absorption yields tantalum-182, whose half-life is 115 days. Decay emits both beta particles and gamma rays. Therefore such stones must be stored for months or years before the activity falls to a safe level. Topaz colored in reactors is known as "London Blue" in the jewelry trade. Diamonds colored in nuclear reactors are blue or green, but subsequent annealing results in a yellow, orange, or pink.

Regulations of the Nuclear Regulatory Commission put limits on radioactivity levels of gemstones artificially colored. These limits vary with the type of radionuclide involved, and range from 0.09 to 20 nanocuries per gram; the figure is 0.4 for topaz. Each human body contains at least 300 nanocuries of potassium-40, carbon-14, etc., and receives a dose equivalent to several thousand more nanocuries from the outside environment (mostly radon). Therefore a few additional nanocuries or so, worn externally a few days as rings or earrings, is safe. Curiously, the gemstone thorianite (chemically, a mixture of thorium and uranium oxides) exceeds the limit of radioactivity by as much as 1700 times, but is not regulated (except for importation) because it is natural.

"Natural" is not necessarily better than "artificial."

Radiation-treated gemstones play an important role in the jewelry trade today. They make it possible for people to purchase beautiful gemstones at affordable prices, and which have colors comparable to Nature's best. Moreover, health hazards from such stones are virtually non-existent.

In the aftermath of the terrorist attacks on American targets on September 11, 2001, another type of terrorism took place. This was sending anthrax spores to unsuspecting recipients in the U.S. mail. The postal service used various procedures to combat this hazard, one of which was sterilization of suspect letters and packages by bombardment with high-energy electrons. A curious unplanned consequence was that certain gemstones being shipped underwent a change in color. Pale blue sapphires turned deep orange, pink kunzites turned green, and cultured pearls turned gray.

6-37 Radioisotope Thermoelectric Generators (RTGs)

RTG Units and Their Fuel—Radioactive decay always releases heat. Advantage can be taken of this to construct electric generators which have no moving parts and last for years without maintenance. They are employed to power remote light houses, Arctic weather stations, space vehicles, and the like.

One of the radioisotopes used for this purpose is strontium-90. It is quite abundant since in nuclear waste it lasts for years (half-life 28.5 years), its decay emits no gamma rays, and its power density is favorable (930 watts per kilogram). A 60 watt generator (known as type SNAP-7) suitable for navigation buoys contains 225,000 curies of strontium-90 in the chemical form of strontium titanate, a refractory substance. Seven kilograms (about 15 pounds) of the material is shaped into rods which are then clad in metal. Clusters of these rods are adjacent to thermocouple junctions; lead telluride is a suitable material of construction of the thermocouples. Multiple thermocouples connected in series form a thermopile; alternate junctions are next to the hot strontium-90 and cold outside. This assembly is surrounded by an 8-cm layer of uranium depleted of its U-235 as a radiation shield, and is welded in a steel casing holding radiation fins. The total weight is 2.3 tons. Smaller units sometimes use strontium fluoride instead of the titanate. Cesium-137, cobalt-60, curium-242, and curium-244 have also been used in generators. Incidentally, depleted uranium finds use not only to absorb gamma radiation, but also, because of its high density, in other civilian applications. Examples are in flywheels, and ballast in aircraft and boats.

One other important radioisotope of great value for thermoelectric generators is plutonium-238. It has a half-life of 87.7 years and a power density of 560 watts per kilogram. It is made by isolating neptunium-237 from spent fuel rods from nuclear reactors, and then irradiating it with neutrons. The Apollo rockets to the moon held 50-watt SNAP generators containing 14 kilograms of plutonium-238 (the acronym SNAP means Systems for Nuclear Auxiliary Power). Their electric power was as high as 400 watts. The aborted Apollo 13 rocket had its SNAP plutonium-238 in the lunar excursion module, which served as a lifeboat to bring the crew back to Earth. It now lies in the Pacific at the bottom of the Tonga Trench. In 1964 an American navigational satellite (type SNAP-9A) containing 17,000 curies of plutonium-238 (about 1 kg) unexpectedly plunged back toward Earth and disintegrated (conversions between mass and number of curies in the case of Pu-238 are complicated by lack of knowledge of the isotopic purity). The plutonium-238 dioxide was released above 100,000 feet over the Indian Ocean. A NIMBUS-B probe failed in 1968, but its plutonium-238 canister was recovered. These generators also powered the Viking landers sent to Mars, and the Pioneer and Voyager spacecraft which sent back those beautiful photographs of Jupiter, Saturn, and their satellites. A Russian probe to Mars carrying plutonium-238 failed in 1996. But in the cases of the Viking missions to Mars, the Voyager and Galileo missions, and the Mars Sojourner, everything functioned flawlessly. None of the failures could be attributed to the radioisotope thermoelectric generators using plutonium-238. These electric generators, having no moving parts, are exceptionally reliable. Production of plutonium-238 by the U.S. slowly decreased until it stopped altogether. In 1992 the United States began negotiations to buy 300 pounds of plutonium-238 from Russia.

Cassini—In a spectacular launch via a Titan IV/Centaur rocket, the Cassini Probe was dispatched on October 15, 1997. It was sponsored by NASA, the European Space Agency, and the Italian Space Agency. Empty, the system weighs 5510 pounds, and it carried 6615 pounds of propellant, making a total of more than six tons. It required seven years to cover the 2.2 billion miles to Saturn, so the probe arrived in July 2004. It was scheduled to fly by Venus twice, Earth once (in August 1999), and Jupiter once, to pick up enough gravitational steam to reach its target. Each of these operations acts as a sling shot to enable Cassini to reach its destination.

Cassini carries a separate probe, Huygens, which was awakened in 2004 and dropped by parachute onto the surface of Titan, one of Saturn's 18 known moons. It will take about 2.5 hours for it to reach the surface. The Italian-French astronomer Cassini (1625-1712) discovered the gap between two of Saturn's rings. Huygens was the Dutch astronomer who discovered Titan (1655).

Cassini holds several radioisotope thermoelectric generators with a total of 32 kilograms of plutonium-238 dioxide. Extreme precautions have been taken to minimize any danger in case of failure of the rocket on launching. The fuel is in the form of ceramic pellets encased in iridium alloy, a metal which maintains its strength even at white heat. The plutonium dioxide is hot-pressed and sintered into large polycrystalline pellets so that, if worst comes to worst and an accident at high altitude occurs, the fuel cannot form a fine dust which would be dangerous if inhaled by humans. In turn, the units are shielded by strong casks made of graphite fibers, which are tough and resilient. Each RTG, initially at about 260 °C, produces 4.4 kilowatts of heat and 285 watts of electricity. By the end of the mission in June 2008, the electric power of each unit will have fallen to about three quarters of its starting level. The generators are 45 inches long and 17 inches wide, and protrude at right angles from the spacecraft so that the gamma ray intensity inside is as low as feasible. The fuel for the Cassini RTGs is 71% Pu-238, 13% Pu-239, 2% Pu-240, 1% Pu-241 and -242, and the remainder is oxygen (that is, the material is PuO_2). The thermocouple material is composed of germanium and silicon. Additional plutonium-238 is used to warm some instrument compartments.

While inefficient in converting heat to electricity, the generators are almost trouble free.

One task of Cassini's Huygens probe is to study Titan's atmosphere, which is thought to be largely nitrogen. Earlier spectrographic examination of that frigid moon revealed that it also contains methane, ethane, propane, and other hydrocarbons. These factors make it resemble the atmosphere of our Earth in its primordial stages. Cassini will probe Saturn and its rings, as well as Titan using instruments based on radiation in the visible, infrared, ultraviolet, and radar ranges. Huygens carries a gas chromatograph/mass spectrometer.

The whole Cassini mission was opposed by a few well-meaning folks on the grounds that it became an unacceptable risk from its plutonium. These critics argue that such substances as plutonium-238 in orbit are hazardous to the world's peoples in case it falls back to Earth. There was some truth to this kind of charge 30 years earlier, but modern RTGs are far safer. Plutonium-238 is more radiotoxic than plutonium-239 owing to its higher specific activity. Photovoltaic solar panels are not sufficient for deep space exploration. Some claim that theft of the plutonium-238 could permit nuclear bombs to be made, but self-heating of plutonium-238 is so high that a critical mass would oxidize or melt. Danger from Cassini is infinitesimal compared to that from the world's supply of nuclear weapons, and few worry about that matter any more.

More information on the Cassini RTGs is available on the web at:

www.jpl.nasa.gov/cassini/rtg

Pacemakers—There are miniature thermoelectric generators based on plutonium-238 which are used to drive pacemakers (type Pulsar N-1). Such devices, encapsulated in titanium, are surgically implanted into a patient's chest and wired to the heart muscle. They rhythmically produce minute electric pulses which regulate heart muscle contraction. They last 20 to 40 years, compared to only two or three years for those with chemical batteries. The amount of plutonium-238 is only about 160 mg in each of these ingenious devices. Very recently notable advances in conventional pacemakers and their batteries have put these in a more favorable position, and no units using plutonium have been implanted for a couple of decades. It might be that artificial hearts can some day be powered utilizing this useful isotope. Another promising nuclide for electricity generation is curium-244. Its half-life is 18 years, and it has a high heat-generation rate.

Minute Electric Generators Based on Nickel-63—In 2002 researchers at Cornell University devised an ingenious means of generating a minute, pulsed electric current which is expected to function for several decades. It consists of a strip of foil made from nickel-63, which is beta active with a half-life of more than 100 years. There is no gamma ray. The nickel-63 foil is mounted parallel to a copper strip about 1 mm wide, 20 mm long, and only 60 μm thick, supported on one end. The assembly is inside an evacuated glass tube. As the beta particles stream out and collide with the copper, the copper strip becomes negative and the nickel, having lost electric charge (that is, beta particles) becomes charged positively. Attraction of opposite charges causes the copper strip to bend down until electrical contact is made with the nickel, when the charge difference is canceled as electrons flow back to the nickel. The copper strip springs back up. A tiny magnet on the end of the copper thus oscillates inside a coil and generates a minuscule electric pulse. This is sufficient to activate an implanted heart pacemaker, to power a light-emitting diode, or perhaps to use in other devices.

6-38 Instruments Based on Radioactivity

Dozens of devices which depend on radioactivity have been invented. If all of them disappeared suddenly, American industry would largely shut down until now-obsolete methods were reinstalled. Small radioactive sources in instruments use no electricity or cooling. These features make them attractive for control operations. A few of the more important instruments are described below.

Radionuclide Gauges, Etc.—Many industrial materials are produced in sheet form: metal, glass, plastic, and paper, to mention a few. Take the case of hot iron being rolled into thinner sheets. The arrangement is illustrated in the sketch. A shielded source of radioactivity shines a beam of gamma rays continuously through the newly-formed sheet of iron. The thicker the iron is, the higher is the degree of absorption of the gamma rays. The detector on the other side has a gauge which reads the thickness of the iron, and this information is recorded. The recorder governs a feedback control. If the sheet begins to grow too thick, more gamma rays are absorbed, and the feedback control pushes the rollers closer together. Uniform thickness is thus insured. Heated glass and plastic are rolled similarly, but require less penetrating radiation. Similar gauges are employed to control the filling of containers. Suppose there is an assembly line of plastic bottles or aluminum cans being filled with liquid. When the level rises to a fixed point near the top, the liquid absorbs the radiation, signaling the control to stop the flow momentarily and shift the next container into place. In the case of photographic film, the radiation beam must be on an edge to prevent exposure of the central area of the film to ionizing radiation.

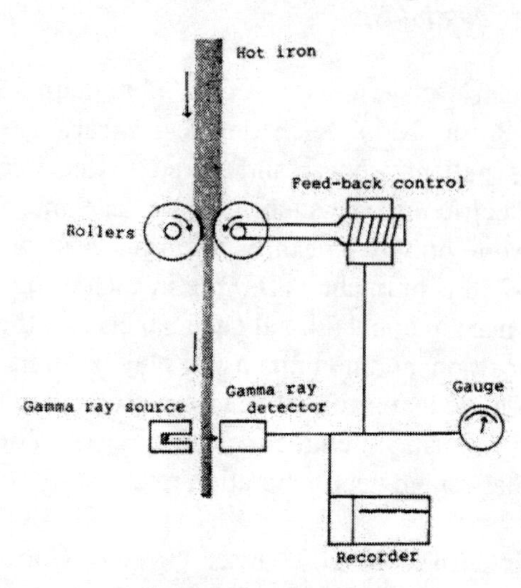

Controlling thickness of rolled sheet iron

Another kind of gauge measures the thickness of one material on top of another. Beta rays are often used. Each material back-scatters beta rays to a different extent, so the source and detector are both on the same side of the object. Paint on wood or metal can be gauged if the instrument is properly calibrated. Ice on airplane wings, plastic coating on paper, silver on mirrors, and tin electroplated on iron are other examples. Gamma ray reflection meters are also in use.

Measuring the density of soil is important in construction work. It permits engineers to determine whether earth refill is being compacted according to specifications. A gauge to measure soil density consists of a gamma ray source which is stuck into the soil to a predetermined depth. By recording the gamma ray intensity coming up through the soil to the surface, the density of the wet soil is measured. Used along with a moisture meter (below), the dry density can also be found.

Formerly, traces of radium were mixed with a phosphor to make a luminous paint for the hands of watches, but more recently beta-active materials such as tritium, strontium-90, and promethium-147 have been employed. They give essentially no radiation dose, and also damage the phosphor less. The three nuclides mentioned emit no gamma rays. Tritium is generally used on watch hands, and the other two are chosen for gauge dials such as in aircraft, ships, and industry. Another use of tritium is in radioluminescent lighting panels to mark runways for aircraft in remote locations. Each panel can contain as much as 300 curies of tritium.

The wear and tear on moving metallic parts can be detected and measured using radionuclides as an alloying component of one or more parts. For example, steel gears are cast which contain a radioactive isotope of chromium. Inserted into a machine, the gears are operated as usual while being lubricated. After a long period of use, the lubricant is analyzed by detecting measuring its radioactive chromium content in the steel which has been abraded off.

Leak Detectors, Etc.—Many methods of detecting leaks in long pipelines have been devised. One method is to dissolve a small amount of radioactive material in the liquid being transported. If it is water, the material may be a salt of sodium-24 (half-life 14.7 hours). As the material flows through the pipe, any leak will allow some of the radioactive material to escape. The pipe is then flushed with pure water, and followed by a person holding a sensitive Geiger counter near the ground. The leak may be discovered even though the pipe is buried a few feet. Underground electric cable hoses are similarly examined, using a radioactive gas. Sometimes a single pipeline is used to pump two or more liquids successively. In order to observe the boundary between the two materials, a radioactive plug is inserted into the line after all the first material has entered, and the plug is pushed along by the second liquid. Periodic stations register the passing of the plug by detecting the gamma rays.

A leak detector saves a thousand times its cost.

Static Electricity Control—Accumulated static electricity often causes sparks, which have ignited fires in industrial facilities. A source of radioactivity which ionizes the air permits the static charges to leak off. One of the most common materials used for this purpose is polonium-210, which is alpha-active. The alpha particles penetrate about 5 cm in air. But the half life of this isotope is only 138 days, so longer-lived beta- or gamma-active nuclides are also employed.

Smoke Detectors, Etc.—Air ionized by a beam of alpha, beta, or gamma rays is electrically conducting, and this property has practical applications. Smoke detectors for homes or other buildings contain a tiny amount (less than a millionth of a curie) of americium-241. This substance is an alpha and gamma emitter with a half-life of 433 years. Alpha particles are particularly effective in ionization. A battery-powered circuit is arranged so that a minute current carried by the short path of ionized air prevents an alarm from sounding; this is the normal condition. If smoke enters, the alpha rays are stopped and the air is no longer conducting, actuating the alarm. The

Smoke detectors have saved thousands of lives.

americium is in the form of its dioxide on a foil. Sales of the devices exceeded 12 million per year by 1985. A person sleeping 8 hours per day, and located six feet from such a smoke detector, could receive a radiation dose of no more than 0.014 millirems per year, a negligible amount. In 1993 an extra-sensitive detector was invented for restaurants which prohibit smoking. Whenever a patron lights up, the device detects the smoke and blares out a stern warning requesting the offender to extinguish his cigarette.

Americium-241 results from the beta decay of plutonium-241, whose half-life is only 14.4 years. The plutonium-241 occurs in abundance in commercial reactor fuel. A problem with these devices if used in smoke detectors is that at the end they are generally thrown out with the trash instead of being returned to the manufacturer.

A photoelectric smoke detector, with no radioactive source, has been developed. They are more costly and are subject to more false alarms.

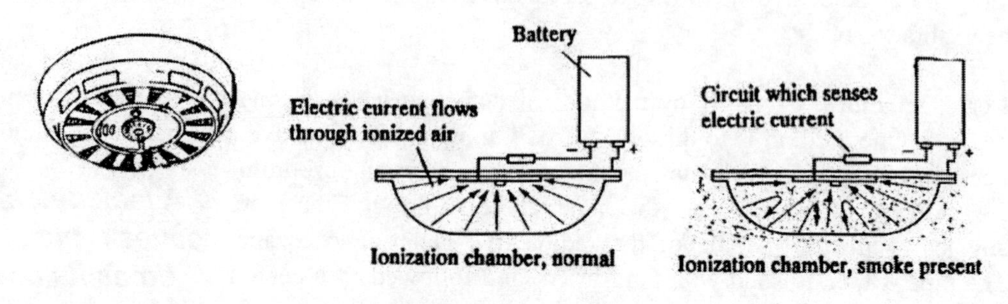

Home smoke detector

Sparking Devices—Some voltage regulators have vacuum tubes. A tiny amount of radioactive material near the spark gaps keeps part of the gas ionized, and this facilitates firing at the set voltage, making for smoother performance. Similarly, the spark gaps of ignition systems need lower voltages and have longer life if an ionization source is maintained nearby. Some lightening rods on the roofs of buildings contain traces of radium, a practice started in 1932. After americium became available, it began to be employed.

Hunting for Oil—Americium-241 is also employed in seeking petroleum. Prospectors looking for oil use radioactive sources in deep wells to characterize geological strata. Disposal of the residues is a problem, but they will probably be dumped in the Waste Isolation Pilot Plan in New Mexico.

Neutron Sources—The earliest source of neutrons in the laboratory was the interaction of alpha particles with the nuclei of light elements. The low atomic number (that is, low positive charge) of these elements is insufficient to repulse the energetic incoming helium nuclei. Thus a mixture of beryllium and a strong alpha emitter such as radium or polonium generates a steady stream of neutrons. Production of neutrons by using radioactive elements makes possible quite a variety of instruments and processes. When the synthetic nuclide americium-241 became available, it began to be used because it is an even more intense source of neutrons when mixed with beryllium.

A more recent neutron source is californium-252. This interesting material decays in two ways. A small fraction, 3%, undergoes spontaneous fission with release of neutrons, the half-life being 85.5 years; the other 97% decays by alpha emission with a half-life of 2.6 years. Alone or mixed with beryllium, californium-252 affords a copious supply of neutrons. The effective half-life is the shorter period, 2.6 years. It is made by extended irradiation of plutonium-239 in high-neutron-flux reactors.

Neutrons from californium-252 are used in a variety of applications: neutron activation analysis (6-10), radiation therapy (6-15), neutron radiography (6-27), neutron radiograms (6-32), nuclear reactor start up (7-5), explosive detection (part I below), moisture meters (part J below), and other instrumentation.

Neutron Generators Based on Fusion—In the late 1950s, an inventor named Farnsworth began working on a device which would cause fusion of deuterium into helium on a small scale, releasing neutrons. His concept of a means to initiate and control the fusion was unique. Instead of generating a plasma, his technique was to ionize the deuterium (which is easily accomplished) and to use an electric field to accelerate the deuterons formed to the point where the individual particles had a temperature corresponding to several million degrees C. He designed the apparatus in such a way that several beams of the charged particles, guided by magnetic fields, were directed precisely to one central point. A small fraction of the energetic deuterons collided and fused.

The reactions involved using deuterium are as follows (release of gamma rays and neutrinos is not shown):

$$^{2}_{1}H + ^{2}_{1}H => ^{3}_{2}He + ^{1}_{0}n \text{ and } ^{2}_{1}H + ^{2}_{1}H => ^{4}_{2}He$$

We see that only the first reaction releases neutrons.

Joined in 1967 by a young physicist named Hirsch, the pair observed that addition of some tritium to the deuterium facilitated production of neutrons. They proved the idea is workable, and achieved a production rate of 10 billion neutrons per second, a quite respectable yield. But the presence of tritium meant that a radioactive material was present, resulting in complications of safety, licensing, and regulation. Hirsch continued the research and developed an improved way of accelerating the positive nuclei. It proved to function well with pure deuterium, that is, no tritium. He inserted a spherical grid about the size of a tennis ball in the center of the device. After evacuating the apparatus, which was a stainless steel sphere about the size of a soccer ball, a small amount of deuterium was admitted. A potential difference of 60,000 volts was applied between the wire grid in the center and the outer sphere, and this was sufficient to ionize the deuterium. The negatively charged grid then attracted the positive deuterons, when they became extremely energetic. Some of them collided with the wires but the rest passed between the wires and collided with others coming in from the opposite sides. Abundant neutrons were released. Hirsch had to abandon the work because of lack of financial support.

Twenty years later a professor of nuclear and computer engineering at the University of Illinois, George Miley, took up the task of perfecting fusion spheres. He was able to increase the yield from a million to a billion neutrons per second, without use of tritium. He modified the electric field by putting dimples into the grid's spherical contour, something like a golf ball. This permits only those deuterons which are headed for the exact center of the sphere to be accelerated. The electric dimples permit the acceleration of only those particles which avoid hitting the wires, preventing erosion and enhancing commercial application. Precise alignment of the incoming beams was no longer necessary. The fusion spheres produce neutrons more cheaply and safely than the beryllium/radium technique or others similar to it. They are expected to go on the market, the cost being about $60,000 each. Users might well be airport security services for luggage inspection, metal smelters who need the composition of their products monitored almost instantly, and mining companies which want to spot ore impurities. A modified form is the neutron generators used in hydrogen bombs.

Detection of Explosives—A recent application of thermal neutron activation analysis is the development of a way to detect explosives in airplane luggage. This costly technique received an impetus from the sabotage of a Pan Am plane over Lockerbie, Scotland, in December 1988. Investigations revealed that an explosive device was responsible, a plastic explosive being most probable. Practically all chemical explosives are rich in nitrogen. The technique consists of passing a beam of neutrons (from californium-252, or generated using a compact accelerator, or neutron generator described above) through the incoming luggage on a conveyer belt. When a nitrogen-14 nucleus absorbs a neutron, an unmistakable gamma ray of energy 10.88 megaelectron volts is emitted. The gamma rays are analyzed using a detector and computer. The detector activates a switch, detouring any suspect luggage onto a sidetrack. While cheese, meat, and other nitrogen-rich food might cause a positive response, these few cases can be dealt with individually. Adjusting the equipment to higher sensitivity triggers too many false alarms, caused by other materials containing nitrogen, such as wool and leather. Airlines call for a false alarm rate of not more than 1%. Cocaine and heroin contain nitrogen, and perhaps it will become possible to detect them similarly.

The early versions of the machine proved to be insufficiently reliable for inspecting airline baggage. As late as fall, 1991, the instruments failed to sniff out explosives to a satisfactory level, and they had to be developed further. By summer 1993 enough improvements had been made to enable a scanner to detect 100 pounds of ammunition at San Francisco airport, and the smuggler was arrested. Each unit currently costs around $1,200,000.

Another luggage-inspection system, called CTX, employs tomographic techniques and X-rays. It reconstructs a cross-sectional image of the baggage at various angles and correlates this with the density and composition of items inside. The procedure was certified by the FAA in 1994.

Some 400 million explosive land mines have been emplaced since World War II and at least 120 million of them are still viable. They lie scattered around in at least 62 countries, grim souvenirs of various wars. It might be possible to make a portable explosive detector, using a neutron source such as californium-252, to locate them. A variant instrument employs pulses of fast and slow neutrons. Since 1975 at least 1 million people have been killed or maimed by these cruel land mines, 30,000 in Cambodia alone. On average, the remaining mines claim a victim somewhere in the world every 20 minutes. The Clinton administration extended a moratorium on export of mines made in the U.S., and the United Nations passed a non-binding resolution asking all countries to stop such exports. Regrettably, the American military convinced Clinton to not enforce the ban. A worldwide ban on manufacture of all mines should be made, classifying them in the same group as war gases. One ray of hope is that the Pentagon has developed a radar technique of detecting mines from robot aircraft using low-frequency radar, even mines buried 10 centimeters deep. The radar method is not able to detect mines made only from plastic, but with further refinement might be able to do this.

Neutron Moisture Meters—A neutron moisture meter or gauge has been devised to measure the moisture content of soil in units of weight per unit volume. The source of the neutrons is 40 millicuries of americium-241 mixed with beryllium. As shown in the sketch, a pipe is driven into the soil, and the probe (neutron source and detector) is lowered to the bottom. Neutrons scatter primarily from the hydrogen atoms of water; the more water present, the more are back-scattered to the detector. This meter has been a boon to farmers who depend on irrigation. Properly calibrated, the meter gives reliable results with mineral soils, but in the cases of soils rich in organic matter, some constraints apply. This is because considerable hydrogen is present which is bonded to carbon (C-H) and to oxygen in chemical linkages such as C-O-H rather than water, where the linkage is H-O-H.

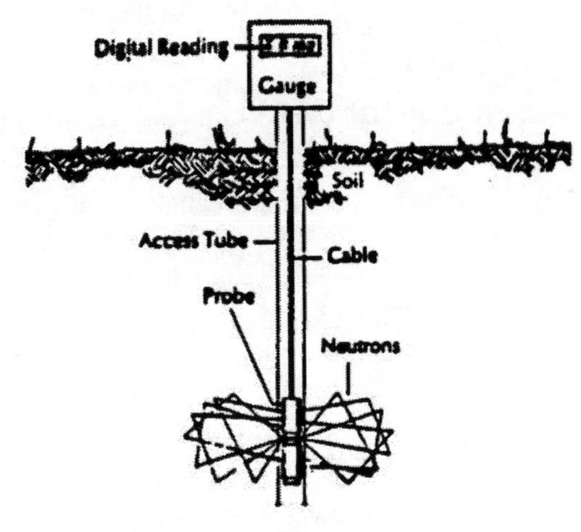

Neutron moisture meter

Positron Transmission Microscope—Electron microscopes have been used for years. The electrons are focused by an electrostatic field in the shape of a lens. The magnification is much greater than that achieved by optical microscopes. In 1987 a microscope was made using positive electrons (positrons) instead of ordinary negative electrons. The positrons are emitted by sodium-22 and pass through a thin slice of the specimen. The image is viewed on a screen. Since positrons interact with matter differently than do electrons, a different kind of image is produced. The two types of microscopes are thus complementary.

6-39 Techniques Using Stable Nuclei

Radioactivity is not the only characteristic of atoms which permits us to utilize their properties with great benefit. In section 6-26 we saw how carbon-13 can be used in diagnosis for stomach ulcers. Deuterium has been used in many experiments to determine the role of hydrogen in chemical reactions. Oxygen-18 permits measuring temperatures during the time millions of years ago (6-8). Other such applications are described briefly below.

Nuclear Magnetic Resonance (NMR) Spectroscopy—The nucleus of an ordinary hydrogen atom is simply a proton. It is known that protons have the property of spin. That nuclei of some elements have spin was suggested by Pauli in 1924. Nuclei with even atomic numbers and even numbers of neutrons have no spin. Examples of nuclei without spin are carbon-12, oxygen-16, and sulfur-32. A hydrogen nucleus (that is, a proton) bonded to a carbon or oxygen atom still spins. Such a spinning charged particle creates a

The north pole of the tiny magnet (spinning proton) tends to be attracted to the south pole of the strong magnetic field.

tiny magnetic field. The magnetic moment of a proton is much smaller than that of an electron because it is much more massive. In a sample of water billions of little magnets normally are pointed in random directions, but if the sample is put into a strong magnetic field, the magnetic moments of the hydrogen nuclei tend to line up. They may line up in two ways: along the imposed magnetic field (parallel) or against the field (antiparallel). The alignment is not complete, that is, each proton's magnetic field is at an angle to the lines of the imposed magnetic field. In addition to spinning, each proton precesses or wobbles about these lines of force, like a child's top spinning and at the same time precessing about a vertical line in the gravitational field.

The two positions, parallel and antiparallel, have slightly different energy levels. The two states are in equilibrium, with continual interchange as protons alternate between the parallel and antiparallel states. Now suppose that we make a coil of wire and connect it to a radiofrequency source, that is, an oscillator. We choose the radio wave region, which is at the low-energy end of the spectrum, because we know that the energy difference between the parallel and antiparallel states will be so small. The electric current which powers the radiowaves is monitored by a sensitive ammeter.

We put a tiny glass tube holding a sample of water under investigation inside the coil, which is in the strong magnetic field. The radiation penetrates the water, but little or none is absorbed. At this point we gradually change the wavelength of the radio waves. Progressively using wavelengths which are shorter and shorter, we eventually come to the point where the photon energy shift matches the difference in energy between the parallel and antiparallel states, and absorption of the radio waves takes place. This is revealed by an increase in the current used to generate the radio waves, that is, an increase in the ammeter reading. This induced transition between the two energy states is called resonance. Instead of changing the wavelength, we can keep it constant, and vary the magnetic field strength; this is easier and is the usual practice.

A graph of the degree of absorption of the radio frequency radiation (as divulged by the current measured by the ammeter) against the wavelength or field strength is a nuclear magnetic resonance spectrum. If water is the sample, there is only one peak (far left in the figure below). This shows that all hydrogen atoms in water are equivalent. But if the material is ethanol (formula: CH_3CH_2OH), three peaks show up, and moreover the areas under the peaks are in the ratio 1:2:3 in the low-resolution spectrum. Three peaks appear because the bonding environments of the three structurally dissimilar kinds of hydrogen

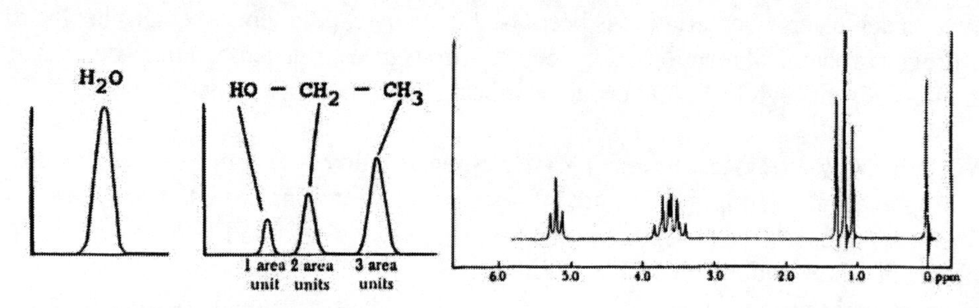

Low resolution NMR spectra of water and ethanol

High resolution NMR spectrum of ethanol

are different; this results because of what is called the chemical shift. The smallest peak corresponds to the hydrogen bonded to oxygen, the middle peak corresponds to the two equivalent hydrogen atoms bonded to a carbon which is in turn bonded to an oxygen, and the largest peak corresponds to the three equivalent hydrogen atoms bonded to the carbon which is not linked to oxygen. Without chemical shift, the technique would have little utility. On the right is a high-resolution NMR spectrum of ethanol, in which each of the three peaks of the first spectrum is further resolved into its components.

Today nuclear magnetic resonance spectroscopy is a highly sophisticated science, and reveals even the most intimate details of molecular structure. Aside from hydrogen, many other kinds of atoms whose nuclei have spin are also studied. The technique of NMR spectroscopy was developed independently by Bloch and by Purcell in 1946.

In the summer of 1994 NMR was adapted to monitoring the concentration of the anticancer medicinal fluorouracil in tumors. The coil receiving the signal was positioned on the patient's skin above the tumor. The response of F-19 in the drug measured its concentration in the area where it was most needed. The results disclosed a great variation in the manner in which various patients retained fluorouracil; in some it was weakly taken up, in others, it washed out rapidly, and in some it was retained for some time and could be effective.

Magnetic Resonance Imaging (MRI)—Since the principles of NMR spectroscopy became well established, it was only natural that they be extended to imaging procedures. This was suggested and accomplished by Damadian (1969) and Lauterbur and Mansfield (1972), taking advantage of the abundant water in living tissues. The first images were those of green peppers and lemons, appearing as tomographic slices (6-22). The procedure is now routinely applied to diagnose the ailments of human beings. No X-rays are involved.

A huge magnet is required. To generate a magnetic field of sufficient strength, an electromagnet using superconducting coils is chosen since this permits strong electric currents. But superconductors require cooling with liquid helium, and this runs the expense up. The radiation is in the radio frequency range, and if the correct wavelength (and thus the correct frequency) is used, it penetrates human bodies deeply. Since various tissues contain differing amounts of water which is bonded to tissues in various ways, the image can be adjusted to show sufficient contrast. Image data are recorded on a computer disk and then reconstructed on a TV screen. The excitation of the hydrogen nuclei is constrained to a thin slice, that is, it is tomographic. This is achieved by using frequency-selective pulses. Fig. 6-39B on Color Plate II shows a magnetic resonance tomograph of the human brain, made during a study to map the visual cortex while being stimulated by various visual images. This study was carried out by J. W. Belliveau and coworkers at Massachusetts General Hospital NMR Center.

No ionizing radiation is involved, unlike X-rays, CT scans, and the use of radionuclides,. In some cases MRI provides contrast superior to that of X-ray CT scans, and in other cases the reverse is true. A disadvantage is that MRI requires several minutes for a scan, and movement by the patient cause image distortion. However, improvements are gradually being made. Metallic implants such as pacemakers can cause problems.

MRI images of schizophrenic patients reveal that the hippocampus is shrunken and the ventricles above and below the hippocampus are engorged with fluid. In 2000, a study in London disclosed an unexpected result. Images of the brains of male cab drivers showed that the region called the posterior hippocampus was larger than in the case of men who did not drive taxis. This is in conformity with the belief that even into adulthood, that part of the human brain, known to be active in spatial memory, mapping, and navigating, responds to repeated mental challenges.

In a modified MRI procedure (magnetic resonance neurosurgery), images of bones, muscles, etc., are subtracted out using the computer, leaving these tissues almost invisible. This permits three-dimensional images of just the nerves. Within about three years after this technique was developed, it has proven to be an enormously valuable tool. Damaged nerves can be discovered without exploratory surgery. Prior to this new technique, surgeons sometimes had to expose the whole length of a nerve to discover a lesion.

Researchers in the National Hospital for Neurology and Neurosurgery in London have also adapted some of the techniques described above to diagnosing degenerative brain diseases such as Alzheimer's disease, Parkinson's disease, and Creutzfeldt-Jacob disease. They found that in Alzheimer's, deterioration usually starts in the hippocampus, an area which plays important roles in memory. The position of the MRI scanner relative to the patient's head is very important, and the image in the computer's memory is used to adjust the angles and distances exactly for subsequent scans. Still another variant of the technique promises to produce images rivaling those in positron emission tomography (PET, 6-25). In 2000, researchers at UCLA mapped growing brain cells using MRI, discovering that neural growth occurs in spurts. In this case three-dimensional images were produced using the graphics produced by about three-dozen super computers. In the case of children, intensive growth was observed in the corpus callosum, which serves as the central communication conduit between the hemispheres of the brain. The studies revealed that the area of the brain linked to language grew fastest at ages 7 to about 14 years, that is, prepuberty. Thus, learning a second language after puberty is much more difficult than before.

Another new variation is functional magnetic resonance imaging (fMRI). It can monitor the metabolism of the brain by tracking blood flow and consumption of oxygen, something like PET techniques do. This modification of MRI is being employed to study dyslexia, and a great deal has been learned about the manner in which the brain processes the images of letters to form words. Recent research at Yale has shown that the area of the brain in which written and phonic versions of words are processed are almost inactive in dyslexics. The technique also revealed that in processing phonics, the left inferior frontal gyrus is activated in men, while both the left and right regions are activated in women. In dyslexics, the angular gyrus has a problem translating letters into sounds. These findings might someday identify dyslexia in children early on, show how to treat it, and monitor the treatments. Employing the information from PET and fMRI imaging studies has enabled new techniques to be developed which greatly aid dyslexics, and when diagnosed at an early age, an acceptably high level of reading ability can be acquired (more on dyslexia in pages 249–250). In 1999 fMRI studies at the University of Medicine and Dentistry of New Jersey presented objective evidence that acupuncture can be effective. Brain activity from light pain induced in the lips of volunteers was imaged. The studies showed that slight relief resulted from ordinary acupuncture, but when a minute electric current was administered through the needle, the alleviation was greatly magnified. Resolution of fMRI is excellent. But it cannot match PET in one respect, and this is revealing particular molecules in specific disease sites.

A study in 2002 using fMRI at Yale University of a large number of children demonstrated that dyslexia can be detected at age 7. The areas in the back of the brain responsible for quickly matching words, sounds, and meaning undergo far less activity than normal. The study demonstrated freshly that speaking comes naturally to human beings, but that reading is a skill we must learn. There is no single neural infrastructure for reading. Dyslexia is so complicated that imaging techniques alone cannot give enough clues to correct many cases.

A minor use of MRI is to test meat, sold as fresh, to determine whether it has ever been frozen. Freezing damages cell walls so the mobility of water molecules and their manner of interaction with proteins changes in an easily detectable way.

MRI is a giant contribution to nearly all branches of medical practice, but is still a bit expensive. One step recently developed (1997) to reduce the cost and at the same time to give brighter images is by incorporating a tiny amount of the paramagnetic rare-earth element gadolinium, injected as a complex ion. When this is done a weaker, and therefore less expensive, magnet is needed. A modern trend is to develop smaller MRI units, cutting costs.

Addiction to Narcotics, Tobacco, and Alcohol—The cost of alcoholism in the United States is estimated at $185 billion per year, while the combined costs of narcotics and tobacco addiction amounts to an additional $115 billion per year. The so-called war on drugs has been mostly unsuccessful. In the last decade or so, studies of addiction using PET and fMRI techniques have contributed great advances in understanding and treating several types of addiction.

The human brain has pleasure circuits and these communicate using the neurotransmitter, dopamine. They are activated by eating favorite foods, success in any endeavor, romantic and sexual episodes, winning a jackpot, and similar experiences. A narcotic does more than merely activate these pleasure circuits, but more or less takes them over, expanding mild happiness into euphoria. Research using fMRI and PET scans has revealed that cocaine, amphetamines, and opiates (morphine and heroin) all target the ventral tegmental region (just above the substantia nigra) in the central and frontal areas of the brain, which are connected to the pleasure circuit. Alcohol affects these same areas of the brain, but also the prefrontal cortex (where conscious thoughts are processed), the cerebellum (controlling movement), and the amygdala (emotions).

The brain quickly becomes addicted to these powerful stimuli. Observing a video of crack cocaine being cooked in a spoon over the flame of a cigarette lighter, all the while being monitored by fMRI imaging, ordinary people showed no particular reaction, but in the case of cocaine addicts, the reaction was wholly different. Almost as if a neurological switch were turned on, the anterior cingulate and part of the prefrontal cortex—which involve learning and mood—lighted up and a surge of craving for crack cocaine suddenly appeared. These scans revealed enduring chemical and physical reconfigurations in addicts' brains. Many scenes, such as any white powder, activate addicts' brains long after they stop using narcotics. These drugs of abuse increase the concentration of dopamine in the pleasure circuits. The neurons have special sites to accommodate dopamine, but cocaine usurps these positions, allowing dopamine to accumulate, continuing to fire the pleasure circuits. Despair and the agony of withdrawal make life seem hardly worthwhile. Repeated use of a narcotic nullifies the body's ability to enjoy simple pleasures, driving the addict to escape through consumption of more and more narcotic. The best news to date is that in most cases, addiction can be overcome with medication and intensive, long-term support, but it is expensive.

Animated Moving Pictures of the Interior of the Human Body—In a medical education project sponsored by General Electric, MRI and CT scans of a male cadaver were made. The resulting tomographs were reconstructed via modern computer techniques. The viewer experiences a "trip" inside various organs, in color and with audio. As of June 1997 "Fly Through Trips" through the torso, heart arteries, lungs, brain, skull, and colon, as well as delivery of a baby, were available. You can download these, along with the necessary programs, into your computer on the Internet at:

www.crd.ge.com/esl/cgsp/projects/medical

Future Imaging Techniques—The radio waves employed in MRI penetrate human tissues easily, and slightly shorter wavelengths do the same. Clear tomographic images have been made of human organs, luggage in airports, and other objects using the so-called T-rays (for terahertz, the frequency range between radio and infrared radiation, wave length a few millimeters). The technique was developed at Rensselaer Polytechnic Institute. More recently, the Japanese corporation Toshiba has also conducted research on imaging via terahertz radiation, especially for dental purposes. Using pulses of the radiation, three-dimensional images of teeth have been made. Toshiba also showed that images which distinguish between muscle, fat, etc., can be generated.

A combination of transcranial magnetic stimulation and PET has been used at Montreal Neurological Institute to image neural maps of the brain. It uses 200 microsecond magnetic pulses combined with PET to yield detailed images. Another procedure, also being developed in Canada, is called Hall effect imaging or HEI. It combines ultrasound waves with a strong magnetic field. Still another is called digital subtraction angiography. Some of these procedures, after full development, might replace X-rays in medicine and thus spare patients any dosage of ionizing radiation.

Atomic Clocks—Contemporary clocks based on a nuclear property have become known as "atomic clocks." They were first made in 1948, and have been greatly improved since then. There are several kinds, and all depend on an exact natural frequency or period. The most common atomic clock uses ordinary cesium-133, the only isotope of this element occurring in Nature. Nuclei of this cesium isotope absorb radiation which is in resonance with its natural frequency, that is, radiation which coincides exactly with its quantized nuclear spin transition. This radiation is in the low-energy radio frequency region. A beam of cesium-133 atoms, numbering perhaps a million per second, is irradiated in vacuum; only those absorbing the exact resonance frequency are deflected by a specially shaped magnetic field. This step blocks all other atoms. This frequency is electronically synchronized with a secondary clock, a quartz crystal vibrator, which is a device for counting vibrations. It provides an oscillating magnetic field. This process

If you're not satisfied with an accuracy of 1 second in a million years, since 1996 there has been another choice, namely 1 second in about 10 billion years.

imparts an incredible precision to the clock. An improvement was made in 1989 by using a laser beam of light rather than a magnetic field to select atoms in the desired energy state. This process has many advantages, such as increased signal strength.

In 1967 one second was defined, based on cesium-133, as the time interval for 9,192,631,770 oscillations to take place. The error in measurements by this type of clock is one second in 300,000 years. An accuracy of one second in three million years was attained in a more recent clock. Examples of the use of atomic clocks are: meticulous tests of relativity theory, precise navigation and guiding military missiles using the Global Positioning Satellite system, deep-space communication, synchronizing colors in TV signals, etc. The clocks promise to make other inventions possible in the future, such as accident-prevention systems.

The most accurate atomic clock to date is called NIST-7 (the letters mean National Institute of Standards and Technology). In the office of its principal developer, Bob Drullinger, there is a wall clock with its numbers 1 to 12 scattered around the face at random, with the message "Who Cares?" in the center.

Mössbauer Spectroscopy—This technique for studying the properties of solids depends on radioactive decay to furnish gamma rays. Mössbauer spectroscopy, named after its German discoverer, gives us an additional tool for investigating molecular structure and bonding, especially in crystals. It depends on the emission of gamma rays by one isotope, and their absorption by another sample of the same isotope or a closely related one.

Under ordinary conditions, when an atomic nucleus emits or absorbs a gamma photon, it recoils strongly. But if the source and target atoms are in crystals which are chilled to a few degrees above absolute zero with liquid helium, then the recoil energy is absorbed by each entire crystal, and makes little impact on the individual atoms. The energy of the photon must exactly equal that of the energy change of the target atom, otherwise resonance absorption does not take place. The energy of the photon which the target atom can absorb depends minutely on its chemical environment. Changes in environment of target atoms produce slight but detectable shifts in frequency of absorption. Thus if the incoming gamma ray is not absorbed, its wavelength (which is inversely proportional to its frequency) can be ever so little altered by moving the source either toward or away from the target. This is the well-known Doppler shift, studied by every physics student. Thus the source is moved at increasing velocities relative to the target until the gamma-ray detector indicates absorption. A plot of the absorption versus source velocity yields the Mössbauer spectrum. The figure shows a spectrum at 4.2° absolute; a shift S of a target of iridium-193 occurs when the source, osmium-193 in platinum, is moved. The inverted peak occurs at a velocity of 0.70 millimeter/second. This type of spectral study has proved to be an unrivaled tool in elucidating fine details of chemical and nuclear structure.

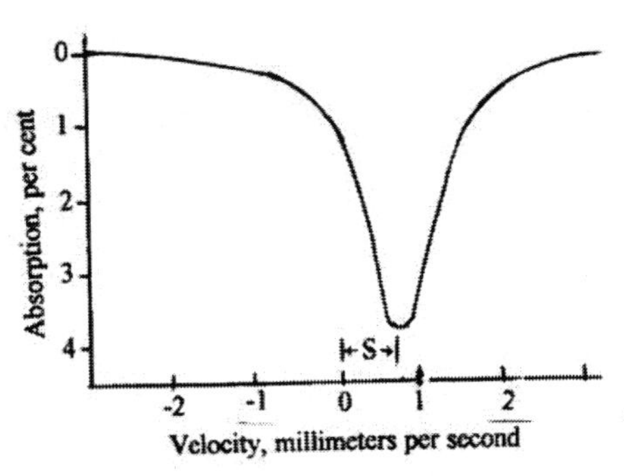

A Mössbauer spectrum

Preservation of Vaccines—Heavy water, chemically known as deuterium oxide, is used as a neutron moderator and coolant in some nuclear reactors, and deuterium is a component of hydrogen bombs. There is satisfaction in learning that heavy water also plays a role in preserving human lives and health. Owing largely to the World Health Organization, small pox- has been virtually eradicated from our Earth and now the WHO is attempting to do the same with that crippling disease, polio. To accomplish this, it is necessary to vaccinate children all over the world. The vaccine consists of genetically disabled polio virus suspended in water. But in the temperatures of sub-Saharan Africa the vaccine deteriorates since refrigeration is usually not available.

During the 1960s, researchers noticed that some microorganisms survive better when very warm if they are kept in heavy water. Later the discovery was made that this applies to vaccines made from enfeebled viruses. The polio vaccine when suspended in heavy water containing some magnesium chloride proved to be about 30 times more heat resistant than that in ordinary water. The preserving power seems to derive from the ability of deuterium to produce stronger bonding (that is, hydrogen bonding) to the virus RNA than ordinary water does, building a sort of scaffold to maintain the molecular shape of the disabled virus. The heavy water has no effect on human health; it is diluted and excreted swiftly. The technique is expected to be equally effective with the yellow fever vaccine.

6-40 Conclusion

In this chapter we have experienced a little taste of how many and how varied are the applications of radioactivity and other nuclear properties. While not as diverse as the uses of electricity, more and more applications are discovered or invented every year. This is the way science should be, serving the world's people, not mastering them, as is the case with nuclear weapons.

Bibliography for Chapter 6: Radioactivity in Human Service

Naomi P. Alazraki and Fred S. Mishkin, *FUNDAMENTALS OF NUCLEAR MEDICINE*, The Society of Nuclear Medicine, 1984.

American Council on Science and Health, *IRRADIATED FOODS*, 1995 Broadway, New York, NY 10023-5860, 1988.

John C. Harbert, William C. Eckelman, and Ronald D. Neumann, editors, *NUCLEAR MEDICINE: DIAGNOSIS AND THERAPY*, Thieme Medical Publishers, NY, 1996.

Robert Henkin, editor, *NUCLEAR MEDICINE*, 2 volumes, Mosby, 1996.

International Consultative Group on Food Irradiation, International Atomic Energy Agency, Vienna, Austria, 1999.

Edward S. Josephson and Martin S. Peterson, *PRESERVATION OF FOOD BY IONIZING RADIATION* (two volumes), CRC Press, Boca Raton, FL, 1983.

Cherry Lewis, *THE DATING GAME: ONE MAN'S SEARCH FOR THE AGE OF THE EARTH*, Cambridge University Press, 2000.

I. P. C. Murray and P. J. Ell, *NUCLEAR MEDICINE IN CLINICAL DIAGNOSIS AND TREATMENT*, Churchill Livingstone, NY 1994.

Martin P. Sandler et al., *DIAGNOSTIC NUCLEAR MEDICINE*, 3rd edition, 2 volumes, Williams and Wilkins, 1996.

Chapter 7: NUCLEAR REACTORS

ABSTRACT—Here we present an account of what nuclear reactors are and how they work. The most important kinds of reactors, several experimental types, special reactors, a number of foreign reactors, and the proposed second and third generation reactors are examined. Breeder reactors and molten salt reactors might become very important in the future. Reactors that occurred in Nature millions of years ago are included. Reactor safety, decommissioning of reactors, and some problems of mining uranium ores are examined. Ill-famed reactor accidents, in particular the most appalling one at Chernobyl, are described. Reactors based on fusion of hydrogen into helium as well as cold fusion as an energy source are analyzed. The economics of nuclear power is studied, as well as use of nuclear energy as a means of avoiding introduction of excessive amounts of the greenhouse gas, carbon dioxide, into our atmosphere.

7-1 Easing into the Subject

Uranium in the metallic state is about as dense as gold. When the surface is freshly cleaned, it is bright and shiny, but on standing in air at room temperature, it slowly oxidizes. First a bronze-colored layer of oxide forms, which gradually darkens to blue-black, and finally becomes black. A massive piece of metal can be stored many years in dry air. If heated, it burns rapidly, forming a black oxide. Natural uranium consists of 99.2837% U-238, 0.7110% U-235, and 0.0053% U-234 by weight, which corresponds to about 138 atoms of the heaviest isotope for every atom of uranium-235.

Imagine that we have two chunks of uranium metal, but this time isotopically pure uranium-235. Each piece of metal weighs 30 kilograms (66 pounds), and is in the shape of a hemisphere. If we take a honeydew melon 18 cm (7 inches) in diameter and slice it in two, we have the size and shape of the uranium pieces. So long as the two pieces of uranium-235 are kept separate, there is nothing exceptional in their behavior.

But if we mount each piece of uranium on a roller skate, and slowly push them closer together (flat sides facing each other), we find that at a certain critical distance the two pieces of metal begin to get hot and emit some gamma rays and neutrons. Move them apart, and they cool off. Push them suddenly close together and they emit a dangerous flash of gamma rays and neutrons, get red hot, melt, and ignite. Now being spread out, the materials cool off. Starting afresh, if one hemisphere is shot by a cannon onto the other, a nuclear explosion occurs, although it would be a mild and inefficient one by modern standards. Two other metals which behave in this curious way are uranium-233 and plutonium-239.

What peculiar behavior!

7-2 Nuclear Chain Reactions and Critical Mass

We can understand why the two pieces of uranium-235 get hot when brought close together on the basis of the nuclear fission process. Earlier (4-16) we saw that when a U-235 nucleus captures a slow neutron, it undergoes fission into two smaller nuclei of familiar but radioactive atoms, simultaneously releasing some more neutrons and gamma rays and much energy (4-9). Some fissions release 1 neutron, some 2, some 3, and some 4 or more, but the average is around 2.5. The fission is represented by the equation below:

$$\text{U-235} + \text{n} \Rightarrow 2 \text{ fission products} + 2.5\text{n}$$

These fission products and neutrons are exceedingly energetic (that is, high velocity), and additional energy is in the form of gamma rays and recoil energy of fission fragments. If 1 neutron is consumed but 2.5 are produced, there is a profit of 1.5 neutrons.

Since more neutrons are produced than consumed, it should be possible to put together enough uranium-235 (metal, oxide, or other suitable material), and use the excess neutrons to initiate more fissions. The neutrons from these would cause still more atoms to undergo fission, etc., and in successive generations the process becomes faster and faster, something like compound interest. This is a nuclear chain reaction, as illustrated.

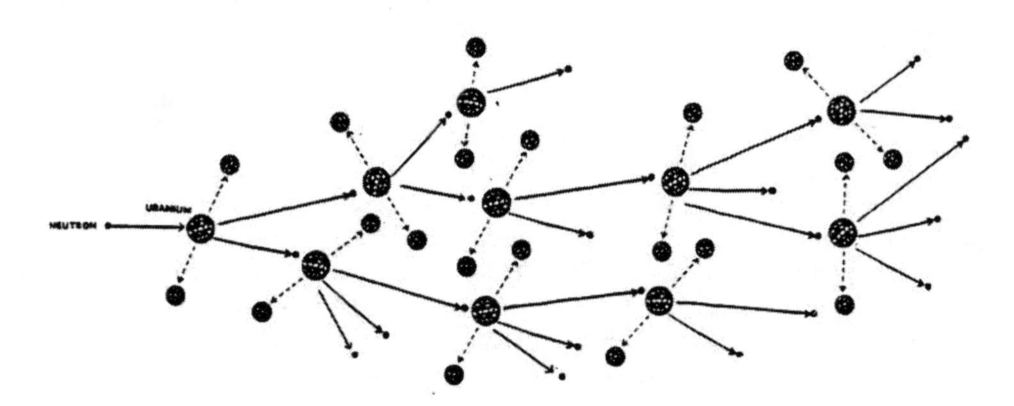

Nuclear chain reaction

In a small piece of uranium-235 no chain reaction occurs spontaneously. There are always some stray neutrons from spontaneous fission and cosmic rays, but only a fraction of the collisions of these with nuclei results in fission. Consequently many neutrons diffuse around inside the metal until they come to the surface, where they escape. The ratio of surface to volume is too high for a nuclear chain reaction to be sustained. If the amount of the uranium-235 is gradually increased (by adding more and more metal), we finally reach the point where the number of neutrons escaping just balances the excess number being generated. The neutron multiplication factor, **k**, is defined as:

$$\mathbf{k} = \frac{\text{number of neutrons in one generation}}{\text{number of neutrons in preceeding generation}}$$

When **k** is exactly equal to 1, the uranium is said to have critical size or mass. Other factors enter into the situation, such as the presence of neutron-absorbing impurities. The critical mass of pure uranium-235 is around 52 kilograms if it is spherical. The critical mass is less than this amount, say only 15 kilograms, if it is surrounded with a material which reflects neutrons back in.

Weapons-grade uranium-235 in metallic form is around 93% in isotopic purity. Specimens of lower and lower U-235 content (the remainder being U-238) require higher and higher masses to become critical. If the composition is 80% U-235, the critical mass is about 21 kilograms, with a neutron reflector. When the U-235 content is 40%, the critical mass is 75 kilograms, again with reflector. Natural uranium, with only 0.711% U-235, cannot be made to become critical no matter how much there is, unless the neutrons from fission (which are fast) are slowed down outside the metal somehow (slow neutrons best induce fission of uranium-235). The reason natural uranium, without a means of externally decelerating neutrons, cannot become critical is that fast neutrons are absorbed by the abundant uranium-238, resulting in U-239. Neptunium-237 is also capable of being used to make nuclear bombs (9-1).

7-3 Slowing Neutrons Down

Neutrons from fission are incredibly energetic, meaning fast or hot. While there is a broad spectrum, their speed is of the order of 10,000 miles per second. To control and maximize the fission process, they must be slowed or cooled down, that is, moderated, to use the technical idiom. This task is accomplished by the *moderator*, a material which absorbs few neutrons and has small, light atoms. Why must the atoms be light? Well, imagine a tiny steel sphere (like buck-shot) shot out of a gun. If it collides with a massive steel sphere, it just bounces off without slowing down very much. But if it collides with a sphere of its own mass, half of its momentum is transferred, and its speed and energy are greatly reduced. Similarly, a neutron, with mass number 1, is not appreciably slowed by bouncing off of heavy nuclei such as those of uranium, but collision with light atoms transfers much energy and thus it loses speed. Substances rich in light atoms which do not absorb neutrons excessively are those used as moderators. Examples are water, heavy water (deuterium oxide or hydrogen-2 oxide), beryllium, and carbon (graphite). The first nuclear reactor ever constructed consisted of hundreds of uranium ingots embedded in graphite.

A bullet ricochets off an anvil, but is stopped by sand.

7-4 Development of Nuclear Reactors

Overview—A nuclear reactor is an assembly of uranium (usually mass numbers 238 and 235), a moderator, a cooling system, and a control system, in which a regulated, self-sustaining nuclear chain reaction is maintained. Fission of the uranium-235 yields energy, fission products, radiation, and excess neutrons. Some of the neutrons cause fission of more uranium-235, perpetuating the chain reaction. Other neutrons are absorbed by the abundant uranium-238, giving uranium-239. This nuclide has a very short half-life (23.5 minutes), decaying by beta emission to neptunium-239 (half-life 2.36 days). This nuclide is beta-active, emitting another beta particle and forming the next element, plutonium-239. Plutonium-239 has a long half-life (24,100 years), and thus accumulates.

There are many types of nuclear reactors and they have a variety of purposes. By 1957 at least 900 different reactor designs had been created, and by 1997 there were probably more than 1200. The most common modern type has uranium fuel enriched in its lighter isotope (U-235) to the extent of 2 to 4.5%, present not as the metal, but as the high-melting dioxide (UO_2). Pellets of the fuel are held in zirconium tubing. Enrichment in uranium-235 is achieved using the gaseous diffusion method, or the newer centrifuge or laser techniques (see 4-20). The price of uranium dioxide enriched to 4% uranium-235 is approximately $600 per pound. Pure, ordinary water (that is, light water, in distinction from heavy water, which is deuterium oxide) is the usual moderator material as well as the fluid of the cooling system. Rods made from substances of high neutron-absorbing power are used to control the rate of operations. A few elements which contain isotopes that avidly absorb or capture neutrons are boron, cadmium, indium, hafnium, and tantalum. These are in the form boron carbide (B_4C), boron-rich steel, the metals hafnium or tantalum, an alloy of cadmium, indium, and silver, or cadmium sheathed in stainless steel.

Components of a nuclear reactor

Wartime Origins—While the ideas of nuclear reactors and bombs with a self-sustaining chain reaction based on fission had spread around the world since January 1939, it took World War II to stimulate their actual development in the United States. The concept was also considered by our adversaries. Physicist Tadayoshi Hikosaka, shortly after the discovery of fission appeared in print, published a paper called "A Method for Utilizing Nuclear Energy," which was a model for fast-breeder nuclear reactors. In Tokyo, under oppressive wartime conditions during the fall of 1944, the Japan Science Congress carried out a symposium on the topic. The idea of a uranium reactor operating on fast neutrons was again examined, but without knowledge of nuclear cross sections (4-16). The Germans considered nuclear reactors but could not devote sufficient resources to the problem (more information in Chapter 9).

Objectives—The most important purpose of modern civilian nuclear reactors is to generate electric power, and of military reactors is to generate plutonium-239 and tritium for weapons. Reactors are also employed as a source of neutrons to make radioactive isotopes for medical and other uses, beams of neutrons for determination of crystal structures by diffraction, as a source of gamma rays, and for other purposes.

Zirconium—Zircaloy is an alloy of zirconium with a little tin, chromium, nickel, and iron. Zirconium, a metal in the same chemical family as titanium, is chosen to manufacture fuel rods because it does not capture neutrons appreciably, is strong, ductile, and resists corrosion by water at high temperatures. Above 1100 °C (a white heat), zirconium does react with water or steam, producing zirconium dioxide and hydrogen. This fact played an important role in the reactor accidents at Three Mile Island and at Chernobyl. Stainless steel was used as cladding material in a few early reactors, but by the mid 1970s all users had switched to Zircaloy. Aside from cladding, zirconium is used in reactor cores to make fuel element supports and instrumentation assemblies.

Zirconium is the eighteenth most abundant element on the Earth's crust, being more plentiful than lead, copper, nickel, or zinc. Its principal ore is zircon; production is around 750,000 tons per year. Australia is the principal source of ore. The supply of

Fortuitously, zirconium has just the right properties.

zirconium is adequate; its price as a milled product is $20 to $50 per pound. One of the largest producers of zirconium is the firm Teledyne, through its subsidiary, Wah Chang Albany. All zirconium ores contain a few percent of hafnium, which must be removed since this element is an avid neutron absorber. The chemical properties of zirconium and hafnium are closely similar, presenting chemists with a nice challenge. Several successful separation processes via liquid-liquid extraction were developed. Zirconium forms a melt with uranium dioxide at about 1900 °C (3450 °F), and the fuel pellets must be cooler than that. The chain reaction maintains the fuel at a bright white heat, like a devil's frying pan.

Historical Note—The first electricity generated by a reactor was in 1951 at Argonne West, Idaho, and small amounts were introduced into the power grid. The reactor was of the breeder type (7-11). The world's first reactor for commercial production of electricity was operated by the Soviets at Obninsk in 1954, and the British similarly opened the reactor at Sellafield in 1956. In 1957, the small town of Moorpark in California was electrified entirely, as a publicity stunt, by a reactor built by Atomics International; the electric power was 6.5 megawatts.

The principal sites of government-sponsored reactors and reactor research are: Oak Ridge, Tennessee; Hanford, Washington; Argonne National Laboratory, Illinois; Aiken, South Carolina (Savannah River); Brookhaven, New York; and Idaho National Engineering Laboratory (near Idaho Falls). The Idaho facility is located in a 900-square-mile complex set amid the brown buttes and dusty lava plains of eastern Idaho's Arco desert. More than 50 different types of reactors were developed there.

Power Reactors—In the United States, commercial reactors are under the control of the Nuclear Regulatory Commission. This commission is to be restructured as the Nuclear Safety Agency. Factors which accelerated the growth of nuclear power in the United States were the interruption of petroleum supplies during the Suez crisis of 1956 and the Middle East oil embargo of the 1970s. The main factors which have curtailed growth of nuclear power in the United States were: the high construction and maintenance costs, the Three Mile Island and Chernobyl accidents, and the problems of radioactive waste. As of 1999 there were 433 nuclear power stations on-line in the world and about 30 more reactors were under construction outside the United States, half of these in Asia. Of the world's reactors about 104 were operating in the United States in 1999, down from 111 in 1991. Very few others have been started and are under construction. A small number were stopped before being finished. The world has more than 300 experimental reactors. The United States in 1994 generated 109 billion watts of electric energy from nuclear sources, which was about 22% of our total electricity, and approximately 6.6% of all energy produced in the country. The United States generates somewhere around 600 billion kilowatt-hours per year. Over the entire world, reactors generate more than 350 billion watts. This is approximately 17% of all electricity made. The list below gives the number of reactors operating during 1995-96 and in 2000 in a few countries, and also the approximate percentages of the total electricity generated in each from nuclear sources. The electric power (in megawatts) for each country is also specified for 2000. Of major countries, France produces the highest percentage of its electricity using nuclear generators.

Country	1995-96	2000
France	55 reactors, 76%	59 reactors, 75.0%, 63,103 MW
Belgium	7 reactors, 56%,	7 reactors, 57.7%, 5712 MW
Sweden	12 reactors, 47%	11 reactors, 46.8%, 9432 MW
Hungary	4 reactors, 50%	4 reactors, 38.3%, 1729 MW
South Korea	15 reactors, 41%	16 reactors, 42.8%, 12,990 MW
Slovakia	5 reactors, 49%	6 reactors, 47.0%, 2408 MW
Switzerland	5 reactors, 41%	5 reactors, 36.0%, 3079 MW
Japan	53 reactors, 36%	52 reactors, 36%, 43,961 MW
Germany	20 reactors, 30%	20 reactors, 31.2%, 22,282 MW
Czech Republic	4 reactors, 28%	4 reactors, 20.8%, 1648 MW
United Kingdom	35 reactors, 27%	35 reactors, 28.9%, 12,968 MW
United States	104 reactors, 22%	103 reactors, 19.8%, 96,080 MW
Canada	22 reactors, 17%	14 reactors, 2.7%, 9998 MW
Russia	26 reactors, 12%	29 reactors, 14.4%, 19,843 MW
China	3 reactors, 1.5%	3 reactors, 1.2%, 2167 MW

On the average, American reactors operated at only 75% of their capacity (called the load factor) until recently because they are shut down for repair so much. South Korean, Swiss and Finnish reactors have the highest load factors, 85% or higher. Between 1990 and 1994 output from Britain's nuclear power stations rose by 43%. Italy built a half dozen or so reactors, but closed them all down by 1990. Since then Italy has been importing nuclear-generated power, prompting accusations of hypocrisy.

In the table above, a drop in the percentage of electricity generally means that the amount generated by other means increased. During the period 1995-2000, the efficiency of American reactors was raised significantly, the load factor being 88.5%. This permitted generation of electricity at a rate of only 1.0 to 1.3 cents per kilowatt-hour. Some experts predict that new reactors will be constructed in the United States within five years.

No new nuclear reactor has been ordered in the United States since the Three Mile Island accident in 1979. One result of this is that expertise in the area has attenuated. When questioned about purchasing American equipment for reactors, Kazuhisa Mori, director of the Japan Atomic Industrial Forum, pointed out the failure of the American industry to keep up-to-date. He does, however, credit American design and software.

After the end of the Cold War about 1990, western European and American firms showered Hungary and Czechoslovakia with offers to build many kinds of nuclear facilities. The idea is to enable these countries to export electricity. Both countries have uranium mines. Westinghouse Electric entered a contract in 1994 to upgrade Czech reactors, grafting American technology to Soviet-built facilities.

Pressurized Water Reactors—A modern nuclear reactor might contain 85 to 200 tons of carefully purified uranium as the dioxide (UO_2), enriched in U-235. This is the fuel, in the form of pellets about the size of the tip of one's little finger. The UO_2 pellets are heated to cause them to sinter into a strong cylinder; in some cases they are covered with a ceramic layer. The pellets are loaded into fourteen-foot tubes made of Zircaloy.

The type called the pressurized light water reactor, such as made by Westinghouse, has two water systems; the primary one cools the reactor core and circulates in a closed loop, while the secondary one connects to the first through a heat exchanger. Steam from the secondary line powers the turbines. There is also an emergency core-cooling system. The fission products and neutrons are born with high kinetic energy, which means they are exceedingly hot. The radiation produced and the energy from beta decay of fission products also ends up as heat. The core-cooling water exits at a temperature typically of 324 °C (615 °F) and a pressure of 2235 pounds per square inch. Since atmospheric pressure is 14.7 pounds per square inch, the pressure cited is 152 times that of the atmosphere. The sketch shows the essential features of a modern nuclear power reactor of the pressurized water type. Such reactors produce up to 3820 megawatts of heat and 1300 megawatts of electricity. In this case the efficiency of converting heat to electricity is 34%.

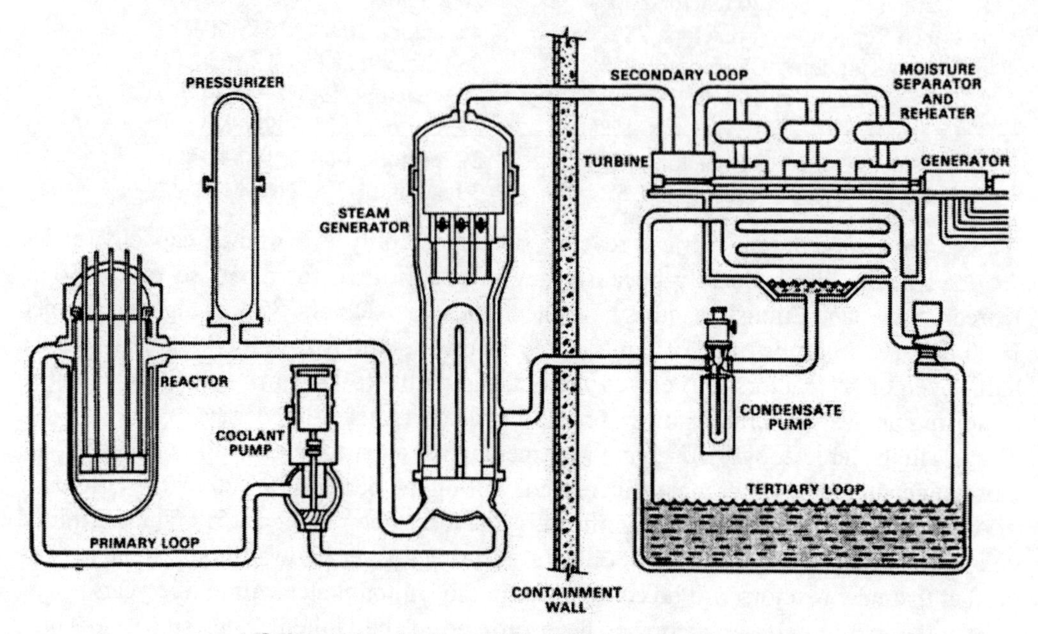

Schematic of a Pressurized Water Reactor Plant

The core of a nuclear reactor containing the fuel is typically cylindrical and about 10 feet in diameter and 40 feet tall. One-fifth to one-third of the fuel is replaced annually. The core is in a steel tank with walls 8.5 inches thick; this is a sort of radioactive inferno. The steel tank is inside two ferroconcrete shields 9 or 10 feet thick. The cooling water exits at high temperature and pressure and vaporizes more water in a heat exchanger; the resulting steam powers turbines to drive the generators. An external cooling system is necessary; it may use cooling towers, river water, or ocean water. The intense neutron irradiation was found to cause embrittlement of the metallic parts in time, shortening the life of the reactor. Embrittlement is the consequence of metal atoms in the steel being displaced by the action of energetic neutrons. Alloys with as much as 40% nickel are less susceptible to embrittlement. Soviet engineers developed a procedure to anneal embrittled steel vessels to relieve the stresses, but their pressure vessels are smaller than American ones. An annealing temperature of 475 °C is used, which is below a red heat. Nevertheless, ways of annealing the larger American vessels are being considered.

Those reactors which are near the ocean generally use sea water in the cooling towers, and they discharge a large amount of heat into the water. These result in some effect on marine life, but mostly benign. They can be likened to ocean-floor thermal vents which are found in many areas of the world. At certain coastal sites, discharge of warm water from the reactor can disturb kelp growth by creating sediment clouds which obscure needed sunlight. This was the case at the San Onofre, California, reactor, but an artificial reef mostly corrected the problem. During the summer of 1991 near Tampa, a baby manatee (291 pounds) was sucked into a seaside utility's intake pipe. Workers managed to free it.

The entire reactor structure is housed in the containment building, a huge shell made of prestressed, reinforced concrete four feet thick. Some newer containments are steel. These types of shells are not strong enough to withstand the crash of a large aircraft, but would absorb so much of the kinetic energy that the massive tank containing the core would not be ruptured. An auxiliary building houses facilities to control the cooling water, radioactive storage tank in the containment sump, and pressurized tanks of radioactive gases. There are many pumps, filters, storage tanks, valves, etc., largely computer controlled. An immense nuclear reactor today costs more than $3.5 billion to construct.

Just think of all those pumps, valves, gauges, and electrical circuits: an engineer's delight.

In the other common type known as boiling water reactors, such as those made by General Electric, there is only one water system, and the water boils inside the core. In this arrangement the steam becomes somewhat contaminated, and thus the turbine blades also pick up radioactive material. The United States has fewer than 40 boiling water reactors. Most types are shut down temporarily for refueling. A typical boiling water reactor produces 2000 megawatts of heat and 640 megawatts of electricity, and is around 32% efficient.

The British did not build commercial pressurized water reactors until rather late. Their first, which is in Suffolk, did not go critical until 1995. Control is accomplished by both control rods and boron (as borax) dissolved in the coolant water. It is designed to produce 1188 megawatts of electricity.

A few reactors in the U.S. have no containment buildings. Four of these (at Hanford, Washington, and Savannah River, South Carolina) are primarily military, are operated by the Department of Energy, and are not subject to the Nuclear Regulatory Commission. The N Reactor at Hanford is now closed. Another reactor without containment was commercial (Fort St. Vrain, Platteville, Colorado), is now decommissioned and its spent fuel has been shipped to Idaho. This experimental reactor had a unique uranium carbide fuel, was gas-cooled, and was constantly besieged by intractable problems. In 1995 a Colorado utility began transforming the Fort St. Vrain reactor into a gas-fired facility to produce 330 megawatts of electricity. Reactors built in the USSR before about 1985 also do not have true containment shells.

Former American reactors without containment shells

Reactor Security—American reactors, as well as those of many other countries, have safeguards against attack by terrorists. To reduce the jeopardy, barriers have been erected to prevent vehicles from approaching closely except those which are authorized and are under surveillance. The barriers consist of steel-reinforced concrete dividers, zig-zag approaches, etc. This system has prevented any planned attack by truck bombs or other such means of sabotage. Attack by aircraft still remains a threatening possibility (see also 10-59).

7-5 Operation of a Water-Cooled Nuclear Reactor

The total power production of a giant reactor is as much as 3 billion watts (3000 megawatts), often expressed as 3000 MWth (th meaning thermal; sometimes it is just MWt,). The thermal efficiency of electricity production is approximately 33%, so electricity generation is one billion watts (1000 MWe, the letter e meaning electricity). The prefix giga- means a billion, so 1 billion watts can also be expressed as 1 gigawatt (GW). Considering generators alone, they convert mechanical energy into electricity with an efficiency of about 95%.

A rule of thumb is that reactors produce 10 million watts of electric power per long ton of uranium fuel; a long ton is 2200 pounds, about the same as a metric tonne or 1000 kilograms. Fuel rods (the most common type of fuel elements) are replaced after three or four years in the reactor. One tonne of natural uranium during its lifetime in a reactor supplies as much energy as burning 12,000,000 barrels of oil. This one tonne of uranium in metallic form would form a cube a little less than 15 inches on edge. It would be much smaller if the fuel were enriched in uranium-235. Supplies of uranium are known to be sufficient for at least 100 years; more ore deposits will almost certainly be discovered if nuclear reactors continue in use.

In pressurized liquid water reactors, as the water heats up it expands and thus becomes less dense. With fewer molecules of water (and fewer atoms of hydrogen to moderate fast neutrons) per unit volume, the fast neutrons are slowed less, and the fission process becomes less efficient. This negative feedback serves as an important safety feature: if the water is lost, the fission reaction stops.

Energy arises from fission of U-235 and U-238, and also from Pu-239 made from U-238.

To make the production of electricity as economical as possible, as much of the uranium-235 as feasible should be consumed. The events inside a huge reactor are quite complicated. At the beginning of operations, uranium-235 undergoes fission, the neutron multiplication factor **k** becomes greater than 1, and the chain reaction commences. Most of the fast neutrons from fission leave the fuel and are moderated by the water of the cooling system, after which they diffuse back into the fuel. But some (around 2.4%) of the uranium-238, which is present in large excess, undergoes fission by the fast neutrons, and this yields a bonus of extra energy. As explained earlier (4-5), uranium-238 also absorbs neutrons (slow ones), forming U-239, which rapidly undergoes two steps of beta decay to form neptunium-239 and then plutonium-239. We have seen that Pu-239, like U-235, readily undergoes fission, so it is fair to ask why that doesn't happen here. The answer is that it does happen. Farther into the effective life of the fuel, more and more plutonium-239 experiences fission and furnishes as much as 40%, in some reactors 50%, of the total energy. Moreover, up to about 8% of the energy derives from fission of uranium-238 by fast, unmoderated neutrons. For a billion-watt (electric) reactor, 2.2 kilograms of U-235 and 2.0 kilograms of U-238 are consumed each day. At the end, three-fourths of the original U-235 has been consumed. By this time each metric tonne of uranium has furnished 35 kilograms of fission products and approximately 12 kilograms of transuranium elements.

Both nuclides—U-235 and Pu-239—absorb neutrons in two different ways, namely, with and without fission. Which process occurs depends mostly on the energy of the neutrons. Consider the case of uranium-235. Its cross section for fission by slow neutrons is 577 barns and for non-fission capture (forming uranium-236) is about 99 barns. Without fission, approximately 15% of the uranium-235 forms U-236, a rather stable isotope, half-life 23 million years. Capture of more neutrons leads to neptunium-237 and plutonium-238. With very fast neutrons, both U-235 and U-236 undergo fission. In the case of plutonium-239, slow neutrons cause fission and also non-fission absorption, forming Pu-240, half-life 6540 years. Capture of more neutrons leads to Pu-241, -242, -243, etc.

We see then that the fate of neutrons spawned by fission is greatly varied. Some are lost by leaking to the outside. Some are absorbed by U-235 resulting in fission or formation of U-236. A few neutrons, not yet moderated, cause some of the U-238 to fission, but slow neutrons convert it to Np-239, which decays to Pu-239; heavier isotopes of this element then build up to some degree. Some of these undergo fission. Certain fission products, xenon-135 and samarium-151 for example, are strong neutron-absorbers (4-15). The control rods, plumbing, and impurities take a share. Even the nuclei of the hydrogen atoms of the cooling water absorb some neutrons, forming hydrogen-2 (deuterium).

As mentioned above, certain fission products readily absorb neutrons, so as they build up they compete in the fission chain for neutrons. For this and other reasons, it is common practice to put some material inside the reactor at the start to absorb neutrons and simulate conditions which prevail later on. Such a material is referred to as a "burnable poison"; the word "burn" in nuclear slang means to be consumed in a nuclear reaction. Boron as boric acid solution pumped into an internal coil, or gadolinium as the solid oxide, is commonly used. Erbium is a rare-earth element which absorbs neutrons at particular energies only, and hence erbium oxide is used to control the reactivity of certain reactors. Incidentally, a neutron source is frequently used to jump-start nuclear reactors in turning them on the first time, although this is not strictly necessary since there are always a few stray neutrons around.

It is natural to wonder whether the control rods of a reactor can be pushed inside fast enough to shut down operations if an emergency arises. Luckily, this can be done because of delayed neutrons. In fission the great majority of the neutrons are released promptly, but a few tenths of a percent are delayed. The number of delayed neutrons in the case of uranium-235 fission amounts to 0.65% of the number formed promptly on fission. Some of the fission products, such as certain isotopes of iodine, continue to emit neutrons up to a minute or so after being created. This factor of delayed neutrons introduces a sort of inertia into the chain reaction. Delayed neutrons set the time scale on which the number of neutrons in the reactor builds up, increasing the time between generations in the chain reaction, and preventing the neutron multiplication factor **k** from rising too quickly. Relatively slow acting control rods are thus able to regulate the power.

If you like nuclear reactors, you will love delayed neutrons.

The intense neutron and gamma ray irradiation of cooling water causes some of it to decompose into hydrogen and oxygen. This process is called radiolysis. The problem is overcome by incorporating a catalytic unit into the line which recombines the elements. A more serious problem is that at the high temperature, the radiation promotes corrosion of the metal plumbing, introducing colloidal oxides into the water; these materials must be flushed out periodically. These colloidal particles of corrosion products contain nuclides such as Mn-54, Mn-56, Co-58, Fe-59, and Co-60, and the radioactivity is typically 37 microcuries per liter of coolant. In addition, a certain amount of fission products leak from or diffuse through the zirconium cladding of the fuel elements at high temperature and form ions, soluble in the water. These fission products are highly radioactive, and pose a serious radiation problem for reactor personnel. The total concentration of fission products is typically around 13 millicuries per liter. The materials are removed in a purification circuit, and the reactor is cleaned chemically after shutdown. During the 1970s, many zirconium-clad fuel rods were defective and leaked badly. This problem has been largely corrected, and the failure rate in reactors currently is of the order of 0.01%.

The amount of energy extracted from a given amount of fuel during its time inside a reactor is measured by the "burn-up." The dimensions of this term are megawatt-days per metric tonne of uranium (MWd/MTU). Fuel in commercial reactors is commonly consumed in the amount of 30,000 to 50,000 MWd/MTU, while low burn-up to produce weapons-grade plutonium runs approximately 1000.

In commercial reactors, the fuel is kept in the reactors as long as feasible in order to yield as much energy as is economically possible. This means the build up of a great deal of plutonium-240 and other plutonium isotopes. The isotopic composition of plutonium in heavily exposed fuel elements on discharge from the reactor (based on plutonium alone, and not including uranium, fission products, etc.) is approximately:

Pu-238 — 1.5%
Pu-239 — 58
Pu-240 — 24
Pu-241 — 11.5
Pu-242 — 5

Of these, the half-lives of two are much shorter than the rest (Pu-238, 87.7 years; Pu-241, 14.4 years). Thus the plutonium-238 is slowly replaced by its alpha-decay product, uranium-234, and the Pu-241 is fairly rapidly replaced with its beta-decay product, americium-241. Other changes occur more slowly. In some cases, as much as 40% of the plutonium commercial spent fuel is Pu-240.

The largest radiation dose to workers at nuclear reactors takes place during shutdown for maintenance and refueling. The average for one year is approximately 400 millirems, somewhat more than the average civilian background level.

7-6 Radionuclides in Spent Fuel

Let's examine the status of reactor fuel after it has been used in a pressurized-water reactor and is ready for discharge. The fuel at the start had been enriched to 3.3% uranium-235. In this case the reactor contained 100 metric tonnes of uranium calculated as the element, that is 3.3 tonnes of U-235 and 96.7 tonnes of U-238. This means that the fuel itself, uranium dioxide, must weigh more than 100 tonnes. A simple calculation shows that the fuel, UO_2, weighs 113.5 tonnes. After the fuel has been used and it has surrendered its allotted energy, it is said to be *spent*, and is ready for discharge. This is done stepwise, and fresh fuel is put in. The thermal power during operation is somewhat more than 3 billion watts and the electric power is one third of that. At this stage the spent fuel rods are lethally radioactive.

Analysis of the spent fuel chemically, by radioactivity measurements and by other techniques, shows that the reactor core contains close to 96.5% U-238 and 0.8% U-235 (basing our computations on the uranium content, that is, ignoring the oxygen content of uranium dioxide). The remaining 2.7% appears as fission products and transuranium elements. The table below is an inventory of some of these materials in terms of weight and in curies. A more nearly complete table is given in 8-16. Both tables are abbreviated because a complete compilation would require about six pages. Actually, quite a high proportion of fission products consists of stable (nonradioactive) nuclides; examples are Sr-88, Zr-92, Zr-93, Zr-94, Zr-96, Mo-95, Xe-134, La-139, and Ce-140. The data are from several government reports with identifications such as NUCREG 0771 and BNWL-1900 NTIS, and also from public sources concerning the San Onofre, California, reactor.

Partial Inventory of Fission Products and Transuranium Elements in a Billion-Watt (electric) Reactor

Atomic Number	*Radionuclide*	*Half-life*	*Amount*	
			Kilograms	*Curies*
36	Krypton-85	10.72 years	1.6	630,000
37	Rubidium-86	18.66 days	0.0077	630,000
38	Strontium-90	28.5 years	29	4,000,000
40	Zirconium-95	64.02 days	7.9	170,000,000
42	Molybdenum-99	65.9 hours	0.38	180,000,000
44	Ruthenium-106	1.02 year	8.5	28,000,000
53	Iodine-131	8.04 days	0.77	95,000,000
54	Xenon-133	5.24 days	1.0	190,000,000
55	Cesium-134	2.06 years	6.4	8,300,000
55	Cesium-137	30.0 years	60	5,200,000
56	Barium-140	12.75 days	2.5	182,000,000
57	Lanthanum-140	40.27 hours	0.32	180,000,000
58	Cerium-144	284.9 days	29	95,000,000
94	Plutonium-238	87.7 years	3.6	62,000
94	Plutonium-239	24,100 years	371	23,000
94	Plutonium-240	6540 years	100	23,000
94	Plutonium-241	14.4 years	36	3,700,000
95	Americium-241	432.7 years	0.53	1800
96	Curium-244	18.1 years	0.31	25,000

The total number of curies in the reactor is close to three billion, a truly colossal sum. The most abundant components inside the reactor core, uranium-238 and uranium-235, have such long half-lives that they contribute only 34 curies to this total.

An estimate of the amount of reactor-grade plutonium (that is, with a high plutonium-240 content) in the entire world is 100 metric tonnes. There is additional plutonium of this quality in high-level waste.

7-7 Other Types of Nuclear Reactors

Nuclear reactors have evolved from many prototypes and experimental designs, earning modern reactors a distinguished ancestry. The table below identifies a small fraction of the reactor types:

Representative Types of Nuclear Reactors

Type	*Fuel*	*Moderator*	*Coolant*	*Purpose*
Original model	Aluminum-clad uranium metal	Graphite	Light water	Pu production
Boiling water	Uranium dioxide in Zircaloy	Light water	Light water	Electric power
Pressurized water	Uranium dioxide in Zircaloy	Light water	Light water	Electric power
Gas cooled	Uranium dioxide in graphite	Graphite	Helium	Electric power
Heavy water	Uranium dioxide in Zircaloy	Heavy water	Heavy or light water	Electric power
Homo-geneous	Uranyl sulfate in heavy water	Heavy water	Heavy water	Experimental
TRIGA	Aluminum-clad uranium and zirconium hydrides	Hydrogen (in hydrides)	Light water	Research and training
Fast breeder	Uranium metal or dioxide	None	Molten sodium	Electric power and breeding plutonium-239
Molten salts	Uranium tetra-fluoride in molten fluoride salts	Graphite	Molten salts	Experimental
TOPAZ (Soviet)	Uranium carbide (90% U-235)	Carbon (in uranium carbide)	Radiant	Electric power in spacecraft

A few use or can use natural uranium, but most are loaded with uranium enriched in U-235. Some are of historical interest only; others are just reaching the point of production. One of the reactors at Oak Ridge is moderated with ordinary water, but has a beryllium neutron shield to reflect neutrons back into the core. It operates with high neutron density, and is used to synthesize radioactive nuclides of many types.

Heavy water (deuterium oxide) has the advantage over ordinary light water in that deuterium (hydrogen-2) absorbs neutrons to a much lower extent than does hydrogen-1. These reactors yield twice as much plutonium as those using light water. Each contains several hundred tons of heavy water. Canada's CANDU reactors are of this type. CANDU (for ***Can**ada **D**euterium-**U**ranium*) reactors are not pressurized and thus do not need strong, heavy reactor vessels. They can be refueled without shutting down. CANDU reactors can use natural (unenriched) uranium as fuel, but there are some economic advantages to using slightly enriched uranium, say up to 1 or 1.5% uranium-235. The sketch illustrates a CANDU 3 reactor, which produces 450 MWe. It has a very high 94% capacity factor and a design life of 40 years. In time, capture of neutrons by the deuterium forms tritium in sufficient quantity to warrant its removal. The tritiated heavy water is shipped to the Darlington Tritium Removal Facility where it is treated with deuterium gas under conditions in which deuterium replaces tritium. The gas containing both deuterium and tritium is condensed at a very low temperature and subjected to fractional distillation. The tritium is converted to uranium or titanium tritide for storage, and the purified heavy water is used again as moderator and coolant in the reactor. A typical facility recovers about 2.5 kilograms of tritium per year.

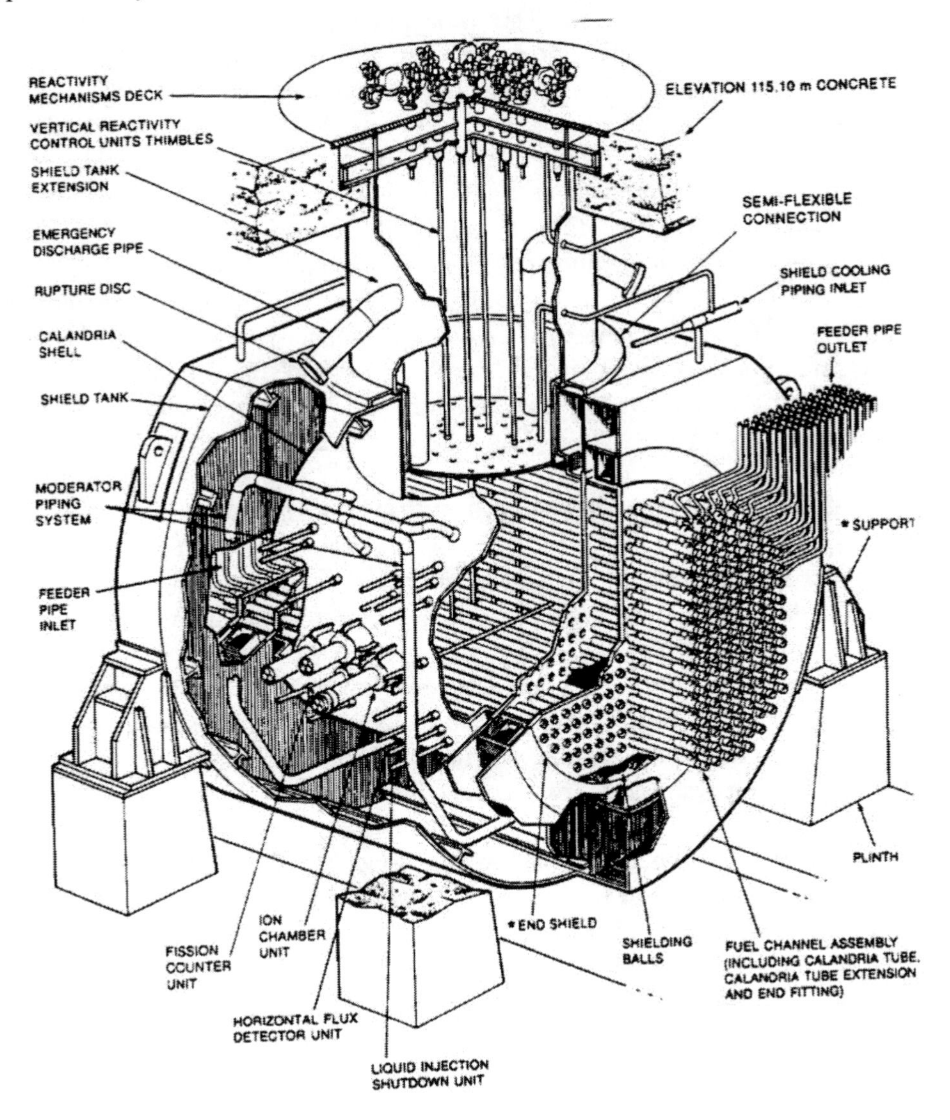

Assembly of the CANDU 3 reactor

In 1997 an internal investigation of Canada's 21 reactors disclosed that one-third of them were defective owing to problems in management rather than in technical matters. They were closed down until the problems were addressed. The remaining reactors will be upgraded. The CANDU reactors proved to be the best regulated.

The reactors at the Savannah River complex in South Carolina (the C, K, L, and P reactors) manufacture plutonium and tritium for military use. Plutonium production peaked at approximately 1500 kilograms per year. The Department of Energy has 50 nuclear facilities, mostly with aged reactors. An estimated $20 billion will be needed to modernize them enough to avoid serious safety problems, and the General Accounting Office projects costs of $155 billion over the next 25 years would be required to pursue this objective.

An aging reactor in Idaho is known as the Power Burst Facility. It is capable of giving concentrated bursts of neutrons. Three scientific studies have recommended that it be decommissioned, but powerful political voices call for spending at least $30 million and convert it into a cancer treatment facility using boron neutron capture therapy (6-18D).

Graphite has its advantages as a moderator, but it has two serious defects. Under intense neutron irradiation, some of the carbon atoms are displaced in the crystal structure, increasing the energy content significantly (Wigner effect). If in this state the graphite is heated somewhat (to 250 °C to 480 °F), this energy can be liberated rapidly, bringing the graphite up to the ignition point (in air). This was the cause of the accident at the Windscale reactor (7-23). If the reactor is operated at an elevated temperature (above about 250 °C) Wigner energy does not accumulate. But in time, the graphite becomes distorted, and must be replaced. This was also a problem in molten salt reactors. The second serious drawback is that graphite burns in air, and this played a role in the Chernobyl accident (7-25).

7-8 The Sad Tale of the Tennessee Valley Authority's Reactors

The rural inhabitants of Tennessee were for decades among our country's poorest; during the depression starting in 1928, the per capita income was only 45% of the comparable national average. The region was also plagued by floods, soil erosion, and other misfortunes. In 1933, President Roosevelt inaugurated the Tennessee Valley Authority, which, by the shock therapy of new electric power, raised the per capita income up to 75% of that of the national average by 1970. Both hydroelectric power and coal-burning generators were used. From these sources, about 1460 megawatts of electric power was produced.

In the 1960s, when nuclear power was alluring, the TVA embraced the idea of building 17 nuclear reactors and becoming the power capitol of the nation. The agency borrowed funds on the bond market. But, alas, destiny was cruel. The TVA is today some $25 billion in debt. Of the 17 reactors planned, eight have been canceled. Only three are actually producing electricity. Two have been licensed but were not operating until 1995, and then at reduced power. The remaining four reactors have been under construction for as long as 25 years. Two of these, near Watts Bar Dam on the Tennessee River, have cost $7.7 billion, more than ten times the original budgeted amount of $625 million. So many cases of defective work occurred that the Nuclear Regulatory Agency pressured the TVA to hire an independent investigating contractor, Quality Technology Company. But after interviewing 1000 employees, this firm was abruptly fired. The Nuclear Regulatory Agency fined TVA $200,000 for intimidating whistleblowers. A clean sweep is clearly needed.

7-9 A Few Foreign Reactors

France—Of all nations, France is just about the most enthusiastic concerning nuclear power. The French have strong ties between civilian and military nuclear facilities, and this makes it difficult to get full information on French reactors. Charles de Gaulle established the world's first civilian organization devoted to exploiting nuclear fission (October 1945). Physicist Frederic Joliot was appointed high commissioner, but was removed from office when it became known that he opposed development of nuclear bombs. The French nuclear efforts are supervised by their Atomic Energy Commission, or CEA (Commisariat à l'Énergie Atomique) Of course, France had to construct facilities for the following: processing of ores; manufacturing uranium tetrafluoride for conversion to metal for reactor fuel or to uranium hexafluoride for enrichment in uranium-235; enriched uranium dioxide and mixed oxides for reactor fuel; centrifuge and atomic vapor laser isotope separation plants; reprocessing spent fuel to separate plutonium; zirconium and stainless steel cladding procedures; lithium-6 separation factories; tritium manufacture facilities; works for vitrification of waste; and much more.

Nuclear gung ho

The earliest reactors in France were air-cooled graphite models fueled with natural uranium. Gradually, reactors moderated and cooled by pressurized light water or heavy water were built. Like the United States, the first light water reactor was constructed to power a submarine. Modern reactors in France are highly standardized and are constructed in about half the time it takes in the United States. The standard pressurized water reactors produce electricity at power levels of 900, 1300, and 1450 megawatts. More than three quarters of the electricity in France comes from reactors. Except maybe for Norway, which has abundant water power, French households and industries enjoy the cheapest electricity in Europe (at least if the decommissioning costs are not included). About 10% of the country's electric power is exported. The French anticipated increased demand for electric power early in the new century, and feel that renewable energy sources will not be adequate. By agreement with Germany, a joint enterprise, Nuclear Power International, has been formed. A 1450 megawatt unit (electric), the European Pressurized Reactor, is planned, and it is said to be ultra safe. Provision is even made to contain the entire core in a worst-case accident, a core meltdown. The premise of such a huge reactor is that only large-scale ones producing considerably more than 1000 megawatts are economical.

There are two heavy-water reactors at Marcoule. Each is 200 megawatts thermal, and they produce weapons-grade plutonium. They are also employed to generate radionuclides for medicine, to make cobalt-60 and plutonium-238, and to produce tritium for fusion warheads.

A number of research reactors are in service. These include three serving as neutron sources near Grenoble and still another at Saclay. Their thermal power ranges from 8 to 57 megawatts. These serve not only to study reactor operation, but also in crystallographic research using neutron diffraction. Four more reactors are employed in training of operators. Fourteen additional miscellaneous reactors of thermal power up to 120 megawatts are used in testing reactors under stress, research, and other purposes.

Cogéma (Compagnie Générale des Matières Nucléaires) is a government-operated establishment which oversees the diverse stages of the nuclear fuel cycle. It also operates on the international level, and is the only company in the world which, through subsidiaries, offers services in mining, reprocessing irradiated fuel, and waste management. It produces lithium deuteride for fusion bombs and fuel for commercial reactors.

The French incorporate the principles of artificial intelligence into their reactors' computers, and also provide for man-machine dialogue. Many of the computers have high-definition, touch-sensitive screens. The French safety programs have provisions for reducing the number of items of information presented to the operators (to avoid overwhelming confusion), but permit calling up status reports of any of 10,000 components within 2 seconds. Nevertheless, several reactors in France have developed cracks in the pressure vessels. Replacing these tanks, which are made of Inconel 600 (an alloy of iron, chromium, and nickel) with Inconel 690 (which has more chromium, and is much more resistant to crack development) will cost several billion dollars. Additional information on French research into reactor accidents is in section 7-35.

China—The Chinese were rather late in production of electricity using reactors. It was not until 1991 that the 300 megawatt reactor in Qinshan, on the southeast coast, went on line, and began supplying part of the power for Shanghai. Some parts were purchased from abroad: the reactor vessel from Japan, the coolant pumps from Germany, and the computer controls from France. Contracts for additional aid have been made with Russia and Canada. There were only three electricity-generating reactors as of 1996, but China expects to have about 100 by 2050.

Look at the situation from the viewpoint of Chinese engineers who foresee their country's energy needs. The burgeoning economy of more than 1.2 billion people requires tremendous amounts of energy, a great deal of it electric. Already many of China's cities have a 20% shortage. Already even Beijing is dreadfully polluted with coal smoke. There are simply not enough petroleum sources. The crowded country might have the potential to generate energy from biomass, but this would be possible only in the far western areas, and take considerable time. There is not enough water power, although the new dam on the Yangtse will help. Yet, for the first time in history, China's citizens are manufacturing and buying refrigerators, air conditioning machines, communication equipment, etc. Where is all that electrical energy coming from? The decision is that nuclear sources should play an important role. Liu Jinhua, director of the China National Nuclear Corp., insists nuclear waste can be contained, perhaps more easily than the truly massive amounts of wastes from fossil fuels which pollute the air and water. This general feeling appears frequently all over Asia. Popular opposition to nuclear power in Asia is in its infancy.

More electricity, no matter what!

South Korea—Having only small resources of coal, and virtually none of petroleum, it is not surprising that South Korea generates about half its electricity using nuclear reactors. Still more reactors were started in 1982 near Yonggwang, in the southwest part of the country. The authoritarian government of that time simply chose a site and built the reactors, without consulting or even informing the local citizens what was going on. But the Chernobyl accident (7-25) of 1986, along with a more democratic government, brought about changes. The prospect of 11 additional reactors stimulated an environmental movement. Farmers whose fields were within a mile or two of a reactor found that their crops could hardly be sold. All the traditional disputes concerning fossil fuels along with their pollution, vs. nuclear reactors with their radioactive waste and other hazards, were rehearsed again. There are plans to purchase two CANDU reactors from Canada; these can make weapons-grade plutonium. The government now tends to use persuasion instead of edict, staging elaborate exhibitions explaining nuclear power and radioactivity. A new, well financed, nuclear research center has also been established, studying advanced reactor design, breeder reactors, and waste disposal.

How not to get public support

India—India has designed and built several of its own nuclear reactors, but the amount of electricity generated has been only about 2% of the country's total. The total electric power from reactors in 1998 was about 1700 megawatts. In recent years, emphasis on nuclear power has declined, along with quality and maintenance. The International Atomic Energy Agency considers four of the Indian reactors to be among the world's least reliable. The two Narora reactors suffered broken turbine blades and fires. The containment dome of the Kaiga reactor simply collapsed in 1994. About the only consolation is that Pakistan's reactors are no better. The innovative 100-megawatt Dhruva reactor is used in research. Government funding for the Nuclear Power Corporation has declined from 50% to 33% of the Corporations' total revenues. By 1996, government support for atomic energy had dwindled to only 30% of its original level. Nevertheless, research into the military aspects of nuclear energy continues.

7-10 Molten Salt Reactors

Early Development—The advantages of a reactor with liquid fuel were recognized early on and this led to homogeneous reactors. Three light water homogeneous reactors were built, the first in 1952 at Oak Ridge, the other two at Los Alamos. They had a thermal power rating of one to two megawatts. Another homogeneous reactor used uranyl sulfate (enriched in U-235) in heavy water; the solvent also acted as the moderator and it was rated at five megawatts (thermal). An evaluation in 1959 indicated that they all demanded excessive maintenance and had other difficulties. At the elevated operating temperature, such water-based reactors must be pressurized, meaning that expensive heavy-walled vessels are required. A liquid-fuel reactor which could operate at ordinary atmospheric pressure would obviously be an advantage, and thus the idea of using a molten salt as a solvent for a uranium compound evolved; moreover, use of the corresponding salt of thorium could convert it into a breeder reactor. The Director of the Oak Ridge National Laboratory, Alvin Weinberg (Fermi Award, 1980), was largely responsible for pushing molten salt reactors.

The advantages of molten salt reactors over light water pressurized reactors using uranium dioxide fuel are: The reactor operates at normal atmospheric pressure, reducing construction costs; the system has a high negative temperature coefficient of reactivity, meaning that it chokes itself off in any emergency; the fuel, being in liquid solution, does not need zirconium cladding and cannot become distorted during operation; the high operating temperature means that the efficiency of electricity production is as high as 44%; they can consume plutonium; makeup fuel can be added as needed; and a much smaller fraction of transuranic waste is produced than with pressurized water reactors. Strictly speaking, no control rods are needed, but are used anyway to facilitate turning the reactor on and off, and in any case are built in for redundant safety.

The advantages of molten salt reactors

First, a suitable salt was needed. Oxides are generally too high-melting, the chlorine in chlorides absorbs too many neutrons, and nitrates and related salts are decomposed by the intense radiation. Fluorides seemed best suited to the purpose. It was already known that certain types of steel and nickel alloys are resistant to chemical attack by molten fluorides. Considering the various metal fluorides, the best choices were soon narrowed down to those of lithium, beryllium, sodium, potassium, and zirconium; the others have too high melting points or other objections. When chemical compounds are mixed, the melting point of the mixture is depressed compared to the components. A composition with a minimum-melting point is called a eutectic.

The Aircraft Reactor Experiment, in Brief—Engineers recognized early on that molten salt reactors could be made small enough to be carried by a plane, and so the planning began as early as 1946. Experimental work began in 1954 at Oak Ridge as the Aircraft Reactor Experiment. About $7 billion was spent on this project. If successful, such a power source would greatly extend the cruising range of aircraft. The metal for the container in the Aircraft Reactor Experiment was Inconel, a nickel alloy. The moderator was beryllium oxide and the coolant was liquid sodium metal. The molten salt consisted of the fluorides of sodium and zirconium, and the fuel was uranium tetrafluoride, UF_4, enriched in U-235. The propulsion was to be accomplished by forcing air into the hot reactor, where it would be heated to a high temperature, causing expansion and exhaust through a jet. The exit temperature was estimated at 700 °C. The reactor was shut down because of corrosion, and this was found to be related to the high content of zirconium tetrafluoride as well to the elevated temperatures. The reactor powered a plane on the ground, but never in flight. To test the level of radiation the crew of a plane would experience in the air, 47 flights were made in 1955 with the reactor operating on board, but not powering the plane. All these tests did provide valuable information on molten salt reactors.

The Molten Salt Reactor Experiment—Laboratory research revealed that lithium and beryllium fluorides are best suited to compound a salt mixture with a sufficiently low melting point, and these two compounds mixed with sodium fluoride proved to be best. By lowering the zirconium fluoride content (relative to the Aircraft Reactor Experiment), employing a somewhat lower temperature than that in the prototype, and using a nickel-molybdenum alloy (Hastelloy) it proved possible to make a molten salt reactor which operated successfully over a three-year period without appreciable corrosion. At the start, the salt composition was ^{7}LiF, 40.5%; BeF_2, 32.8%; ZrF_4, 20.0%; and UF_4, 6.7% (all by weight; the UF_4 was enriched in U-235). Control rods holding a strong neutron absorber (gadolinium oxide) were employed. The operating temperature was close to 663 °C (1225 °F), a dull red heat. The moderator was graphite, which is not wet by the molten salts. To remove heat from the reactors, a secondary salt mixture of lithium-7 and beryllium fluorides in a separate loop was employed. Outside of the reactor, the hot salt was cooled by air, but a heat exchanger with water to form steam would be used in a facility to generate electricity. When fission occurs, the fission products include the noble gases krypton-85 and xenon-133, and these were continually stripped out using helium. The experiments began at Oak Ridge in 1962 and lasted about a dozen years. The reactor developed a power of 8 megawatts (thermal).

The shortcomings of molten salt reactors

The most severe question encountered with the Molten Salt Reactor Experiment involved the use of lithium-7 as a component in the salt mixture. Natural lithium consists of the two isotopes Li-6 and Li-7, the lighter one making up 6.50% by weight of the total. Lithium-6 has a terrific appetite for neutrons, which interact to form tritium and helium (see 9-13). Any tritium would find its way into the steam system in an actual power plant if it is not trapped and removed. For these reasons only lithium-7 can be used. As it happened, lithium-7 began to be available as a result of the separation of lithium-6 for hydrogen bomb production (9-14). Therefore a mixture of lithium-7 fluoride, beryllium fluoride and sodium fluoride was selected as the solvent for the molten salt reactor. The expense of an isotopically pure component is a definite shortcoming of this type of molten salt reactor, but it is possible to recover and recycle lithium and beryllium fluorides by distillation in high vacuum.

The Molten Salt Breeder Reactor—The breeder fuel salt, consisting of the fluorides of lithium-7, beryllium, thorium, and uranium, melts at 500 °C. Operating as a breeder, the salt temperature was 705 °C, a red heat. The fuel of the reactor was uranium tetrafluoride (33% enrichment in uranium-235). The hot molten salt in the reactor was then pumped through an external heat exchanger, when an intermediate coolant was heated to 538 °C. This material could transfer its energy to water to form steam, which would be used to generate electricity in an actual power station. The secondary coolant consisted of sodium fluoride and sodium tetrafluoroborate at the eutectic composition of 81.5% sodium fluoride by weight. It melts at 385 °C. Lithium-7 was omitted in the interest of economy. To prevent decomposition of the sodium

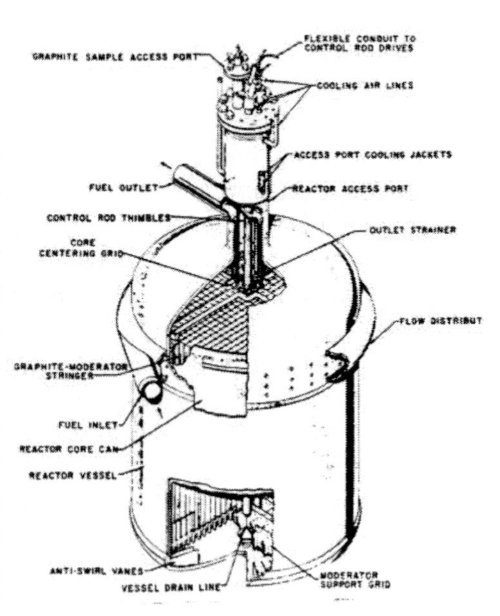

Core of molten salt reactor

tetrafluoroborate a certain pressure of boron trifluoride gas must be maintained in the cooling coils.

When used in breeder mode, the molten salt contains thorium tetrafluoride. The idea is that thorium-232, the common isotope, absorbs the surplus neutrons to form Th-233, which decays quickly (half-life 22 minutes) to the next element protactinium-233, and this decays further, yielding uranium-233. This last material is fissile like uranium-235 or plutonium-239. After some operating time during the runs starting in 1965, the uranium fuel was removed by bubbling fluorine through the molten salt, where it converts all uranium to its hexafluoride, UF_6. This substance is very volatile, and the fluorine treatment elegantly lifts the uranium out of the reactor. Experiments were subsequently carried out in which the reactor was successfully fueled for a year with uranium-233 bred in earlier runs. These tests proved that thorium can be utilized to breed a fissile nuclide. Plutonium can also be used to some extent. Altogether the reactor operated about 2½ years. Even though the breeding capacity of the reactor was not its strong point, this success is important because our world has more than three times as much thorium as uranium, and breeding uranium-233 can in principle furnish abundant energy for millennia.

Another complication with the molten salt breeder reactor lies with the protactinium-233 mentioned above. While beta decay yields the desired uranium-233, the process is a bit slow (half-life 27 days). This means that the protactinium-233 formed in the reactor accumulates and consumes excessive neutrons, lowering the breeding yield of uranium-233; in fact, if the protactinium is not removed, practically no breeding takes place. The problem can be managed by removing the protactinium-233 and transporting it outside the reactor where it can decay to uranium-233. This is accomplished by allowing molten bismuth metal containing dissolved lithium to fall as droplets through the molten salt when the protactinium is displaced by the lithium. The result is that the protactinium and some rare-earth fission products are extracted by the bismuth, and the heavy molten bismuth layer is removed at the bottom. The protactinium is removed from the bismuth, which is recycled. Thus the problem can be managed, but only with the expenditure of extra time, effort, and funds. If ever a great demand for energy from thorium arises, better techniques will probably have to be developed. Despite the attractive advantages of molten salt reactors, their problems and unique designs were deemed sufficient to close down the research.

Breeders based on uranium have the disadvantage of generating plutonium, which is now in surplus and is not a fuel of choice for reactors. Breeders based on thorium generate uranium-233, which not only is an excellent fuel for reactors, but is also easily rendered unsuitable for manufacture of nuclear weapons by blending it with depleted uranium (4-20), which is abundant. Moreover, some uranium-232 is produced, a nuclide which emits dangerous gamma rays and thus confers an element of self-protection against theft. It might be worthwhile to evaluate some type of molten salt reactor to consume all that plutonium-239 and uranium-235 from dismantled nuclear warheads.

Uranium-233 Reactor in India—On October 29, 1996, at Kalpakkam, India, a reactor using uranium-233 as fuel started operation. The reactor, known as Kamini, gives 30 kilowatts of electric power. The uranium-233 was bred in a 50 megawatt (thermal) reactor, also at Kalpakkam, and was constructed by the Bhabha Atomic Research Center. India has vast reserves of thorium, and is thus one of the few countries sponsoring its conversion to uranium-233.

7-11 Fast Breeder Reactors

Breeder reactors generate (that is, "breed") fissile nuclides from relatively abundant uranium-238 or thorium-232. In principal, breeder reactors hold the promise of permitting use of as much as about 75% of uranium-238 as an energy source. The concept of breeder reactors, first suggested in 1943, is ingenious. Their attractive feature is that they produce easily fissionable atoms from uranium-238 or thorium-232, which cannot be used alone in reactors. Thorium is about 3.5 times as abundant as uranium in the earth's crust. Uranium-238 yields plutonium-239 and thorium-232 yields uranium-233. In fact, molten salt reactors using thorium to breed uranium-233 (7-10) were thought directly after World War II to have a great future, but they were never fully developed.

In breeder reactors, uranium-238 is converted to plutonium-239 as in other reactors. The plutonium is separated (by reprocessing) and is mixed with uranium to be used as fuel to produce more plutonium from the copious uranium-238. Breeder reactors operate on fast neutrons and thus have no moderator. Fission by fast neutrons generates more excess neutrons than is the case with slow-neutron fission. Fast neutrons cause fission of all plutonium isotopes, including plutonium-240, which is always abundant in plutonium from commercial reactors. In fact, all isotopes of uranium and of all transuranium elements are fissioned by fast neutrons. Ordinary reactors, cooled with water, convert about 3% of the potentially available energy in uranium into heat, whereas breeders can recover roughly 75%.

Depending on design, fast breeder reactors can use fuel in either oxide or metallic form. Adjustments can be made to employ uranium dioxide enriched in U-235 or mixed oxides (MOX) of enriched uranium and plutonium as fuel (see 9-69 through 9-72). Plutonium recovered by recycling spent fuel need not be cleanly separated from fission products. In fact, a partial reprocessing technique, the CIVEX process, leaves the fuel usable in a breeder reactor but far too dangerous to be stolen. The coolant in breeders is generally molten sodium metal, which, having the relatively high mass number of 23 (that is, 23 times the mass of a neutron), exerts but little moderating effect on the fast neutrons from fission, hence the name *fast* breeder. The sodium coolant is not under pressure. The fuel rods in the core are surrounded by uranium which is more than 99% uranium-238, a fertile nuclide; this uranium blankets the core and stainless steel parts and is thus rather unimaginatively called the blanket. It might be natural uranium (0.7% U-235) or depleted uranium (0.2 to 0.3% U-235). Some of the uranium-238 absorbs the surplus neutrons, finally forming plutonium-239. It too is cooled by liquid sodium and is surrounded by shielding. The plutonium in the blanket is separated and put back into the core as fuel.

Like other reactors, breeders have their advantages and disadvantages, but on average have not won wide approval.

Fast breeder reactors can be adjusted and operated in three different modes. In "breeder mode," more plutonium is produced than is consumed. This is accomplished by surrounding the core with uranium-238. In "burner mode" (also called "incinerator mode"), no uranium blanket is employed, just steel, and more plutonium is consumed than is produced. The third modification is "converter mode," and just as much plutonium is consumed as is produced. In this case, the blanket contains both uranium and steel in the correct proportion. By 2010, Japan plans to have 17 reactors using MOX as fuel. At present, MOX fuel is several times as expensive as low-enriched uranium fuel. Breeders can consume depleted uranium.

One reactor design, proposed by General Electric, could consume or produce plutonium at any ratio from 0.6 to 1.23. When adjusted to breeder mode, 1.23 gram of plutonium is produced per gram consumed. When adjusted to burner mode, 0.6 gram of plutonium is produced for each gram consumed. Recycling cannot be continued indefinitely because the quality of the residual plutonium is degraded (more plutonium-240 is made) with each use. At the end, some must be buried with other waste.

The molten sodium coolant undergoes very little damage by the high-energy neutrons and gamma rays. Natural sodium consists entirely of sodium-23. A very little sodium-24 is formed by neutron absorption, but its half-life is only about 15 hours, and so it does not build up much. The most minute traces of sodium-22 are formed, and while the half-life is 2.6 years, so little is formed that it is not a problem. Control rods for fast breeder reactors frequently contain europium boride. Both europium and boron readily absorb neutrons. The reactor which first generated electricity for civilian consumption, in Idaho in 1951, was a breeder using liquid metal for cooling.

It is possible to extract energy from thorium in a fast breeder reactor if a small amount of uranium enriched to the 20% level in U-235 is mixed in. The Radkowsky Thorium Power Corporation promotes this concept, with assurances that very little plutonium is produced. In fact, it is said that excess plutonium from weapons can be consumed. The company plans to test the concepts in a Russian reactor.

7-12 American Fast Breeders

The first fast-neutron reactor cooled with a liquid metal was built in Los Alamos in 1943. It was a cute little thing, the core being only six inches high and the same distance wide. The reactor was affectionately nicknamed Clementine, an appellation derived from the familiar song. Not only was the reactor in a canyon, but also a wartime code word for element 94 (plutonium) was simply 49, the digits being reversed for greater security. Sometimes the Los Alamos scientists were called the forty-niners. Anyway, Clementine was cooled with mercury, which hardly absorbs fast neutrons. The fast neutrons from fission were not moderated, and the reactor ran on fast neutrons only. It had plutonium-239 as fuel and was not a breeder. The power was 25 kilowatts (thermal). Natural uranium was used as a neutron reflector. Another reactor, Los Alamos Molten Plutonium Reactor Experiment (LAMPRE-1), started in 1961, employed a fuel of molten plutonium cooled with liquid sodium. Its power was 1000 kilowatts (thermal) and its operating temperature was 510 °C in the regions just outside of the fuel.

Experimental Breeder Reactor I in Idaho began to produce electric power in December, 1951, the first electricity produced by a reactor. The power was low, only 170 kilowatts. A great deal of experience was gained about breeders from this reactor, which was deliberately subjected to extremes of operating conditions to test its response. In 1955, during one of these tests, there was a partial meltdown of the core. The core was replaced and operation was resumed until the reactor was shut down in view of its successor, Experimental Breeder Reactor II (EBR-II). It was constructed at Argonne West in southeast Idaho and started up in 1965. It ran for 30 years, being put in standby status in 1995. It produced about one megawatt of heat and 300 kilowatts of electricity, but was capable of producing much more. The fuel consisted of uranium rods or "elements" or "pins" which were 10% zirconium; they were 5 millimeters in diameter (like a pencil). This fuel was 67% uranium-235 when fresh and approximately 65% on removal; the difference became fission products. Each fuel element was inserted into a thin-walled stainless steel tube and a small amount of sodium metal was also put in (see sketch). The tube was welded shut at the top to form a unit 29 inches long. The purpose of the sodium was to function as a heat-transfer agent. In operation, as more and more of the uranium undergoes fission, it develops fissures and the sodium enters the voids. It extracts an important fission product, cesium-137, and hence becomes intensely radioactive. The void above the uranium collects fission gases, mainly krypton-85. Clusters of the pins inside hexagonal stainless steel jackets 92 inches long are assembled honeycomb-like; each unit has about 10 pounds of uranium. All together, the core contains about 680 pounds of uranium fuel, and this part is called the driver.

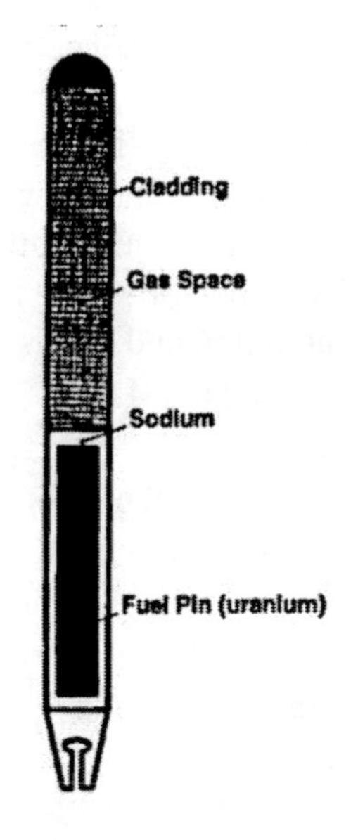

Fuel element of Experimental Breeder Reactor II

Outside the driver is a similar collection of stainless steel hexagonal bars, and outside that is a large amount of depleted uranium, that is, uranium stripped of most of its U-235, and there are vast stores of this material. This uranium (the blanket) has the purpose of stopping or reflecting the fast neutrons streaming out of the core (the steel does not moderate them). The blanket, made of uranium-238, undergoes fission in part and absorbs the excess neutrons to form plutonium-239, that is, the process is breeding. EBR II is cooled by liquid sodium. There is a primary cooling system whose sodium, entering the core, is subject to intense gamma ray and neutron bombardment. It transfers its heat to a secondary system whose sodium boils water to generate steam and the electric power. The blanket too must be cooled by liquid sodium. The reactor and first heat exchanger are immersed in the huge tank of liquid sodium. Control is achieved by lowering or raising rods containing boron carbide. The steam produced in the secondary heat exchanger is at 455 °C (851 °F). In an experiment the reactor was going full blast and the sodium pumps were deliberately stopped. The reactor has a negative temperature coefficient of reactivity, and soon shut itself off. This is because the reactor is barely critical, and expansion of the metallic uranium fuel lowers the neutron flux, the opposite of the effect of compression on implosion.

Breeder reactors might be necessary some day.

A technique has been developed at Argonne West to remove the unchanged uranium from the spent fuel driver assembly and blanket and to collect the fission products and transuranic elements (neptunium, plutonium, americium, and curium). This is described in section 8-10. The reactor can use plutonium-uranium alloy as fuel and thus contribute to reducing the supply of plutonium from dismantled warheads, but it is not efficient at this task. While not immune from possible dangers, Experimental Breeder Reactor II represents a distinct advance in reactor technology in many ways. While the reactor can consume plutonium-239, the rate is too low to be practical. In principle, however, electrometallurgical techniques can be readily adapted to separating weapon-grade plutonium, and this is cause for concern.

The Hanford site, in Washington state, has the Fast Flux Test Facility, an experimental, sodium-cooled reactor of 400 megawatts. Its high density of neutrons makes it suitable for training purposes and for testing fuels, thus simulating breeder reactor conditions. It was capable of making medical isotopes. Over fierce opposition, it was scheduled for closure in 2002, largely on account of its multimillion dollar annual budget. There is another fast reactor installation in the U.S., namely the Enrico Fermi Atomic Power Plant, located in Michigan.

7-13 The Integral Fast Reactor System

A series of fast breeder reactors has been proposed by the Department of Energy whose objective is to generate electricity while consuming surplus actinide metals. This program, known as the Advanced Liquid Metal Reactor/Integral Fast Breeder program, would require up to 40 breeder reactors and some reprocessing and fuel refabrication plants. A waste handling system would also be needed. These activities, along with accompanying high-temperature electrolytic reprocessing (8-10), might at the present level of development increase the cost of nuclear power with little or no decrease in health risk. Heavily shielded argon-filled areas (hot cells) would be needed for some of these operations on account of the intense radioactivity. Neutron activation of the materials of construction, causing decommissioning complications later on, is still another worry. Repair of jammed equipment inside would be extremely difficult. The entire project is ill conceived in its present form, and could not become operational for decades. Nevertheless, its basic premise has value. When operating, all fissile metals, that is, uranium, plutonium, americium and other transplutonium elements, could be completely consumed, not only getting rid of these nuclides, but also furnishing power (and radioactive waste).

One net effect of the Integral Fast Breeder programs as presently visualized would be to increase the volume of high-level waste. The chlorides of the fission products left behind would be in the worst possible chemical form, namely soluble salts mobile in the environment. The vitrification procedure would be able to void this problem, however.

It is also worrisome that any effort to find cheaper and easier processes for plutonium separation increases proliferation risks, despite the relatively high plutonium-240 content in the fuel. The risk would not be from freshly-separated transuranic metals: there is too much radioactivity involved. The major risk would come later, during storage or transportation. The procedure used in the Experimental Breeder does not separate the plutonium from fission products, but if this feature is preserved, then plutonium which is generated in the fuel and blanket (that is, the fissile material which makes a breeder what it is) cannot be used as fuel. Perfection of the electrolytic separation processes might enhance potential use of the technique by developing countries, such as Pakistan and Iran.

Most breeder reactor programs have two potential flaws at their present level of development. The first is that plutonium-239 is produced in the blanket of uranium-238; if separated, it is of weapons grade, and hence a proliferation danger. After 3 years of operation, the plutonium-240 content is typically only about 4.3%. Breeders can be operated in a mode which does not generate plutonium in the uranium blanket. The second flaw is that successful operation requires reprocessing of spent fuel to separate the transuranic elements to be used as additional fuel. These processes might be at present too dangerous and too expensive to be acceptable. At some point in the future these shortcomings could probably be overcome. For the time being, the entire Integral Fast Reactor program has been terminated by Congress (1994). A related activity, the Actinide Recycle Program, met the same fate. It was aimed at treating spent fuel for reuse in light-water reactors.

It does not seem reasonable to make a sweeping condemnation of all breeder reactor research. After all, breeders can extract a far higher fraction of the energy which is in uranium and thorium than other reactors. The energy is there. Human beings will need it in time. The problems are enormous, so a good case can be made for plugging away in research programs with the long-range view in mind. If problems in exploiting nuclear energy can be satisfactorily managed, breeders could supply the world's needs for millennia.

7-14 Foreign Breeder Reactors

The Soviets built the world's first commercial-size breeder, the BN-600, in the central Urals (Beloyarsk, Kazakhstan). It began operating in 1980. Today the Russians still maintain a modest breeder program. In April 1994 at the Beloyarsk breeder reactor a ruptured pipe permitted the coolant (liquid sodium) to escape into the air. It caught fire and made quite a mess, but there was no escape of radioactivity. The breeder program in Great Britain has been essentially closed down. The prototype reactor at Dounreay has 1000 metric tonnes of sodium; it stopped operating in March 1994. Another at Dounreay used sodium-potassium alloy as coolant; this alloy is liquid at room temperature. It was shut down in 1977. An experimental breeder has been built in the town of Kalpakkam, India.

In Germany, a fast breeder was started at Karlsruhe, but construction has now been stopped. Another breeder at Kalkar, on the Rhine River near the Dutch border, was completed except for fueling, but it was never operated because of intense public opposition. The Kalkar reactor met a titillating fate in 1995. A Dutch investor contracted to turn it into an amusement park, the Nuclear Water Wonderland. The water rides are fed by the pumps intended for the reactor's turbines. In late 2001, Germany decided to close all its 19 reactors over the next 20 years.

Just think, fun for the nuclear family!

The French have the Phénix experimental fast reactor, which is cooled with 700 metric tonnes of sodium. It was closed in 1994 because of safety concerns, but plans were made in 1998 to restart the reactor. Another breeder, in the village of Crey-Malville near Lyon, is known as Superphénix (see sketch below). The reactor was built as a prototype for commercial breeders. It was designed to use mixed uranium/plutonium dioxide fuel

(MOX). It has 4000 metric tonnes of sodium, an amount so large that the reactor has high thermal inertia, a definite safety advantage. On shutdown, decay heat is removed by natural convection; no pumps are necessary. While operating at maximum power, it produced 1240 megawatts of electricity at 41.3% efficiency. After only 174 days of such operation, the reactor had to be shut down in 1990 owing to leakage of air into the sodium. During this and other less serious malfunctions, no radioactivity escaped. In 1994, Superphénix was reopened as a nonbreeder (that is, burner mode). This was achieved by replacing the first row of uranium blanket assemblies with steel neutron reflectors. As of 1996 the power was adjusted to 30% of maximum. The plan is to fission the transuranic wastes, that is, plutonium, etc. The French regard this step as one in managing the plutonium stockpile, which reached about 180 metric tonnes in 2000 (the British will have separated about 119 tonnes of plutonium by 2010). This program (using Superphénix alone) could at best dispose of a fifth of a metric tonne of plutonium per year, while around 10 metric tonnes are being produced per year by France's 54 reactors. In any case a new reprocessing unit would be required. In spite of the difficulties with their breeders, the French still regard spent fuel as a resource, not a waste. A vigorous opposition movement to Superphénix has arisen in France, aided by many in nuclear communities in other countries. The French decided to dismantle Superphénix by 2005 at a cost of about $1.5 billion.

The dangers of destroying large amounts of sodium metal were illustrated with the breeder at Cadarache, in southern France. In March 1994, during removal of the sodium, it was permitted to react with an alcohol, liberating hydrogen gas. The accumulated gas in air exploded, killing one engineer and injuring four others. Almost no radioactivity was ejected.

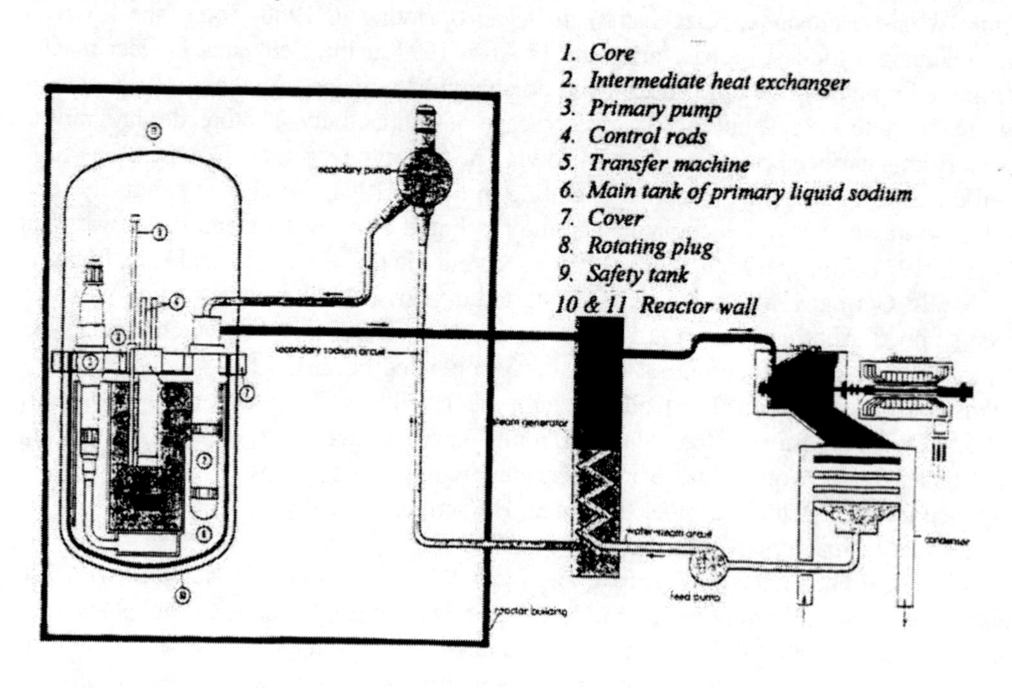

Schematic flow diagram of Superphénix breeder reactor

7-15 Japan's Nuclear Complexes

From the early post-war years (March 1954), Japan has been an enthusiastic supporter of nuclear power. This support derives from the lack of abundant energy supplies in the island country. But since about 1992, a series of accidents at nuclear facilities has been eroding popular support for the nuclear industry.

Along Japan's spectacular western coast in Fukui prefecture, there is a string of 15 nuclear reactors, dubbed "Nuclear Ginza" by the local residents. The prefecture receives some $100 million annually in subsidies and taxes on the electricity produced. It includes new fast breeder reactors (7-16).

The government has undertaken construction of a second titanic nuclear complex on the hatchet-shaped Shimokita peninsula, a bleak territory on the northern tip of Honshu in Aomori Prefecture. The complex comprises four pressurized-water reactors, an advanced plutonium-consuming thermal reactor at Oma, a uranium-235 enrichment facility, waste vitrification works, two radioactive waste repositories, a reprocessing facility at Rokkasho, and an experimental nuclear-powered ship program. All the physical structures were built to meet rigorous earthquake standards. The facilities on Shimokita Peninsula were subjected to scrutiny by no fewer than 1777 inspectors from the International Atomic Energy Agency during 1990 alone.

Opposition to the Shimokita Peninsula complex has been largely neutralized by government-sponsored benefits to local citizens, and by propaganda. Classy public buildings were constructed, and educational programs featuring attractive young women were presented. All opposing initiatives by the locals were mostly inactivated, sometimes by forceful dramatizations of their protests against bringing in electricity several generations ago. The nuclear lobby even invented a cartoon character, "Pluto Boy," who grumbles that plutonium has been given a bad press, and that the element does not produce cancer. This propaganda produced temporary acquiescence. The allegation that plutonium does not produce cancer is false. Secretary of the U.S. Department of Energy, Hazel O'Leary, issued a public rebuke to the Japanese corporation. In spite of the rewards to the people of Aomori Prefecture, when a British ship arrived in March 1998 bearing 30 tons of high-level nuclear waste from France, local farmers and antinuclear activists staged a sit-in and blocked unloading the ship for three days at the port in Rokkasho.

In summer 1996 an unprecedented event shook up Japan's nuclear establishment. The little town called Maki, situated on the west coast of Honshu about 200 miles north of Tokyo, held a referendum on whether to approve construction of a new nuclear reactor. The proposal to build the reactor was resoundingly defeated, 61% of the voters disapproving. While technically nonbinding, the mayor refused to sell the needed land to Tohoku Electric Company. A Government spokesman warned that blocking additional reactors by the public means that the public is also agreeing to use less electric power. Prime Minister Hashimoto added that "in the absence of substitutes, we must consider nuclear power the central part of our future energy strategy." Along the same lines, voters in Russia turned down a proposed reactor in December, 1996, in the Kostroma region 250 miles northeast of Moscow. The future of nuclear power in Japan has been clouded lately by increasingly doubtful public opinion. This downward turn of approval was accelerated by bungled cover-up attempts, such as the one after the accident at Monju (7-

16). Accidents at the Tokai-mura nuclear waste processing plant and loss of radioactive water from the Michama reactor near Osaka further eroded confidence.

The Japanese government might have no intention of stockpiling plutonium, but many tonnes will unavoidably accumulate unless a vigorous program of breeder reactors in "burner" mode (7-11) is undertaken. In "burner" mode for every metric tonne of plutonium consumed, about 0.6 metric tonne is produced. This is a source of worry since such large amounts of plutonium could be used to manufacture hundreds of nuclear bombs, although this would be difficult owing to the high plutonium-240 content. Instead of buying plutonium, Japan might be better advised to stockpile uranium. Nevertheless, the nonproliferation credentials of Japan are excellent, and their constitution stipulates that the country will never develop nuclear bombs. An influential Japanese diplomat remarked that "if you visited Hiroshima, you would understand that is beyond our imagination."

7-16 Japanese Breeder Reactors and the Tokai-mura Accidents

The world's most ambitious breeder reactor program is run by the Japanese. This development can be traced to a feeling of insecurity induced by the absence of significant energy resources in Japan, that is, coal, oil and gas, and also uranium and thorium. The amount of hydroelectric power is simply insufficient, and space to generate biomass and solar power is too limited. Imports account for approximately 80% of Japan's energy needs.

Monju reactor

Japan's Breeder Reactors—Japan's first breeder reactor, known as Joyo, was built at a nuclear complex near Tokai-mura, Ibaragi prefecture, on the east coast about 60 miles northeast of Tokyo. It started operations in 1977, producing 50 megawatts of electric power. Later its core was reconfigured to double the power, and this is to be increased to140 megawatts. Its fuel is 18% uranium-235.

Near Tsuruga, on the Sea of Japan about half way along the length of Honshu, there are two important reactors. One is known as Fugen, a heavy-water moderated reactor producing 148 megawatts of electricity. It uses mixed oxides of uranium and plutonium as fuel and thus helps consume surplus plutonium. The other reactor, named Monju (sketch), is a new fast breeder. It started operation at low power in April, 1994, as Buddhist monks and others protested outside the plant. The name Monju derives from Buddhist mythology, in which a Bodhisattva sits serenely on a lion's back and controls raw nature through wisdom. Whether this choice of names is appropriate remains to be seen. In early 1992, Japan imported a metric tonne of plutonium (containing 22% Pu-240) from France to fuel its fast breeder. The shipment by sea was the largest ever made, the cargo ship was accompanied by a protective convoy, and was monitored by satellite to insure that there was no terrorist attack. In summer 1994 Japan's Atomic Energy Commission announced a partial retreat from the unpopular, uneconomic strategy, and plans to convert Monju into nonbreeder mode at a later date. In December 1995 a leak occurred in the secondary cooling system, allowing a ton of molten sodium to escape. No radioactivity was released. The reactor had to be shut down for repairs.

Monju's concrete containment dome is tastefully colored leaf green. The installation is impressive from an engineering viewpoint. It is designed to produce 280 megawatts of electricity. The cooling system uses 1700 metric tonnes of molten sodium which is in two cooling circuits. Only the primary coolant enters the reactor's core. The temperature on entering is 397 °C and on exiting it is 529 °C. It is considered to be a prototype, not a commercial reactor. In 1992 the Japanese were negotiating with Russian engineers to aid in the fast breeder program.

In response to Japan's original nuclear fuel cycle system, in which plutonium was to be separated from spent fuel and blankets of breeder reactors, the intention to develop a new kind of reprocessing was announced in 1994. The new system, whose details are not yet public, is said to avoid isolation of plutonium of bomb quality. Neptunium and curium are evidently to be separated and used as nuclear fuel. Available information is as yet lacking to evaluate the proposed system.

Accidents at Tokai-mura—Japan's first nuclear reactor, JRR-1, which used an aqueous solution of uranyl sulfate (UO_2SO_4) as fuel, was built in Tokai-mura; the author was present when it first became critical (August 27, 1957). Today the city accommodates at least 15 separate nuclear agencies.

In March 1997 a fire broke out in a waste-treatment plant where residues with low levels of radioactivity were being imbedded in bitumen. The severity of the fire was under-estimated, and the burning bitumen exploded, causing quite a predicament.

Another accident was far more serious. The small fuel-preparation plant is operated by a subsidiary of the Sumitomo Metal Mining conglomerate. Each year, it produces 715 metric tonnes of uranium (3 to 5% U-235) for ordinary reactors and 3 tonnes of uranium for the Joyo breeder reactor. The uranium for the breeder reactor had been enriched to 18.8% uranium-235 in France; such a high level of enrichment means it is especially prone to criticality accidents, described in 5-22. At the Tokai-mura facility, the imported uranium hexafluoride (UF_6) is converted to uranium dioxide (UO_2), which is the chemical form of reactor fuel. One intermediate step required dissolving uranium oxide in nitric acid to form uranyl nitrate, adding ammonia to precipitate ammonium diuranate ("yellow cake"), decomposing this by heat to triuranium octoxide (U_3O_8), and reducing this to uranium dioxide by heating in hydrogen. The procedure for dissolving the oxide in nitric acid, as described in the work manual, was an elaborate one and this step was slow: the uranium oxide was added little by little, followed by piping the solution into the main tank using metering devices. The workers found this to be tedious, and apparently devised their own shortcut procedure of dissolving the uranium oxide in stainless steel buckets. This had been written up in what was later described as an "illegal manual." This particular day, September 30, 1999, their luck ran out. According to the published accounts, the main tank was enclosed in a larger tank which was flushed with cooling water. It held 2.5 kilograms of the uranium (18.8% U-235), and an additional 16 kg was added. Keep in mind that the critical masses of fissile materials in aqueous solution are much smaller than the critical mass in the free metallic form (9-2). A dry process, in which all aqueous solutions are avoided, would be much safer.

Complacence became the rule. The workers were wearing T-shirts and did not have the required radiation badges and protective gear. Their training regarding criticality accidents was shallow and minimized learning about similar accidents elsewhere in the world. When the excess uranium-235 was added, a chain reaction began instantly, accelerated by reflection of the neutrons released back into the central tank by the cooling water outside. The solution erupted out the top and produced the tell-tale blue flash. Falling back, a second supercritical reaction occurred , and then a third, etc., oscillating for nearly 20 hours until some boric acid was added (the boron absorbs the neutrons avidly, stopping the chain reaction). Neutron counters were located 1.7 and 2.0 kilometers from the building. The fast, penetrating neutrons were registered instantly by the two counters, appearing as sharp spikes in the graph. This was at 10:38 in the morning. Three workers received high radiation doses, later determined to be approximately as shown below:

Absorbed dose, rads

	Neutron	Gamma	Total
Worker 1	550	850	1400
Worker 2	290	450	740
Worker 3	81	130	211

Since the semilethal dose is 450 rads, it is not surprising that worker 1 died 83 days after the accident, and that worker 2 died after 211 days, despite the best of care. Worker 3 was discharged from the hospital after 82 days. Very little uranium or fission products escaped the building, but nearly 50 people outside received small doses by neutron exposure. Calculations showed that during the accident, approximately 0.74 milligram of U-235 underwent fission. Even this small quantity was enough to cause major damage. Siting the plant in a residential area came under heavy, well deserved criticism. This was Japan's worst nuclear accident.

The internal organs of the worker exposed most seriously, 35-year-old Hisashi Ouchi, began to fail, and he lost so much blood from his intestines that he received ten liters of blood daily by transfusion. He also underwent aggressive new therapy techniques, including stem-cell transfusion (5-20). Toward the end of November he lapsed into a coma, and died 83 days after the accident. Since he received excellent care, his death required considerable more time than is generally the case. The second workman passed away in April, 2000, while the third continued to improve.

Up until the accident, signs at the city limits proudly proclaimed: Tokai-mura, Town of Nuclear Energy. A couple of months after the accident, the signs were replaced with those reading: Welcome to Tokai-mura. Japan has come under criticism for hiring a very high fraction of their nuclear employees on a subcontract basis; these workers are less rigorously trained. Many such day laborers are assigned the most dangerous work, and their radiation exposure is frequently excessive.

7-17 Second and Third Generation Reactors

A new class of reactors, designed with safety uppermost in mind, is designated as "inherently safe," a term which some have criticized as meaning "accident-proof." The safety features arise from passive controls such as convection currents, and do not depend on motors or similar moving parts. A reactor of Swedish design has the improbable name "*p*rocess *i*nherent *u*ltimate *s*afety" reactor (acronym PIUS). Its rather radical design calls for the core to be immersed in a borax solution; in an emergency the core is flooded with the boron-rich water, stopping the chain reaction. There are no control rods. Cooling water circulated by convection takes over if pumps fail. It is said to be virtually immune to meltdown. These types of reactors are also more resistant to human tampering. Quite a number of designs are now available, all with passive stability. Some are gas-cooled. The sketch in section 7-20 shows a helium-cooled design. Such reactors produce 640 megawatts of electricity. Reactors with a power of about 650 megawatts or below can be operated without pumps for cooling since the amount of heat is low enough that convection alone can handle the situation. The water is also a bit cooler. The newer reactors can also last 60 years, and have a lower percentage of down time, around 15% versus 30% for older models.

Westinghouse's Advanced Passive reactor (AP600) has a power of 600 megawatts, and is a simplified pressurized water unit. It is much less expensive to build than earlier models. This type combines proven pressurized water reactor technology with passive safety systems. Each unit has electric power at 600 megawatts. But the high-power reactors have not lost favor completely. In 1993 an American consortium of 16 power companies announced intent to help underwrite a $100 million project to design a standardized, advanced type of reactor. It would be 1350- megawatt boiling water reactors designed by General Electric. More fabrication would be completed at automated manufacturing facilities with improved quality control and new types of stainless steel. Less labor would be required at the final construction site. Newer designs would have a larger core, a smaller mass of fission products, and much larger water reservoirs for the coolant, allowing a longer time to recover from emergencies. The AP600 is about a thousand times less likely than older models to experience a serious accident.

7-18 Natural Nuclear Reactors

When the pioneers of nuclear energy first considered reactors based on a self-sustaining chain reaction, they often asked themselves, "If all we must do is assemble several tons of uranium into one big pile, then why haven't huge deposits of uranium ore acted as nuclear reactors ages ago?" They answered that such uranium ores contained too much neutron-absorbing impurities to permit a chain reaction, and in addition most of the ores were dry, so that any fast neutrons had no water to moderate them. This appears to be generally the case. Although several suggestions of natural reactors had been made, it remained for an American scientist of Japanese origin, P. K. Kuroda, to publish a paper in 1956 pointing out that approximately two billion years ago the U-235 content of natural uranium must have been much higher than the present 0.711%, and that a pure ore deposit in the presence of water could have acted as a natural reactor. He predicted that natural nuclear reactors would one day be discovered. He was correct.

The country of Gabon lies on the west coast of Africa at the equator. Formerly a French colony, it has been selling its extensive uranium ores to France. The French use this ore as a source of uranium-235 in their enrichment facilities. But in 1972, a batch of ore arrived which had a slight deficiency of U-235. This aroused the suspicions of the analyst, but another sample proved to be so deficient that it caused alarm: it checked out repeatedly at only 0.434% U-235 (all figures by weight). At least one sample registered at 0.346%, somewhat less than half of the normal 0.711% level. Up until that time all other ores in the world had been found to contain 0.711% U-235, constant within about 0.01%. Indeed, even natural uranium in meteorites and in Moon rocks also were found to contain 0.711%. The low analytical results proved not to be in error. The physicist, H. Bouzigues, and the French Atomic Energy Commission resolved to solve the mystery.

Other ores began to arrive which were low in U-235, running 0.35 to 0.44%. This was a serious matter, since the price paid depends on the uranium-235 content. The area in Gabon called Oklo contains hundreds of thousands of tons of ore, in huge deposits which range from 10 to as high as 60% uranium. The yellow ore is found in slanting strata 1 to 10 meters thick in a sandstone matrix. The material is uraninite and is of sedimentary origin. Newly-evolved blue-green algae, one of the first life forms to produce oxygen by photosynthesis, raised the oxygen content of the water present and oxidized the primordial igneous ore bodies. This caused dissolution of uranium by conversion to its higher oxidation state, +6 (uranyl ion, UO_2^{2+}). The now-mobilized uranium washed to a river delta, where oxygen-poor organic matter prevailed. There is abundant evidence today that a kind of bacteria, with the unimposing name GS-15, actually utilize this oxidized uranium as a source of energy, reducing it to oxidation state +4; in this form it precipitates as uraninite, as mentioned above. This is a hydrated uranium dioxide. Reduced to insoluble form, it settled onto the sandstone strata, and eventually was covered. In time, geologic uplift resulted in the slanting strata inland observed today. We might note in passing that a "bioreactor" has been made which employs the microbe GS-15. Waste containing uranium in the oxidized state is allowed to run through the reactor, which precipitates the uranium out as hydrated dioxide. This process permits collection and disposal much easier.

Nuclear reactors occurred in Nature before the human race emerged.

The only apparent cause of a low uranium-235 content was that it is a consequence of its consumption in a natural nuclear reactor eons ago. No other explanation was credible, but this idea was so bizarre that it had to be tested by other means. To analyze the hypothesis the French first determined the geologic age of the ores, and found it to be 1.74 billion years, perhaps a little more, a time before mammals evolved. At that time, the uranium strata were under the ocean about 5000 meters. Today Oklo is about 225 miles inland.

Knowing the half-lives of both U-235 and U-238, they calculated that at that time the U-235 content must have been 3.0% (when our Earth was formed 4.6 billion years ago, U-235 made up 25% of the total uranium, but the lighter isotope has a shorter half-life). Studies were made of fission products which do not leach out with water, such as the rare-earth elements. Neodymium is a rare-earth element particularly well suited for the investigation. It is found in trace quantities all over the land areas of the Earth. It has seven stable isotopes, but only six of these are actual fission products. Neodymium from all other sources in the world contain 27% neodymium-142 and 12% neodymium-143. The lighter isotope is known not to be a fission product or any nuclide which decays to form it, and the Oklo neodymium is very low (less than 5%) in this variety, far less than the normal 27%. But 29% of the neodymium from fission is known to be neodymium-143, and the Oklo material contains 24% of this isotope, twice as much as the normal 12%. When the observed spectrum of neodymium isotopes is corrected for the natural composition, what is left corresponds exactly to the fission product spectrum. This involves consideration of the conversion of newly produced neodymium-143 into neodymium-144 by neutrons.

The French carried out some superbly competent science concerning these primordial reactors.

The uranium, abnormally low in its uranium-235, can be considered to be a natural depleted uranium, as opposed to the man-made material (4-20). It was found in at least 15 sites, and in each there was a spectrum of fission products so distinctive that only a long-lasting decay chain reaction could have accounted for it. Capture of neutrons by uranium-235 causes most to undergo fission, but about one atom in six does not, and merely exists as U-236 (half-life 23 million years). On decay, the product from U-236 is thorium-232, which is only weakly radioactive because of its extremely long half-life (14 billion years). This thorium is found only in the reactor zones. Of course, plutonium-239 was produced as in modern reactors; some underwent fission, but most decayed (alpha emission), producing uranium-235. Much other supporting evidence has been accumulated. It is impossible to escape the conclusion that these rich, reasonably pure uranium deposits were at one time natural nuclear reactors. No more can exist today because the uranium-235 content is too low.

The French scientists concluded that water acted as moderator; the ore contains both water of crystallization (6%) and ground water. The internal temperature of a typical natural reactor, which was under pressure, reached 250-370 °C. Six fossil reactors are known to have endured over a million years; there might be more not yet discovered. At least 5 tons of fission products were generated, as well as 2 tons of plutonium-239. This plutonium, bred in its natural nursery, has decayed away, since 70,000 half-lives have passed. The decay product of plutonium-239 is none other than uranium-235, so a constant enrichment in this nuclide occurred. The power in each reactor, which was generally a meter thick and 10 to 20 meters long, was typically 2 to 100 kilowatts. When our Earth was very young the proportion of uranium-235 was about 25%, 35 times higher than it is today, and natural reactors might have been fairly common.

Most of the fission products remained in the ore body despite being leached with water for years. The cesium-137 and strontium-90 did dissolve and drain away. The plutonium formed was immobilized. These data give valuable information concerning the disposal of radioactive waste (Chapter 8). The behavior of each nuclide has been studied with great care, but more research should be carried out. Regrettably, 14 of the 15 natural reactors have been destroyed by mining. The 15th, at Bangombé, is 30 kilometers southeast of Oklo. It should be preserved.

In 2003, geophysicist J. Marvin Herndon suggested another kind of natural reactor. His idea was that the metallic core of the Earth is a gigantic nuclear reactor using uranium fuel. He estimated its power at around four trillion watts, but fluctuating strongly with a period of about 200,000 years, corresponding to the reversal of the polarity of Earth's magnetic field. The evidence is weak, and most scientists who have considered the matter concluded that it is mostly speculation.

7-19 Some Special Nuclear Reactors

Since the Three Mile Island accident in 1979, American nuclear technology has accomplished significant improvements in safety and efficiency. Some of the most promising developments have been in reactors of the inherently safe type cooled with liquid sodium. Sodium has excellent nuclear properties, is high boiling, and does not attack stainless steel. Types such as the EBR-II reactor operate at atmospheric pressure. They have negative temperature coefficients of reactivity, that is, negative feedback. Simulated accidents showed that if the coolant is stopped, the reactor slowly shuts itself off.

The TRIGA Reactor—The TRIGA (for Training, Research, and Isotope production of General Atomics) reactor has aluminum-clad fuel rods containing uranium and zirconium hydrides. Thus the fuel contains its own moderator, hydrogen; cooling is accomplished with ordinary water. This arrangement makes the small reactor almost foolproof; rapid withdrawal of the control rods can be tolerated. In ordinary reactors, rapid removal of the control rods could lead to fuel melting, or worse. (Indeed, a small nuclear reactor at Jackass Flats, Nevada, was deliberately exploded in 1965 by rapid withdrawal of the control rods.)

In the TRIGA reactor, the uranium is 20% U-235, considered a medium level of enrichment. Commercial reactors use uranium enriched up to about 5% U-235; this is low-enriched uranium (LEU). If the enrichment in U-235 reaches approximately 50% or higher, it is high-enriched uranium (HEU). Bomb grade uranium is of course in this category, being near 93.5% U-235. Some versions of TRIGA can be pulsed, giving short, intense neutron bursts. An important use of TRIGA is to produce radioactive isotopes for medical use. Short lived nuclides are often preferred, and they can be made on site. The British VIPER reactor allows production of intense gamma rays and neutrons in millisecond bursts.

The Chinese built a small heavy-water reactor just outside Beijing in 1956. Most of the materials were supplied by the Soviets. The reactor was for training and production of radionuclides.

Relatively small nuclear reactors are used to power aircraft carriers, submarines, ice breakers, etc. The first nuclear-powered merchant ship, the N.S. (for Nuclear Ship) Savannah, was launched in 1955. This was part of the Atoms for Peace program.

Reactors as Neutron Sources—A special reactor called the Advanced Neutron Source was built in Oak Ridge. It has a power level of around 350 megawatts, and its neutron density or flux is 5 or 10 times that of any other reactor in the world. The Laue-Langevin reactor near Grenoble, France, produces the world's most intense neutron beams. It uses

93% uranium-235. Germany is planning to build a reactor in Garching, near Munich, which will still be another strong source of neutrons.

The N Reactor—The Hanford reservation in Washington, the site of the reactors on the Columbia River which made plutonium during World War II, is huge, being about half the size of the state of Rhode Island. It had one reactor operating up until recently. This one, started in 1963, was first called the New Products Reactor, then NP Reactor, and finally just the N Reactor. It used metallic uranium as fuel; the uranium and its zirconium cladding were coextruded. The sketch below gives a general view.

The reactor contained 1980 metric tonnes of graphite and 366 metric tonnes

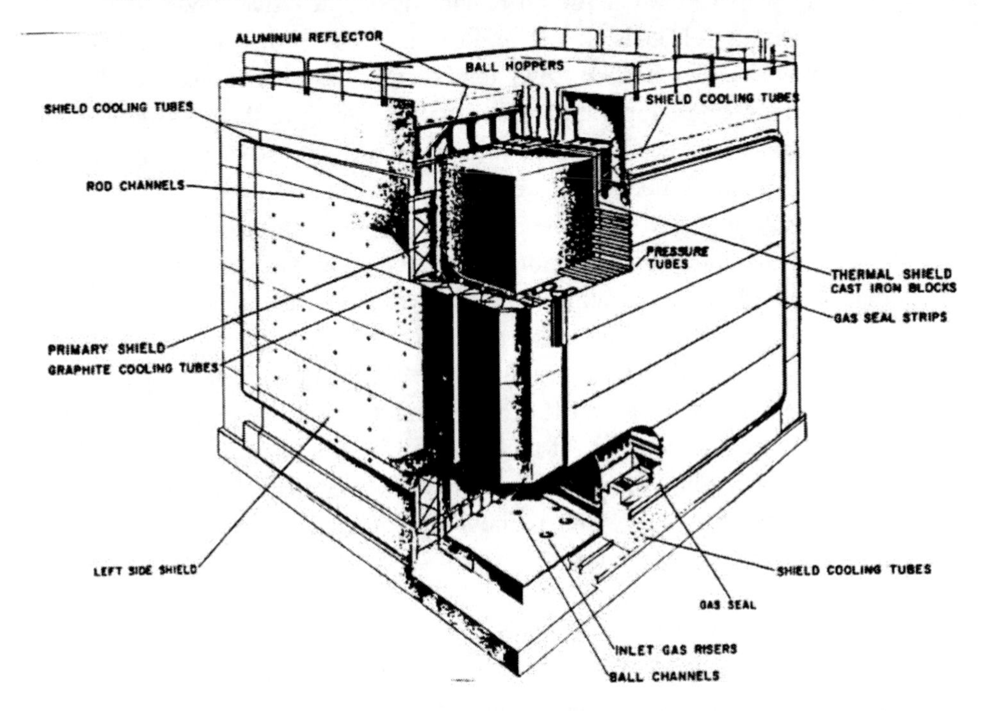

The N Reactor

of low-enriched uranium (0.94 to 1.25% U-235). When operating, one-third of the fuel was renewed every 33 days or so. The short fuel cycle kept the plutonium-240 content low. If consumed exhaustively, over a prolonged period, reactor fuel consisting of uranium metal tends to become distorted and is difficult to remove from the reactor. Cooling was effected by a network of zirconium tubing which held circulating water under pressure (to prevent boiling). This extremely hot water went through heat exchangers to create steam for the turbines. The total electricity production was 860 megawatts. The principal purpose of the plant, however, was to produce plutonium for weapons; about a quarter of American military plutonium was made here (the rest was made in the Savannah River reactors in South Carolina). During the ten-year

It is a dangerous precedent to produce commercial electricity and weapons plutonium in the same reactor at the same time.

period 1976-1985, 4804 kilograms of weapons-grade plutonium was made. At times, tritium was also produced at the N Reactor; in this mode, it was said to be a "triple-play reactor," that is, it produced plutonium, tritium, and electricity.

There was no containment dome over the N Reactor. Instead it had a "confinement" vented to the outside through filters. The graphite core was in a helium atmosphere. Elaborate safety measures had been provided. Aside from automatic control rods, the reactor could be scrammed (suddenly stopped) by dropping in balls of boron carbide. Two cooling systems with independent diesel power were on standby. Each fuel channel was monitored during operation for escaping radioactivity to detect failed zirconium cladding. Unlike the Chernobyl reactor, it had negative *power feedback* as a function of temperature. That is, if the temperature rose above the specified level, the power automatically fell until normal temperature was reestablished. This was accomplished because rising temperatures caused more steam in the boiling tubes, and since fewer water molecules were present in a given volume of steam than in liquid water, there was less neutron moderation, and thus a lower fission rate. This situation is also described by the term *negative void coefficient*. In spite of these qualities, many feel that the reactor represented an unacceptable risk, since there was some resemblance to the Chernobyl reactor. After all, uranium metal is pyrogenic. Just about the time of the Chernobyl disaster in 1986, the author was a member of a team inspecting the N Reactor; a recommendation to shut it down was submitted. In 1988 the Energy Department did just that. The reactor's budget was tapered off in 1993, and dropped to maintenance levels in 1994. As of 1996, the accumulated spent fuel was still in storage under water, and signs of corrosion are now evident. The material consists of 2133 metric tonnes of irradiated fuel in the form of metallic uranium. This is about 80% of the 2646 metric tonnes of spent fuel inventory in Department of Energy facilities.

Reactors in Space—The USSR used small reactors in orbit to power its Radar Ocean Reconnaissance Satellites (ROSATS). They were used to track U.S. naval ships. The earliest was called the Romashka, which generated about 500 watts of electric power. The Topaz reactors were larger, producing up to perhaps 10 kilowatts of electrical energy. They had about 12 kilograms of uranium carbide fuel, 90% uranium-235. The United States purchased a small (1 ton) Soviet Topaz-2 reactor in 1991 for $14,000,000. While it is of the advanced type used in satellites orbiting the Earth and in outer space, the objective was in part to study Soviet technology; but the main purpose was use in the Star Wars program (10-14). Scrutiny of Topaz-2 disclosed that here was an area where Soviet technology exceeded the American.

The Soviets also introduced the Cosmos series of reactors into space. One of these, number 954, was of a different design. In 1978 a Cosmos broke up over Canada, and analysis of the recovered fragments revealed that it contained a uranium-molybdenum alloy (uranium enriched to 90% U-235), and beryllium neutron reflectors.

The United States has mostly relied on radioisotope generators for use in outer space. Plutonium-238 dioxide serves as a favorite power source in SNAP-9A and Cassini (see 6-37B). SNAP is an acronym meaning Systems for Nuclear Auxiliary Power.

The near orbit regions in space, ranging from about 125 to 600 miles above Earth, are today cluttered with about 7700 objects big enough to track, and thousands more of smaller objects. Some of these are radioactive (mostly reactor cores).

7-20 High-Temperature Gas-Cooled Reactors

General Atomics designed the Modular High Temperature Gas-Cooled Reactor, which uses helium as a coolant. Modular reactors operating at high temperatures and cooled by gas have attracted much attention lately. The entire core and primary cooling loop are enclosed in a heavy steel vessel to prevent release of fission products in case of an accident. It is cooled with helium gas, which carries the heat through a heat exchanger to water coolant, generating steam. Helium is the one substance not affected by high-intensity gamma rays. Fuel pellets, encapsulated in graphite balls coated with silicon carbide, are introduced into a pebble-bed reactor core. The fuel is of two types: fissile uranium oxocarbide, enriched to 20% uranium-235, and fertile thorium dioxide. The core is refueled every 20 months. Provisions are made to remove decay heat in case of shut-down. There are no valves, circulating fans, or other active components. This type, producing electricity at power levels up to roughly 100 megawatts, has proven to be considerably more efficient (as high as 40%) in electricity production than the pressurized water reactor. The sketch shows one design. The high-temperature gas reactors are very accident resistant. They have strongly negative temperature coefficients of reactivity. Tests in Germany have demonstrated that loss of all coolant causes the reactor to shut down automatically. Some of the newer reactors display a certain artistry, unlike their graceless ancestors.

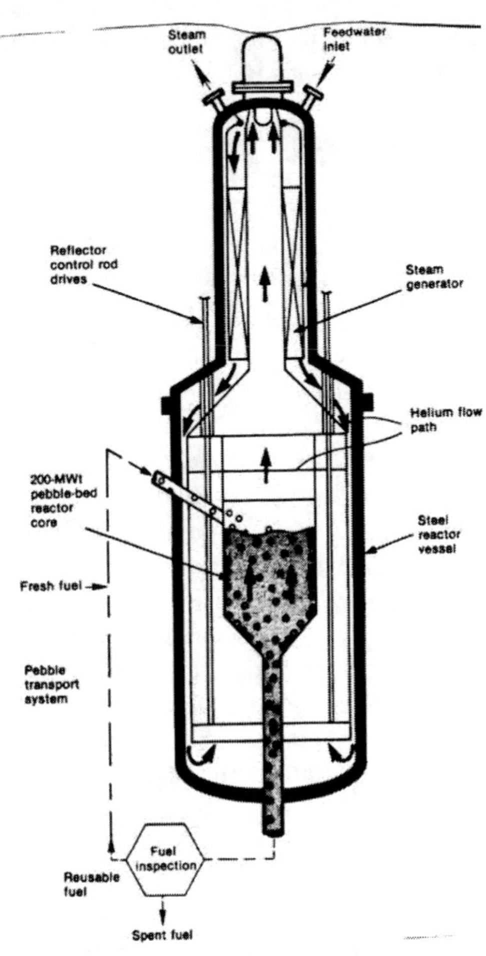

High temparature gas-cooled reactor

7-21 Reactor Safety

Being aware of the hazards of high-level radioactivity, nuclear engineers have designed reactors with extreme safety features and with redundancy, that is, with backup safety systems if the first should fail. The result of this is an excellent, but not perfect, record in safety. There have been many fatalities in mining uranium, some from accidents and some delayed deaths caused by radon inhalation. Other fatalities have resulted from falls from scaffolding in constructing cooling towers, in uranium-235 enrichment work, and in the Soviet accident at Chernobyl. This last emphasizes that the potential for an overwhelming catastrophe still exists. Most shutdowns arise from the same sources as in conventional coal- or oil-burning electricity generating facilities: pump leakage or failures, plugged or ruptured pipes, or fire. The safety and nuclear waste disposal issues are paramount in motivating the knowledgeable and able antinuclear community. No man-made system is 100% safe. The more effort put into any engineering plan, the safer it becomes, but the costs rise in proportion, or higher. If we examine nuclear reactors and radioactive waste disposal systems, we can decide what level of safety is appropriate, and then attain that level by corresponding expenditures. This could well price these endeavors out of the market in the absence of political considerations. The term "human error" is often used, and failure of a mechanical component can in a sense be ultimately ascribed to human error.

Large reactors have three kinds of control rods. What are called shim rods are used to give gross adjustments in power. Finer adjustments are made with control rods which number in the thousands to insure evenly-distributed power production. About 10 "scram" rods are activated by gravity and springs in case an emergency shutdown is necessary. These can arrest the chain reaction within three seconds. In water-cooled reactors chemical scramming can be effected by switching in a boric acid solution; the boron rapidly captures neutrons and paralyzes the chain reaction. But in all of these cases, it is necessary to continue cooling even after shutdown, because the radioactive decay of the massive amount of fission products of course continues. This decay heat amounts to approximately 10% of the normal energy production, drops to around 7% in perhaps half an hour, and to only 1% within several hours. Modern reactors are designed so that rising temperature causes the neutron multiplication factor to fall, and thus it goes below 1 and the chain reaction automatically stops. In the case of water-moderated and -cooled reactors, this negative void coefficient is caused mostly by the formation of steam bubbles or voids and to a lesser degree by the expansion of water as it heats up. Both effects reduce the amount of water in a given volume, and lessen the neutron moderation and reactor power. Thus there is a sort of negative feedback. Reactors with graphite moderators exhibit positive void coefficients and positive feedback, and as the temperature rises, the power rises, making their smooth operation more difficult; in fact, they can go out of control.

After the chain reaction is stopped, heat production from radioactive decay continues.

An important source of trouble is failure of the cooling system. At the Three Mile Island pressurized-water reactor, this type of emergency scrammed the reactor in 1979, but since cooling could not continue, the heat from rapid decay of fission products continued to build up until the core partially melted. An unexpected surge in power (such as from loss of water coolant and moderator) can also be a cause of a reactor accident, and probably was the case at Chernobyl. Nuclear Regulatory Commission rules require that for each step which must be taken during the course of an accident, there must be two or more safety measures, either of which is sufficient to prevent escape of significant radioactivity. All experts in nuclear matters agree that no reactor can detonate as a nuclear bomb.

While reactors can withstand all but the most destructive earthquakes, their emergency cooling units are probably more vulnerable, and are certainly susceptible to sabotage. On January 31, 1986, an earthquake registering 5.0 on the Richter scale struck ten miles from the reactor at Perry, Ohio, 35 miles from Cleveland. The shock exceeded the design capacity of the reactor, and caused numerous leaks and cracks. But the jolt also knocked out nearby roads and bridges, thwarting evacuation plans. The savage earthquake of 1988 in Armenia had little effect on a 400-megawatt reactor west of Yerevan; nevertheless, this reactor and a second similar one were shut down. This deprived Armenia of a third of its electricity. Incidentally, even the Russians agree that safety in American nuclear reactors greatly exceeds that in their country.

Japanese reactors have about the best safety record of all. Shielding is so effective that each worker at power plants receives an annual dose below 50 millirems, about half that of American workers. In Japan, the rate of fuel leakage is less than one per million fuel rods, and the automatic scram rate is only once per two years for each reactor. The Japanese experience helps point the way to safer reactor operation. Still, there was an accident at the Mihama reactor near Osaka in February, 1991. A few tons of slightly radioactive water was released, the most serious case in Japan except for the one in Tokai-mura (7-16). One consequence has been a stimulus to Japan's growing anti-nuclear movement. In 1992 an accident at the Okuma reactor resulted when an engineer accidentally left an aluminum rod in the electrical console of the control bank, causing the failure of three pumps simultaneously. This resulted in the automatic emergency core-cooling system to shut the reactor down. But confidence in nuclear power is still strong, and Japan plans to build 40 more reactors to bring electricity production from nuclear sources up to 43% of the total.

More nuclear reactors spawn anti-nuclear sentiments

The Institute of Nuclear Power Operators was established in Atlanta after the Three Mile Island accident. It is a forum to exchange experiences and to pool information about running nuclear plants. It cooperates closely with the World Association of Nuclear Operators, with regional headquarters in Atlanta, Moscow, Tokyo, and Paris. This organization was formed directly after the Chernobyl accident. It uses a scale (the International Nuclear Event Scale) running from 1 to 7 to quantify accidents at nuclear reactors. According to this Three Mile Island rated 5 and Chernobyl rated 7. With accumulating experience, the probability of nuclear disasters is falling.

The most modern reactors incorporate features of intrinsic (also called passive) safety. These internal governors provide for emergency cooling by convection and do not require power. They are simpler and more rugged than the reactors built in the 1960s and 1970s, and their life spans are longer, perhaps as long as 60 years. They use modular designs which permit more construction in factories and less at the building site.

7-22 Decommissioning Reactors

Commercial nuclear plants built before about 1980 were generally licensed to operate for approximately forty years. It is too soon to see how many reactors last that long: by 1995, only one had survived more than thirty years. The Connecticut Yankee reactor was shut down in 1996 after 29 years of service. This reduced the number of operating reactors in the U.S. to 109. Only one plant has been fully decommissioned. In 1988 the Nuclear Regulatory Commission mandated that public utility companies make deposits into a trust fund to cover the costs of decommissioning. The companies started by putting in 0.08 cent per kilowatt-hour, but that has proven insufficient, and the fund is at least $25 billion short. In 2000 decommissioning Unit I of the three reactors at San Onofre, California, commenced. The cost of dismantling this 540-megawatt reactor is estimated to be about $460 million, and the time required will be approximately six years.

The spent fuel is removed before moth balling the reactors in preparation for dismantling. One danger in the work arises from the long-lived isotopes of nickel and niobium, which are components in the steel used in construction, and arise from neutron activation. The danger to workers is not great because the steel is inert, resembling stainless steel, and thus radioactive nuclides do not wash out.

The British are exploring a scheme in which, at the end of a reactor's useful life, the fuel is removed and the site is simply covered with earth. It would be planted with vegetation. The site would be kept under surveillance and monitored for around 100 years, after which it could be dismantled with minimum exposure to the work crew. Funds to cover the costs would be required to be set aside into the custody of independent trustees. The French set 15% of their nuclear budget aside for investment in safety, for handling nuclear waste and conducting research in this area, and decommissioning plants at the end of their working lives.

7-23 Accidents at Nuclear Reactors

A one billion watt (electric) reactor has about 5 billion curies of radioactive material in the core, and many of these stations are near population centers. These facts alone show that the potential for a catastrophe exists. During the first 30 years of reactor operation, there were only four fatalities directly associated with commercial reactors in the U.S.; additional deaths from other aspects (such as mining uranium, uranium-235 enrichment, building reactors, and operation of military reactors) have taken place. Fatalities also occurred at the Chernobyl reactor in Ukraine during Soviet times. Of course, accidents occur in all other aspects (nonnuclear) of energy production. For example, in 1988 an explosion on a North Sea oil rig killed 166 persons.

Contrary to the beliefs of some, deaths have occured in American reactor work.

Considering the direct damage which radioactive materials inflict on living things, there are four elements among the fission products which are especially dangerous. These are iodine, cesium, strontium, and barium. Iodine is an indispensable element; quickly taken up from food; it is carried by the blood to the thyroid gland, where it becomes an essential component of the hormone thyroxine. If the iodine is a radioactive isotope, the body assimilates it just the same. This causes irradiation and possibly enlargement and cancer of the thyroid gland. With proper treatment it is usually not fatal. Cesium is a metal resembling potassium. Its ion mimics the potassium ion, and thus goes all over any living body which absorbs it, especially the liver, spleen, and muscles. It is cesium-137 from the 1954 hydrogen bomb test which contributes heavily to the radioactivity of the atoll

Four nasty nuclides

of Bikini today. Similarly, strontium-90 mimics calcium, essential for bone growth and other biological functions; thus radiostrontium is a dangerous material. It lodges in the bone marrow and ultimately causes leukemia. The element barium resembles strontium.

In addition, the two elements krypton and xenon are noble gases, that is, they are chemically inert. If inhaled in sufficient amounts (and they are produced in large amounts), irradiation of the lungs could induce cancer, but the risk is low. Studies of the Marshallese people who were exposed to radioactive fallout in 1954 showed that in addition to the above cases, the rare-earth elements are also absorbed by the body. Citizens have a justifiable reason to be fearful of exposure to all these nuclear rogues.

There are many possible kinds of accidents at nuclear reactors; some have already occurred, and others remain hypothetical. Possibilities include: loss of coolant from plugged lines or pump failure; core meltdown; steam line break; flooding; fire; faulty fuel rod handling; damage from earthquake; steam generator tube rupture; transient power surge without quenching the chain reaction; reactor vessel rupture; steam explosion; high-pressure molten core ejection; containment failure; and sabotage of essential equipment (this last is not accidental). During the great flood of the Mississippi River in 1993, the reactor at Prairie Island, Minnesota, experienced a critical test. Massive dikes, hastily built, saved the reactor from disaster. Accidents at nuclear waste disposal or storage sites have also occurred.

The accident at Sellafield

The accident at the Sellafield (formerly Windscale) reactor in England occurred in 1957. Accumulated Wigner energy (7-7) in the graphite moderator of the air-cooled reactor was released when a faulty maneuver by a physicist caused uranium fuel cartridges to burst and burn. Graphite is difficult to ignite in air, but once started it stubbornly resists being extinguished. Burning uranium ignited the graphite and large quantities of fission products were ejected into the environment. Estimates of the amounts are: iodine-131, 20,000 to 30,000 curies; tellurium-132, 12,000 curies; cesium-137 and -144, 680 curies; strontium-89 and -90, 82 curies. In addition, the British were making a special polonium isotope (polonium-210) for nuclear bomb neutron generators, and much of this was also released. An area of 200 square miles was contaminated and declared off limits for 25 days. Important vital statistics on the accident were made available, but not until 30 years later! The last reports were that there were 260 cases of thyroid cancer and 13 deaths attributable to the accident. In 1993 reports appeared that the amount of strontium reported to be released in the 1950s might have been too low by 75%. The Windscale incident was the world's worst nuclear accident except for Chernobyl. While a few graphite-moderated reactors are still in use, they are operated at a temperature high enough so that Wigner energy cannot be stored. Even so, excessive exposure of graphite to neutrons causes it to suffer radiation damage and become distorted.

A steam explosion (7-24) took place at an SL-1 Navy reactor near Idaho Falls, Idaho, and killed three servicemen in 1961. The experimental reactor, used to supply power to a military installation, experienced the accident owing to human error (the central control rod was accidentally withdrawn much too fast; it had stuck and its chain hoist was jerked). The control rod skewered an operator, pinning him to the ceiling. The reactor used 93% U-235. Between 5 and 10% of the fission products were released.

After the end of the Cold War, some details became available of another accident in a Soviet nuclear-powered submarine in the summer of 1961. The vessel, known as the K-19, was constructed hurriedly in a slipshod manner. It carried three nuclear warheads. A steam pipe ruptured while the crew was on a training exercise in the north Atlantic. Since the cooling system was now faulty, a meltdown was feared. The captain sent a series of volunteer brigades into the engine room full of radioactive steam, each for ten-minute periods, and sufficient repairs were made to avoid loss of the submarine. All of the 22 volunteers died, eight in a matter of days, and the rest within two years. The dose of radiation was about three times the lethal level for the eight victims who perished within days. Their skin reddened, their features became so swollen that they could not be recognized, and they died in agony. In May 1968 a serious accident on an experimental sub, the K-27, killed five crew members. In April 1989 the Soviet nuclear submarine Komsolets sank off the coast of Norway, with loss of 42 lives. It carried two nuclear torpedoes containing 12.7 kilograms of plutonium. So far there has been very little loss of radioactive material from the vessel. Another disaster whose clock is ticking is near Murmansk, where a ship called the *Lepse* is a repository for all sorts or spent fuel. About 50 nuclear subs still with their fuel are laid up in the harbor.

In August 1985 at Chazma Bay near Vladivostok, Soviet sailors were refueling a Victor-class nuclear submarine. The reactor went out of control, belching steam and fire. Ten men were killed instantly. Vladivostok Bay is now an environmental nightmare full of the skeletons of corroded combat vessels. Another nuclear submarine lies in Golden Horn Bay, near Vladivostok. Bolshoi Kamen, a city of 42,000, was the site where the reactors of nuclear submarines were serviced. The tombstones in its cemetery record its grim story: the workers died at ages between 30 and 40.

In March 1994, on board a French nuclear submarine in the Mediterranean, a mishap caused superheated steam to roar out of control inside the turbine room. Ten sailors were killed. Partial melting of a core also took place at Saint-Laurent, France, in 1969.

In 1965, an American plutonium-test reactor, using mixed uranium/plutonium dioxide fuel, underwent an episode during a test of faulty fuel rods. One rod had been made defective by drilling a small hole in the zirconium cladding. The result was that fission products were ejected, and settled as particulate matter inside the containment. The core of an experimental breeder reactor partially melted at the Fermi installation near Detroit in 1972. More than 50,000 gallons of water containing radioactive waste spilled into the Mississippi River in 1971. At Brown's Ferry, Alabama, a large reactor was shut down in 1975 by a fire; only luck prevented a disaster. Costs of $150 million were involved.

Accident on purpose

A few of the other reactor accidents which have occurred include those at Lemont, Illinois (1952, blue glow, four employees irradiated); Irwin, Tennessee (1979, 1000 people contaminated slightly); Sequoyah (Tennessee Valley Authority, 1981); Ginna, N. Y., (1982); Oak Harbor, Ohio (1985); and in several foreign countries. External water coolers are subject to fouling by algae or other forms of water life, and several closures have arisen from this cause. On December 9, 1986, a 16-inch pipe carrying water at 350 °F, broke open at the Surry reactor near Newport News, Virginia. The superheated water

Fatalities at an American reactor

flashed into steam and burned eight workers, four of whom died. The pipe wall was originally one-half inch thick, but after 16 years service had thinned to one-sixteenth inch. It seems as if the stresses on equipment in nuclear reactors from radiation and high temperatures result in more rapid deterioration than expected. In 1988 the Department of Energy released a great deal of information concerning accidents and leaks at the facilities at Hanford, Savannah River, Fernald, and other sites. The Fernald uranium processing plant known as the Feed Materials Production Center, leaked uranium over the surrounding Ohio countryside for years. Compensation payments to Fernald's neighbors have started.

The most serious accident in the U.S. to date was that at Three Mile Island, and the worst in history was that at Chernobyl, USSR. There have been at least three cases of sabotage by disgruntled or unbalanced insiders at American nuclear facilities. The danger remains, and is not imaginary, but security steps have been taken to make such events extremely rare.

7-24 The Accident at Three Mile Island

Three Mile Island, in the Susquehanna River near Middletown, Pennsylvania, is the site of two pressurized-water reactors with 1.7 billion watts (electric) total power. At 4:00 a.m. on March 28, 1979, the most serious reactor accident in American experience began to unfold in Unit 2. It had been in operation at full power for only three months. Two weeks later a Presidential Commission was established to investigate the matter. The general conclusion was that the incident was initiated by human error, which triggered mechanical failure, which in turn was greatly worsened by more human errors responding to it. Unprecedented public concern and anxiety followed.

100-Alarm emergency

There is some doubt as to the exact cause of the event which initiated the mishap, but it was probably associated with the maintenance of the ion-exchange resin used to remove the small amounts of fission products which leak from the fuel rods into the coolant water. Some resin particles had clogged a transfer line, and a faulty valve had allowed some water to leak into the resin control system. This triggered the automatic shutdown of a feedwater pump, which in turn stopped a series of others. The trouble continued to escalate with the station operating at 97% of capacity. With the flow of water in the primary coolant loop stopped, the steam turbines automatically shut down. The temperature and pressure of the coolant water in the core began to rise rapidly. A pressure-relief valve opened and water began to flow out of the coolant lines into a tank. The relief valve failed to close when the pressure dropped sufficiently, but no signal indicated this fact. More than a hundred alarms sounded, creating an eerie aria and giving far more information than the luckless operators could handle. Here is a chronology of events with time elapsed after the start:

8 seconds: Reactor was scrammed automatically and the fission chain reaction arrested. The heat produced was now only from decay of fission products, and while this was only 6 or 7% of the former level, without cooling the core would melt.

5 minutes: The temperature in the coolant system rose so high that despite the high pressure, steam formed and displaced coolant water. Operators were misled into thinking there was plenty of water inside.

8 minutes: Operators discovered that no emergency feedwater was reaching the steam generators.

11 minutes: An alarm signaled high water in the containment, indicating a bad leak or break. Later it was found that enough water to cover the floor to 8.5 feet had flowed out.

1 hour: Water was actively boiling out of the core, even into the coolant pumps, causing them to vibrate dangerously. They were shut down. The water level soon sank below the level of the fuel rods, allowing them to heat up.

1 hour 45 minutes: The steam generators boiled dry.

2 hours: Radiation inside the containment and auxiliary building was noted. More than half of the fuel rods were uncovered.

2 hours 20 minutes: The pressure-relief valve was closed manually, but one-third of the coolant water had drained out. The core was heating up. Zirconium cladding began to be oxidized.

3 hours 20 minutes: A monitor in the dome of the containment registered 800 rads/hour. Radioactive water began to leak from the auxiliary building into the environment. Oxides of uranium and zirconium began to melt.

3 hours 45 minutes: The molten mass broke free and fell to the bottom of the reactor. About 20 tons had melted.

8 hours: Some spots in the auxiliary building registered 1000 rads/hour.

10 hours: The extremely hot zirconium cladding had reacted with the water to form hydrogen. This caused an explosion, not very powerful, to occur inside the containment, which could withstand a much more energetic explosion.

Finally the operators got the high-pressure injection pumps working, and began to cool the core down. The level of radiation in the control room grew to unacceptable heights. Off site, in Middletown about three miles north, the reading was 1 to 2 millirads per hour. Helicopters detected quite high radiation levels above Unit 2 of Three Mile Island. The Governor anguished over whether to evacuate the population within a radius of ten miles. He was sure that there would be a toll of fatalities in moving babies in incubators, people in intensive care units, the elderly, etc., in heavy traffic. General evacuation was not ordered, but it was recommended that pregnant women and very young children move farther away. Approximately 90% of the citizens of Goldboro (1or 2 miles from the reactor) left on their own. Contradictory announcements from public officials, the utility company executives, and the Nuclear Regulatory Commission (none of whom had the credentials of a rock star or television anchor), as well as ignorance of how serious the accident might be, conspired to degrade public confidence and impose anxiety and severe mental stress.

Anxiety from not knowing the facts

Nearly a quarter of a million one-ounce bottles of potassium iodide were rushed into Middletown. Taking a small dose of this substance by mouth is known to saturate the thyroid gland with iodine, which practically blocks uptake of radioactive iodine. Use of the potassium iodide proved to be unnecessary.

The cost of cleaning up the Three Mile Island facility, including payments for replacement power, is estimated at over one billion dollars. Eight years after the accident, examination showed that about 70% of the core had been damaged, and about 40% had actually melted, including 10% of the fuel rods. This means that the temperature exceeded 2840 °C (5144 °F). A core meltdown was formerly considered the ultimate disaster in power reactors, but this case was not really very close. Recent studies indicate that in a worst case, a molten core of mostly uranium dioxide might penetrate the reactor floor and earth for a few feet, and then slowly solidify. Breaching of the containment would constitute a worse accident, but this was most unlikely. Incidentally, the water in the Three Mile Island reactor assembly eight years after the accident was found to be swarming with hardy bacteria which fed on the hydraulic fluid that had leaked in. The workers who removed the spent fuel received an extra radiation dose of about 6 millirads per day. The deadly remains of the core and other debris were freighted to Idaho for disposal at taxpayer expense.

How close to a meltdown?

The containment, the auxiliary building, and the primary water loop which was inside the core and connected to a heat exchanger outside, were contaminated with a broth of fission products equivalent to millions of curies. Of 64 million curies of fission-product iodine in the reactor core, only a tiny fraction—15 curies—escaped into the environment (some revised calculations gave higher values). Roughly 35 curies of other fission products got out, not counting a much greater quantity of krypton and xenon which escaped, 13 million curies. This must have added to the world level of atmospheric radioactivity, increasing the probability of lung cancer ever so little (though negligible compared to the damage caused by smoking tobacco). The highest dose to a person over a 30-day period was less than 0.1 rad. Governments of all countries which push nuclear energy or weapons have consistently minimized the dangers to the public from small levels of radiation.

The containment, a prison for fission products

Just the same, calculations have been made of the increased number of cancers induced into the population by this small exposure. Out of a million people receiving 20 millirads, the estimate is that there will be eventually about 74 additional fatalities; there would be 200,000 such cases anyway. No one can prove that any particular cancer was caused by the accident. General Public Utilities, the owner of the Three Mile Island plants, settled claims against it for $20 million out of court in order to avoid a trial. By the fall of 1990 a study disclosed that any increase in the cancer rate was barely measurable, if at all. In fact, people living near the site were subjected to higher radiation doses in their homes, mostly from radon, than they received as a result of the accident. Predictions of the amount of iodine which would escape into the atmosphere in an accident of the Three Mile Island type were thousands of times higher than the amount actually released. Investigators concluded that, unlike the Windscale and Chernobyl reactors (in which oxidizing conditions prevailed), reactors such as those at Three Mile Island had reducing (opposite of oxidizing) conditions and that most iodine was therefore fixed as a solid iodide. Since there is a tenfold excess of cesium over iodine, the iodine exists as cesium iodide, a relatively nonvolatile salt. Free (elemental) iodine easily vaporizes. There still exists the possibility of forming aerosols of solid fission products during a core meltdown, which would include any cesium iodide present.

Valiant efforts have been made to assess the actual danger from accidents at nuclear reactors. These calculations are fraught with enormous uncertainties. A worst-case scenario reported by the Nuclear Regulatory Commission postulated that the following percentages of the total fission products could be released: krypton/xenon, 100%; iodine, 30 to 70%; cesium, 30 to 70%; tellurium, 30 to 70%; and strontium, 1 to 10%.

A steam explosion results when water contacts a mass of exceedingly hot matter. In a true core meltdown, a hundred-ton mass of lava-like molten metal and slag might penetrate the heavy steel bottom of the core and go on to the concrete floor. If a melted core drops into water, a nasty steam explosion would result. A violent steam explosion might propel the heavy reactor core as a missile through the containment roof. Examination in 1990 of the steel vessel holding the core of the Three Mile Island reactor disclosed that it had come through almost unscathed.

The accident dealt a shattering blow to the American nuclear industry. No new reactors have been ordered in the U.S. since that time. There is no doubt that after Three Mile Island, the media began to stress the negative aspects of nuclear power, even to the point of morbidity. Polls indicated that in the public mind, nuclear reactors represent a tremendous danger, while in fact smoking, narcotics, alcohol, guns, and cars have proven to be far more hazardous.

7-25 The Accident at Chernobyl

Fission products respect no borders.

On April 26, 1986, radiation monitors at a nuclear power plant at Forsmark in Sweden began to sound alarms. It appeared as if radioactive materials were being carried by air currents from the southeast. Krypton-85 and iodine-131 were detected, certain signs of trouble at a nuclear reactor. Later, radioactive isotopes of xenon, cesium, barium, and even curium were found. Still later iodine-134 was also detected, and since this nuclide has the short half-life of 53 minutes, the meaning was that substantial quantities of fission products must have been released. The most serious industrial accident in history had just occurred.

It was soon realized that the source of the radioactivity was Chernobyl (Chornobyl in Ukrainian) in the Soviet Ukraine, at a site about 60 miles north of Kiev, where there was a complex of four large reactors, with two more under construction. Each produced 925 megawatts of electric power and was cooled by river water which flows into the Pripyat and Dnieper rivers. Reactors of this type, identified by the initials RBMK (from the Russian *Reactor Bolshoi Moschnosti Kanalynyi,* meaning Channelized Large Power Reactor), are of a highly automated design which the Soviets considered so safe that no containments were built over them, even those constructed after the Three Mile Island accident. Instead, they were equipped with a confinement, which is much less substantial. The philosophy of redundant safety systems was not followed in constructing Soviet reactors.

The RBMK reactors have graphite as the neutron moderator. They are boiling-water reactors, and thus the water coolant is at a relatively low pressure, permitting boiling in the 1660 zirconium pressure tubes. Actually, the metal is not pure zirconium since it contains a small proportion of niobium, the element one space to the right of zirconium in the periodic table; this is the Soviet equivalent of the American Zircaloy. In RBMK reactors, water serves as a heat transfer agent, and plays only a small role as moderator. The steam exits at 284 °C (543 °F). Each reactor has approximately 190 metric tonnes of uranium (2% U-235) as the dioxide in 1700 metric tonnes of graphite. The reactor core is almost 39 feet in diameter and 23 feet high. It sits in a steel-lined concrete shaft about 66 feet high and 56 feet in diameter. The fuel elements are in nearly 1700 vertical channels and can be replaced without shutting down the reactor. Power is regulated by 211 control rods containing boron carbide. The reactor vault is in an inert atmosphere consisting of helium and nitrogen. The figure shows the general layout. Fifteen or so of the 50 reactors in the former USSR were of this type. Unlike the N Reactor, they do not produce plutonium for weapons. They are capable of producing tritium, a component of hydrogen bombs.

RBMK reactor at Chernobyl

In water-moderated, water-cooled reactors, such as the type at Three Mile Island, a rise in temperature causes a decrease in power (*negative feedback*; 7-19, 7-29). In contrast, the Chernobyl reactors have an instability which is dangerous, especially at low power. Liquid water in the boiler tubes is largely displaced with steam, resulting in higher reactivity, that is, the power increases and this causes still more steam and less liquid water (*positive feedback* or *void coefficient*). The graphite continues to moderate the fast neutrons regardless of the status of water in the tubes. At higher power (above 640 megawatts thermal), the feedback becomes negative, and the instability decreases. At low power the fission process accelerates, another case of positive feedback. These factors are believed to have played a major role in the accident.

Engineer A. Yadrikhinski, who was stationed at the Kursk power station, pointed out the dangers of the RBMK reactors. Six months before the Chernobyl calamity, he had sent a letter to the State Committee on Nuclear Energy in which he pointed out the potential for just such an accident. He recommended a commission to study the matter. His suggestions were ignored.

The accident involved unit 4, the newest and most advanced (type RBMK-1000); it had been operating three years. The mishap began to unfold at 1:00 a.m. on April 25, 1986. Since routine maintenance required a shut-down, the operators decided to use the opportunity to conduct an experiment with the main objective of finding out whether the momentum of the two massive turbines could be used to generate enough power to drive emergency systems such as lights and cooling pumps during accidental station blackout until diesel motors with generators take over (some other reactors in the ex-Soviet Union have no diesel backup). Even when scrammed and power from fission is very low or zero, cooling is essential to remove heat from radioactive decay of the fission products. Thus the Chernobyl operators disconnected the plant from the electric power grid and began their test. The procedures just described and much of what followed is an example of enthusiastic mismanagement. A chronology follows, in terms of time elapsed after the start of the first step of the fatal experiment:

An RBMK can be refueled while operating.

Start: April 25. Power was reduced and turbine 7 was shut down, disabling one set of automatic emergency cooling systems.

12 hours: Turbine 8 was shut down, along with a second set of emergency systems, to prevent the reactor from turning itself off. The operators disconnected a computer that recorded data on reactor conditions, and used it to record data in their tests. They also disabled a key part of the emergency shutdown system.

22 hours 10 minutes: The power had been gradually stabilized at approximately 200 megawatts thermal. The test required a power of 700 megawatts thermal. Unexplained fluctuations occurred, involving sharp drops in power.

24 hours: April 26. The power stabilized at 200 megawatts thermal, but the fission product xenon-135 (half-life, 9.1 hours), which captures neutrons avidly, was building up. This caused further loss of power and increased instability, causing the operators to recklessly withdraw many control rods. Power had dropped to about 30 megawatts thermal. There was no sense of impending danger.

24 hours 23 minutes: Erratic behavior of the reactor arose from voids in the cooling water pipes. Any experienced operator would have scrammed the reactor. Nevertheless, the experiment was continued. Within 3 seconds, the power shot up from 30 megawatts thermal to one or two hundred times the capacity of the reactor. The temperature could have reached 7000 °C, hotter than the surface of the sun.

24 hours 24 minutes: The operators attempted an emergency shut-down. The giant reactor shuddered, jamming the control rods. The water lines and fuel rods overheated and burst. A mighty explosion took place, killing two operators instantly. Not a single body part of one of them, an engineer named Khodimchuk, was ever found. The explosion was from the sudden formation of steam; it lifted and toppled a 1000-ton refueling crane, snapped off 1600 water pipes, and blew out concrete walls. The heavy crane ripped a hole in the confinement, opening the helium-nitrogen protective blanket to the air. Chemical reaction of the steam with the white hot zirconium and graphite produced a large quantity of hydrogen and carbon monoxide, which mixed with air in the refueling room above and a second explosion might have taken place, although this is not certain. Continued reaction of steam with the hot graphite formed more hydrogen and carbon monoxide, feeding the flames. The vault holding the graphite was now breached, and the graphite in the core began to burn fiercely, the vertical channels acting as chimneys.

The fire of course consumed the fuel rods and their fission products, making it especially dirty. Hundreds of tons of water under high temperature (380 °C) and pressure (70 atmospheres) were released instantly; the amount of energy has been estimated at 1200 gigajoules. While nuclear energy was the source of this energy, the explosion was not truly a nuclear explosion. There was no blinding fireball. Convection currents sucked up radioactive iodine vapor and particulate matter, forming a plume almost a mile high and depositing solids on the landscape as fallout. The accident occurred at the worst possible stage in the reactor's life, just before a planned shutdown, when so much fission products (around three billion curies) had accumulated. About 3.5% of the total fission products were released into the environment. In technical jargon, the amounts and types of such radioactive materials discharged outside are known by the innocuous expression *source terms*. This corresponded to about 12 million curies in the initial explosion and fire, millions of curies more during the next ten days, and an additional 45 million curies of radioactive xenon (one of the least harmful). The amount of radioactivity escaping amounted to some 30 or 40 times the amount inflicted on Hiroshima, but the types differed somewhat in that the reactor material had aged enough so that the shorter-lived nuclides had decayed. Apparently a partial meltdown took place.

A ferroconcrete containment dome would have been far cheaper.

A tremendous cloud containing dangerous radioactive iodine, cesium, strontium, and other elements spitting out beta particles, passed over Minsk, northeast Poland, and Scandinavia. Two reactors in its path, namely the huge 1380 megawatt (electric) reactor at Ignalina and the one at Rovno, had automatic sensors which caused them to shut down. When their operators realized that the radioactivity came from outside, they resumed power production.

The fire at Chernobyl, which consumed about 10% of the graphite, was extinguished in ten days using clay and sand (800 tons), dolomite (800 tons), and liquid nitrogen. In addition, attempts were made to stop all chain reaction by dropping lead shot (2400 tons), boron carbide (40 tons) and borax (boron absorbs neutrons readily).

АВАРИЯ НА ЧЕРНОБЫЛЬСКОЙ АЭС
И ЕЕ ПОСЛЕДСТВИЯ

THE ACCIDENT AT THE CHERNOBYL AES AND ITS CONSEQUENCES

Six thousand tons of these substances were dropped from helicopters. These materials insulated the radioactive wreckage thermally, causing decay heat to accumulate. This resulted in release of still more fission products during days six to nine after the original accident. Examination years later showed that most of the sand, lead, and boron carbide dropped had missed the mark and landed on the floor of the central hall.

The U.S. Department of Energy nuclear engineer Edward Purvis studied the Chernobyl accident starting shortly after it took place, and revisited the site in 1993. His study led him to conclude that the main explosion did not occur in the concrete reactor shaft, but rather that a steam explosion catapulted the core out of the shaft, where it exploded. Many details are in harmony with this hypothesis, but it has met vigorous opposition.

The Soviets gave no warnings, and indeed their public relations can only be described as clumsy. The reasons why the Soviets were slow to acknowledge the accident and respond to it quickly on both the domestic and international scale were: it took some time before they realized its dimensions; to avoid panic; to avoid embarrassment of high officials; and deeply ingrained habits of secrecy. These are essentially the same reasons for similar action or inaction in western countries. An ironic sideline is that the American reconnaissance satellite KH-11 took excellent photos of the Chernobyl site during the eruption, but the Reagan administration did not wish this known because one of its principal arguments against new arms control agreements was based on the contention that that verification would be too difficult.

An American spy satellite photographed the Chernobyl site.

7-26 The Amounts of Radioactive Materials Ejected from the Chernobyl Reactor

In August 1986, four months after the disaster, the Soviets presented estimates of the total amounts of radionuclides discharged from the Chernobyl reactor. These figures were based on analyses of fallout on many areas of land, including gamma ray measurements carried out from low-flying aircraft, and were integrated to cover the entire affected areas. The inert gases krypton and xenon were estimated in other ways. The radionuclides lofted a mile into the atmosphere were not included, and much of them were carried outside the Soviet Union.

Various western sources (American, British, and German) also published estimates of the amounts of radionuclides and also in some cases broke the releases down into the amounts discharged on each of the ten days of the accident. The western estimates are in general higher than the Soviet figures, in part because the material carried high into the air was included. The early Soviet estimates (1986) are presented in the table below. They total 76,700,000 curies. In addition, Russian (Dobrynin) and Japanese (Imanaka) estimates, both made in 1993, are given for five radionuclides.

Radionuclides Ejected from Chernobyl Reactor

Radionuclide	*Half-life*		*Number of curies*	
		Soviet 1986	*Dobrynin 1993*	*Imanaka 1993*
Krypton-85	4.48 hours	900,000		
Strontium-89	50.6 days	2,200,000		
Strontium-90	28.5 years	220,000		
Zirconium-95	64.0 days	3,800,000	4,000,000	5,900,000
Molybdenum-99	2.75 days	300,000		
Ruthenium-103	39.3 days	3,200,000	3,800,000	3,300,000
Ruthenium-106	1.0 year	160,000		
Tellurium-132	3.26 days	1,300,000		
Iodine-131	8.04 days	7,300,000	19,000,000	17,000,000
Xenon-133	2.19 days	45,000,000		
Cesium-134	2.06 years	500,000		
Cesium-137	30.0 years	1,000,000	2,300,000	2,500,000
Barium-140	12.75 days	4,300,000		
Cerium-141	32.5 days	2,800,000		
Cerium-144	283 days	2,400,000	3,600,000	3,400,000
Neptunium-239	2.36 days	1,200,000		
Plutonium-238	87.7 years	800		
Plutonium-239	24,100 years	800		
Plutonium-240	6,540 years	1,000		
Plutonium-241	14.4 years	140,000		
Plutonium-242	376,000 years	2		
Curium-242	163 days	21,000		

Probably the best studied of the fission products released is cesium. The most reliable estimates of the total amount of cesium-137 discharged from Chernobyl is about 2,500,000 curies. This count includes the 1,000,000 curies listed by the Soviets in the table above, another 1,000,000 curies in Europe outside the Soviet Union, and about 500,000 curies elsewhere, as shown below. A year after the disaster the pattern of fallout over Europe had been mapped. It was found that irregular and unpredictable "hot spots" appeared as islands in southern France, the British Isles, and Scandinavia. Ten years after the accident (that is, in 1996), only about 3.5% of the shorter-lived isotope, Cs-134, remained, but about 80% of the longer-lived isotope Cs-137 survived. Studies of cesium-137 all over the northern hemisphere disclosed the following distribution of this fission product:

European USSR 38%
Rest of Europe 41%
Asian USSR 18%
Canada and USA 0.5%

One might wryly note that Marxist fission products are identical with capitalist fission products.

The average age of the fuel in Unit 4 at Chernobyl was 610 days, and consequently most of the nuclides with short half-lives had decayed. Only the amounts formed by fission during the last few days before the accident were present, but their amounts were nevertheless substantial. The largest percentage of fission products and fuel particles was ejected on day 1 (April 26). Following that, the amounts decreased and then increased again until day 10, when there was a sudden decrease. In percentages of the total, the amounts of radioactive debris disgorged day by day were: day 1, **25.0**%; day 2, **7.9**%; day 3, **6.7**%; day 4, **5.1**%; day 5, **3.9**%; day 6, **3.9**%; day 7, **7.9**%; day 8, **9.8**%; day 9, **13.8**%; day 10, **15.7**%; and day 11, **0.2**% (total **99.9**%). The buildup of discharge rate after the initial blast, reaching a maximum on day 10, was caused by heat from the radioactive decay of the fuel which at this stage had no cooling. The temperature reached the point where the more volatile fission products began to distill out. These included the most volatile, iodine and tellurium, and later the less volatile cesium. At higher temperatures the more refractory materials, such as barium, strontium, cerium, and plutonium, are discharged. Considerable actinide elements were ejected as particulate matter rather than distillation.

The land area most heavily contaminated by fallout was that north of the reactor within a 30 kilometer zone. Radiometric measurements made there on May 17, 1986, showed the following typical concentrations (in curies per square kilometer):

Zirconium-95	640
Ruthenium-103	560
Cerium-141	510
Iodine-131	510
Barium-140	290
Cesium-137	270
Cesium-134	250
Ruthenium-106	150
Tellurium-132	54

The responsibility for the accident was ascribed to a number of factors. These included gross negligence and insufficient technical training of the operators, more or less as at Three Mile Island, but worse. The Soviet operators must have had a complacent, even cavalier attitude, toward safety to have made so many foolish errors. Six of them were tried and sentenced to years of hard labor in prison. The chief engineer in charge of the reactor at the time of the accident, Anatoly Dyatlov, served about five years, and was released early in a general amnesty for Chernobyl workers. He had received an almost fatal dose of radiation. It would not be just to hold the workers entirely responsible for the accident. Serious design flaws in the reactor were revealed and are being addressed. More safety measures have been introduced such as improved control rods. The original rods could not halt rapidly rising power. Emergency core-cooling systems have been installed. By October 1986 units 1 and 2 at Chernobyl had been restarted. Late in 1999 Ukrainian authorities started up unit 3. The newest Russian reactors have no graphite, are of the pressurized-water type, and equipped with containment domes.

Learning to take reactors seriously

The Chernobyl accident, a result of a sort of technological arrogance, was a pivotal point for the nuclear power industry worldwide. One consequence of the accident was stimulation of American authorities to shut down the N Reactor for installation of new safety devices; the final decision was not to start it up again. Another consequence was putting interlocking devices into commercial reactors which cause scramming if anyone tries to bypass critical safety features.

7-27 The Sarcophagus

A concrete icon

After a considerable time, few choices for action were apparent and the Soviets tunneled under the ill-fated reactor, emplacing concrete in order to insure against leakage of fission products into the ground water. They covered the site, with some of its melted nuclear fuel now resolidified into grotesque shapes, constructing a sort of concrete sarcophagus some 200 feet high. This was regarded as a short-term measure to lessen immediate risk. The gigantic coffin required 300,000 tons of concrete. It was initially cooled with liquid nitrogen, and now is cooled via ventilation shafts. Cooling is necessary to remove the heat from fission product decay. Thus the dangerous debris will be entombed for centuries. Sensors to monitor temperature and radioactivity were installed. This monument to the god of technological folly illustrates the immaturity of nuclear methodology. Doubting the stability of the sarcophagus, newly independent Ukraine is seeking western help in repairs. By 1994 cracks in the concrete shell had begun to appear. This is due in part to a significant temperature difference between the inner and outer faces. In 1995 scientists from the European Union confirmed that dangerous cracks are growing, and that portions of the structure might collapse. The United Nations inspectors reported "numerous safety violations" in the two remaining plants, and in 1994 international pressure was being brought to bear on Ukraine to close them down.

By 1994, much of the short-lived radionuclides had decayed, and volunteers began burrowing into the sarcophagus. Excessive radiation doses were avoided by a maximum exposure time of 30 to 40 minutes. Passages have been cleared so that inspections can be made within a few minutes. The bowels of the sarcophagus are like a strange planet. The melted components, collectively called "chernobylite," have various colors, and some resemble a frozen waterfall made of anthracite coal. A second, more secure, sarcophagus built over the first is being considered, but it would cost somewhere around $1 billion.

Sunlight streams into the sarcophagus through cracks. Birds, animals, and insects have begun to make their homes inside the structure. The dose rate in front of the sarcophagus in 2000 was 10 to 20 microsieverts (1 to 2 millirems) per hour. Chemists at the Kurchatov Institute in Moscow have developed a silicone-based plastic called Ekor which is extremely resistant to ionizing radiation. Curiously enough, it was an American firm, Eurotech of La Jolla in California, which was awarded the contract for applying the plastic as a foam to seal the holes in the sarcophagus in 1997 at a cost of about $200 million. It seems likely that the silicone plastic will also be useful in transporting and storing radioactive waste. The Group of 7 industrialized nations agreed to finance (estimated at $768 million) the construction of a huge semi-cylindrical structure some 370 feet high and about 800 feet wide, mounted on rails, which can be

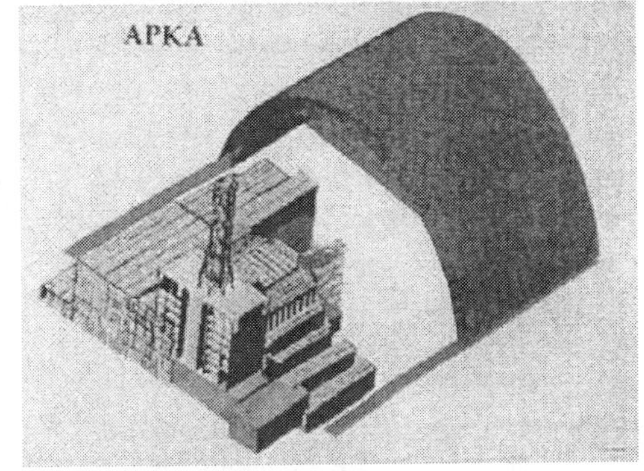

Enclosure for Chernobyl ruins (The Cyrillic letters APKA mean 'the arch').

moved to enclose the derelict reactor (see sketch). Inside, robotic cranes are planned to pry apart the wreckage, where feasible, and load sections of the core into shielded canisters. Steel beams, still highly radioactive, are to be cut up and packaged. By that time, Ukraine hopes to have developed a suitable repository.

The science editor of Pravda, Vladimir Gubaryev, wrote a powerful drama on the Chernobyl accident, titled "Sarcophagus;" the play has been presented before Soviet, European, and American audiences. The play was presented in Los Angeles, and the author gave a lecture at the end, and breakfasted with Gubaryev the next morning.

7-28 Costs in Human Terms

Soviet sources first reported that only a dozen or so persons lost their lives in the first two weeks. Later the official figure was set at 32 deaths, mostly of firemen, and 500 people had to be hospitalized. Only two of these were saved through bone marrow transplants. The 32 deaths mentioned would be 33 if a news photographer who received a heavy dose of radiation, causing his death in a year, is included. His films were spectacular (though fogged by the radiation). To decide how many fatalities were incurred at Chernobyl is not easy, and requires some arbitrary decisions. Are only those killed during the active phase of the debacle to be counted? How about those who expire within one month, or a year, or five years? Soviet sources in 1990 raised the estimate of the number who died at Chernobyl or immediately afterwards to 300, and another appraisal in 1998 gave 7,000 to 10,000 deaths counting those who volunteered to fight the fire. The numerous cleanup workers returned to the far-flung regions of the USSR, and there is practically no way today to get reliable data about their exposure and fate. It is not clear just which standards were applied in the various estimates, but there is no doubt that the earlier numbers are far too low.

Dr. Tetsuji Imanaka of the Research Reactor Institute in Japan, along with his Japanese team, and corresponding Russian, Belarussian, and Ukrainian scientific teams, finished a thorough study of the aftereffects of the accident in 1998 (see bibliography). They recognize five main groups of victims:

1. The reactor personnel, firemen, and emergency workers involved directly in the accident (1000 - 2000 persons);
2. Those called the liquidators who cleaned up the main wreckage of the reactor; these included soldiers and workers who built the sarcophagus (600,000 - 800,000 persons);
3. Early evacuees from the 30-kilometer zone (135,000 persons);
4. People resettled from the contaminated areas (more than 115,000 persons);
5. Residents in the contaminated areas (more than 6 million persons).

After several months the radio-iodine had decayed, and the most dangerous nuclides were cesium-134 (half-life 2.1 years), cesium-137 (half-life 30 years), and strontium-90 (half-life 28.5 years). Of the total radiation dose inflicted by these cesium isotopes over their entire life spans, about 50% had taken place by 1996 and about two-thirds of the total will have been delivered by 2011.

We do not know how many will die or develop cancer altogether, but there will be an increase over the natural rate, which is about 20% of deaths. This amounts to about 9.5 million cases of cancer in this case. Consider a radiation exposure of 10,000 person-rems. How many deaths result from cancer over the natural rate (the risk factor) result? A benchmark figure used by the International Atomic Energy Agency since 1977 is 1 fatal cancer per 10,000 person-rems. The Environmental Protection Agency uses a figure of 2, while the Department of Energy asserts that 2.3 deaths per 10,000 person-rem exposure is more realistic (this is the same as 23 deaths per 100,000 person-rems). This last risk factor means that 10,000 to 12,000 excess cancer deaths will occur in the European regions of the former USSR, and approximately 39,000 excess deaths over the northern hemisphere. Some authorities, such as Dr. John Gofman, estimate the number of fatal cancers as high as between 600,000 and 1,000,000, including leukemia. Whatever the number, it will not be obvious because it will be submerged in the high natural rate.

By 1990 the incidence of leukemia in the Minsk area had doubled. Just the increase in deaths from cancer is not an adequate measure of the hazard; one also needs to gauge the number of years the victims are robbed of life. Heavy doses of ionizing radiation, in most cases here accumulated over years, cause some cases of cancer but even more disorders of various other types. There is evidence that the immune systems of many people, especially children, have been damaged. Symptoms of chronic radiation exposure, such as lymph gland inflammation, digestive tract and kidney failure, and anemia, are common in the areas hardest hit. Still other ailments include general weakness, pain in the joints, enlarged thyroid and lymphatic glands, headaches, stomach troubles, and chronic throat infections. The grim biomedical consequences of Chernobyl will be monitored for years in an attempt to reveal the hidden dimensions of the disaster. All these must be weighed against the unhealthy lifestyles of many Soviet or Russian adults: heavy smoking and drinking, poor nutrition, and polluted air and water. Almost certainly the debilitation by Chernobyl contributed to the new policy of *glasnost*, and indeed quickened the collapse of the Soviet Union itself in 1990-91.

Tumors other than thyroid cancer increased in Balarus. Dr. Rose Goncharova, of the Institute of Genetics and Cytology in Minsk, in 1998 reported the numbers of cases of congenital malformations in children. These include cleft palate, Down's syndrome, and deformations of limbs and organs, which had increased by 83% in the heavily contaminated regions. She was able to discount another possible cause, toxic chemicals.

No radiological emergency plans were in place beforehand. No protective clothing was available. No radiation measurements were taken at the nearby town of Pripyat. The residents were not informed until 35 hours after the accident, and former plant director Bryukhanov received a 10-year sentence for this negligence. Eventually, nearly 84,000 people were evacuated from the immediate area using city buses from Kiev, and 60,000 more were moved from southern Belarus. An exclusion zone of radius 30 kilometer (19 mile) was set up. This dangerous area, encompassing more than 1000 square miles, bulges toward the northwest, the direction of the winds during the first two days when most of the radioactive release took place. Livestock within 12 miles were slaughtered. Warnings against eating local

The exclusion zone came to be known as the Zone of Alienation.

vegetables were issued, but contaminated crops nevertheless found their way to other Soviet Republics. After all, the accident occurred during the growing season.

Within one mile of the Chernobyl reactor site, many persons received more than 100 rads. People between 2 and 6 miles away received an average of about 50 rads and the ring outside that, 6 to 9 miles from the source, got an average of 35 rads. The average exposure of all evacuees was reported as about 12 rads. Certain spots were contaminated much more seriously than others. Since few counting instruments were available, the true figures will never be known. The town called Krasnoe is in Belarus, nearly 4 miles north of the reactor. During the first two days or so after the eruption of Chernobyl, the dose rate to the inhabitants of Krasnoe was about 330 millirads per hour. This means one rad per three hours, a dreadfully high rate, and it was the highest rate observed.

In Poland the maximum activity in the air, reached on April 29, was approximately 0.015 millicuries per cubic meter. In some areas, people were subjected to a radiation dose of as much as 1 or 2 rads per day for a few days. In Poland a mass program was undertaken to give children potassium iodide in order to reduce the uptake of radioactive iodine by their thyroid glands. An excess of ordinary iodine "fills up," so to speak, the thyroid gland, preventing much radioactive iodine from being absorbed. In Sweden, whole-body doses were about 1 millirad, and thyroid gland doses were 5 millirads. Unsafe radiation levels were reported in mutton, fish, reindeer venison, and berries.

The immediate landscape was dusted with solid fission products and plutonium (Pu-239, -240, and -241). The first two plutonium isotopes are very long-lived, but Pu-241 has the rather short half-life of 14 years, and beta decays to americium, a gamma emitter with half-life of 433 years. This substance might pose a hazard for many years. Based on experience with fallout from the hydrogen bomb test at Bikini in 1954, two other important nuclides which will cause long-term trouble are cesium-137 and strontium-90. Topsoil near the reactor site has been scooped up and removed. Pripyat is now a surreal ghost town; abandoned cars sit rusting, all the trees killed by radiation. The gamma ray dose rate there in year 2000 was 1 to 2 microsieverts per hour.

7-29 Consequences of the Chernobyl Tragedy

In early 1988 the Politburo announced that the financial cost of the Chernobyl accident was about $14 billion, but this was a gross underestimate. In 1990 another $26 billion in aid was authorized. The total cost of cleanup, resettlement, and medical care was said to be as high as $416 billion, $235 billion in Belarus alone. All of these estimates are too low. Belarus has levied a "Chernobyl tax." Greater cleanup efforts were demanded at rallies of 60,000 people in Kiev. Radionuclides entered the Pripyat River and washed into the reservoir of Kiev; authorities said the level was too low to be dangerous. Chernobyl stimulated resurgent Ukrainian nationalism.

Nearly three years after the accident, 20 additional villages in Belarus had been evacuated, and one-fifth of the arable land in the republic was too contaminated for agricultural use. Belarus got about 70% of the fallout. Its scientists propose that the level of cesium-137 in soil should be no higher than 5 curies per square kilometer, while Moscow claimed that three times this concentration can be tolerated.

Five years after the Chernobyl accident, its true dimensions began to become apparent as the veil of secrecy was lifted. In the Belarus capitol city of Minsk, the dosage was about 200 times that from the natural background for two days after the accident, and yet no iodine preventive was administered to children. Today there is widespread cancer of the thyroid gland, and increased incidence of birth defects, leukemia, and respiratory, gastrointestinal, and cardiovascular diseases. By 1995 nearly 700 cases of thyroid cancer had been diagnosed and many operations to remove the gland had been performed. If treated early on, most of the thyroid cancers can be managed successfully, but if neglected for some time, they become particularly aggressive and tend to invade adjacent tissue. The children will be dependent on regular doses of thyroxine for the rest of their lives. By some estimates, between 4000 and 8000 cases are anticipated from the Chernobyl accident, of which 10% will be fatal.

People living in the vicinity have developed a tendency to blame any and all ills on radiation (radiophobia), and some are referred to as "nuclear lepers." Depression of the immune system by exposure to radiation, resulting in respiratory tract inflammation among children, constant coughing, and chronic fatigue, have been colloquially called "Chernobyl AIDS," an unhappy term. It might not be an exaggeration to state that Chernobyl initiated a great wave of morbidity and accelerated the sudden collapse of the Soviet regime.

"Nuclear lepers?"

Nearly one-fourth of the Belarus population was killed during World War II, and now about one-fifth more have been affected by the radiation. The dust holding radioactive fallout is blown everywhere: in food, in water, in the homes, all pervasive. Tens of thousands of Belarussians, afflicted by radiation from Chernobyl, have fled to Israel. It was Soviet policy for some time to distribute radioactive foodstuffs from the contaminated areas to uncontaminated areas outside, thus diluting the dangers. This appeared to reduce the radiation dose to some consumers, but increased it to others; the total number of person-rems remained unchanged.

Some time after the accident, a physician in Belarus faxed the Irish Campaign for Nuclear Disarmament to request that afflicted children be brought to Ireland for treatment. Thus the Chernobyl Children's Project was born. By 1996 this organization had delivered $3.75 million worth of medicinals, ambulances, and other aid to Belarus. This sum exceeds the amount given by the United Nations. Soviet bureaucracy consistently downplayed the effects of radioactivity on the people living in the lands surrounding Chernobyl, except for one courageous woman, Prof. Elena Burlakova, a biologist and a member of the Academy of Sciences and chair of a council for radiological problems. She traveled extensively in the afflicted areas and became convinced that thousands and thousands of children were slowly being destroyed. She did all in her power to get these victims moved out to more distant and cleaner regions, but with limited success. She compared the pathology of the sufferers from Chernobyl fallout to the similar cases of those who lived along the Techa River (8-7A). The range of medical problems in the two groups was distinctly alike and collating symptoms of the two populations was clearly valuable, but the bureaucracy was still in denial.

A true heroine, Prof. Elena Burlakova

By 1992 some peasants were drifting back into the contaminated lands; four years later they numbered at least 500. Their experience with government has led them to be hypercritical and disbelieving. They have scant knowledge of radiation damage. They see wild animals which seem to thrive in the deserted lands. Rabbits flourish in the empty streets of villages. The government brings in workers to clean up the contamination. Thieves come to steal abandoned radioactive vehicles. A few drifters and lost souls have found a haven in forsaken homes and weed-filled gardens. The ultimate fate of these people is yet to be seen. The off-limits Chernobyl zone encompasses large areas in which wild animals have multiplied. It is now one of Europe's largest wildlife habitats. There are boars, moose, eagles, cranes, roebucks, wolves, and a few rarities such as booted eagles and black storks. A few animals have been captured or shot to test for radioactivity, and all tests were positive, especially for cesium-137 and strontium-90. The antlers of an elk which had been shot were so radioactive from cesium and strontium that they could not be legally removed from the zone. In 1998 some wild, rare, robust Przewalski horses were introduced. Their foals have grown to adolescence without any visible effects from their radioactive diet.

Nine years after the accident, an American study was made of rodents (voles) which lived within 30 km of the reactor. These animals gave the researchers a surprise because they found 46 mutations in just one gene; this seemed to be of no major importance, however. The voles and mice are about the most contaminated animals known, and yet they appear to be healthy and to reproduce normally. Considering the base pairs in DNA as "letters," under normal circumstances one error (mutation) appears in every million letters of genetic code per generation. In the Chernobyl animals the rate is one error for every 10,000 letters. Barn swallows from the Chernobyl area and from distant, uncontaminated sites, showed some visible differences. A mutant in the exposed swallows had white feathers in spots where the normal birds had colored feathers.

In 1992, six years after the Chernobyl disaster, an international group of physicians published an analysis of the incidence of thyroid cancer in children who had been exposed to iodine-131 in affected areas. One region, Gormel, is in Belarus immediately to the north of Chernobyl. The incidence of thyroid cancer in children under15 in a general population is 1 per million per year. By 1992 in Gormel, the incidence had jumped, after a latency period of six years, to about 80 cases per million per year, and by 1995 it was much higher. The younger the children, the higher the dosages were. The growing thyroid glands of fetuses were especially susceptible. The radiation doses were comparable to those received by Marshallese children in the Pacific (9-19), but the number of cases was several hundred times higher.

Ten years after the Chernobyl disaster, Russian geneticist Dubrova and English biologist Jeffreys finished research on the DNA of 79 families living in the Mogilev region of Belarus, 120 miles from Chernobyl, which was the area most tragically affected. They collected blood from children born in 1994 and also from their parents. Control samples were taken from 109 families in England. The results disclosed that the children whose parents had been exposed to the fallout had twice the mutation rate as the English children. The higher the level of soil contamination, the higher was the rate of mutation. Mutations occurred not only in the genes, but also those regions of DNA in between the genes. No effects of mutations visible to the naked eye were detected. A fifth of all farmland in Belarus became extremely dangerous to human life, some contaminated with as much as 140 curies per square kilometer.

The northern parts of Scandinavian countries have large reindeer populations tended by the Laplanders, and the animals forage on lichen. Rather large quantities of cesium-137 from the Chernobyl accident were absorbed by the lichen, and thus contaminated the meat from reindeer. Norwegian biochemists developed a means of greatly reducing the level of cesium. They found that the ammonium form of Prussian blue, an insoluble iron-cyanide complex, would readily exchange the ammonium ion for the cesium ion. Therefore, if reindeer (or sheep or cattle) which had been eating contaminated fodder are given Prussian blue, the cesium is adsorbed and excreted. The Prussian blue is given in a salt lick and also as a bolus inserted into the reticulum (the second compartment of a ruminant's stomach). This can reduce the radiation levels of meat by 50 to 75%. The biological half-life of cesium in contaminated animals which are fed clean fodder is about 20 days. In Finland, the average radiation dose one month after the accident had grown to 50 microsieverts per month, double the normal background.

Reducing the concentration of cesium-137 in food

Aside from the radionuclides from Chernobyl, fallout from atmospheric nuclear tests has fallen steadily in the arctic, where it is more readily picked up by lichen than is the case in cultivated land further south. The result is that the inhabitants of the Arctic regions, who eat a great deal of reindeer meat, suffer a much higher dose than those further south, in fact, as much as 15 rads each per year.

Milk contaminated with strontium-90 and cesium-137 can be processed into cheese and butter; this step removed most of the dangerous nuclides, since they stay in the whey, which is discarded. By 1993, western Europe had established a limit of 370 becquerels of cesium-137 per liter of milk imported from the contaminated areas. British chemists modified the Prussian blue technique for removing the cesium-137. The milk is mixed with particles of the sodium iron cyanide complex, and the cesium ions replace the sodium ions and are trapped. About 95% of the radioactive cesium is removed. The particulate matter is separated by filtration. Meat from lambs slaughtered in Britain a few weeks after the accident showed a radioactivity level of cesium-137 of 1.8 nanocuries per pound, exceeding by 50% what was considered to be acceptable.

7-30 Coping with the Aftereffects of Chernobyl

One technique developed for decontaminating the farmland around Chernobyl is to grow grass, and then rolling up the turf for processing. The grass takes up much of the radioactivity. It is put into a plastic-lined hole and allowed to rot under water. The water is pumped out and the radioactive components are removed and dumped in a make-shift repository. In any case, every year rainwater percolating through the earth extracts fission products to lower levels, and sometime will reach the water table, but by that time much of the radioactivity will have died out.

A special plow has been invented in Denmark which makes cultivation of contaminated soil possible. Tests began in 1992 in the area around Chernobyl. The plow operates in two steps. In the first, it digs a furrow about 20 inches deep, and in the second step it scoops the top couple of inches or so from an adjacent strip. This top layer, holding nearly all the cesium-137 and strontium-90, is dumped into the furrow; these two radionuclides are strongly adsorbed in this top layer of soil. The plow then pushes the next top layer sideways to cover the furrow. Such a device might turn out to be of immense value. Treating the soil with calcium and potassium greatly lowers the take-up of strontium and cesium and in any case, cesium is only adsorbed at very low levels. A group of Russian scientists in the city of Tula have found that an abundant type of brown coal, when powdered and mixed with the contaminated soil, so strongly adsorbs radionuclides that the plants grown contain only half of the radioactivity as those without treatment.

Experiments at the University of Georgia (USA, not former-Soviet Georgia) have provided data of great interest to farmers who live in the Chernobyl vicinity. The data indicate that if chickens are raised on radioactive soil, they pick up considerable contamination, such as cesium-137. But their metabolism rate is so high that in just a week on uncontaminated feed, their bodies are pretty well cleaned out of radionuclides. Radioactive land can also be used to grow nonfood crops such as cotton or flax, or biomass to be fermented to fuel alcohol.

With the transition of the old Soviet system into a society more like western countries, the personnel are leaving the state-operated reactors to accept higher-paying jobs at private companies or cooperatives. Alexander Rimsky-Korsakov, grandson of the great composer, is deputy director of the Radium Institute in St. Petersburg, and he complains that his scientists are leaving. "How can we keep them?" he asks. Help from the West is sorely needed, and it would be in the self interest of Europe. Little aid is in the offing.

By 1994, effects on the health of those living in the contaminated areas were very much in evidence. There has been an enormous rise in thyroid cancer rate in Belarus, especially in children. There are other oncological diseases, anemia, immunodisfunction, and infants with Down's syndrome. The birth rate has dropped, and many deformed fetuses have miscarried. About 5% of Ukraine's national budget is devoted to cleanup.

By 1994, radiation damage to the health of Chernobyl cleanup workers had become more obvious. Approximately half a million soldiers, military veterans, and miners had worked in shifts over a three year period. More than 7000 of these men, of average age 29, are reported to have died, and perhaps three-fourths of the rest suffer various disorders. Of the 7000 who perished, about 1250 had committed suicide, unable to cope with radiation effects.

Massive radiation doses

Just before the tenth anniversary of the accident, a group of Ukrainians was paying a nostalgic visit to their old villages, now ghost towns, near Chernobyl. A quick-spreading fire in the exclusion zone burned large areas of grasslands and hundreds of houses. Most of the cesium-137 and strontium-90 had been washed from the structures by rain, but the plant life had taken up considerable amounts of these fission products. A helicopter flown through the smoke cloud disclosed a slight increase in radiation levels due to particulate matter.

The presence of so many radioactive trees, both living and dead, poses a problem. Forest fires could spread their cesium, strontium, and other radionuclides over farm lands and raise contamination levels. In 1996 a joint project of Belarus and the Sandia National Laboratories in California designed an electric power station which burns timber from the affected trees. Better than 99.9% of the radionuclides in the ash is captured. New trees are planted as the old ones are removed. Since Belarus imports 90% of its energy, this extra electric power is very welcome.

An international study by 59 scientists of the effects of flooding of the contaminated area was finished in 1996. In just the area around the ruins of the reactor, an estimated total of 10,000 curies of strontium-90 and plutonium was found. Rainwater is washing the radioactive materials down the Pripyat River into the Dnieper River, which empties into the Black Sea. Strangely, the most contaminated lake is Lake Kojanovskoe, which is in Russia about 150 miles away from the reactor. Evidently, unexpected wind currents were responsible for this. Perch and pike from the lake in 1994 contained at the level of 1 microcurie of cesium-137 per kilogram, 65 times the European Union safety limit. Rather few cases of leukemia seemed to have been linked to the disaster, but in 1996 children who were *in utero* during exposure began to come down with this disorder. Some of these cases occurred outside the old Soviet Union, such as Greece, where radiation doses were far lower. In spring of 2000, the Ukrainian health ministry reported that about 3.5 million citizens were suffering from long after-effects of Chernobyl.

Thus we see that the legacy of Chernobyl lives on, resembling a radioactive boomerang coming back to haunt the innocent and the guilty alike.

7-31 Post-Chernobyl Policies

In March of 1992 a small accident at an RBMK reactor at Sosnovy Bor, 60 miles west of St. Petersburg, was reported instantly to the world press. Soviet nuclear engineers developed mathematical computer models for testing every conceivable accident. Far-reaching new standards of safety have been installed. An RBMK reactor at Smolensk has been extensively upgraded. One factor which inhibits western contractors from helping the urgently needed repairs is lack of insurance which would protect them in case of an accident during or after the work.

By 1992 the European Community had pledged $270 million toward upgrading the most hazardous Soviet-built reactors. Soon afterward, the Scandinavian countries promised the same amount. The Group of Seven industrialized nations agreed on $100 million more. These funds will buy at least short-term emergency improvement, but there is no guarantee that international assistance will produce safer reactors. Some in the West feel that the aid so far is merely extending the time the old Soviet-built reactors will be used. By the twelfth anniversary of the Chernobyl accident (1998), most of the promised funds had not arrived, and the last RBMK at Chernobyl had not been shut down. While all 15 of those rickety RBMK reactors are to be eventually phased out, no intention is apparent to reduce development of nuclear energy. Even Belarus, hurt badly by fallout, is evidently planning on building ten more reactors; these are to be the "Supersafe" type. By 1996, after accumulating considerable experience with the technology of RBMK reactors, some American and western European experts concluded that they can be upgraded sufficiently to warrant continued use for a few more years. The backfitting steps include installation of better control rods, faster emergency shut down procedures and core cooling, and even building a containment in some cases.

Patching up those rattletrap old reactors to squeeze out a few more years service

Not much could be done to improve the stability of those RBMK reactors still operating, but some steps were taken. The new fuel has a higher degree of uranium-235 enrichment, shutdown time was reduced, and rigorously strict rules about disabling safety mechanisms were introduced. Another consequence of the Chernobyl catastrophe was that Moscow acutely reduced its ambitious plans to quadruple nuclear generation before 2000. Construction at 16 sites was halted, nine plants were closed down, and plans for about 30 new reactors were scrapped.

As of 1996 there were 13 RBMK reactors (925 megawatts electric each), and two RBMK-1500 reactors (1380 megawatts electric each) operating in Russia, Ukraine, and Lithuania. Another in Kursk came online in 2000. As of 1997 the remaining reactors at Chernobyl produce 5% of Ukraine's electricity. The country has many coal-burning generators but insufficient fuel. An agreement was reached to close the remaining Chernobyl reactor by approximately 2000, and this was actually accomplished in December of that year.

The Russian government has started a Center for Public Information on Atomic Energy to try to gain acceptance of new reactors. This Center advocates building 30 new reactors, and several of these are already under construction. There is a requirement that ecological standards be met. Russian and Ukrainian nuclear engineers, driven by anguish from Chernobyl, had by 1994 vastly improved the design of new reactors. The first of these, built near Smolensk, generates 1000 megawatts of electricity. But three of the half-built reactors (at Baku, Gorky, and Minsk) have been converted to gas-fired plants, and an American firm has contracted to the conversion of the Tomsk and Krasnoyarsk-26 plutonium-producing reactors to coal or gas alternatives. In 1994 the Russian and American governments signed agreements to shut down the last three reactors which produce military-grade plutonium. In return, the American Department of Energy is helping the Russians to get financing to build power plants using gas, oil, or coal. Export of Russian uranium reserves has raised more than $500 million toward these ends.

Consider the demeaning fate of the reactor at Kharkov: it has suffered the indignity of being converted into a chicken farm. Ukraine and Russia have small but sophisticated wind turbine efforts and they are expanding. Ukraine had placed a substantial order for wind turbines with the San Francisco-based Kenetech Windpower, but that firm went bankrupt, thus canceling the project. Photovoltaic cells were built for satellites and their technology is being applied for civilian use, again on a small scale. But these alternative energy sources so far are paltry.

Pity the unfortunate reactor at Kharkov

7-32 Newer Russian Reactors

There are three types of VVER reactors, models 440/230 (the early type), 440/213 (second generation), and model 1000. The letters VVER stand for the Russian words "water-cooled and water-moderated reactor." There are 18 model 440 reactors and 16 model 1000 reactors. A number are in Russia and in Ukraine, and some are in Bulgaria, Hungary, the Czech Republic, and Slovakia. All Soviet-built reactors fail to meet modern western safety standards, and should be shut down whenever practical.

The VVER reactors are not without advantages, however. They have twice the cooling water/moderator as western pressurized-water reactors, providing a higher margin of safety by giving operators more time in emergencies to take corrective action. There are about a dozen reactors in Russia where electricity is so badly needed that the government wants to continue their operation through their "design lives." A German firm has been upgrading a VVER 440/230 unit at Kola; this includes simple steps such as installing microphones to detect the sound of any escaping steam. Two such events were detected in 1994.

After Chernobyl, we may well ask why the eastern countries don't just shut all those precarious reactors down. The main reason the reactors are kept going is energy; a secondary reason is jobs. Since 1990, production of petroleum has fallen 15% each year, as more and more of that which is produced is exported for foreign currency. Production of electricity from oil and coal has fallen so low it is rationed in Russia. Reactors furnish about 11% of the total electricity currently.

Russia is planning to finish construction of three reactors which were under construction before the Chernobyl accident, and also to begin building four new reactors. Two of the four new ones are to be fast breeders, one at Beloyarsk in Siberia and the other at Ozersk, in the southern Urals. Western observers are skeptical that funding for these projects can be found.

In 1997 Russia announced that it is building a floating nuclear power station to service Pevek, a remote region in eastern Siberia. Later it was disclosed that other floating reactors might be sold and towed to Indonesia, China, and India. Several countries sounded alarm at this prospect. Nevertheless, the Russians have pressed on with the idea, and more details have emerged. Russian nuclear engineers say that their new generation reactors have a new design and are genuinely safe. Each barge is to have two reactors which produce 60 megawatts of electricity. There is to be storage facilities for spent fuel and living quarters for the crew. Every 12 years, each barge is to be towed back to St. Petersburg for refueling, repairs, and removal of spent fuel. The first units were scheduled to begin operating early in the 21st century. When the reactors are rented by a country which is short on fresh water, desalination units will also be incorporated.

7-33 Reactors in the Post-Soviet Republics and Satellites

In Ukraine, of the three operating reactors at the Chernobyl site, a fire in 1991 closed one. But shutting down the remaining two reactors is proving to be onerous, since they produce 1800 megawatts, about 6% of Ukraine's electricity. Ukrainian officials agree that the other two should be closed down in time, but urge completion of five half-built reactors of another type first. These are VVER reactors (7-32), and are of the pressurized-water type. Each would supply 1000 megawatts of power. But Ukraine can hardly handle the nuclear waste it already produces. President Kravchuk said, "Ukraine cannot currently do without nuclear energy, for economic reasons." Indeed, in 1993 a decision was made to keep those reactors operating on the grounds that Ukraine is being crippled by energy shortages. Russia has been raising prices of oil and gas to international levels, throwing Ukraine's economy into decline. In April 1995 Ukraine announced its willingness to close all reactors at Chernobyl, and replace them with gas-powered generators. American DOE officials say that improving energy efficiency would also help greatly because it is so cost-effective.

In 1988 a remarkable demonstration took place at the Ignalina reactor in Soviet Lithuania. Members of an environmental movement, generated by the Chernobyl accident two years earlier, marched on the reactor and formed a living ring of 15,000 people around the Ignalina plant, which is also a water-cooled graphite reactor. In the end, the Soviet government agreed to cancel an additional reactor already under construction. This was about the earliest example of how popular pressure could be effective against that government.

Lithuanians bitterly criticized Soviet operation of the giant Ignalina reactor complex, but after independence they changed their tune and kept it running. In fact, Lithuania produces 81% of its electricity from nuclear reactors.

Armenia shut down its two reactors after the1988 earthquake, but resumed their operation after a bitter winter. The reactors were again closed down, and the country experienced several years of electricity starvation, worsened by dissipation of resources in a seven-year war with Azerbaijan. But the Armenians did make repairs and upgrade safety; the cost was $42 million, and much of the aid for this came from Russia. By this time, the Armenian people had had their fill of reading by candlelight, doing the family laundry by hand, of walking upstairs past stationary elevators, of doing without refrigeration, and of being unable to use computers. Armenia has no oil or coal, and is in dire need of energy sources. Trees in public parks have been cut for fuel. During the recent winters many people died of hypothermia. The reactor at Medzamor was started up in summer 1995 in a decision which met practically no opposition. As much as there is fear of another nuclear accident, there is the certainty of tragedy in hospitals, homes, industry, etc., if there is insufficient electricity. The question transcends politics; it is a matter of life and death.

Kazakhstan has only a single reactor, called BN-350, at Aktau; its electric power is 135 to 150 megawatts. Its heat is used for desalination of water. The BN-350, which started operating in 1972, is a breeder reactor. It experienced a sodium fire in an accident, but no radioactivity escaped. At first, the plans were to retire the BN-350, but the latest news is that maybe this decision will be postponed. The Kazakh government is planning several new reactors, including a new breeder. The republic inherited the Semipalatinsk nuclear testing ground. The country has quite a number of nuclear experts who need jobs.

Bulgaria has six Soviet-built reactors. Though seriously flawed, some are kept operating because of the need for electricity. The Kozloduy site has more than 700 tons of spent fuel rods stored under water. The Russians no longer accept the waste for reprocessing or storage. Kozloduy is a sleepy town a ten-minute donkey trot south of the Danube. Cooling water from the Danube is pumped through an elevated canal. The six reactors generate 40% of Bulgaria's electricity. Power outages are common in Sofia, the capital. When all are operating, two of the reactors produce 1000 megawatts, and the other four produce 440 megawatts each. The Russian technicians have left, and the anemic pay and miserable living conditions have prompted most trained Bulgarian technicians to quit. The complex has the distinction of having the least safe reactors in the world. In February 1990, 40,000 Bulgarians demonstrated in Belene against a planned VVER reactor, and its construction was halted. The West is so worried about these old clunkers in Bulgaria that the European Union

Accidents waiting to happen

offered free electricity and coal to shut down the oldest one. One unit of the elderly 440-megawatt reactors, known as model 230, is particularly dangerous. Its welds are brittle, owing to too high phosphorus content in the steel, and no way is known to remedy this problem. It should be shut down.

The case of Slovakia represents the Catch 22 dilemma in the eastern countries. The need for electricity is so great that the old reactors have not been shut down, but western powers are reluctant to upgrade them for fear that they will be held responsible in case of serious accident. But finally it might be that this problem can be circumvented. Slovakia has four reactors of the Soviet VVER pressurized-water model 213 type near the city of Mochovce, each producing 440 megawatts, as in Bulgaria. Three western agencies have inspected these facilities. The British investigator recommended that the VVER model 213 units be shut down on the grounds that they cannot be brought up to acceptable standards. The German team, with experience at similar reactors in Greifswald (in former East Germany) suggested the reactors could be upgraded to German standards for $1.2 billion or so. The French inspectors were most optimistic, quoting a much lower cost. The most serious shortcoming of the VVER reactors is lack of a real containment; instead, they have 12 pipes to a bubble tower, an unproven system. Even if the four VVER units are put in operation, two other VVER reactors of a different type in Bohunice might not be closed down: the demand for electricity is simply too great. The Slovaks hope to join the European Union and receive aid, but completion of the reactors in an unsafe way would offend those from whom they seek help. Quite a dilemma.

7-34 Iran

A nuclear program was started in Iran in 1959 with the purchase of a 5 megawatt (thermal) reactor from the United States under the Atoms for Peace program. The Shah began to send Iranian students abroad to study nuclear theory and practice. The government made investments in German and French nuclear industries and contracted with German concerns to build two huge reactors on the Persian Gulf near Bushehr. They were to be 1300 megawatts (electric) each.

The fundamentalist government of Ayatollah Khomeini, taking power in 1979, inherited the unfinished Bushehr reactors from the Shah, as well as an embryonic nuclear research program, along with a ballistic missile program. The new government took care to safeguard these resources, but the reactors, about 70% complete for the first unit, had been subject to corrosion in the Gulf's salty air, and not much could be done about it. The nuclear aspirations of Iran were largely suspended during the long war with Iraq, but in 1984, right in the middle of that conflict, the Iranian government did open a nuclear research facility in Isfahan.

In 1987 Iran contracted with Argentina for $5 billion worth of uranium enriched to 20% uranium-235, shipping some of it to Pakistan for upgrading. In 1985 uranium ore deposits were discovered in Yazd Province in central Iran, and several more have since been found.

On ending the war with Iraq, Iran assigned higher priority to its nuclear efforts. Some thousands of students have been sent abroad for study. A major new nuclear facility is being built in Qavzin, on the Caspian Sea. By 1991 American and Israeli intelligence services were collecting signs that Iran was conducting intense research on uranium enrichment and related matters. Later, evidence began to accumulate that Iranian agents were scouring world markets for materials and parts which could be useful only in bomb production. The country has purchased formidable aid in nuclear technology from China, including a second reactor at Qavzin. The Chinese also supplied a calutron. Iran has hired ex-Soviet scientists and engineers, reportedly at least 150 in number, who specialize in nuclear fields.

When Americans point out that Iran has plenty of petroleum for electricity production, the Iranians answer that in less than 50 years that resource will be exhausted.

The Iranians announced in 1995 that they had contracted with Russia to complete one of the two nuclear power plants near Bushehr. The Russians plan to adapt their VVER-1000 pressurized-water reactors to the German-built containment. The cost is estimated at $940 million. Intense opposition to the deal was voiced by the American Secretary of State. So strong was American displeasure that a cooperative treaty, the Peaceful Uses of Atomic Energy Agreement, was not extended. This treaty, dating from 1973, supports many American scientists who collaborate with their Russian counterparts in fusion energy, nuclear safety, subatomic particles, growing optical crystals for lasers, etc. In their defense, the Russians point out that subsidiaries of American petroleum companies are permitted to deal in Iranian oil, and may even be permitted to develop a new Iranian petroleum field, but President Clinton was inclined to stop these practices. Russia agreed not to sell uranium-enriching centrifuges, and the Iranians announced they are willing to send spent fuel back to Russia, and to accept inspection by the International Atomic Energy Agency.

A small reactor at Tehran University Amirabad Nuclear Center has a laboratory where reprocessing techniques can be studied. It is difficult to escape deep suspicions that Iran is preparing for nuclear weapons for some future time; recent testing nuclear warheads by India and Pakistan will without doubt reinforce this ambition.

7-35 Research in Reactor Accidents

Plans are afoot to carry out a series of simulated reactor accidents. The experiments were begun in late 1993 in southern France at the Cadarache Nuclear Research Center with the participation of the European Community's Joint Research Center, the United States, Canada, Japan, and South Korea. A 40-megawatt experimental reactor, the Phebus, is being used. Six tests covering six years will study simulated core meltdown, loss of backup cooling, leakage into the containment structure, and related events.

Near the Cadarache site the French have also constructed a special greenhouse whose soil was deliberately contaminated with miscellaneous radioactive debris collected from seven reactors in Europe. The main objective is to find ways to limit uptake of radionuclides by crops in case a disaster such as Chernobyl strikes.

The simulation program is called Phebus PF (the PF being for *produits de fission*, French for fission products). The first tests used undersized, pre-irradiated fuel rods. Some 400 sensors monitored temperatures, pressures, and flow rates in the core, as well as steam production, types of radioactivity released inside the containment, and many other parameters. A 100 cubic meter tank was attached to simulate an external environment so that no radioactivity could escape outside. The temperature reached 2850°C, and partial meltdown occurred. Robots were employed to collect samples of the radionuclides in the tank.

Russia is hosting a joint project with several other nuclear nations to investigate the interaction of molten core materials (*corium*) with the lower parts of a reactor pressure vessel. This is Project *Rasplav* (Russian for melt), sited near the Kurchatov Institute near Moscow. The plan is to melt core-materials electrically, using graphite electrodes, in a model of a reactor pressure vessel, and study the nature and rates of interactions. A test using 200 kilograms of corium was carried out in October 1996. The material consisted of uranium dioxide (81.5%), with smaller amounts of zirconium metal and zirconium dioxide, but no fission products. The maximum temperature was 2500 °C. The results of these experiments are exceedingly valuable in preparations for reactor accidents of all types and reduce much of the uncertainty in calculation of source terms (7-25) for accident scenarios.

7-36 Uranium Ores and Mining

Uranium ores are found widely distributed over the Earth, and millions of tons of the element occur as traces in the oceans and in granite. The two most important ores are uraninite and carnotite. Uraninite is a heavy black mineral which is 50 to 85% uranium, primarily as oxide. Pitchblende is a variety of this material. Carnotite is yellow to orange in color, and besides uranium contains vanadium; it is 50 to 60% uranium. The richest ores are found in Canada, Africa, and Europe; substantial deposits occur in the United States, Brazil, Australia, and the former Soviet Union. Canada is the largest exporter of uranium ores. Uranium also occurs in monazite (a thorium-uranium phosphate), and in small amounts in phosphate rocks. Florida phosphate rock contains 40 to 120 parts per million uranium; most is removed in processing. Ores with 0.05 to 0.3% uranium are routinely mined. Such ores generally contain a form of uraninite mixed with huge amounts of earth of one type or another. Our Earth's crust contains more uranium than silver, mercury, or iodine. In 1995 the cost of uranium ore was about $59 per pound of uranium content. The costs must be raised for poorer ores on account of the greater costs of concentration.

About 1982 a deposit of uranium ore was discovered in northeastern Saskatchewan, near Cigar Lake. It was estimated to contain around 150,000 metric tonnes of uranium ore. Since it was at a depth of about 1500 feet in wet clay, a special mining technique had to be developed. This consisted of freezing the soil solid and excavating the ore from underneath using water jets. The ore proved to be between 13.2 and 14.7% uranium.

Uranium ore is mined in open pits when possible, because the radium in it emits the injurious radioactive gas radon-222. Another radon isotope, with mass number 220, occurs in the thorium series. If uranium is mined underground, efficient ventilation must be provided to prevent accumulation of radon. The world's biggest open pit uranium mine is in the Rossing complex in Namibia. During the Cold-War years, American miners were not given much protection from radon, and most later paid the price with their health. A great deal of American ore was mined by Navajos in Red Valley, Arizona. Many of the uranium miners in Soviet times were political prisoners, and were seriously injured by radon.

The ore from the Colorado Plateau, which is 0.5% uranium or less, is crushed and concentrated by a flotation process. In 1982 approximately 11 million tons of ore were mined, and 13,000 tons of uranium oxide separated. The uranium was extracted by an acid leaching method and then processed in additional chemical steps. The residues, still holding about 4% of the original uranium, are known as mill tailings.

More trouble from radon

These mill tailings have given us a four-billion dollar headache. For years they were just dumped, and now amount to more than 190 million tons, 84 million tons being in New Mexico alone. The detritus is scattered by the wind. Radium is being leached out by rain water, contaminating the ground water. At one time mill tailings were actually mixed with cement to make concrete, which was used to build homes and schools. But radon kept leaking into the buildings constructed with this concrete. The health hazards were just too serious. Much of the mill tailings are in Native American lands, and outside the reach of the Environmental Protection Agency regulations. Stabilizing these poisonous pyramids of mill-tailings will cost the taxpayers hundreds of millions of dollars. At the very least the piles of rubble should be covered by clay and/or plastic tarps to prevent rainwater from entering and to confine most of the radon. This procedure is more or less successful because of the short half-life of radon-222 (3.8 days). The Department of Energy devised its Uranium Mill Tailings Remedial Action project in the early 1980s, in which mounds of mill tailings are covered with clay (which is almost impervious to radon if intact), then earth, and then rock. But roots and animals make holes in the cover and water leaks in. This extracts the acid-laced tailings and ultimately contaminates the aquifer with uranium, aluminum, sulfates, and some nitrates. In eastern Utah, just above the Canyonlands National Park, lies a pile of mill tailings weighing about 10 million tons. Some drainage into the Colorado River is occurring. At one time ore holding 500 tons of uranium was processed each day; operations stopped in 1988. Radium leaching from the pile of mill tailings poses a certain level of danger, not yet quantified. Plans are underway to cap the pile with clay.

Mining uranium and processing the ore releases radon as well as dust carrying radioactive materials. A study of mill tailings in 1987 near Pana Marie, Texas, disclosed that nearly 1000 curies of radon was released each year. Consumption of uranium in nuclear reactors means that there is less radon contributing to natural background radiation, but this is minimal.

Mining uranium during the 1950s and 1960s represents a shameful chapter in American history. There were around 15,000 miners, one-fifth of them Navajos, working in underground sites. The mines were unventilated and dusty. A radon count of 500 picocuries per liter was not uncommon. The EPA action level is 4 picocuries per liter. The miners were never told that their health was endangered; hazards were deliberately downplayed by government and employer sources. At least 450 of the miners have already died of lung cancer, and the body count is still rising. The Public Health Service, a small agency with little power at the time, did recommend ventilating the mines to the Atomic Energy Commission. But with Cold War pressures and fear of McCarthyism, nothing was done. In late 1990 the Radiation Exposure Compensation Act was passed by Congress, benefiting surviving miners to some extent. By 1993 some compensation was being paid to survivors.

In situ uranium mining comprises leaching using sulfuric acid, hydrogen peroxide, and other materials. After the uranium is dissolved, the solution is pumped to the surface and recovered. Many such mines are found in Texas, Wyoming, Colorado, and Utah. Contamination of aquifers is likely, and the procedure is hardly environmentally sound. A step in further processing of the dissolved uranium consists of precipitating sodium or ammonium diuranate, both known as *yellow cake*.

The mountain range between Germany and Czechoslovakia, called Erzgebirge, is rich in pitchblende. The series of mines of the Wismut mining concern was closed after reunification of the two Germanys. The region is an ecological disaster area. The miners received annual doses to the lungs from radon estimated to exceed 30 rems. Current international standards for uranium miners limit yearly exposure to 5 rems, and this will probably be lowered to 1.5 rems. Considerable uranium is also mined in France.

7-37 Comparison of Three Power Stations

Consider three power-generating stations, each producing electricity at the level of a billion watts. One burns oil, one burns coal, and one is nuclear. The two fossil fuels contain some sulfur. Coal leaves about 10% of its weight as ash. The table below compares the fuel requirements, the most important air emissions, and solid wastes from the three installations. Ash from coal is dumped into landfills. Rainwater leaches out traces of selenium, vanadium, and other toxic elements. Some of these materials end up in aquifers. The volume of solid wastes from the coal-burning plant is far greater than that of the high-level radioactive waste from the nuclear reactor per year, even counting the mill tailings from uranium production.

Combustion of oil and coal is still introducing many tons of the oxides of carbon, sulfur and nitrogen into the air. Carbon dioxide is a greenhouse gas. The atmospheric pollution from sulfur and nitrogen oxides results in acid rain, damage to trees, and killing of fish in lakes. These injuries to the environment are especially distressing in eastern U.S. and Canada, and in parts of Europe. Coal contains traces of radioactive materials. American coal contains an average of about 1.3 parts per million uranium and 3.2 ppm thorium. Most (99.0%) of the light fly-ash from combustion of coal is captured by precipitation from the stacks of a modern electricity-generating installation. Since 1.0% escapes, this percentage of uranium and thorium also is discharged into the atmosphere, as well as their decay products, such as radium. All the radon is discharged, since it is a gas. The net result is that such a generating station discharges about 100 times more radioactivity into the environment than a normally functioning nuclear power plant of the same capacity. The radiological doses to the population from both sources are relatively minor. There are additional health effects caused by sulfur and nitrogen oxides from coal-burning plants. Of course, a nuclear reactor, containing a huge inventory of radioactive nuclides, represents a greater potential danger in case of serious accident.

Comparison of Three Power-Generating Stations

	Oil	*Hard Coal*	*Natural Uranium*
Heat produced per ton of fuel . . .	0.41 trillion joules	0.27 trillion joules	4320 trillion joules
Fuel consumption per year	1.6 million tons	2.3 million tons	143 tons
Air emissions per year	5 million tons of carbon dioxide	7 million tons of carbon dioxide	10,000 curies of of hydrogen-3
	21,000 tons of nitrogen oxides	19,000 tons of nitrogen oxides	220,000 curies of krypton-85
	10,000 tons of sulfur oxides	12,000 tons of sulfur oxides	
Solid wastes	2000 tons of ash from filters	230,000 tons of ash from filters	100 tons of low radioactive waste 5-10 tons of high-radioactive waste
	360,000 tons from de-sulferization	440,000 tons from de-sulfurization	65,000 tons of mill tailings

Coal also contains mercury. Combustion of coal introduces considerable mercury into the atmosphere, even more than incineration of municipal waste does. The toxic effects of mercury have been well documented. A measure of the mercury contamination of the human body is the mercury content of hair. The WHO safety limit of mercury in human hair is 10 parts per million, but the EPA is pushing for a limit of about one-tenth of this level. It would be terribly expensive to install equipment to remove traces of mercury from exhaust gases of coal-burning generating plants. An invisible assumption in the statement that the problem of radioactive waste from reactors has not been solved is that the problems of waste from coal-burning utilities have been. Supporters of nuclear power point out that fission products do decay, while mercury and similar toxic elements are forever.

7-38 Power from Fusion

Realization in 1920 that the Sun's energy derives from thermonuclear fusion of hydrogen to helium was one factor much later in stimulating development of hydrogen bombs. These bombs were enormously successful, so to speak. After power from nuclear reactors, based on fission, became a reality, it was only natural to wonder whether power from controlled fusion of hydrogen might also be feasible.

Considerable study and research have been carried out on the subject. It develops that the most promising technique which depends on the brute force conditions described below lies in fusion not of hydrogen-1, but hydrogen-2 (deuterium), along with some hydrogen-3 (tritium). If successful and practical, there would be enough energy to supply all the world's needs for many millions of years, with no fission products, although there would be much radioactive waste, largely tritium, and radioactive reactor parts. One estimate is that for a given amount of energy, a fusion reactor would generate 100,000 times less radioactivity than a fission reactor. One gallon of ordinary water contains

The dream of limitless energy

enough deuterium to yield the energy equivalent to that of 360 gallons of gasoline. Surplus neutrons, if moderated, could be used to breed plutonium-239 from uranium-238, or to breed uranium-233 from thorium-232. The plutonium-239 and uranium-233 are readily fissionable. Fusion reactors would not involve a chain reaction.

To effect fusion in a man-made reactor, temperatures of 50 to 400 million degrees C or so, depending on the pressure, are necessary, and the atoms must be confined sufficiently long to react. Problems of introducing raw materials and removing the products would have to be solved. Since no material can withstand such high temperatures, the hydrogen (as a plasma) would have to be confined magnetically, although other techniques could conceivably be developed. The closest approach to success up to about 1988 was achieved by the Soviets in their tokamak apparatus, a huge doughnut-shaped ring (see sketch). The word *tokamak* is an acronym for the Russian term meaning torus, chamber, and magnetic. A temperature of 90 million degrees C has been achieved in the Tokamak-10.

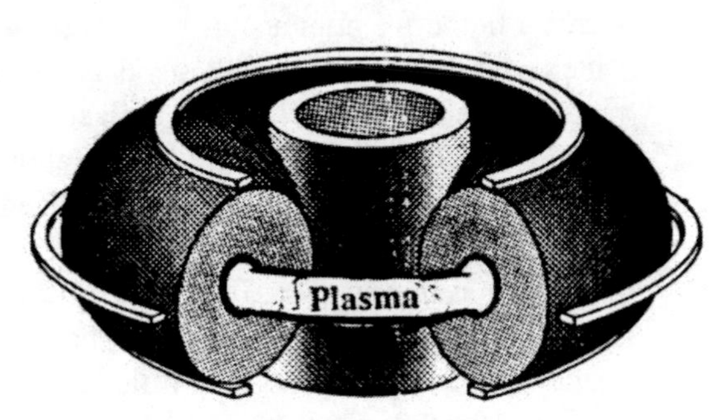

Schematic of a tokamak

The United States has spent more than $10 billion on fusion research since 1955. The six main laboratories are at Princeton, MIT, Oak Ridge, Los Alamos, Livermore, and General Atomics in San Diego. In addition, an International Thermonuclear Experimental Reactor is being built at the University of California at San Diego, along with its design base in Germany, with a multibillion dollar budget. It is attracting an expected 90 scientists from Japan, Europe, and Russia. In 1996 three American physicists said they have computer models which indicate that too much heat would escape from the proposed tokamak, resulting in failure of the reactor as planned. Changes are under consideration. Another project, the Tokamak Physics Experiment, also has high priority. While not achieving sustainable fusion, it would yield valuable data on how to do this. A massive, 50-foot-tall American tokamak was built at the Princeton Plasma Physics Laboratory. Starting in 1992, the United States began funding fusion research at Russia's Kurchatov Institute in Moscow at a bargain-basement price, only about $100,000 per year. A tokamak called JT-60 has been built in Japan. There are three fusion research facilities in France (Fontenay-aux-Roses, Grenoble, and Cadarache). The British are constructing a tokamak which is more or less spherical, and it is expected to have advantages over the older models. Another spherical reactor (NSTX) was built by the Princeton Plasma Physics Laboratory.

Fusion temperatures are sufficient to prepare roast ghost.

In operation of a tokamak, a plasma which is electrically conducting is generated from deuterium using microwaves. The circulating stream of deuterons and electrons which results is confined by enormous, properly-shaped magnetic fields to the extent that the pressure becomes sufficient to overcome the repulsion of two like charges, and fusion can take place. Since each deuteron consists of a proton and a neutron, the newborn nucleus has two protons and two neutrons, and is helium-4, but it

Controlled power from fusion is a long time off

still has a great deal of the energy used in overcoming the original repulsion. This excited helium nucleus achieves greater stability via three different pathways. A tiny fraction of its atoms emits a high-energy gamma ray (23.8 MeV), and eventually ends up as ordinary helium-4. The remainder, in nearly equal amounts, either emits a neutron (2.2 MeV) and forms a helium-3 nucleus, or emits a proton and forms a hydrogen-3 nucleus (a triton). Much heat is liberated simultaneously. Testing for these various nuclides or energy forms reveals whether fusion had taken place.

The Joint European Torus Laboratory, situated in England, conducted a test during the fall of 1991 which produced enormous power, 1.7 megawatts, for two seconds. This impressive milestone was accomplished using deuterium and some tritium. Abundant neutrons were produced, and their energy corresponded to that expected for deuterium-tritium fusion, showing that fusion had occurred beyond doubt. In 1997, 12 megawatts was achieved for a little less than a second.

The Princeton laboratory was in the race to produce high power from fusion. The basic reason why the Europeans won this stage of the race is that financing for American research has been steadily cut; by 1990, the budget had been slashed to less than half its1980 level. Nevertheless, the Princeton team succeeded in December of 1993 in operating the tokamak for 4 seconds at 6.2 megawatts, a notable accomplishment. A power level of 9 to 10.7 megawatts was achieved in May 1994. This victory might be the last for many years; the laboratory was largely shut down in April 1997. Only a budget of about $50 million remains, mostly to support some theoretical studies. The Department of Energy plans to close several other fusion research facilities, including the Oak Ridge Advanced Toroidal Facility. This is especially unfortunate, since unlike tokamaks, the Oak Ridge machine was designed to run continuously rather than in short pulses. All this retrenching has devastated the morale of the American fusion researchers.

Suggestions have been made, most prominently in Japan, that controlled fusion can also be accomplished using deuterium with helium-3 rather than tritium. The advantage would be that high-energy protons are produced instead of neutrons; protons, being charged, can be manipulated by magnetic fields and thus steered away from the reactor walls. One problem with this idea is that helium-3 is exceedingly scarce on earth. The Moon has large stores of helium-3 (of solar origin) adsorbed in its top layers, but mining it would be quite a task. Attempts are also being made to accomplish fusion by zapping a pellet of frozen deuterium-tritium fuel with an array of powerful laser beams. The instantaneous heating evaporates some fuel, compressing the interior and hopefully causing some fusion. In some regards, the technique resembles the implosion of hydrogen bombs by pressure generated from radiation (9-15). Fusion on a minor scale has been accomplished at Brookhaven National Laboratory, NY, by first generating microcrystals of deuterium oxide (heavy water), giving them a positive electric charge, and accelerating them in an electrostatic field. At high energy, the particles collide with a target of deuterium-rich material such as titanium deuteride. Under these conditions, a few atoms fuse, as proven by detecting the products: protons, tritium nuclei, and helium-3 nuclei. Still another technique, which dates from the 1950s, is called "pinch" fusion. It consists of a filament of frozen deuterium/tritium (in a metallic wire) which is converted to a plasma and heated by discharge of an electric current through it. This is done by discharging capacitors. The electric current generates a magnetic field that constricts the particles, hence the name of the process.

An alternative to a tokamak is the stellarator. This depends more or less on the same principles of magnetic confinement, but are more leak-proof. They consist of intertwined spiral magnets and several ring magnets. No large-scale tests have been made, but Japan's National Institute of Fusion Science is preparing to undertake the required studies.

But the practical difficulties in harnessing fusion energy seem almost insuperable, and no industrially successful fusion reactor of any type is in sight. But Sandia National Laboratory announced in 1998 that a new fusion device, called the Z machine, might provide a means of accomplishing controlled fusion.

It might not be charitable to mention this, but no one seems to have considered that a large part of our society's problems could stem from expenditure of too much energy, not too little. What if endless, cheap energy became available? Without a drastic change in human breeding habits, our crowded Earth would in time have people everywhere, without forests or wilderness. After all, in the period 1950-1970, energy use doubled, and yet average quality of life in the world declined. The most important human problems are social, economic, and political, not technological. A point which restrains too much speculation on the subject of too much energy is this. Even if fuel or other primary energy source costs nothing, the cost of residential electricity would drop at most by about a third. This is because of the fixed costs. These include interest payments, depreciation, maintenance, labor, profits, insurance, taxes, safety measures, environmental impacts, and other factors.

What? Too much energy?

7-39 Cold Fusion

The development of science and its theories has been marked by a few events which aroused a great deal of interest in both the public and scientific communities, and yet in the end turned out to be duds. One of these occurred in 1927, seven years after the colossal energy production by our Sun was first understood in some detail as a consequence of thermonuclear fusion (4-12). In Sweden, researcher Tandberg electrolyzed water using palladium electrodes and alleged that excess energy, as well as helium, was produced by fusion, soon dubbed cold fusion. He applied for a patent, but his claim did not stand up. A British announcement in 1958 of a "Zeta reactor," which was said to effect controlled fusion, caused quite a stir. That dream was soon punctured too.

In March 1989 claims were made by chemists Fleischmann and Pons that they had accomplished cold fusion. This announcement galvanized many communities of scientists, especially those working on controlled thermonuclear fusion. If true, a simple table-top apparatus achieved what billion-dollar assemblies had not. The chemists electrolyzed heavy water (deuterium oxide) containing lithium deuteroxide using palladium electrodes; platinum and titanium were also said to be suitable. These metals are known to avidly absorb hydrogen or its heavier isotopes deuterium and tritium. It was reported that more power was produced (mostly as heat) than was consumed. The products were variously said to be neutrons and helium-3 or helium-4, possibly with some tritium.

The lure of limitless energy

Some of the papers stated that gamma rays were detected. There was evidence that the number of neutrons liberated was suspiciously less than the number proportional to the power produced. The barrier to fusion is the repulsion of the two positively-charged deuterium nuclei (deuterons), and heroic measures are generally required to overcome this obstacle. In this case absorption of the deuterium by the palladium was supposed to have played a role in fusion by forcing the deuterium nuclei close together. "Hot fusion" has been carried out by zapping a frozen cluster of deuterium with a powerful laser beam, producing helium-3 and neutrons. Each joule of laser energy produces 100,000 fusion neutrons. More energy is consumed than is produced. The announcement of cold fusion kindled enormous interest in all mass media and scientific circles. Within a couple of years as many as 1000 laboratories in many countries had started investigations. Claims and counterclaims of success or failure were made, sometimes acrimoniously. Some scientific meetings began to assume the quality of a political convention. Explanations appeared trying to rationalize fusion inside the palladium despite the apparent violation of known physical laws. One invoked hydrogen-2 (i.e., deuterium) with a negative muon (4-15) in place of an electron; this arrangement was supposed to permit the muon to attract two deuterons together to less than a hundredth of their normal separation distance. Such were the symptoms of fusion fever.

The crucial debunking experiments were carried out in Britain, in the United States, and by a team of five French laboratories. The French carried out their experiments in an Alpine tunnel to attain a low neutron background. These definitive studies, with sophisticated instrumentation, appeared to discredit the putative cold fusion process. So far as science itself is concerned, it suffered a minor bruise perhaps, but recovered quickly through the process of exposing its own errors and folly. The harsh lessons of reality prevailed, as usual. In the end most scientists knowledgeable in the field concluded that the cold fusion process simply did not occur. Proper controls were lacking in the original work. Neutron measurements were especially faulty. Even very careful researchers were bedeviled by utterly unexpected contamination of their palladium with tritium, and thus were deceived into thinking the tritium arose from fusion. Proper experiments must consider not only possible contamination, but also helium-4 and background gamma rays from radon in the air, blank and control experiments, and background neutrons from cosmic rays. The drive to be first in the race encouraged shortcuts in these precautions, and thus resulted in error. State-of-the-art equipment was not employed in much of the early work. There was never any intent to deceive.

Reality check!

Nevertheless, a few true believers remain. Cold fusion proponents are still intrigued by hints of some unknown nuclear process. Attempts to accomplish cold fusion continue in the United States, Europe, and Japan. There have been quite a number of instances in science when the establishment proved to be wrong and some upstart iconoclasts proved to be correct. It is too early to come to any firm and final conclusion about cold fusion. A few competent physicists continue both experimental and theoretical work. One group proposes that the wave nature of matter is involved in some way (the transmission resonance model); this is said to permit fusion, and thus excess heat. This concept led to the hypothesis that under the electrolytic conditions, cold fusion of protons or deuterons with alkali metal nuclei (lithium, sodium, potassium, and rubidium) could occur; claims have been made that this has been verified. There is even a company in Dallas, Clean Energy Technologies, Inc., which sells the Patterson Power Cell in which cold fusion is alleged to take place. The burden of unchallengeable proof of such astonishing events rests on the scientists making the claims. While the last studies have calmed this fun-filled tempest in the heavy-water pot, at the very least this case of cold fusion fever has inspired thought on how to achieve fusion in new ways.

7-40 Household Consumption of Electricity in the United States

Electricity consumption in American homes varies greatly. In urban areas, household electricity consumption for one person averages 150 kilowatt-hours per month, very roughly. Depending on circumstances, the amount might be half or twice this value, or even more divergent. This amount, 150 kilowatt-hours per 30-day month, figures out to be equivalent to a constant energy consumption at the rate of 208 watts. To change kilowatt-hours per month to watts, multiply by 1.39. This counts household use only. The total urban consumption, including business, industry, street lighting, etc., is a little more than twice this value, or somewhere around 400 watts per person. Thus for a city of one million, the electricity demand would be 400 times one million, which is 400 megawatts of electricity. One must keep in mind that these values vary greatly depending on climate, industrial density, season, and other factors.

7-41 The Economics of Nuclear Power

Whether nuclear energy is economical depends to some degree on how the accounting is carried out, but the costs of electricity from coal and from uranium are roughly the same. Data from the utility companies and other sources gave the following costs for production of electricity (cents per kilowatt-hour).

	1975	*1980*	*1985*
Using oil	0.927	6.9	7.3
Using coal	0.476	3.2	3.4
Using uranium	0.347	2.7	4.3

The cost of electricity produced by the N Reactor at Hanford in 1986 was quoted at 1.8 cents per kilowatt-hour. The householder in the United States typically paid 8 to 12 cents per kilowatt-hour in the 1990s. In 1988, the cost of generating electricity using new reactors was about 13 cents per kilowatt-hour. Electric grid systems were installed before nuclear energy came on the scene; was a prorated share of their costs counted in? Costs in their entirety would be included in a critical accounting. Obvious expenses in production of energy are those of mining, ore processing, accessories, turbines and generators, transmission lines, waste management and disposal, insurance, and decommissioning. Nuclear reactors entail expenses for uranium enrichment, and fuel rod preparation, and extra expenses for waste disposal. Decommissioning can be nearly as expensive as the original reactor construction price. One reason for this is that the cobalt, nickel and niobium used in alloy steel become Co-60, Ni-59, and Nb-94, all dangerous nuclides. Stabilization of mill tailings must also be included. An imponderable factor is possible military use of the plutonium produced. Of course, corresponding costs for oil- and coal-burning electricity generating plants must be included, as well as environmental costs of acid rain and the greenhouse effect. A great deal of the uranium, oil, and coal deposits in the U.S. are owned by a few companies.

A 1984 study compared the human costs of coal and nuclear fuel cycles. Considering coal and uranium mined underground, transported by rail, and consumed to produce 1 gigawatt-year of electricity, there were 279 cases of illness and 18 deaths connected with coal, and 17 cases of illness and 1 death connected with uranium. Environmental damage from coal mining is also far greater. It increasingly comes from strip mines, which damages large areas of land.

Both the Department of Energy and the utilities companies grossly overestimated the need for expansion of the nuclear reactor business. The result was the mothballing of one of three gaseous diffusion plants for production of uranium enriched in U-235, and halting construction of a new plant for enrichment by the gas centrifuge technique, which is less expensive to operate. These steps resulted in a loss of at least $3 billion. But since 1984, demand for electricity in the U.S. has been rising; consumption rose nearly 5% in 1987, and is currently rising 2.5 to 3% per year. In 1993 General Electric estimated that demand for electricity in Asia will grow at twice the world rate, and orders for many power plants will materialize. Over $1.7 billion in new orders were received during 1992-93. Indonesia, whose economy improved during the period about 1990 to 1997, is planning to install its first power-producing reactor, but this seems to have been put on hold in 1999, when depression set in. Westinghouse is lobbying for its latest model, the AP600, using such tactics as training Indonesian engineers. The Japanese are also trying to sell its reactors to Indonesia. Indonesia is planning, in time, to establish nine new reactors in Java with a generating capacity of 7000 megawatts. The Electric Power Research Institute estimates that global demand for electricity will become two to four times the present level by 2050.

The five major companies in the nuclear business have experienced rapidly rising costs in electricity generation, so much that only the best managed plants are competitive with coal-burning stations. Expenses are still rising, and profits are falling. Costs in 1988 of nuclear power reactors averaged about $3.10 per watt, that is, $3.1 billion for a one billion watt plant. Erosion of investor confidence has been a major factor in halting new construction. Future demand for electric power is tricky to estimate. No new power reactors are being constructed in the U.S. The gestation period for construction now averages 12 years, and interest on the financing is not inconsiderable. The cost of building reactors has quadrupled since 1980. Michigan's largest reactor has been converted to run on natural gas. The exhaust heat is employed in the process and the efficiency is increased. One bright spot for the nuclear industry is that the newer high-

Nuclear reactors are only marginally competitive.

temperature, gas-cooled reactors convert about 40% of their thermal energy to electricity, compared with 33% for the pressurized water type, but it must be remembered that the cost of uranium fuel is relatively low. The low degree of standardization of American reactors has raised their cost. Design and engineering expenses are less when spread out over many plants. Public support is an essential ingredient for nuclear power, and currently this is only at about the 50% level; even this has been falling since Chernobyl. Steps which can be taken to reduce costs include making reactors smaller.

Despite the nuclear industry's decline, Congress appropriated $203 million in 1994 for fission research, and $366 million for fusion research. But in 1995, about a third of these amounts were cut off. Federal support for helium-cooled reactors was canceled, but its sponsor, General Atomics, says it will continue the research.

Finally, one might imagine that dependence on imported uranium will foster formation of something like OUEC (Organization of Uranium Exporting Countries), corresponding to OPEC.

In summary, it is not clear that electricity from nuclear sources is really economical at the present time in the United States. In Japan, energy from coal is more expensive than from nuclear sources, at least if decommissioning and waste costs are neglected. The above discussion is clearly not the last word.

7-42 Does Nuclear Power Reduce Carbon Dioxide Emissions?

Obvious expenses in the case of nuclear energy are those of mining, ore processing, isotope enrichment, preparation of fuel elements and the reactor and accessories, turbines and generators. Additional costs are those of waste management and disposal, insurance, and decommissioning after the reactor is finally closed down. In the case of breeders, there is an additional cost of reprocessing.

Occasionally a proponent of nuclear power touts this source of energy as avoiding pollution by excessive carbon dioxide and thus an enhanced greenhouse effect (4-31). If the argument is restricted to just the operational stage of nuclear reactors, then it is without doubt true. Valid comparisons of nuclear *vs.* combustion sources are difficult, but some are available.

A great deal of carbon dioxide is evolved from burning fossil fuels to generate energy used in mining uranium, enriching it in uranium-235 by gaseous diffusion or the centrifuge process, transporting the materials, disposing of waste, and other operations. Another source of carbon dioxide is use of diesel-driven generators during power shut down of reactors while refueling. To make the claim of lowered total carbon dioxide emissions from nuclear energy credible, the energy used to build and supply a reactor must also come from a nuclear source itself, or at least from a renewable energy source.

The Nuclear Power Oversight Committee, representing the nuclear industries, made an analysis of the matter (1990). The result was that for each 1000 megawatts of generating capacity, coal-fired plants emit 5,500,000 tons of carbon dioxide per year, while nuclear plants cause 970,000 tons to be discharged, that is, about 18% as much. In generating electricity in the United States, 5.33 tons of carbon dioxide per capita are emitted annually. In France, with its large nuclear power input, the number is 1.56 tons (it was 2.60 tons in 1973). While the figures above might be challenged quantitatively, it appears to be true that if reactors are made to pay their own way fully, they contribute less carbon dioxide to the atmosphere per unit of energy than combustion plants do, but this has not been achieved yet on any appreciable scale. Breeder reactors present a different scenario. But as the richer uranium ores are exhausted and leaner sources are tapped, there must come a point of futility where as much energy is used to generate nuclear power as is produced. This point is somewhere below 100 parts per million uranium in the ore, the exact value depending on the ore type, depth, rock hardness, and location.

7-43 Reactors: Shall We Shut Them Down or Not?

Early in the nuclear age, the promise of cheap, almost limitless energy dazzled the peoples of both the developed and developing worlds (these words refer to economic development, not cultural). Somewhere along the way, intractable realities began to become apparent. The energy was neither as abundant nor as cheap as had been imagined, and fearsome dangers accompanied it. A generation of unfulfilled promises took its toll. In physicist Freeman Dyson's words, "Sometime between 1960 and 1970, the fun went out of the business. The adventurers, the experimenters, the inventors, were driven out, and the accountants and managers took control." Utility companies were reluctant to build nuclear power stations until their financial responsibility to victims of possible accidents was limited. At first this limit was set by Congress at $700 million per accident (Price-Anderson Act, 1957). Actually, utilities may deduct legal expenses, and pay claims only from what is left. Moreover, indirect losses resulting from temporary breakdown of a city's economy caused by a nuclear accident are not covered. A bill introduced into Congress in 1988 and now in effect raises the limit from $700 million to $7 billion. After the Chernobyl accident, the Soviet government paid out $1.12 billion to 116,000 people, not counting construction of new houses for the evacuees.

The danger and insurance costs make reactors hard to love.

It seems probable that the world's governments which have the capacity to develop nuclear power reactors have jumped in too fast, trying to gain immediate profit and benefit, without examining sufficiently the long-term situation. Were it not for nuclear weapons, reactors would have had much less attraction. The use of the existing nonmilitary power reactors can recoup the enormous financial investments in them, and give time to develop alternative (and less hazardous) energy sources, as well as furnish additional experience in reactor operation. The utilities industries should carry out more critical safety studies. This means finding ways to lessen still further the dangers from accidents. It means putting more effort into the methods of disposing of nuclear waste safely. The new reactors should be designed keeping in mind that they will eventually be decommissioned and disassembled. Service life of reactors will have to be extended. Greater safety also means developing better control over mine mill tailings. It means harnessing the heat now wasted in reactor operations; for example, it could be used to heat greenhouses (hothouses) in colder areas. These steps are part of an overall program of sensible energy management.

We Americans especially seem prone to quickly burn up all the fuel we can get our hands on, although we have improved in recent years. But if we persist in an insatiable appetite for luxurious energy to pamper every whim, no matter how trivial, then we must also accept the accompanying risks.

One reason that all nuclear reactors should not be phased out is that small reactors, such as the TRIGA type, should be kept for medical and scientific purposes. They produce the short-lived nuclides necessary for these ends. They are also needed in training reactor operators.

Another reason is that certain reactors offer one of the principal means of safely destroying all the uranium-235 and plutonium-239 which has been accumulated in the world's nuclear arsenals. The arms race ran, in part, on the threat from uranium-235 made for power reactors, and plutonium generated in them.

A decision today to commit our future to capital-intensive nuclear power exclusively is premature. Like driving a car in traffic, the technology is inherently unsafe. A positive decision to use more and more nuclear energy would be to commit the human race to exercising tenacious and eternal vigilance over all steps in production of nuclear power, from mining to disposal of wastes. But if the public is subjected to risk or benefit, the public should have the principal voice in the decisions. Many news media, especially television, present nuclear power and other nuclear issues as being outrageously dangerous, magnifying the risks thousands of times over the true values. The public can hardly be expected to make enlightened decisions in the absence of facts. Any feeling on the part of the people that they have been excluded from the decision-making process leads to their unremitting opposition to whatever decision is made. Virtually no new reactors have been ordered in the United States in recent years. This might be viewed as nuclear power having had its chance in the market place, and having failed the test. After the Three Mile Island and Chernobyl accidents, polls showed that 73% of Americans opposed construction of new reactors within five miles of their homes. Reactors lost their luster in the U.S., as manifested by the closure of training reactors on university campuses. The numbers of students majoring in nuclear science and engineering have fallen dramatically. By 1997 the number of students in the entire USA majoring in nuclear engineering had fallen to 570; five years earlier, the number was around 1500. About 1994 or so an undercurrent supporting modern, inherently safe reactors began to appear, and this intensified about the year 2000. Many openings are beginning to appear, and foreigners are beginning to fill the gaps.

In 1991 Germany decided to shelve a project in North Rhine-Westphalia on which $2.6 billion had already been spent. In 1988 a decision was made to scuttle the $6 billion Shoreham reactor on Long Island, New York, before it sold any electricity. It had the capacity of 1000 megawatts of electric power in an area where there are chronic shortages. It could well be, but is unlikely, that this trend will continue into the future until very few of these caldrons of nuclear fire, perceived as frightfully perilous, are constructed and until a higher stage of civilization is attained by the human race. In 1978 the people of Austria decided by ballot not to use a newly-built reactor; after Chernobyl, its dismantling was begun. This decision was eased by abundant hydroelectric power in mountainous Austria, an option not available everywhere. Denmark shelved its plans for nuclear power stations. Switzerland, which has five nuclear reactors, has steadily improved efficiency. In 1991, the average capacity factor was an impressive 87.6%. China decided in 1991 to build a second 300 megawatt (electric) reactor at Qinshan, and to order two 1000-MWe reactors from Russia.

The trends are not all downward: in 1987, a referendum in Maine which would have shut down the Yankee Nuclear Power Plant was defeated 59% to 41%. Sweden, which generates about half of its electric power using nuclear reactors, was planning to phase out all of its dozen units by the year 2010, the result of a referendum. But in 1991, this mandate, now beginning to get moldy, was slowed down by a complicated political compromise in which the actualities were recognized of the huge costs (tens of billions of dollars) of the premature shutdown of the nuclear power plants. Unlike Norway, the Swedes have about reached the limit of their hydroelectric power generation. They have little or no oil or gas. Their analyses of alternative or renewable energy supplies are not very optimistic. By 1998 not one reactor had been closed. Like the French, intractable realities seem to be forcing them to live with nuclear power. Norway and Denmark have no power reactors.

But consider nonnuclear sources of energy, primarily combustion of oil, gas, and coal. There is the acid-rain problem, resulting in polluted water and destroyed forests. This obstacle can be managed with modern technology (4-28B). The favorable energy supply from petroleum which the world enjoys today cannot endure for an extended time. There is the possibility of the greenhouse effect (4-31) from excessive carbon dioxide production, resulting in raising the Earth's temperature, melting polar ice caps, and rising sea levels. No visible solution to this problem is on the horizon, although the degree of its damage is not fully clear. Taking into account the best features of nuclear reactors and the remarkable new ways of disposing of waste, a good case can be made in favor of continuing to develop nuclear sources of energy. Risks are involved, but they are minor compared to nuclear weapons. Thus a reasonable policy is to oppose the operation of military reactors (to produce plutonium or tritium) all over the world. Nevertheless, nuclear weapons are here to stay for the foreseeable future; various countries will maintain their arsenals until some sort of world organization or government has the power to prevent it. This means that uranium-235 enrichment and reactor technology will not be lost.

Whatever course we choose, the risks are high.

Quite a number of people, some well informed, feel that all commercial power nuclear reactors should be phased out. The message in this is that the human race simply cannot cope with such a potentially dangerous technique. Yet there is an enormous amount of energy locked up in atoms, so there is the constant temptation to tap it. A nuclear program in which development of ultra safe reactors is emphasized would be best, assuming a more or less satisfactory solution to the waste problem is found. A great deal of additional research on waste disposal is thus needed. At the same time, we need an accelerated educational program, so the public increasingly understands that a high standard of living requires abundant energy, but that this comes with a cost. The merits of a limited world population need to be emphasized. Regardless of one's attitude toward nuclear energy, most of us support increased research to win inexhaustible, nonpolluting energy. These techniques were discussed in section 4-29B. Petroleum is really too valuable a resource to be used simply as a fuel.

7-44 A World Without Nuclear Power

As mentioned above, a great many experts in energy-generating fields feel that all reactors should be phased out and terminated permanently. The principal reasons cited are:

- The stubborn problems of nuclear waste;
- The dangers of accidents, Chernobyl ranking first to date;
- The fact that most types of plutonium-based weapons can be made from spent fuel, tempting rogue nations, terrorists, and others.

Closure of all reactors would not prevent clandestine development of bombs based on uranium-235, which can be separated from natural uranium using equipment more difficult to detect.

What would it mean to halt all nuclear energy sources? The energy lost (approximately 7% of the world's supply) would have to be replaced. In the short run this would be from fossil fuels, but with dedication, renewable energy sources could be phased in and fill the gap. Intense efforts worldwide would have to be undertaken to conserve energy and use it efficiently, something we ought to be doing anyway. A lower population on earth would contribute mightily to making the above steps possible.

For each gigawatt of electricity-generating capacity, commercial reactors today produce approximately 200 kilograms of plutonium (mostly Pu-239, with a high proportion of Pu-240) per year. About 70 metric tonnes of plutonium are now produced annually. Modern developments in bomb detonation makes it possible to employ some of this material to manufacture a nuclear arsenal. In principal, breeder reactors can avoid this problem because they can be operated in consumer (incinerator) mode, destroying all the plutonium produced. But even in this case, it is not difficult to switch into breeder mode. None of this addresses the uranium-235 question.

The views of those for and against nuclear power seem irreconcilable, but the arguments are not so much about the facts as about which facts are chosen to emphasize.

7-45 The Future of Nuclear Power

In 1946, the United States proposed the Acheson-Lilienthal-Baruch plan in the United Nations Atomic Energy Commission, a plan which called for creation of a global agency to govern nuclear energy. No decision was made to establish such a commission, but the United Nations later on did institute the International Atomic Energy Agency, with a more limited scope. Whatever the means, it seems wise to have a strong international hand in all nuclear power developments. This could help insure a sustainable environment.

The vast potential of nuclear energy can be harnessed with confidence only if all issues of safety, waste disposal, and weapon proliferation are monitored by an international agency. Such an agency could avoid construction of unsafe reactors, such as the Chernobyl type, and could issue guidelines for accident prevention, waste treatment and disposal, and means of combating smuggling and sale of nuclear materials for possible clandestine bomb manufacture. Looking far into the future, we realize that present reactors just won't do. These reactors extract only about 0.6% of the energy stored in uranium. With this low efficiency, the supply of reasonably rich uranium ore could be exhausted within perhaps a century or so. Fossil fuels will also be scarce in a few centuries. The higher- and medium-grade uranium ores might last that long, but low-grade supplies are sufficient for millennia.

Breeder reactors can produce 75 to 100 times as much energy from a given amount of uranium as in current reactors. But breeders require reprocessing, and at the present stage of development of nuclear energy, this makes them almost unacceptable to many for the time being. By maintaining research efforts constantly, it seems very likely that in a few decades, acceptable techniques can be developed. Continued laboratory research, pilot plants, and computer modeling should be continued. The exploitation of thorium-232 might be similarly possible. Who knows? Maybe even processes based on fusion will eventually emerge.

Whether reprocessing or recycling is a good idea, as opposed to simply storing spent fuel rods in a repository of some kind, depends on how far into the future we look. Bertrand Barré, Director of the Center for Atomic Energy in Paris, thinks that as uranium resources run low and the demand for electricity continues to grow, reprocessing will become a necessity. He states: "If a country is going to use nuclear power as a long-term resource, it has to recycle." Considering these views, it might make sense to dispose of spent fuel in a manner in which it could be retrieved.

One can make a case that the danger is in not going nuclear. Even with furious development, alternative and renewable energy sources are diffuse, and cannot meet the enormous demands of a growing world population which aspires to a high standard of living. The Electric Power Research Institute in California estimates that demand for electricity over the next 50 years will grow by 400%. It is difficult to see any way this can be accomplished without some contribution from nuclear sources. It seems as if the American public is suspicious of nuclear power on the one hand, but intrigued by it on the other, and might be increasingly ready to accept it as the lesser of many evils.

Our people have become imbued with intense emotions and fears concerning nuclear matters, especially considering the weapons issue. Maybe these feelings are a way the populace is saying that any nuclear cataclysm is just totally unacceptable. In summary, the skepticism of the general public regarding nuclear power stems from: fears of a reactor accident as at Chernobyl; concern over low-level radiation from routine emissions; deep disturbance over nuclear warhead proliferation; doubts about adequate radioactive waste disposal; and uncertainty about decommissioning of nuclear power plants. All these are substantive matters. The human spirit and soul are enormously more complex than mere technology.

Bibliography for Chapter 7: Nuclear Reactors

Manson Benedict, Thomas H. Pigford, and Hans Wolfgang Levi, *NUCLEAR CHEMICAL ENGINEERING*, McGraw-Hill, NY, 1979.

D. J. Bennet and J. R. Thomson, *THE ELEMENTS OF NUCLEAR POWER*, John Wiley & Sons, NY, 1989.

Allen B. Benson, *HANFORD RADIOACTIVE FALLOUT* (Iodine-131 Releases, 1944-56), High Impact Press, P.O. Box 262, Cheney, WA 99004,1989.

Joan Bromberg, *FUSION: SCIENCE, POLITICS, AND THE INVENTION OF A NEW ENERGY SOURCE*, MIT Press, Boston, 1982.

Frank Close, *TOO HOT TO HANDLE: THE RACE FOR COLD FUSION*, Princeton University Press, 1991.

Bernard L. Cohen, *THE NUCLEAR ENERGY OPTION*: An Alternative for the 90s, Plenum Press, New York, 1990.

Mary D. Davis, *THE MILITARY-CIVILIAN NUCLEAR LINK: A GUIDE TO THE FRENCH* NUCLEAR INDUSTRY, Westview Press, 1988.

T. Kenneth Fowler, *THE FUSION QUEST*, The Johns Hopkins University Press, Baltimore, 1997.

Nigel Hawkes, Geoffrey Lean, David Leigh, Robin McKie, Peter Pringle and Andrew Wilson, *CHERNOBYL: THE END OF THE NUCLEAR DREAM*, Vintage Books, 1987.

Robin Herman, *FUSION: THE SEARCH FOR ENDLESS ENERGY*, Cambridge University Press, 1990.

John R. Huizenga, *COLD FUSION: THE SCIENTIFIC FIASCO OF THE CENTURY*, University of Rochester Press, 1992.

Andrey Illesh, *CHERNOBYL*, Richardson & Steirman, 1987.

Tetsuji Imanaka, *RESEARCH ACTIVITIES ABOUT THE RADIOLOGICAL CONSEQUENCES OF THE CHERNOBYL ACCIDENT*, Research Reactor Institute, Kyoto University, Japan, 1998.

Tetsuji Imanaka, *RECENT RESEARCH ACTIVITIES ABOUT THE CHERNOBYL NPP ACCIDENT IN BELARUS, UKRAINE, AND RUSSIA*, Research Reactor Institute, Kyoto University, Japan, 2002.

International Atomic Energy Agency, THE ACCIDENT AT CHERNOBYL REACTOR AND ITS CONSEQUENCES (translated from the Russian), Vienna, August, 1986.

John G. Kemeny, chairman, *THE ACCIDENT AT THREE MILE ISLAND*, Report of the President's Commission, Pergamon, 1979.

Eugene F. Mallove, *FIRE FROM ICE: SEARCHING FOR THE TRUTH BEHIND THE COLD FUSION FUROR*, Wiley, 1991.

David R. Marples, *THE SOCIAL IMPACT OF THE CHERNOBYL DISASTER*, St. Martin's Press, 1988.

Grigori Medvedev, *THE TRUTH ABOUT CHERNOBYL*, Basic Books, 1991.

Zhores A. Medvedev, *NUCLEAR DISASTER IN THE URALS*, W.W. Norton & Co., 1979.

Zhores A. Medvedev, *THE LEGACY OF CHERNOBYL*, W.W. Norton & Co., 1990.

Richard Munson, *THE ENERGY SWITCH: ALTERNATIVES TO NUCLEAR POWER*, Union of Concerned Scientists, 1987.

Bennett Ramberg, *NUCLEAR POWER PLANTS AS WEAPONS FOR THE ENEMY*, University of California Press, 1980.

Bennett Ramberg, *GLOBAL NUCLEAR ENERGY RISKS*, Westview Press, Boulder, CO 80301, 1987.

Charles Ramsey and Mohammad Modarres, *COMMERCIAL NUCLEAR POWER*, Wiley, 1998.

Gary Taubes, *BAD SCIENCE: THE SHORT LIFE AND WEIRD TIMES OF COLD FUSION*, Random House, 1993.

Union of Concerned Scientists, *SAFETY SECOND: THE NRC AND AMERICA'S NUCLEAR POWER PLANTS, 26* Church St., Cambridge, MA 02238, 1987.

Frederick Warner and Roy Harrison, *RADIOECOLOGY AFTER CHERNOBYL*, Wiley, 1993.

Alla Yaroshinskaya, *CHERNOBYL: THE FORBIDDEN TRUTH*, University of Nebraska Press, Lincoln, NE, 1995.

Herbert F. York, *THE ADVISORS: OPPENHEIMER, TELLER, AND THE SUPERBOMB,* Stanford University Press, Stanford, CA 94305-2235, 1991.

Herbert F. York, *ARMS AND THE PHYSICIST*, American Institute of Physics, Williston, VT, 1995.

Chapter 8: MANAGING RADIOACTIVE WASTE

ABSTRACT—Many feel that the fatal flaw of nuclear energy is the "insoluble" problem of its radioactive waste, and this view has a certain merit. Here we examine the types and classes of nuclear waste, its amounts and sources, and our options in disposing of it. Reprocessing, and the world's surplus of plutonium, uranium-235, and depleted uranium, might play a central role. The costs and difficulties of cleaning up contaminated sites are discussed. Some of the corresponding problems in the former Soviet Union are compared. Research in treating spent fuel is briefly described. The highly-engineered repository for high-level waste, at Yucca Mountain, is scrutinized. Various alternatives are contrasted, including disposal in geological repositories, storage above ground, and other possibilities. Vitrification of old wastes, both military and civilian, is outlined. Management of wastes in other countries is covered.

8-1 The Problems of Nuclear Waste

What to do with radioactive rubbish

In addition to an accident strewing fission products over a populated area, another vexing problem stemming from power generation using nuclear reactors is what to do with the inordinately dangerous fission products and actinide elements produced. We dare not let this toxic, radioactive garbage get into the food chain via the oceans or underground water. If radioactive waste is simply dumped or thoughtlessly buried in flimsy containers, some of the components of the material eventually spreads through millions of tons of earth, and the problem becomes virtually uncorrectable. While some of the most hazardous nuclides decay quite rapidly, others linger on for thousands of years. Ways must be found to isolate this threatening junk from the environment for centuries if we are to benefit from nuclear energy. The waste from past military reactors represent still another source of danger. We sometimes hear that the problem of nuclear waste has not been solved, and therefore power-generating nuclear reactors should be shut down. What if we applied this criterion to coal-burning power plants? Have the problems of waste from them been solved? We know that these facilities discharge millions of tons of carbon dioxide into the atmosphere, that thousands of tons of ash are generated, that oxides of nitrogen and sulfur are formed, and that traces of dangerous metals (uranium, thorium, mercury, etc.) are set free to pollute the air (see 7-37). A reliable estimate is that burning coal is responsible for the deaths of about 30,000 citizens each year in the United States. In all great industries, waste products are generated. We gradually learn how to manage them to some extent, but rarely "solve" the problems.

In some ways, the problems of nuclear waste are more amenable to resolution than those of coal burning. This is true because the actual mass and volume of these materials is not really very large, considering industrial scales of operations in general. In 1980, world production of high-level nuclear wastes was around 10,000 tons per year. By 1990 the U.S. alone was producing 2500 tons per year. The radioactivity of 10,000 tons of waste, after ten years storage so that the short-lived nuclides can decay, will be around three or four billion curies. For comparison, there are more than a billion curies (a thousand metric tonnes) of radium in the oceans, and it is quite long-lived (half-life, 1600 years). The world's oceans hold approximately five billion tons of uranium.

Some say that we have no right to devolve on to our descendants the dangerous wastes from nuclear industries. This is a powerful and ethical argument. But others say future generations will curse us for consuming so much precious oil, gas, and coal when there is plenty of energy in abundant uranium and thorium, and will find it hard to understand why we are so slow to adopt new technologies. We ourselves might ponder about how earlier generations feared steam boilers, automobiles, radios, and electricity.

There's something wrong with every energy choice.

Unfortunately, there is little precedent for the actual practice of each generation thinking more than two or maybe three generations ahead. For example, the human race today is sharply increasing the levels of carbon dioxide in the atmosphere through combustion of coal and oil, with little consideration for the future.

We might note in passing that Enrico Fermi warned of impending problems of radioactive waste in 1943, saying:

> It is not clear that the public will accept an energy source that produces this much radioactivity and that can be subject to diversion of materials for bombs.

8-2 Nuclear Waste and Its Management

Nuclear waste is any unwanted radioactive material. By far the greatest amount of such radioactivity comes from the spent fuel. Management of radioactive waste is a complex of multifaceted procedures. The manner of permanent disposal depends on the radioactivity level (that is, number of curies), type of decay, decay rates (in terms of half-lives), and chemical and physical properties of the various substances. Spent commercial fuel rods present the most demanding challenge of all waste problems because they represent such high levels of radioactivity. By statute, the government, through the Department of Energy's Office of Civilian Radioactive Waste Management, has promised to provide disposal capacity for the nation's nuclear power plants.

The fuel rods, almost harmless before entering the reactor, emerge glowing with alchemist's fire, having become dreadfully radioactive. They are stored under water in a pool inside the reactor containment at least two years; further under-water storage usually up to ten years is done in nearby structures. The zirconium cladding of the fuel elements is extremely stable during underwater storage, and no case of failure has been recorded without mechanical damage.

Spent fuel rods are deadly!

The water is inside the containment in pools equipped with circulators for cooling. During a two-year period of cooling, the heat liberated from radioactive decay decreases to about one-sixteenth of its original value. Now that the Cold War has ended, about 95% of the nation's radioactive waste is produced by civilian nuclear power plants. At the present rate, most pools near reactors will be filled by about 2010.

Since the problem of finding permanent repositories has not been completely resolved, storage space for spent fuel rods at reactor sites is becoming critical. This situation has forced developing interim methods, such as dry storage technologies. Several types of metal and concrete casks were designed to accept spent fuel rods after removal from the pools. One type is known as Ventilated Storage Casks, and they are emplaced vertically. After loading, the casks are dried and capped. Some are stored in thick-walled concrete vaults, and cooled by natural convection. Dry storage in a similar manner was approved for spent fuel in Scotland after a detailed study. This procedure is probably safe for 100 years at least, but is not a satisfactory permanent disposal method.

Pools containing spent fuel which are outside a reactor's containment dome present a possible terrorist target. This is especially true for those few which are situated above ground level. If the water is drained by a terrorist bomb or otherwise, the fuel rods would self-heat, possibility to the ignition point. The zirconium cladding would burn furiously, scattering fission products all over the area.

8-3 Modern Classification of Radioactive Waste

In the early days, three levels of nuclear waste were distinguished: low-level waste of up to 0.01 curie per cubic meter; intermediate-level waste of 0.01 up to 1000 curies per cubic meter; and high-level waste of above 1000 curies per cubic meter. Today the criteria are considerably more complicated. The level of radioactivity is measured in terms of amount (number of curies) and concentration (number of curies per kilogram or per cubic meter). Half-lives also play a role. High-level waste consists of spent fuel (commercial and from naval propulsion reactors) and components of old military waste. The total amount in the United States is approximately 94.3 million gallons (357,000 cubic meters), 93% of which is at three sites. These are: Hanford, 53 million gallons in 177 tanks; Savanah River, 34 million gallons in 51 tanks; and Idaho Nuclear Engineering Laboratory, 900,000 gallons in 11 tanks.

The changes in classification were stimulated in large part by irresponsible disposal practices of low-level waste in earlier years, for example just loading it into cardboard boxes and dumping it on the ground. Such procedures have been strictly prohibited. Liquids generally must be solidified in cement or adsorbed in a solid. Containers must be structurally strong enough so they are not crushed. Waste with pathogenic or infectious material must be treated to eliminate the hazard. Chemically reactive materials such as sodium or uranium in metallic form are not allowed.

For near-surface disposal there are three main classes, A, B, and C. Class A is the least tightly defined. The number of curies allowed of each nuclide depends in some cases on whether it is in activated metal, that is, whether it had been formed by neutron activation. For example, there is a limit of 0.8 curies per cubic meter of carbon-14 if it is in the form of chemical compounds, but if it is a constituent of steel, the limit is 8 curies. For nickel-59 in steel, 22 curies per cubic meter is the limit. The steel serves as a prison of the radioactive nuclides, rendering them far less harmful. For the long-lived isotope technetium-99, generally from medical work, the limit is 0.3 curie per cubic meter. For plutonium-241, a beta emitter with half-life 14.4 years, the limit is 350 curies, while for curium-242, an alpha emitter with the much shorter half-life of 163 days, 2000 curies are allowed. Class A also includes gloves and other disposable items, as well as most medical waste.

Class B is for more dangerous radioactive substances, and there are more rigorous specifications to protect against inadvertent intrusion. It includes reactor filter resins and may include some transuranics. Class C has a limit ten times that in Classes A and B; if the number of curies per cubic meter exceeds this, then the material cannot be put into a near-surface site and must be emplaced in a geological repository.

Nevertheless, many of the modern regulations are simply arcane. Waste with mixtures of radionuclides given in a regulatory table are evaluated by a "sum of fractions" rule. The fraction of the limit of each nuclide is calculated by dividing the actual number of curies per cubic meter by its appropriate tabular limit. Each of the nuclides has amounts specified in three columns with increasing limits. If the sum of the fractions is less than unity for that column, then the column used determines the class and disposal is allowed. This is an abbreviated treatment of the procedure, but serves to show how formerly simple topics can become convoluted.

Classes without class

The upper end of low-level waste is 10,000 curies per cubic meter. Thus waste officially called "low level" can be 10,000 times as radioactive as some "high-level" waste, a bizarre state of affairs. Low-level waste is waste which is not classified as high level. There is plenty of room for improvement of our classification system. In 1994, 734,000 cubic feet of low-level waste was generated in the U.S. The average cost for burial in repositories was about $152 per cubic foot. To follow current news about such waste see: *www.llrw.org*.

In France, there are three classifications of radioactive waste. Category A waste is weakly to moderately radioactive with beta/gamma emitters of half-life 30 years or less. Any alpha emitters in this class, based on the calculated level of radioactivity after 300 years, must contribute10 millicuries or less per metric tonne. Medical and most research waste falls into Category A. Liquid waste of this level is solidified or converted to a sludge. Oil containing tritium, as well as animal carcasses which contain radionuclides, are incinerated and the entrained particulate matter and ash are collected. Other forms of waste are encapsulated in bitumen. Final disposal of Category A waste is at la Manche, where the containers are stored on the surface, or in concrete monoliths for the more radioactive material. Other such facilities are being made. Category B waste has about the same radioactivity limits as Category A, but contains long-lived alpha emitters, primarily plutonium. Some of it can be incinerated. Category C waste is highly radioactive, being spent fuel and vitrified waste (8-21) from reprocessing (see below). It is vitrified and stored on the surface until put into a deep repository. A type of container safe for shipment of plutonium by air is being developed.

France, which generates 80% of its electricity using reactors, produces 4,000 metric tonnes of packaged high-level waste annually, but the nonradioactive toxic waste amounts to 4,000,000 tonnes. Many French engineers consider nuclear energy one of the safest ways to produce electricity.

Even though some people feel that studying nuclear waste is about as exciting as watching a glacier race, the topic is too important to be ignored.

8-4 Reprocessing

The term reprocessing means chemically treating spent fuel from nuclear reactors by techniques designed to isolate valuable components. In practice, this generally means separation of plutonium, but can also include uranium itself in the case of spent fuel from breeder reactors. The first step used during World War II was dissolving the dangerously reactive material in a suitable acid, generally nitric acid. During the early Manhattan

Project days, the plutonium was then coprecipitated on a host carrier to effect preliminary separation, and the precipitate was redissolved and the plutonium was extracted. After the war, a solvent extraction process was developed called PUREX (8-9). Later the process was supplemented with one called TRUEX (8-9), which still has some use in processing old waste from the cold-war years.

Bertrand Goldschmidt was a French chemist who went to England before the German invasion of France, and he transferred to the Canadian nuclear reactor project in Montreal. He later traveled to the University of Chicago in the early 1940s and worked with the radiochemical group, studying irradiated uranium from the first reactor. In 1950 he was back in France as Director of the Commissariat's Plutonium Service and began research on extraction of plutonium from the fuel of France's new reactors. In 1951 Goldschmidt learned of the author's publication on butyl phosphate (8-9) as an extractant, and he and his group developed a modification of the PUREX process. They also advanced another process, DIAMEX, for extracting minor actinides from high-level liquid waste.

There are two main alternatives in addressing the problem of spent fuel rods: (1) to simply prepare the fuel for indefinite storage without this reprocessing, and (2) to reprocess the fuel rods so as to recover and recycle the valuable uranium and plutonium, and perhaps other materials. The first choice is called the once-through process, and currently is employed by most American reactors. The second choice was employed during World War II and the Cold War and is no longer in practice in the U.S., but might be revived some day if breeder reactors are employed.

The fate of spent fuel

Hanford has many tons of zirconium-clad spent fuel rods in storage. They are washed and dried at 75 °C in vacuum and further dehydrated at 300 °C. They are collected in steel tubing, flushed with argon, and sealed for dry storage. Currently, no commercial reprocessing is carried out in the United States (although it continued until the end of the Cold War in connection with military reactors to recover plutonium-239 for weapons). One of the reasons for halting reprocessing is that much more uranium ore has been discovered since the 1960s, so there is no pressing need to carry out the expensive extraction processes. Another is that separated plutonium always presents the potential of theft by terrorists. Thus American policy is to emplace spent fuel in geological repositories for disposal. The two fission products which are most radioactive in spent fuel are cesium-137 and strontium-90. Their radiations are sufficient to prevent any theft, but after ten of their half-lives (about 300 years) have passed, this self-protection feature has largely disappeared. It might be possible then that the disposal sites would be mined for plutonium.

Just imagine, someone digging in an ancient dump to get plutonium 1,000 years from now.

Reprocessing continues in Britain, France, and Russia; small-scale reprocessing continues in India and Pakistan. The British plant at Sellafield reprocesses 1000 metric tonnes of spent fuel annually. Japan is preparing to reprocess spent fuel from power plants, some of them fast breeders (7-11). The English are treaty-bound to reprocess waste from Japan, and plan to return the separated wastes to Japan. The British plan to service 30 power companies in 9 countries in their Thermal Oxide Reprocessing Plant (THORP), and realize a profit of nearly $1 billion in ten years.

Regardless of which fuel cycle is followed (once-through or recycling), there will still be a need for permanent repositories for high-level waste. This is because fission products from reprocessing must be accommodated.

8-5 Cleanup and Its Costs

A 1988 report from the Department of Energy estimated that it might cost in excess of $91 billion to clean up all military waste in the United States, and an additional $80 to $200 billion to remedy the cumulative neglect at the many sites of the nuclear weapons complex. The term cleanup is often seen in discussions of old nuclear facilities. It is vague, and unless quantified is of little value. Depending on the level of cleanliness to be achieved, cost estimates of cleaning up our nuclear sites range from $200 billion to $1 trillion. The polluted sites will never be pristine in our lifetimes. The enterprise could become the largest civil works project in history. Some of the most heavily contaminated sites might have to be sealed off indefinitely, becoming national sacrifice zones. Still, even the worst-case estimate comes at a cost less than that of the Cold War. The two areas in the United States with the most contamination, Cold War battlefields so to speak, are at Hanford (Washington) and at Savannah River (South Carolina). Corresponding areas exist in the territories of the former Soviet Union.

What a dreadful thought, national sacrifice zones!

During World War II and the Cold War, environmental concerns involving radioactive waste were given short shrift. But now that all excuses are clearly no longer valid, the Department of Energy finds itself in an unaccustomed role, namely subject to meaningful external direction, regulation, and criticism. It no longer enjoys an open-ended budget. In response, the DOE created its Office of Environmental Management, whose own budget is $6 billion yearly. This exceeds the annual amount still spent on nuclear weapons, $3.4 billion. By 1996, the DOE actually began making progress in cleaning up several contaminated sites. In summer 1996 a contract was made with Fluor Daniel Inc., amounting to $4.8 billion, to begin the clean up work at Hanford. At the same time, a slightly smaller contract was signed with Westinghouse Corp. for similar remediation at Savannah River, South Carolina.

A supplementary contract is planned with British Nuclear Fuels Ltd. The original cost estimate was $6.9 billion, but by April 2000 it had risen to $15.2 billion. The company is to take responsibility for the over-all cleanup at Hanford. The plan is to first vitrify about 13% of Hanford's 53 million gallons of high-level waste. The sludge is to be centrifuged, and the solid and liquid components treated separately. The solids hold about 90% of the radioactivity. Each pound of dry solid is mixed with three pounds of glass constituents and melted at 1150 °C (see vitrification, 8-21). The molten glass is cast in stainless steel canisters, each 15 feet long and two feet in diameter, and weighing 9200 pounds. The borosilicate glass is black, like obsidian. The liquid waste is evaporated and similarly vitrified.

A rough estimate of the total radioactive contamination thrown out into the world's environment by the USA and the old USSR is 1.7 billion curies, at its 1996 level. As large as this amount is, it is less than half a percent of the amount of radioactivity in the oceans, which approximates 430 billion curies (most of this is due to potassium-40).

The contamination by the Soviets was far greater than that by the United States. The amount of radioactivity from old Soviet plants reprocessing spent nuclear fuel is much in excess of that from the accident at Chernobyl. In Russia, the three sites most responsible for the contamination are Mayak, Tomsk-7, and Krasnoyarsk-26. Russian scientists today are aware of the problem. For example Alexei Yabokov, a member of the Russian Academy of Sciences, said in 1999: "The Cold War has created environmental problems with which future generations will have to contend."

8-6 The World's Surplus of Plutonium

By the year 2000 the stockpile of plutonium in the spent fuel rods of the world's electricity-producing reactors reached nearly 1900 tons. Of course, this is not weapons-grade plutonium, since it contains up to 25% plutonium-240. Nevertheless, such plutonium has been used to make a bomb (9-9). Consumption of this plutonium as fuel, after reprocessing, in specially constructed reactors is one way to dispose of it. A great deal of fission products is produced, but it might be safer to cope with the problem in this way than leaving the plutonium unchanged. A curious bit of information is that storage of reactor-grade plutonium containing 30% Pu-240 for approximately 24,000 years (the half-life of Pu-239) converts it to bomb-grade plutonium (about 6% Pu-240). This is because the half-life of the 240 isotope is shorter than that of the 239 isotope. Maybe the repositories will someday serve as plutonium mines.

Do you suppose that after 24,000 years our descendants will know what plutonium is and what it can be used for?

A disposal problem which has become important since the end of the Cold War is how to cope with the sudden surplus of uranium-235 and plutonium-239 from disassembled nuclear warheads (9-70). In the case of the plutonium warheads, up to 1% gallium is present, and this complicates the matter. The world is awash with unwanted plutonium.

8-7 The Tragedies of Soviet Waste

Contamination of Towns—The way in which radioactive waste was dumped during the early days of the Soviet weapons effort is utterly appalling. But it can be understood in terms of the urgencies of the Cold War. In Chelyabinsk-40 near the town of Mayak, in the southern Urals, a nuclear reprocessing plant for the first Soviet reactors had been built; and eventually there were three. At once (1949), it began discharging its radioactive rubbish into the Techa River and shortly afterwards residents downstream began to fall ill. The water supply for 125,000 people had been fouled with strontium-90, cesium-137, plutonium, and other radionuclides. The total waste dumped into the river exceeded 150 million curies by 1956 when five reactors were operating. Physicians were not allowed to inform their patients that their illness was a consequence of poisoning by radioactivity. Over an eight year period, the average radiation dose in towns such as Muslimova was 350 rems, and many were afflicted with more. More than 8000 died. Their burden of ill health was enormous. Chronic fatigue and damaged immune systems

The Soviet leaders were sane, but behaved insanely.

were common. Other morbid disorders were heart disease, high blood pressure, asthma, and anemia. One-third of the newborn had some physical defect. There seemed to be some inescapable evil which no one knew how to avoid. The Techa River flows northeast into the Tobal River, which enters the Ob River, and radioactivity eventually began to run into the Arctic Ocean. The discharges were stopped in 1956, and the Techa River is clean today except for its sand and silt. This recovery is in part due to construction of a cascade of reservoirs along the Techa River to store waste. Some leakage is occurring, and the river has shown increased radioactivity lately.

By 1995 cooperation between radiation scientists from the West and Japan with their Russian colleagues at Chelyabinsk and its environs was underway. Data collected at the Urals Research Center for Radiation Medicine have now been released. Around 64,000 people unfortunate enough to live near the nuclear complex, as well as workers at the Mayak plant, were examined over about 40 years. The results appear to yield information available nowhere else, since large numbers of people along the Techa River downstream from the source of contamination were exposed to varying amounts of plutonium, cesium-137, and strontium-90. While there are many uncertainties, it is possible to link the leukemia and other cancer rates to the radiation doses. The exposure was gradual, unlike that at Hiroshima and Nagasaki, where exposure was instantaneous. Exposure was external (gamma rays from radioactive material deposited on the river banks) and internal (mostly cesium in drinking water). Doses were around 115 rads within 10 kilometers of Mayak, 40 rads at 50 kilometers, and 7 rads at 75 kilometers.

Nuclear Cesspools—A great deal of radioactive waste, totaling some 120 million curies, were simply drained into Lake Karachai, which has no outlet and therefore was considered safe. Not only did some nuclides seep into groundwater from this lagoon full of radioactive refuse, but droughts in the 1960s and 1970s caused a drop in the water level. This exposed the newly dried shores to wind, and particles carrying about 600 curies were blown over the countryside. The lake currently contains some 120 million curies, mostly strontium-90 and cesium-137. The cesium is strongly adsorbed by the clay on the lake bottom, but the strontium migrates downward to a larger extent. There is slow drainage into the Asanov swamp at the head of the Techa River. Nearby Lake Staroe Boloto was used as a dump for the medium-level waste. In 1991, the World Watch Institute designated the Lake Karachai and Chelyabinsk-Mayak regions the world's most radioactively polluted areas.

Some distinction, to be the world's most radioactively contaminated spot! Well, at least real estate prices are low.

By 1994 a plan to stabilize Lake Karachai had been developed. More than 5000 hollow concrete cubes were dumped into the lake, which was then covered with stones. This prevents the wind from blowing radioactive sand, and the area will dry up, except during wet seasons which might cause more fission products to seep into the ground water. At present a person standing 30 to 40 feet from the lake's shore gets a radiation dose of 300 to 600 millirems per hour.

Explosion in a Waste Plant—Western intelligence reported an accident of some type involving nuclear waste on September 29, 1957, at the Mayak plant in Novogorny, near Kyshtym, which is north of Chelyabinsk in the southern Urals. In 1989, under the influence of *glasnost*, the Soviets released some information about the disaster, and it conforms fairly well with data from other sources. Many details of the incident are still lacking, but it arose from a chemical explosion, not nuclear. Improperly stored waste evidently had nitric acid, sodium nitrate, and organic materials, and its refrigeration system broke down, allowing heat from radioactive decay to raise the temperature to the ignition point. The tank held 360,000 liters (95,000 gallons) of high-level waste. The radioactive material was blown upwards as a plume and amounted to about two million curies, a large fraction of which was strontium-90. An additional 18 million curies was scattered on nearby grounds. The area most severely contaminated was a narrow strip of somewhere around 400 square miles, and more than 5000 additional square miles were also affected. There were deaths and injuries by radiation; at least 450,000 people were contaminated. By 1994 much more information had become available about a series of hamlets along the Techa River. This area, to the north of Chelyabinsk, was seriously contaminated by the plume from the 1957 explosion.

And Still More Radioactive Defilement—A joint Norwegian and Russian study reported in 1997 that the Mayak area was contaminated with 250 million curies of strontium-90 and cesium-137 alone, which is nearly six times the amount formed by all atmospheric tests combined.

Russian scientists at Mayak have perfected a technique for vitrification of waste which differs in important ways from the American and French procedures. It uses a phosphate-based glass. At least 250 million curies have been bonded in this glass and cast in cylindrical canisters. These are stored above ground.

At Tomsk-7, a large release of radioactive materials, amounting to some 130 million curies, took place. In addition a great deal of waste was injected approximately 1000 feet deep. Perhaps one billion curies has been disposed of in this manner. In Krasnoyarsk-26, now renamed Zheleznogorsk, a huge reactor and reprocessing facility were built under ground. Much waste was injected several hundred feet deep. Altogether, approximately 130 million curies from Mayak, 1130 million curies from Tomsk-7, and 450 million curies from Krasnoyarsk-26 were released into the Russian environment. There is still more contamination from uranium mine tailings.

Millions of curies here, millions of curies there

Sale of Radio-Isotopes—By 1992, all seven reactors producing plutonium had been shut down. Two small heavy-water reactors continue to operate because they make a profit by selling radioactive nuclides for medical and industrial use. One half of the materials goes abroad. Spent fuel from old Soviet submarines is reprocessed in Mayak. Nuclear warheads are being dismantled there, with an American subsidy. Commercially valuable by-products are isolated; the U.S. Department of Energy has a $57.3 million contract to buy 40 kilograms of one isotope, plutonium-238. There are even plans to build three BN-800 breeder reactors to consume excess plutonium and generate electricity. More than 800 million curies of waste is stored nearby.

Cleaning Up Moscow—The area of Moscow is now about twice what it was 50 years ago. The city has expanded into regions where many laboratories, dumps, and factories were originally situated. Quite a number of such facilities used radioactive materials and simply left or dumped them on evacuation. The new occupants are constantly running across them. A city agency called Radon (of all things!) deals with these situations. More than 1000 radioactive sites have been treated. Cesium-137, radium, and tritium are the most common offenders. They were used in military, medical, and energy projects. Contaminated soil is removed and replaced with clean earth or sand.

8-8 Old Soviet Waste in the Arctic

Recently it was revealed that off the shores of Novaya Zemlya, the Arctic island where many nuclear bomb tests were carried out, the reactors from 15 antiquated nuclear-powered submarines were dumped on the ocean floor. These were part of the 407 reactors which powered 225 submarines, three battleships, and seven icebreakers. Still more submarines are scheduled to be taken out of service. Thousands of containers of radioactive waste were also sunk in the Arctic. The total amount of radioactive substances so cavalierly dumped was in excess of 2.5 million curies. A 1994 study of the area by an American team revealed that movement of the radioactive matter is barely detectable. Evidently, leakage has been slight and seabed materials strongly bond to and adsorb the ions of fission products and transuranium elements.

Bonding of all that radioactive material on the ocean floor was the result of good luck, not foresight.

The center of the facilities of the Northern Fleet and the Murmansk Shipping Line are on the Kola Peninsula on the banks of a fjord. It harbors six nuclear icebreakers, more than 100 nuclear submarines with nuclear weapons, two nuclear cruisers, hundreds of nuclear propulsion reactors, and thousands of nuclear warheads. In 1998 Norway and Russia agreed to establish a program to start cleaning up the area, with the Norwegians paying most of the costs. The intention is to start by dismantling the most precarious nuclear submarines.

In the northwest near the Norwegian border 32 cracked and corroded casks of spent nuclear submarine fuel sit in a field. A 370-foot ship, the Lepse, is anchored in Murmansk harbor. It holds 624 spent fuel assemblies. In the areas south, there are many more nuclear facilities. There are 21,000 tanks holding spent fuel rods. All this means that the potential for contamination of the Arctic is high. The expense of dismantling these reactors and weapons safely is at present simply beyond the economic resources of Russia. Weather reports list the temperature, barometric pressure, and radiation level. A small green movement advocates harnessing wind energy.

8-9 Reprocessing Techniques: Generating Radioactive Waste

The Non-Proliferation Treaty of 1976 prohibits reprocessing spent nuclear fuel from civilian power reactors to separate plutonium, and in 1977 President Carter reaffirmed the decision "to defer indefinitely the commercial reprocessing and recycling of the plutonium produced in the United States' nuclear power programs." No subsequent president has changed that policy. When carried out using either commercial or military spent fuel, the following considerations apply: Spent fuel from a reactor consists of two main classes of materials, namely actinide elements and their fission products. They consist of 700 to 800 different isotopic species, most of them beta active; many are gamma active as well. They contribute by far most of the total radioactivity. The actinides which are important here consist primarily of uranium, neptunium, plutonium, americium, and curium. Alpha activity dominates in this group. Out of 100 metric tonnes (based on uranium content) of fresh spent fuel, there are about 3.85 tonnes of fission products, 600 kilograms of actinide elements beyond uranium, and the rest is uranium itself.

The reprocessing must be done in shielded enclosures with remote control, owing to the extreme levels of radioactivity. After being broken up, the fuel material is dissolved in nitric acid, leaving the zirconium cladding fairly clean. During dissolving, gaseous fission products such as krypton, xenon, and iodine vapor are released and adsorbed; the adsorption process is about 99% efficient. An alternative procedure for capturing the krypton is to condense it out using liquid nitrogen. After fractional distillation, the radioactive krypton is stored compressed in steel cylinders. Americans and Soviets both originally allowed the krypton, mostly krypton-85 with a half-life of 10.7 years, to escape into the air. Analysis of the atmosphere for this material gave an index of worldwide plutonium production.

For chemists, this sort of work is absolutely fascinating, at least until one realizes the consequences.

Solvent extraction procedures are well suited to remote-controlled operations, and by application of the appropriate chemical techniques, separation of the uranium, the plutonium, and certain of the fission products is accomplished. The PUREX (***p***lutonium, ***ur***anium ***ex***traction) process employs tributyl phosphate as the solvent (it is the author who first suggested this solvent and who holds the patents on it; Ray Fisher suggested it use here). The butyl phosphate is diluted with hexane or kerosine. Essentially all countries which reprocess spent fuel to recover plutonium use tributyl phosphate extraction. Using moderately strong nitric acid solutions, more than 99.5% of the uranium (with oxidation number six) and plutonium (with oxidation number four) are extracted from the fission products. Chemical reduction of the plutonium (to oxidation number three) permits re-extraction and separation from the uranium. The radiation is so intense that some of the solvent is decomposed, and the efficiency of the process falls off. This can be remedied by purification of the solvent. All of the plutonium except a few tenths of a percent is removed. Most of the fission products remaining after extraction of the actinide metals are not separated from each other, but collected as a mixed precipitate, which is dried. Precautions must be taken to insure that no concentration step of U-235 or Pu-239 causes exceeding a critical mass in aqueous media; otherwise, a flash of gamma rays is emitted and the solution boils out of control. The TRUEX process was developed at Hanford for separating the actinides. It removes all transuranics left over in the PUREX waste stream. It employs the same solvent as in PUREX but with addition of 8% of one of those compounds with formidable names (octyl(phenyl)-N,N-diisobutylcarbamoyl-methylphosphine oxide, in case you just have to know). This permits extraction of neptunium, americium, and curium, much of which is missed by PUREX. TRUEX also

Reprocessing spent fuel

removes some fission products, such as rare earths.

A serious problem in the operation of any large-scale separation plant is the precise accounting for plutonium. Quite a large amount might be missing (from theft or otherwise) and it would not be known.

8-10 Alternative Reprocessing Techniques: Attempts to Lessen Waste Produced

The process of separating plutonium from spent reactor fuel which was employed during World War II to make the first nuclear bomb possible depended on coprecipitation of the plutonium on a bismuth salt. In the post-war years, this primitive technology was quickly replaced by liquid extraction techniques, evolving into the PUREX process (8-9). These methods generate a great deal of wastes. In recent years several alternative ways have been studied, as well as simpler and more specific liquid extraction procedures. Some of the newer methodologies avoid aqueous and organic solutions and depend on molten salts or molten metals as the working medium. The International Atomic Energy Agency sponsors seminars on the topic.

A technique has been developed at Argonne West in connection with the Experimental Breeder Reactor II (7-12) to remove the unchanged uranium from the spent fuel driver assembly and blanket and to collect the fission products and transuranic elements (neptunium, plutonium, americium, and curium) into a mineral-like material which is then vitrified. The hexagonal steel assemblies of pins, which are deadly radioactive, are pulled from the top of the core into lead shielding weighing 30 tons. After aging to allow the short-lived radio-nuclides to decay, the spent fuel is taken through a lock into a round chamber inerted with argon. Operators outside the argon cell, as it is called, look through five-foot lead-glass windows and manipulate the apparatus inside. No one ever enters the argon cell. The pins are removed from their steel casings and are chopped into small lengths. The pieces are dumped into a steel basket and lowered into the electrorefiner. This consists of a steel container holding a molten mixture of potassium chloride and lithium chloride; its temperature is 500 °C (932 °F). There is also a steel electrode in the molten salt. A direct current is passed through the molten salt, causing the spent fuel to dissolve from the basket (positive) and its uranium to electroplate out onto the other steel electrode (negative). The fission products and transuranic metals stay in the molten salt; several fission products, including zirconium-95 and technetium-99, are reduced to the metallic state. The molten salt is then pumped through a bed of an aluminosilicate called zeolite. Several kinds of zeolite are known, some occurring naturally as minerals and others are made synthetically. They have open crystal structures with channels and contain light metals such as sodium, potassium, or calcium. Light metals are readily exchanged for heavier metal ions, resembling a process employed in water softening. Therefore the molten potassium/lithium chloride is pumped through dry zeolite in the potassium form, when the fission products and transuranic metals are adsorbed out by displacing the potassium ions. After draining, the zeolite is mixed with the components of glass, fused, and is ready for a geological repository.

The use of uranium-235 and plutonium-239 as the engines of nuclear bombs has tainted their use as fuel in reactors.

During the past few years still another technique for removing metal ions from waste has been developed. At Pacific Northwest National Laboratory, a treated silica with pores of diameter typically 5 or 6 nanometers is made which selectively and voraciously removes heavy metals from aqueous waste streams. The inside walls of the micro-channels are covered with a monolayer, formed by bonding one end of elongated organic molecules to the silica. The free ends of these tethered molecules can now adsorb and sequester selected metal ions. The surface area of the free space of the pores can be as high as 1000 square meters per gram. One type removes cesium from solutions which are rich in sodium and potassium ions. This type is being used to separate cesium-137 from the stored waste at Hanford, a step which promises to greatly simplify disposal of the waste. Another type of treated silica removes uranium, plutonium, or americium. Still other types of treated silica remove mercury, lead, silver, etc.

The uranium metal which is recovered by the electrolytic procedure contains about 65% U-235, and is melted down with depleted uranium (only 0.3% U-235; see 4-20) to produce metal with less than 20% U-235. Since the uranium has been removed, the volume of the waste is reduced significantly, and disposal is less expensive.

Waste disposal regulations prohibit emplacement of metallic uranium in repositories since it is a reactive metal, that is, not stable chemically. The N Reactor and the Enrico Fermi breeder reactor (Chapter 7) used metallic uranium fuel. Therefore consideration has been given to processing old spent fuel from these reactors at the Argonne West facility.

Officially, the electrorefining procedure described is not, definitely not, classified as reprocessing. Interpreted from the standpoint of intent to separate plutonium, this is correct, but with some modifications, plutonium could be produced, in which case it would definitely be reprocessing. Theft of weapons-grade uranium-235 from the argon cell is virtually impossible, but shipping the material cross country to the site always poses some hazard of theft. The labor costs of the electrorefining step might be unacceptably high, but further development could possibly solve this aspect. Probably the greatest hazard arises from spreading sophisticated technologies around the world, technologies which make reprocessing spent fuel easier and possible in facilities small enough to conceal underground.

DOE officials are really touchy concerning the question of electrorefining being reprocessing.

8-11 Research in Treating Spent Fuel for Disposal

Other studies to separate the actinide elements from fission products by related electrorefining techniques have been undertaken. One of these, now shut down, had the ponderous title Transuranic Management by Pyropartitioning Separation, or TRUMP-S. The developmental research was carried out under the auspices of Rockwell International and with Japanese financing. These types of procedures are under consideration for treatment of wastes (below). They are also considered for possible use in processing spent fuel and in preparing fuel for breeder reactors.

Old military waste is largely a mixture of sludge and alkaline solutions stored in tanks at Hanford, Washington, and at the Savannah River Plant in South Carolina. The sludge contains fission products and many metals from earlier processing and treatment. In one possible procedure to separate out the actinide metals (U, Np, Pu, Am) the sludge is resuspended, pumped out, centrifuged, washed, and dried. This removes most of the sodium nitrate in the aqueous phase. The remaining nitrates are decomposed chemically and the mass is chlorinated at high temperature with carbon tetrachloride vapor. The resulting metal chlorides are dissolved in a molten salt (a mixture of potassium and lithium chlorides), inside an argon cell. Cadmium metal, or in the more recent experiments, bismuth metal, is introduced. The metal melts and forms a heavy layer on the bottom of the salt melt. Next is a step called pyrochemical reduction: lithium metal (as an alloy with cadmium or bismuth) is added, and this reduces essentially all of the actinide elements to the metallic form. The metals are separated from each other by electrolytic refining, if necessary (below). Modified procedures are to be investigated for use in treating waste from Rocky Flats and other sites.

If applied to spent fuel rods, they would be processed by (1) chopping up the fuel elements, and (2) converting the spent fuel itself (metal oxides) to metallic form by pyrochemical reduction with metallic lithium in a molten salt mixture (potassium and lithium chlorides). All the metals dissolve except the fragmented cladding. Under an inert atmosphere such as argon, the mixture is subjected to electrolysis at 450 to 500 °C (842-932 °F). One electrode is molten cadmium or bismuth, the other metallic iron, on which some of the actinide metals deposit. With proper control of voltage, it is possible to separate the uranium, as in the Argonne West procedure. The transuranic metals could be removed to the extent of at least 99.9%, or they could be left in the molten salt. The cesium and strontium stay mostly in the molten salt mixture, while the remaining metals dissolve in the molten cadmium or bismuth. The less active fission products (ruthenium, molybdenum, technetium, etc.) also go into the liquid metal phase. Most of the plutonium, as well as the neptunium, americium, curium, and some rare earth metals, end up in the liquid cadmium or bismuth. Thus the separations are anything but clean. The advantages of the process are said to be to permit disposing of the two groups (actinides and fission products) separately and the production of very little liquid waste. The shorter-lived fission products, solidified in cement, could be put into less expensive geologic repositories, while the actinides could be either buried in vitrified form (since there is not much heat liberated on radioactive decay) or could be put back into a nuclear reactor. The whole procedure is often referred to as pyroprocessing. All such processes are terribly expensive and have yet to prove their economic viability.

On an industrial scale the operations described above, with billions of curies being processed, would be hazardous in the extreme. One must cope with volatilization of some fission products, much as krypton-85 and iodine-129. In casting the recovered fissile metals to make new fuel elements for a breeder reactor, the relatively volatile element americium tends to distill out of the hot mass, causing complications. Accumulated rare earths and other radionuclides in the molten salt would require periodic zeolite treatment or replacement, resulting in still more expense. Contaminated processing equipment would constitute additional material for eventual disposal. The gains of the process might well be outweighed by the disadvantages.

Include me out of this one.

A very promising technique for immobilizing actinide elements has been recently developed by French chemists at the Institute of Nuclear Physics in Orsay, not far from Paris. Thorium is about 3.5 times as abundant as uranium in the Earth's crust, and it is found in ores such as monazite, which is basically a thorium phosphate. It generally contains considerable uranium. Such minerals are exceptionally stable and hold their thorium and uranium for millions of years even through massive geological changes. The thorium in monazite can be partially replaced by uranium, neptunium, or plutonium, that is, synthetic monazite is made incorporating these actinide metals. The host matrix freezes in the metals for millions of years. Pellets of the material can be incorporated into a ceramic. It might be suitable for disposing of uranium-235 or plutonium-239 warheads.

Other studies of spent fuel treatment are being carried out at Argonne National Laboratory near Chicago. For example, the spent fuel, consisting mostly of uranium dioxide, is mixed with metallic calcium and is then heated. This process is carried out under a molten metal, which is a copper-magnesium alloy, and a molten salt; the temperature is 800 °C. The uranium is reduced to the metallic state, which forms a solid, while most of the transuranic metals dissolve in the copper. The cesium and strontium, as well as the iodine, dissolve in the molten salt. Modifications of this procedure involve pyrochemical reduction with magnesium in various molten metals. A case can be made to pursue these studies and research with the aim of separating actinides from waste for breeder reactors, treating accumulated military waste, which is mostly PUREX process residues, and cleanup of contaminated sites such as Rocky Flats. Grave difficulties are to be expected.

Two of the most dangerous and most abundant fission products are strontium-90 and cesium-137. These nuclides, on beta decay, contribute a great deal of heat to the total generated by the waste, so if they are removed, the remaining material can be packed more densely in repositories. These properties have stimulated developing means of removing them from the mass of other waste at an early stage. A technique was developed in 1990 in which strontium-90 can be selectively extracted from liquid waste such as that from military sources. The process uses a compound known as a crown ether to complex the strontium, and a solvent to extract it; the expensive crown ether is recycled. All except 0.001% is removed. The strontium-90 finds a use in thermonuclear generators (6-37), and it is also the source of yttrium-90, a beta active nuclide (half-life 64 hours) used in nuclear medicine and other fields. Joint efforts by Czech and Russian chemists have developed another unique means of extracting both strontium and cesium. It uses a complexing agent known as dicarbollide, a synthetic molecule containing carbon and boron, or its cobalt derivative, and the technique is being investigated by the DOE.

Clever ideas here: they deserve study.

Similarly, in 1992 chemists perfected a technique for removing both cesium and strontium from aqueous waste solutions. It employs a crystalline silico-titanate which selectively removes cesium from aqueous waste solutions, even those with a high sodium concentration. A hydrated, noncrystalline titanate removes strontium. These methods are promising in coping with all that accumulated military waste from Cold War years. Another troublesome fission product is technetium-99, with the long half-life of 213,000 years. A process for extracting it was announced in 1994. It employs a reagent containing phosphorus, nitrogen and silicon. Another technique is use of beads made from a magnetic material and coated with an organic resin which selectively adsorbs cesium, strontium, or transuranium metals. The beads can be lifted out using an electromagnet. Research on numerous other separation technologies is underway.

Some spent fuel rods were still being reprocessed or otherwise treated in 1997 at the Savannah River site. These are "at risk" fuel assemblies, including those from foreign sources, old fuel rods clad in aluminum, and damaged and leaking rods. The purpose is to achieve a higher level of safety, not to recover plutonium, which is a glut on the market. The "Atoms for Peace" program of the 1950s had as one of its objectives a promise by recipient countries not to start any nuclear bomb program, in return for which the U.S. would accept their spent fuel. Other sources of "at risk" spent fuel rods are various American experimental reactors.

The "Atoms for Peace" program was admirable in its objectives.

Finally, it should be pointed out that waste containing transuranic elements which is put in geological repositories might be a backup in the future. After many generations, they could serve, if need be, as a source for transuranic materials. Of course, they might be regarded as plutonium mines by any party which wants to make bombs.

8-12 The Problem of Depleted Uranium

A distressing issue which has not yet been faced fully is how to cope with all that depleted uranium which accumulated during WW II and the long Cold War (see 4-20). There is a huge amount of it, more than 700,000 metric tonnes. Most exists as the volatile compound uranium hexafluoride (UF_6), held in some 60,000 steel cylinders stored near Paducah, Kentucky. The cylinders are four feet in diameter and 12 feet long, and cost about $1600 each. Filled with uranium hexafluoride, each weighs around 13 tons. Some of the material has been used, after reduction to metallic uranium, in military projectiles, as shielding in radioisotope thermoelectric generators and other extremely radioactive devices, as a constituent in certain types of steel, in flywheels, as ballast, etc., but the amount available exceeds the demand thousands of times over.

Uranium hexafluoride is a very interesting substance. It forms beautiful, colorless crystals. Even at room temperature solid uranium hexafluoride readily passes directly from the solid to the gaseous state (sublimation, as in the well-known case of dry ice, which is solid carbon dioxide). If some UF_6 is put into a tube, chilled in liquid nitrogen, evacuated, and sealed, the internal pressure is essentially zero. On warming, the solid begins to sublime and the pressure rises. Measurement of the UF_6 vapor pressure from the solid held at the freezing point of water (zero degrees C) shows it is about 20 mm of mercury (normal atmospheric pressure is 760 mm). At 25 °C (room temperature), the vapor pressure is around 125 mm. At 55.7 °C, it is 760 mm, that is, it reaches atmospheric pressure. Warmed a bit more, the pressure exceeds atmospheric, and the crystals melt at 65.6 °C. These properties permit manipulating the compound in converting it to a less dangerous form, such as the oxide. The fluorine in uranium hexafluoride can be converted to industrial hydrogen fluoride, or the hexafluoride can in principle be used as a fluorinating agent in manufacturing substances such as Teflon.

8-13 Used Cars and New Reprocessing Equipment for Sale

A bizarre incident took place in Pocatello, Idaho, starting in June 1993. Tom Johansen was proprietor of a used car lot, and he branched into salvaging scrap metal. The nearby Idaho National Engineering Laboratory was the source of much of the scrap. Mr. Johansen noted a bid solicitation from a contractor at the Idaho Laboratory, and examined the merchandise. It consisted of massive quantities of chemical processing equipment, largely stainless steel, from an incomplete, discontinued experimental reprocessing facility. Using the Freedom of Information Act, he was able to get the papers, blueprints and X-ray prints. These revealed that the "surplus" constituted about one-third of a reprocessing plant for nuclear fuel, designed to produce plutonium for bombs. Its value was around $10 million; Mr. Johansen bought it for a mere $154,000. As news of the deal spread, the new owner began to get inquiries from foreign governments through their agents, but a condition of sale was that the equipment was not exportable.

How to get a nuclear bargain

The State Department was finally alerted, and the Department of Energy also investigated. The State Department export-control director characterized the affair as a "dangerous lapse." In the end, the DOE paid Mr. Johansen $600,000 more to cover the costs of converting the equipment to scrap, and he had to return the blueprints, etc.

8-14 Nuclear Incineration of Waste by Transmutation

Soon after commercial generation of electricity via reactors started and their high-level waste began to accumulate, ways to simplify and manage the problem were sought. Among these was reprocessing to separate the waste into several fractions, and then, using neutrons, to transmute via fission the transuranium elements (neptunium, plutonium, americium, etc.) into nuclides which have relatively short half-lives so that they lose their radioactive sting in a repository during an abbreviated storage time. The transuranium elements would require sequestering in a repository for thousands of years, while the fission products would need only several hundred years for their radioactivity to drop to innocuous levels.

Considerable research has been carried out recently on these nuclear incineration techniques. Tests are being conducted at Hanford, Los Alamos, and Brookhaven National Laboratory on Long Island, as well as at the CERN laboratories in Switzerland. Success of the proposed procedure depends on first reprocessing spent fuel by either the PUREX process or some other technique. The actinides would then be reintroduced into the reactor or bombarded with neutrons generated using an accelerator. Thus neutron sources might be either nuclear reactors, perhaps of the breeder type, or linear accelerators to produce high-energy protons, which collide with lead, bismuth, or tungsten targets. This produces abundant neutrons, which can be moderated using heavy water. The neutrons then cause fission of the actinides, and liberation of huge amounts of energy, as in a nuclear reactor. The idea is that each nuclide has a certain narrow band of neutron resonance energies which in theory permits transmutation of each nuclide to short-lived derivatives. The

Exploring alternative ways of coping with radioactive waste

problems involved are immense. The Russians have found a way to prevent molten lead from corroding metallic containers (bubbling in some oxygen, which causes a protective oxide coating to form), and this could help in the neutron-generating step.

Disposal of wastes by transmutation is intimately related to fast breeder reactors. While American reactors of this type were phased out by Congress in 1983, a new type, the Integral Fast Reactor, was being studied up until 1994. They were being promoted as a way to cope with nuclear waste.

The outlook for nuclear incineration is quite unpromising. The accelerator procedure is highly unfavorable from the standpoint of energy consumption. The steel and other parts would be activated by neutrons, and become radioactive. It seems that about as much radioactive waste would be produced as is consumed, if not more. Reprocessing would be an essential step. Costs would be fantastic. The procedure could not easily be used with fission products, although fast neutrons can transmute nearly all nuclei, even those of cesium-137. They absorb neutrons poorly; after all, they were in a neutron environment for years, and survived. Only two, iodine-129 and technetium-99, are easily transmuted to nonradioactive nuclides, and these are not particularly important. Technetium-99 (half-life nearly a quarter of a million years) is converted by neutrons into technetium-100 (half-life only 16 seconds). Thus the next nuclide, ruthenium-100, results, and it is stable. If this process is carried out while a stream of ozone is passed through the apparatus, volatile ruthenium tetroxide is constantly removed. Transmutation might be successful in this case, and perhaps that of iodine-129, but in general the technique is probably unsatisfactory. Actinide separation and transmutation cannot be considered a satisfactory substitute for geological disposal.

In 1992 a group of nine qualified experts finished an exhaustive assessment of disposing of waste through transmutation via fast breeder reactors, accelerators, and high-temperature electrolysis techniques. These scientists are associated with the Lawrence Livermore National Laboratory, two universities, and a private firm. The study concluded that high-temperature electrolysis procedures for separating actinide metals in reprocessing high-level waste offers no economic incentives or safety advantages. The Organization for Economic Cooperation and Development estimates the cost of reprocessing at $720 per kilogram of spent fuel, which is in harmony with the charge of the French and British, approximately $1000 per kilogram of actinide metal. Uranium would have to become15 times more expensive before the electrolytic process would become attractive. According to a 1991 report by the Electric Power Research Institute, the cost of high-temperature electrolytic reprocessing of spent fuel is $729 per kilogram of actinide metal (investor financed).

The report pointed out that even if actinides are separated, this does not solve the problem of radioactive waste since the obstacle is primarily the soluble fission products. It emphasized that removing the fission products from the waste to be buried in a geological repository (usually earth called tuff) lowers the amount of heat liberated on radioactive decay, but that this may actually be a disadvantage. Centuries of drying out by the heat permits the waste to remain intact even after failure of the containers.

In order for advanced liquid-metal breeder reactors to be effective in destroying actinides, it would require between 10 and 40 reactors, reprocessing plants, a fuel refabrication plant, and other facilities. These would not be popular with the American public. These procedures, along with the accompanying high-temperature electrolysis reprocessing, would increase the cost of nuclear power with little or no decrease in health risk. The problem of what to do with the recovered uranium has not been solved. The fate of the accumulated uranium-236 has not been addressed. It seems best at present to abandon all transmutation and high-temperature processes, at least for the foreseeable future.

This procedure will probably be buried.

8-15 More Alternative Processes of Waste Treatment

A technique for handling liquid waste which is currently in use consists of first adding aluminum nitrate, which dissolves. Then the liquid is sprayed into a heated chamber (fluidized bed) where evaporation takes place. The aluminum nitrate decomposes to inert granules of aluminum oxide. The granules, incorporating the waste residues, are then calcined into a stable, sandlike solid for disposal. A pilot plant in Idaho had processed two million gallons of waste as early as 1973.

A great deal of waste from reprocessing spent fuel consists of aqueous solutions mixed with solid sludge. Many tanks at Hanford are filled with these materials. There is a high content of sodium nitrate, formed by neutralizing the nitric acid from dissolving the spent fuel; sodium hydroxide was used. A simple process for removal of the sodium nitrate from the aqueous phase is to make the solution slightly acidic and evaporate it until the sodium nitrate begins to crystallize out. After filtering and washing, the material is recrystallized half a dozen times for purification. The sodium nitrate recovered is practically pure, with only a background level of radioactivity. This process will save $2 billion in cleanup costs. Another process involves vacuum distillation of sodium and potassium chlorides from oxides of uranium and plutonium.

Australians have developed a new substance for immobilizing radioactive waste. Called Synroc, it incorporates the waste into a titanium oxide matrix, forming a rocklike material. Evidence to date indicates that the dangerous material is locked inside securely. Extensive tests are being started in China, which is seeking a suitable technology. American chemists have devised a similar procedure which uses a crystalline silicotitanate, a material which is especially effective in removing strontium-90 and cesium-137. The resulting solids are then vitrified to immobilize the radioactive components.

Nearly all waste from reprocessing contains uranium. Research at the University of Idaho has adapted the solvent ability of supercritical carbon dioxide (best known for decaffeinating coffee beans) to selectively removing uranium. The uranium is converted to uranyl nitrate, tributyl phosphate is added, and the mixture is extracted with the carbon dioxide under heat and pressure. After separation of the gas phase and cooling, the carbon dioxide is removed and recycled. If successful, there might be the possibility of applying the process to plutonium.

Testing every conceivable procedure to solve a difficult problem

In addition to the above, some low-level waste is produced as follows. Reactors cooled with water accumulate small amounts of radioactive nuclides of tritium (H-3) and oxygen-19. Impurities in the water form traces of nitrogen-13, nitrogen-16, fluorine-18, and carbon-14, all radioactive. As mentioned earlier, radioactive hydrated oxides in colloidal solution result from corrosion of metal parts. In certain cases some cesium-137 and strontium-90 are leached into the water. All of these cause the turbine blades to become active in some stations. Filters, ion exchange resins, and charcoal adsorbers are satisfactory in controlling these problems. The solids containing these materials, amounting to 200 to 500 curies per year for a billion watt (electric) power station, are mixed with cement or bitumen, covered with concrete in concrete boxes, and shipped out for disposal.

A novel means of detoxifying soil is to use certain plants whose roots selectively pick up many soluble nuclides. The plants are grasses, shrubs, and trees. The harvested biomass is incinerated and the ashes disposed of as low- or intermediate-level waste. The technique is called phytoremediation.

8-16 The Fission Products and Transuranium Elements

Consider a pressurized-water nuclear reactor of one billion watt (electric) output. At the end of a normal fuel cycle, the reactor contains more than 5 billion curies of radioactive materials, a worrisome quantity. The amount of fuel at the start was100 metric tonnes of uranium, and the original U-235 content was 3.3%. Most of the radioactivity is from the fission products, which amount to 3,500 kilograms (7,700 pounds). There are about 600 kilograms (1,320 pounds) of elements beyond uranium. Each commercial reactor in the United States generates around 20 metric tonnes of spent fuel rods annually. In addition, some 210 cubic meters of low-level waste is produced.

The list below gives an inventory of the most important fission products and transuranium elements and gives their half-lives and amounts in the billion-watt reactor.

Partial Inventory of Important Fission Products and Transuranium Elements in a Billion-watt (electric) Reactor (100 Tonnes of Uranium)

Atomic Number	*Radionuclide*	*Half-life*	*Amount*	
			kilograms	*curies*
36	Krypton-85	10.72 years	1.6	630,000
38	Strontium-90	28.8 years	29	4,000,000
40	Zirconium-95	64.0 days	7.9	170,000,000
40	Zirconium-97	16.9 hours	0.09	160,000,000
44	Ruthenium-106	1.0 year	8.5	28,000,000
53	Iodine-131	8.04 days	0.77	95,000,000
53	Iodine-133	20.9 hours	0.16	180,000,000
54	Xenon-133	5.24 days	1.0	190,000,000
55	Cesium-137	30.0 years	60	5,200,000
56	Barium-140	12.75 days	2.5	182,000,000
57	Lanthanum-140	40.27 hours	0.32	180,000,000
58	Cerium-141	32.5 days	5.6	160,000,000
58	Cerium-143	33.1 hours	2.1	140,000,000
58	Cerium-144	285 days	29	95,000,000
59	Praseodymium-143	13.6 days	2.09	140,000,000
94	Plutonium-238	87.7 years	3.6	62,000
94	Plutonium-239	24,100 years	371	23,000
94	Plutonium-240	6540 years	100	22,800
94	Plutonium-241	14.4 years	36	3,700,000
95	Americium-241	433 years	0.53	1,800
96	Curium-242	163 days	0.17	540,000
96	Curium-244	18.1 years	0.31	25,000

Spent fuel rods and high level waste from them present the most challenging problem because the fission products and transuranium elements are involved. If a person stands unprotected one meter from a one-year-old spent fuel rod, he receives a fatal dose of radiation within a short time. In the United States, about 2200 tons (2000 metric tonnes) of spent fuel rods per year are generated, and more than 5 million spent fuel rods (33,000 tons or 30,000 metric tonnes) were in storage in 1992. About 80% of these are in storage at Hanford and 10% at the Idaho National Engineering Laboratory. By the end of the century the amount was expected to reach about 45,000 tons. The United States also has nearly 23,000 spent fuel rods from foreign countries. If the transuranic elements are separated from this commercial spent fuel (33,000 MWd/MTU burn-up, 3.25% U-235 at start), the composition immediately after removal from the reactor is as below:

Pu-238	0.7 %
Pu-239	72.5
Pu-240	19.6
Pu-241	7.05
Am-241	0.10
Cm-242	.003
Cm-244	.002

Each gram of this material would have a level of radioactivity of 8.5 curies, and also emit 6000 to 7000 neutrons per second. The half-life of plutonium-241 is relatively short (14.4 years, beta active), and it decays to americium-241. After two half-lives, the plutonium-241 content drops to 1.76%, and the americium-241 content has built up to about 5.39%. All the decay processes are accompanied by some gamma and X-rays.

The heat generated by spent reactor fuel of course falls off as it ages. Most of the heat comes from the strontium-90 and cesium-137 at the start, but the longer-lived actinides produce relatively more in later years. For each metric tonne of spent fuel, the heat liberated is approximately as follows:

Rate of Heat Liberation During Storage of Nuclear Waste (per metric tonne)

Age (years)	*Rate of heat liberated (watts)*	*Percent of heat from strontium and cesium*
1	12,300	67
5	2260	69
10	1300	72
20	950	68
50	572	56
100	312	31
200	183	5

The heat generated by americium-241 is 114 watts per kilogram. Since americium-241 arises from the decay of plutonium-241, the result is increased self-heating of separated plutonium from fuel as it ages.

8-17 Disposal of Radioactive Wastes

Shortsighted means of disposal of radioactive wastes at Hanford during and immediately after World War II paved the way for lack of public confidence in later years. Some wastes which were not of the very highest level of radioactivity were dumped directly into holes in the ground. Plants like tumbleweed and rabbit brush have deep roots and pick up strontium-90 and cesium-137. They break off when dry and are wind-blown into piles, where they present a hazard if a fire occurs. Rabbits eat contaminated plants and have left more than 200 curies of radioactive droppings around the Hanford reservation. Speaking of rabbits, we might note that the French had a similar experience. Rabbits trapped in an old low-level radioactive storage site just south of Paris were found to be three times as radioactive as expected.

In 1945 a large amount of radioactive waste was pumped directly into the aquifer at the Hanford site. Spillage from a tank in 1973 disgorged thousands of curies of strontium-90 and cesium-137, and a large quantity of other fission products; this material is slowly sinking down, and the water table is only 100 to 200 feet below. Tests made in 1997-98 disclosed that part of the cesium had actually migrated down to the aquifer through what is called the vadose zone, which is moist soil, but with hardly any liquid water.

In 1992 the dumping of tons of soil heavily contaminated with radioactive fallout from Nevada was divulged. The event took place in 1960 near Point Hope in northern Alaska. Between 1952 and 1984 low-level waste was discharged directly into the Snake River Plain aquifer in Idaho through an injection well and seepage ponds. In 1989 it was revealed that several million cubic feet of low-level waste had been carelessly buried just above the Snake River aquifer, the primary source of drinking water for 200,000 people. More than a tonne of plutonium in cardboard boxes, wooden boxes, and steel drums had been dumped into shallow trenches of the Idaho National Engineering Laboratory. By 1998 several radionuclides were detected in the aquifer, including Sr-90, Cs-137, Tc-99, and Np-237. Similar negligence occurred in Tennessee; the waste had been buried in shallow trenches. North of the Oak Ridge National Laboratory, the transuranic nuclides Am-241 and Cm-244 were detected. It was shown that the metal ions had been complexed by natural organic matter. Radioactive emissions carried by air or water entered the surrounding territories, some finding its way into garden vegetables and milk. Between1944 and 1957 a total of 530,000 curies of iodine-131 vapor was intentionally released into the atmosphere from Hanford. This cavalier action had grave consequences (5-23).

What, me worry?

In November 1990, 16,000 South Korean villagers rioted in protest to siting a low-level nuclear waste dump on their island, Anmyon, 80 miles southwest of Seoul. A police station was destroyed. The government has suspended the dump operation. In Taiwan, the proto-Malay aboriginal minority has been protesting the government's choice of Orchid Island, home of one tribe, as a holding area for nuclear waste. Taiwan generates considerable low-level waste, and came to an agreement with North Korea to ship 200,000 barrels of it for disposal in a disused North Korean mine. The payment is said to be around $250 million. Neither nation is a member of the International Atomic Energy Agency, so no external supervision is required.

In 1982 Congress passed the Nuclear Waste Policy Act to accommodate commercial nuclear waste; it was modified three years later to cover military waste as well. The act established a timetable for choosing sites, with a deadline in 1998; this was later extended to the year 2003. No matter which site is proposed, influential local groups spring up in opposition; even the most pro-nuclear politicians resist putting repositories in their own states. The Not-In-My-Backyard syndrome has been expressed so often that it is frequently made into an acronym: NIMBY. The public perception seems to be that waste repositories are a source of endless misfortune. It seems as if people just don't like the idea of radioactive wastes being buried for thousands of years, even though Nature has interred uranium and thorium ores for billions of years, and these are not in salt formations or other protective environments. The Department of Energy has the unenviable responsibility of locating the repository sites, and has made some halting progress through the political jungle.

In 1990 the governor of Idaho, feeling that his state had done more than its share of accepting radioactive waste, closed the state borders to further import of waste. There had been a steady stream of plutonium-bearing refuse from the Rocky Flats nuclear weapons plant in Colorado, and finally enough was enough. At the Rocky Flats site itself, not far from Denver, an ill-conceived scheme to evaporate aqueous radioactive waste consisted of simply dumping the solutions into ponds. Heavy metals in solution are usually immobilized by soil, but in this case, the liquids were so acidic that the metals just sank deeply, and some radioactive contaminants reached the ground water.

Nobody wants it.

One aspect of nuclear waste which has earned a considerable level of confidence is the method of transporting it by rail or truck. The waste is confined in casks which are made with radiation shielding and cooling fins. They are so sturdily constructed that they have withstood dramatic tests. Trucks with the casks were crashed into brick walls at 60 miles per hour; locomotives moving at 80 miles per hour have smashed into them; they have been dropped from planes onto concrete, dropped onto huge steel spikes, submerged for extended periods in water; and all of this was with virtually no cracking or leakage. Other hazardous materials are routinely shipped around the country and there have been a few accidents, all with minor consequences. Hundreds of spent fuel rods have been shipped via truck or rail without incident. Their principal vulnerability is from fire. Spent fuel rods on shipboard in a harbor could spew a plume of deadly radiotoxic material over a city in case of a severe fire, and thus should not be allowed into urban harbors.

8-18 High Level Waste

A repository is supposed to be more than an elegant word for a dump; in modern usage it connotes careful, ordered storage in a monitored fashion. The deposits are not planned on being recoverable in some cases, but are retrievable in other scenarios (Monitored Retrievable Storage, or MRS, section 8-27). The two versions have been dubbed "throw away" and "stow away" modes. While present American policies are mostly based on throw-away, the Nuclear Regulatory Commission calls for at least 50 years storage in an accessible manner before back-filling underground burial holes; after all, policies can change. The monitoring process need not be 10,000 years, but only for shorter periods capable of being extended. Some worry that since a test repository cannot be overseen by human beings for a full cycle, thus violating certain engineering principles, they should not be constructed at all. Since the storage period is so long, it is impossible to fully test prototype storage facilities. Therefore redundant safety steps must be taken, and this is expensive.

Storage above ground the first 60 years or so seems sensible.

A temporary storage area for high-level waste in Nevada not far from Yucca Mountain has been proposed. It would accept thousands of tons of waste destined for the mountain repository. The courts have ordered the DOE to accept this material, and the House voted in favor of the plan, but there is still much opposition.

The best practical disposal method known to date consists of sealing the zirconium-clad spent fuel rods, without reprocessing, in copper or steel canisters, or perhaps in porcelain containers in certain cases, and storing these in a manner where they can be monitored. The spent fuel rods should first be allowed to stand about ten years under water so that most (nearly 90%) of the initial radioactivity decays away. Storage during this first period is at the site of the reactors. The second stage is storage for perhaps 50 or 100 years. During this above-ground storage it seems quite likely that still better canisters can be developed. The waste is then ready for a geologic repository. This procedure is the once-through fuel cycle, as opposed to the multiple cycles used in breeder reactors (7-11). The repositories must have multibarriers.

The canisters are arranged so that air can circulate through for cooling after disposal. The waste density must not exceed the level at which heat from decay is conducted away . Candidate sites have been tentatively chosen in the states of Nevada (Yucca Mountain), Washington (Hanford), and Texas (Deaf Smith County). Two other candidate sites for spent fuel rods are at Maybell, Colorado, and at Pineville, West Virginia. Yucca Mountain and most of the other sites are also to accept vitrified military waste from Hanford and Savannah River. Hazel O'Leary, appointed by President Clinton as Secretary of the Department of Energy, has said that before utilities order a new generation of reactors, the problem of their waste must be worked out.

The objective is to build the repositories in such a way that they present less danger than uranium and thorium ores, not in the sense of having less radioactivity per unit volume, but in the sense of being in durable confinement; after all, the ore deposits have no canisters or liners. The ores produce the radon which cause a good fraction of the natural radiation dose to all living things, and radium is leached from many of the ores and gets into the food chain. All scientists working in the area of geological repositories are aware that the containers of waste will eventually fail, mostly owing to corrosion, but by then the levels of radioactivity have been greatly reduced by radioactive decay.

8-19 The Yucca Mountain Repository

Political Issues—Yucca Mountain is on the west side of the Nevada Test Site and not far from Death Valley in California. It has been chosen for the repository for high-level waste, but the final decision has not yet been confirmed by Congress. The initial repository is priced at about $15 billion, and can be expanded by expenditure of another $15 billion. The anticipated cost on completion might be about $60 billion, according to

The challenging obstacles of permanently disposing of high-level radioactive waste have several dimensions: technical, political, regulatory, psychological., economic, and social.

a study at the end of 2001. Much of these funds derive from a tax of 0.1 cent per kilowatt-hour on nuclear electricity. The site is designed for emplacement of 77,000 tons of high-level waste, but this limit is only statutory, and can be increased. About 2000 tons of reactor waste is generated annually. Ten percent of its capacity has been reserved for defense waste. The Yucca Mountain repository cannot open before 2010, maybe 2015, if it ever is. The site is designed to contain the waste for thousands of years. Natural geological barriers will delay and dilute the radioactive substances if it migrates from the repository.

During the 1980s an opposition group of citizens sprang up quickly. Nevadans do not appreciate the idea of other states shipping their waste to Yucca Mountain; after all, Nevada has no nuclear reactors. The repository is perceived by many as a source of potential harm with no visible benefits. The bitter and paralyzing debate focuses on public health. All of this action is another step in what might be called atomic power politics, an unending drama. The nuclear waste problem is a blend of political and scientific issues. Thus the topic has become a contentious arena, with opposing factions trying to ensnare the issue to further their own political agenda. Switching to an alternative site would gain nothing.

One suggested plan is to store spent fuel rods in concrete and stainless steel casks above ground but near Yucca Mountain. This type of interim storage does not qualify as Monitored, Retrievable Storage (8-27). The Senate approved this stepping-stone plan in summer 1996 and reaffirmed it in spring 1997. The monitored above-ground storage of waste for 50 to 100 years could be accomplished at many sites in several states, and this would help defuse the antagonism.

Nevadans did tolerate, even welcomed, nuclear testing in their state for many years. The Nevada Test Site today looks like a lunar landscape. It is a nuclear waste dump of sorts because of the fission products and actinides left in the Earth from the tests. So, how could these citizens welcome the use of their wide open spaces to test bombs but oppose the Yucca Mountain project? The answer is probably that an immense danger to the United States lay in the Soviet nuclear arsenal, and it was a patriotic duty to host the tests. The Yucca Mountain repository, on the other hand, was initially regarded as a danger inequitably forced on the state by Congress. By 1994 subtle changes in public attitudes could be detected. Already hundreds of millions of dollars are being spent on the repository, and this means jobs. Some citizens openly favor the project, and several polls have revealed decreasing hostility to the endeavor.

In contrast to the American chronicle in Nevada, two towns in northern Sweden are actually competing to be chosen for high-level radioactive waste repositories. These are Storuman and Mala, just south of the Arctic Circle. They have vast areas with hard bedrock, and the citizens welcome not only the funding, but also the liveliness and excitement. The Swedes have crafted "inherently safe" canisters in which to package waste, said to be impervious to water for thousands of years.

Technical Issues—Doomsday scenarios of flooding of the proposed disposal site at Yucca Mountain by ground water have been presented in newspapers (but not the scientific literature). These accounts have served to stimulate extensive research of past ground water movements using isotopic techniques. Studies of carbon-13 and oxygen-18 abundance in calcium carbonate minerals from Yucca Mountain give strong evidence that the regional water table has remained well below the disposal levels for at least 300,000 years. The element strontium consists of four stable isotopes, two of which, Sr-86 and Sr-87, afford a reliable means of determining the age of ground water and minerals deposited from it. This is possible because only Sr-87 is constantly being generated by the slow radioactive decay of natural rubidium-87; thus there is a slight but measurable variation in the ratio of the two isotopes. The results conclusively demonstrate that calcite from veins in Yucca Mountain did not arise from ground water. The same results come from uranium and lead isotopic work. Moreover, age measurements of the nearby Lathrop Wells volcanic center by the argon-40/argon-39 technique demonstrated that the last two eruptions, about 100 years apart, took place close to 140,000 years ago. It was shown that a previous study of this point, giving only 20,000 years, was in error due to a miscalibration. Another advantage Yucca Mountain presents is that its parched earth contains zeolite, a mineral which can capture most escaping fission products by an ion exchange process.

The ground water in many areas flows through earth rich in calcite, that is, calcium carbonate ($CaCO_3$). Such water is rich in many kinds of microbes. Research in 1999 showed that strontium-90 which is present in such water can be immobilized by injecting urea solutions. The microbes decompose the urea into ammonia and carbon dioxide, a process which brings about precipitation of more calcite. Since strontium is quite similar to calcium, it is coprecipitated and held firmly until the strontium-90 has decayed to yttrium-90 and zirconium-90, which is stable.

The proposed disposal area is 300 to 400 meters (1000 to 1300 feet) above the water table, and there is no evidence that the water level has shifted more than 10 meters from earthquakes or other causes over the past several thousand years. The repository is about 1000 feet below the air-earth surface above it. A medium-size earthquake in spring 1992 caused the groundwater table to rise temporarily about five inches. The ground water moves at a rate of approximately 1 foot per year, and the nearest surface where it flows out is 30 miles away, requiring more than 150,000 years.

Tuff is a kind of pyroclastic rock consisting mainly of ancient lithified volcanic ash. There are two main types. The Yucca Mountain soil has a layer of what is called welded tuff, which has a very low porosity but is easily fractured. Beneath that is a stratum of nonwelded tuff, which is very porous. Below this is another layer of welded tuff, and this is where the proposed repository is to be situated. Below this second stratum of welded tuff is a layer containing a high proportion of zeolite, a mineral with strong ion-exchange properties which would adsorb any ionic materials which might ever leak into it.

So much fuss has been raised about the proposed Yucca Mountain site that still another intense investigation was carried out, and was finished in 1992. It involved a panel of 17 experts assembled by the National Research Council. This makes that particular piece of real estate about the world's most exhaustively studied. The assessment and scrutiny concluded that there is essentially no likelihood that ground water can flood the upper reaches of the mountain, where spent fuel rods are to be stored. Veins filled with carbonate and silicate minerals were shown to result from water trickling downward, not from ground water forced upward, in agreement with the conclusions presented above.

There is almost no chance that groundwater will rise as high as the waste.

Colloids are congregates of atoms, assemblies less than a micrometer across. Chemical reactions such as corrosion involve colloid formation, and coagulation of these particles yield precipitates. Colloids are stable because the particles hold like electric charges, which repel each other. Considerable attention has been paid to colloid formation during weathering of high-level nuclear waste, especially that in glass. The solubility of plutonium-bearing waste exposed to water underestimates the potential of release into the environment. Colloids of clay matrix holding plutonium and other actinides cannot escape a properly engineered barrier.

The waste is to be monitored remotely for up to 300 years. Human beings will take the waste through the access tubes in shielded locomotives to the storage sites, but from there on it is to be managed remotely and monitored by sensors and robotics.

Heat from Radioactive Decay—The Department of Energy has conducted extensive research on other geotechnical issues, including the problem of heating by decay of radioactive waste in repositories, in particular Yucca Mountain. Thermal conductivity measurements were made on the various kinds of rock present, mostly tuff and basalt. First, computer simulations indicated the rate of temperature rise in the canisters and in the surrounding rock for various levels of thermal loading. Then actual field tests were made using electrical and other heat sources to supply measured amounts of energy, and temperature changes were recorded. These results showed that thermal loading of 57 kilowatts per acre (14 watts per square meter) could be accommodated with sufficient margin of safety. This caused a maximum measured temperature, without ventilation, in the monolith of 150 °C (302 °F), although 235 °C (455 °F) is tolerable. The canisters themselves have a design peak temperature of 350 °C (662 °F), whereas the bore-hole wall is cooler than 275 °C (527 °F). The packages of waste fuel have a thermal output of 1.3 to 3.3 kilowatts each, while the glass cylinders (see 8-21) holding waste give out less than 0.5 kilowatt. The great bulk of the heat comes from the fission products; the transuranics have such long half-lives that their thermal output is small. The surface temperature of the land above the repository is limited to a rise of 6 °C (11 °F). One must keep in mind that spent fuel rods are stored at least ten years under water so that about 88% of the decay heat has already been dissipated and there is additional storage above ground before being emplaced in the repository. The average worker received a dose of 3 millirems per handling operation, mostly from neutrons.

Where repositories are in cold climates, how about building hothouses for growing crops?

Could Heat from Radioactive Decay Be an Advantage?—Early studies of using a geological repository indicated that centuries of drying out by the heat liberated by decay permits the waste to remain intact even after failure of the containers. A 1995 investigation concluded that it might be possible to space the canisters closer together than first planned, but in tunnels somewhat farther apart (around 100 meters). This would heat the surrounding earth and boil out the corrosive moisture. Covering the canisters with gravel would aid this process. This study concluded that such storage would be safe for at least 10,000 years, long after almost all of the fission products had decayed away. Critics suspect that the prolonged heating would change the rock's porosity, perhaps allowing liquid to seep back into the tunnels.

Glass Logs—The Yucca Mountain repository is scheduled to accept logs of vitrified high-level radioactive waste. Hanford's allocation is at present only 6000 glass logs. Yet if all of the old waste at Hanford were vitrified, somewhere between 20,000 and 60,000 logs would be made. Clearly, additional and perhaps different approaches are needed.

The New Casks—The type of casks now planned for Yucca Mountain, each loaded with canisters of spent fuel or vitrified waste, is robust and double-walled. They will last at least 10,000 years, under the most credible assumptions. In this respect they resemble those manufactured by Sweden. Each cask has outer walls made of four-inch-thick carbon steel and a three-fourths-inch thick inner wall, made of a resistant nickel alloy. The outer skin is stainless steel, and there is another stainless steel liner. Each has a gamma ray shield made of depleted uranium, and also a neutron shield. Only about 10% of the mass is radioactive waste. Each has aluminum honeycomb impact shielding one each end.

Drilling—An immense tunnel-boring machine to drill into Yucca Mountain has been purchased. The cutting face of the machine, known as the "Yucca Mucker," is around 25 feet in diameter. The tunnel goes down 600 to 900 feet in a slight grade. The tunnels total 40 miles. The age of samples of water taken from strategic sites along the tunnel path were measured by analysis for chlorine-36. This nuclide, with a half-life of 300,000 years, is formed in the upper atmosphere via cosmic rays (the background level) and also was made during hydrogen-bomb tests a few decades ago. It is washed down by rainwater and affords a means of dating. Except for water found near faults, the water in Yucca mountain has been there for 5000 to 10,000 years. Near faults, the water is above background in chlorine-36, and is thus newer, but the fraction of this late-precipitated water is very low.

Earthquake—On June 29, 1992, an earthquake of Richter magnitude 5.6 shattered the pre-dawn calm at Little Skull Mountain, situated 14 miles from Yucca Mountain. The shaking at the Yucca site confirmed the fears of those opposed to the dump, while those favoring the repository regarded the quake as a marvelous learning opportunity, testing the site's resistance to damage. Engineered to withstand a quake of Richter 6.5 to 7.0, no detectable damage was done. Another quake, of magnitude 4.7, occurred in January, 1999, centered about 35 miles away. No damage was apparent.

A Repository Blowing Up?—In 1995 a report surfaced in Los Alamos which claimed that a catastrophic scenario was possible in a repository such as Yucca Mountain. This was considered especially in case plutonium-239 from dismantled warheads is vitrified in quantity and emplaced underground. The course of events was envisioned as collapse of the tunnels in time, erosion of the metals by ground water, and dispersion of the plutonium in the surrounding rock. This was supposed to create conditions in which a chain reaction and explosion could occur.

As mentioned earlier, there is evidence that the parts of Yucca Mountain where the waste is to be stored has been well above ground water for 300,000 years. In any case, the glass is very resistant to water. Nonradioactive neutron-absorbing elements (boron, cadmium, others) have been put into the waste. Even if the plutonium is attacked by erosion and is reconfigured in a concentrated form, at worst a nuclear reactor could be produced, like those in nature in Gabon (7-18). If geochemical processes separated the plutonium from the neutron absorbers and concentrated it, perhaps in time a reactor could result. The time scale of 10,000 years was mentioned. To make an explosion, a quick assembly or compression of the fissile material is required (Chapter 9), and no satisfactory tamper is evident. Corrosion products are much more difficult to detonate than metallic fissile elements. Another team of Los Alamos experts concluded that the alleged sequence of events leading to explosion is simply not credible.

Finally, something not to worry about.

Tentative Acceptance of the Yucca Mountain Site—In summer 1999 the Department of Energy issued a 1400-page report which outlined the years of scrutiny of the Yucca Mountain repository, covering its geology, environmental factors, and long-range predictions. It acknowledged that there is a certain level of uncertainty in the integrity of the site over tens of thousands of years. The provisional verdict was that no factors uncovered so far would cause rejection of the site, which cannot open before 2010. In 2002, the Secretary of the Department of Energy recommended to the President that the Yucca Mountain site is suitable as a long-term repository for high-level nuclear waste. He notified Nevada officials, and he next presented his decision to the President. Congress makes the final decision.

8-20 Chronicle of Kinney County

Kinney County, Texas—If you were seeking a site for a radioactive dump, what features of the area would be favorable? The answer was furnished by a Los Angeles consulting firm in a report to the California Waste Management Board and Conoco Inc., which closed its giant Conquista Project uranium mine in 1982, and was shutting down its uranium mill tailings pond in south Texas. The report gave a profile with the following qualities: a remote and arid area whose inhabitants are rural, preferably rather poor, not well educated, and older. A dumpsite was needed for the solid, naturally-occurring radioactive material in the huge pond. While all the radioactive material is natural, some of its waste is relatively more concentrated in radium than that of uranium ore.

A search disclosed a place which seemed to fill the bill exactly. There are no earthquake fault lines, and there is no agriculture. It was in Kinney County, Texas, not far north of the Mexican border. The site is an isolated, mesquite-studded, parched, former ranch of 1440 acres. The soil is suitably impermeable. It was purchased in 1988 from the owner, who was staggering under a $250,000 lien. Kinney County survives mostly from sale of livestock.

In the end, the attempt to establish a dumpsite in Kinney County became a bitter and unresolved collision between two different worlds. The local residents proved to be canny, adaptive, and resourceful, altogether unlike their stereotype. They did not take kindly to accepting waste produced elsewhere, despite a powerful public relations campaign promising well-paying jobs. Their homelands did not appear desolate in their eyes. A NIMBY activist group sprang up, consisting of crusty cattle ranchers and goat herders, Spanish-speaking laborers, feminists, and others. The supposedly naive ranchers learned quickly.

How to stimulate a NIMBY movement in the populace

The conflict inspires questions such as these: Is it fair to make one group accept a burden they do not want for the benefit of other people? Should the welfare of a few be forgone for the benefit of many? Is it right to inflict the waste of a dead-end industry on a clean, unpolluted region? Why not store the waste where it was produced? Why stigmatize Kinney County so that its livestock cannot be sold?

The Texas Department of Health has a Bureau of Radiation Control, and this bureau had concluded that the dumping of this low-level radioactive waste "would not be detrimental to the public health and safety or have significant adverse impacts on the environment." Licensing of the facility was recommended.

The issue is complicated by many other factors. One is that the real safety of the dump has hardly been addressed by the populace. This is in part because there are few technically-trained individuals among them. The common statement that "We didn't produce this waste, so we should not be responsible for it" suffers from the imprecision of the word "we." Does it mean only the folks of Kinney County, or the state of Texas, or the whole United States? After all, Texans eagerly accepted the Pantex nuclear bomb facility near Amarillo, in the Texas panhandle. They benefit from the electricity produced by nuclear reactors. The exigencies of World War II and the Cold War have distorted many values.

8-21 Vitrification

In the case of old waste from reprocessing, nearly all of military origin, it is to be incorporated into a matrix of glass or semi-crystalline ceramic. By 1993 a test program was under way by DOE and the Westinghouse Savannah River Company in South Carolina to prepare durable borosilicate glass-encapsulated waste containing dried fission products and transuranium elements. First, care must be taken to remove any organic material, such as residual solvents. If too much water-soluble salts, such as sodium nitrate, are present, a filtering or centrifuging step is required. The dried residue is mixed with the components of glass and frit, which is crushed, recycled glass. The composition (expressed as oxides) of one kind of glass suitable for fission products is:

silicon dioxide (sand) 45.6%	potassium oxide 3.6%
sodium oxide 11.0	lithium oxide 3.2
boron oxide 10.3	uranium oxide 2.2
iron oxides 10.1	manganese oxide 2.0
aluminum oxide 4.0	other components 8.0

Phosphates deteriorate the quality of the glass. If the waste contains more than trace amounts of plutonium, the above composition is not suitable since the plutonium tends to aggregate into clusters which cause embrittlement and other problems. Continued research in the field made a long step forward in 1995 when it was discovered that adding heavy metals whose ions have a +3 charge or, still better, a +4 charge, causes formation of nonbridging oxide ions, which harbor a reduced negative charge. Tin and zirconium (ionic charge +4) are suitable metals to achieve this. The result is that glass containing silicates, alkali metals (lithium, sodium, potassium, cesium), and tin or zirconium disperse plutonium uniformly. This is because of the electrostatic attraction of the highly-charged plutonium ions to the nonbridging oxide ions. Such glasses can hold up to 10% plutonium. Tests show that they are stable on exposure to heat and moisture to about the same degree as the natural glass obsidian, which survives for millions of years. There might be a problem with all glasses containing alpha emitters since the alpha particles are helium nuclei, and helium gas accumulates. Fractures from pressure can result in time if too much helium accumulates.

Ah, um, see how clever chemists are?

After melting at around 1200 °C and mixing, the glass is poured into stainless steel cylinders or canisters, which are welded shut. These units in some cases are then enclosed in barriers made of lead, titanium, cast iron, ferroconcrete, and/or asphalt or bitumen, all in multiple layers. Note that the glass contains abundant boron, a strong neutron absorber which insures that the waste cannot become critical, although even without the boron this would not be the case. The glass "logs" are around 10 feet long and 2 feet in diameter. Care must be taken to avoid loading the glass with excessive radioactive material lest the irradiation cause deterioration. The vitrification process immobilizes the waste elements so that they are not appreciably leached out in case they ever come into contact with groundwater, which is the most likely pathway they could somehow come into contact with human beings.

The South Carolina plant finally went into operation in early 1996, under contract with the Westinghouse Electric Corp. The cost of building it was about $2.4 billion, roughly twice the original estimate. The operating cost is approximately $140 million annually. The Savannah River site, which covers 310 square miles, had 34 million gallons of waste in 51 underground tanks in 1995. By the end of 1997, 500 tons of high-level waste had been vitrified. Each canister weighs 5100 pounds and costs $1.4 million. About 21,600 canisters will be required for all American high-level waste, and 20 to 25 years will be required to finish the job. The plant is the world's largest of its kind. France and Russia also operate vitrification plants. Those in Russia employ a phosphate glass, which is less durable than borosilicate glass.

In some types of radioactive sludge, it is hardened by mixing with an excess of Portland cement. In experimentation with this technique, two sludge tanks at Savannah River have undergone this treatment.

Several alternative techniques of vitrification are promising, one being melting the glass using microwaves. Actually a huge vitrification facility was started at Hanford, but it was abandoned after incurring a cost of $286 million. In 1996, contracts were signed to build pilot plants and see what must be done to start up again. The French have had more than 25 years of experience in vitrification, and willingly advise American experts.

Shards of Babylonian glass have endured more than 3,000 years in running water with negligible signs of dissolution. Volcanic glass lasts for millions of years in the elements.

Even borosilicate glass undergoes corrosion if it becomes wet, but it is incredibly slow. By the time of significant failure, most of the radioactivity would have decayed away. Using lithium as a tracer, measurements have shown that the dissolution of the glass is at a rate causing loss of 0.002% per year of the by now low level radioactive waste. In 2000, new classes of radiation-resistant substances were developed to encapsulate the most damaging radioactive materials, such as plutonium. These are fluorides and zirconia-based materials.

Whenever a new procedure of such vast scope is undertaken, there are always a certain number of failures, errors, and delays. This is to be expected, and intemperate outbursts by inexperienced critics are hardly helpful. About $6 billion was spent on development in 1994. Regrettably, the Department of Energy more or less handicapped itself by signing legal agreements with states which it could not carry out for lack of funds and technology. This left the Department open to lawsuits, and thus some technical decisions are being made by courts, the side with the most powerful Congressional delegations and most aggressive attorneys winning.

After the long-lived actinide metals are removed from spent fuel by reprocessing, the radioactivity of the remaining, shorter-lived fission products reach the level of, say, uranium ores, much more quickly than spent fuel itself. In addition, less heat is generated and this permits a reduction in repository size. Several countries have concluded that these factors lowers disposal costs, but, as explained earlier, such processes are fraught with grave difficulties.

8-22 Thorium-230, Another Dangerous Waste Product

Another waste the nuclear industry must cope with is thorium-230. This nuclide is a natural disintegration product of uranium-238, being the fourth step in the uranium series (4-9). All uranium ores contain about 16 grams of this nuclide per metric tonne of uranium. When the ore is processed and the uranium is extracted, the thorium is left in the residues. It has a half-life of 75,400 years, and is a dangerous emitter of alpha particles; radium-226 results. During World War II, many tens of kilograms of thorium-230 accumulated, and the material was simply dumped into old mines or excavations or the like. Still more is currently being generated in production of uranium for reactors.

8-23 Waste at Hanford

The Hanford reservation has 1377 waste sites, totaling perhaps 1.4 billion cubic meters of material, some two thirds of the total in the U.S. A fraction of the sand-covered pits and underground storage sites, called cribs, have leaked badly. Vast quantities of radioactive waste from military operations await disposal. Some is toxic, but not radioactive. An estimated quarter million gallons of toxic carbon tetrachloride has flowed from the cribs into the soil, forming an underground plume which has contaminated the ground water. Some waste containing plutonium and americium was pumped into the ground. At least 2100 tons of spent fuel is in storage. There are 64 million gallons of liquid or semiliquid waste in 228 tanks, 177 of these being the huge underground type. Only 28 of the tanks are of the newer double-shell type; the rest of the old types were never intended for such a long storage period. Normally, the temperature inside the tanks is somewhere around 60 °C (140 °F), but on July 31, 1994, in one tank it reached the boiling point of water. Several of these stark monuments to the Cold War have developed leaks. For example, tank 106-T, constructed during the war and holding exceedingly radioactive waste, sprung a leak in 1973. The liquid soaked into the sandy soil. The loss was estimated at 115,000 gallons, containing 40,000 curies of cesium-137 and 14,000 curies of strontium-90, and 97,000 curies of other fission products. Evidently no waste entered the pristine Columbia River nearby. The level of radioactivity downstream from Hanford proved to be only half that naturally present in the Potomac River. A study in 1998 disclosed that just four of the leaking tanks had lost more than a million curies of cesium-137. By 2001, all leaking tanks had been pumped out and emptied into newer, sound tanks.

A site for storing spent fuel rods might be the huge cave system headquartering the NORAD facility, but the objections of the military would have to be overcome.

The amount of nuclear materials at Hanford is staggering. An estimated 446 million curies of radioactive elements is there. This totals 6900 tons, of which 4100 tons is uranium, 15 tons is cesium-137, and 11 tons is plutonium. Aside from this, hazardous nonradioactive chemical compounds were mixed in; examples are carbon tetrachloride, chromates, and unknown other substances. What a mind-boggling potpourri!

Within a few years all of the leaking tanks had been drained into double-shell tanks. The double-shell tanks hold up to a million gallons. They have walls 11 feet thick made from reinforced concrete, and the walls have two steel liners. The softer sludge has the consistency of cold peanut butter, and that lower down is still harder. It must be loosened with a special water jet (“water lance”) for removal. The water slams into the semisolids at a speed about three times that of sound. A temporary technique to arrest the flow of radioactive liquid from leaks has recently been developed. Pipes are sunk into the wet earth around the area, and a refrigerant is evaporated inside. This creates a wall of ice 50 to 75 feet thick, acting as an effective barrier. About the only good use of this sludge is as a dewormer for dragons.

Hanford wastes have solids which form sludge because their acidic components have been neutralized with sodium hydroxide, precipitating hydroxides of metals. This makes the waste less corrosive, but more voluminous and more difficult to pump. European practice is to leave the solutions acidic to avoid sludge, and prevent corrosion by using the more expensive stainless steel to build the tanks.

There are five sturdily-reinforced “concrete canyons” at Hanford, built during World War II to reprocess the spent fuel from the nearby reactors. These facilities produced the plutonium for the Trinity test and Nagasaki bomb and for building the early nuclear arsenal. Hanford is also planning to cocoon its long-idle reactors.

8-24 Cauldron Chemistry

The 177 waste cauldrons in Hanford's tank farm hold a chemical witch's brew which crackles with radioactivity. Some of them are leaking. One of the most notorious containers is waste tank 241-SY-101, holding 1.1 million gallons of sludge which contains organic matter (complexing agents, solvent residues and the like). Hanford's waste is much more complicated than that at Savannah River. The radiation not only decomposes the water to hydrogen and oxygen, but also converts nitrates to nitrous oxide, a powerful oxidizing agent. During the 1950s the tank was doctored with sodium ferrocyanide and nickel sulfate, in an attempt to precipitate out the cesium-137 and strontium-90, and later about two dozen other tanks were treated similarly. Operators fear that the mixture of gases in the upper reaches of the tank might explode. The exact nature of the malevolent chemical reactions is not known. A thick crust has formed over the top of the sludge, and this is ruptured approximately every hundred days by gigantic burps of gas, mostly hydrogen. A powerful pump to mix the waste was installed during the summer of 1993. Seventeen other such tanks also have burping problems. The investigations associated with this potpourri of chemical unpleasantness are enough to drive the analytical chemists bonkers.

The plan is to ultimately process the contents of the tanks and produce high- and low-level fractions. The high-level material is to be vitrified (destination: Yucca Mountain), and the low-level material will be made into a grout and stored in underground vaults (many at Hanford). About 85 million curies of the strontium and cesium have already been recovered and converted into capsules 2.5 inches in diameter and 20 inches long, and are stored under water. The capsules are high-level waste and must eventually be put into a permanent geologic repository.

When the spent fuel is submerged in water-filled pools, as mentioned above, the radiation from radioactive decay causes the water to emit a blue glow, beautiful in a ghostly way. The light emitted is called Cherenkov radiation, having been discovered by Russian physicist P. A. Cherenkov in 1934. This radiation arises when gamma rays or beta particles pass through a liquid or glass. Light traveling in air is slowed down when it enters water (to an extent depending on the refractive index), and a charged particle can exceed this velocity in water. This is a sort of shock-wave effect. The eerie light is generated with a continuous spectrum, mostly in the blue, violet, and ultraviolet regions. Advantage is taken of the effect to measure radiation. By using a photomultiplier tube individual charged particles or photons can be detected. Cherenkov counters are now a standard type of ionizing radiation meter.

Another process under investigation at the Hanford site is in situ vitrification. Study of the procedure was begun about 1984. The idea is to drive electrodes into the soil at strategic points and apply megawatts of electricity for a week or two. This process fuses the sand into a glassy rock, which immobilizes the radioactive waste. At least 150 tests have been carried out, and the process seems to be promising.

Looking for solutions

A number of research projects in 1995 illustrated some trends in waste research. One process under study deals with a highly selective complexing agent derived from natural materials which is used to remove plutonium selectively from aqueous wastes. Another study uses phosphates to immobilize actinides in soil. Still another employs sodium titanate to generate a hydrated titanium oxide, a material which carries strontium-90, uranium, and transuranium metals as a precipitate. This mixture is dried and vitrified.

In 1992, 16 Russian and Ukrainian scientists visited Hanford to exchange information on waste handling with their American counterparts. This proved highly productive. For example, the U.S. is buying patent rights on use of a separations technology which uses an inorganic extractant, meaning the radioactive material removed can be converted to a glass directly. Another process involves using electromigration to move ionic metals through the soil, effecting decontamination.

At the Idaho Nuclear Engineering Laboratory, there are nine 300,000-gallon tanks and two 315,000-gallon tanks of radioactive waste. The tanks are made of stainless steel, but they do not have double walls. Their resistance to corrosion is much superior to the carbon-steel tanks at Hanford.

8-25 Robots and Radioactive Waste

Dealing at close quarters with high-level waste, which constantly emits deadly gamma radiation, is not a job for human beings. To better cope with tanks and drums of such waste, the Department of Energy has contracted to have high-tech robots built which are immune to the radioactivity and also to temperature extremes. With an annual budget of $28 million, the Robotics Technology Development Program is developing automatons which have the capability of movement (even in the space between the walls of double-wall tanks), take samples, measure temperature and radioactivity levels, send back TV pictures over fiber-optic cables, and even perform certain instrumental analyses. The contents of many tanks are partly or mostly unknown and the robots will speed up operations. A robotic arm is attached to a 65-foot mast and it and the robot can be lowered into tanks through the portal in the center of the tank's top. The robots body stays in the space above the tank contents. The 36-foot arm can reach in every direction, inspect the walls optically or using ultrasound for cracks or corrosion, and can bend around obstructions. The hand can carry tools to crack open any crust. Using a laser range-finder, the robot can map the topography of each tank.

8-26 Waste at Savannah River

It will cost billions of dollars to repackage the military waste stored precariously at the Savannah River Plant, which holds at least 837 million curies in 34 million gallons of waste. Most of it, as liquid or sludge, lies in 51 underground tanks, some of which are leaking. The site is about 100 miles from the most intense shock zone of the great Charleston earthquake of 1886; if the tanks are ruptured, it would be an unimaginable catastrophe. A plant, the Defense Waste Processing Facility, is now under construction among the pines of South Carolina. Opening after 1998, it will in time reduce some of the radioactive waste to glass and the rest to a concrete. Earlier, low-level waste was dumped into unlined seepage basins and there might be danger of contamination of the Tuscaloosa aquifer which supplies water to several southern states. In 1997 a program was begun at Savannah in which the liquid contents of certain tanks of waste were converted to a hard grout.

Military waste is most expensive.

The solidified glass cylinders are encapsulated in copper, titanium, or ceramic vessels. These, along with canisters of spent fuel rods in their zirconium jackets, are then sequestered in safe repositories, such as vaults cut from granite, basalt, tuff, or in arid mesas such as the Yucca Mountain site discussed earlier. The areas chosen must be proven to be geologically stable since a time period of 100,000 years is necessary. Such disposal is undoubtedly safer environmentally than unsecured mill tailings from uranium mines, and no more dangerous than deposits of uranium ore. Costs for disposal are estimated to be 6 to 9% of the sales price of the electricity generated, which comes to about $320 per pound of waste.

8-27 Monitored, Retrievable Waste Storage

A plan to store high-level waste temporarily at a Mescalero Apache reservation in New Mexico has stirred up a lively dispute. Such above-ground storage permits decay heat to dissipate into the air. Such monitored, retrievable storage (MRS) facilities are under serious consideration, despite controversy on their merits. A feasibility study, funded in 1992, recommended storing up to 15,000 metric tonnes of spent fuel rods in canisters above ground. It would cover about 450 acres, less than 0.1% of the tribe's land. It is not in flood plains, wetlands, a zone seriously threatened by earthquakes, the habitat of an endangered species, or near any urban area. A detailed study indicated that workers in such sites would be exposed to lower radiation doses than those at the Yucca Mountain site. New Mexico state officials have pledged to fight the plan. Other MRS strategies under consideration are with the Chickasaw Nation in Oklahoma and the Yakima Indian Nation in Washington. Some communities have expressed interest and considered offering to host storage facilities in Nye County, Nevada, Morgan County, Tennessee, Grant County, North Dakota, and Fremont County, Wyoming,

A compelling point is the high unemployment rate: an estimated $15 million per year could be generated for the tribe.

Monitored storage in retrievable form is attractive in that repackaging, if necessary, could be done many years in the future, after much of the radioactivity had decayed away. A study completed by the Center for Nuclear Waste Regulatory Analyses in San Antonio (May 1993) estimates that storage of dry fuel rods in air will result in stresses, deformation, and oxidation. It might be that storage under water for more than ten years will be necessary.

8-28 The Waste Isolation Pilot Plant

The Department of Energy excavated the Waste Isolation Pilot Plant (WIPP) in arid salt beds 230 million years old in the New Mexico desert near Carlsbad. More than 2150 feet underground and below the Culebra Dolomite aquifer, many rooms and more than 11 miles of tunnels were burrowed. There is space for 176,000 cubic meters of waste. At a cost somewhat in excess of $2 billion, the repository was first scheduled to open in summer 1998 but this was delayed until 1999. The repository is to accommodate steel barrels of low- and medium-level waste, such as plutonium-contaminated clothes and tools, largely from weapons production. Other low-level waste comes from biomedical

Safe disposal is costly.

research facilities, and consists of glassware, syringes, filters, and animal carcasses. Over 95% of the material is labeled "contact-handled" waste, meaning that so long as the drums are not opened, they can be handled with little special protection. After emplacing the barrels, the caverns are to be back-filled with mined salt, sealing each space as a cocoon which should be stable for millennia. Salt under pressure is somewhat plastic and recrystallizes, so if cracks develop from any cause, they are expected to seal spontaneously. A factor which accelerates this process is the presence of some brine between the crystals. A test and research program was finished at the beginning of 1999. Hydrogen gas resulting from the action of alpha particles on organic matter must be vented. There is some concern of premature collapse of salt ceilings.

About four truckloads of waste per week are to be deposited in WIPP. The radioactive cargo is loaded into large steel cylinders or casks for safe shipment. The trucks are equipped with GPS devices permitting them to be tracked by satellite. In 1991, shipment of 8500 barrels of waste to the WIPP site was scheduled by the Department of Energy. In summer 1998, the job-hungry citizens of Carlsbad had readied street celebrations and a ribbon cutting to mark the first delivery. But a restraining order and threats of a lawsuit have delayed operations, supposedly because of nonradioactive toxic waste mixed with some containers. Familiar political impediments handicap the work at every stage.

It is hard to believe, but a New Mexico man in 1998 was actually able to convince more than a dozen people to buy and breed his "California Red Superworms," which were supposed to eat the radioactive waste to be shipped to WIPP. The cost was $500 for 4 pounds of worms. In court the swindler pleaded no contest.

A French nuclear official who visited the site observed the redundant safety features and inquired how such expensive "overkill" could be justified. In nearby Carlsbad, the WIPP project has not awakened much opposition, in part because of the jobs it has brought. But in Santa Fe, 250 miles distant, antagonism is strong.

In the fall of 1996 a National Research Council panel finished a study of the WIPP repository and concluded that it is safe and feasible. Provided it is sealed effectively and is not disturbed by human beings, the committee found that the waste, including transuranic elements, can be safely isolated for at least 10,000 years. The first truckload of waste arrived and was loaded into the repository in March, 1999, to the accompaniment of both cheers and jeers.

8-29 Commercial Repositories for Low- and Medium-Level Waste

Some commercial disposal sites for low- and medium-level waste are at the following locations:

Beatty, Nevada. Licensed in 1962, closed in 1993.
Maxey Flats, eastern Kentucky. Licensed in 1963, closed in 1977.
West Valley, western New York. Licensed in 1963, closed in 1975.
Hanford Reservation, Richland, Washington. Licensed in 1965.
Sheffield, Illinois. Licensed in 1967, closed in 1978.
Barnwell, South Carolina. Licensed in 1971.
Clive, Utah. Licensed in 1991.

The West Valley site, closed in 1975, has a history that is a summary of how any waste dump should not be handled, and contributed heavily to the ignoble and nasty reputation which became associated with all nuclear waste repositories. A process of extracting cesium-137 removed 5.2 million curies, and this was mixed with cement. Over 2 million cubic feet of various classes of waste were dumped into unlined trenches, although it was known that annual rainfall is heavy. More than 10,000 drums were filled. Clean-up costs of around $3.4 billion were involved. The dump was low level in name only.

In 1977 the Maxey Flats site, and in 1978 the Sheffield site, were closed because of penetration of ground water and consequent plutonium leaks. The Barnwell site contains about 211,000 curies of waste, 95% of which is from commercial reactors. It also contains tritium, and in 1992, at least 100 curies of this nuclide had leaked off site. But Barnwell was reopened in late 1995, primarily because South Carolina needed the revenue, amounting to approximately $140 million per year. The Beatty site also underwent stepwise closure. A proposed repository at Martinsville, Illinois, was scrapped in the fall of 1992.

A low-level repository has been proposed for Eagle Flat, in west Texas about 65 miles southeast of El Paso. A 16,000 acre site has been purchased. The waste, in concrete canisters and filled with concrete grout, is to be buried in a retrievable manner, and covered with a water-proof overlay.

Another procedure is to use decommissioned reactor sites to store low-level waste. For example, the now idle Rancho Seco plant near Sacramento, California, could be converted into a facility to hold virtually all of the radioactive waste from hospitals, bio-tech laboratories, and universities in California. With additional alterations, perhaps ion exchange resins from cleaning the cooling water of reactors could be safely accommodated. The possibility should be examined.

8-30 The Proposed Ward Valley Repository

A dump site, officially called a low-level waste repository, was under consideration at Ward Valley, California, in a wind-swept stretch of the Mojave desert 20 miles west of the town of Needles, which lies on the Colorado River. The valley is 1700 feet above the river. The aquifer is some 650-700 feet below the surface, and the soil is mostly gravel. To city folks, the site seems desolate, bleak, empty, and hot; to the Mojave Indians and other locals, the words which spring to mind are peaceful, serene, scenic, and hot. Naturally, a vigorous not-in-my-backyard movement has emerged.

The design of the dump seems to be short on redundant safety features, primarily in the name of economy. For example, it is planned to just dump mild steel (and some plastic) drums of waste into unlined trenches. Those who defend unlined trenches assert that this quality is an asset, since water would drain downward instead of flooding a lined area (a sort of "bathtub" effect). This view ignores the possibility that unlined trenches would permit soluble radionuclides to be carried downward, just what a repository is supposed to avoid. No modern nation, not even China, would ever permit such a primitive technology. Even nonradioactive toxic waste dumps must be lined. The repository at Beatty, Nevada, almost a twin

Ward Valley gives us a lesson in how not to go about building a waste repository.

of the proposed one in Ward Valley, failed to hold its radioactive contents. Radioactivity sensors are planned. A double-lined trench, with proper drainage provisions, sensors, and pumps to remove any liquid leachings would seem to be warranted, as well as coating the drums with bitumen, rubber or plastic.

Somewhere between 1% and 3% of the total number of curies would arise from medical and academic waste if most of the tritium is recovered rather than being dumped. Mandatory tritium recovery should be considered whenever this is feasible, which is almost always the case. Present requirements are that tritiated water, to qualify for being dumped, must be sealed in glass ampoules, which are embedded in cement inside of steel pipes which are welded shut and put into special plastic canisters. This procedure is expected to be satisfactory until the tritium decays into insignificance. After six half-lives (about 75 years), only 1.56% of the tritium remains. Tritium is an especially mobile form of low-level waste. A new technique for removing tritium from water has been developed at the Hanford site. It employs a special membrane which passes ordinary water freely, but holds back the tritium. A single pass removed 34% of the tritium at a concentration level of under a microcurie per liter. Using a cascade of many membranes could remove nearly all tritium from water.

Another nuclide in medical waste whose half-life is too long to permit local storage until almost complete decay is carbon-14. A third is technetium-99, which results after the decay of technetium-99m. Except for these three, medical waste can in general be stored safely where it is used until it decays to insignificance, when it can be safely combined with ordinary trash. If no repository is approved, then low-level waste will continue to be stored at hundreds of urban locations, a situation which might pose a higher risk than the proposed repository, and in any case would require constant monitoring. The Ward Valley facility was to accept nuclear power plant decontamination refuse, which might total about 320,000 curies during the projected life of the repository, hence the doubt about the accuracy of the term low-level waste. This reactor waste includes considerable amounts of plutonium. Such wastes would constitute more than three-fourths of the total.

While Ward Valley itself is a closed basin with respect to surface water, its underground water and that of the nearby Piute Valley aquifer (which supplies water to the city of Needles) are interconnected. Water head differences are so small that flow in the aquifers can be reversed, so that water could conceivably sometimes enter the Piute Valley aquifer. Ward Valley drains into Danby Lake, which is usually dry. Leakage of radioactive materials into this depression might end as dust during the summers, and it could become airborne and be inhaled by humans and animals. A berm system around the repository must be constructed to protect it from the occasional floods. Infiltration of the waste-filled trenches by shallow subsurface flow must be considered. Indeed, three U.S. Geological Service geologists have provided some evidence that there might be hydrologic connections between Ward Valley and the Colorado River.

One could be excused for suspecting that officialdom almost willfully compounds public anxieties about repositories. Officials of Needles expressed their fears that the city is gaining a reputation of being a "Nuclear Dump," with loss of development, tourists, and business. During the last days of the Bush Senior administration, sale of the land to California was approved, but the new Interior Secretary under Clinton halted completion of the transaction until he was satisfied it is legal.

One unresolved aspect of the Ward Valley repository is the degree of liability the State of California and the city of Needles would have in case of radioactivity release. City officials are concerned that the repository has been represented as requiring only 77 acres, yet the request for land was for 1000 acres. Does this mean a large expansion in the future? The Nuclear Regulatory Commission apparently has the power to declare an emergency and then order the facility to accept unanticipated waste. City officials fear that the Ward Valley aquifer, a potentially valuable source of water in the desert land, might be sacrificed. Addressing these concerns by State and Federal authorities would help defuse apprehension. Starting Ward Valley has been delayed time and again, and it might never be constructed.

The contractor, American Ecology or a subsidiary, if successful, would use the dump over a 30-year period, and monitor it for five more, at which time the State of California would maintain it for 100 more years. A resourceful and spirited Los Angeles organization, Committee to Bridge the Gap (President, Daniel Hirsch), played a decisive role in finally getting the Ward Valley proposal defeated.

In any case, the amount of low-level waste generated in the United States has been steadily decreasing. In 1980 the amount was 3,770 thousand cubic feet, and this figure dropped to 422 thousand cubic feet in 1996. The decrease is attributed to use of less radioactive tracers and advances in incineration and compaction techniques. A study by the U.S. General Accounting office concluded that the repository is not needed at all. In 1998, the Department of Interior officially halted the necessary transfer of land to the state of California. In 1999, the final legal decision was made which authorized the administration to refuse to turn over the federal land to California, thus terminating the proposed repository.

One might think from all this that the decision not to construct the dump at Ward Valley was final, but in late 1999 attempts were renewed to get authorization for building it. Its proponents seem never to give up.

Experience to date suggests that a great deal of hostility to low-level radioactive waste repositories could be avoided by a number of steps. One measure is inviting public participation in the siting process from the beginning. Making grants of state funds available to interested public groups would help achieve a feeling of participation. It is necessary that clear and accurate explanations be given of the waste, its origin, its isotopic composition and radioactivity levels, half-life data, and risks. The benefits which accrue to the public on generating the waste must be conspicuous. Moreover, the situation must be explained in terms which the public can understand; this itself is a demanding task. Finally, the risks must be stated with no pretense that they are zero. Any attempt to force a repository into unwilling localities is seen as a colossal intrusion. Communities in general, when well informed, are much more likely to accept waste facilities if the process of selection is and is perceived as fair and not coercive.

A little common sense in the process helps.

8-31 Management of Radioactive Waste in Other Countries

Shimokita Peninsula, Japan—The Tsugaru Strait separates Japan's main island of Honshu from the northern island of Hokkaido. The Shimokita Peninsula is a hatchet-shaped promontory which juts out from the north end of Honshu. The land is infertile, the climate is inhospitable, and the people are poor fisherfolk. In 1992, after a 27-year dispute, most opposition to a proposed giant nuclear complex had been subverted and co-opted, and a $20 billion nuclear complex had been started.

To effect this transition, the government/nuclear industry combine seems to be driven by a feeling of energy insecurity. This is a powerful national force in an industrial country without coal or petroleum. Opposition to the nuclear complex crumbled as construction created hundreds, even thousands, of well-paying jobs. Hotels were filled with engineers and technicians. A $25-million visitor center in Rokkasho is a high-tech ode to nuclear power. The project calls for building four new reactors, with space for 20 more. A breeder reactor which consumes plutonium as fuel (7-11) is being planned. A low-level waste dump near a picturesque marsh has been completed, and there are plans for a high-level waste repository. A uranium-enrichment plant is ready to operate. Lined trenches, vaults, and salt formations are also considered. Although it is realized that the relatively low international price of uranium does not warrant construction of new reprocessing facilities to extract plutonium from spent fuel, the pervasive view of energy insufficiency is enough to override mere economics, at least in its passing phase, so a reprocessing facility is planned. Supporters of the new age point out that only about 80 years ago the ignorant villagers opposed bringing electricity into the peninsula, claiming it produced deformed babies, etc.

Lack of reliable energy sources can drive any country to desperate measures.

United Kingdom—In the United Kingdom, spent fuel rods are reprocessed, and the high-level waste produced is vitrified and air-cooled until the heat generation is low enough to permit deep burial. In this regard, the practice is the same as in France. Waste is classified according to the rate of heat release. The English consortium of waste generators, Nuclear Industry Radioactive Waste Executive (Nirex), was planning underground repositories for intermediate- and low-level waste, and expected construction to begin after the year 2000. The amount to be accommodated was planned to be about 50,000 cbic meters of accumulated intermediate waste, and 5000 cubic meters more each year in the future, until 2050 at least. The main disposal site considered, expected to cost around $3 billion, is near Sellafield, on the west coast. The average density of the waste was to be about 1.65 metric tonnes per cubic meter. The cost works out to be one or two tenths of a cent per kilowatt-hour of electricity generated.

The sketch displays a typical proposed Nirex repository. Studies convinced the British engineers that by using suitable waste forms and containers, and backfilling the vaults, the special alkaline concrete employed can achieve safe containment of the radioactive waste. This is by virtue of both physical and chemical containment. Accelerated test procedures indicated trustworthy sequestering of the waste for tens of thousands of years. The physical barriers confining the waste are most valuable for the more soluble fission products, such as cesium-137 and strontium-90, since they can provide a measure of containment until more than 99% has decayed. The repository is expected to remain alkaline (pH above 10.5) for about one million years. The Nirex company testily asserts that "by no stretch of the imagination" can their repository be considered a dump.

Examination of the cement-based grout foundation in Hadrian's Wall, finished in AD 123 to protect Roman Britain from northern tribes, shows enduring structural integrity (Roman cement was superior to that of the Greeks). The alkaline condition of the cement and grout helps to prevent migration of radioactive ions by immobilizing most of them as exceedingly insoluble hydroxides and by adsorption of the radionuclides. Such alkaline cements absorb carbon dioxide from the air so slowly that the interior regions are not fully carbonated after 2000 years. An American firm has patented a process for carbonating such cements using supercritical carbon dioxide. This step can be carried out in a few minutes. Such cement or concrete does not permit leaching of radionuclides from radioactive waste.

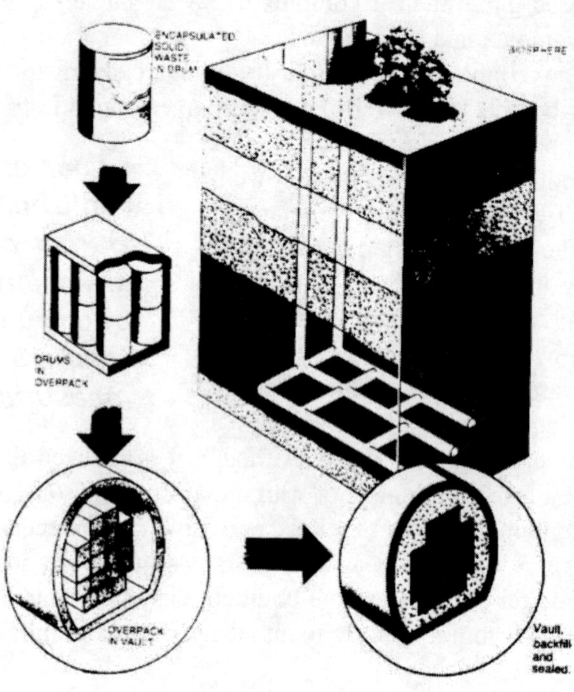

Proposed Multi-Barrier Nirex Repository

The Nirex repositories were planned for construction in unfaulted granite, one of the most studied rock structures in the world. The volcanic rock is about 450 million years old. Mostly, caverns 82 feet wide, 115 feet high, and 820 feet long were envisioned. These were to be more than 1600 feet deep. Some criticism has recently been directed at the proposed Nirex facility after it was discovered that ground water moves upward in the area. Concrete-lined vaults in sedimentary rock are thought to be suitable for certain wastes. In England too there is a developing NIMBY movement which exacerbates the radioactive waste problem. Vitrification techniques (8-21) for high-level wastes have been developed in Britain, France, Belgium, Russia, and Japan.

Nirex had planned to excavate a subterranean research laboratory in the rock, making two 680-meter-deep shafts, but the U. K. Environmental Secretary canceled the operation in March 1997. The opinion expressed was that the rock below Sellafield is simply too porous. This step might have doomed the whole Nirex repository and conceivably the future of British nuclear power.

Scotland has decided to build its own repositories. Scottish Nuclear plans to house spent fuel in a series of air-cooled concrete vaults. After perhaps 50 years a decision will be made as to whether to reprocess the material or bury it. The British nuclear authority made a dreadful mistake in 1959 when it authorized digging a shaft at the Dounreay reactor on Scotland's north coast, and simply dumping in more than 1000 tonnes of all kinds of waste. Aside from radioactive materials, there was a great deal of sodium and potassium metals. In 1977 the dump exploded and showered the surrounding territory with dangerous junk. As of 1998, little remedial action had been taken.

France—In France, research on improved disposal techniques continues. There is a growing not-in-my-backyard movement. Most of the waste is handled through a special agency, ANDRA (Agence Nationale pour la Gestion des Déchets Radioactifs). The least harmful waste (gloves, masks, rags, plastic, etc.) is packaged in steel drums and compacted. The drums are incorporated in concrete monoliths at Cap La Hague. Medium-level waste is put into concrete barrels and concrete boxes. In many cases the waste container is filled with bitumen or concrete before closing. The repository has a capacity of 400,000 cubic meters and is nearly full. A Cogema dump is located on marshy ground in Normandy near La Hague and is leaking tritium and some fission products, according to a study by Greenpeace. A new site, started in 1992 and called the Aube Disposal Facility, is being developed near Troyes. Its capacity is 1,000,000 cubic meters. There is no evidence of appreciable seismic activity in the Auge area since the tenth century. The French favor lined trenches and vaults. Currently the French store high-level waste, mostly from reprocessing, in shallow underground chambers, planning to keep it there around 40 years, at which time it will have decayed to the point that dense-packed, deeper storage will be possible. Much high-level waste from reprocessing is vitrified at two facilities (Marcoule and La Hague), and the 150-liter steel-encased glass blocks are stored in air-cooled structures until they can be put into deep storage.

Approximately a million cubic meters per year of uranium mine tailings are generated in France. Much of it is transferred into depleted mines. The remainder is dumped into special basins and slurried with water. After settling, the water is removed and treated with barium chloride and a sulfate in order to precipitate the radium along with insoluble barium sulfate. The supernatant water from this process can be safely put into streams or rivers.

Civilian and military wastes are not kept separate in France.

For each resident of France, the amount of radioactive waste produced in the nuclear enterprises averages 1 kilogram per year.

Germany—The Germans are investigating disposal in salt caverns near Gorleben, and have carried out studies on the thermal characteristics of salt and surrounding rock to be sure that there is no overloading. This site is for high-level waste. Delivery of the first waste to Gorleben in April 1995 were met by angry protesters; police responded with water cannon. An old iron mine at Konrad, 800 to 1200 meters deep and insulated from aquifers underneath by thick layers of clay, is being developed for low-level and intermediate level waste.

Other Countries—In Sweden an interim storage facility, consisting of pools of water, was opened in the mid 1980s at the Oskarshamn reactor. It has a capacity of 5000 metric tonnes and is now about half full. The plan is to store the spent fuel 30 to 40 years before transferring to a geological repository. A repository for spent fuel, one square kilometer in size, has been opened near Oskarshamn. It is 500 meters below ground in the Baltic Shield, a mass of crystalline rock, mostly granite. Spent fuel rods are thoroughly dried and sealed in copper containers with steel inserts. Another site being studied is the old Stripa iron mine. Still other sites are under preparation. The canisters are retrievable. Swedish sources claim the canisters have a life time of 100,000 years. Finland also has an underground repository, and more are planned by Canada and Switzerland; above ground bunkers are also in the works. In Belgium, a waste laboratory has been set up at Mol 650 feet below thick clay deposits. Lined bunkers are to be tested.

Here is a brief summary of the techniques a few other nations have adopted to cope with low-level nuclear waste:

- China: Lined trenches; caves, tunnels, and mines. High-level waste from reactors in China are stored under water initially, and studies are under way to decide their future fate. The power plants at Daya Bay and Qinshan have sent up to 1000 tonnes of spent fuel to an under-water storage facility at Lan Zhou. The Chinese are also considering permanent repositories in the Gobi Desert and other dry areas. They have even announced a willingness to accept nuclear waste from other countries, for a price, but so far there have been no takers.
- Hungary: Lined trenches, caves and mines.
- India: Shallow unlined trenches for short-lived nuclides and lined trenches for long-lived nuclides.
- Russia: Lined trenches, deep injection, boreholes, salt deposits, permafrost.
- Spain: Concrete vaults, excavations in granite.
- Taiwan: Lined trenches.

8-32 Learning from Mother Nature

The natural nuclear reactors at Oklo (7-18) demonstrated that the plutonium and most metallic fission products did not leach out, even over thousands of centuries. Even the strontium-90 stayed in place until it decayed. The cesium-137 did migrate out, and the iodine evaporated. Despite this favorable result, strictly speaking it applies only to the particular geology of that area.

Another natural site teaches us valuable lessons about the behavior of radioactive materials on long storage. This is a hill called Morro do Ferro in Brazil where there are 30,000 tons of thorium and 100,000 tons of rare earths. Much of fission products are rare earths. Chemically, thorium resembles plutonium in some ways and the rare earths resemble curium and americium. Again, the evidence is that migration of the most dangerous materials from the surface over eons of weathering has been negligible.

Still another area whose study yields useful information is the Koongarra ore body in Australia. This is a giant deposit of uranium ore in a common type of geological formation through which groundwater has been flowing for millions of years. Movement of uranium and its decay products has been investigated by drilling a series of holes through the ore body and surrounding layers. The results indicate that migration of only a few tens of meters has occurred on the weathered surface, and virtually no movement has taken place underground.

A resourceful teacher, Mother Nature

Here is a bit of perspective about how the amount of nuclear waste compares with the natural levels of radioactive materials. The ground, composed of soil, rocks, sand, etc., contains radioactive substances. The most abundant radionuclide is potassium, and others are uranium, thorium, and their disintegration products, such as radium. The total number of curies in the top 2000 feet of soil and rock in the United States is millions of times the amount in all our nuclear waste.

The four series of radioactive actinide decay have mass numbers 4n, 4n + 1, 4n + 2, and 4n +3 (see 4-9). The decay products of one, namely the uranium-238 series (4n + 2), are far more menacing than those of the other three. Uranium ores constantly form radium-226 (half-life 1600 years) and radon-222 (half-life a few days). These two nuclides cause more exposure to human beings than any others in the series. Radium is constantly being extracted from uranium ore bodies and mine tailings and ends up in spring water, lakes, rivers, and finally the oceans. More than a thousand metric tonnes of radium are in the oceans. Since it resembles calcium chemically, it is taken up by plants and animals and enters the food chain. It contributes to the natural background of radiation which each of us endures. Some of the radon enters the atmosphere, and contributes significantly to the natural radiation background. Radium and radon isotopes from the other series are too short lived to contribute materially to the natural background.

In short, by sequestering the transuranium elements in fuel rods, along with the other components of spent fuel elements (primarily fission products), most hazards can be averted. It is the escape of soluble fission products formed in higher yields, such as cesium-137 and strontium-90, which we have mainly to fear. These bad actors resemble elements which play essential biological roles, and thus are most treacherous.

During World War II at the Hanford site aqueous solutions of radioactive waste were dumped into trenches, directly onto the bare earth. The operators felt that the adsorptive properties of the soil would immobilize the fission products. Now, 50 years later, analysis of the soil revealed only shallow penetration, still far from the groundwater, and no migration off site. Of course, rainfall is scarce there, and the soil has favorable characteristics.

While one cannot yet say that the radioactive waste problem has been solved fully, many experts feel that the prognosis for a satisfactory management is favorable. Such management would require inspection and retrieval capability.

8-33 How Long Must Nuclear Waste Be Stored?

Nuclear reactors confront us with a problem of paramount importance: How long must their hazardous waste be sequestered until the radioactivity dies down to an acceptable level? The answer depends on how much radioactive material we begin with, how rapidly it decays, the solubility of the waste in water, and what we mean by "acceptable level."

Consider a reactor producing one billion watts of electrical energy. Typically, it started with 100 metric tonnes of enriched uranium (3.0 to 4.3% U-235). While the exact quantities vary somewhat among various reactors, the table below summarizes the amount of radioactivity arising from the fission products and from the transuranium elements for the 100 metric tonnes of initial uranium. This spent fuel is heavily exposed, and the total radioactivity is approximately 5 billion curies. During the first year after shutdown, a huge fraction of the radionuclides with very short half-lives decay. About 700,000 years are required for the radioactivity to drop to that of a typical uranium ore, namely one with 0.115% uranium and a radioactivity level of 4.8 curies per metric tonne.

Radioactivity from 100 Metric Tonnes of Spent Fuel
After Increasing Time Periods
(3.3% U-235 at Start)

Time, Years	*Radioactivity of fission products, curies*	*Radioactivity of transuranium elements, curies*	*Total radioactivity, (round numbers), curies*
1	240,000,000	924,000	241,000,000
10	30,000,000	952,000	30,900,000
100	2,680,000	1,040,000	3,720,000
1,000	32,200	700,000	732,000
10,000	4,620	420,000	425,000
100,000	1,670	23,000	24,700

An extremely important point is that about 88% of the radioactivity present one year after reactor shutdown disappears by year ten. During this time the fuel rods are stored under water and can be monitored. This is standard practice at commercial reactors; the storage pools are at the reactor site. After 10 years storage, spent fuel rods still give off heat at the rate of 1.2 watts per kilogram of uranium. Another important point is that the initial radioactivity arises overwhelmingly (more than 99%) from the fission products, but they decay faster than the transuranium elements, which become preponderant in less than 1000 years.

In 10 years, about 88% of the radioactivity is gone.

Notice also that the radioactivity level of the transuranics rises to a maximum and then falls, a feature which will be clarified later in this section.

The two fission products formed in highest yields and which have half-lives of around 30 years are strontium-90 and cesium-137. After the short-lived substances have mostly decayed away (60 years or so), these two nuclides dominate the fission product radioactivity for the next 300 years. The levels of radioactivity (in curies) from these two materials in our 100 metric tonnes of spent fuel are roughly as follows:

	1 year	*10 years*	*100 years*	*500 years*	*1000 years*
Sr-90	4,000,000	3,140,000	350,000	21	trace
Cs-137	5,200,000	4,100,000	516,000	50	trace

There are at least seven fission products with half-lives of 100,000 years or more (technetium-99, cesium-135, zirconium-93, tin-126, iodine-129, rubidium-87, and palladium-107), but only the first two are produced in fission yields high enough to merit consideration. They decay so slowly that they pose little danger. These two, with their half-lives and radioactivity levels (curies) in the 100 tonnes of spent fuel after various elapsed time intervals, are:

	Half-life, years	*1 year*	*100 years*	*1000 years*	*10,000 years*
Tc-99	213,000	1430	1430	1425	1384
Cs-135	3,000,000	29	29	29	29

The very long-term hazard from nuclear waste originates mostly from the transuranium nuclides neptunium, plutonium, americium, and curium. Some of them build up to a higher activity and then die down. This behavior is a consequence of three factors: (a) the alpha activity of many radionuclides, (b) neutron generation by certain nuclides, and (c) decay of some transuranics to produce uranium-235, plutonium, etc. In regard to the first, we recall that neutrons were first discovered by the action of energetic alpha particles from radium or polonium on beryllium (3-4). The low nuclear charge of the light element is insufficient to repel the energetic like-charged alpha particles, and it is disrupted, releasing neutrons at a low rate. In the waste on long storage, decay of the plutonium, uranium, etc., generates alpha particles, and there is an abundance of the light element oxygen (as oxide ion in the uranium dioxide matrix).

Neutrons are thus generated, and absorption by the abundant uranium-238 gives rise to additional plutonium (as in a reactor). Regarding the second factor, a few neutrons are also emitted on spontaneous fission of americium-241, but californium-254, and plutonium-240 are much richer sources. In regard to the third mode, americium-243 (half-life 7370 years) decays to neptunium-239, which quickly emits a beta particle and becomes plutonium-239. Curium-243 decays directly to plutonium-239. Curium-244 decays directly to plutonium-240. The build up of plutonium-239 exceeds its decay rate, and thus there is a net increase. In a bit more than 10,000 years, the amount of plutonium-239 in a waste repository more than doubles.

The short table below shows the slow buildup of the two most important isotopes of plutonium in our 100 metric tonnes of spent reactor fuel, followed by their decay.

Changes in Number of Curies of Plutonium in
100 Metric Tonnes of Spent Fuel on Long Storage

	Half-life, Years	*1 year*	*100 years*	*1000 years*	*10,000 years*	*100,000 years*
Pu-239	24,100	23,000	23,800	31,000	61,000	12,000
Pu-240	6570	22,800	73,000	65,000	32,000	3

The graph above illustrates many of the points discussed above. Normally, in graphs involving radioactivity and time, it is the logarithm of the activity which is plotted against time on a linear axis since this gives a simple straight line (4-6B). But here we are dealing with extremely long periods of time, and such plots are inconvenient. When logarithms of large numbers are taken, they change one unit per ten units of the number, thus compressing large numbers and expanding the smaller ones. Therefore the logarithms of the radioactivity are plotted against the logarithms of time, even though these yield nonlinear curves. After 100 years about 1.5% of its starting radioactivity remains. After 10,000 years, the level has dropped to about 0.2% of its starting value.

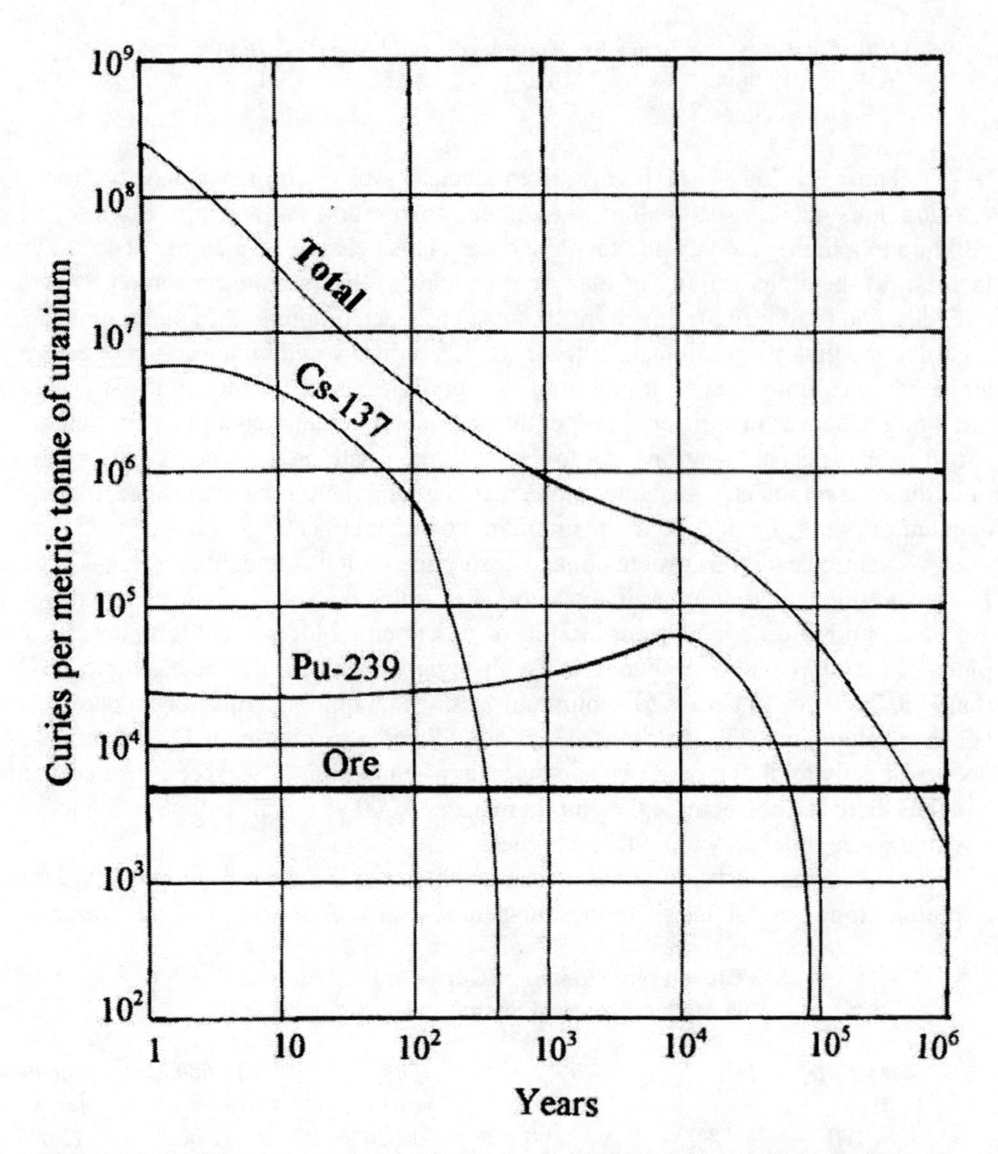

Decrease in radioactivity on aging of spent reeactor fuel. Only one important fission product and one transuranic are depicted. The heavy horizontal line represents a typical uranium ore. The fuel was initially 3.1% uranium-235 and went through a burn-up of 33,000 MW (th) days per tonnes of uranium.

Thus we see from the tables and graph that spent fuel poses an extreme peril when fresh. Separation of the transuranium elements from fission products by reprocessing does not lessen the menace; it only divides it into two parts. But just think about it: 10,000 years! The sturdy buildings of the ancient Greeks, now in ruins, are only about 2,500 years old. But buried salt deposits are dry and stable for millions of years.

8-34 Other Waste Disposal Means

Another disposal method is called hydrofracture. A hole is bored several hundred feet deep in a shale formation. A high-strength casing with its bottom end welded shut is lowered into the hole, and the annular space around the steel is filled with cement. An explosive charge is lowered down almost to the bottom and detonated. Water at high pressure is pumped in when it cracks the shale layers apart and forms a thin cavity of large area. Then radioactive waste is mixed with cement and clay, and this grout is pumped into the thin cavity. The grout spreads out into a roughly circular sheet only about a quarter of an inch thick. Then a second hole is blasted in the casing wall, and the process is repeated. This technique is not intended for high-level waste.

Alternatively, some low-level waste can be mixed with cement and water, allowed to harden in the form of slabs, and stored above ground, but under cover. Indeed, consideration has been given to disposal of intermediate- and high-level waste in concrete mausoleums located near-surface or above-ground. The immobilization of waste with cement is not suitable if too much salts are present because the product is unstable. In fund-short Russia as late as 1996, even high-level liquid waste was being injected into sand strata between clay layers some 300 meters below the surface.

Low-level wastes, such as filters, charcoal absorbers, radioactive pharmaceuticals and other refuse from hospitals, etc., sealed in bitumen or concrete, are generally disposed of in desert trenches or stored above ground. Some very low-level waste formerly was encapsulated in concrete and dropped in the sea, but this practice was stopped in 1970. Very low-level waste may be compacted, and still not exceed the limit in curies per cubic meter. A rotary kiln incinerator for waste (Process Experimental Pilot Plant) is being developed at the Idaho National Engineering Laboratory. The United States generated 1,140,000 cubic feet of low-level waste in 1990, about 65,000 cubic feet of it in California. In 1993 Russia began dumping low-level liquid waste into the Sea of Japan, near Hokkaido. Officials claimed they simply had no other choice, and would have to continue until Japan and the West help build facilities to solidify and bury the waste, which arises from servicing nuclear submarines.

Six proposed methods of disposal not in use are:

1. Marine—The first idea was simply dumping the canisters of radioactive waste in the clay or mud sediments of the oceans, in tranquil channels three miles deep, especially in the Arctic and Antarctic. The fear of irreversibly contaminating the seas is so strong that ocean dumping has been banned for years, except for some very low-level waste. But since about 1993 there has been a revival of interest in sub-seabed dumping. The argument is that in the vast oceans there are continent-sized areas of bottom clays and muds which have strong affinity for positively charged ions of fission products and transuranic elements, being superior in this regard to volcanic tuff. This has been demonstrated by studying such materials dredged up from the seabed. Further evidence is that the Soviets have dumped many old military nuclear reactors and other radioactive trash in the Arctic, and scarcely any radioactivity has leaked out.

Additional investigations in the period 1976-1986 by the Nuclear Energy Agency of the organization for Economic Cooperation and Development. The results indicate that the most favorable and stable sites would be the vast mudflats near the middle of tectonic plates, not the ocean trenches where tectonic plates meet. Bottoms some five kilometers deep have only traces of life in the upper mud layers. These sites have remained geologically inert for tens of millions of years. Radioactive waste, in the form of spent zirconium-clad fuel rods or vitrified logs in stainless steel, would be inserted into boreholes up to 100 meters in the sediments, thus forming a graveyard for spent fuel.

This matter deserves more study and serious consideration.

Uranium-235 and plutonium from warheads could also be accommodated after treatment. The technology for these operations has been pretty well developed by the petroleum industry. The containers would probably corrode through within a few thousand years, easily long enough for nearly all fission products to decay. The uranium and plutonium glasses or oxides would slowly be attacked, but migration outside the ion-adsorbing confinement would not occur.

2. Subduction by Tectonic Plates—The theory of global tectonics addresses the structure, history, and dynamics of the earth's crust. There is evidence that most of the earth's crust consists of 13 vast semirigid plates which move extremely slowly, generating earthquakes and volcanic eruptions near their boundaries. On collision, one plate slides under another (subduction), generating much heat. The lower plate is drawn into the earth's mantle and melted, producing new magma. Burying nuclear waste on a plate which is being subducted has been proposed as an ideal means of disposing of it, but until recently the process was thought to be impractical.

Seismic reflection data of the Canadian Lithoprobe Project have indicated that near Brooks Peninsula on the west coast of Vancouver Island, where the plate known as Explorer is being subducted, the plate is covered with about 2 kilometers of sediment and 2 additional kilometers of ocean water. Canadian J. Baird (*http://www.island.net/~bairdjr)* believes that existing technology is capable of drilling to the top of Explorer Plate, and thus that the Subductive Waste Disposal Method might be practical. The rate of movement is said to be 2.1 centimeters per year. The plan calls for boring cavities to accommodate the waste in the basaltic layer of the plate under the ocean sediments. The proposed technique certainly deserves investigation.

3. Antarctica—This idea is to deposit the vessels on the Antarctic Ice Cap, when the heat generated will allow them to sink slowly through a mile or so of ice to the earth. Alternatively, disposal on the surface of ice-free areas has been considered. The plan has been more or less abandoned.

4. Space—Since the mass, especially of the transuranium elements, is not so great, the cost of shipping some radioactive waste by rocket into the Sun or out of the solar system might not be too high. Despite the danger during launch, the method might some day be used, but only for a few of the most dangerous nuclides. All the waste cannot be sent into space because the costs would be excessive, and the dangers to the public would be too great. Consider, for example, the explosion of a Titan-4A rocket, costing $1-billion, forty seconds after launch from Cape Canaveral on August 12, 1998. The strategy is not considered seriously at present.

5. Bomb Test Cavities—Given the already contaminated underground cavities made by bomb-testing in Nevada, a logical option would appear to be the use of these voids for permanent waste disposal. The Soviets have had some experience in this matter, such as using such cavities to store natural gas (6-2). An important factor to be considered is the high level of radioactivity already present within those cavities. While leaks into the air occurred in some cases, in most American tests all of the radioactivity from the explosions was confined. After all, this was the bomb-testing option of choice to prevent contamination of the atmosphere. A typical test was the Chesire experiment, conducted on February 14, 1976. It was a hydrogen bomb with a yield between 200 and 500 kilotons. It was detonated at a depth of 3830 feet, which was 1760 feet below the water table.

There is already considerable experience in drilling into bomb cavities. The purpose of earlier drillings was to sample the radioactive materials after a test explosion for analysis in order to estimate the yield and the efficiency (which is the percentage U-235 and/or Pu-239 which underwent fission). If the deeper cavities are chosen (to insure that they are well below the water table), it would be easiest to drill the shafts in the same places as the original ones. By today, the fission products which are most dangerous, such as iodine-131, have all decayed. The only gaseous fission product left is krypton-85, with half-life 10.7 years. It is not nearly as dangerous as radon, and in any case only a small amount would diffuse out. Casks of wastewould be lowered into the cavity using a cable suspended from a derrick, with the operator inside a housing, shielded if necessary. At the end, the cavity is filled with earth, and the shaft is closed.

It could be that creating new bomb cavities for the express purpose of use as repositories could become attractive someday. In this case, the site would be carefully chosen with the water table in mind, and the cavity would be blasted very deep. In some cases it might be necessary to seal the shaft through the porous rock holding the ground water, using concrete. Hydrogen bombs would be best in making the cavity since most of the energy comes from fusion, thus minimizing the amount of radioactivity produced. It is by no means certain that this technique of disposing of hazardous waste would be satisfactory.

There might be some problems, but how about shipping all highly radioactive waste to hell?

The Department of Energy policy toward waste disposal in bomb cavities is negative. This opinion, that such a practice is impracticable, stems from geological and engineering uncertainties. Disposal in this fashion would not be retrievable prior to closure, as required by the Nuclear Waste Policy Act. Seismic perturbations from the blast would cause unknown long-term uncertainties.

6. Boreholes—In Great Britain, Fergus Gibb, of the University of Sheffield, has offered a new approach for disposing of high-level waste which is a modified technique using deep bore-holes. In this method, boreholes are drilled about 4 kilometers deep into granite. Spent fuel rods, densely clustered, are lowered in and the hole is backfilled. The heat from radioactive decay is enough to melt the surrounding granite. The temperature is estimated to reach 800 to 900 °C. The molten rock solidifies in time. The sponsor of the research, British Nuclear Fuels, has not made any decision about adopting the technique, but it seems to warrant further study.

A report by the American National Research Council, published in 2001 after a thorough study of all waste-disposal procedures, concluded that geological disposal remains the only long-term solution available.

8-35 Perspective

It is well to get another slant about very low-level radioactive material. New York City releases around 20 curies of carbon-14 into the air each year from incinerators and landfills. Yet there was vocal opposition to the release of 0.005 curie of carbon-14 by Rockefeller University in the early 1980s. The population of Denver receives twice the background radiation as New Yorkers do, owing to their higher elevation. Yet they have a lower cancer incidence, resulting from a healthier lifestyle.

In 1990 the Nuclear Regulatory Commission stirred up a hornet's nest with a proposal to deregulate certain low-level waste, calling it "below regulatory concern." Such materials would be permitted to be dumped into ordinary landfills as if it were not radioactive. At once environmental, consumer, and antinuclear groups protested loudly, labeling it linguistic detoxification. The nuclear industries, perceived to be behind the move, were dealt another blow to their already low credibility. The new regulation would affect 200,000 cubic feet annually, which is about 30% of the volume and 0.01% of the radioactivity of very low-level waste from nuclear power stations. The NRC claims that the dose exposure of the populace resulting from the policy could be up to 3% of that from natural background radiation. A number of states have already outlawed putting the new dumping procedure into practice. Many opponents seem to feel that, although the problem has been studied to death, future generations will not have the intelligence to handle buried wastes properly.

A future inducement to dig up reactor waste in the future might be that it contains appreciable rhodium, a valuable metal in the platinum group. Having a short half-life, it will be practically dead from the radioactive point of view.

Irreversible radioactive waste disposal is most unwise. Leakage might expose future generations. No one believes that repositories are perfect; there will be some leakage, just as is the case with natural uranium ores. Monitored, retrievable storage has its merits. All disposal techniques should be retrievable for repackaging. While disposal methods for radioactive waste can still be improved, as is the case for practically all problems, it is within the power of human beings to deal with the matter in a way at least as satisfactory as, say, the case of wastes from burning coal, and hopefully in a more satisfactory way. With responsible behavior in designing and implementing waste systems, there is reasonable historical assurance that future disasters will probably be avoided even if some failures should occur.

Bibliography for Chapter 8: Management of Radioactive Waste

Donald L. Barlett and James B. Steele, *FOREVERMORE: NUCLEAR WASTE IN AMERICA*, Norton & Co., 1985.

Manson Benedict, Thomas H. Pigford, and Hans Wolfgang Levi, *NUCLEAR CHEMICAL ENGINEERING*, McGraw-Hill, Inc., 1981.

Luther J. Carter, *NUCLEAR IMPERATIVE & PUBLIC TRUST: DEALING WITH RADIOACTIVE WASTE*, Resources for the Future, P.O. Box 3852, Hampden Station, Baltimore, MD 21211, 1988.

League of Women Voters Education Fund, *THE NUCLEAR WASTE PRIMER: A HANDBOOK FOR CITIZENS*, Shocken, 1986.

A. Makhijani, H. Hu, and K. Yih, editors, *NUCLEAR WASTELANDS*, The MIT Press, 1995.

L. Murray, *UNDERSTANDING RADIOACTIVE WASTE*, Battelle Press, Columbus, Ohio, 1989.

National Research Council, *DISPOSITION OF HIGH-LEVEL WASTE AND SPENT NUCLEAR FUEL,* National Academy Press, Washington, D.C.

Radioactive Waste Campaign, *DEADLY DEFENSE*, 625 Broadway, NY, NY 10012, 1988.

Fred C. Shapiro, RADWASTE: *A REPORTER'S INVESTIGATION OF A GROWING NUCLEAR MENACE*, Random House, 1981.

Chapter 9 NUCLEAR WEAPONS: PRINCIPLES AND DEVELOPMENT

ABSTRACT—In this chapter we take a look first at some of the scientific aspects of these monstrous weapons, and cover a few of the associated military and political components. The nature of fissionable metals, critical mass, and uncontrolled nuclear chain reactions are explained. An account of the development of the first nuclear bomb by the Manhattan Project is chronicled. Terms such as nuclear bomb yield in kilo- or megatons, shock waves, neutron generators, implosion, and gun-assembly are explained. The blooming of the nuclear bomb industry during the Cold War is described. The history of fission bombs and hydrogen bombs, production of deuterium, tritium, and lithium-6, as well as details on the construction of fission and fusion bombs are presented. How boosting yields with tritium is made possible is explained. Seemingly endless testing of all kinds of nuclear warheads took place at the Nevada Test Site. The effect of the fallout on the inhabitants and their farm animals was dreadful. Irradiation of soldiers on the atomic battlefield is described. The security of nuclear bombs in case of theft is addressed.

The extensive and sometimes frenzied development of fission and hydrogen bombs by the Soviet Union is covered. Details of their first nuclear test and events such as creating "Atomic Lake" are given. The Soviets also carried out prolonged testing. The fate of the Russian nuclear arsenal after the collapse of the Soviet Union is discussed. An account of the explosion of Soviet superbombs, the world's mightiest, is given. Neutron bombs were made by both sides. The nature of electromagnetic pulses, discovered in 1962, and considered as a weapon of war, is explained. Testing nuclear warheads underground continued after being banned in the atmosphere. The peculiar story of the "Red Mercury Scare" is related.

The corresponding nuclear weapons programs of Great Britain, France, and China are recorded. Nuclear programs of India and Pakistan are briefly described, as well as their joining the Nuclear Club. Short analyses are given of the nuclear programs of Israel, South Africa, South and North Korea, Iraq, Latin American countries, and others. Tables of data are presented showing the total numbers of nuclear tests by all nations.

Modern research by the U.S. in an area called hydronuclear testing is discussed. The objectives are to develop small nuclear bombs, of yield 25 to 200 tons; this would endanger world peace. Estimates are made of the numbers of nuclear warheads in the world today. Techniques for detecting them are considered. The meaning of a megaton explosion is analyzed in graphic terms. The shortcomings of a dreadful idea, namely radiological warfare, are described. Estimates of the amount of weapons-grade uranium-235 and plutonium-239 in the various countries are given. Techniques for disabling all the uranium-235 and plutonium recovered from dismantled bombs are outlined. The problems of cleaning up the old weapons sites are analyzed. Finally, the author presents some ideas on the depth of the problems discussed earlier.

9-1 Metals for Fission in Nuclear Bombs

For substances which have irreversibly twisted the course of human history all askew, uranium and plutonium metals don't look like much. Both are shiny when freshly cleaned, and are only slightly tarnished after a week in dry air. In humid air, uranium slowly oxidizes, becoming first yellowish, then golden, brown, gray, and black; plutonium in humid air tarnishes, turning light yellowish, and then slowly darkens to a dirty gray. If it is protected from air, plutonium can be stored safely for years, although some stresses slowly build up inside because its radioactive decay liberates alpha particles, which soon become bubbles of helium trapped in the metal matrix. This property reduces the shelf life of plutonium warheads. Both metals, in the form of high surface area (chips, turnings, and especially powder), oxidize readily and become pyrophoric (self-igniting).

The use of uranium-235 and plutonium-239 to make bombs depends on their being *fissile.* The word fissile is used in nuclear work to describe a nuclide which undergoes fission by both slow and fast neutrons. Two additional nuclides which are fissile are uranium-233 and plutonium-241. The first was used by the Soviets to make several bombs for testing, but not for their nuclear arsenal. The half-life of plutonium-241 (14.4 years) is too short for it to be used in warheads. Four other fissile nuclides are neptunium-237, americium-241, -242m, and -243. Only the first of these (half-life 2.14 million years) is considered a usable bomb material; all americium isotopes are either too short-lived or too scarce. Los Alamos researchers in 2002 achieved criticality using neptunium-237, and confirmed that it is capable of being used in fission and hydrogen bombs.

The energy of nuclear bombs derives from fission of uranium-235 or plutonium-239.

Nuclides which are fissioned by fast neutrons, but not slow ones, include uranium-238, thorium-232, and plutonium-240; they are *fissionable*, but not fissile. We have seen that atomic bombs are of two main types, the earlier kind based on fission alone, and the later kind, far more powerful, based on fusion of hydrogen (hydrogen or thermonuclear bombs, actually using the heavier hydrogen isotopes, deuterium and tritium). Both reactors and bombs depend on nuclear chain reactions. The difference is that in most reactors the fast neutrons arising from fission are moderated by water, graphite, or other materials with light atoms, and the neutron multiplication factor is barely above 1; the system is strictly controlled. But in a bomb the chain reaction is uncontrolled, is based on fast neutrons only, and the neutron multiplication factor is as high as possible, sometimes more than 2. Fission by fast neutrons yields more surplus neutrons than is the case in slow-neutron fission. There is no moderator in bombs. One might say that the out-of-control chain reaction in an explosion is a sort of unchained reaction.

9-2 Critical Mass

As more and more pure uranium-235 is accumulated into a single piece, it reaches a critical stage or mass in which the chain reaction (initiated by any stray neutrons) is barely self-sustaining. At this point the loss of neutrons from the surface is compensated by generation of excess neutrons within. The metal begins to heat up, and if not cooled it will melt and ignite. Melting increases the surface and stops the chain reaction. Plutonium-239 behaves similarly.

Each fissile nuclide in the pure state has a certain critical mass. If it is diluted with nonfissile isotopes, the critical mass of course increases because the proportion of atoms which can easily undergo fission is reduced. But if we surround the metal with a neutron reflector such as uranium-238 (depleted uranium, 4-20), beryllium, graphite, or tungsten carbide, it reduces the critical mass to a half or a third of its original value. Neutrons which would have been lost to the outside are reflected back in. Other neutron reflectors are hydrogen-rich substances such as paraffin, uranium hydride, or even the human body. Blocks of air-stabilized uranium hydride (UH_3) were used to surround uranium-235 metal in order to reflect neutrons back into a nearly critical mass; moving the blocks closer caused the uranium metal to become barely supercritical. Uranium hydride as a powder ignites spontaneously in air, and the blocks must be compressed and encased in a protective coating to become air-stable. Wartime experiments conducted in Los Alamos probed the behavior of critical masses by several techniques. Otto Frisch, nephew of Lise Meitner, played a prominent role in these tests. In one type of experiment, a subcritical amount of uranium-235 as the hydride in the shape of a cylinder was allowed to fall through a channel in a second subcritical mass of uranium hydride; together, for a tiny fraction of a second, the total mass became just supercritical and a burst of neutrons and gamma rays was emitted. This is barely safe with the hydride; two samples of metallic uranium-235 would be more dangerous. Richard Feynman called this type of experiment tickling the tail of a sleeping dragon. The work afforded proof that an explosion of uranium-235 metal could be carried out by fast assembly of a supercritical mass. By April 1945 final plans were made for the gun-assembly bomb.

Use of a neutron reflector reduces the critical mass.

When plutonium-239 undergoes fission by fast neutrons, each atom fissioned releases an average nearly of 3 neutrons, a higher number than the 2.88 released by slow-neutron fission. In the case of uranium-235, slow-neutron fission generates 2.5 neutrons per fission, while fast neutrons cause about 2.6 to be released. The critical masses listed below depend on the presence or absence of neutron reflectors, and even with reflectors, exact values depend on shape and purity; thus the figures below are subject to slight variations.

Critical Masses (Metallic Form without Neutron Reflector)

100% uranium-235	52	kilograms
100% plutonium-239	10	kilograms
100% uranium-233	16	kilograms

Critical Masses (Metallic Form with Neutron Reflector)

100% uranium-235	15	kilograms
93% uranium-235, 7% uranium-238	17	kilograms
80% uranium-235, 20% uranium-238	21	kilograms
40% uranium-235, 60% uranium-238	75	kilograms
100% uranium-233	7.5	kilograms
100% plutonium-239	4.4	kilograms
95% plutonium-239, 5% plutonium-240	5	kilograms
80% plutonium-239, 20% plutonium-240	5.6	kilograms
10% plutonium-239, 90% plutonium-240	17	kilograms
100% plutonium-241	3	kilograms

The critical mass of fissile elements is much smaller than the values shown above when salts of the metal are dissolved in water, even with no external neutron reflector. Thus an aqueous solution of uranyl sulfate, UO_2SO_4 (the uranium being U-235), becomes critical when as little as 820 grams (only 1.8 pounds) of U-235 (as uranyl sulfate) in enough water to make 6.3 liters of solution flows from a pipe quickly into a vessel of spherical or approximately spherical shape. In the pipe, the surface area is large and neutrons can continuously escape; the solution is stable. But when shaped into a sphere, the surface area is suddenly reduced, fewer neutrons can escape, and a chain reaction is possible. When made quickly supercritical, the temperature jumps far above the boiling point of the water and the resulting eruption expels much of the solution outside. A number of accidents have occurred in which supercritical amounts of solutions were produced by such innocent acts as picking up one end of a pipe containing the solution and allowing the contents to flow toward the lower, closed end. The sudden chain reactions under these circumstances can hardly be described as explosions, but the boiling is violent and of short duration. The corresponding conditions for plutonium-239 are 510 grams in 4.5 liters of solution, and for uranium-233, 590 grams in 3.3 liters of solution. In reprocessing spent fuel from reactors to separate the plutonium-239 for warheads, great care must be exercised to avoid critical conditions in which a chain reaction can take place. The 1999 accident at Tokai-mura, involving uranium-235, (page 321) was of this type.

Accidents from supercriticality occur also when neutron reflectors are placed near barely subcritical uranium-235 or plutonium-239. In 1945 in Los Alamos, Harry Daghlian was killed after he dropped a block of tungsten on some plutonium-239; reflection of the neutrons back into the plutonium caused it to emit a blue flash of deadly gamma rays and fast neutrons. Aleksander Zakharov, working in Arzamas-16 in Russia, placed a shell of copper over weapons-grade uranium-235. Neutrons reflected by the copper caused a supercriticality accident, causing fatal injuries to the scientist.

Uranium whose U-235 content is 90% or more is generally considered weapons-grade material. Samples with uranium-235 content down to 20% can be made to explode, though with smaller fission efficiency and yield. These less enriched materials are said to be weapons-usable.

Two ways have been devised to initiate a fission explosion: the *implosion technique* and the *gun-assembly technique*. In the first, a subcritical mass is surrounded by high explosive, which on detonation compresses the core inside, reducing the surface and causing it to become supercritical (details in 9-5). In the second, the fissile material consists of two subcritical pieces, and one is shot from a cannon through a hole in the other, which is ring-shaped; the two pieces together are supercritical (details in 9-6). Los Alamos scientists soon found that the gun-assembly technique is not easily practical with plutonium (see 9-6). Historically, the implosion technique was employed in the first test (Trinity site, 3-10), but the gun-assembly procedure was the first used in warfare (Hiroshima, 3-11).

Actually, the two simple processes as described above would result in relatively low-yield explosions. Several steps are taken in practice to create a higher fission efficiency (the fraction or percent of the total fissile metal which undergoes fission) and thus achieve higher yield or energy release. In making a bomb based on implosion, the subcritical mass is surrounded with a neutron reflector, usually uranium-238, which lowers loss of neutrons to the outside. The bomb is also surrounded by a large quantity of an extremely dense material called the tamper. The purpose of the tamper is to delay the expansion of the fissile mass a little in the explosion, thus permitting more fission to take place. This is accomplished by its sheer inertia, and has no relation to its strength. Since uranium-238 is exceedingly dense, it serves not only as neutron reflector but also as tamper. If beryllium or another neutron reflector is used, the tamper may be steel, tungsten or tungsten carbide, gold, or lead. Beryllium reflectors have made possible the construction of small fission bombs which still have fairly high efficiencies. Finally, a neutron generator or initiator is employed to insure that the chain reaction starts promptly and vigorously.

The tamper is a shell of dense metal outside the fissile core.

9-3 Neutron Generators

Neutron generators (or initiators) are employed in nuclear bombs to by-pass the first few generations of the chain reaction and thus greatly enhance the yield. Neutrons are readily generated when alpha particles impact light nuclei such as those of beryllium. The reaction is:

$$^{9}_{4}\text{Be} + ^{4}_{2}\text{He} \Rightarrow ^{12}_{6}\text{C} + ^{1}_{0}\text{n}$$

The process yields neutrons of several megaelectron-volt energy. Radium-226 has a specific activity of 1 curie per gram, while that of polonium-210 is close to 4500 curies per gram. Therefore polonium is far superior to radium for the purpose. An additional advantage of polonium is that it gives off only low intensity gamma rays, while radium is a powerhouse in this regard. A weakness of polonium is that its half-life is only 138 days. To prevent flooding the warhead with neutrons prematurely, the two components of the neutron initiator must be kept separate and combined at the instant of explosion. This can be accomplished by employing foils of beryllium and polonium metals separated by thin sheets of gold or platinum, which protect the beryllium from alpha particles. In the early implosion bombs, this combination was packed inside a beryllium sphere whose inner surface was grooved to induce shock-wave turbulence or a shaped-charge effect; this insured thorough mixing at the instant needed. One must keep in mind that the neutron initiator can only operate less than a microsecond or so before it is destroyed. These neutron generators were picturesquely referred to as "urchins." On detonation the inward pressure causes instant mixing of the beryllium and the polonium as the materials melted together in the very center of the nuclear bomb. The polonium used in the weapons program of the U.S. was produced in the Hanford reactors.

In modern warheads, and in particular hydrogen bombs, the neutron generators contain deuterium and tritium. These high-voltage devices involve fusion of deuterium with tritium, a process with a high yield of neutrons, patterned after the fusion spheres previously described (page 278). Some are as small as one's fist. These fusion-sphere neutron generators are external, that is, not in the center of the plutonium sphere. If tritium is employed, the generator must be accessible so it can be replenished periodically. They are important in raising the yield of fission bombs (9-5).

9-4 Energy Released in Nuclear Explosions

From the first days of nuclear explosions, a scale was needed to measure the immense amounts of energy released (called the yield), and thus their size and destructiveness. Since chemical explosives had been thoroughly studied, it was only natural to find equivalent energy levels between them and nuclear explosives. Engineers chose TNT as the standard explosive and the short ton (2000 pounds) as the unit. Although not a metric unit, metric multiples of tons of TNT came to be used:1000 tons of TNT is one kiloton and 1,000,000 tons is one megaton. One short ton of TNT on explosion liberates very nearly one billion calories (4.2 billion joules). Today the definition of a yield of one ton is the release of one billion calories, although this is not exactly one short ton of TNT. Only the immediately released energy (in the first minute) is counted, not the delayed energy of fission product decay. In that first minute about 90% of the energy is liberated.

The yield of a nuclear explosion quantifies its potency.

When all of exactly one kilogram of uranium-235 undergoes fission, the immediate energy released is equivalent to that of 17.7 thousand tons of TNT, that is, 17.7 kilotons. For one kilogram of plutonium-239, the figure is 17.4 kilotons of TNT. It is only the thermal energy and mechanical forces which are equivalent in comparing chemical and nuclear explosives; nuclear explosions also emit radioactive materials and much more radiant energy such as gamma rays, and are more dangerous. When one gram of mass is converted to energy in a nuclear explosion, Einstein's equation shows that the energy is equivalent to 21.5 kilotons of TNT.

In a classical explosion of chemical compounds such as TNT or nitroglycerin, the temperature reaches a few thousand degrees C, resulting in release of visible light, as well as some ultraviolet and infrared radiations. In contrast, a nuclear explosion involves temperatures of tens of millions of degrees, and approximately 70% of the energy is born as X-rays and 3.5% as gamma rays (the remainder is kinetic energy of fission products, unfissioned uranium or plutonium, and bomb debris). We can call all this the primary energy released.

Now there are secondary stages. Most of the high energy radiation (gamma and X- rays) is absorbed by the air surrounding the burst point, causing the air to become incredibly hot; this is the fireball. This incandescent air re-radiates its energy as ultraviolet, visible, and infrared light, as well as some micro and radio waves. Thus the air is instantly heated to an inconceivable temperature, and expands in a shock wave. The kinetic energy of the fission products, unfissioned uranium or plutonium, and bomb debris is also transferred to the surrounding air, contributing to the shock wave being created. When the explosion takes place on or under the surface, a ground wave, like an earthquake, results. It travels somewhat faster than the shock wave in air. The point on the ground directly under the explosion is called the hypocenter or ground zero.

Origin of shock waves

The total energy of the explosion in air, now assessed in terms of the secondary processes, comes out to be 50% in the shock wave, 35% as ultraviolet, visible and infrared radiation (mostly the last), 5% as gamma, X-ray, and neutron radiation, and 10% as the radioactivity of the fission products.

For each kiloton yield, approximately 30 billion curies of radioactivity results one minute after explosion. Thus the Hiroshima burst of 15 kilotons released about 450 billion curies. The great bulk of this total decays exceedingly fast. When a 20 kiloton warhead explodes, dosage 500 meters (1640 feet) from the hypocenter is approximately 7000 rads, and at 1100 meters (3600 feet) it is 400 rads (see Chapters 6 and 10). In nuclear bursts at high altitudes, very little of the energy goes into shock waves (because in the rarefied air there is almost nothing to shock), and much more exists as radiant energy.

A great deal of the information on nuclear warheads in the following sections is based on information in the excellent book *US Nuclear Weapons: the Secret History*, by Chuck Hansen (see bibliography at end of chapter).

9-5 Detonation Using the Implosion Principle

The next few sections describe in some detail how the two nuclear bombs used to destroy Hiroshima and Nagasaki were made and how they functioned. They were most certainly weapons of war, hence the use of the word weapons in the title of this chapter. But by the present time, there has been a change. Most nuclear warheads in today's world are so powerful that they cannot be employed to win battles. They serve only as threats, or deterrents, or perhaps as national icons of insuperable power. For this reason, they can hardly be considered as true *weapons* of war. There are no justifiable scenarios for fighting nuclear wars.

In the table of critical masses above, we see that the critical mass of plutonium-239 of 95% purity is 5 kilograms if a neutron reflector is supplied. This is the case when the plutonium is in the shape of a solid sphere. Suppose we reshape the metal into a hollow sphere. It now has a larger surface area and thus neutrons can escape at a greater rate. We can now use an extra kilogram or two of plutonium without the mass becoming supercritical. It is made with a hole inside to accommodates a neutron generator.

To effect compression of a metal ball, the principle of implosion is employed; in this, the ball is centered in a mass of high explosive which is then detonated as uniformly as possible in a special way. This concept was first described by Richard Tolman in 1942. Years before World War II the American explosives expert Charles Munroe discovered that if letters are inscribed in a block of high explosive, and this is laid on a steel sheet with the inscribed surface on the steel, after detonation the letters are clearly seen as depressions in the sheet. There is a sort of hollow charge or shaped charge action at work: the Munroe effect. This topic has been extensively researched. It appears as if the shock waves (also called the detonation waves) inside the exploding material converge at the surface of the steel substrate. This happens because the shock waves, when they reach the internal surface of the engraved letters, then refract and focus on the steel surface. This results in extraordinarily high pressures and temperatures which impress indentations in the steel in the exact shape of the letters. The technique has led to the development of armor-piercing shells, as in the bazooka, and anti-tank cannon. The effect has also been used to pierce casings in oil wells. Some meteorites happen to have shapes which produce the effect on impact.

The Monroe effect, an amazing phenomenon

The neutron initiators in post-war implosion bombs were constructed to take advantage of the Munroe effect for more efficient action. Cone-shaped holes in their heavy metal foil and polonium-beryllium components resulted in focusing the shock wave from implosion onto the neutron initiator, causing instant mixing and neutron release from the alpha particle-beryllium action.

Development of a successful implosion technique began at Los Alamos in summer, 1943, under the overall oversight and direction of J. Robert Oppenheimer. Many were skeptical that it could be done, at least in time to use in the war. The group leader, physicist Seth Neddermeyer (Fermi Award, 1982), however, was fairly confident by April 1943 that it could be done; he was following the lead of Tolman. Neddermeyer concluded that the implosion technique was much superior to the gun assembly method. This belief was strongly reinforced by the cooperation of mathematician von Neumann, one of the foremost mathematicians of the 20th century. Among other techniques, X-ray photos were taken of metal cores being imploded by high explosives. The X-ray source was protected inside one block house, the radiographic equipment was in a second, and the test explosion was in between. Flashes of X-rays in rapid pulses were used, each about a tenth of a microsecond in length. An alternative approach employed gamma-emitting radiolanthanum, a fission product, inside the core.

During the research on implosion at Los Alamos, the first tests compressed iron pipes and other cylindrical metals using explosives. Later steel balls as a core and a shell of high explosive outside were used. When many points were detonated at the same time on the outside surface, each started a shock wave as the explosive reaction moved inwards. These waves, which are really intense sound waves, intersected to produce points of extra high pressure, the result being uneven compression of the steel core. By devising a design that would permit the waves to converge during their movement inward, made possible by using two different kinds of high explosive, uniform pressure could be exerted on the metal core, compressing it like a stiff spring. Such instantaneous pressure heated the metal above its melting point. This development of explosives focused the shock waves and thus became known as explosive lenses.

Mathematical analysis helped point the direction to go to perfect explosive lenses. Kistiakowsky realized that a knowledge of the velocity of shock waves and the use of two kinds of high explosive would make it possible to make the shock front converge at the metal surface, arriving at very nearly the same time. In constructing of the Trinity bomb, the uranium tamper (with plutonium and neutron initiator inside) was surrounded with blocks of high explosive shaped something like pyramids so they could surround the core spherically. The narrow ends of the pyramids pointed inwards. The bases of the pyramids were made of a fast-acting explosive called Composition B, which consisted of TNT and RDX (an explosive more powerful than TNT), and a wax. Each was cast with a hemispherical cavity, that is, lens-shaped, with the curved surface toward the outside. The cavity contained a slower-acting explosive called Baratol, which consisted of barium nitrate, aluminum powder, TNT, guncotton, and a binder. Each block of explosive was X-rayed to insure that there were no voids. Below the pyramids was more Composition B. The total amount of high explosive was about 5000 pounds.

Crafting a big ball of high explosives to deliver a compressive blow to a metal ball via the shaped charge effect

To explode the bomb, detonators on the surface set off the fast-burning explosive. Thus all of the explosive charges detonating simultaneously generated a shock wave traveling inward, in turn detonating the slower-burning explosive. The wave front changed from convex to concave. This resulted in a lens effect to focus the spherical wave front on the tamper in the center. The instant compression of the metallic core liquefied it. The design of the Trinity implosion bomb was largely due to Robert Christy. The explosive lenses were mainly the suggestion of James Tuck, an English scientist at Los Alamos. Arnold Kramish was in charge of the detonators.

Implosion of uranium-235 was shown to be possible (though the yields are lower), and thus plutonium-239 appeared to be much superior. Since much more uranium-235 was available than plutonium-239, composite cores were made from both plutonium and uranium-235. Tests in the Pacific in 1948 showed that these bombs, representing a second generation with improved techniques, had high efficiency. For example, the *Yoke* test had a yield of 49 kilotons. A Soviet battleship and submarines were snooping in the distance.

At one time consideration was given to using uranium hydride, UH_3, in place of uranium metal in implosion bombs. The idea was that the moderation of fast neutrons by the hydrogen atoms would result in increased efficiency and yield, despite the much lower density of the hydride. But the time between fission steps in the chain reaction proved to be more than enough to overcome any gain, so the idea was not pursued at the time. In 1952 more tests of uranium hydride bombs were carried out, but resulted in fizzles.

The design described above is dated, and must be considered schematic only. With hundreds of talented physicists toiling for decades perfecting more and more efficient warheads, modern weapons are much more complicated, but the basic principles are much the same. A warhead manufactured in the 1980s is incredibly complex. It is loaded with precision electronics, carefully machined mechanical parts, shaped explosive charges based on decades of experience, exotic metallic parts (many gold-plated), and lovingly designed plutonium or uranium-235 nuclear charges. The model of warhead known as MK 61 has over 4000 components.

These points can be illustrated using a fission bomb such as the one tested at the Trinity site in 1945. The crude sketch below shows its main components in a plausible schematic form. The progression of events and the stages of its explosion can be reconstructed approximately as follows. The core contained 6.2 kilograms of plutonium-239 (with a low percentage of Pu-240). The metal formed a ball (actually two half-balls) about the size of a grapefruit. This component of the bomb became known as the pit from the obvious similarity of the arrangement to that of seed in a plum or similar fruit. The plutonium was alloyed with about 1% gallium, which stabilized a single crystal structure, the delta phase. Otherwise, changing temperatures would cause transformation to new crystalline forms and consequent expansion or contraction, and difficulties in fitting the parts. The fabrication of plutonium is in general a difficult task. The plutonium was nickel plated to protect it from oxidation. The flat surfaces of the hemispheres were covered with gold foil. The purpose of the heavy gold was to prevent any jets formed during implosion from entering and activating the neutron initiator prematurely.

***The word* pit *derives from the similarity in configuration to the pit or seed of a fruit, not from the term* pit bull.**

Dynamite is commonly exploded using blasting caps, also called percussion caps, which can be fired using a burning fuse or electric resistance filament. The small caps are filled with a sensitive explosive such as lead azide. To begin the implosion of the Trinity bomb, however, a more reliable detonation technique had been developed, namely imbedding a metallic filament inside the high explosive itself and firing it by discharging an electrical capacitor. The filament was simply vaporized instantly. Simultaneous firing of 32 such detonation points on the outside of the peripheral chemical explosive lenses caused shock waves to travel inward and merge into a nearly spherical shock wave as described earlier. Arriving at the tamper, the incredibly powerful shock wave subjected the uranium-238 tamper to an enormous compressive force. Tampers need not be a single piece of metal; they can be fitted together in parts. There was a spherical space between the heavy tamper and the fissile core inside; this was to allow the tamper to build up momentum and strike a hammer blow at the core for more effective compression. This principle was well known for years before the war. The result of this procedure was to make the compression more than a hundred times as high as it would be without the space to build up momentum. The space mentioned was actually a rigid, spongelike plastic like that in a polystyrene drinking cup, serving only to hold the central core in position. In later models of implosion bombs, the core of plutonium was mounted on aluminum or steel supports in a spherical air gap.

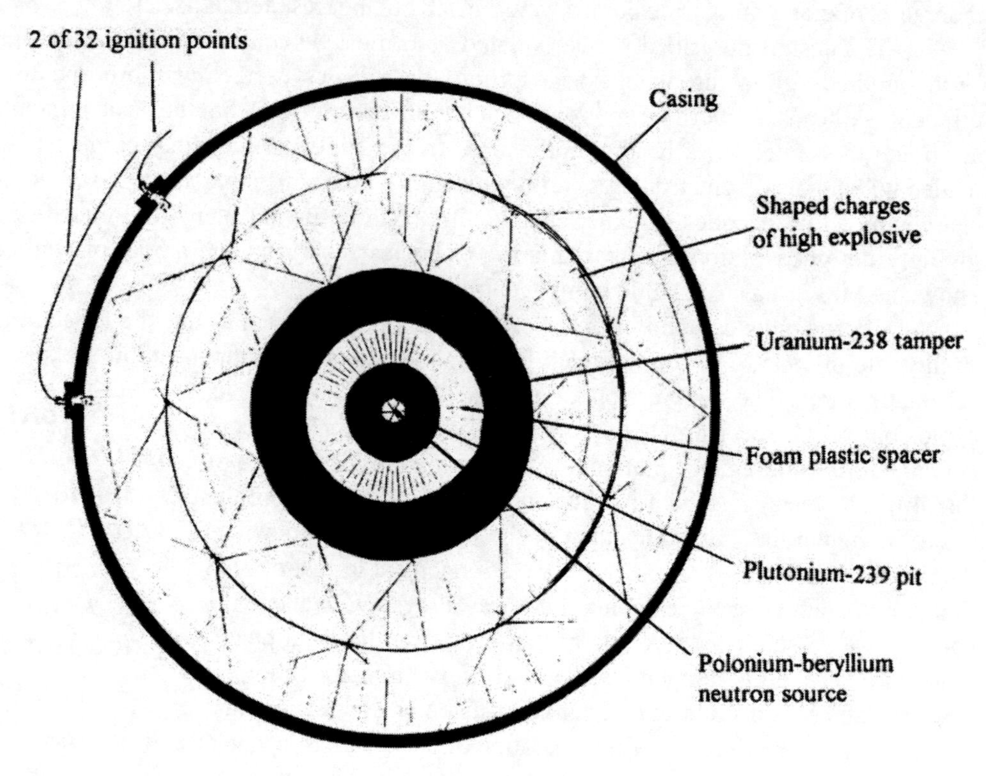

Schematic cross-section of Trinity fission bomb

The center of the core had a cavity to accommodate the neutron initiator so that it could deliver a blast of neutrons into the interior during implosion, thus insuring that the fast-neutron nuclear chain reaction was vigorously started. A twofold reduction in volume of the core meant that about four critical masses suddenly existed, as described below. An advantage of the implosion technique is that the process is so fast that predetonation was avoided. Predetonation (or pre-ignition or pre-initiation) means the beginning of a fission chain reaction before a maximum yield can be achieved, resulting in a low yield or even a fizzle. The surfaces of the tamper were covered with a boron-containing material to lessen any tendency for predetonation; boron strongly absorbs the neutrons released from the various radioactive materials present.

It turns out that when a fissile metal is compressed, the critical mass decreases roughly according to the square of the compression factor. Thus if plutonium is imploded so that its volume becomes half of the original, the critical mass is reduced to one-fourth its normal value, or, to put it another way, one critical mass becomes four. This rule of thumb is an approximation, and one critical mass might become anywhere between three and six. The effect results not only from a reduction of the surface area and lowering of the escape rate of neutrons, but also from the fact that if compressed, the distance between atoms is reduced, thus shortening the time of each generation of neutrons. Compression factors of up to about 30 have been achieved, and much of the research on implosion has been directed toward this objective.

How imposion multiplies the number of critical masses

If we imagine these steps on a slow-motion scale, it is advantageous to make an unaccustomed adjustment to our units of time. From the point when the plutonium was compressed until it flew apart in explosion, only 0.000,000,560 second was required; this is an approximation chosen to illustrate the principles involved. This is 560 billionths of a second. For greater convenience, we will use the term *nanosecond* for a billionth of a second, which is standard in all scientific work (light, traveling at its enormous speed, goes almost a foot in one nanosecond). Thus the total time of implosion-explosion is 560 nanoseconds. The length of time between neutron generations in an exploding bomb averages about 10 nanoseconds, so there were 56 generations (give or take a few) of neutrons in the whole event. Since about 3 neutrons are released for each plutonium-239 atom fissioned by fast neutrons, the neutron multiplication factor k has a value of nearly 2 (1 being consumed in causing fission). Knowing this, it is possible to calculate the rate of fission and number of neutrons released as each nanosecond passed. The results show that the number of neutrons (and corresponding fissions and energy release) rose exponentially so steeply that an amazing 99.5% of the energy release occurred in the last 4 generations. This illustrates how important the tamper was: by its inertia alone, it confined the incandescent mass an additional 40 or 50 nanoseconds, and increased the percentage of atoms fissioned from 2 or 3% to 20 or 30%, or considerably more in modern bombs. This illustrates the advantages of the neutron initiator (9-3): flooding with extra neutrons at the start more or less short-circuits the time for the first few generations. Moreover, the fast (unmoderated) neutrons

There are perhaps 50 to 100 links in the neutron chain reaction before the explosion occurs.

About 99.5% of the energy is released during the last four neutron generations.

from plutonium fission caused fission of some of the uranium-238 tamper, increasing the explosive yield. By 1998, computer modeling of the above steps had become extremely sophisticated. This was made possible by the development of supercomputers capable of performing as many as 12 trillion calculation steps per second, equivalent to 12,000 steps per nanosecond. This speed is much more than enough to model one generation of neutrons after another during a fission bomb explosion. The calculations must consider the decreasing amount of plutonium as it is consumed.

So at this point there existed a ball in which some ten million million (ten trillion) joules of energy had been almost instantly generated. The temperature jumped to several tens of millions of degrees C, hotter that the center of the Sun. It is as if a chunk from the interior of a massive star had just been instantly created on our Earth. The unfissioned plutonium and uranium, fission products, uranium tamper, and weapon components were converted into a plasma, and the colossal internal pressure compelled immediate outward expansion: a nuclear explosion. The instantaneous internal pressure has been estimated at 10 or 20 trillion pounds per square inch; these numbers average 15,000,000,000,000! Such a figure is almost beyond imagination. Most of the radiant energy was in the form of X- and gamma rays, which were absorbed by the air surrounding the bomb. This ionized the air, converted it to a plasma, and heated it to exceedingly high temperatures; this was the fireball. An awesome shock wave sounded in the air: visible light, infrared, radio waves, ultraviolet, X-rays, gamma rays, and neutrons burst out; the fission products and surviving plutonium vapors were ejected into the environment and slowly condensed. Of the original 6 kilograms of fissile material, approximately 1.2 kilograms underwent fission (this was the *efficiency*, assumed here to be about 20%). The explosion released an amount of energy about equal to that of 21,000 tons of TNT, that is, 21 kilotons. Aside from the X-rays and gamma rays liberated at the instant of explosion, short-lived fission products continued to emit gamma rays for some time.

An exploding nuclear bomb, in its early stages, is by no means homogeneous. Photographs taken with exposures of a hundred-millionth of a second (10 nanoseconds) reveal that the growing incandescent mass is shaped something like a skull, with cavities and indentations. Sockets with spikes protruding from them are visible. The whole ball has a shape not unlike that of the spore of some weird fern, greatly magnified. At some stages the fireball has a reddish hue, owing to the presence of strontium, whose isotopes Sr-89 and Sr-90 are important fission products. The size, shape, and colors of the hot cloud seen right after explosion of a fission warhead varies with yield and distance above the ground at which detonation occurred. In general, the radioactive mass rises like a hot air balloon to produce the familiar mushroom shape, or, as some say, the toadstool shape. The colors change constantly. Of the hundreds of fission explosions filmed in the air, the shapes and general characteristics are by no means uniform.

The rate of neutron generation and fission during an atomic explosion is similar to the amassment of rice on a chessboard in a legend from India. A payment in rice was involved which consisted of 1 grain on the first square, 2 grains on the second, 4 grains on the third, doubling for each square until the 64th square was reached. At first thought, this doesn't seem to be an excessive amount. But calculation shows that the last square corresponds to 9.22 million million million grains of rice! Counting 50 grains of rice per gram,

High stakes: rice grains on a chess board

the total for the chessboard comes out to be 369 billion metric tonnes, and the last 4 squares account for nearly 94% of the total. This calculation, applied to chain-reaction fission in a plutonium-239 bomb, over-estimates the number of fission events because it does not take into account the depletion of the plutonium. Exponential multiplication is a powerful engine for growth.

9-6 Detonation by the Gun-Assembly Technique

The basic ideas can be presented by a description of *Little Boy*, the bomb which employed the gun-assembly technique to destroy Hiroshima. Theoretical physicist Robert Serber was largely responsible for its design (refer to the figure below). Two subcritical masses of uranium-235 were used; the isotopic purity was probably 70 to 80%. The projectile, also known as the bullet or plug, had been shaped into a cylinder to fit in the cannon, and it made up 42% of the total uranium-235. Together, the amount of uranium has been variously reported, but was approximately 140 pounds. The target was in the form of a cylinder, constituting the remainder of the uranium-235, and was situated at the end of the cannon barrel. It weighed somewhere around 80 pounds. It was inserted as a sleeve into a cylindrical hole drilled in massive steel rings, which weighed more than 5000 pounds. The uranium tube was inserted as a sleeve. Thus the uranium-235 target rings were surrounded by the massive steel, which served as a tamper. A polonium-beryllium neutron initiator (see 9-3) was located on the target rings, and was crushed by the projectile after firing. The total mass of the bomb was 8900 pounds. The bore of the cannon was 3 inches, it had no rifling, and was 6 feet long. The exterior casing of the bomb was about 28 inches in diameter and overall it was 10.5 feet long. The explosive used to propel the bullet was several pounds of cordite, a mixture consisting mostly of nitroglycerin and guncotton.

The gun-assembly technique

On firing, a high muzzle velocity (1000 feet per second) was attained. The bullet did not impact the target, but entered the hole in the uranium-235 target, and struck the neutron initiator. The mass became greater than critical almost instantaneously. In fall 1943 Segrè measured the rate of spontaneous fission of uranium which Flerov had discovered in 1940. This result made it possible to predict the minimum muzzle velocity of the uranium-235 bullet to reduce any tendency toward predetonation. The term predetonation (or pre-ignition) means increasing numbers of fissions approaching the

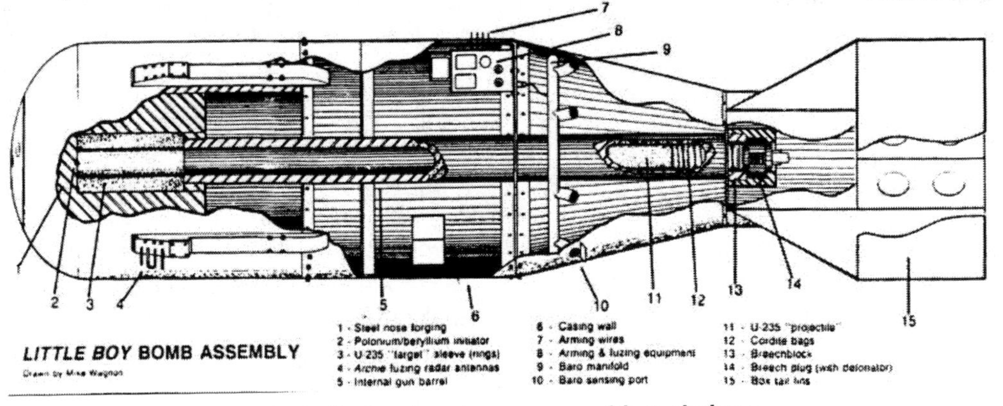

Early fission bomb, gun-assembly technique

point at which a self-sustaining chain reaction can occur. In the gun-assembly technique, a too low muzzle velocity would mean that as the projectile approached the target to achieve supercriticality, it and the target rings would be melted and the resulting explosion would be weak. Cosmic rays generate a few neutrons, and at high altitudes, where cosmic rays are stronger, more neutrons result. These neutrons are capable of causing U-235 to undergo fission, just as neutrons from spontaneous fission of uranium-238 can. (U-238 is present in the tamper of bombs, and to some extent in the U-235). The lower the number of neutrons from these sources, the less the danger of predetonation, and the less the muzzle velocity the bullet must have in the gun-assembly bomb. Shielding from stray neutrons would permit shorter and lighter gun-assembly components.

Originally, the plan was to employ plutonium in the gun-assembly bomb. But the plutonium-239 contained about 6% plutonium-240, a strong neutron emitter from spontaneous fission, and this would cause pre-ignition unless a truly extraordinarily high muzzle velocity of the projectile was achieved (at least 3000 feet per second). For these reasons, uranium-235 was chosen, even though it was not of true bomb quality by today's standards. While yields are lower than in implosion-initiated explosions, they are still enormous.

The gun-assembly method is simple and reliable. Nuclear artillery shells, generally six to eight inches in diameter, operate on the gun-assembly principle using uranium-235; uranium-233 has also been employed. Reports have appeared to the effect that the latest gun-assembly weapons do contain some plutonium. The cylindrical U-235/Pu-239 bullet is barely subcritical. It is designed so that the two ends detonate first, forcing the middle section into a more nearly spherical shape for higher yield. The Soviets also developed gun-assembly warheads of various types employing uranium-235.

When you think about it, you have to wonder how the delicate mechanisms of a nuclear warhead could survive and still function inside an artillery shell on firing from its cannon. Yet these problems have been solved. On firing, the projectile is accelerated to 2000 feet per second in a fraction of a second. In addition it spins several thousand times per second. The projectile is mounted in the rear of the shell and its target and tamper are in its nose. The 11-inch MK 9 shell weighs 803 pounds, while the 16-inch MK 23 shell weighs 1900 pounds. An innovative artillery shell, the W48, is plutonium-fueled. The plutonium is shaped into a rod, which is embedded in a mass of high explosive. To detonate the device, the explosive is caused to go off in a linear fashion, rather like the secondary in a hydrogen bomb (9-15).

9-7 The Yield of the Hiroshima Bomb

Since no bomb of the Hiroshima type (uranium-235) had ever been tested before, there was some difficulty in determining its energy and yield. The earliest estimates of yield were between 12 and 22 kilotons. In later years, after calibration studies of data from the Trinity and Nagasaki plutonium-239 bombs, and much additional information, a more accurate yield estimate could be made. This work involved theoretical calculations, radiochemistry, the radius of the fireball, thermal radiation intensity (as measured by charring of cypress trees), gamma-ray effects, blast wave observations, luminescence studies, and measurements of neutron-induced radioactivity. The last involved determination of the radioactivity of sulfur (in certain roof tiles), cobalt (in steel), and copper (from electric wires) when activated by neutrons. Reports by the Radiation Effects Research Foundation document these studies. Additional work by American and Japanese physicists employed the very sensitive accelerator mass spectrometer (6-6) to determine minute traces of chlorine-35 and chlorine-36. Their ratio give us an index of the number of slow neutrons involved. This number proved to be several times higher than the calculated value. Since the slow neutrons arise from fast ones, which are much more dangerous to human tissue, it means that some serious errors might have been introduced into the ionizing radiation doses of the population. This work indicates that the most reliable estimate of the yield of the Hiroshima bomb was 15 kilotons. Assuming the yield was this number, approximately 850 grams of uranium-235 underwent fission, and this was only about 1.5% of the total present; thus the bomb was very inefficient. The gun-assembly technique is inherently considerably less efficient than the implosion method because the two subcritical components are merely united, not compressed. The whole topic is still being reevaluated.

9-8 Nuclear Bomb Production

About 90,000 persons were employed in nuclear warhead manufacture during most of the Cold War years. The major nuclear weapon research and production facilities are shown on the map below.

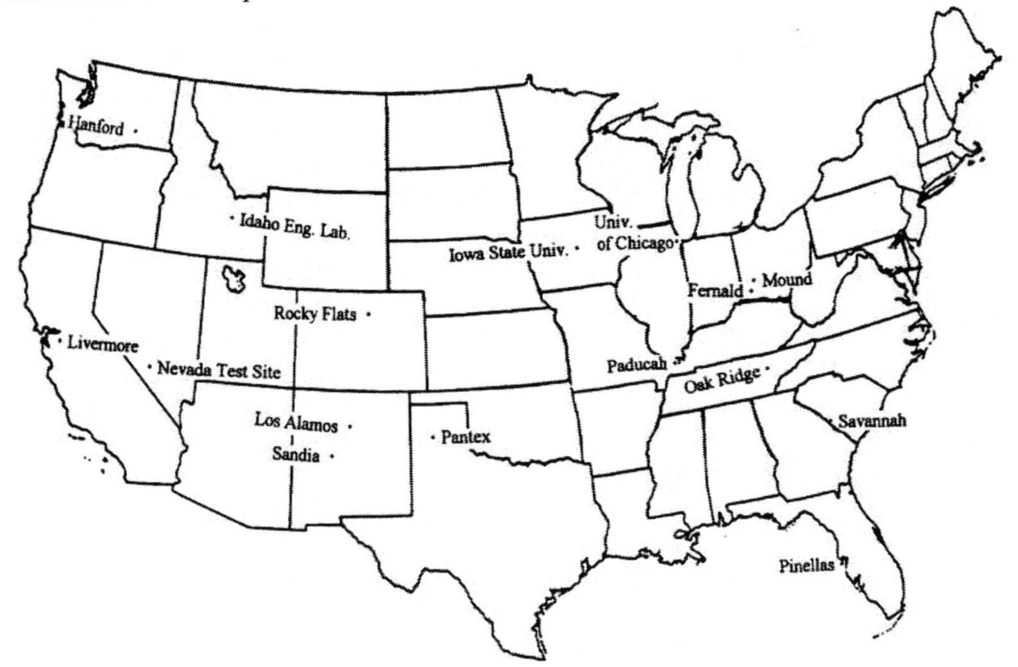

Location of Manhattan Project Installations in the United States

Research—The principal nuclear weapons research laboratories are at Los Alamos, New Mexico, Livermore, California, and Sandia National Laboratory, with one branch near Livermore and the other in Los Alamos. During the Cold War, Los Alamos was half university town and half military base.

Plutonium Production—Plutonium was manufactured at the Hanford site in Washington up until recently (production by the N Reactor: 4804 kilograms, 1976-85) and at the heavy water-moderated K, L, and P Reactors at the Savannah River Plant in South Carolina (production:11,960 kilograms,1976-85; these are currently operating at reduced power or are shut down). To keep the content of plutonium-240 low (not over 6%), the fuel was removed from reactors producing weapons-grade plutonium-239 every few months. The plutonium was extracted using the PUREX process (8-9).

The Rocky Flats Plant—The plutonium was fabricated up until recently at the Rocky Flats Plant, Golden, Colorado, on the doorstep of Denver, and old warheads were recycled there. The facility was started in1951. At the time the local citizens considered the plant an economic boon and patriotic duty, but over the years patriotism turned into outrage. Rockwell International took control under the Department of Energy in 1975. With 6000 to 8000 jobs and an annual payroll of $220 million, Rocky Flats was an economic force of importance. About 1980 an undisputed case of malignant brain tumor caused the death of a 40-year-old worker. An attorney charged that the DOE is "lost in a time warp of patriotism that what they are doing is important to national security." About 1990, plutonium production was stopped. Supplies from old warheads are more than sufficient for new ones, especially in light of the START Treaty signed in 1991, and the demise of the Cold War.

During its peak years of operation, there were many fires in the Rocky Flats installation. The most serious one was in 1965, and it involved plutonium metal. It evidently started spontaneously from chips or turnings of the metal in the presence of machining oil. A considerable amount of the deadly material, variously estimated from "slight" to 20 kilograms, escaped into the surroundings, and there was a minute amount of plutonium dioxide which continually eluded the filters. At least 41 firefighters and others sustained radiation doses. The escape of some plutonium from the site was discovered by a citizens group, and was confirmed by Rocky Flats authorities only afterward, a development which helped to undermine the credibility of management. Machining plutonium requires much oil, solvents, and degreasing agents, and these become contaminated, thus presenting disposal problems. A new process for cleaning plutonium metal uses supercritical carbon dioxide, and this simplifies the process and greatly reduces the amounts of waste solvents. An estimated 62 pounds of plutonium remains in the air ducts. Actually more than a thousand pounds of plutonium is missing, but most of this is probably now in a dump in Idaho, having been carried along with regular shipments of radioactive waste. The total damages in the 1965 fire amounted to some $70.7 million, a record for industrial accidents in the United States.

Missing plutonium

Uranium-235—Uranium-235 enrichment plants are at Paducah, Kentucky, at Piketon, Ohio, and at Oak Ridge, Tennessee. The Ohio facility, known as the Portsmouth Gaseous Diffusion Plant, is the only one which can produce highly enriched uranium for bombs. The Feed Material Production Center for uranium was at Fernald, Ohio; it closed in 1989. No weapons-grade material (93.5% U-235) has been made since 1964.

In 1994 the Department of Energy announced that altogether 994 metric tonnes (1093 short tons) of weapons-grade uranium-235 had been manufactured. Of this, 259 metric tonnes remains unused, and is stockpiled.

Warhead Parts—Neutron initiators are built at the Pinellas Plant, St. Petersburg, Florida. Additional parts are made at Idaho National Engineering Laboratory. Sandia National Laboratory in New Mexico engineered detonators and triggers, and fabricated large numbers of field-ready weapons during the years following World War II. Some nonnuclear components for warheads are produced at the Mound Laboratory, Miamisburg, Ohio.

A trivial off-shoot of a device used in nuclear weapons is the semiconductor bridge igniter. Buena Vista Pictures, a subsidiary of the Walt Disney Company, has contracted with Sandia to make these timing devices to detonate fireworks in the company's theme parks. Thus spectacular displays could be synchronized with a climax in the music.

Final Assembly of Warheads—New warheads were assembled at the Pantex (*Pan*handle of *Tex*as) plant near Amarillo, Texas. It is here that the chemical high explosives were shaped by casting and machining to specifications and the final assembly of high explosives and fissile materials was carried out. To minimize danger from any accidental explosion, this work was done in underground concrete cylinders covered with a thick layer of gravel. Older weapons are modernized at the Pantex plant, and retired warheads are disassembled. At the end of 1947 the American arsenal contained 56 fission bombs; at the end of 1950 there were 298; by 1956 the figure had reached 3620 bombs; and by 1962, there were more than 27,000. The Soviets had five bombs at the end of 1950. During the early 1960s the United States was producing 25 nuclear warheads per day. By 1982, the rate had dropped to two per day. In excess of 30 kinds of nuclear warheads have been assembled at Pantex, numbering several tens of thousands. They ranged from gravity bombs to be dropped from aircraft to sleek models for cruise missiles. A tornado, with heavy rain and hail, struck the Pantex plant in September, 1967. The extensive damage done was concealed until 1989. The sudden storm blew the roofs from several buildings, knocking a few incomplete warheads from their pallets, and flooding a number of facilities. After the Cold War, production stopped. Today public tours are conducted through the grounds. A local battle is shaping up over the issue of whether to support transfer of former Rocky Flats operations from Colorado to Pantex.

9-9 The Problem of Plutonium-240

From the start, weapons work with plutonium was plagued by the problems of self-heating from alpha decay (and resulting expansion of the metal components). A second problem appeared too: neutron release by the plutonium-240 which was always present, drenching everything with a neutron shower. In the spring of 1944 in Los Alamos, this second problem was feared by some nuclear scientists to threaten the success of plutonium bombs. The tiny amounts of plutonium made in the cyclotron were pure Pu-238; the Pu-239 produced in reactors in kilogram quantities had several percent Pu-240. The only practical way of producing plutonium-239 in quantity is by nuclear reactors, and this always forms some plutonium-240 and lesser amounts of heavier isotopes. The half-life of plutonium-239 is 24,100 years, and of plutonium-240, 6570 years. These two isotopes undergoing alpha decay liberate enough energy to self-heat the plutonium metal components of bombs. The metals are warm to the touch. Each kilogram of isotopically pure plutonium-239 gives off heat at the rate of 1.93 watts, while the figures for plutonium-240 and plutonium-241 are 6.8 and 4.2 respectively. Since the bomb components have different sizes and configurations, they self-heat and expand to different degrees, and precision-tooled parts might not fit perfectly when they are assembled. This problem can be managed by refrigeration or phase stabilization by incorporation of gallium (9-5).

Plutonium-240 undergoes spontaneous fission (in addition to alpha decay), producing neutrons and gamma rays. Each gram of weapons-grade plutonium emits approximately 60 neutrons per second, and more if the Pu-240 content is high. Thus the plutonium-239, which is the major component of the bomb core, is awash in neutrons, a circumstance which tends to initiate premature chain reaction (pre-ignition). This means that the higher the plutonium-240 content in a bomb core, the more below critical size it must be and the more surface its component parts must have in order to permit the escape of the excess neutrons to prevent a chain reaction. It also means that the implosion must be all the more powerful to cause the intended uncontrolled explosive chain reaction on detonation. The presence of plutonium-240 complicates fabrication and degrades reliability. On implosion, if the chain reaction begins too soon, the bomb yield will be low, even a fizzle. Up to about 2% of plutonium-238 might also be present, while in bomb-grade material it is only about a hundredth of that figure. Since this nuclide produces much heat on decay (560 watts per kilogram), a mass of 6 kilograms of reactor-grade plutonium has the equivalent of a heat source of 85 watts or so inside. This would heat the chemical explosive outside the tamper and cause it to degrade in time. Also, some plutonium-241 is unavoidably present, and this requires heavier shielding. In spite of all these negative factors, reactor-grade plutonium can be and has been made to serve as fuel for nuclear explosions.

The fly in the nuclear ointment

Weapons-grade plutonium generally contains 6% Pu-240 or less. Since plutonium-240 does not undergo fission appreciably by slow neutrons (as do U-235 and Pu-239), it tends to accumulate in the fuel of nuclear reactors. Freshly prepared weapons-grade plutonium has various compositions, but typically might show the following isotopic analysis (percent by weight):

Pu-238	0.02%
Pu-239	93.6
Pu-240	5.8
Pu-241	0.55
Pu-242	0.03

Plutonium of this isotopic composition would exhibit a level of radioactivity of very near 0.64 curie per gram. The plutonium isotope among those listed above which has the shortest half-life (14.4 years) is plutonium-241. It decays by beta emission into americium-241, which has a 433-year half-life. Therefore after storage for 14.4 years, the Pu-241 content drops from 0.55 to about 0.27%, and its decay product, americium-241, appears in its place. Thus each isotope is now close to 0.27%, and the total radioactivity has fallen to 0.30 curies per gram. After storage another 14.4 years, the level reaches 0.16 curies per gram. It is the beta-active plutonium-241, with the short half-life and correspondingly high specific activity (103 curies/gram), which is responsible for most of the radioactivity in fresh plutonium. In addition, spontaneous fission of the plutonium-240 gives neutrons, as mentioned above. Decay of americium-241 is by alpha and gamma emission. The gamma ray has the energy of 60 kiloelectron volts and it provides a useful specific marker to detect plutonium.

The standards for American weapons-grade plutonium (per cent by weight)

Pu-238, maximum	0.05%
Pu-240, maximum	6.2
Pu-241, maximum (at start)	0.75
Pu-242, maximum	0.1
Am-241, maximum (at start)	0.02
U (all isotopes)	0.07
Pu-239	92.81

Its minimum plutonium content, counting all isotopes, is 99.89%. Typical weapons grade plutonium generates approximately 2.5 watts of heat per kilogram through alpha decay, and feels warm to the fingers. Americium-242 produces heat at a high rate so care must be taken to keep its content low in order to reduce expansion of the bomb components from self-heating.

The question arises whether the plutonium from commercial, power-generating reactors can be employed in bombs. The answer is definitely yes. Such plutonium generally contains 15 to 25% plutonium-240, and while troublesome, it can be made into a weapon. Test bombs using commercial plutonium have been exploded successfully in the Nevada desert as early as 1962; yields were low. Such bombs require especially powerful implosion. Although plutonium-240 can be fissioned by fast neutrons, much survives in explosions, making them extraordinarily dirty. The word "dirty" here means that the fission product debris, already deadly, also contains much plutonium-240, a particularly dangerous substance. All isotopes of plutonium undergo fission under suitable conditions. Bombs made using reactor-grade plutonium would be expected to have unpredictable yields unless prior calibration tests are carried out.

Bombs have been made from reactor-grade plutonium.

Warheads containing several percent plutonium-240 emit both neutrons and gamma rays, posing a danger to personnel, especially in confined quarters such as submarines. This is one of the motivations for preparing plutonium which contains little or no plutonium-240. One way to lower the content of the unwanted isotope is to blend it with plutonium containing about 3% of the 240 variety (called supergrade, made in the Savannah River reactors) and this is actually done. The americium-241 which accumulates in plutonium can be removed by chemical procedures, resulting in more user-friendly bombs.

Plutonium nitrate decomposes to the dioxide when heated strongly. This dioxide is reduced directly in molten calcium chloride to metallic plutonium using calcium metal. The americium impurity in the plutonium is removed by extracting the molten metal with molten magnesium chloride. Electrorefining of the liquid plutonium accomplishes removal of much of the remaining impurities. This technique is also employed in recycling some of the plutonium from retired warheads.

A newer, more sophisticated technique is the physical separation of Pu-240 (and Pu-241) from Pu-239. A factory for this purpose had been proposed to be built at Idaho Nuclear Engineering Laboratory. This is by a process called atomic vapor laser isotope separation (AVLIS).

In this process, liquid plutonium metal is vaporized in vacuum by electron bombardment, and the vapor is irradiated by finely-tuned laser beams; only the heavier isotopes in a vapor are ionized and drawn off in an electrostatic field. The process is expensive. The author took part in a hearing on the AVLIS matter in Boise, Idaho, in 1987, and recommended that no facilities be built for this purpose. But in 1989 Congress approved $101 million for the factory; this would be a down payment on the roughly $1 billion which would be required. The project was dropped in 1990, as the Cold War died down. In 1994 the Clinton administration canceled the AVLIS project, saving $246 million. A large pilot plant for this purpose was finished in late 1991 at great expense at Lawrence Livermore Laboratory. The U.S. already has a great surplus of uranium-235.

More than 280 tons of plutonium in spent fuel rods from commercial reactors are on hand in the United States. If this had been converted into weapons-grade plutonium by removal of its Pu-240, it would end several decades of careful separation of military and civilian nuclear programs and invite all countries to follow suit. It should be noted that verification of arms limitation treaties depends in part on detection of neutron and gamma-ray emanations from suspected warheads; if plutonium free of the isotope with mass number 240 is available, it would complicate such inspections. A completely different discovery bears on this matter. Until 1991, physicists considered a lens for gamma rays impossible. But one is said to have been invented. It consists of silicon or germanium crystals in place of glass. Such a lens, with a 35-foot focal length, can focus gamma rays onto a tiny spot. This might be of considerable use in verification of nuclear arms treaties.

Diverting plutonium from civilian fuel could mean an international black market in this commodity. The possibilities are endless, limited only by one's imagination (and paranoia). Casting plutonium metal is tricky. Its properties are extremely sensitive to impurities. Assembling the parts of a bomb can be dangerous. When an essential component is removed, a bomb is said to be in the "safe configuration." Even plutonium dioxide (rather than the metal) can be made into a bomb, but it would be large (pit size: 40 to 70 kilograms).

9-10 Regulating the Energy of Fission Bombs

We have seen that the two bombs exploded in Japan during World War II had different energy yields, 15 kilotons and 22 kilotons. Tests with fission bombs in the years following led to a tremendous variety of weapons. The more important variables one can control include: mass and isotopic purity of the uranium-235 or plutonium-239; the degree of compression on implosion; presence or absence of a reflector; and type and amount of tamper. Use of, say, one-fifth of the critical mass of weapons-grade plutonium (around 1 kilogram) without a reflector necessitates an exceedingly effective implosion, and even this might lead to weak, inefficient explosion, or possibly a dud. The smallest nuclear weapon in the U.S. stockpile is known as W54. Its yield is only 0.25 kiloton, that is, 250 tons of TNT. There are reports that it can be adjusted to the low yield of 0.01 kiloton, or only 10 tons of TNT. The W54 was used in the Davy Crockett rocket, now obsolete, and was also designed as a demolition bomb, although its use for this purpose would be complicated by the fission products. It could be carried by a single man. One important factor in manufacturing miniature nuclear warheads is the use of beryllium metal for many of the parts; beryllium is lighter than aluminum, very strong, and has compatible nuclear properties.

One man can carry a small nuclear bomb.

The largest fission bomb ever detonated had a yield of 500 kilotons (that is, half a megaton). It contained only uranium-235, and was known as the Super Oralloy or MK 18 bomb. It was dropped from a B-36 plane over the Pacific on November 15, 1952. Since 1 kilogram of uranium-235 on complete fission yields 17.7 kilotons yield (9-4), a 500 kiloton yield corresponds to 28.2 kilograms of uranium-235 undergoing fission. The bomb, containing 60 to 90 kilograms of uranium-235, must have been near criticality at all times, and might have been stabilized by use of neutron-absorbing control rods. Such high-yield fission bombs are considered uneconomical when compared to hydrogen bombs. Another type of bomb whose yield requires adjustment is the nuclear depth bomb. Dropped from a plane, it is an antisubmarine weapon, and they average about 10 kilotons yield.

9-11 The Beginnings of Hydrogen Bombs

Harnessing Fusion Energy for Bombs—Physicists realized in the early1920s that the energy source of the Sun and other stars is fusion of hydrogen into helium. After nuclear fission was discovered in late 1938, it became known world-wide soon after its publication in early 1939 that atomic bombs are possible. This was true in many laboratories: German, English, French, American, Italian, Soviet, Japanese, and others.

In his authoritative account (see bibliography at end of chapter) of the hydrogen bomb development, Richard Rhodes attributed to the Japanese chemist Tokutaro Hagiwara (1897-1971) the distinction of being the first to suggest using a fission bomb to trigger fusion of hydrogen to helium, thus creating a hydrogen bomb explosion. This was in a lecture on May 23, 1941, at the Japanese Navy's Second Arsenal, near Yokohama. It was written up by Hagiwara and was printed in an unclassified internal journal of the Navy, dated July 24, 1941. An official of the Army's Tonizo laboratory read this report and prepared a summary in hand-written *kanji* characters. This was in April, 1943, and the summary became known as the Tonizo document. Just before the occupation by American armed forces in 1945, the printed copies were destroyed, but Hagiwara had already taken one of them to his home. A copy of the Tonizo document was brought to the United States after World War II by Dr. P. K. Kuroda, and in translation it eventually became available to Rhodes. Investigations by the author, cooperating with Japanese nuclear physicists

Prof. Shuji Fukui, Dr. Tetsuji Imanaka, and Prof. Kunio Ozawa, found out about the Navy internal journal's original printed typescript which Hagiwara had taken home. It was kindly supplied to us by Hagiwara's daughter in Kyoto. Comparison of Rhodes' key sentence based on the hand-written Tonizo report which ascribed priority to Hagiwara for the concept of hydrogen bombs, with the same sentence in the newly-available printed document, disclosed an error in a crucial *kanji* character. There are two *kanji* characters in Japanese which are closely similar in appearance but which have very different meanings, namely "initiating" and "super." The flawed paper available to Rhodes had the character meaning "initiating," while in the original printed one the character meaning "super" appeared ("super" explosion at that date meant atomic explosion; a dozen years later, Americans applied it to hydrogen bombs). This is the origin of the incorrect translation, and we conclude that Hagiwara did not have the concept of a hydrogen bomb in mind.

The idea of using a fission bomb to trigger fusion of hydrogen (as its isotope deuterium) did occur to Fermi and he informed Teller of it in September, 1941. In the end, it turned out that deuterium alone could not be made to fuse into helium, but if tritium is added, then a successful bomb could be made (9-11, 9-15).

The idea of a thermonuclear fusion bomb was actively discussed early on by leading nuclear physicists, even though it began to be overshadowed by the burgeoning development of the fission bomb. Still, the idea of a superbomb was very much alive, and in 1942 American physicist Emil Konopinski suggested incorporating some hydrogen-3 (tritium) with the deuterium on the grounds that this third isotope of hydrogen is less stable than deuterium at the temperature of an exploding fission bomb, and this would promote fusion by lowering the required temperature. The temperature of the interior of our sun is around 15 million degrees C, and fusion of hydrogen to helium occurs. But the temperature stated is the average; in fact there is a distribution of velocities of hydrogen nuclei, and the fastest or most energetic are at temperatures much higher than the average. Deuterium-deuterium fusion requires a temperature of about 400 million degrees C for the fastest nuclei, while deuterium-tritium fusion needs only 40 million degrees C or less. We might note that a temperature of 1 keV (kiloelectron volt) corresponds to 11.6 million degrees C. Except for calculations, not much was done in the laboratory concerning these ideas until after the war.

One way or another, so-called nuclear secrets become publicly known.

Still later, essentially the same concept occurred to Soviet physicist Y. I. Frenkel', as evidenced by his letter dated September 22, 1945 to Kurchatov, and the suggestion was independent of information deriving from Soviet espionage. The Soviets started a low-priority theoretical study of the possibility of fusion bombs. This was about the same time that the London Times published an article on a superbomb (October 24, 1945).

Postwar Research—The Soviet test of a nuclear warhead in 1949 accelerated research on the hydrogen bomb in the United States and this was later intensified by the war in Korea. Most of the scientists were aware that this second generation of nuclear weapons was a giant step in the arms race, and that the new bomb would spur the Soviets and others to develop their own. The General Advisory Committee of the Atomic Energy Commission came out against a high-priority program to develop the bomb, but President Truman, Edward Teller, and others felt that the Soviets would not refrain, and so orders were given to push ahead. Oppenheimer, asked whether he would have approved dropping a hydrogen bomb on Hiroshima, replied no, on the grounds that "The target is too small."

Tests soon confirmed that it would be much easier to cause fusion of hydrogen into helium if the heavier isotopes of hydrogen are used, that is, hydrogen-2 (deuterium or D) and hydrogen-3 (tritium or T). The equations for fusion of two deuterium atoms and one deuterium atom with a tritium atom (omitting the neutrinos and gamma rays involved) are:

$$^{2}_{1}H + ^{2}_{1}H \Rightarrow ^{3}_{2}He + ^{1}_{0}n + 3.27 \text{ MeV}$$

$$^{2}_{1}H + ^{3}_{1}H \Rightarrow ^{4}_{2}He + ^{1}_{0}n + 17.6 \text{ MeV}$$

The 17.6 MeV per atom of helium-4 comes out to be 1.70 x 10^9 kJ/mole, only about two-thirds of the 2.57 x 10^9 kJ/mole for the fusion of 4 hydrogen-1 atoms to helium-4 (4-12), but is still an enormous amount of energy. The above reactions are the principal source of energy in explosions of hydrogen bombs of the more advanced types. Thus abundant energetic neutrons are also generated, and this process using tritium increases the efficiency of fission bombs, a process which came to be known as boosting (9-17).

Teller came up with an idea for a hydrogen bomb which he referred to as the Super, and soon suggested a simplified version. The smaller one, referred to as the Alarm Clock, would derive only a small part of its energy from fusion, and it required an extraordinarily powerful primary fission bomb to trigger it. These were to be steps in investigating the practicality of fusion bombs. Both versions would require liquid deuterium.

The physicists laboring to develop hydrogen bombs were hampered by lack of adequate computers at that time. In addition they had to address the question of whether, if a fusion reaction in a bomb had been started, it would lose energy faster than it was being generated and simply fizzle out. Indeed, rigorous calculations by Ulam and Everett introduced credible doubt as to whether the early proposed assembly would work; this original configuration was fatally flawed. This was in 1950, and soon afterwards the calculations were confirmed using the new, more powerful computers just available. The indications were that after an initial flash of fusion, the fuel mass would cool down. It was not until Ulam showed how important compression is that notable progress on the hydrogen bomb was made. By 1951, however, new designs of the components and an arrangement which promised to overcome the difficulties were presented by Teller and Ulam, and this became known as the Teller-Ulam configuration. By 1952 still more advanced computers, such as MANIAC (Mathematical Analyzer, Numerator, Integrator, and Calculator), and others, were available. The Alarm Clock design appeared unpromising and Teller devoted his attention to the alternative Super design.

MANIAC, a cuter computer

A few years were required to construct facilities to separate deuterium in large quantities, to synthesize tritium in modest quantities, and to prepare adequate amounts of lithium-6 (9-13). Many construction and engineering problems remained to be solved. Thermonuclear tests were to begin in the Pacific, and many variations in the geometry of construction were included.

Early Test of a Fusion Device—The first test explosion of fusion incorporating these new concepts was the *George* shot, conducted on a tower on May 8, 1951 at Enewetak. The yield was 225 kilotons, the highest ever up to that date. A steel tower 200 feet tall and 283 tons of equipment were vaporized. The mushroom cloud climbed to 15 miles. The results (such as production of high-energy neutrons) showed that indeed some fusion of deuterium with tritium had taken place (an estimated 10% of the energy released was from fusion). In the following month Teller and de Hoffmann issued a report on the effectiveness of using lithium deuteride in the new superbomb since tritium is formed from lithium-6 under explosion conditions (9-13). Thus at this time the need for concentrated lithium-6, rather than natural lithium (which is 92.5% lithium-7) was confirmed. In May 1952 a facility for separating lithium-6 was started. Investigations of lithium-6 deuteride and tritide were undertaken.

As in the case of fission bombs, few official details of hydrogen bomb construction have been released. But five governments have devised and exploded hydrogen bombs, so there are no essential secrets. Teller once said, "The most difficult thing about making a nuclear weapon is to make one that doesn't work." At first thought, one might suggest that a hydrogen bomb could be made on the same principles of an implosion fission bomb, by construction concentric spheres of chemical high explosive, a uranium-238 tamper, lithium deuteride, and a fissile core. Mathematical analysis shows that this design is not feasible; the degree of compression is simply insufficient. In both fission and fusion bombs, high compression is the key to achieving high yields. The fusion fuel is cold at the very start of compression, but heats up when the pressure is instantly elevated.

A conceivable design of a hydrogen bomb is associated with a colorful story. Howard Morland, a young peace activist with only a little training in physics and chemistry, researched the subject of hydrogen bomb construction in public libraries and other open sources. When his paper was about to appear in *The Progressive* in 1979, the magazine suddenly was prohibited from publishing by an order from the Department of Energy through the Attorney General, presumably at the request of the nuclear weaponeers' priesthood. This attempted prior restraint, via a compliant judge, was unprecedented in American press experience, but serves to show how emotional and sensitive authorities are about information concerning our supposed supersecrets. Any step which tends to debunk our nuclear mystique is still sharply opposed. Morland published his story in a book, "The Secret That Exploded," in 1981 (see bibliography at end of chapter).

By this time it was clear that large-scale production of hydrogen bombs would require a great deal of three key substances, namely deuterium, tritium, and lithium-6. The facilities for generating these are described below.

9-12 Production of Heavy Water and Deuterium

Deuterium is rather rare, constituting only one atom in every 6750 atoms of ordinary hydrogen. Nevertheless, chemists have devised efficient ways of extracting deuterium from water, and hundreds of tons are now available.

There are quite a number of ways to separate deuterium from ordinary water. One of the most successful is the isotope exchange between water and hydrogen sulfide

(H_2S). The apparatus consists of two towers, one above the other, in which ordinary water is allowed to trickle down from the top, while a countercurrent of hydrogen sulfide gas is forced in at the bottom. In the lower tower, which is hot, the intimate contact causes exchange which results in the hydrogen sulfide becoming relatively enriched in deuterium. On passing into the upper tower, which is cool, the water picks up the excess deuterium from the hydrogen sulfide, and exits the tower enriched in deuterium. No hydrogen sulfide is consumed; it serves only as the agent for exchange.

In a series of five units, ordinary water containing 0.014% heavy water (deuterium oxide, D_2O) is enriched to 15%. Further concentration through fractional distillation raises the concentration to 90%. Finally, an electrolytic procedure results in 99.97% deuterium oxide. A single large plant can produce 400 tons per year. The cost of such heavy water is around $100 per kilogram.

The heavier isotopes of hydrogen are needed.

9-13 Production of Tritium

The other isotope of hydrogen, tritium, is formed naturally in ultratrace quantities in the upper atmosphere. Neutrons generated by cosmic rays convert nitrogen-14 to tritium and carbon-12. The amount is so small that our entire atmosphere before 1954 (before tritium from hydrogen bombs was set free) contained only about 1800 grams! For weapons purposes it must be made artificially, generally in nuclear reactors. This was first accomplished by manufacturing lithium-6 fluoride or lithium-aluminum alloy clad in aluminum or stainless steel, and then exposing it to neutrons in the K Reactor at the Savannah River complex. This reactor uses heavy water as a moderator and has an extraordinarily high neutron density. This high flux of neutrons results if the reactor fuel contains 20% or more uranium-235. The lithium is enriched in lithium-6. The equation is:

$${}^{6}_{3}\text{Li} + {}^{1}_{0}\text{n} \Rightarrow {}^{3}_{1}\text{H} + {}^{4}_{2}\text{He}$$

The radioactive tritium gas is trapped inside the solid (fluoride or aluminum alloy) where it is generated, and this material is removed for processing. A certain amount of tritium was made in the N Reactor. Total production reached about 12 kilograms per year. Tritium production was stopped in 1988 owing to reactor safety problems, but after spending almost a billion dollars on modernization, production was authorized to be resumed.

The Department of Energy was for a time pressing for the prototype of a New Production Reactor, to be built in Idaho. This would be of the Modular High-Temperature Gas-cooled Reactor type. The purpose would be to make more tritium and other materials of military interest. Just with the demise of the Cold War, the Bush (Sr.) Administration was pressing for more and more materials for hydrogen bombs. There is the possibility of purchasing tritium from India, or even Russia; Canada produces much tritium, but refuses to sell it for military purposes. Actually, buying nuclear weapons from the cash-starved Russians and others would help insure a safer world.

Official policy of the United States is, in the words of President Clinton (1997): "Nuclear weapons serve as a hedge against an uncertain future, a guarantee of our security commitments to allies, and a disincentive to those who would contemplate developing or otherwise acquiring their own nuclear weapons." If this doctrine is uncritically accepted, then it follows that new tritium production facilities must be constructed, since by 2005 supplies will be exhausted (except for a covert extra five-year supply). All nuclear weapons in the modern American arsenal employ a small amount of tritium to boost yield.

The reactor at Watts Bar Nuclear Plant, Spring City, Tennessee, was chosen to demonstrate that a modified technology produces tritium more efficiently. In 1995 a dispute arose concerning a stratagem to produce tritium for the American military using commercial nuclear reactors. By late 1998, a definite decision was made to manufacture tritium in the Watts Bar reactor. This action to produce a key nuclear warhead material in a reactor generating electricity blurred the demarcation between military and civilian uses, setting a regrettable precedent. The claim was made that even in the time when the Cold War no longer exists, the U.S. still needs more tritium for its bombs, despite a great deal being recovered from dismantled warheads. It was the planned production of tritium in civilian reactors which the U.S. found so objectionable when North Korea and Iraq were considering to do so.

Don't do as I do; do as I say.

Reactors of the Watts Bar type use boron-10 in ceramic form in the control rods, and in the new production technique, lithium-6 aluminate or fluoride in ceramic form is employed. This material is surrounded by zirconium tubing, which picks up the tritium as it is formed, forming zirconium tritide (that is, zirconium hydride, the hydrogen being H-3). The tritium is recovered at the Savannah River Site by heating to 1000 °C under vacuum, causing decomposition of the zirconium tritide.

If the number of warheads is reduced to 1000, current supplies of tritium from dismantled bombs are adequate until at least the year 2020. Old gladiators from the Cold War seem never to give up. In 1996-98 the Department of Energy, in a reversal of earlier policy, was again pressing for resumed tritium production on the grounds that it is needed to support a 5000-warhead arsenal after 2011.

An alternative way to synthesize tritium is via linear accelerators. The lithium is encased in lead, which when impacted by high-energy protons from hydrogen generated in the accelerator, releases neutrons. The neutrons interact with the lithium to form tritium, as discussed above. This process is less economical than use of a reactor. A steady input of 800 megawatts of electrical power would be required. In another type of linear accelerator, the target is tungsten, and the energetic neutrons released interact with helium-3 to form tritium. A decision was made in 1999 not to construct an accelerator to make tritium.

In 1991, the commercial price of tritium was $30,600 per gram. It is sold for research purposes, to make self-luminous dials, airport lights in remote areas, etc.

Since elemental hydrogen (H-1, H-2 or D, and H-3 or T, each with two atoms per molecule, H_2) is a gas, relatively small quantities can be confined under pressure in tanks of reasonable size; storing it in liquid form requires temperatures a few degrees above absolute zero, which is impractical for long periods. Therefore, for the purpose of warheads in hydrogen bombs, the hydrogen is converted into a hydride (in this case, a deuteride or tritide) of a metal, substances long known to chemists. These solids are easy to prepare. Which metal should be chosen? The obvious choice is

Lithium deutride, a choice obvious to every chemist, cannot be kept secret.

lithium in the form of its isotope with mass number 6 because it reacts with neutrons under conditions of nuclear explosion to form more hydrogen-3; alpha particles are also released, as shown in the equation above. Lithium hydride (and its isotopic modifications, lithium deuteride and lithium tritide) are exceedingly sensitive to moisture, and it must be made and handled under strictly anhydrous conditions. After lithium-6 deuteride is prepared, it is compacted, sintered, and machined to the specified shape, all operations being in special dry rooms. Long storage of hydrogen bombs requires regular inspection for deterioration. Possible alternative means of incorporating deuterium and tritium into fusion bombs are the use of the deuterides or tritides of uranium-235 or plutonium-239. Since only about 4 grams of tritium is required per warhead of the fission type, a small steel cylinder filled with tritium gas under pressure is merely inserted. A stockpile of about 70 kilograms of tritium was at hand (as of 1999), and approximately 11 more kilograms was made annually up until recently.

Removal of these small cylinders of tritium provides a means of de-alerting bombs, that is, disabling or crippling them, greatly reducing the yield until the tritium is restored. This is a step which reduces chances of unauthorized use and is a step to avoid launching bombs in panic. Another technique has been suggested which disables nuclear warheads even more severely. This is to feed an iron wire through the tube which conducts tritium into the cavity in the very center of the pit. Enough wire is pushed inside to stuff the cavity, and then the end of the wire is forced inside with a rod so it cannot be withdrawn.

9-14 Production of Lithium-6

A plant for preparing lithium-6 was built at Oak Ridge, Tennessee. Natural lithium consists of 7.5% lithium-6 and 92.5% lithium-7. The enrichment in the lighter isotope is accomplished by a chemical exchange process in which lithium amalgam is mixed with aqueous lithium hydroxide in numerous stages or steps. Both isotopes distribute themselves between the mercury and aqueous phases, but lithium-7 preferentially concentrates in the amalgam phase. Huge quantities of mercury are required. As much as 750,000 pounds of mercury was inadvertently lost in a stream near Oak Ridge over the years, causing a terrible pollution problem.

Removal of lithium-6 left so much lithium-7 that its price fell and lithium batteries became popular.

Production of lithium-6 was halted in 1963, since enough for current warhead manufacture was available. Actually, lithium-7 also interacts with neutrons to form some tritium, provided the conversion is initiated by fusion using lithium-6 deuteride. Consequently relatively cheap natural lithium (both isotopes), as the hydride or deuteride, is also a component of hydrogen bombs.

9-15 Further Advancements in the Hydrogen Bomb

One difference between the American and Soviet intercontinental ballistic missiles (ICBM) systems was that while the first American hydrogen bombs weighed many tons, nevertheless a decision was made to concentrate on medium-size rockets. This was based on the conviction that the size of hydrogen bombs could be reduced a great deal, and this proved to be the case. The Soviets concluded that the larger rockets would be necessary, and developed them, ending in the gigantic booster rocket called Proton. The Soviet hydrogen bombs were also made smaller at a later date.

In spring of 1946 Klaus Fuchs, seizing a hint from von Neuman, came up with the idea of transferring the deuterium-tritium mixture to the zone heated by the primary explosion, thereby establishing conditions for its thermonuclear ignition. To confine the radiation within the tamper volume, Fuchs suggested enclosing the system in a radiation-impervious casing. This seems to be the first idea of implosion by pressure generated from radiation. Thus was born the radiation implosion principle, served as the prototype for the future Teller-Ulam configuration. On May 28, 1946, Fuchs and von Neumann jointly filed a patent application for the invention of a new scheme for the initiator of the classical superbomb using radiation implosion.

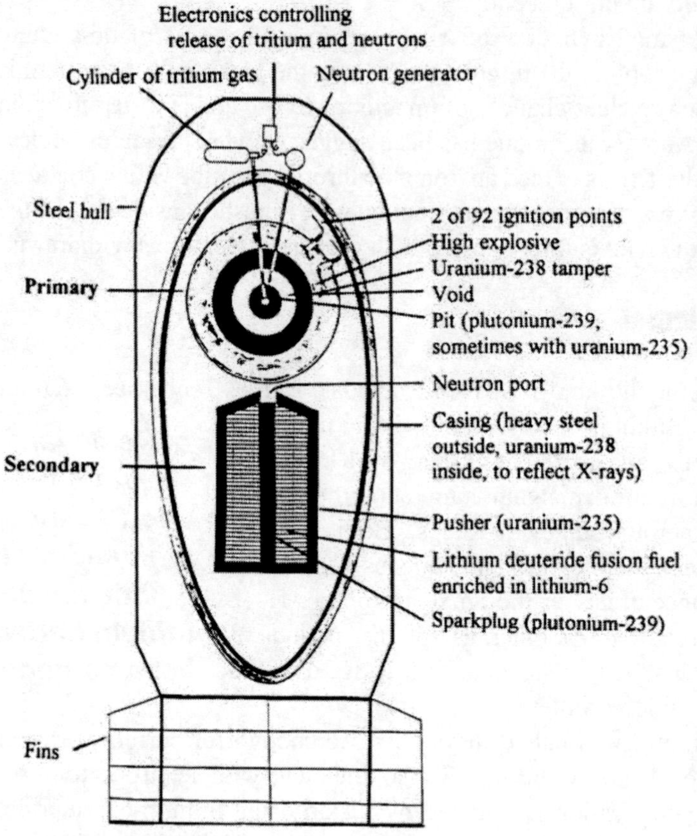

Schematic cross-section of early two-stage hydrogen bomb

That the early superbomb design would be a failure was inferred from the results of approximate calculations in 1950 by Ulam, Cornelius Everett, and Fermi, and confirmed at the end of that year by von Neumann's computations using ENIAC. The newer ideas for the superbomb were employed by Teller and Ulam, and they included the ideas of Fermi, Emil Konopinski, von Neumann, and Fuchs. The design was importantly modified by contributions by the mathematicians Ulam and Metropolis. The Teller-Ulam configuration is basically a fission bomb trigger (the first stage, or primary) inside a reflective casing so that X- and γ-radiation can cause compression and thus fusion of tritium (generated from both the deuterium and lithium-6 components of lithium-6 deuteride) and by fission of a plutonium-239 rod. The design is described and crudely sketched above. The claim that Fuchs gave the Teller-Ulam configuration to the Soviets cannot be true, since it was not developed until Fuchs had been in a British prison about two years.

The following account of hydrogen bomb construction is patterned largely on the ideas of Ulam, with contributions by Teller, Richard L. Garwin, and others. The construction comprises a cylindrical steel hull enclosing a massive steel and metallic uranium casing. Inside is a fission bomb at the top, the primary, which is the trigger to initiate the fusion process (that is, to "ignite" the deuterium-tritium fusion reaction) in the second stage below. The primary is boosted with about four grams of tritium (9-17), and is expected to fission with an efficiency of 35 to 40%. Wherever any component is required to reflect neutrons, metallic beryllium is employed.

Just a few centimeters below the primary is the secondary, an elongated cylinder up to 30 centimeters in diameter and made of uranium-238 and/or uranium-235. The walls of this heavy cylinder (the "pusher") are 2 or 3 centimeters thick. A rod made of plutonium-239 or uranium-235 (the "sparkplug") runs along the axis of the fusion fuel mass (this idea was one of Teller's contributions). The annular space between the cylinder walls and the rod is filled with the fusion fuel, lithium deuteride. Some of the necessary tritium might be present as the gaseous element in a separate container. The lithium is enriched in its lighter isotope, lithium-6. A channel or port at the top of the secondary, just above the end of the sparkplug, serves to admit neutrons from the primary on detonation. All the remaining space is filled with a special dense plastic foam to hold the various components in place; in some cases steel or aluminum supports are used.

A series of complex interactions takes place on detonation of the fission bomb, and one must keep in mind that the intensities of radiation which prevail are almost beyond imagination. The primary bomb is converted instantly into a plasma, creating a colossal flux of soft X-rays as well as a great deal of gamma rays and neutrons. The X- and gamma rays, being electromagnetic radiation, travel at the speed of light and thus easily outpace any particles or shock wave of debris from bomb parts. The X- and gamma rays normally travel in all directions from the exploding primary fusion bomb but for this purpose the primary is configured to emit its radiations preferentially toward the secondary. The rays are reflected from the walls of the heavy uranium casing to the wall of the secondary unit. The reflection process does not resemble the case of light reflecting from a mirror. Instead, the surface layers of the casing walls, consisting of uranium (natural or depleted, both more than 99% uranium-238), absorb the radiation and are instantly converted to a dense plasma, which reradiates the X- and gamma rays.

This account is without doubt quite incomplete.

To be successful, the outer casing of uranium and steel must be shaped so as to focus the X-rays to the secondary. One possibility is to make the outer casing in the shape of an ellipsoid, with the primary at one focal point and the secondary at the other, making the reflected rays concentrate on the secondary. Another possibility is to make the outer shell around the primary parabolic in shape. It required a great deal of testing hydrogen bombs to find the most successful focusing arrangement. In any case, on detonation, the whole assembly is vaporized in less than a millisecond.

The outer layers of the uranium walls of the secondary are similarly converted to a plasma, ablating off and evaporating uranium. The recoil forces from the departing uranium vapor amount to shock waves and compress the lithium-6 deuteride instantly, hence the name "pusher." These events create a more or less uniform inward pressure, compressing the uranium cylinder holding the fission fuel. To improve the reflective properties of the inner walls of the pusher, the uranium is covered with gold foil; gold was chosen after testing many metals. The pressure on the fission fuel and plutonium sparkplug become far higher than chemical explosives can generate. The uranium walls of the secondary serve as a tamper. The enormous pressure resulting from the instantly created plasma implode the sparkplug, causing it to become supercritical ("radiation implosion" or "radiative compression"). Thus its fission chain reaction, starting at the end near the primary, triggers the thermonuclear fusion reactions. Neutrons from the fission of the sparkplug convert the lithium-6 to tritium (9-13) and its thermonuclear fusion with the deuterium commences. Recall that neutrons from the primary explosion could travel through the neutron channel and serve as the initiator. The higher the efficiency of the primary, the greater is the degree of compression of the sparkplug, and thus the overall yield. It is essential for the lithium deuteride be compressed to a fraction, say 1/20th or 1/30th, of its original volume. This is to enhance the probability of fusion and its rate, which is proportional to the square of the density. Thus if the compression is 25-fold, the rate of fusion is increased 25^2 or 625 times. The inertia of the matter being compressed also helps to confine the mass a bit longer. The deuterium from lithium deuteride and the tritium, mostly arising instantly from the neutron-lithium-6 interaction, undergo fusion under these extreme conditions of pressure and temperature, liberating phenomenal quantities of energy and neutrons. The fusion reactions are tritium-tritium, tritium-deuterium, and deuterium-deuterium, all releasing prodigious amounts of energy. It has been found that even a certain amount of inexpensive, ordinary hydrogen (H-1, as lithium hydride) can be made to fuse in hydrogen bomb explosions if it is mixed with the lithium deuteride. Since the X-rays instantly cover the whole length of the secondary nuclear assembly, implosion is quite uniform and the problems encountered with implosion of fission bombs do not arise.

Another important point is that the energy liberated by explosion of hydrogen bombs is increased by still another factor. Under the conditions of the explosion, abundant neutrons with energy of several megaelectron volts are released during fusion, which are capable of causing fission in the plentiful uranium-238 from the pusher walls and the uranium-238 casing (4-16). Thus the fusion fuel at this stage is in between two media exploding via fission, the pusher inside and the uranium-238 outside. Such bombs are sometimes described by the term fission-fusion-fission and they release inconceivably large amounts of energy in truly vast explosions. Hydrogen bombs tested at the Pacific Proving Grounds in 1956 derived 10% to as high as 95% of their energy from fusion. Explosion of uranium-238 caused by very energetic neutrons may be regarded as a third technique of inducing nuclear explosions, the other two being implosion and gun assembly. The concept of critical mass does not apply to fast-neutron fission of uranium-238.

9-16 Three-Stage Hydrogen Bombs

In order to construct still more powerful bombs, additional fusion stages can be added. Thus if a tertiary stage is put below the secondary, the assembly becomes all the more devastating. This is shown in the sketch below. Neutrons from the secondary travel through the neutron channel of the tertiary, and it undergoes fission/fusion just as the secondary did, only an infinitesimal fraction of a second later. The first three-stage, multi-megaton-yield hydrogen bombs, coded MK 17 (as well as the closely-related MK 24) were tested and entered the American stockpiles in 1954, but were retired by 1957, being replaced by the MK 36, a bomb with a lower yield. The MK 17 bomb was the most powerful one ever in the standard American nuclear arsenal, having yields of 15 to 20 megatons. The bomb was 24 feet 8 inches long and weighed 21 tons (about 70% of which was uranium or steel casing and tamper). The heavy bombs were carried by B-36 aircraft. The tail of the bomb had a retarding parachute to allow the delivering plane more time to distance itself before detonation. In 1957, during a practice run, an MK 17 hydrogen bomb was accidentally released from a B-36 bomber. It crashed through the closed bomb bay doors onto the New Mexico desert. The chemical high explosive of the primary exploded on impact, but there was no nuclear explosion or release of radioactivity.

During explosion of hydrogen bombs, a surplus of neutrons is generated, and both helium-3 and helium-4 are produced by fusion. The ratio of yield to weight in the case of hydrogen bombs is considerably higher than in the case of fission warheads. The ratio in fission bombs can be regulated to values between half a ton to a hundred tons of TNT explosive equivalency per kilogram of bomb material. For hydrogen bombs, the ratio is as high as 6 kilotons per kilogram of assembled warhead weight. The outer casing of a hydrogen bomb, made of thick depleted uranium and steel, reflects X-rays back inside so long as its structural integrity prevails; at the end, its uranium-238 also undergoes some fast-neutron fission, contributing to the overall yield. In principle, many additional stages can be added, a concept which makes one shudder. The time required for a three-stage hydrogen bomb to explode is only about five microseconds. Except for the fission bomb trigger, the concept of critical mass does not apply to hydrogen bombs.

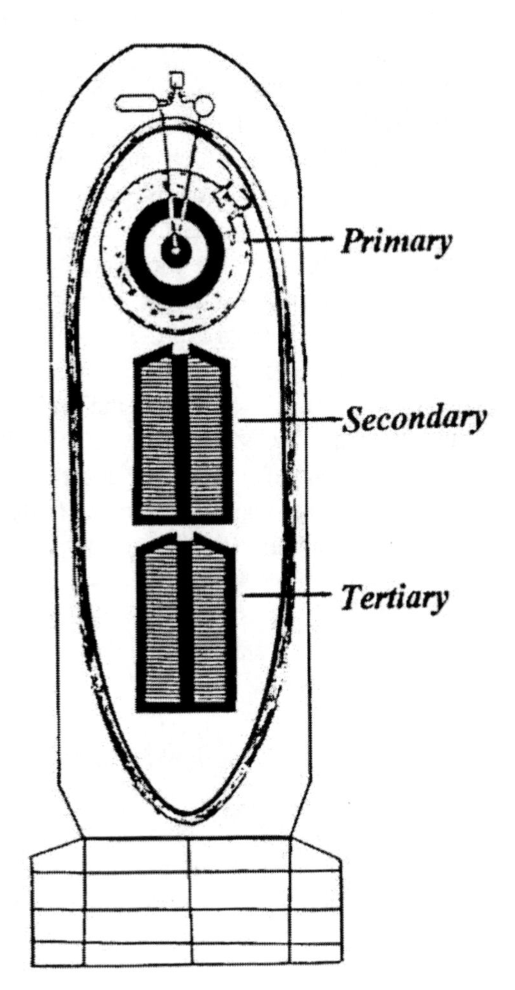

Schematic cross-section of three-stage hydrogen bomb

Thus we see that a hydrogen bomb, alias fusion or thermonuclear bomb, consists of a primary stage (a fission bomb) which ignites a secondary stage consisting of lithium deuteride, along with tritium. This could serve to kindle a third stage, and this a fourth, releasing truly unimaginable, absolutely staggering amounts of energy. It is possible to construct hydrogen bombs of energy more than 200 megatons, but 200 separate one megaton bombs are much more destructive because of less overkill, so they are favored by the military. The 58 megaton superbomb exploded by the Soviets in 1961 (9-26) was probably constructed along these lines. The design of nuclear warheads became a demanding sub-discipline of physics, employing an eager guild of warrior-scientists. One must not imagine that real hydrogen bombs are as simple as the sketches indicate; they are far more sophisticated. A B-61 bomb consists of at least 6000 components; some are made using gold, titanium, or zirconium.

Various other configurations are conceivable. For example, the fusion fuel might be coupled to two fission bombs, one at each end, or the primary could be situated between the two fusion stages. Compression and detonation by shock wave would probably work as well as compression by radiation.

The storage life of modern nuclear warheads is 15 to 25 years for the fission type. The chemical explosive used to implode and trigger a nuclear explosion undergoes slow deterioration, although some new types are much improved in this regard. The lithium deuteride of fusion weapons is stable so long as it is sealed perfectly to prevent exposure to atmospheric moisture. Tritium is radioactive (4-3): it decays by beta emission with a half-life of 12.3 years, which is the same as 5.5% each year. This means that when tritium is incorporated into hydrogen bombs, every year 5.5% of it disappears, and provisions must be made to replace this perishable component periodically. The shelf life of hydrogen bombs might be considered to be somewhat less than the half-life of tritium.

One of the most advanced American hydrogen bombs is model W 88, which is small enough so that eight of them can be carried by a MIRVed Trident II ballistic missile, which is designed to be launched from a submarine. The yield of the W 88 is 475 kilotons. After the end of the Cold War, the United States stopped production of new hydrogen bombs such as type W 88; this was in 1992.

It is wise to reflect now and then on the purpose of making these bombs. Their purpose is to wage war or to threaten to do so. One big hydrogen bomb detonated over a large city could annihilate 15 million people or more.

By about 1980, many encyclopedias, physics texts, and reports by independent researchers had published many sketches and conceptual designs of fission and fusion bombs. The sketches above are simply other examples. The genie has long been out of his bottle.

9-17 Boosting the Yield of Nuclear Warheads using Tritium

Raising the yields of nuclear bombs

It is common practice to boost the efficiency (and thus the yield) of fission bombs by incorporating some deuterium and tritium. This gives rise to an added burst of neutrons just at the critical time, and thus jump-starts a robust fission chain reaction. The efficiency and thus the yield can be boosted by a factor as large as ten. The conditions in the center of an exploding sphere of plutonium (several trillion times atmospheric pressure and tens of millions of degrees C) are sufficient to cause fusion of deuterium and tritium nuclei. The abundant energetic neutrons (12 to 18 MeV) produced initiate extra fission of plutonium, liberating still more neutrons. This fission-fusion synergistic interaction greatly accelerates the fission chain reaction, meaning that a considerably higher proportion of plutonium undergoes fission (before the pit or whole mass flies apart) than otherwise would be the case. Boosting permits a given yield to be accomplished using substantially less plutonium, and lessens the weight of the bomb. Strongly boosted fission bombs are of high yield, and can be several hundred kilotons, up to about half a megaton.

Lithium-6 deuteride is not a favorable source for deuterium in boosting because the lithium consumes too many neutrons, which are needed for dynamic fission via chain reaction. The way finally developed for introducing the deuterium and tritium was to use a small external cylinder of the mixed gases under a pressure of a several thousand pounds per square inch. A tube leads to the center of the pit. A timing device, accurate to less than a microsecond, injects the gas mixture, amounting to several grams, just as the fission reactions begins. The timing of the gas injection is performed by a complicated electronic device. Boosted warheads are always equipped with external neutron generators.

Use of tritium has permitted developing light-weight warheads, such as those used in artillery shells. The practicality of boosted bombs was first demonstrated in one of the Enewetak shots on May 24, 1951. Fusion-boosted bombs are also used as triggers in hydrogen bombs.

9-18 Radioactive Fallout

With the enormously increased energy released by hydrogen bomb explosions, enhanced by fission of the uranium-238 tamper, correspondingly larger amounts of fission products are also formed. In addition, the high yield of free neutrons converts more of the elements in the environment into radioactive nuclides. The fission products which are responsible for the radioactivity of fallout have about the same composition as fission products in nuclear reactors, except that more short-lived ones are present (these have time to die out in reactors). When the fireball touches the Earth, the high temperatures cause soil to be vaporized and carried up into the angry, malignant mushroom cloud. About 65% of the deadly material falls out onto the surface over an area of several thousand square miles downwind of the explosion site (*local fallout*), while the remainder is carried upward into the troposphere and stratosphere and is distributed around the world (*global fallout*). The eruption of the volcano Krakatoa between Java and Sumatra in 1883, for example, injected a vast amount of dust into the stratosphere and demonstrated how particulate matter circles our Earth.

Radioactive fallout is a mixture of bomb debris, fission products, and earth.

The local fallout poses the immediate danger, and these ghosts of fission afflict the just and unjust alike with cosmic impartiality. The global fallout is spread around the Earth in the high atmosphere, and although some does drift downward, it is comparatively much less dangerous. The extent and nature of fallout ranges between wide extremes, depending on weather, yield, and height at explosion. The Hiroshima and Nagasaki bombs did not touch the surface and there was little local fallout, but considerable neutron activation of soil and other materials. Fallout is discussed more fully in sections 10-40 to 10-44.

9-19 Tests in the Pacific

In 1946 the American military sought a testing site for megaton-yield bombs, and chose the Marshall Islands in the Pacific. The first test was conducted on Enewetak Atoll. The obliging islanders, in a painful involuntary departure, were moved to a dot of an island named Kili, about 600 miles to the southeast. They are still there today, leading miserable lives on the American dole. "It is like a prison island," said Juda, the son of the former leader. They were told at the time that their homeland was needed for a project "for the progress of mankind all over the world," and that they could return when it was over.

Let us consider two hydrogen bombs which Americans exploded, first (the *Mike* test) and the largest, (the *Bravo* test). Both, described as devices, not true bombs, were to test thermonuclear principles. They were monitored and analyzed with numerous instruments protected in distant bunkers, at great expense. Drone planes collected mushroom cloud debris. In these tests hundreds of tons of equipment and thousands of scientists, engineers, and military personnel, each with their supporting staff, had to be accommodated. During the twelve years following 1946, more than 60 nuclear bombs were exploded in the area.

A one-megaton burst creates a fireball more than a mile in diameter. There is an initial flash (0.1 second) of ethereal violet radiation, followed by most intense, prolonged (perhaps half a minute) emission of pure white light. Various shots display reddish-brown, peach, or other colors in their later stages. Lithium atoms, from the lithium deuteride, under these conditions emit a brilliant red color, and this is visible at a certain stage. The cloud finally looks white owing to condensed water vapor. The air up to about half a mile from the center is convulsed, being ionized and converted into a plasma of fantastically high temperature; this is the fireball. Just outside this region a violet glow is visible surrounding the fireball; this results from further ionization of the air by gamma and X-rays. Ozone and nitrogen oxides are formed from constituents of air. The fireball behaves like a hot air balloon and rises rapidly, reaching 12 miles in 4 minutes. The upward motion causes violent internal circulation and churning of gases, resulting in a doughnut-shaped ring (toroid), as the figure below shows. The stem is around half a mile in diameter. A strong current of air, called the after-wind, is drawn upward along the stem. Roughly 90% of the total radioactivity is in the mushroom head, and 10% is in the stem. The diameter of the fireball of a nuclear explosion depends on the yield and the explosion height. At ground level, the diameter of the fireball of a 20 kiloton explosion is 760 feet, while that of a 1-megaton explosion is 5700 feet.

The fireball is highly ionized air—a plasma; bouyancy and convection currents cause the mushroom shape.

The *Mike* shot, on Enewetak Atoll in 1952, involved a cryogenic system to manage extensive quantities of liquid hydrogen, liquid deuterium, and liquid nitrogen, all in 530-gallon steel Dewars (vacuum-wall bottles), and the unit weighed a little more than 62 tons. Its primary, the fission bomb, had 92 detonation points. With such a large number of detonation points, bulky high-explosive lenses are not necessary, and smaller amounts of such explosive are satisfactory. The yield of the *Mike* shot was 10.4 megatons (about a quarter of this from fusion), and the fireball was 3.5 miles in diameter. The mushroom cloud rose 20 miles. The islet of Elugelab was vaporized. Some 80 millions tons of material were lofted into the atmosphere. The blast made a crater 164 feet deep and 6240 feet across. The closest islands were denuded of their vegetation and wildlife was wiped out by the shock wave. Fish found three miles from ground zero had been denuded of their skin on one side. The vegetation on Rigili, an island 14 miles away, was scorched. The radioactive debris was found to contain two new chemical elements, now called einsteinium (mass number 254) and fermium (mass number 257), synthesized in the violent blast. A photograph of the Mike test is shown.

Just imagine, handling hundreds of gallons of liquid hydrogen (boiling point: minus 423°F) and liquid deuterium (boiling point: minus 417 °F) on a remote Pacific island!

A total of five hydrogen bombs were tested in the air or water at Bikini in 1954. Bikini Atoll, about 220 miles east of Enewetak, was the most densely populated area, and its population was also evacuated. The *Bravo* test, conducted on February 28, 1954, on a reef in the atoll had a fission bomb component (the primary, with plutonium boosted by tritium and an extremely high yield). The secondary contained lithium enriched to 40% Li-6 (present as the deuteride) and a massive uranium tamper. The expected energy release was 6 megatons, that is, 6,000,000 tons of TNT. But the actual energy released was close to 15 megatons, more than twice the expected amount. It soon became apparent that much of this extra energy arose indirectly from the 60% lithium-7 which was present. The lithium, enriched to 40% lithium-6, was the source of abundant neutrons (9-13), but these energetic neutrons converted lithium-7 into additional lithium-6:

Mike test, October 31, 1952

$$^{7}_{3}\mathrm{Li} + ^{1}_{0}\mathrm{n} \Rightarrow ^{6}_{3}\mathrm{Li} + 2\ ^{1}_{0}\mathrm{n}$$

Thus the result was conversion of much of the lithium-7 to lithium-6, which was rapidly transformed to tritium, which yielded still more neutrons. The transient excess of these abundant high-energy neutrons caused fission of some of the uranium-238 casing, unexpectedly increasing the enormous yield still more. This fission process was not a self-sustaining chain reaction. The mushroom cloud of this truly colossal 15 megaton burst was nine miles across, and the fireball inside was nearly four miles in diameter, "like a diseased brain," in the

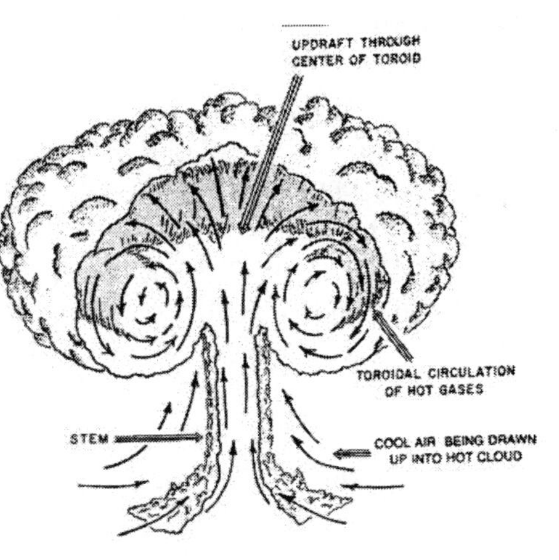

Illustration of circulation pattern in mushroom cloud of nuclear explosion

words of one observer. Ten minutes after the initial blast, the mushroom cloud was 70 miles across. The cloud rose nine miles in the first minute and reached a height of 22 miles. The explosion annihilated an islet named Bokonejen, which was an adjacent reef, leaving a 6500-foot crater 240 feet deep, and parts of neighboring islands were heavily damaged as well.

The firing bunker was on Enyu, a small island in the Bikini Atoll. On setting off the *Bravo* shot, the firing crew could see its light instantly, and after some seconds, they felt the seismic shock coming through the earth just under the seabed. It resembled an earthquake, shaking the bunker with its three-foot concrete walls. Still later the violent sonic shock wave in the atmosphere reached them. Radioactive fallout from the *Bravo* shot contaminated the bunker so badly that it had to be abandoned.

The fission of the plutonium-239 and uranium-238 mentioned above created a mass of deadly fission products. These substances, mixed with the vaporized earth, formed the nasty cloud of radioactive fallout. In both fission and fusion bomb explosions, there is first the searing flash of radiation, followed by the shock wave. The momentum of this blast was so great that partial vacuum resulted at ground zero and air rushed backwards, drawing matter with it. The wind-borne radioactive ash showered on Rongelap Atoll, 120 miles away. Its inhabitants had not been warned, and curious children played in the funny ash falling from the sky. Rain washed the fallout into the ground and water tanks. Whole body exposures were around 175 rads, causing nausea, vomiting, diarrhea, skin and eye irritation, and other effects. The inhabitants of Rongelap were hastily evacuated some 44 hours after the fallout began. In 1996 a budget of $45 million was provided by the Department of Interior to bring the surviving islanders and their descendants back. The payment covered safe water, electrical power, and all necessary construction.

Fallout from the big Bikini blast left the island uninhabitable and killed or injured quite a number of people.

Thyroid cancer is normally a rather rare disease. But when a person is subjected to radioactive iodine, its incidence rises. This may arise by breathing in iodine vapor or consuming food which has absorbed it. Drinking water is contaminated as well. Radioactive iodine isotopes are produced with rather high fission yields. Iodine-131 is the most dangerous iodine fission product, but the other isotopes, I-132, I-133, and I-135, are also hazardous. After entering the lungs or alimentary canal, the iodine enters the blood and is rapidly taken up by the thyroid gland. The gland is exposed unevenly, and local radiation doses can be very high. The result is either destruction of the thyroid or, after a period of latency, development of cancer. Three-fourths of the children of Rongelap under age ten later developed thyroid tumors or cancers, and some died from leukemia. On Utirik Atoll, 290 miles east of Bikini, the 157 inhabitants had similar experiences. All of these people had obviously been traumatized by their involuntary involvement in nuclear testing.

A recent review of the health status of the islanders revealed that Atomic Energy Commission had kept poor records of their exposure levels and subsequent condition. An independent study of their thyroid disorders indicated that the contamination by fallout from the *Bravo* test was far wider than officially admitted. Radiation doses of inhabitants of Rongelap were estimated in 1980 as 175 rems whole-body gamma dose and 810 to 1800 rems thyroid dose for children up to age ten. Most of these people are now taking thyroxine tablets, and will continue this for life.

Twenty-eight men of the staff of a weather station on Rongerik Atoll and 23 Japanese fishermen on the "Lucky Dragon No. 5" (80 miles distant from the explosion) were irradiated by fallout from *Bravo*. One of the fishermen died. These incidents resulted in part from the unexpectedly high yield of the *Bravo* test and in part an unforeseen shift of wind direction from the south to the west. The chairman of the Atomic Energy Agency, with no trace of compassion and no shred of evidence, dismissed the incident on the grounds that the fishing boat was probably a "Red spy ship."

A prime example of doctrinaire stupidity

The hydrogen bombs implanted so much fission products and plutonium-239 into the soil of Bikini and Rongelap and surrounding islands that the native inhabitants cannot return. The principal culprit is plutonium, but cesium-137 and strontium-90 are also present. In 1968, President Johnson, anxious to demonstrate how safe testing is, simply declared Bikini safe, and the nuclear nomads were returned. But they soon showed signs of radiation sickness, and had to be evacuated again. It will certainly not be safe enough for their descendants to return before the year 2035, and most probably long afterward. Application of additional potassium to the soil greatly reduces the amount of cesium-137 taken up by plants. The island of Runit in Enewetak Atoll was sealed over with a concrete dome to confine its fission products and plutonium. Two other tests made in 1954 with enormous yields were called *Romeo* (11 megatons, three times the expected yield) and *Yankee* (13.5 megatons). Many more tests were conducted.

From the military viewpoint, the series of tests did demonstrate the practicality of solid-fueled hydrogen bombs, meaning lithium-6 deuteride, rather than liquid deuterium. These new discoveries were quickly incorporated into the American nuclear arsenal. The accompanying reductions in weight meant that unmanned intercontinental rockets could be made. Incidentally, several of the hydrogen bombs tested in 1956 derived as much as 95% of their energy from fusion alone. In 1956, detonations of hydrogen bombs lofted by rockets to altitudes of 19 to 47 miles were made. These tests were monitored using instruments to record neutron spectra, neutron flux, gamma ray spectra and flux, electromagnetic pulse (9-29), fission and fusion yields, and other parameters. By 1958 the emphasis had shifted to "clean bombs" (9-28). These would employ nonradioactive pushers in the secondary units, replacing uranium. The new materials were either tungsten metal or tungsten carbide, both hard, dense materials. These successes did advance military power, but also intensified the Cold War. News that the Soviets had also carried out successful thermonuclear tests in August 1953 and September 1954 stimulated American efforts forcefully.

By 1972 around 1.15 billion curies had been deposited in the Pacific. The great bulk of this was tritium from hydrogen bomb explosions. By 1996, about three-fourths of this tritium had decayed. As of the middle 1990s, the Department of Energy has been making some efforts to restore the atolls so that the islanders could return at a date earlier than first anticipated. After their 50-year exile, resulting in severe cultural and sociological damage, the islanders began a campaign to be allowed to return. In three lawsuits federal courts ruled that the United States had violated the terms of the trusteeship under which it took possession of the Marshall Islands. The Islands, now independent, won $100 million, an amount nowhere near the damage. Scraping off the topsoil has been considered, but is impractical except for the village areas themselves. Application of high concentrations of potassium will reduce but not eliminate the amount of cesium-137 taken up by plants. The whole situation is simply wretched.

It appears as if the callous and cavalier treatment of native peoples exposed to radiation by nuclear testing by both the USSR and the USA was about equal from the standpoints of ethics.

9-20 Security in Arming and Firing Nuclear Bombs

Much effort has been expended to insure that no strategic nuclear weapon can be exploded without authorization, which must come from the President. Most American bombs are equipped with electronic locks employing a system known as "permissive action links" (PALs). The system employs a coded electronic switch on a computer chip which prevents arming each weapon without permission and the arming code from a central command post. Essentially, this procedure renders a weapon unusable if it is stolen. There is practically no possibility of kidnapping officers and forcing them to arm a stolen bomb because the arming requires special equipment and several people from different divisions. Moreover, the permissive action link codes are frequently changed. The Navy did not use the permissive action link or its methodology. It used a system of human cross-checks in which the commanding officer and several others must turn keys to arm a weapon. In the 1990s safety enhancements in arming bombs began which employed glass fiber optics and laser activation, and in 1994, permissive action links were installed on all U.S. nuclear weapons. Arming all American nuclear warheads is based on complex electronic devices. Their codes include operating electronic switches in a particular sequence, a sort of labyrinthine puzzle. Nuclear bombs on aircraft must be unarmed; the arming, if ordered, can be done quickly by the crew. An alternative arming procedure is transmitted only after a warhead has been released from its carrier. Many safety devices have also been installed. There is essentially no chance that a deranged or narcotic-frenzied person could arm a weapon. Tactical warheads, such as artillery shells, are riskier than strategic warheads because the former type is not generally equipped with complicated codes for arming; in addition, their storage is less secure.

Thieves could not explode a warhead if they stole it.

The former Soviet Union employed a control system even more stringent than the American one. A military unit assigned to the top Soviet leadership was to help them generate a secret code. The defense minister had to make a launch code simultaneously.

Both codes were to be transmitted to the Operations Directorate of the General Staff. Using computer algorithms, this Directorate combined the two codes electronically to make an encrypted 12-digit number. This was then to be sent on a secure frequency to the ICBM silos, submarines, etc. With the end of the Cold War, these security steps have probably become less dependable. Nuclear reactors have their safety problems, but bombs are in a sense 100% unsafe.

9-21 More Testing, Real and Virtual, of Nuclear Weapons

The purposes of testing nuclear bombs are many: to increase the yield, to miniaturize the bomb assemblies, to measure lethality, to observe air blast, shock, heat, and radiation effects of various types, to test the survivability of weapons in a nuclear environment, to estimate the level of effectiveness of various defenses, to investigate the electromagnetic pulse, to perfect tailored warheads such as those for nuclear artillery, to study the X-ray laser, and others. Tests with these motives in mind were begun by the American military soon after the war, using old battleships as targets. Warheads have been tested on towers, dropped from planes with or without parachutes, on the surface of the land or water, under land or water, on barges, suspended from balloons, by rocket, using artillery, and even in outer space. Some tests have yielded less than a ton of TNT explosive equivalent; others have utterly failed.

From the military viewpoint, there are many reasons to test warheads.

At least 71 different types of nuclear warheads had been developed in American laboratories by 1995. They are configured for every conceivable military mission. These include bombs for missiles, nuclear artillery shells (some as small as six inches in diameter), nuclear land mines, shoulder-fired bazookas, nuclear torpedoes, nuclear depth charges, warheads for rockets, and more.

Recent testing has had still other objectives (6-23). Experiments have been carried out to make nuclear blast effects directional, as opposed to spherical. One kind is to use the blast energy to focus into laser beams of X-rays or other high-energy radiation, or to use antennas for longer wavelengths.

The Limited Test Ban Treaty of 1963 stopped atmospheric tests by its signatories. Among other reasons, parents were alarmed by the accumulation of the dangerous fission product strontium-90 in milk. Some who advocated a ban in atmospheric testing, such as the eminent American chemist and Nobelist Linus Pauling, were considered subversive by the more conservative elements. Nonsignatories, such as the French and Chinese, continued atmospheric testing until they considered that they had achieved near parity. In 1974 the U.S. and USSR signed the Threshold Test Ban Treaty, which limited underground tests to 150 kilotons. It took effect in 1976, but has not been fully ratified.

One way of testing nuclear warheads underground without being detected is to build the device so that it just barely goes critical. Thus the nuclear yield is small, but data are gained which permit construction of a reliable, larger bomb. This technique might be considered by smaller powers which are just developing their nuclear arsenals.

It is not necessary actually to test a bomb; modern computer simulations can come very close to doing the job. One must remember that the first nuclear bomb exploded in New Mexico of necessity was based on calculations alone. Moreover, the bomb which destroyed Hiroshima was of a type never before tested. In fact, all of the seven nations which have carried out tests of nuclear warheads were successful on the first attempt. Despite success in computer tests, case-hardened military men would probably not be satisfied with anything less than an actual successful test.

The whole topic of intense development by the United States of nuclear warheads, of implosion type, gun-assembly type, and hydrogen bombs, in model after model, is described in detail by the late Chuck Hansen (see bibliography at end of chapter).

9-22 Early Soviet Tests

The first Soviet bomb (which Americans called *Joe 1*, 1949) exploded in Kazakhstan, contained plutonium-239, and had a uranium tamper. Its energy was equivalent to that of approximately 20 thousand tons of TNT (20 kilotons), that is, about the same as the first American warhead. The second test explosion, two years later, also contained plutonium and had an energy level equal to that of 25 kilotons of TNT. The third bomb, also exploded in 1951, contained both plutonium and uranium-235, and its yield was around 50 kilotons. All three were atmospheric. The main driving force of the Soviet scientists was knowledge that the United States had nuclear bombs and they didn't.

Trinity test, redux

The Soviet scientists were laboring with primitive equipment and frustrating supply problems, but were experts in improvisation. They called their first fission bomb RDS-1, the letters being a code term in Russian, standing for Stalin's Rocket Engine, although it was a near duplicate of the Trinity bomb tested in New Mexico on July 16, 1945. The test of this fission bomb, code named *First Lightning*, in the Kazakh steppes took place on August 29, 1949 (3-21). The hundred-foot tower had a covered freight elevator. Structures of various types had been built around the base, both near and far, to measure the level of destructiveness. Army tanks, artillery, penned animals, and even a locomotive, had been brought in so that the effects of a nuclear bomb could be studied. Soviet observers who had seen American tests in the Pacific were summoned, as well as many other military personnel. Many of the leading scientists participated: Kurchatov, Flerov, Khariton, and others. The bomb was assembled the day and evening before the test. It had 64 detonation points instead of the 32 in the Trinity bomb. It fired at seven in the morning, the ninth nuclear explosion in human history, with the typical mushroom cloud drifting southward. Samples of the blue-black melted soil were collected from the area around the base where the tower had been. The yield of the bomb was 20 kilotons or somewhat below (for the author's visit to the explosion site, see 9-25F). The scientific team members were rewarded with honors, automobiles, and dachas.

Specially equipped American and British planes ("sniffers") collected debris from the atmosphere using filters, whose analysis by radioactivity measurements provided enough data to detect this first test, *First Lightning*. Good estimates of the date of the test and its site were made. The American estimates were accurate to one hour of the actual date and time, and established that it was a plutonium bomb with a uranium tamper.

Nuclear detectives called "sniffer planes"

Two more fission bombs were tested in 1951, as mentioned above. While RDS-1 was more or less a copy of its American prototype, RDS-2 (*Joe 2*) was a Soviet innovation. It was half the diameter and two-thirds the weight of RDS-1, and yet had a considerably higher yield, although it's core was plutonium-239. Its efficiency (the percentage of fissile metals to undergo fission) was about 35%. *Joe 3* used a composite of plutonium and uranium-235.

The Soviet test conducted on November 22, 1955 in Kazakhstan (see also 9-25H) had a yield of 1600 kilotons and, unexpected by American experts, used both uranium-235 and uranium-233. It also had a uranium-238 tamper. It was a hydrogen bomb, but used no tritium, according to Khariton. The bomb was dropped from a plane and the explosion occurred at several thousand feet (more on this test in 9-23). Uranium-233 is made from thorium-232 (7-10). A difficulty in working with it is that it always contains some uranium-232 (7-10D), a fierce emitter of alpha particles and gamma rays; the former generate neutrons by bombarding any impurities, promoting pre-ignition.

About half of the Soviet tests (1949-1989) occurred in the steppes near Semipalatinsk in Kazakhstan, and about a fifth were conducted on the island of Novaya Zemlya, 400 miles north of the Arctic Circle. The remainder were exploded all over Siberia, and some underground tests were conducted in Ukraine, southern Russia, and along the Arctic coast. Atmospheric tests were also conducted during the late 1950s in Siberia, especially the Chukotka peninsula just west of Alaska. In the 1950s, the USSR Ministry of Health issued a directive setting the threshold dose of ionizing radiation for the population at 50 rads per year, about 200 times natural background! The health effects of the fallout on the local Chukchi reindeer herders and their animals were dreadful. The population developed the world's highest death rate from esophageal cancer and life expectancy dropped to 45 years.

9-23 Soviet Hydrogen Bomb Developments

The account below of further development of Soviet hydrogen bombs is based on numerous sources, prominent among which are Richard Rhodes' *Dark Sun* and Russian physicist German (or Herman) Goncherov writing in the American journal *Physics Today* some half-dozen years after the end of the Cold War.

In September 1945 Soviet intelligence began to find the first hints that American physicists had been planning a thermonuclear bomb employing both deuterium and tritium. This was simultaneous with the same idea of Soviet physicist Frenkel'. Analyses by the Soviets of debris from the first American tests of bombs designed to accomplish fusion, the *George* shot in May 1951 followed by the *Mike* shot in 1952 and the *Bravo* shot in 1954, disclosed that tritium had been an ingredient, that primary and secondary stages had been employed, and that enormous pressures must have been achieved. The most useful data would have come from creation of elements much heavier than uranium from an extraordinarily high pressure and neutron density.

In March 1948 in London, Fuchs gave a Soviet agent papers containing reports of American progress on hydrogen bombs. The report contained information on the classical Super, which had the two-stage configuration operating on the radiation implosion principle. The secondary unit was a liquid deuterium-tritium mixture. A heavy jacket of radiation-impervious material was used to achieve radiation confinement in the cylindrical chamber. The initiator was joined to a long cylinder containing liquid deuterium. Tritium was mixed in with the deuterium in the initial section of the cylinder. The use of tritium for this purpose was perhaps the point most important to the Soviets. Data (cross-sections) on the fusion reaction to give helium-3 were included. The result was that Stalin, after consulting with his physicists, concluded the US had made major progress. Kurchatov and his team analyzed the data. By summer orders to carry out theoretical studies and experimental verification of the data were given.

In October 1948 Sakharov thought of an alternative solution to the problem and began to explore the possibility of building a combined bomb in which deuterium would be used in conjunction with uranium. His scheme used alternating layers containing a deuterium compound and uranium-238, like Teller's "Alarm Clock." Sakharov called his arrangement the *sloika* (Russian for layer cake). It was based on radiation-ionization compression of thermonuclear fuel. Late in 1948 physicist V. L. Ginzburg came up with the idea of using lithium-6 deuteride instead of liquid deuterium. Interaction of lithium-6 with neutrons yields tritium, helium-4, and energy, and is thus a rich tritium source. This concept was incorporated into Sakharov's *Layer Cake* design in 1949. The fission of the uranium-238 in the tamper by fast neutrons was also taken into account. By 1950 orders went out to develop ways of isolating lithium-6 from the natural element and to synthesize tritium. The Soviets had a reactor with heavy water as moderator and coolant. It had a high neutron flux and was used to manufacture tritium. Lithium deuteride was prepared, and all the expensive equipment to shape it in dry rooms was constructed.

The upcoming hydrogen bomb was coded RDS-6s for the *sloika* type or RDS-6t for the tube type (the idea gained via espionage). In summer 1953 Sakharov, along with Tamm and Zel'dovich, made their report which authorized completion of the first model of the *sloika* hydrogen bomb. One of the Soviet physicists who carried out the mathematical calculations concerning the *sloika* bomb was Lev Landau. He computed the dynamics of the upcoming bomb so skillfully that he predicted the yield quite accurately, a task then beyond American competence. In 1938 he had been arrested by the KGB and he spent a year in prison allegedly because he led a counter-revolutionary organization. Landau did not want to help develop hydrogen bombs, but there was the threat of prison or worse. As soon as Stalin died (1953), he quit the nuclear weapons program (cf. Rotblat, 3-24). The *sloika* bomb was detonated on August 12, 1953, at the Kazakh testing grounds, the fourth Soviet nuclear explosion. Americans dubbed the bomb *Joe 4*. It was a true thermonuclear bomb, exploded on a tower, but capable of being carried by plane. There are differing statements concerning its yield; values ranging from 200 to 470 kilotons have been reported. The post-Cold War value given by Russian scientists, such as Khariton, was 400 kilotons (more data on this test in 9-25G). The bomb was of a single-stage configuration; this and other data were discovered in Los Alamos by analysis of debris from the Joe 4 test. Lithium-6 deuteride and possibly a considerable amount of lithium tritide were incorporated in some layers to generate extra neutrons during explosion, while other layers held uranium-238. This use of lithium-6, as well as air-dropping a thermonuclear bomb, preceded that of Americans. About one-fifth of the yield was from fusion. Compression of the single-stage bomb was achieved via high explosives, not radiation compression. The success of the test gave the Soviets confidence that their future developments of hydrogen bombs would be even more spectacular.

Lev Landau (1908–1968), physicist of positively paramount intelligence and supreme accomplishment. In 1929 he worked with Bohr in Copenhagen, at Cambridge, and at other Western universities. His fertile mind came up with penetrating theories about diamagnetism, quantified states in an electron gas, electron showers from cosmic rays, and the existence of neutron stars. He gave a lucid explanation of superconductivity and superfluidity in liquid helium. He worked on plasma physics and numerous other topics. Landau served a year in a Soviet prison. He received notable Soviet awards and the Nobel Prize in physics.

The earlier American thermonuclear explosion (the *Mike* shot, October 31, 1952; see 3-22 , 9-19, and 9-23) used liquid deuterium containing tritium, weighed 65 to 70 tons, and the bomb was not deliverable. It was euphemistically called a "device." Espionage had revealed Teller's "tube" type of hydrogen bomb, i.e., second stage. By 1953 the Soviets concluded that this approach was a dead end. This decision was based on the work of Zel'dovich, Tamm, Landau, and Pomeranchuk. A pivotal event took place when physicists Zavenyagin and Frank Kamenetskii came up with the idea of a two-stage thermonuclear bomb. The primary stage was a fission bomb and the secondary stage was the fusion components, each in a massive casing. The compression of the secondary stage was supposed to be achieved by gases emanating from the primary into the secondary; the principle of compression by radiation was not yet realized. When assembled, it still retained the layer-cake design, but there was no tritium. It contained uranium-235 and uranium-233, as well as a uranium-238 tamper. The test of this thermonuclear bomb was conducted November 22, 1955 in Kazakhstan (9-23; see photo below). Dropped from a plane, its yield was 1.6 megatons. That yield could easily have been made twice as high. Andrei Sakharov was a witness. Subsequently, the United States also tested several bombs containing uranium-233. The shock wave from that 1.6-megaton bomb, even though it was detonated at a height of 10,000 feet, nevertheless compacted the earth at ground zero, forming a crater. The American test of a hydrogen bomb with a yield of 15 megatons in 1954 (the *Bravo* test, 9-19 and 9-23) greatly stimulated the Soviets to push their own research along these lines.

These bombs with megaton yields frightened both American and Soviet scientists.

The layer-cake concept was abandoned in later Soviet hydrogen bombs in favor of radiation-pressure implosion in two stages. These ideas, parallel to the Teller-Ulam configuration but independent, resulted largely from the work of Sakharov, Zel'dovich, and V. A. Davidenko. The physical processes involved in explosion of thermonuclear charges were so complex that only high-level mathematical modeling and computer work could make them manageable. This was true in the cases of all five countries which have developed hydrogen bombs.

Reports came in about the American test (*Bravo*) of February 28, March 1, 1954, at Bikini. With its gigantic yield of 15 megatons, the Soviets realized that the U.S. had achieved awesome advances in thermonuclear weapons. Only a two-stage warhead made sense. The Soviet teams at once joined the race with enthusiasm, Sakharov taking the lead. The United States and the Soviet Union were approximately on a par by 1955 in regard to the theoretical and practical aspects of thermonuclear bombs. The Soviet Union was actually the first to employ lithium-6 deuteride thermonuclear fuel and to air-drop such bombs. The tremendous advancements in hydrogen bomb construction by both superpowers in the period 1952-56 undeniably opened the floodgates for the nuclear arms race, causing it to erupt into savage, dangerous competition. The drain on the Soviet economy was proportionately higher.

Soviet hydrogen bomb test, November 22, 1955

9-24 Further Development of Soviet Nuclear Bombs

After it was certain that the early Soviet nuclear reactors would generate a sufficient supply of plutonium, a secret site was needed for research and for testing techniques of detonation of the bombs to be manufactured, a sort of Soviet Los Alamos. The urban Kurchatov Institute in Moscow was obviously not suitable.

The old monastery city of Sarov, 250 miles east of Moscow, was chosen for warhead research. It was considered a holy city until Soviet times. The forbidden city of Arzamas-16 was constructed at the site. Starting in spring 1946, ten such secret atomic cities were built. They did not appear on any map. Arzamas was fenced in and carefully guarded. Sakharov made his first trip to Sarov/Arzamas-16 in March 1949. He familiarized himself with the status of the first Soviet fission bomb, soon to be completed, and also participated in a series of conferences on hydrogen bombs. Yuli Khariton was appointed scientific director; he is considered by some to be the father of the first Soviet nuclear bomb, although

Among themselves, the scientists sometimes referred to Arzamas-16 as "Los Arzamas."

others ascribe that distinction to Kurchatov. Top-notch physicists such as Lev Altshuler and Yakov Zel'dovich worked there, often commuting to Moscow. Andrei Sakharov later had a villa in Arzamas-16, and a park was named after him. Living conditions for these elite scientists were first class. Secrecy was strictly enforced by tight security and compartmentalization of information. The ethics of developing atomic bombs, particularly after the effects on Hiroshima and Nagasaki were known, were often debated. Their subscription to the *Bulletin of the Atomic Scientists* helped to stimulate discussion of the moral and social issues of making atomic and hydrogen bombs. They considered Leo Szilard to be a leading conscience of humanity. There was general agreement along the lines that the Soviet Union could not afford to be defenseless, relative to the U.S., and that the work was necessary to maintain a balance in the world. The first Soviet nuclear bomb, the one exploded near Semipalatinsk in Kazakhstan in August 1949, was made in Arzamas-16, as well as the first few dozen of the rest.

The most extensive manufacturing facilities for nuclear materials for warheads were located in the southern Ural Mountains, and are often referred to as the Chelyabinsk-Sverdlovsk complex. The city was first called Chelyabinsk-40, later Chelyabinsk-65, and today is known as Ozersk. In some ways, it more or less corresponded to Livermore in California. It is about 15 miles east of Kyshtym and is the site of the first Soviet reactor (the A Reactor) for production of plutonium. It began operating in June 1948 and reached a power level of 100 megawatts. The operators had to cope with distortion of the uranium metal, but were able to get it producing about 100 grams of plutonium every 24 hours. The reactor contained 365 tonnes of pure graphite and 150 tonnes of pure uranium metal. Soviet intelligence had already found out about the poisoning effect of the fission product xenon-135 (4-16), so the reactor had been constructed large enough to produce a neutron multiplication factor of 1.035, large enough to overcome the difficulty. In 1947 construction of reactors to power ships and submarines was authorized.

In April 1946 construction of a nuclear center was started in the town of Mayak in the Southern Urals. Its first facility was a metallurgical laboratory. A reprocessing plant was constructed in nearby Chelyabinsk-40 shortly afterwards, and its waste was dumped directly into the Techa River (8-7). Much of the construction was carried out by prisoners. Safety measures were so lax that the annual dose to workers frequently exceeded 100 rems per year. At first the Soviets separated plutonium using a primitive coprecipitation process based on sodium uranyl acetate, but during the Cold War years they switched to their version of the PUREX extraction process based on use of tributyl phosphate (8-9).

Another secret city was Nizhnaya Tura, north of Yekaterinburg in the Urals. It was also called Sverdlovsk-45. A second facility was known as Pensa-19, and a third as Zlatoust. In these plants, final assembly of nuclear warheads was carried out, as well as component fabrication; after the fall of the Soviet Union, dismantling of bombs was also conducted. Thus they functioned much as the Pantex, Texas, plants had (9-8F).

Pampered in Soviet times, impoverished in the 1990s

Chelyabinsk-40 was also the site where warheads were designed, especially hydrogen bombs, beginning in 1957. Other such cities were Tomsk-7 and Krasnoyarsk-26. This last city is sited on the Yenesei River about 35 miles northeast of the parent industrial city Krasnoyarsk. The secret city is in an area heavily wooded with birch and pine, and even today shows signs of its former elegant status of serving a pampered scientific elite. By this date, an estimated 350,000 people were busy in the Soviet nuclear effort. A subterranean complex of 3500 rooms had been excavated for nuclear laboratories and reprocessing facilities. Its chief, Andrei Sokolov, remained at least through 1998. With the meltdown of the Soviet economy, Krasnoyarsk-26 had to endure a restive workforce and months of unpaid wages. Guards abandoned their posts to forage for food. Even its lone nuclear reactor had to be shut down temporarily, a disastrous development in the Siberian winter. The Russian government plans to convert Krasnoyarsk-26 into a site manufacturing silicon chips and other civilian commodities.

Facilities for separating uranium-235 from uranium-238 by the centrifugal method were well developed by Zippe (see 4-20). The enriched uranium was used as fuel in nuclear reactors to manufacture plutonium, and in addition weapons-grade uranium-235 was prepared abundantly. Another captured scientist, the German Nikolaus Riehl, helped the Soviets develop techniques for manufacturing pure uranium metal for use as reactor fuel and to fabricate gun-assembly uranium-235 bombs. He worked from 1945 to 1955.

In the late 1950s, there were many overflights of the Soviet Union by American pilots in B-45 jets, spying by photography and radar. At least 20 planes were shot down, and more than 100 American airmen were captured or killed. The town of Kyshtym lies in the area and a serious accident had taken place there on September 29, 1957. The CIA wished to learn more about this area and its reactors, waste facilities, weapons factories, and the recent accident. A U-2 spy plane, piloted by one Francis Gary Powers, was sent from Peshawar, Pakistan, on May 1, 1960. He flew northwest over the Aral Sea and then north over the Urals, intending to land in northern Norway. Approaching the Chelyabinsk-Sverdlovsk area at 72,000 feet, the U-2 was hit by a Soviet SA-2 missile. Powers parachuted to safety, and was captured. The incident aborted an Eisenhower-Khrushchev summit conference in Paris. A French-Swedish satellite and an American Landsat satellite photographed the area of the accident in the southern Urals in 1987-88. Computer enhancement of the photos revealed that the region, larger than Connecticut in area, was still abandoned, including 30 villages which appeared on pre-1950 maps. It is now known that the refrigeration in a reprocessing plant failed, allowing a solution of plutonium and uranium nitrates to go dry, overheat, and oxidize organic matter. The force was enough to blow off a 3-foot-thick concrete cover.

A CIA spy plane was downed over the Urals in 1960.

In 1989, under the influence of *glasnost*, the Soviets released more information about the disaster, and it conforms fairly well with data from other sources. The total radioactivity release was about two million curies, a large fraction of which was strontium-90. The area contaminated was a narrow strip of somewhere around 400 square miles. There were deaths and injuries by radiation, but the numbers are not known. The region was also the site of weapons construction facilities.

At one time the Soviets had 13 weapons-grade plutonium production facilities, but by 1995 all but three had been shut down. It was said that they were needed to produce electricity for nearby towns, but some reprocessing to separate plutonium continued. This came to light when there was an accident near the Siberian town of Tomsk-7, a major nuclear weapons facility east of Chelyabinsk. The Russians agreed to shut down these three reactors by about 2010. Tomsk-7 is one of ten "atomic cities" still closed, more or less. These

Aftermath of the disintegration of a great power

cities have been quaintly renamed, Tomsk-7 becoming Seversk. From the information published, it appears as if a nonnuclear explosion took place when a large tank was being cleaned with nitric acid and a chemical reaction with waste occurred. A few hundred curies of radioactivity escaped, mostly air-borne, moving northeast over sparsely-occupied land. Russia, like the U.S., has a glut of plutonium already, and the plant has reportedly been closed, although a rumor in 1996 was that it was still in operation in order to maintain employment.

Workers at Arzamas-16 and Chelyabinsk-40 have been disassembling warheads under international agreements. But their pay, already anemic from inflation, has often been delayed and some workers have been threatening to strike. Under the Soviet regime, they had high prestige and living standards. Many are now considering lucrative jobs abroad. But in a strange twist of fate, an agreement with the United States in 1995 has proven to stabilize the situation for a while. This was an agreement to conduct coordinated research on nuclear fusion at Arzamas and Los Alamos. For the United States, the arrangement is a bargain: only about $10 million per year has been enough to keep the 9500 world-class scientists and engineers at Arzamas on the job, and prevent them from seeking foreign employment. Moreover the fusion work, following a concept of Sakharov, is of a new kind called pulsed power. The general idea is to use ordinary high explosives to implode deuterium-tritium mixtures, generating a controlled electromagnetic pulse, whose energy is harnessed. The technique is too new to evaluate at present.

Conditions at Chelyabinsk-40, however, continued to deteriorate. Its director, Vladimir Nechai, a competent physicist, just could not watch his life's work fall apart any longer and he took his own life in the fall of 1996. He and his fellow scientists had not been paid for months. The true status of affairs was revealed by the destitute character of his funeral. It was held in a cafeteria, without a single wreath. The pride of Russia's science attended, dressed in their threadbare clothing. No telegrams from Moscow arrived.

A Russian company, Chetek, says it is planning to destroy toxic chemical weapons (war gas) by incinerating them in underground chambers a kilometer deep using old nuclear bombs. Up to 3000 tons of toxics could be incinerated per blast. The cost, between $300 and $1200 per kilogram, is estimated to be about a fifth of the cost of conventional incineration. The plan is to sell this service to any buyer. Questions of safety have not been fully answered. There is, of course, the little matter that such explosions would violate international agreements.

There is an incredible report that the Walt Disney Company began negotiating with Russia for establishing a theme park in central Russia. The site? Arzamas-16.

9-25 The Semipalatinsk Testing Grounds in Kazakhstan

Trip to Kazakhstan—The author traveled to Kazakhstan in the summer of 1994 as a member of a scientific team to conduct a study of the test sites and of the effects of fallout on the population.* The country, which became independent in late 1991, is huge, having almost four times the area of Texas. It is mostly steppes, and has much mineral wealth. The city of Semipalatinsk, in northeastern Kazakhstan, is the site of the Kazakh Scientific

*This trip was sponsored by the United Methodist Church, which conducted a compassionate aid project for the Kazakh victims of radioactive fallout.

Research Institute of Radiology and Ecology, whose director is Dr. Boris Gusev. He and his staff have been studying and documenting the effects of radioactive fallout from testing nuclear bombs for more than two generations. Let us hope that an international research foundation of some type can be established with Dr. Gusev as director. He is most familiar with the data and archives, and two or three generations are covered. Support should be international: United Nations, and the nuclear establishments of the U.S., England, France, Russia, Japan, and maybe China. During one translucent evening our group, during a banquet in a yurt, listened to a Kazakh chieftain as he explained that "We now have our own country, and no one will use our people as guinea pigs again."

The Number of Test Explosions in Kazakhstan—The number of Soviet tests of nuclear warheads from 1949 to 1989 was 715, and 489 of these were in Kazakhstan. In the period 1949-63, 116 of these tests were carried out in the atmosphere and in the period 1964-89, 340 tests were made underground. Most of the air blasts were made on towers; a few were carried out by dropping from planes or suspension from balloons. Of the underground tests, only 176 were completely contained. Radioactive nuclides (fission products and plutonium) and/or radioactive gases leaked out in the rest, 52 cases being severe. In quite a number of tests, two to eight warheads were detonated simultaneously, but such cases count as a single test in accordance with the Protocol to the Threshold Test Ban Treaty (9-59). Dr. Gusev, who had close contact with the victims of the resulting radiation, puts the figure for the atmospheric tests higher than the above 116 since he counts shallow underground tests and those with severe leakage as equivalent to air blasts. The most damaging results of the nuclear nightmare began to end in 1963, when the Limited Test Ban Treaty was signed. It banned atmospheric tests. In 1991 a nuclear bomb was put in a tunnel 126 meters deep at the Semipalatinsk site, but the Soviet Union collapsed before it could be exploded. In summer 1995 Russian and Kazakh engineers placed a charge of 400 kilograms of chemical high explosive on the bomb and pulverized it in a blast. The tunnel was then sealed.

Radiation from Fallout—The bombs exploded in the atmosphere were mostly in the steppes to the south and west of Semipalatinsk. The citizens of the city itself received only a relatively small exposure, 1.5 to 2 rads per inhabitant. But several villages were near ground zero, and were covered with the highly radioactive dust of fallout. Each inhabitant was afflicted with a dose of between 200 and 300 rads. Consider, for example, Dolon, a beautiful village framed by pine trees on the banks of the Irtysh River. It is 74 miles from ground zero. The usual consequences were observed: anemia, low white blood cell count, general weakness, fatigue, depression, nosebleeds, loss of hair, stomach and lung and liver cancer, and other disorders (see also 5-20). The consequences of the radioactive fallout on the populace was dreadful beyond imagination. Many fetuses were miscarried, and many of those born alive suffered from blindness, mental retardation, grossly shortened legs, thyroid cancer, damaged immune systems, microcephaly, or other defects. About a quarter of the women were rendered sterile, and menopause came at an age under 40. Just consider the anguish this irradiation

Any testing of nuclear bombs is awful enough, but exploding them in the atmosphere is complete lunacy.

must have caused the victims and their parents. Our group was taken to a museum which featured miscarried fetuses preserved in formaldehyde. While no true genetic mutations were found, as opposed to congenital deformities, there were genetic markers, as was the case in Hiroshima. A particularly grotesque deformation, known as the cyclops case (single eye in the forehead and misplaced ears) was probably of natural origin, rather than resulting from ionizing radiation. Efforts to reconstruct the radiation dose to various tissues are underway employing electron-spin resonance studies of tooth enamel.

The plume of fallout from the first Soviet test was carried northeast on a brisk wind, crossed the border with Russia and gave quite a heavy radiation dose to the inhabitants of Talmenka, a village in the Altai region. This single test was the most damaging of all. One estimate is that it inflicted a collective radiation dose of 3,200,000 person-rems, making up nearly 90% of the total of all tests in the region. There were the usual radiation effects on the health of the citizens; even the second generation of children were prone to weakness and jaundice. In the Russian district of Uglovsky the average dose was 80 rems, but it was not uniform, and some people received up to 180 rads. There was a great increase in eye cataracts. At least 100,000 people were exposed. Dr. Gusev believes that the radiological damage inflicted on the Kazakhs was worse than that at Hiroshima and Nagasaki. This is because the Soviet population received exposure of the internal organs from radionuclides in food and inhaled dust, and also were exposed repeatedly. The Kazakhs born of parents who had been exposed suffered from poor immune systems, and blood and nervous system disorders more frequently than those born of unexposed parents.

Incidentally, a recently-declassified photograph taken by an early American spy satellite in 1966 clearly showed Soviet long-range bombers (the Bison type) on a base not far from Dolon; the planes probably were dusted with fallout at some time during the series of tests. The spy satellite was in the Discoverer series; so many had failed that the CIA concocted a story about them carrying mice for medical experiments. It was number 14 in the series which first finally took photographs successfully.

Radioactivity of Soil in Eastern Kazakhstan—During travels over hundreds of miles of steppe land in the Semipalatinsk area, the author made numerous radioactivity measurements using a sensitive Geiger counter. The samples were soil, foodstuffs, vegetative matter, and animal dung. In all cases the results were at background level, except for areas in the vicinity of actual bomb test sites. The last serious fallout from nuclear explosions in the air occurred in 1963; after that date, they were underground. Counting natural decay and washout by rain, nearly all the land today is safe for agriculture.

Almost all of the land is safe to grow food crops.

The Secret City of Kurchatov—One of a series of secret, cloistered atomic cities in the Soviet nuclear effort was called Kurchatov City, after the physicist who was director of the work for years (3-19, 3-24). Its construction was begun in 1947, in anticipation of the need for a headquarters to accommodate the scientific team testing the bombs to be manufactured. The site selected was an ancient Kazakh village named Nadejda, which was taken over. Our group was driven to the isolated town in the endless steppes. There was a fenced area many miles across, with a walled compound inside. The structures had clearly been built to last. The houses for the scientific elite had marble and hardwood floors, spacious rooms, and fine carpets and drapes. Amenities included schools, tennis courts, pools, theaters, and an airfield. During the Cold War, its population was about 18,000.

After independence, Kurchatov City was converted into a national laboratory devoted to peaceful uses of radioactive substances in medicine, industry, and other areas. The author was able to speak freely with a Russian physicist (but Kazakh citizen) about all the formerly secret nuclear matters, stimulating a virtually surrealist sensation.

Visit to the Site of the First Soviet Test—Our study team was driven to the site of the first atomic test explosion, which the Soviet scientists carried out at 7 a.m. on August 29, 1949. This first Soviet nuclear warhead, dubbed *Joe 1* by Americans, had been largely based on espionage data of the Trinity bomb tested in New Mexico a little more than four years earlier. The site was at the hind end of nowhere, not a house, not a tree, not an animal. At about two miles from the site (upwind), the soil registered at background radioactivity, but at one mile, it was 1500 counts per minute, even inside the vehicle. As we approached closer, the activity increased rapidly, registering around 100,000 counts per minute at the rim of the crater. The bomb had been detonated on a tower about 100 feet tall, and the downward force compacted the earth enough to form a crater roughly 30 feet deep. It was half full of water. At the time of the explosion, the wind velocity was around 28 miles per hour, blowing northwest. Walking downwind from ground zero, the activity rose to 600,000 counts per minute. Analyzing a sample of the soil back in California, it was found to be approximately 0.2 nanocuries per gram (gamma activity). Telephone poles had been sheared off by the shock wave for several miles along the access road. Steel-and-concrete bunkers which housed cameras and other devices had been crumpled. Vestiges of cages were visible which held sheep, cattle, horses, and desert animals. Such studies had also been carried out during American tests.

First Thermonuclear Test—The Soviets conducted a test on August 12, 1953, and this was evidently the first true warhead with a hydrogen bomb ever exploded (9-23). Americans dubbed the bomb *Joe 4*, the Soviets called it RDS-6s. Knowing that the blast would be unusually vehement the nearby town of Karaul, 106 miles distant, had been evacuated, except for 42 men. These men were not informed about what was about to happen. The explosion, which took place on a tower and probably had a yield of around 400 kilotons, generated an intense gamma ray pulse. Sheep were killed, chickens blinded. Of the 42 men, one happened to be standing behind a pillar and was sheltered; the remainder received heavy gamma ray exposure, and all 41 lived only a few more years. During our visit the surviving sheltered man described the bright flash and the spectacular mushroom and its shadow. He was active and healthy at the time of our visit. Not all people could be completely evacuated, and 291 while traveling were exposed to the radioactive cloud directly. By 1994, only three were still alive. No more evacuations were conducted in subsequent tests. By 1955 some 350,000 persons had been exposed repeatedly.

Gamma ray damage by an H-bomb 100 miles away

According to Soviet physicist Khariton (in a paper written in 1996), this bomb was the first true hydrogen warhead ever tested. The earlier American test (1952) of a heavy thermonuclear device cannot be considered to be a warhead. The Soviet bomb (*Joe 4*) was constructed according to a design by Sakharov and was of the *sloika* type. Lithium deuteride and perhaps a considerable amount of lithium tritide was incorporated in some layers to generate extra tritium during explosion, while other layers held uranium-238. About one-fifth of the yield was from fusion. Bombs based on the *sloika* design were limited in scope, that is, their yield could not be increased without limit. This conclusion caused Sakharov and Zel'dovich to design a new configuration; its first test is described below.

The Second Soviet Hydrogen Bomb—After the preliminary thermonuclear test was made in 1953 (above), the Soviets detonated another thermonuclear warhead on November 22, 1955 (9-22). This model was of the two-stage type and had a potent yield of 1600 kilotons. It was dropped from a plane. A passing eagle had its wings singed so badly it could not fly. Altogether, some 700,000 people were affected by the radiation. The inhabitants of a dozen or so villages suffered appalling damage to their health; fetuses were especially susceptible. The Kazakh people also were exposed to fallout from tests at Lap Nor in China; this occurred on the uncommon occasions when the wind was blowing to the west. The Soviets monitored the air-borne radioactive debris from American, French, and Chinese tests during the 1960s. All of this weighed heavily on Sakharov, and he began thinking in terms of limiting nuclear bomb tests. He used his influence to force future tests underground, leading to the atmospheric test ban of 1963.

The Kazakhs got Soviet fallout from the west and Chinese fallout from the east.

Atomic Lake—Although atmospheric tests were halted by the Limited Test Ban Treaty in 1963, the Soviet military did make a test of a hydrogen bomb of intermediate yield (150-200 kilotons) on January 16, 1965. It was buried in such a shallow hole that it was certain to blow fallout into the air. Its depth was approximately 360 feet and rocks were blown more than six miles away. It resembles Sedan Crater at the Nevada Test Site (9-30). A radioactive cloud swept over several settlements. The test was touted as a peaceful use of nuclear explosions, in this case to make a lake. The site was a short distance from the confluence of the Shagan and Aschi-Su Rivers, and a canal had been dug before the blast by young military conscripts, thus connecting the site to one of the rivers. The soldiers were from central Asian Republics, that is, non-Russian. The conscripts were brought back for further construction at the explosion site 21 days after the explosion. They had no protective gear to shield them from the radioactive debris and nearly all received severe radiation exposures. Thus Lake Atomkul, usually known as "Atomic Lake" was born. It is difficult to avoid the suspicion that the real objective of the test was to see how soldiers would function in the nuclear battlefield.

Wild rodents, such as hamsters (which are indigenous to the area), mice, and rats would drink from this nuclear booby trap and die. In 1973 algae was found growing in the lake and, since it was the food of a certain fish, the lake was stocked with this species. The fish grew rapidly to twice their normal size, and laid eggs. But the hatchlings were blind and had no tails or fins, and so died. Radiometric measurements of the fish revealed hazardous concentrations of strontium-90 and cesium-137 in their bodies. After a few more years, fish could survive and reproduce, and after 1985 limited consumption of them was allowed.

The author brought back a liter of water from Atomic Lake in an old vodka bottle. Analysis in California disclosed that its radioactivity was quite low, being only 150 nanocuries per liter owing to the presence of tritium. This level is so low that tiny creatures (almost 1 mm long) were living in the water. The water contained 1.6% dissolved solids, and these residues were very weakly radioactive by gamma emission.

The Nevada-Semipalatinsk Movement—One of the world's most remarkable occurrences was the birth of a popular anti-nuclear bomb movement during the last years of Soviet power. With excruciating sensitivity, it was named Nevada-Semipalatinsk. It started outside the gates of Kurchatov City in March, 1989. The leader of the movement was Olzhas Suleimenov, a Kazakh poet, writer, stirring orator, and masterful organizer. Demonstrations were held in the capitol, Alma-Ata (Almaty in Kazakh), and some of the activists were shot by security police, but that action galvanized more protesters, who collected more than two million signatures. The movement played a decisive role in shutting down the test sites (August 29, 1991).

9-26 Soviet Superbombs

To each action of either the U.S. or the USSR, the other reacted again and again, driving the arms race more and more perilously. For their part, the Soviets decided to develop a variety of hydrogen bombs in the early 1960s. At their testing grounds on the frigid island of Novaya Zemlya, on October 30, 1961, they exploded the most monstrous thermonuclear device in human history. This robust bomb had a yield of 58 megatons, that is 58 million tons of TNT (some sources quote a yield of 50 megatons). Just think about this number; it is equivalent to 116,000,000,000 pounds of TNT, or nearly 20 pounds for every human being on Earth, in just one explosion! This bomb probably had three stages (an extra powerful primary, a secondary, and a tertiary; see 9-16). It used a tamper made of lead for the fusion stage; if uranium-238, ordinarily used for tampers, had been employed, its yield would have been perhaps 2½ to 3 times as great. Since the bomb was tamped with lead, there was only a relatively small amount of fission products released. The immense bomb was dropped from an airplane. Detonated at 3:30 a.m., night became day for a thousand miles around. The device was never weaponized. The thermonuclear energy undoubtedly came from fusion of deuterium in lithium deuteride, in cylinders arranged in a series so that each stage ignites the next. In 1962, four more huge hydrogen bombs were tested, with yields ranging from 20 to 30 megatons.

The mightiest bomb ever exploded

These mighty bombs are not considered of military value. Ten half-megaton bombs are much more destructive than a single five megaton one, even though the total yield energy is the same. Besides, the heavier weapons are less easily delivered by rockets. Teller has written that there is no theoretical reason why truly colossal superbombs of 20,000 megatons yield could not be constructed. These less-than-useless devices, on explosion, would blow some of Earth's atmosphere out into space. Even the most lunatic of Earth's inhabitants would have no reason to test such a monstrosity.

9-27 J. Robert Oppenheimer as Scapegoat

As we have seen, both super powers began to expand the types of their nuclear weapons, their numbers, and their power soon after the Soviets tested their first bomb in 1949. The political miasma known as McCarthyism appeared on the American scene about this time. After it became clear that the USSR could and did begin to develop a countervailing nuclear arsenal, reactionary forces on the American scene needed and soon found a scapegoat, namely J. Robert Oppenheimer. Ignoring the truly monumental contributions which Oppenheimer had made to the American nuclear program, the superpatriots began to whisper that Oppenheimer was a "hardened communist," or had "more probably than not . . . been functioning as an espionage agent," or has "acted under a Soviet directive . . ." Teller made claims to the FBI that Oppenheimer's opposition to the hydrogen bomb had delayed the progress on this project, ignoring the opposition of other notable scientists, such as Hans Bethe and James Conant. The FBI even tapped Oppenheimer's home phone conversations with his attorneys and secretly provided copies to Lewis Straus, chairman of the Atomic Energy Commission, who saw that copies were given to the attorneys acting as prosecutors in what was supposed to be an impartial inquiry. Clandestinely recorded conversations of Oppenheimer, not made available to the defense earlier, were sprung during the hearing, of course damaging the testimony of the accused, as planned. In 1953, Oppenheimer was suspended as a security risk in what essentially was a heresy trial, and this banished a voice of reason in regard to the Cold War. In a sense, Oppenheimer had the last laugh: he received the Fermi Prize in 1963.

Heresy in America

Oppenheimer's punishment on counterfeit charges of being a "hardened communist" are parallel to Sakharov's punishment on the equally absurd charge of being a "dupe of the CIA." Sakharov was physically exiled to Gorky (3-24), but was later rehabilitated. Oppenheimer was never rehabilitated.

9-28 The Neutron Bomb

Faced with a supposedly superior Warsaw Pact tank force, American nuclear scientists devised a bomb (1977-78) which kills more by radiation than by blast. This enhanced radiation bomb, or neutron bomb, is a low-yield hydrogen bomb for tactical use. It maximizes the lethal effects of high-energy neutrons and gamma rays produced in fusion. The fission efficiency is low and the fusion efficiency is high. This is accomplished by either eliminating the uranium tamper or replacing it with a nonfissionable metal, such as lead or tungsten. The neutron bomb has a high requirement for tritium, and is strongly boosted. In an ordinary fusion bomb, about 5% of the total energy released on explosion is carried by neutrons; in a neutron bomb, the figure is about 30%. Fast neutrons are deadly and can travel considerable distance in air. They penetrate steel, and thus kill soldiers in tanks.

Clean killing, another step in the arms race

A low-altitude burst of a one kiloton neutron bomb, while still very destructive by blast effects, is lethal by radiation up to a distance of 1 to 2 kilometers. Quick death results up to 850 meters, where the dose is 8000 rads or more. The weapon was introduced as a more refined method of killing, falling into a class deceitfully dubbed "clean bombs," clean in the sense that there is less fallout compared with pure fission bombs. The claim that the bombs are clean has gradually expired. Since President Reagan authorized production of neutron bombs in 1981, there has of course been a similar response by the Soviets. In addition, both sides began to equip their tanks to make them more radiation resistant, especially to neutrons. France soon announced its own neutron bomb, and in 1988 the Chinese tested their first, bringing the total to four nations which have developed it. The neutron bomb represented another notch in the growth of a perilous arms race.

9-29 Electromagnetic Pulse

In August 1958 a hydrogen bomb was carried by rocket about 26 miles above Johnson Island in the Pacific. Its explosion caused some disturbances in the ionosphere, which reflects radio waves, and cut communications to Australia for some time. It also produced some strange interferences in Hawaii, but they were not investigated further at the time. This shot had been spiked with some radioactive isotopes of metals which do not appear as fission products, namely tungsten-185 and rhodium-102. This permitted tracing the course of the fallout over the Earth, without confusing it with debris from other tests. At this great height, it was found to be more or less evenly distributed over the Earth except at the poles, where it was strangely concentrated.

The next act in this drama took place at 11 o'clock on a July night in 1962 when the sky was brilliantly lighted by a 1.4 megaton hydrogen bomb exploding 248 miles above Johnson Island, approximately 800 miles from Hawaii. Instantly many street lights went out as circuit breakers opened, burglar arms began to sound, and some electronic equipment with the newly introduced transistors failed. These events puzzled physicists for some time, even though the phenomenon was not entirely new. In 1958 the American military had set off six nuclear bursts at altitudes 25 to 50 miles, still within the thin atmosphere. In 1961 the Soviets exploded nuclear bombs at high altitude over Asia. All space tests were stopped by the Limited Test Ban Treaty of 1963 and the Outer Space Treaty of 1967.

Unexpected events from a nuclear blast in space

The odd results of the space shots over Johnson Island have become known as the electromagnetic pulse (EMP) or nuclear pulse in the U.S. and as radio flash in England and the USSR/Russia. Physically, the course of events is as follows. In nuclear explosions in vacuum, nearly three-quarters of the total energy is emitted as X rays and gamma rays. If the explosion is in the vacuum of space above the Earth's atmosphere, the radiation of course travels in all directions; that part going downward is absorbed on reaching the attenuated atmosphere. X-rays and gamma rays are extremely energetic, and their absorption by air molecules strips electrons from them; these electrons are also very energetic. This process is ionization, and the air molecules are left positively charged. Each electron, being negatively charged, energetic, and in the Earth's magnetic field, moves rapidly away, following a spiral path along the geomagnetic lines of force. The tsunami of electrons gyrate several hundred feet in the tenuous atmosphere before coming to rest. Under these circumstances the decelerating electrons emit radiation of long wavelength (a few meters) and low frequency, at the opposite end of the spectrum from X- and gamma rays. This is in the radio and microwave region. The surge of radio waves is of unprecedented intensity.

Traveling downward to the Earth's surface, the burst of radiation is the electromagnetic pulse. It is picked up just as any radio antenna picks up a radio signal. Any conductor of electricity acts as an antenna: all electric power lines and grid systems, telephone lines, radio and television broadcasting stations, radar systems, rails, water pipes, etc. When power lines lead to electronic equipment, the sensitive components, especially transistors and silicon chips in integrated circuits, are disabled or degraded by the surge, and thus unprotected computers are crippled. A typical germanium transistor requires only 0.0001 joule of energy to melt its soldered points. Induced electric current can spark across gaps, meaning that actual contact between conductors is not necessary. Even an electric motor can be damaged by a powerful pulse. Transformers may be burned out. Old fashioned vacuum tubes are not sensitive to electromagnetic pulse, and most radios in Hawaii in 1962 had not yet been equipped with transistors. The strength of such pulses is measured in volts per meter. This value might be as much as 100,000 volts per meter on the surface under the nuclear blast, and typically half this value further away. The pulse is practically harmless to nonconductors, such as living things.

Burning out electronic equipment

An electromagnetic pulse rises to a maximum intensity in an unimaginably short time, only around 10 billionths of a second. Lightning is 100 times slower. Thus an electromagnetic pulse can go through a lightning arrestor circuit and wreak its damage before the circuit opens. One two-megaton nuclear burst in outer space 200 miles over Nebraska would lobotomize most unprotected communication equipment across the continent, causing instant chaos. Steps are now being taken to protect commercial radio stations. Nuclear bursts higher than about 19 miles are most destructive. Detection of an electromagnetic pulse is a way of detecting high altitude nuclear explosions. An artificial aurora was observed in the southern hemisphere after the 1962 test.

Explosion of a nuclear bomb in space produces an electromagnetic pulse on Earth below, but the X- and gamma rays which hit satellites also cause damage. The ionization of their metallic surfaces creates an intense electric field inside, up to a million volts per meter. This in turn induces enormous currents (several thousand amps). The result is another kind of electromagnetic pulse, causing burnouts of electronic equipment inside. Commercial communication satellites are vulnerable. Moreover, the band of radioactive fission products and trapped electrons created by the blast damages any spacecraft which travel through it. This occurred after the 1962 test.

The Pentagon was rather slow to appreciate that electromagnetic pulses might be employed as a weapon of war to disable telecommunications. Today there is a keen awareness, and much effort is going into "hardening" electronic components to make them EMP-resistant. The costs run into hundreds of millions of dollars per year. Hardening is accomplished in two ways: building more resistant components, and shielding with well-grounded conductive cages. Nuclear explosions on the Earth's surface produce only a weak electromagnetic pulse, owing to the dense atmosphere; nevertheless, some tests can be made, and this is one objective of underground explosions. Fiber optics are immune to the electromagnetic pulse, and are being increasingly employed. Nuclear weapons sent via rocket are now hardened. It is commonly believed that the Soviets have achieved parity in protection from electromagnetic pulses. Recent research has the objective of making the yield of radio or microwaves as strong as possible, to knock out even hardened electronics.

There are tenable reports that, during the Persian Gulf War, just before American attacks on Iraq began in January 1991, Gen. Schwartzkopf requested authorization to detonate a nuclear warhead high over Iraq. This was to employ the resulting electromagnetic pulse in incapacitating most electronic devices in Iraq. The proposal was rejected.

Still another consequence of electromagnetic pulse is "transient radiation effects on electronics" (TREE). It is a combination of the effects of X-rays, gamma rays, and neutrons on electronic components. Its outcome is the disabling of integrated circuits. Neutron bombs are efficient electromagnetic pulse generators.

The French operate a research center at Gramat to study the electromagnetic pulse. It uses an abandoned railway tunnel and simulates EMP. The center also investigates ways to harden material for protection against nuclear blasts, and the effects of heat from the explosions.

By 1998 worries about electromagnetic pulses had turned to protecting ("rad-hardening") the Pentium chips in microprocessors in the Pentagon's fleet of defense and spy spacecraft. They are already invulnerable to cosmic rays and solar flares. The U.S. communications infrastructure is vulnerable to electromagnetic pulses from strategically placed nuclear explosions. There are about 325 commercial satellites.

9-30 Testing, Testing: More Testing Aboveground

After the tests in the Pacific immediately following the war, a series of test explosions was carried out at the Nevada Test Site, starting in 1951. This huge area, amounting to 1350 square miles, is 30% larger than the state of Rhode Island. The section called Yucca Flat is where most of the tests occurred; others are Frenchman Flat, Mercury, Rainier Mesa, and Pahute Mesa. Altogether 126 tests were made in the atmosphere. By the end of the Cold War, 928 nuclear test explosions had been conducted. The warheads were exploded on or under the surface, slightly above the surface, on towers several hundred feet high, from balloons, shot from cannons, or dropped from planes. Most bursts were below 1500 feet, and caused considerable local fallout. In the test code-named the *Grable* Shot, an artillery shell was detonated at 524 feet on May 25, 1953, with a yield of 15 kilotons (Color Plate II, Fig. 9-30). Since the winds were to the east and northeast, American citizens all the way to the Atlantic coast were exposed, but the closer inhabitants in Nevada, Utah, and New Mexico received the highest doses of radioactivity. In many of the tests livestock were corralled at various distances from near-surface blasts in order to study the effects of shock waves and nuclear radiation (direct gamma rays and neutrons).

Tests in about any configuration one can think of

In 1953 a mock American community ("Doom Town") was constructed near ground zero of an air blast. It was complete with cars, mannequin families, houses, and shelters. Nearly all were destroyed. A Japanese-style town was built in 1962 and a test was made to determine the degree of shielding residents of Hiroshima and Nagasaki had experienced. A 36-acre farm was maintained on the site to study the effects of radiation on cattle and crops. A warhead with 37 kiloton yield was suspended from a balloon 700 feet above ground in 1957, and detonated to test its effects on heavy, reinforced structures. These included concrete domes, underground garages, and steel bridges. Nearly all were severely damaged, but a bank vault survived.

From the air the site looks like a moonscape. One warhead, of 104 kiloton yield, was buried only 635 feet deep. It lifted 12 million tons of ejecta into the sky and left a crater 1250 feet in diameter and 320 feet deep. The Apollo 14 astronauts trained in this site, Sedan Crater, for their later trips to the Moon. More than 200 deep explosions of small low-yield bombs were kept secret until recently.

Many photos of nuclear explosions are available on the web at:

www.atomicarchive.com/Photos/LANL/image19.shtml

By 1994, after the Cold War had been buried, parts of the Nevada test site became a tourist attraction of sorts. The hamlet called Mercury had once served as a base camp for test workers. Today it has perhaps 7000 inhabitants. Nearby is a pair of holding pens where peace demonstrators, who carried out the largest civil disobedience actions in U.S. history, were held until they could be bused away to be booked.

Recently a marketing program has been initiated in which, for a hefty fee, tests are permitted of the type not allowed anywhere else. Since the area has already been pummeled by so many bombs, a little more destruction is thought to be inconsequential. Experiments are carried out in which large amounts of toxic mixtures are spewed out onto the earth and cleanup techniques are performed. One firm cleans massive industrial carbon filters, full of unpleasant materials. New fuels are tested in experimental vehicles; these are not allowed on public roads. Outcast industries, being refugees from suburbia, include Fluid Tech, headquartered near Las Vegas, cleans apparatus contaminated by radioactive materials. If you need to blow up a building to test a new anti-terrorism design or to try out a new flame-smothering foam, Nevada Test Site is the place to go.

9-31 Victims of Fallout: The Downwinders

The Atomic Energy Commission and military officials displayed a malignant cunning. Some officials in the know had taken care to relocate their own families away from the fallout zones. The fervently patriotic, rural citizens of Nevada and nearby states who were downwind (indeed, they have become known as "The Downwinders") from the explosion sites at first welcomed the tests, but when first their sheep and later their children showed signs of radiation exposure, they became deeply radicalized, and many today feel that their government lied to them. They had not been warned to shower after exposure to fallout, or to wear protective clothing. They received only fraudulent reassurances.

How to convert conservatives into radicals

The first sheep began to die in 1953. Tests with Geiger counters disclosed intense radioactivity in the thyroid glands of the animals, confirming that radio-iodine had been taken in. Later there was evidence that the intestines of the sheep had received doses of around 5000 rads from eating grass and leaves covered with fallout. At first the Atomic Energy Commission tried to blame it all on malnutrition and poisonous weeds eaten by the animals. Stories of deformed lambs and other animals arose, but the reports are anecdotal, and have not been reproduced by laboratory exposure of sheep.

The town of St. George lies 100 miles east of the test site, and was dusted frequently with fallout. For example, the plume from a 32-kiloton blast on May 19, 1953, hovered over the town while rain clouds gathered. By sheer good fortune, no rain fell; if it had, the inhabitants below would have been severely irradiated. The only warning was an improvised notice by radio which few residents heard. Stewart Udall described the decision makers as "intoxicated by bloated conceptions of 'national security' that imbued them with pitiless arrogance." Public fears began to accelerate about 1958. Just too many cases of cancer developed in the areas most heavily exposed. One by one, the loyal American citizens became convinced that the fallout was killing them and their families. When seven cases of leukemia arose within a block, it was just too much, and soothing official words did not suffice.

Take the case of Arlene Davis, born in 1955 and raised in southern Utah. She reported that "We used to eat dinner on our back lawn to watch the fallout clouds roll in. They told us we were safe. And if we saw the clouds, we'd call the whole neighborhood to watch. I remember my mother taking her finger and drawing on the dust that fell on the cars." Arlene Davis developed breast cancer later. It is not that the dangers of fallout were unknown. For example, Dr. Stafford Warren, an Atomic Energy Commission health expert, warned that minute amounts of fallout particles inside the body can cause cancer years later.

The problem was not ignorance; it was blind fervor inspired by the Cold War. Measurements of the exposure to radioactive fallout of the citizens of Nevada, Utah, and other areas later showed an average value of around 5 rads. Officialdom generally pointed to this information as evidence that nuclear testing was safe. But the fallout was not evenly distributed, and some areas definitely received much more than the average, as shown in the various examples described above. Moreover, some radionuclides were concentrated by the bodies of the people, causing large doses to certain organs. The fresh fallout contained iodine-131 and this was taken up by grazing milk cows.

Goat milk was even worse than cow milk. Infants and children ingested enough to give their thyroid glands an average radiation dose of about 2 rads, but those in the most afflicted areas received as much as 16 rads, on average, and a few were exposed to much more, as much as 50 rads. The most harmful shot at the Nevada Test Site took place August 31, 1957. The test, code named Smoky, was at the top of a 700-foot tower, and its yield was 44 kilotons. The fallout was 10 to 20 times greater than that of the other detonations of the series. In 1997, additional data on exposure of the American population was released. It turns out that the fallout was carried to a dozen states or so, in irregular patterns. Aside from Nevada and Utah, the most heavily affected states were Montana, Idaho, Colorado, and South Dakota. An estimated 160 million curies, a

Fallout, fallout, unholy fallout

staggering amount, had been released into the atmosphere. In August 2001, the National Cancer Institute released the results of a study which concluded that between 11,000 and 12,000 Americans died of cancer induced by the fallout from the Nevada nuclear testing during the Cold War.

9-32 Soldiers and the Atomic Battlefield

The army was anxious to train soldiers to carry out maneuvers on the atomic battlefield. A typical exercise was code-named Smoky, mentioned above. A 44-kiloton warhead atop a 700-foot tower was detonated on August 31, 1957. Troops were positioned in trenches only three miles from ground zero. The blinding flash was visible in both Los Angeles and San Francisco. Some soldiers reported that they could see the bones in their arms as if in an X-ray photo; this was because of the intense light. The Joshua trees ignited, the shock wave was unbearable. After four minutes a truckload of men raced off toward ground zero. Soon they reached another world: no life of any kind, just greenish glass, crunching under their boots. Readings as high as 50 rads per hour were recorded in some cases. Over the 12-year testing period, around 200,000 American troops from all branches of the services were exposed in 235 atmospheric tests.

Soldiers as guinea pigs

All this time the official word was that the fallout was harmless. The Atomic Energy Commission urged "official interpretations." Public Health Service officials suppressed or altered damaging reports on orders from their superiors. Around $30 million was spent on "public relations" to reassure the public that there were no health hazards and that the tests were patriotic. Officials consistently misinformed the westerners, sometimes implying that these scientific matters were beyond the meager intellects of mere ranchers. A recently declassified document referred to those downwind from the test site as "a low-use segment of the population." This arrogance implanted mistrust of officialdom which persists till this day.

One must keep in mind the tenor of the times. The development of a variety of nuclear warheads was seen by government officials as the only means of survival for the United States in the struggle with the Soviet Union. When two scientists at the University of Colorado Medical Center publicly opposed testing, the governor of Colorado said, "The two scientists should be arrested." A Nevada Senator insinuated that stories about fallout being harmful were "communist inspired." A military report of 1947 recommended, concerning fallout, that it is "a matter of reeducation" of the U.S. public "to accept the possibility of an atomic explosion within a matter of a hundred or so miles of their homes."

In the end, it became generally accepted that the American public and many soldiers were truly injured, some seriously, and in many cases killed by cancer caused by radioactive fallout. Despite a letter in 1952 to the effect that the military was ready "to accept full responsibility for the physical and radiological safety of troops," the soldiers who were exposed received no special compensation. Similarly, in 1988 the Supreme Court refused to consider civilian cases. But in 1993 the Clinton administration authorized a new study and reevaluation. By 2000 about $244 million had been paid to 3300 sick and dying fallout victims, including some miners. Compensation was expanded later in that year to award as much as $150,000 each to workers damaged by radiation or by toxic exposures to elements such as beryllium. The total cost has been estimated at around $1.9 billion over ten years.

A corresponding story unraveled in the Soviet Union: the notorious Totsk test. On September 14, 1954, a military exercise in the Orenburg region of the southern Ural Mountains killed and injured numerous servicemen. About 45,000 troops were marched through the epicenter six hours after an explosion, and without protection against radiation. The bomb, of yield between 20 and 40 kilotons, was detonated at 1150 feet. The event was recorded by movie cameras. Thousands suffered long-term effects of radiation sickness, and fewer than 1% of the soldiers were still alive in 1994. The story was kept secret for nearly 40 years.

Soviet military and civilians suffered even more than their American counterparts.

In addition, documented accounts were made of numerous cases of cancer, especially leukemia, in the inhabitants near Semipalatinsk, the main nuclear testing grounds. In 1993 a study revealed that the number of breast cancer cases per 100,000 inhabitants in the Semipalatinsk region rose from 13.7 in 1981 to 23.7 in 1991. In the absence of data on previous health status, the radiation dosages, and other data, no thorough and scientifically sound analysis of the matter can be established. It was that very first Soviet test (August 29, 1949) which inflicted approximately 90% of the radiation dosage (3.2 million person-rems) on the Kazakh people. A grassroots anti-nuclear movement in Kazakhstan (the Nevada-Semipalatinsk Movement, page 482) began to have influence, and it played a role in causing the dismemberment of the Soviet Union.

9-33 Still More Testing: Underground Nuclear Explosions

After the ban on atmospheric testing in 1963, the nuclear arms race continued enthusiastically in other ways. American tests began to be carried out underground at the Nevada Test Site. Vertical shafts 3 to 12 feet in diameter were drilled 500 to 5000 feet deep, depending on the energy of the bomb. The warhead, in a long canister, was lowered to the bottom. A massive bundle of electrical cables (totaling as much as 33 miles) was used for control and for the diagnostic systems. The hole was closed by backfilling with sand and gravel. In about 10% of the tests, the explosion was initiated in a horizontal tunnel which radiated out from the bottom of the shaft. In far less than a thousandth of a second after detonation, the cables, sensors, etc., were destroyed, but not before the data had been sent to the recording stations.

Disturbing the devil in a suburb of hell

On explosion, the earth is compacted so that a large cavity is formed. Its inner surface is molten rock, which begins to flow to the bottom. As the mass cools, the fluid rock becomes a solid glass, and material falls in from the top. Thus the void works its way upward, frequently to the point where a crater is formed by subsidence. In quite a number of cases, radioactivity escaped into the air; the venting of 1970 was especially serious. Tests cost $20 million to $40 million each, sometimes more, in the 1960s and 1970s, and as much as $100 million in the 1980s. More than 650 such tests were carried out up to the end of 1986, pockmarking the Nevada desert, and inflicting a case of subterranean indigestion to our Earth.

Actually, a second kind of test evolved during the late 1980s. The earlier type was simply to explore new or modified warhead designs. These tests cost about $40 million each in the 1980s and 1990s. The new type, called "effects tests," was to investigate the effects of radiation and heat on other warheads and electronic equipment. These were supposed to insure that during an actual war, nuclear weapons would survive nuclear blasts. Effects tests involve drilling horizontal tunnels from underground blast sites, tunnels which are a mile or so long. Radiation from the nuclear bomb races ahead of the shock wave to the warhead to be tested, and then a huge blast door closes before the shock wave arrives. These tests cost about $80 million each. The weaponeers conducting these tests, as if frozen in a Cold War time zone, evidently had a nearly absolute belief that they were advancing the security of the United States.

Crater from test of underground nuclear warhead

To evaluate a test, samples of gas and solids from the cavity were withdrawn using previously drilled test holes, whose lower ends had to be rebored. Analysis of these samples by nuclear chemists established the yield (number of kilotons), efficiency (the fraction of uranium-235 and/or plutonium-239 which underwent fission), and other features. A typical test was called the Chesire experiment, and the detonation took place on February 14, 1976. It had a powerful yield of 200 to 500 kilotons, and occurred at a depth of 3830 feet, which was 1760 feet below the water table. The cavity, after much rubble had fallen in, extended high enough to reach the water table. The Soviets and other powers of course undertook their own program of underground testing of nuclear warheads.

9-34 Earth-Penetrating Bombs

In the 1950s gun-assembly type bombs were made designed to penetrate soil, concrete, etc., and explode deep down. The first model was the TX-8, with a yield of 15 to 29 kilotons. Each slender bomb was less than 15 inches in diameter. The targets in mind were fortifications, harbors, and airfields. One could go down 40 feet in sand, 60 feet in loam, and 100 feet in clay.

Later on, when the Soviets buried more and more of their key military facilities deep underground, penetrating warheads with hydrogen bombs of yield perhaps 1 to 5 megatons were manufactured. They were supposed to be able to destroy missile silos and underground communications headquarters. They would create huge amounts of lethal local fallout. These high-yield weapons have been discontinued and replaced by warheads of 1 to 10 kiloton yield. An example is the B61-11 bomb, deployed

How to eradicate moles

in 1997 and light enough to be carried by B-1B and B-2A bombers, as well as by F-16 fighter planes. The MK 11 penetration bomb, which is well streamlined, can burrow as deep as 22 feet into reinforced concrete. These are well suited for first-strike weapons.

Incidentally, nonnuclear earth-penetrating bombs were constructed just in time to use at the end of the Persian Gulf War in 1991. They were made by boring out old Army eight-inch artillery gun barrels and filling them with molten explosive. Clustered into assemblies weighing 4700 pounds, the devices, called GBU-28, were equipped with laser-guidance systems. Several were dropped by F-111 bombers on Iraqi command bunkers north of Baghdad, and they killed a number of senior officers. They are thought to be able to penetrate 50 to 100 feet of earth or 20 feet of reinforced concrete. By 2002, more advanced earth-penetrating bombs had been developed, such as the BLU-116, a 2000-pound weapon now in the U.S. arsenal. Several others are in the works, such as Deep Digger, which operates on the principles of dry drilling used in oil exploration. Once underground, the device fires projectiles like a cannon which hammer the soil, compacting earth and enlarging the hole, allowing the payload to reach close to the target (also see the Robust Earth Penetrator in 9-61).

9-35 Acceleration of the Cold War

Shortly after the first Soviet nuclear bomb test in 1949, American military preparations accelerated. More uranium ore deposits were found and stockpiled. Mammoth new gaseous production plants for uranium-235 at Oak Ridge were constructed, doubling production. Hanford doubled plutonium production. The numbers of nuclear bombs grew steadily, each generation incorporating the advantages gained from hundreds of tests. The kinds of warheads grew in number, including artillery. Later in the 1950s and 1960s, ballistic missiles were being constructed (Chapter 10). In general, the Soviets kept pace. Oppenheimer wrote, when analyzing the standoff between two great nuclear powers, that "We may be likened to two scorpions in a bottle, each capable of killing the other, but only at the risk of his own life."

During the 1950s, some higher American military officers, especially those in the Air Force, began to advocate preventive war, giving an ultimatum to the USSR, and similar appalling, bizarre ideas. During the Cuban missile crisis in 1962, an Atlas intercontinental ballistic missile (without a warhead) was launched over the Pacific for a test. Planes carrying hydrogen bombs kept a 24-hour alert. Sixty-six bombers were airborne over the Mediterranean, and others were ready for action over Greenland, Canada, and Alaska. Submarines on both sides were on alert. In 1989 Moscow revealed that 20 nuclear warheads had been transferred to Cuba. Sometimes squadrons of American bombers would fly provocatively toward the Soviet Pacific coast, only to turn back near the line marking the end of international waters. Our world was indeed fortunate to survive these irrational times until the end of the Cold War; even today, liberal doses of sanity are badly needed. Incidentally, a collection of documents covering these developments during period 1965 to 1968, amounting to more than 20,000 pages, is now available on microfiche (see under William Burr et al. in the bibliography at the end of this chapter; the cost is $4,200).

Preventive war, an oxymoron

9-36 The Red Mercury Scare

In the spring of 1995, impenetrable reports began to appear from Russia of a mysterious substance called "red mercury" whose explosive power was so great that it could implode small amounts of plutonium or cause fusion of deuterium with tritium without employing any uranium-235 or plutonium-239. Those processes without uranium or plutonium are known as "pure fusion." In another version a small amount of plutonium, far from critical size, is used. If true, either type would permit construction of lightweight bantam nuclear bombs which are relatively cheap, a genuinely alarming prospect. While the power would be tiny compared to ordinary hydrogen bombs, it would still be gigantic, and would generate free neutrons in abundance, like neutron bombs.

The available reports, which are obscure and on some points contradictory, give garbled information, but something like the following is claimed. A mixture of mercury with a double oxide of mercury and antimony (i.e., dimercuric pyroantimonate) is irradiated 20 days in a nuclear reactor, according to one report. The resulting semiliquid is mixed with an unnamed radionuclide according to another source. This material was called red mercury 2020 (a term also written as RM 20/20). This cherry-red mixture is supposed to be the explosive. Whether it is neutron or gamma ray bombardment which was employed was not specified. The material was allegedly first prepared in 1965 by cyclotron bombardment in Dubna, near Moscow, apparently by deuteron bombardment. Just how and what this activation step achieves remains a riddle.

To make a fission bomb, a tiny sphere of plutonium-239 is centered in a red mercury sphere, which is caused to explode by detonators, imploding the plutonium. A neutron generator is probably included. To make a pure fusion bomb, deuterium (as lithium deuteride) and tritium (probably as lithium tritide, or perhaps compressed tritium in a small tank) would be placed inside a sphere of red mercury, and this would be surrounded by the unique, mercury-based high explosive. Such bombs are said to weigh only 10 kilograms or so. It is said that such pure fusion bombs could be made as small as a baseball, and could pack a yield of 300 tons of TNT. These would be a type of neutron bombs, and lethal quantities of neutrons would be released. These would activate soil and other materials and generate some radioactivity. Lurid tales of smuggling red mercury to third-world countries abound; a price of $100,000 per kilogram has been mentioned. If red mercury turns out to be authentic, it would be a terrorist's dream and a dreadful development for our world.

The information is so scant that no definitive opinion on red mercury can yet be given. Experts in nuclear bomb design seem to be divided in their opinions, some claiming the whole matter is a fraud, and others thinking that there might be some unexplained phenomenon which makes the idea credible. In any case, there is general agreement that tritium should be subject to the same safeguards as plutonium and highly enriched uranium.

To succeed, the energy liberated on explosion of red mercury must be far, far higher than that of classical chemical explosives. In general, conventional explosives are made from light atoms (H, C, N, O mostly), and thus carry much energy per unit weight. Known explosives made using heavy elements tend to be sensitive, but less energetic per unit weight than, say, TNT. In the 1950s experiments on pure fusion bombs were

In the author's opinion, the chances are more than 95% that the whole red mercury matter is fortunately a hoax.

carried out at Livermore National Laboratory; the program was code-named DOVE. Success was minimal. In later years, attempts to fuse deuterium with tritium have succeeded to the extent of generating up to 10^{13} neutrons, still far short of the numbers needed for a pure fusion bomb. If such weapons are ever developed, they would transform warfare and greatly complicate nonproliferation. By 2002, nearly ten years after the first rumors appeared, the subject had disappeared from the scene.

9-37 The British Nuclear Weapon Program

Directly after the end of World War II, Great Britain renewed its earlier nuclear research in earnest. Klaus Fuchs, on returning to England in 1946, shared his knowledge of American developments with his British employers; he was, after all, a British citizen. Thus Fuchs shared his expertise with both the British and the Soviets. The McMahon Act, passed by Congress in August 1946, severely limited nuclear cooperation with the British. After the first Soviet bomb was exploded in 1949, the British were keen to join the nuclear club. The British bomb effort was led mainly by physicist William Penney, who had experience in Los Alamos during 1944-45. He became director of the Atomic Weapons Research Establishment in the 1950s and chair of the U. K. Atomic Energy Authority in the 1960s. His work notably reduced the size of the critical amount of uranium-235 needed in bombs.

In their nuclear weapons program, the scientists in Great Britain produced some of their uranium-235, and bought more from the United States. They generated almost all of their plutonium-239, but did purchase some from Canada. In the early stages of their work, they imported tritium from the USA, but later manufactured their own. Their program of course included expensive development of submarines with underwater missile launch capacity, many aircraft, and all the other components required for nuclear warfare. Altogether, 790 warheads of eight types had been produced, and perhaps 300 remain in the year 2000.

The first British test of a nuclear warhead was conducted in 1952 off the coast of Western Australia at the Monte Bello Islands. The first test of a two-stage hydrogen bomb with the Teller-Ulam configuration took place April 28, 1958. The bomb was detonated at 7700 feet near Christmas Island, and had a yield in excess of a megaton. Later, starting March 1, 1962, the British carried out some tests at the Nevada Test Site.

British bombs: fission and thermonuclear

In the early 1960s, under the thrust of the Cold War, the United Kingdom formalized a second agreement with the Australian government, permitting a series of tests at Maralinga, in south central Australia in Aboriginal lands. Nuclear powers seem to have a proclivity to conduct dangerous tests in the homelands of defenseless, less technically advanced peoples, and to be economical with the truth about the matter.

Thirty preliminary tests were conducted at Taranaki, near the south central coast. Using conventional explosives, in 12 of these tests molten plutonium metal was blasted more than 3000 feet into the air. The purpose was to test component parts of bombs in case of accidents with bomb-carrying aircraft. Nine nuclear explosions were carried out at Maralinga and nearby Emu. The British subsequently carried out a cursory cleanup operation. A team from the Australian Radiation Laboratory in 1984 checked the area and was stunned by the high level of contamination. They found fragments of equipment, one of which held three grams of plutonium. Activity levels of 10 microcuries per square meter were found. Much of this arises from the gamma rays emitted by americium-241; this point had been overlooked by the British, who had measured alpha particles only. The Aborigines will get back their land except for about 175 square miles of the most heavily contaminated part. A quarrel is in the making between Australia and Great Britain concerning who pays cleanup costs, and compensation to the Tjarutja Aboriginal tribe, who have been deprived of much of their land. In 1993 Britain agreed to pay for part of the cleanup.

Australian journalists Bartol and Knill visited Bikini in 1988 and reported the almost uncanny parallels between the indigenous people there and those in Australia. Indeed, the two peoples have formed a network to cooperate, combining their voices in opposition to nuclear tests.

9-38 The French Nuclear Weapons Program

Based on pioneering French research in radioactivity and development of nuclear bombs in the USA during World War II, the French began their nuclear program, Commissariat à l'Énergie Atomique, in October, 1945, and have pursued it vigorously. They procured uranium oxide (from African ores) from Belgium and heavy water from Norway. They recovered eight tons of uranium oxide which had been hidden in a Moroccan mine during German occupation. A nuclear reactor was built in an old fortress near Paris. The first milligram of plutonium was extracted in 1949. From the start military and civilian aspects have been integrated. Plutonium from electricity production is employed in bomb manufacture although two reactors are strictly military. Two events which stimulated the French nuclear effort were the loss of Dien Bien Phu in Vietnam in 1954 and the Suez Canal crisis of 1956. Today France ranks third in the world as a nuclear military power. Its laws differ from those in the United States in that civilians have only ineffectual means of challenging or stopping nuclear projects through Parliament.

Sources of uranium for the French nuclear program, in addition to purchase from Belgium, were first the mines in the colonies, most notably Gabon, Congo, Madagascar, Ivory Coast, and Niger. The French also helped exploit the vast, rich uranium ores at Cigar Lake, Canada. Later important sources were discovered within France itself.

Enriched uranium for civilian nuclear reactors was purchased from the United States up to the mid-1960s. Construction of a facility for separating uranium-235 by thermal diffusion was started in 1964 to get enriched fuel for submarines. Weapons-grade uranium-235 was also made for gun-assembly bombs. There are reprocessing facilities for separating plutonium from spent fuel, lithium-6 isotope separation services, tritium production plants (using lithium-aluminum alloys), and atomic vapor laser isotope facilities.

The French exploded their first nuclear warhead in 1960; this was in the Algerian Sahara desert, on a 344-foot tower. It was a fission bomb based on implosion of plutonium-239, and had a high yield (60 to 70 kilotons). Altogether, the French tested 17 warheads in Algeria, four of them in the atmosphere and 13 in tunnels. When the

Algerian Sahara was no longer available to test warheads, these studies were transferred to the uninhabited Mururoa and Fangataufa Atolls in the South Pacific in 1966. Bombs boosted with tritium came in the mid 1960s, and some of these had very high yield (several hundred kilotons). The first two-stage hydrogen bomb (yield, 2.6 megatons) was tested in 1968. Miniaturized bombs followed, and also those in MIRVed systems. The U.S. permitted the French to study the Nevada Test Site in 1957.

For the South Pacific testing, some boreholes were drilled on land, but most were drilled in the earth under water in a lagoon using a barge. The bore holes were 1.5 to 2 meters in diameter, and typically 600 to 1200 meters deep. Coral is soft, but the hole reached into the underlying basalt. In a typical test, a 70-ton cylinder containing the bomb was lowered to the bottom of the hole. A long cylinder or canister holding the diagnostic equipment (roughly five feet in diameter and 35 feet long) was lowered in the borehole, which was then plugged with rock and concrete. The French say that the molten lava formed by the blast solidifies to a glass and imprisons the fission products firmly. Geophysicist Yves Caristan of the French Atomic Energy Commission reported that a 150 kiloton blast in basalt about 1100 meters deep makes a cavity 80 meters (260 feet) across, and that 98% of the fission products are trapped in the liquid rock, which slowly solidifies. But fractures reaching several hundred meters might admit ocean water in time. After shifting to the South Pacific, they carried out 179 tests at Mururoa Atoll and 14 at Fangataufa Atoll in French Polynesia.

Nuclear weapons: the key to making a medium-sized country a major military power

As expected, the French also developed neutron bombs. This was in the period 1979-83. Their explosive yields were mostly in the 5 to 15 kiloton range. In a feeble attempt to sanitize the concept of neutron bombs, French politicians refer to them as "limited collateral effects weapons."

The person most closely associated with developing the French fission bomb was a military man, Gen. Charles Ailleret. The physicist responsible for leading the hydrogen bomb project was Roger Dautray. The chemist who developed the French extraction process of plutonium from spent reactor fuel was Bertrand Goldschmidt. The number of French warheads reached a maximum of 538 in 1991.

Today the French have the entire range of tactical and strategic nuclear warheads and the means of delivering them: aircraft carriers, several types of Mirage strategic bombers, ballistic missiles, some MIRVed missiles such as the one-megaton TN-61 in silos, command centers deep underground, seven nuclear powered submarines carrying missiles with nuclear warheads and others with conventional weapons, nuclear artillery, mobile missile-firing vehicles, a range of hydrogen bombs, neutron bombs, cruise missiles. This war machine has adequate support systems. France had a total 122 megatons in nuclear weapon yield by 1986. Clearly, France is a military force to be reckoned with.

9-39 The Controversy over Renewed Testing by France

With the end of the Cold War, France followed the U.S., Russia, and Great Britain in stopping nuclear testing. But with the election of the conservative president Chirac, the announcement was made that a series of eight tests would be made in 1995-

96. The ostensible reasons were to learn how to improve model nuclear explosions by computer and to facilitate a planned laser program (PALEN) near Bordeaux to simulate nuclear explosions. PALEN is a multibillion-dollar program to develop a laser producing million-joule beams to trigger thermonuclear explosions.

The result of Chirac's announcement was an explosion in anti-French demonstrations and outbursts. The claims just didn't ring true. Thousands of demonstrators marched through Paris. It all created quite a fuss. After the first test in the series in September 1995, criticisms poured in from around the world. There were riots in Tahiti. In Australia and New Zealand, condemnations were particularly shrill. Boycotts of French products were promoted. Ambassadors were recalled.

That 1995 test had a yield of 20 kilotons. The second test, under Fangataufa atoll on October 1, had a yield of "less than 110 kilotons." Its purpose was really to make sure that a new warhead, the TN-75 for submarine-launched ballistic missiles, worked without trouble. The third, fourth, and fifth tests, at Muruoa, had yields of 30 to 60 kilotons. The sixth test, in January 1996 at Fangutaufa, was the most powerful, 120 kilotons. It was France's 208th test.

Some opponents asked, if nuclear tests are so safe, why not conduct them under Paris?

The French nuclear establishment seems to have copied the claims of American weaponeers to the effect that their modern warheads have evolved to be so sophisticated that testing is necessary to have confidence in their successful operation. The French apparently have difficulty understanding the depth of the movement for a nuclear-free and independent Pacific. Their policies fed the discord, as for example in their refusal to permit independent groups to monitor the site by taking samples.

After the sixth blast Chirac canceled the other detonations and suddenly transformed himself into an opponent of such tests. He began to sermonize about how France would "spare no effort" to persuade other countries to prohibit "all nuclear tests." Calling France's arsenal weapons "in the service of peace," Chirac evidently never considered that India, Pakistan, or Israel, for example, might take the same lines and nuclear proliferation would go on and on.

9-40 The Chinese Nuclear Weapon Program

It has proven in general more difficult to acquire reliable information on Chinese nuclear efforts than in the case of the other major powers. The leadership of the Chinese Communist revolutionaries was alert to the attraction and importance of nuclear weapons even before their victory in 1949. Of course, at the same time it was recognized that delivery systems would also have to be developed, meaning planes, missiles, submarines (some nuclear powered), etc., and all the necessary infrastructure. From 1949 until about 1959 China received substantial assistance from the Soviet Union. Another factor stimulating rapid progress of the nuclear program was the perceived threat of attack by the United States. The official decision to manufacture nuclear bombs was made in 1955. Within a remarkably short time, considering the background of poverty, an extreme shortage of scientific personnel and apparatus, and political problems, China did succeed in constructing a creditable arsenal of nuclear warheads of several types, as well as a corresponding missile and aircraft potential.

China has produced a small but steady stream of able scientists of world-class caliber since the turn of the 20th century. Most received their later scientific education in the United States or Europe. An example is the first director of the nuclear weapons program, Qian Sanqiang. After earning an undergraduate degree in China (1936), he went to France and graduated with a doctor's degree from the University of Paris and worked at the Curie Institute with Joliot. Returning to China in 1948, Qian later became director under the Communist government of the Institute of Atomic Energy. He worked with Soviet scientists in Dubna. He was largely responsible for China's rapid progress in the nuclear field. Qian's wife, Ho Tse-hue, was also a prominent nuclear physicist.

Deng Jiaxian was a nuclear physicist who studied at Purdue University, receiving a Ph.D. in 1950. He returned to China and devised many creative designs for both fission and fusion bombs. He became an expert in detonation physics, theory of plasmas, etc. He directed at least 15 nuclear tests. Some regard him as the "father of the Chinese hydrogen bomb." Peng Huanwu, after studying in China, went to Great Britain, earning a Ph. D. degree in physics. He returned to China in 1947, and in the 1950s made important contributions to the fission and fusion warhead work. Wang Ganchang went to Germany in 1930 and returned to China with a Ph.D. degree in physics shortly after Hitler took power. In 1956 he joined a Soviet team at Dubna institute in the Soviet Union, and on returning to China participated in the early atomic and hydrogen bomb projects. Chen Nengkuan went to the U.S. in 1947 and was graduated from Yale University with the Ph.D. degree. He did not return to China until 1958, when he contributed forcefully to the atomic and hydrogen bomb work. A Deputy Director of the Institute of Atomic Energy was Qao Chungyao. After graduating with a Ph.D. in nuclear physics from Cal Tech, he observed American tests of fission bombs in the Pacific. Another Deputy Director was Qang Chiahua, Ph.D. in nuclear physics from Washington University in St. Louis. There was quite a number of such gifted individuals.

9-41 Soviet Aid to China

A preliminary geophysical survey of Xinjiang (Sinkiang) and other sites was conducted in 1949. In 1950 two uranium mines started operation near Ürümchi, the capital of Xinjiang, with Soviet aid. At first, the ore was sent to Czechoslovakia for processing, the payment being a fraction of the ore. In the early 1960s uranium mines at Chenxi and at Linxian began production, and later there were many more.

Most of the manufacturing sites were dummies to deceive the spy planes sent by the CIA with pilots from Taiwan, and also Soviet spy satellites.

In 1950 the USSR and China signed a Treaty of Friendship, Alliance and Mutual Assistance. Many Soviet advisors began to arrive and participate in numerous enterprises, especially nuclear. A Soviet nuclear reactor and a cyclotron were donated. China's first reactor began to operate in 1958. It was built near Beijing with Soviet help. It was of the heavy water type, and had a power of ten megawatts. Increasingly, the Soviets began to express their irritation at the Chinese demands for independence in regard to nuclear capacity and policy, and in rejecting joint control. These nationalistic requirements by the Chinese caused endless quarrels between the two powers and eventually caused the Soviets to withdraw their scientists and engineers in 1959-60, leaving many projects half completed.

9-42 Nuclear Self-Development in China

The Chinese accelerated their efforts to overcome the handicap of losing Soviet aid. By making great sacrifices, the Chinese completed their gaseous diffusion plant near Lanzhou to separate uranium-235, following the Soviet pullout in 1960. The plant became operational in late 1963. It produced 300 to 400 kilograms of weapons-grade uranium-235 annually, and other plants raised production to at least 1000 kilograms per year. Research began in the centrifuge method of enriching uranium in U-235, as well as other techniques. Reprocessing plants for plutonium-239 were constructed. The first of these was finished in 1955, but it used an obsolete technique (precipitation of sodium uranyl acetate) introduced by the Soviets. The Chinese rebuilt the plant, basing it on extraction using tributyl phosphate. To test the warheads made from these materials, a dozen sites were prepared in the Taklimakan Desert of Xinjiang. The first warhead was exploded on a 335-foot tower on October 16, 1964; it contained uranium-235 and had a yield of 22 kilotons. This bomb employed the implosion principle, not gun-assembly. Within a few months this model was weaponized and one bomb was tested in a drop from a plane in May, 1965.

Nationalistic pride in a first nuclear warhead test is illustrated in the following incident. The author happened to be in Indonesia when the first test by the People's Republic of China was announced over the radio. This was during lunch with a Chinese-Indonesian business man, a capitalist's capitalist. He said, with obvious pride, "No country is going to push China around anymore."

Studies of the theoretical aspects of hydrogen bombs were undertaken in 1960, and later experiments were made to test the concepts. A fission warhead boosted with tritium was tested in May, 1966, with a yield of 200 kilotons. In December of that year an explosion was made to test the design of a two-stage fusion device; its yield was in excess of 300 kilotons. The first true hydrogen bomb was tested by dropping it with a parachute from a plane on June 17, 1967. It was also a two-stage device, with lithium-6 deuteride; no plutonium was employed, only uranium-235. The yield was 3.3 megatons. A rocket was launched into the cloud to sample radioactive material. The first plutonium bomb was tested on December 27, 1968. In 1976 a hydrogen bomb was detonated with a 4 megaton yield. An ambitious missile program was undertaken. By 1984 the Chinese felt secure enough to join the International Atomic Energy Agency.

In order to carry out these accomplishments, constantly coping with insufficient trained personnel and a deficiency of equipment, the Chinese set up a series of research laboratories and institutes. Among the research laboratories are the following. The Institute of Nuclear Physics, in Shanghai, has a cyclotron, neutron-generating equipment, isotope-separation facilities, and strong cobalt-60 sources of gamma rays for studies in radiation damage, sterilization, etc. The Institute of High-Energy Physics, in Beijing, has a synchrotron, linear accelerator, subnuclear particle division, and a cosmic ray laboratory. The Institute of Atomic Energy, also in Beijing, has a cyclotron, a heavy-water reactor, a section for study of the chemistry of transplutonium elements, and facilities for preparing various radioisotopes. One section even substitutes tritium for the hydrogen in traditional Chinese herbs to aid in investigations of their medical effects. Beijing is also the site of the Nuclear Weapons Research Institute, established about the time when difficulties with the Soviets began. In so far as possible, the Chinese emphasize making their own instruments, although some are bought from the USA, Europe, or Russia. The Nuclear Power Institute of China is in Chengdu. The Chinese Academy of Engineering Physics (consisting of a dozen or so institutes), and also the Nuclear Weapons Research and Design Academy and other institutes, often considered the Los Alamos of China, are in Mianyang, situated in Sichuan in central China. Some of its work has been transferred to Haiyan. Another gaseous diffusion plant is located in Heping; a branch is also in Sichuan near Chengdu. It produced tons of weapons-grade uranium-235.

China's largest plutonium production reactor and reprocessing plant are in Guangyuan. Jiuquan, located in a desert in the north central part of the country, is the site of an Atomic Energy Complex, and it is the core of nuclear weapons production. It includes the facility for producing uranium hexafluoride for gaseous diffusion and reduction of the enriched material to weapons-grade uranium metal. It has a Plutonium Processing Plant and could be compared to Golden, Colorado (9-8C). The weapons testing site near Lop Nor in Xinjiang, developed beginning in 1959, is by far the world's largest. Its headquarters is in Malan. One might say it corresponds to the Soviet's Kurchatov City in Kazakhstan (page 479). Lithium-6 deuteride is produced in Baotou, in north central China below the Gobi desert.

Mao Zedong at first feared that the Americans might try to destroy China's nuclear facilities, and later this suspicion was enlarged to include fear of the Soviets. The government decided to create a secret "Third-Line" of more modern nuclear weapons facilities, with all necessary infrastructure. Construction of this massive, duplicate industrial base was begun in 1964 and continued until nearly 1980. It had its own uranium mines, steel-manufacturing plants, reactors, gaseous diffusion plants, reprocessing facilities, etc., all situated in western and southwestern provinces well away from more vulnerable eastern and northern facilities. The scale of the Third-Line operations surpassed Roosevelt's New Deal and Stalin's Five-Year Plans. It consumed an average of nearly half of China's capital budget from 1963 to 1975. So much plutonium was generated that production was stopped in 1991. The number of nuclear warheads in China's arsenal in 2000 has been estimated at approximately 400.

China's missile program more or less paralleled the nuclear program: starting from near zero, intense efforts with initial Soviet aid finally came up with a reliable armada of ballistic rockets. In 1990 China still had only 18 missiles (type DF-5), and these were liquid-fueled. Their warheads were stored separately. Solid-fueled missiles of the Dong Feng (East Wind) types, DF-31 and DF-41, are being built currently. Missiles remain the mainstay of China's defense, but nuclear capable aircraft were also built. All systems are being continually upgraded.

The remarkable success of the Chinese nuclear program again illustrates the futility of trying to suppress the efforts of a determined and resourceful country from acquiring nuclear arms.

9-43 China in Perspective

In August 1991 China, by then a more secure nuclear power, announced its intention to sign the Nuclear Non-Proliferation Treaty. This decision was welcomed with enthusiasm in Asia, especially by Japan. Despite this announcement, in September 1992 China tested its first tactical nuclear warhead (15 kilotons). The country tested a 90-kiloton warhead in fall 1993; this was part of its efforts to downsize its weapons to make them more accurate and easier to deploy. In 1994 China announced its intention to continue to conduct underground tests unless a Comprehensive Test Ban Treaty is negotiated. Also by 1994, the military had greatly upgraded its missile systems, converting to solid-state fuel, and equipping the rockets to carry nuclear warheads of several types, mostly DF-31 and DF-41. In summer 1999 China tested its newest missile, probably the DF-31 or DF-41, with a range of 5000 miles. The test was within Chinese territory. Its payload was 1500 pounds. An official report announced that China "had developed scores of missiles, many of which can match the leading missiles of the world." The Chinese DF-25 ICBM can reach the Midwest of the United States. They will soon have multiple-warhead capacity, if that has not already been accomplished. The mainstay of Chinese nuclear forces is the ballistic missile.

Like France, China had come under dynamic criticism for its continued testing. In August 1995 another underground blast was carried out, its 43rd. Its energy is not known with certainty, but was perhaps 50 kilotons, give or take 10 or 15 kilotons. The White House urged China to refrain from further testing. The Japanese lodged a formal protest. France's comments were muted. Two more tests at Lop Nor were conducted in 1995. One of them, directly after the fiftieth anniversary of Hiroshima, so offended the Japanese that Japan froze a proposed grant to aid Chinese development. In June of 1996, China conducted another test, and in July one more (number 47). It was announced that this was the last one, and that a moratorium on testing was now in effect.

China has all the necessary capabilities for operation bootstrap, but progress will be slow. The Chinese navy is expanding. The sensitivity of China concerning its sovereignty can at times seem exaggerated. For example, in October 1994 an American aircraft carrier was in the Yellow Sea, between the Chinese coast and two the Koreas. A Chinese nuclear submarine was detected by American electronic monitoring devices called sonobuoys, dropped by aircraft. The Chinese sent a shrill message to a U.S. military official in Beijing. It was to the effect that next time in such a situation, the Chinese would shoot to kill. This growing potential for conflict is enhanced by China's continued purchases of advanced military equipment from Russia and elsewhere. These include submarines, jet fighters, helicopters, tanks, transport planes, missiles, rocket engines, missile guidance technology, and uranium-235 enrichment technology.

From a long-range viewpoint, China seems determined to bring itself up to superpower status from the nuclear-weapon standpoint, befitting its status in the world.

Is a new Cold War possible, this time with China? Some elements of American society would welcome such a development. Signs portending this eventuality have appeared; other evidence has been to the contrary. American unease about China's future power has recently prompted a few military and diplomatic officials to discuss containment of China. Some other observers consider that a nuclear threat from China is in the making. One factor goading the Chinese to scale up its armaments is that their defense budget and military resources are far smaller than the American. Another sign of the times is that the Chinese have shown indications of backing away from any intention to sign the Non-Proliferation Treaty. After the Senate refused to ratify this treaty, the Chinese are almost certain not to sign. When pressed on the matter in May 1996, an announcement was publicized in China that continuing research on nuclear armaments is necessary in case an asteroid is heading for the Earth, and must be destroyed before hitting our planet. It was pretended that this was said seriously. Such an inventive excuse leaves the door open on the question of whether reason really stands a chance. The next 50 or 75 years might find the world with a dreadful but familiar kind of anxiety.

One development which acts as a deterrent of a Cold War with China is mutual economic investment of each side in the other's economy. Currently, numerous American businesses have been established in China, while the Chinese have as many as 3000 state-owned companies in the U.S. This web of mutual investment never took place in the case of the Soviet Union.

Anti-Chinese propaganda appears periodically in the United States, often coupled with indirect attempts to revive a new Cold War. A recent (1999) example is a 900-page Congressional report, sponsored by Representative Cox (R-CA), charging that China had been spying on American nuclear laboratories and had stolen the "secrets" of hydrogen bombs, neutron bombs, and more. The committee which compiled the report did not have a single expert on nuclear arms. All great powers spy on each other to some degree, but the claims made in the Cox report were extreme. A naturalized citizen from Taiwan, Wen Ho Lee, was implicated and dismissed from his position in Los Alamos. In December, 1999, Lee was arrested and charged with 59 counts of mishandling classified defense information, seemingly a case of overkill. After this incident, not before, the classification of the documents involved was apparently upgraded to "secret." The "mishandling" consisted of downloading the data from a secure computer to an "open" one, and related careless behavior. Similar cases were known to occur in other laboratories, as in the case of former CIA director Deutsch; these cases went unpunished. The American Association for the Advancement of Science and the American Physical Society sent letters to the Attorney General protesting mistreatment of Lee in prison, revealing that he is confined to a cell 23 hours per day and is shackled when moved about in prison, which is extraordinarily harsh handling. Three prestigious organizations, the National Academy of Sciences, the National Academy of Engineering, and the Institute of Medicine, all complained that the arrest of Lee was unfair, and that nearly all the information downloaded had already been public. How such inequitable affronts can backfire is shown by the case of Tsien Hsue-Shen, formerly a Chinese rocket scientist at Caltech. In 1955 he was labeled a Communist and deported; there were no hearings. Back in China he became the director of the Chinese missile program, and developed the Silkworm and Dong Feng missiles.

The Chinese had developed hydrogen bombs much earlier, as well as its modified form, the neutron bomb (which was tested in Xinjiang in 1988). Much of the information the Chinese were accused of stealing is available in scientific journals and on the internet. The so-called secrets have been well known for years to the Russians, the British, and the French. The publication *Arms Control Today* pointed out that the Cox report uses "little evidence and flawed logic," and that "dates of events, payloads, and dimensions are inaccurate."

The Cox report appeared just before the Senators and representatives were set to vote on ratifying the Comprehensive Test Ban Treaty. In general, those who supported the Cox report opposed the Test Ban Treaty, and this makes no sense at all. With no Test Ban Treaty, China would be free to do all the testing it wanted to perfect the warhead whose details were allegedly gained by spying. Now that the Senate killed the Treaty by declining its ratification, China and other countries are free to make more tests of nuclear bombs with impunity. The Lee case has come to be viewed as the result of a sort of anti-foreigner policy. We should keep in mind that international collaboration is the essential nature of science. Many of the creative leaders of the Manhattan Project were foreign born. Recruiting of foreign nationals into American government laboratories has by now already begun to slow down as a result of the new restrictions.

Rep. Weldon (R-PA) repeatedly and maliciously made speeches in 1999 on the House floor to attack the President and the Secretary of Energy, claiming they leaked the design of the W87 nuclear warhead to a newsmagazine. Here is some of his inflammatory, highly crafted rubbish:

> On July 31,1995, this administration, not the Reagan administration, not the Bush administration, not the Carter administration, this administration leaked the design for our W87 warhead to U.S. News and World Report. Not just the Chinese, the North Koreans, the Iraqis and Iranians, anyone who would buy U.S. News and World Report on July 31, 1995 got a documented diagram of the W87, which up until that point in time was classified.
>
> Here is the color version of what the Department of Energy released to U.S. News and World Report. This design shows in some detail the way our most capable nuclear warhead works. It shows and explains the process, it shows and locates the technology, the fuel, the process, the activity, the physics of the way America's most capable warhead would work. This was not secretly stolen by the Chinese, that this administration maintains they found in 1995. This diagram was given to U.S. News and World Report by this administration in 1995, and reproduced in *U.S. News and World Report.*

Steven Aftergood, of the Federation of American Scientists, analyzed the above statements and wrote the following rebuttal:

> Every assertion in this harangue is wrong. The "design" of the W87 warhead that appeared in *U.S. News and World Report* is not a design at all. It is an artist's conception based entirely on sources in the public domain. It was not a DOE document and could not have been given to the magazine by anyone in the Clinton Administration. Since it was never a government document, it was never classified. Nor did the underlying information originate with Hazel O'Leary or the Department of Energy. It was not "leaked" at all; rather, it came from the Natural Resources Defense Council (NDRC), which was explicitly credited by the *U.S. News* graphic artist. Christopher Paine of the NDRC confirmed that in 1995 he had indeed provided the information on which the illustration was based in 1995, and in retrospect he voiced doubts about the accuracy of the *U.S. News* artist's rendering.
>
> Although plainly false, the allegation was evidently too seductive for Rep. Weldon, an influential member of the Republican right wing, to let pass, and he erupted again and again.

The examples above demonstrate how ingrained the idea is that there are "secrets of the atomic bomb" which can be kept secret. Even the FBI, ten years after the end of the Cold War, seems to accept such nonsense.

The following data, comparing the USA and China in 1997, are from the International Institute for Strategic Studies and the Natural Resources Defense Council; the figures are about the most reliable available at the time they were published, but constantly change. They reveal some stark realities.

	Gross Domestic Product:	*Modern Tactical Aircraft:*
U.S.	$7,200 billion	4,450
China	$560 billion	697
	Military Budget:	*Transport Ships:*
U.S.	$263.9 billion	205
China	$31.7 billion	55
	Strategic Nuclear Weapons:	*Transport Aircraft:*
U.S.	7150	1070
China	484	149
	Long-Range Strategic Bombers:	*Helicopters:*
U.S.	178	7,925
China	0	513
	Ballistic Missile Submarines:	*Attack Submarines:*
U.S.	17	78
China	1	61
	ICBMs:	*Active Duty Personnel:*
U.S.	580	1,483,800
China	17	2,935,000
	Aircraft Carriers:	*Allies:*
U.S.	11 (& 1 more soon)	NATO, 18 countries Central Europe, Japan, South Korea, New Zealand, Australia
China	0	North Korea, possibly Pakistan

The whole idea of a Cold War II with China is a topic which deserves our highest priority for consideration. Contemplate the historical perspective. China has one fifth of the world's population, which is now six billion. During the past several centuries the country has been humiliated by Western powers and Japan on quite a number of occasions, and resentments on account of these affronts still simmer. China is now united as never before. Its economy is blossoming and modernizing currently at an unprecedented rate; some observers believe that within a few decades China's economy will be the world's largest. Its classical military forces and its nuclear capabilities are growing in strength. Its people are industrious and inventive. It is abundantly clear that any Cold War II with China should be avoided by cultivating the land as a natural friend.

9-44 Nuclear Weapons Efforts in Other Countries

The chief psychological factors which drive the quest for nuclear weapons by industrializing countries are power, prestige, and fear, essentially the same motives which operated between the superpowers. Historical hostilities have conditioned most countries to regard potential rivals as aggressive, diabolical, and untrustworthy. Smaller nations might view nuclear bombs as equalizers.

9-45 India's Nuclear Effort

India carried out a successful nuclear bomb test on May 11, 1974 (3-23), at the Pokaran test range in the western Rajasthan Desert. It was a plutonium-239 bomb detonated 320 feet underground. Its yield was announced as 12 kilotons, but there is evidence that it was lower, perhaps as low as 5 kilotons. The test was popular at home, but was criticized abroad. Part of the plutonium was bred in a pressurized heavy water reactor, which is a Canadian-built reactor of the CANDU type (7-7). Its heavy water was supplied by the United States. Some of the plutonium came from the 100-megawatt Dhurva reactor at the Bhabha Atomic Research Center. India has two large reactors at Tarapur, just north of Bombay, largely devoted to plutonium production, and eight other heavy-water reactors. The plutonium was extracted in Indian-built reprocessing plants. India has two reprocessing plants, the Trombay plant associated with the Bhabha center and the second at Tarapur. Together they are capable of separating approximately 180 kilograms of plutonium-239 per year. A third reprocessing plant is being prepared at Kalpakkam. All use the tributyl phosphate extraction technique (PUREX). India currently produces uranium-235 in a small, problem-plagued centrifugal plant near Mysore. India's first chief of the nuclear weapons program was Homi Bhabha, who died in a plane crash in Europe in 1966. He was a sort of Indian Oppenheimer. The chief of India's Atomic Energy Commission, appointed in 2000, is Dr. Anil Kakodkar. Previous directors have visited Israel's nuclear facilities, and some of Israel's scientists reciprocated with visits to India's. Engineer A.P.J. Abdul Kalam heads India's nuclear missile program, and helped direct India's 1998 nuclear bomb tests. He was elected to the office of President of India in the summer of 2002.

Religion or nationalism? India's Kalam was born to Muslim parents but is non-practicing

The bomb used in India's "peaceful" nuclear explosion in 1974 was large and unwieldy, but, galvanized by Pakistani research, newer models which can be delivered by plane or missile were later developed. Neither India nor Pakistan has signed the Non-Proliferation Treaty. A reasonable estimate of India's stockpile of plutonium-239 is 350 to 375 kilograms, from which possibly 55 to 110 warheads have been made, or can be assembled quickly. There is no public evidence to support these speculations, but it would be surprising if India did not have a substantial arsenal.

Little clues leak out indicating that both India and Pakistan have more extensive weapons programs than suspected earlier. Deliverable nuclear warheads can be made with less weight if modern very energetic high explosives are used for implosion and beryllium metal is used in certain parts. India imported about 100 kilograms of this metal from West Germany in 1984, and in addition has constructed its own beryllium production facility. Tritium is also produced, some for civilian purposes. Early in 1996 India conducted a successful test of its Prithvi missile, a nuclear-capable liquid-fuel rocket of intermediate range.

During 1995 United States intelligence, based largely on spy satellites, began to find evidence that India might be preparing to conduct another test of more warheads. The place being prepared was at the Pokaran site in the Rajasthan desert, where the first test was conducted. The signs were strong enough to prompt the American ambassador to caution New Delhi that this would trigger a 1994 statute, the Glenn Amendment, causing a cutoff of aid and American opposition to World Bank loans to India, as well as a series of other actions. India carried out it first test in 1998 (see 9-47).

9-46 Pakistan

Pakistan produces weapons-grade uranium-235 at its Kahuta enrichment plant near Islamabad. The facility employs the centrifugal method of isotope separation and was quite expensive. It can probably produce enough highly enriched uranium-235 for a maximum of six warheads per year. An estimated 100 to 200 kilograms of weapons-grade uranium-235 had been produced by 1992. There is evidence that Pakistan has a small reprocessing plant for separating plutonium from reactor fuel near Rawalpindi. Beryllium metal has been imported for use as a neutron reflector and bomb components. In 1987, Pakistani agents succeeded in smuggling in 800 milligrams of tritium from Germany, and this material can be used in neutron initiators and as a fission bomb booster. Dozens of high-speed cathode-ray oscilloscopes were procured one way or another from American sources. They are used to calibrate the uniformity of compression on implosion of a warhead. Considerable effort has been made to master nuclear bomb detonation techniques, including construction of neutron initiators. Chemical high explosives have been used to test implosion of dummy bomb cores.

By now, at least half of that tritium has decayed; Pakistan has probably started making its own.

All during the Soviet invasion of Afghanistan, Pakistan received enormous American military support, much of which went to the Afghan rebels. Now that that war has stopped, Pakistan probably began to feel that it is no longer to its advantage to restrain nuclear warhead development, despite the American bombing of Afghanistan in 2001-2002.

American satellites and other espionage techniques have spotted what appears to be a nuclear-storage facility in Baluchistan, in the mountains of southwestern Pakistan. Tests of high explosives which could implode warheads had been conducted nearby. Pakistan insists that its nuclear program is "essentially" for peaceful purposes.

Abdul Q. Khan, a German-educated metallurgist known to many foreigners outside of Pakistan as the father of their bomb, said that it is "correct" that they have the bomb, and is reported to have reconfirmed this status in the fall of 1991. Later Foreign Minister Sardar Ali disputed the statement, saying that while the country had all the know-how and components, it "does not have nuclear weapons and does not intend to make" them. A rumor has it that Pakistan tested a bomb at China's proving grounds. Nevertheless Kahn maintains that Kahuta is a peaceful nuclear facility and that Pakistan will sign the Nuclear Non-Proliferation Treaty if India does.

The Kashmir issue remains a thorn which festers constant dispute with India. Early in 1994 Pakistan's Foreign Minister warned of possible nuclear war over the area. India and Pakistan have concluded an agreement not to bomb each other's nuclear facilities in case they go to war again, and have exchanged lists of each other's plants.

A sidelight on Pakistan's bomb efforts is afforded by a scandal of sorts, revealed in 1991, involving The Bank of Credit & Commerce International. The Bank had built up an image in philanthropy. Its single largest donation was $10 million to a private institute for science and technology in Pakistan. It later turned out that the director of this institute was none other than the Abdul Q. Khan, mentioned above, and identified with paternity of the Pakistani bomb. Another beneficiary was a smaller foundation headed by I. H. Usmani, who directed Pakistan's nuclear programs.

In May 1990 Pakistan and India were on the edge of going to war again. The confrontation was at least as frightening as the Cuban missile crisis of 1962. United States surveillance indicated that Pakistan would carry out a nuclear strike rather than suffer another military defeat by India. The Indians had decided to stage a gigantic military exercise in the desert of Rajasthan, about 100 miles south of the Pakistani border. Pakistani officers were convinced that the Indian army had tactical nuclear weapons. They had modified some American-supplied F-16 bombers to deliver nuclear warheads. Hostilities were defused in part by American efforts. Pakistan has a few nuclear-capable M-11 missiles of Chinese manufacture.

A chief disturbance in Pakistan-American relations is the Pressler Amendment, in effect since 1990, which bars economic or military aid if the U.S. suspects Islamabad is seeking nuclear arms. In 1991-92, the U.S. cut $280 million from economic and military aid after President Bush (Senior) told Congress that he could no longer certify that Islamabad did not have nuclear bombs. Pakistan is commonly regarded as the Islamic world's most advanced nuclear power.

Here are the words of former Prime Minister Zulfikar Ali Bhutto of Pakistan, concerning nuclear bombs: "Christian, Jewish, and Hindu civilizations have this capability. The Communist powers also possess it. Only the Islamic civilization is without it. But that position is about to change. . . Even if we have to eat grass or leaves or remain hungry, we will get one of our own." Bhutto evidently agreed with Charles de Gaulle, who said "No country without an atomic bomb could consider itself independent." A Gallup poll in 1991 disclosed that 87% of the Pakistani people want their government to build nuclear weapons. The bomb has deep roots.

American efforts to mediate the antagonisms between Pakistan and India in the spring of 1994 were in general rebuffed. In March 1996 American intelligence learned of Pakistani preparations of what looked like a test site in the Chagai Hills in Baluchistan, close to the Afghan border.

The number of Pakistani nuclear warheads was estimated at 24 to 48 in 2002. Most are based on the implosion technique using uranium-235, not plutonium-239. Pakistan carried out its first tests in 1998 (see 9-47 below).

9-47 India and Pakistan Join the Nuclear Club

On May 11, 1998, India carried out (some would say, *brazenly* carried out) simultaneous tests of three nuclear bombs, and on May 13 two more (though these two are in doubt). President Clinton called the tests a "fundamental mistake." Pakistan responded with five or more tests of its own on May 28 and 30. Thus a new nuclear arms race was born. The Indian tests were made in the Pokaran Desert, where the 1974 test was carried out. Indian scientists said one test had a yield of 12 to 15 kilotons, another 43 kilotons, and the third 0.2 kilotons. The claim was made that the 43 kiloton device was thermonuclear, and that its yield had been adjusted to make it low to avoid damaging nearby villages, one being only three miles from ground zero. The other two bombs had small yields, namely 0.2 and 0.6 kilotons, approximately, but there were no seismic data to back these assertions. The fission bombs were probably fueled with plutonium-239.

Cold War redux and déjà vu all over again

Analysis of seismic data by experts outside India cast doubt on the claims concerning yields quoted above. The tests were detected worldwide, and the information permitted estimating the combined yield of the first three devices at 25 to 30 kilotons maximum, not the 54 to 57 kilotons indicated in the Indian announcements. The U.S. Geological Survey results were based on data from 125 stations. Inaccuracies in yield estimates arise from lack of knowledge about the character of the soil at the explosion site. There is doubt that any of the bombs was thermonuclear, although there is ample evidence that India had been working on such weapons. It might be that the second stage of the hydrogen bomb failed to ignite. The claims of both nations are probably inflated. Whatever the truth, though, there is little doubt that India can deploy a range of fission warheads, ultimately including successful hydrogen bombs.

Exaggerations of bomb yeilds stem from inner feelings of insecurity.

India's Prime Minister Atal Bihari Vajpayee is the chief of the Bharatiya Janata Party (BJP), currently India's largest. It is a conservative organization dating from 1980. It is aggressively anti-Islamic. The BJP received only 25.46% of the popular vote in the preceding election. It has 180 seats in the 543-member Lower House of Parliament. The popularity of the BJP shot upward to a reported 87% directly after the first nuclear tests. The euphoric flush of nuclear vainglory was short-lived. The BJP's statement that there was a "national consensus" is false; the monumental decision to test nuclear warheads was made without national debate. It seems never to occur to leaders of political parties such as the BJP that continued progress in India's economy of 9% annually will attain the coveted international prestige more surely than flaunting nuclear weaponry.

Both India and Pakistan have long felt that the Non-Proliferation Treaty is hypocritical. Why should the U.S., which has detonated more that 1000 warheads, object to the few tested in south Asia? The Indians and Pakistanis were driven not only by their mutual hostility, but also by determination to benefit from the perceived status of becoming nuclear states. In fact, their meager nuclear prowess hardly impresses the rest of the world. Another driving factor was Western attitudes of condescension and ignorance toward both countries.

The Pakistanis conducted their tests in the desolate Chagai region of southwestern Baluchistan. According to the first reports, the May 28 tests involved five (maybe six) devices, the total yield being 40 to 45 kilotons; one of them was tritium-boosted. But seismic data available to experts outside Pakistan gave smaller estimates in the range of 15 kilotons. The Pakistan government claimed that the May 30 bomb (uranium-235) had a yield of 15 to 18 kilotons; Western seismologists estimated two kilotons. Pakistani Prime Minister Nawaz Sharif, in announcing the tests, said "Today the flames of nuclear fire are all over. . . . [We] have jumped into these flames."

While mutual deterrence is a consequence of the new tests, the situation is fragile because few of the safeguards developed by the superpowers during the Cold War are in place. These include monitoring each other's progress, surveillance by satellite, and double codes for launching missiles. Suppose we wait a few years without significant progress, and India and Pakistan go to war again, which is quite possible considering their blowtorch attitudes toward each other. The result could be 20 million Pakistanis and 30 million Indians dead within a few hours, with more than 100 million killed eventually. In December, 2001, Islamic suicide terrorists raided the Indian Parliament, and threats of nuclear war were heard again. Tensions became high in mid-2002.

According to the definition of nuclear tests made under the Threshold Test Ban Treaty (9-21), the number of Indian tests in 1998 was three, and the number for Pakistan was two.

Both India and Pakistan have been developing delivery systems suitable for nuclear warfare. These include planes, missiles, and will probably include submarines in the future. India's Agni missiles have a range of 1600 miles, and its Prithvi missiles, with a 200-mile range, can hit most areas of Pakistan. The country is also pursuing programs to build cruise missiles capable of being launched from land or sea. India keeps one eye on China, which will now see India more decisively as a rival. A high-level Chinese military delegation was in India when Vajpayee announced the tests, and a blast of anti-China rhetoric then from New Delhi didn't help matters. Xenophobic BJP supporters stormed a meeting of scientists who protested the tests.

The economy of India is damaged less by the expenditures for these steps than is the case of Pakistan because India is no longer as poor as it was 25 years ago, while Pakistan is. India spends more than twice as much on its military as it does on health, education, and social welfare combined. The great tradition of Gandhi has been abandoned. About the only positive statement which can be made is that since nuclear weapons are politically unusable, neither side has gained much in military strength. In 1998 Pakistan tested its Ghauri missile, which can reach any part of India. Pakistan also has several dozen M-11 missiles, with a 170-mile range. With each country claiming that its own nuclear program is "peaceful" while the other's is "military" presents a supreme diplomatic challenge.

Around one billion dollars in foreign aid will likely be lost to India at once and much more later. Within two months after the tests, the Indian rupee had fallen 8% in value and the Pakistani rupee had dropped 20%. It is difficult to see any genuine benefit to India and Pakistan from possession of these weapons.

The latest nuclear tests have spurred development of missile and antimissile systems and submarines. In August 1999 the Indian government advocated deployment of aircraft and mobile land and sea missiles capable of delivering nuclear warheads. Such policies definitely increase the risk that nuclear weapons will be used in any future hostilities.

Remarkably, a group of 33 retired officers from the Indian and Pakistani armed forces (and one Bangladeshi) signed a manifesto including the statement: "We are of the considered view that nuclear weapons should be banished from the South Asia region, and indeed from the entire globe. We urge India and Pakistan to take the lead by doing away with nuclear weapons in a manifest and verifiable manner, and to confine nuclear research and development strictly to peaceful and beneficient spheres."

9-48 Israel

Development of Nuclear Weapons—Israel's nuclear program, masterminded by Ernst Bergmann, is surprisingly extensive considering the size and resources of the country. Its plutonium-producing reactor at an underground desert site called Dimona is aging, but it produced enough plutonium-239 to make an estimated 100 to 250 Nagasaki-sized warheads by the year 2000. Israel has not signed the Non-Proliferation Treaty. The facility at Dimona was constructed with a great deal of assistance from the French. The reactor fuel reprocessing plant was also built underground. As early as 1974 the CIA issued a report saying "We believe that Israel already has produced nuclear weapons." There is a report that Israel acquired about 100 kilograms of highly enriched uranium-235 from American sources, material which was "lost" in processing. In 1983, 15 tons of heavy water from Norway disappeared en route to West Germany. There is some evidence it ended up in India, although this is officially denied. But it is known that Israel has procured, one way or another, a great deal of Norwegian heavy water.

Hardly anyone believes that Israel does not have nuclear bombs.

Israel uses the centrifugal method for separating uranium-235, and is conducting tests with the laser technique. The country has manufactured a nuclear-capable missile called Jericho II, able to fly approximately 900 miles, as well as another, called Gabriel, with a shorter range. In May 2000, Israel successfully tested long-range, nuclear-capable cruise missiles launched from two German-built submarines. They hit targets 930 miles distant. In 1995 the country put a satellite, called Ofek-3, into orbit, thus erasing any doubt as to its ability to deliver warheads anywhere on earth. Israel uses the tributyl phosphate/PUREX process to separate plutonium.

If Iraq had hit Israel with poison gas or biological weapons during the Persian Gulf conflict (1990-91), Israel might well have responded with nuclear weapons. Had this sequence of events actually occurred, it would have vastly damaged Israel's ability to secure financial aid from the West, and would have reduced its chances of being accepted by its neighbors to zero for an indefinite time.

In September 1993 Israel and the Palestine Liberation Organization agreed to mutual recognition and to negotiate a peace treaty. Many observers feel that Israel concurred in this bold but tortured step from a sense of security made possible by its nuclear shield. The accord also demonstrated that Israel's nuclear status is not an absolute prohibition to peace in the area. Any invasion of Israel by combined Arab armies would of course be countered first using conventional weapons, and if those were not successful, devastating nuclear retaliation would be almost certain.

Israel has consistently refused to sign the Non-Proliferation Treaty, but is a signatory to the treaty to ban nuclear tests.

The Vanunu Case—Technician Mordechai Vanunu, who worked at Dimona, began to have serious doubts about his country's pledge not to be the first to introduce nuclear weapons in the Middle East. He experienced the anguish of testing the limits of loyalty to one's government when there is evidence that that government is lying to its people. He secretly made a series of photographs of the Dimona nuclear facilities just before he took a vacation to Australia and other countries in 1986. In Sydney, after contacting an Anglican church social justice community, Vanunu was contacted by the Sunday Times of London, which brought him to England. He displayed about 60 of his photos and was interrogated by British nuclear scientists about Israel's worst-kept secret. The story was that Israel had 100 to 200 nuclear warheads; other estimates are between 50 and 300 warheads. These numbers are far in excess of any reasonable need of Israel to deter aggression. There is practically no antinuclear movement in Israel.

Vanunu's punishment is indeed cruel, and does not fit the crime

The Mossad soon found out about Vanunu's activities in London and lured him from England to Rome using as bait a lovely young woman—known in the trade as a "honey trap." The woman was American-born Cheryl BenTov, known to Vanunu as Cindy. Mossad agents drugged and kidnapped him and took him back to Israel. In 1988 he was convicted in a secret trial for spying, and he was sentenced to 18 years in prison. Although the court did not require solitary confinement, the security forces nevertheless imposed this condition. For the first 2½ years, his cell was illuminated 24 hours per day. Two of his brothers were allowed to visit weekly but only with a heavy screen between the prisoner and the visitors. After 12 years in solitary, Vanunu was allowed to talk with other prisoners, but by then his mind had shown signs of psychosis and his health had been irreversibly damaged. Vanunu considered his action to be civil disobedience, saying "I am not a spy, but a man who helped all the world to end the madness of the nuclear age." Indeed,18 Nobelists, including Joseph Rotblat (3-24), have praised his "lonely courage" and noted "a moral imperative" in his case. Amnesty International observed his "cruel, inhuman, and degrading" treatment, but also acknowledged that he had violated Israel's security laws. Israeli protest movements demand his release from confinement. The European Parliament has called on Israel to release him on humanitarian grounds. Other groups, such as the Federation of American Scientists, the American Physical Society, the International Peace Bureau, a group of Israeli physicists, and others have requested his release. It should be noted that Vanunu's revelations did not damage Israel's security; if anything they reinforced the deterrent value of Israel's nuclear arsenal. For a country which claims to be a democratic nation, Vanunu's brutal treatment is a festering sore on its soul.

Incidentally, high-resolution aerial photographs of Israel's nuclear facilities, taken by a civilian satellite, were posted on the internet by the Federation of American Scientists. A photo gallery is available at *www.nonviolence.org/vanunu/photos.html.*

As might be expected, Israeli nuclear weapon production has goaded Islamic powers to heighten their own efforts. A senior Iranian official said Israel's nuclear arsenal "leaves us no choice but to acquire the same weaponry." The recent nuclearization of India and Pakistan leaves Iran and North Korea as the next prime candidates.

9-49 South Africa

We have seen that seven countries are members of the Nuclear Club (USA, Russia, Great Britain, France, China, India, and Pakistan). For a while there was another. On September 22, 1979, a mysterious flash was detected in the region of the Prince Edward Islands off South Africa by two sensors on a U.S. Air Force VELA satellite orbiting at 65,000 miles. This instrument had already detected other nuclear explosions and was believed to be reliable. At the same time a new American radiotelescope detected a "ripple" in the ionosphere which could have been made by a nuclear blast. The U.S. Naval Research Laboratory registered echoes from the Antarctic ice shelf. In November there were reports of some radioactive fallout in Australia; the thyroid glands of sheep had about five times the normal level of radioactive iodine. Later tests cast doubt on these conclusions.

Enigmatic nuclear flash

At the time, some thought that the flash could have been a test by South Africa; others pointed their fingers at Israel, or perhaps the two countries jointly. Both countries denied that they exploded a nuclear bomb. While there is no absolutely conclusive evidence that a nuclear bomb was tested, a CIA document declassified in 1990 concluded that it was. This paper indicated that it was a South African bomb with a yield of less than three kilotons. The test was carried out in darkness and under heavy cloud cover; authorities had declared the nearby harbor and naval base at Simonstown to be off-limits to the public. That a warhead was tested seems all the more probable in view of South Africa's admission in 1993 of manufacturing a number of bombs. In 1997 an Israeli newspaper reported that South African Foreign Minister Aziz Pahad admitted that Israel had helped develop the South African arsenal and that the 1979 flare was a test.

Recent reports from South Africa, which did not sign the Nuclear Non-Proliferation Treaty until 1991, give firm evidence that a facility for separation of uranium-235 had been completed at Valindaba which probably could produce enough of this material to make two or three warheads per year. The plant was shut down in 1990. There was a second nuclear facility at Pelindaba. South Africa has considerable uranium deposits. In 1977 the Soviet Union notified the U.S. that one of its surveillance satellites had spotted what appeared to be a nuclear test site in the Kalahari Desert, a report which American satellites confirmed. But seismic political changes in South Africa, bringing in a much more democratic government after1990, impelled the country to rethink its position on nuclear weapons. In 1993, the South African government revealed that it had built six (by some accounts, seven) uranium-235 fission bombs, of yield about 20 kilotons each. Up until then, vigorous denials had been made that South Africa had the bomb. According to the published reports, the warheads were finished about 1979, and none was ever tested by detonation. According to government

Imagine, a country actually gave up its nuclear bombs!

documents, all the bombs, presumably of the gun-assembly type, have been dismantled and their blueprints destroyed. The International Atomic Energy Agency has vigorously investigated this assertion and has found no basis for doubt. The uranium-enrichment facility is still in operation to make fuel for reactors. South Africa destroyed its small arsenal of uranium-235 bombs, the only case so far of unilateral nuclear disarmament.

The United States is considering buying South Africa's enriched uranium, and converting it to nuclear reactor fuel; a similar deal to purchase the enriched uranium from dismantled Russian warheads is also underway.

9-50 South Korea

As of 1998 South Korea had 20 nuclear reactors, 14 of which were in operation. The country initially had been bent on developing nuclear weapons, and in the 1970s established Daeduk Science Town with major research facilities, experimental reactors, and a reprocessing plant. These activities were curtailed under American pressure. South Korea has begun to purchase Russian uranium, a step which weakens the American veto power. The South also is considering shipping its spent fuel rods to Russia for reprocessing. South Korea is scheduled to buy two CANDU reactors from Canada, and these are capable of making weapons-grade plutonium.

On learning that Japan had imported a metric tonne of plutonium from France, the government announced that it would counter by building its own fast breeder reactor, "which we need in the long run because, like Japan, our country is lacking in energy resources." In the eyes of South Korean officials, Japan's Rokkasho reprocessing plant is ominous, and cannot be viewed merely as a strategy for energy security. An editorial in the Korean Daily said that "If Japan next acquires the capacity to build nuclear weapons any time it wants . . . we shudder at the implications for Northwest Asia."

9-51 North Korea

Some time after the war in Korea, the Soviet Union provided North Korea with experimental graphite-moderated nuclear reactors. They generated 25 megawatts of power each, but of course also produced plutonium. By changing the fuel frequently, bomb-grade plutonium could be generated. The possibility of North Korea producing even one nuclear bomb was very disturbing to South Korea, Japan, and the U.S. The North Korean reactors use natural uranium (i.e., unenriched) and are cooled with carbon dioxide. The fuel rods are clad in a magnesium-zirconium alloy. A radiochemical laboratory large enough to separate plutonium has been built; its director is Dr. Li Sang Gun. The nuclear complex is about ten miles south of Yongbyon. Separation of some plutonium has been accomplished using the tributyl phosphate extraction technique (8-9). Twenty tons of this extractant was purchased from China in 2000.

Sometimes old hostilities can be subdued.

Satellite surveillance disclosed a large excavation being prepared close to the reactor site near Yongbyon, and suspicions that a hidden, larger reprocessing plant was being built proliferated. Years of acrimonious negotiations with the truculent North Korean government followed. After the economy of North Korea dropped to the point at which some of the population was starving, difficult bargaining did produce tenuous agreements in 1994, during the Clinton administration; this was the "Agreed Framework." It was to the effect that North Korea would receive two American pressurized-water reactors (1000 megawatts each) to ease the energy shortage, as well as fuel oil (500,000 tons annually), and also a certain amount of foodstuffs. The reactors were financed mostly by South Korea and Japan. In 1997 officials from North Korea, South Korea, Japan, and the United States broke ground for the construction of the reactors in Kumho, on the North's isolated northeast coast near the border with Russia. North Korea agreed to abandon any plans it had to construct nuclear bombs. The 8000 spent fuel rods from the old reactors were also removed, and the International Atomic Energy Agency will be allowed to conduct inspections. No fuel for the new reactors will be delivered until the International Atomic Energy Agency is satisfied that all is in order with the old reactors. American experts were also permitted to inspect the excavation near Yongbyon. It was found to be a tunnel complex, and to be empty: no equipment was there.

With the second Bush administration in 2000, relations with North Korea degenerated. Right-wing ideologues shamefully overestimated North Korea's nuclear capabilities. By 2002, construction of the reactors was still in lethargic progress.

9-52 Two Islamic Antagonists: Iraq and Iran

Iraq—As Iraq's French-built nuclear reactor, of the so-called Osirak type, was nearing completion, it was destroyed by Israel on June 7,1981. Eight bombers, each carrying two 2000-pound bombs, were escorted by six fighter planes. The first bombs were fused to go off on impact with the concrete shell. The rest of the bombs entered the holes blasted out and thus exploded inside. One French engineer was killed. The reactor was about 14 kilometers from Baghdad.

Iraq had two other small reactors (power less than 5 megawatts). They were at Al Tuwaitha, near Baghdad. One was a Soviet model, the other was French. These reactors were destroyed during the Persian Gulf War, but their enriched uranium had evidently been removed beforehand. Iraq had earlier signed the Non-Proliferation Treaty, and had allowed United Nations inspectors to visit the facilities. A great deal of hype was published in the American press during the Gulf war, suggesting that Iraq would have a nuclear arsenal soon. Iraq had been working to acquire nuclear capability for about 15 years, and had evidently made some primitive calutrons (3-9). Urenco centrifuges of German design to separate uranium-235 had been acquired, but they had not became operational. Bombs can be constructed with less than state-of-the-art technology. A team of Iraqis experienced with computer modems was trained to become hackers, and they were able to transfer a great deal of design data from Germany to Baghdad on uranium enrichment via centrifuges, thus evading export control restrictions.

The drive to become nuclear-capable was so strong that Iraq spent enormous funds from its petroleum revenues toward this end. In 1990 the British seized some Iraq-bound krytons, capable of being used to trigger nuclear bombs. After the Gulf war, inspections revealed additional facilities at Tarmiya, Mosul, Al-Qaim, Al-Atheer, and other sites; some of these were demolished by the United Nations after the war. A "secret uranium mine" was alleged to exist at Akashat, but this turned out to be a hoax.

A United Nations inspection team claimed that the Iraqis had even begun research on separation of lithium-6, which is only used to make tritium and hydrogen bombs. There are unconfirmed reports that by March 1992 Iraq had recruited 50 nuclear scientists from the former Soviet Union. There is also evidence that Iraqi scientists had deliberately deceived Saddam, leading him to believe that they had made much more progress than in truth they had.

The earliest chief nuclear scientist in Iraq's program was Dr. Khidhir Abdul Abas Hamza, who was trained in physics and nuclear science in the United States (MIT and Florida State University). He returned home in 1970. Living in a police state, scientists who had brought back foreign wives were ordered to divorce them and marry Iraqi women. Hamza fled Iraq in 1994 and in summer 1998 was accepted by the U.S. He wrote a chilling account of Saddam's nuclear effort which exaggerated his own role in it (see Bibliography at end of chapter). Another leading nuclear scientist was Dr. Hossein Shahristan. He was a man of conscience and resigned rather than comply with orders to make uranium-235 warheads. He was arrested and spent ten years in prison, when he managed to escape in 1991. At least one senior scientist, J. D. Jaafar, was deemed not productive enough and was arrested and tortured. The main weapons laboratory was built at Al Atheer. The number of scientists and engineers rose from 400 to 7000. Most of the installations at Al Atheer were not damaged by the American bombings of the Gulf War.

Some Iraqi scientists lived perilous lives.

Iraqi armies overran Kuwait in August, 1990, and by March, 1991 had been driven out by a coalition of forces, mostly American. To help drum up pro-war public support in the United States, the Bush (Sr.) Administration shamelessly manufactured propaganda to the effect that Iraq was on the verge of manufacturing nuclear weapons. It was believed that the only fissile materials in Iraqi hands were 12.3 kg of 93% uranium-235 (in metallic form) of French origin, and 10 kg of 80% uranium-235 (in oxide form) of Soviet origin. The Iraqis had also salvaged about 12 kilograms of enriched uranium from the Osirak reactor, but it was not of bomb grade.

Although the amount of uranium-235 was sufficient for one or maybe two gun-assembly bombs, the Iraqis did not yet have sufficient background in nuclear matters to manufacture one. During this time there were around 500 nuclear bombs on board U.S. ships in the area, and another 100 in Turkey on American bases. If Saddam Hussein had used even a single bomb, and this is an enormous if, the nuclear retaliation would have been swift and deadly. Deterrence was thus far more than sufficient.

During the Gulf War, Newsweek magazine reported that Gen. Schwarzkopf requested a nuclear bomb be exploded high over Baghdad to generate an electromagnetic pulse (9-29), but this proposal was rejected. Early in the bombing phase, Iraq's defenses were blinded. The war claimed the lives of perhaps 100,000 Iraqi military personnel and a like number of civilians. Major motivation for the war, aside from considerations based on oil, stemmed from the Pentagon, which was encumbered with huge stockpiles of surplus weapons and ammunition. Moreover, it was getting more difficult to justify additional funding from Congress.

Only three years after the Gulf War, the sands of history had already deflated its righteousness, exposed the overestimation of Iraqi power, and caused many Americans to come to think of it as almost inconsequential. By summer 1995 there were stories in the press to the effect that Iraq had again launched a crash program to acquire nuclear weapons. This pathetic effort was to be achieved by taking the fuel from Iraqi nuclear reactors, right under the noses of international inspectors. It was an exercise in virtual unreality. Late in 1995 reports surfaced that Iraq had also tried to develop radiological weapons. Even if true, it would have not amounted to much. A United Nations arms inspector characterized the idea as "a pretty dumb weapon." In summer 1997 a report by the General Accounting Office further deflated bloated claims made during the Gulf War about the effectiveness of high-technology weapons: aircraft, smart bombs, the F-117 stealth fighter, and other systems.

More intrigue and propaganda

Many American veterans returning from the Gulf War complained of sickness (Gulf War syndrome). This was commonly attributed to the tons of depleted uranium spread over the country by American munitions. Saddam Hussein had positioned reservoirs of nerve gas and biological weapons in the south of Iraq, and some of these were hit during American attacks. It might be that these materials are responsible of some of the Gulf War syndrome.

Khidhir Hamza in the U.S. has kept track of Iraqi progress in making nuclear armaments. In 2002 he reported to the Foreign Relations Committee that Saddam was completing centrifuges to separate uranium-235. If successful, peace in that region of the world would become a step more fragile, as it did in the India-Pakistan balance.

In 1998 the U.N. inspectors were forced to leave, but a senior inspector, Scott Ritter, was satisfied that the Iraqi nuclear program was dead and buried. This point was ignored by the second Bush administration in its drumming up support for a new attack on Iraq in 2003.

Iran—It was in 1959 when Iran began acquiring nuclear reactors (section 7-34), and there is evidence that investigations related to starting a nuclear weapons project began about 1991. There is a small experimental reactor at Tehran University, as well as investigations of reprocessing nuclear fuel. Visiting scientists from Russia, China, North Korea, and Pakistan support Iran's efforts. There are so many from North Korea that a resort on the Caspian coast is reserved for them. Samples of uranium taken by U.N. inspectors from several laboratories in 2002 tested far too high in uranium-235 content to be compatible with use as ordinary nuclear fuel. Iran has mineral sources of uranium. Several factories strongly suspected of conducting bomb research are concealed. Iran has contacted several European manufacturers, asking to purchase machines which can forge uranium metal or means to handle dangerously radioactive materials. Inquiries were made about switches which could be used in triggers for nuclear warheads. Mohamed ElBaradei, director of the International Atomic Energy Agency, criticized Iran for hiding so much of its nuclear efforts. Satellite photos have revealed what appear to be centrifuges for separating uranium-235 in Natanz. IAEA officials were finally allowed to visit the plant, and they found 160 assembled centrifuges and components for 1000 more. An Iranian exile group revealed a secret site near Arak, in western Iran, which has a special nuclear reactor to make plutonium. About 35 miles away is a plant to separate heavy water, the standard source of deuterium.

Considering the above information and Iran's considerable wealth from petroleum sales, it seems very likely that the country is determined to manufacture nuclear weapons, despite having signed the Nuclear Nonproliferation Treaty in 1970. In 2003 Iran's Foreign Minister declared: "Allegations that Iran was working with countries in order to attain nuclear technology are sheer lies."

9-53 Latin America

Of the Latin American countries, Argentina has had the most advanced nuclear program. It has a gaseous diffusion plant at Pilcaniyeu, near the border with Chili. There is a pilot plant for reprocessing reactor fuel to separate plutonium. Brazil also has an accelerated nuclear program, which includes a centrifugal enrichment facility for uranium-235 at Aramar. Neither country has signed the Non-Proliferation Treaty. The recent near bankruptcy of Argentina makes any nuclear bomb program even less tenable.

In a momentous development, both countries in 1990 abandoned their efforts to make nuclear bombs. Each country has agreed to permit the other to inspect its nuclear facilities. The fate of 220 kilograms of enriched uranium purchased by Brazil was not revealed.

9-54 Algeria and Syria

In 1991 American intelligence learned of a 40-megawatt reactor capable of making weapons-grade plutonium near Ein Ousseira in Algeria. It was built with Chinese aid. Beijing has also announced an agreement with Syria to build a research laboratory. While it is conceivable that these reactors are intended for medical and other peaceful purposes only, realities of the modern world indicate otherwise.

9-55 Vietnam

Vietnam has only an embryonic nuclear program, none of which is weapons-oriented so far as is known. Incidentally, when American forces retreated from South Vietnam in 1975, about three ounces of weapons-grade plutonium-239 was left behind. The material is stored at the Dalat Nuclear Research Institute. The present government says not to worry; it is stored safely.

9-56 Japan

A shift rich in historical irony has forced us to think the unthinkable. Strict opposition to the spread of nuclear weapons has been the lodestar of Japanese foreign policy. But in the summer of 1993, at a summit meeting of the Group of Seven leading industrialized nations, Japanese officials seemed to begin edging away from nuclear pacifism by declining to endorse indefinite extension of the Non-Proliferation Treaty. They pointed to the nuclear program of North Korea, just as that country cited Japan's stocks of plutonium as a threat to its security. Some officials expressed fears that Japan will find itself "naked with other countries having increased nuclear capabilities," in an over-armed world. These sentiments are expressed mostly by conservative, nationalistic elements.

There is no doubt that Japan could quickly manufacture a family of nuclear warheads if a decision is ever made to do so.

Reference has been made (7-16) to Japan's fast breeder reactors, Joyo and Monju. Depleted uranium, with only about 0.2% U-235, was chosen for the blankets. Thus absorption of neutrons by U-238 produces Pu-239, and is accompanied by only a low rate of fission of U-235. If the blanket is changed frequently, the result is production of plutonium of isotopic composition about 98% Pu-239 and 2% Pu-240. Such plutonium would emit a low level of neutrons by spontaneous fission (see 7-13), and be ideal for nuclear bombs, especially tactical bombs. There is an estimated 40 kilograms of high-quality plutonium in the blanket of Joyo, and extracting it by reprocessing was originally scheduled. Still more such plutonium could become available from Monju.

When it became public knowledge that Japan planned to produce bomb-grade plutonium in reprocessing the blankets from breeder reactors, there were poignant protests at home and abroad. In the end the government announced that it aims to develop a new kind of nuclear fuel cycle which does not produce pure plutonium, and thus avoid the potentially dangerous, destabilizing steps.

Another worrisome development was the statement of Hiromi Yuzawa on resigning from Japan's Atomic Energy Commission: "They [government officials] were constantly asking us for permission to do basic research on how to build an atomic bomb. Naturally I rejected the idea."

In the spring of 2002 there was still another rumble from Japan, reflecting continuing debate on Japanese nuclear neutrality. Discussions had been taking place in certain government circles concerning whether Japan should break a half-century of pacifism and amend the constitution to permit manufacture of nuclear weapons. This turn of events was stimulated by the rising nuclear power of Asian nations, especially China. Remarks by the Prime Minister's chief aide, Yasuo Fukuda, indicated that a shift in security policies is under way.

9-57 Germany

Acquiring nuclear arms by Germany has been much more muted than in most other countries, advocacy being limited to ultra-nationalists so far. This situation could change if Russia begins to take on a totalitarian character. Several American scholars suggest that such weapons in Japanese and German hands would help maintain peace by making the countries more secure and more cautious. But such a development would also encourage many other nations in the world to go nuclear.

9-58 Proliferation

Just as any country which has a relatively high level of scientific and industrial development can, if a policy decision is made for the necessary expenditure of time and effort, manufacture ballistic missiles, it can also fabricate fission bombs. Reprocessing spent reactor fuel to separate plutonium can be carried out on a small scale and is no obstacle. The following countries have built and successfully operated reprocessing facilities: Argentina, Belgium, Brazil, Canada, China, France, Germany, India, Iran, Iraq,

Israel, Italy, Japan, North Korea, Pakistan, Russia, Sweden, Taiwan, United Kingdom, and the USA, and either have or could, in time, construct nuclear weapons. In some such cases, progress in developing a nuclear arsenal would be accelerated by help from a major power. In the eyes of quite a number of underdog countries, nuclear weapons are the great equalizer. Uranium is widely distributed on Earth, and ores are easy to purchase. There are no scientific secrets which would delay progress for long, although all countries pretend that this is so. Smaller countries, with less abundant resources, would experience economic deprivation and lower standards of living in attempts to create a bomb. A number of Third World countries have scientific elites trained abroad. Some Western countries, most prominently Germany, has been selling technical products and services to almost any buyer. These include computers, beryllium, centrifuges, krytons, complete nuclear reactors, and much more. The Reagan Administration actually tried to pressure the United Nations into freezing the budget of the International Atomic Energy Agency and its funds for safeguarding inspections around the world.

Countries, aside from the above which would probably be capable of manufacturing their own nuclear weapons in time, include Spain, Switzerland, Holland, Canada, Australia, Sweden, and Finland. Others which might also succeed, but require more time, include Norway, Poland, the Czech Republic, Egypt, and Mexico. After the end of World War II, Switzerland actually considered building its own nuclear weapon system, an idea which was strengthened after Germany rebuilt its economy. It wasn't until 1988 that the Swiss gave up its modest nuclear ambitions. Sweden undertook a nuclear weapon program early on, but soon shut it down.

Security through secrecy is an illusion.

Indonesia, whose economy became quite robust for a period of 15 years or so, undertook the construction of several nuclear reactors and might have considered taking steps toward building its own nuclear bombs except for its now-depressed economy. The idea that separation of uranium-235 from uranium-238 to the degree of weapons-grade enrichment is beyond the capability of all but advanced industrial countries is incorrect; advances in centrifuge techniques have made it possible for smaller countries to succeed.

Several countries manufacture ballistic missiles. India's Prithvi has a payload of 2000 pounds and a range of 150 miles. Brazil, Egypt, India, North Korea, and Taiwan also make missiles. In 1993, Brazil became the sixteenth country to launch a satellite into Earth orbit.

9-59 Numbers of Bombs, Tests and Total Yield

How many nuclear warheads have been made and how many exist now, counting all those in our world? Precise figures are lacking, but the Natural Resources Defense Committee has made an inventory based on the best data available. The table below, which has been abbreviated, gives the number of nuclear bombs at the end of 1945 and for each fifth year following. The few made in India and Pakistan are not included.

The totals in the table are expanded in graphical form under it. Note that in 1967 the number of warheads reached a bit more than 40,000 and then actually decreased somewhat, but soon began to build up again. In 1986 the number of warheads in the world reached a maximum of 69,490 and has been decreasing ever since. The number of warheads in the world was reported as 36,110 in 1997, but since many in Russia are non-operational due to neglect, the number which is operational in the global stockpile, at the end of 2000, is estimated to be between 22,000 and 30,000.

Global stockpiles of nuclear warheads

Year	U.S.	Soviet Union	U.K.	France	China	Total
1945	6	-	-	-	-	6
1950	369	5	-	-	-	374
1955	3,067	200	10	-	-	3267
1960	20,434	1,605	30	-	-	22,069
1965	32,135	6,129	310	32	5	38,611
1970	26,492	11,643	280	36	75	38,526
1975	27,235	19,443	350	188	185	47,401
1980	23,916	30,062	350	250	280	54,858
1985	23,510	39,197	300	360	425	63,792
1990*	21,781	37,000	300	505	435	60,021
1995*	14,111	27,000	300**	485	425	42,321

**The years marked with an asterisk indicate that the numbers include active, operational warheads, retired warheads awaiting dismantlement, and weapons in reserve.*
*** In 1999 the UK's Strategic Defense Review announced that this number has been reduced to fewer than 200.*

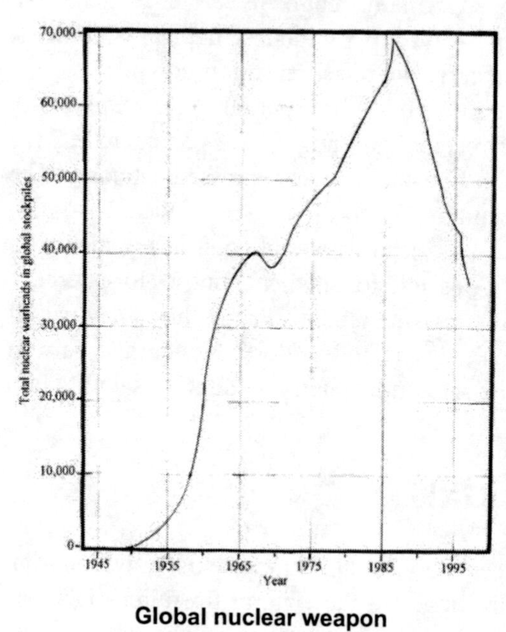

Global nuclear weapon stockpiles, 1945–1997

In the early stages of accumulating nuclear bombs, there were always more potential Soviet targets than American warheads. By the middle 1960s, the reverse situation prevailed. Sometimes dozens of warheads were aimed at the same target, even though a single bomb would be sufficient to render the installation inoperable.

There are seven acknowledged nuclear-bomb powers: the United States, Russia/Soviet Union, Great Britain, France, China, India, and Pakistan. One might think that since each country carefully monitors the test explosions of the others, we would have an accurate account of their total, but this turns out not to be the case. Some warheads were of small yield, a few of them being hydronuclear (see 9-61) which were buried deeply, and there might have been doubt as to whether a seismic wave detected far away was caused by a genuine nuclear explosion. Hydronuclear tests are omitted from the list. Another source of confusion was simultaneous detonation of several warheads in one shaft or nearby shafts. By 1996 the United States, France, and Russia had released previously secret data, so more accurate information is available today. So far as is known, 2051 nuclear tests have been carried out since 1945; this does not count the two which destroyed Hiroshima and Nagasaki.

Concerning multiple warheads in a single test, the 1990 Protocol on the matter adopted as an addendum to the Threshold Test Ban Treaty, defined the meaning of a test explosion. According to this document, a test is either the explosion of a single bomb or two or more bombs fired within 0.1 second of one another and within the area of a circle having a radius of one kilometer. The test yield is the combined yields of all bombs in the test explosion.

In 1993 the Department of Energy shed another cloak of Cold War secrecy and revealed that the United States had actually tested 204 warheads more than had been publicly announced. Of the 1030 American tests, 27 are classified as peaceful. Quite a number had multiple bombs exploded simultaneously.

Included in these 204 unannounced tests are several underground shots outside of the usual proving grounds. These included two near Hattiesberg, Mississippi, two in Colorado, three near Amchitka, Alaska, and three in New Mexico. The U.S. and British tests totaled 1054, and altogether 1149 bombs were detonated. This means that 95 bombs were exploded in multi-bomb tests.

Very recently, Russia released a list of Soviet tests, which totaled 715. Of these, 124 are regarded as peaceful. The Russians recognized the Protocol of the Threshold Test Ban Treaty in regard to multiple bombs exploded simultaneously; they too conducted many multi-bomb tests. Although the Soviets carried out 715 tests, they detonated 969 bombs, meaning that 254 were exploded in multi-bomb tests. Sometimes as many as eight warheads were placed in the same shaft or tunnel. A curious development was that during the Cold War the United States routinely announced only a fraction of the Soviet tests which were actually detected, presumably to conceal how sensitively its detection facilities functioned. This deception persisted despite widely published reports from Sweden and other countries, as well as private organizations, which gave complete data.

The French published a complete list of tests its military carried out up to 1991. Since that date most of the French tests, carried out in the South Pacific, were devoted to improving nuclear explosion yields using tritium. This was conducted for the French warhead known as TN 75, to be fitted into submarine-launched missiles. The recent Chinese tests seem designed to raise yield-to-weight ratios and to improve safety features. China is also developing multiple independently-targeted reentry vehicles.

The numbers of tests carried out during the half-century following World War II by the various nuclear-capable countries are given in the table below. The date 1963 refers to the beginning of the Limited Test Ban Treaty which halted tests in the atmosphere by its signatories.

Just look at the data on the next page. Nearly 70,000 nuclear bombs at one point in time, and the equivalent of more that 500 million tons of TNT expended in more that 2000 tests. Now ponder the meaning of all this, and what it tells us about the nature of human beings, willing to seriously risk the deaths of hundreds of millions of people.

Numbers and distribution of nuclear tests, 1945–1996

	U.S.	USSR	Britain	France	China	India	Pakistan
1945 through 1963							
Air and space	215	219	21	4	0	0	0
Underground	132	2	2	5	0	0	0
1964 through 1998							
Air and space	0	0	0	46	23	0	0
Underground	683	494	22	155	20	4	2
Totals, 1945–1996	**1030**	**715**	**45**	**210**	**43**	**4**	**2**
Grand Total: 2049							
Percentages	50.3%	34.9%	2.2%	10.2%	2.1%	0.2%	0.1%

Notes on above table: *The bombs which destroyed Hiroshima and Nagasaki are not included (because they were not tests). The world total nuclear explosion yield, up through 1998, was 427.9 megatons in the atmosphere and outer space, 82.4 megatons underground, totaling 510.3 megatons.*

It is instructive to compare the total bomb yields in megatons of TNT (9-4). For the period 1945 through 1995, the yields of all bombs are estimated as follows

United States—179 megatons
Soviet Union—285 megatons
Britain—8.9 megatons
France—14 megatons
China—23.4 megatons
Total—510.3 megatons

Keeping in mind that the Hiroshima bomb had a yield of 15 kilotons (15,000 tons) and that the above total is 510.3 megatons (510,300,000 tons), we see that the total explosive energy released by Cold War testing was equivalent to that of more than 34,000 Hiroshima-sized bombs.

As an aside, we might mention a recent analysis of the mysterious explosion high above the Tunguska River in Siberia in 1908 which has shed some light on that event. It felled trees over an uninhabited area of approximately 860 square miles. At first the falling object was thought to be a comet, but modern data from NASA undermined this idea. Measurements of the density of Halley's comet showed it to have a density about the same as that of ice. The explosion over the Tunguska occurred at an altitude of six miles, and its energy was10 to 20 megatons. This information is inconsistent with the behavior expected of a comet. The falling object was probably a stony meteorite or miniature asteroid somewhat more than 100 feet in diameter, and traveling at around 10 miles per second.

9-60 How Much Potential Nuclear Explosive Power?

The United States possessed an amount of fissile materials in 1960 equivalent to 19,000 megatons in yield. Since that date, the amount had been cut down, and is currently somewhere around 5,500 megatons actually in warheads. This reduction is a consequence of the much greater accuracy of modern rocket delivery systems, especially MIRVs. This means the total lethality has risen sharply despite less megatonnage.

The United States has more than 500 metric tonnes of weapons-grade uranium-235 and 120 metric tonnes of plutonium-239. Estimates of Soviet amounts were near these figures, but Viktor Mikhailov, head of the Ministry of Atomic Energy, said in 1993 that their stockpile of uranium-235 was closer to 1200 metric tonnes. In 1967 the number of American warheads, after a prolonged orgy of production, peaked at about 32,500; the number has been reduced by retiring some tactical and sea-launched missiles. Nuclear warheads in 1991 numbered close to 19,000, and arms control initiatives reduced that number to about 6,300 by 2000. Although the number of warheads has been reduced somewhat, they are much more accurately targeted, and the lethality is greater. The Department of Energy announced in 1990 that no more weapons-grade plutonium would be produced.

Joseph Rotblat, leader of the Pugwash group of scientists and Nobelist in Peace in 1995, with all the human species in mind, stated the matter succinctly: "If we were stupid enough—or mad enough—to accumulate [more than 50,000 nuclear warheads], who can assume that we would not be mad enough to use them, even if this would be global suicide?"

A new technique for recycling warheads was developed at the Livermore laboratory in 1991. Formerly, each new type of warhead had each component custom made, a costly procedure. Parts were not interchangeable. The recent change will permit the cores of older warheads to be repositioned in more modern designs without rebuilding. One effect is to render the Rocky Flats plutonium works unnecessary.

Tens of thousands of warheads!

The Soviet Union had an estimated 7,750 megatons total yield in perhaps 25,000 warheads, according to estimates of about 1988. But after the Cold War, there have been some claims that the true number was at one time as high as 45,000 warheads.

An estimate of the total megatonnage yield of nuclear weapons in the entire world as of 1989 was 10,000 to 13,000 megatons. It is estimated that there were nearly 70,000 nuclear warheads in the world at the time when they peaked. By 1995, more than 100,000 nuclear warheads had been manufactured by the various nations with the capability to do so, but this figure counts recycled bombs.

Between 1945 and 1986 the United States produced approximately 60,000 nuclear warheads of 71 different types. As mentioned above, this number has been reduced, but their deadliness has increased. Some 90,000 people were employed in manufacturing these weapons. Undoubtedly, target lists have been promulgated to justify larger strategic nuclear forces.

In 1996 the Department of Energy revealed that between 1944 and the end of 1995 the United States had produced 104 metric tonnes of weapons-grade plutonium, acquired 5.7 tonnes from foreign countries, and 1.7 tonnes from the nuclear power industry, making 111.4 metric tonnes total. Continued production of plutonium-239 is accompanied by the inevitable accumulation of fission products. This is high-level waste, in the form of solution or sludge after chemically extracting the plutonium (reprocessing). The French have a reprocessing plant at Cap de la Hague, and the English have one at Sellafield. The Japanese are constructing a reprocessing plant at Rokkasho; it is expected to be completed during the year 2005.

Those who think all this armament will insure peace should contemplate the belief of Alfred Nobel, who concluded that his invention of dynamite would prevent future wars. Similar ideas were often expressed following the bombing of Hiroshima and Nagasaki.

9-61 Hydronuclear and Hydrodynamic Testing

With the growing sophistication of computers, programs with numerous parameters which simulate nuclear explosions were gradually developed. The variables are tied to the performance of actual explosions insofar as possible. Very small explosions, meaning those with yield starting at only about four pounds of TNT, have become known as hydronuclear tests. The term hydronuclear arises because it represents the beginning of the point where the bomb materials behave like a fluid under the high temperature and pressure from the chemical explosive used (the prefix hydr- or hydro- having its original meaning of water or any other fluid). The upper limit of yield is not exact, but is generally a few tens of pounds of TNT. These and others up to a yield of few hundred tons give crucial information about the functioning of the warhead and help develop bombs without carrying out full-scale tests. It is well to keep in sight that the "few hundred tons" mentioned refer to the energy of that amount of TNT on exploding. The smaller hydronuclear tests can be confined, and are not detectable by distant sensors. They date from 1960-61, when 35 tiny nuclear tests were secretly carried out; this was during a three-year moratorium agreed to by the U.S., Britain, and the Soviet Union. The explosions were carried out 20 to 30 meters underground, the nuclear yields being around a thousandth of a pound in most cases, but nearly half a pound in one case. The British made similar tests in Australia.

The yield from that four pounds of of TNT is only 0.000,002 kiloton!

According to computer modeling, it is possible to make low-yield fission bombs using as little as 1 kilogram of 93% uranium-235 or 0.5 kilogram of plutonium-239. By using an efficient neutron reflector, addition of tritium, and especially vigorous compression, it has proved actually possible to make as little as 1 kilogram of plutonium-239 explode, not just in theory, but in practice. The yield of such a bomb might be about 1 kiloton. This technique could be attractive to a nation which is desperate for a bomb but which has only small amounts of fissile metals. The metals would be fashioned as hollow spheres which collapse on implosion, allowing exceptional acceleration and consequent compression. This compression would not be expected to be uniform, and to be greatest in the center where it is most effective. Presumably there would be a neutron generator inside, and boosting by tritium. The yield of such bombs might be around 0.1 kiloton, that is, equivalent to a 100 tons of TNT. This is tiny

100 pounds of TNT, just a little bomb?

compared to the larger fission or hydrogen bombs, but still capable of causing enormous havoc to a city. Depending on the level of sophistication of the imploding high explosive, 2 kilograms of weapons-grade uranium-235 can produce a 1-kiloton yield. Actually, American testing in Nevada during the 1950s resulted in several explosions of 300 to 500 tons yield. Examples are the tests known as Pascal-B (August 27, 1957) and Coulomb-C (December 5, 1957). During the development of nuclear artillery one stage was a 7-inch shell with a yield of 100 tons of TNT.

Still another aspect of testing low-yield warheads is deliberate designing an assembly to undergo a chain reaction which is self-sustaining only for an instant, or come right up to that point. The compression is designed to attain a state just short of supercritical, that is, no sustained chain reaction. Data from such studies can be employed in construction nuclear bombs which have high yields. The U.S. is building a testing center, dubbed the Dual Axis Radiographic Hydrodynamic Test Facility, at Los Alamos, funded at $48 million. In this operation two X-ray machines produce beams which intersect in a warhead, making moving pictures of the compression of the fissile metal on implosion (cf. 9-5). Such work during the post-Cold War period seems to have little trouble in getting funds. The weaponeers requested authorization for six underground tests in which the implosion stops just short of triggering the chain reaction (zero yield tests). One must keep in mind that seismic data cannot determine what fraction of the energy from an underground explosion was nuclear.

Aside from the Dual Axis Radiographic Hydrodynamic Test Facility mentioned above, there are still other related test programs. These include the following: Advanced Hydrotest Facility (4 to 6 axes, $422 million); Low-Yield Nuclear Experimental Research facility and the Big Explosives Experimental Facility for larger scale experiments, both to be built in Nevada; Explosive Components Facility, (Sandia Laboratory, $27.8 million); Contained Firing Facility (a single-axis pulsed technique, $48.5 million); High Explosives Applications Facility (Livermore); Flash X-Ray (Livermore); and at least three other related laboratories pursuing these small-scale nuclear bombs. On May 9, 2003, the Senate Arms Services Committee voted to repeal the Spratt-Furse Amendment, which had banned research and development that could lead to production of low-yield warheads. Sometimes one feels that the end of the Cold War is slipping into reverse.

All nuclear powers, but especially the United States, have been conducting research programs on new types of chemical high explosives. The objectives are to develop explosives with extraordinarily high values of energy per unit weight (to implode small, subcritical charges), to find those whose storage life is longest, and to be sure that while highly energetic, the materials are rather insensitive to mechanical shock, as in an airplane crash. An example of the newer explosives is triaminotrinitrobenzene. The chemistry and technology emerging constitute closely-guarded and classified branches of weapons development. Another area for research has been inventing means of more uniformly detonating the spherical surface of the high explosive charge used for implosion. Raising the number of detonator points from 32 (as in the Trinity bomb) to 60 or 90 or more makes the imploding shock wave more nearly spherical. One result of this research was to reduce the amount of necessary high explosive in implosion warheads to levels as low as 15 to 40 pounds.

At the bomb-pocked Nevada Test Site, with its labyrinthine tunnels, subcritical tests were undertaken beginning in July, 1997. A suitable amount of chemical explosive (160 pounds) was detonated in a tunnel 960 feet underground, imploding 3.3 pounds of plutonium in a nonspherical shape (various sources give somewhat different figures). One purpose was to study the behavior of shock waves inside the metal. On long storage, tiny bubbles of helium from alpha decay form inside the plutonium in warheads, and there is some concern that these might interfere with effective implosion. To hear the nukemeisters talk, one would be led to believe that they are only innocently interested in the way metals behave under these high-stress conditions; yet they do not confine their tests to, say, ordinary iron. The Department of Energy made the claim that the test was "fully consistent with the spirit and letter" of the CTBT, which is simply not true. Some view the tests as a bribe to the personnel of the weapons laboratories. In 2000, the mayor of Nagasaki protested to the U.S. about the planned tenth hydronuclear test. The Russians also have conducted such subcritical tests, in their case, in the site on Novaya Zemlya.

There is a truly frightening aspect to these recent developments. The weaponeer community is pressing for authorization to resume certain underground test explosions, to which the present Bush administration seems favorably disposed. If bombs of yield, say, 50 to 100 tons are developed, they pose a tremendous threat. The older bombs, with yields of around 10 kilotons or higher, are too big to be used except in a real war. But these new bantam bombs (by nuclear standards) cause limited damage, and so are more likely to be used in, say, little wars of the scope of the Persian Gulf conflicts. Research to perfect the miniature warheads would contaminate still more sites in the United States, although not so badly as in the cases of the major nuclear sites. In 1992, Los Alamos weapons analysts advocated designing a "tiny- nuke" warhead with a yield of about 1000 tons, a "mininuke" warhead of about 100 tons, and a "micronuke" bomb of 10 tons.

Bantam bombs, if nuclear, would be exceedingly dangerous because they are more likely to be used in local conflicts.

The new Robust Nuclear Earth Penetrator is another new objective (2003). It is to have a rather large yield, 450 to 1000 kilotons, and is supposed to destroy enemy bunkers. Of course, such bunkers would have to be located first, a challenging task.

The French also seem bent on conducting tests in the hydronuclear range. Such tests would blur the distinction between chemical and nuclear warheads and cripple or subvert the spirit and intent of the Non-Proliferation Treaty or Comprehensive Test Ban. Strictly interpreted, the CTB signed in 1996 prohibits all low-yield nuclear tests, including the hydrothermal tests. It does not prohibit tests which do not employ fissile materials. Still, one wonders what the reaction in China or Russia might be to these tests. The reaction of the Japanese is already in. In fall, 1998, a few months after subcritical tests began, the mayors of Hiroshima and Nagasaki condemned such testing, touted as only checking the reliability of stockpiled warheads.

One of the frightening consequences of the development and manufacture of these relatively small nuclear warheads, combined with the September 11, 2001, terrorist attacks, was an initiative by the President George W. Bush Administration called the Nuclear Posture Review, which was sent to Congress in January, 2002. Though technically still classified, enough of the document has appeared in the press to evaluate its intent. It listed seven nations as capable of attacking the U.S. with nuclear, biological, or chemical weapons (Russia, China, Iraq, Iran, Libya, Syria, and North Korea), and promised devastating retaliation in case any chose to launch an attack. The low-yield nuclear bombs were touted as useable even against nonnuclear powers or terrorists, a serious departure from the past. The plan would incorporate nuclear bombs into ordinary war, not reserving them just as weapons of last resort. The document described precision bombs, newly nuclear, along with covert operations. Its bellicose language can only encourage nonnuclear nations to work even harder to get them, a lamentable outcome.

In 2002, and repeated in 2003, the Bush administration asked Congress for an extra $15.5 million to support the Robust Nuclear Earth Penetrator program. It would, its supporters say, penetrate the earth carrying a nuclear (of up to around 70 kilotons yield) warhead to destroy buried bunkers sheltering high enemy officials or other sites. Ominously, $25 million was requested to improve the nuclear test site in Nevada. Such developments have alarmed arms control advocates and stimulated the mayor of Hiroshima to write Bush, saying that these developments represent a "frontal attack on the process of nuclear disarmament."

Virtually no attention was given to violation of treaties or raining fission products onto civilians.

9-62 Nuclear Suitcase Bombs

The Cold War years stimulated production of nuclear bombs small enough to be carried in suitcases. Some could be dismantled and reassembled after being smuggled piecewise into a target country. During the 1960s the United States produced its Special Atomic Demolition Munition, weighing 80 to100 pounds. Its purpose was mainly for sabotage of bridges, dams, and other strategic sites, to be delivered by parachutists. The yields were around 1 kiloton, that is (equivalent to 1000 tons of TNT!). The weapons have now been dismantled. Of course, the Soviets manufactured their own version of these bombs for use by the KGB. In general, these small nuclear munitions need rather frequent servicing, for example, to replace the tritium which decays. This quality makes them less threatening than they would be otherwise. (See also the modern development of hydronuclear weapons, 9-61).

9-63 Comprehensive Test Ban

As early as 1963 President Kennedy noted that a total end to nuclear weapon tests "would check the spiraling arms race in one of its most dangerous areas. It would increase our security." Attempting to attain American agreement to such a Comprehensive Test Ban, in 1985 the Russians unilaterally stopped all testing for more than a year and a half. The Reagan administration refused to follow suit, citing the scarcely credible objection that continued testing was essential to insure reliability of weapons (this can be done by disassembling sample weapons and subjecting the components to nonnuclear tests). The real reasons involved research in techniques useful for the Strategic Defense Initiative (Star Wars). Another reason lay in the development of convertible weapons, that is, a technology of converting conventional weapons into nuclear by use of a "clip-in" or "insertable" warhead. This procedure could be used with naval torpedoes and short-range missiles such as the Lance missile. Such a system would make arms control even more nightmarish (more on Comprehensive Test Ban Treaty is in section 11-7).

One encouraging development was the agreement by the Russians to permit American scientists to monitor seismic stations within the Soviet Union, beginning in 1988. It permitted a network of seismic stations at Karkaralinsk near the primary testing site in Kazakhstan. The plan was arranged not by government, but by a private environmental organization, the Natural Resources Defense Council, headquartered in Washington. The driving force in this work was Thomas Cochran, a feisty nuclear scientist dedicated to squeezing the nuclear genie back into his bottle, or at least locking him up in a deep subterranean dungeon. He has taken on quite a number of establishment entities by litigation, and has made significant contributions to world peace in the nuclear age.

A Comprehensive Test Ban can be verified.

Later, a Soviet team set up for similar tests near Deep Springs, California, not far from the Nevada test site. The Reagan Administration seemed uninterested. The visas of the Soviet scientists were delayed nearly a year, and there has been minimal government cooperation. The Russians brought their own samovar to the cactus-covered canyon.

Underground testing of warheads was halted as of 1992 by the United States, but was still continued by China into 1996. Most, but not all, countries without nuclear arsenals approve a Comprehensive Test Ban. The United States, which has a gigantic and thoroughly reliable arsenal, had not ratified the ban on testing. The British similarly at first opposed any CTB. In review conferences on the Non-Proliferation Treaty, the United States and Great Britain have consistently expressed an unwillingness to accept any commitment to seek a Comprehensive Test Ban. In 1990 when Mexico requested a time schedule to achieve such a ban, it found itself in an isolated position. The United States conducted tests in 1992, and China did the same two days later. One Chinese test explosion was huge, amounting to one megaton. In October 1993 China tested a bomb of 80 to 90 kiloton yield, stimulating the United States to begin to ready additional tests. China exploded two more bombs (June 1994 and October 1994), always claiming the purpose was defense. Old habits die hard. China has not signed the 1974 threshold treaty, limiting the energy of tests to 150 kilotons, but did join the Non-Proliferation Treaty in 1991 (finalized in 1992). In 1995 the Clinton Administration extended a moratorium on underground testing until an international treaty banning tests is signed. There is still one unsettled point: weapons scientists are still clamoring for "laboratory-scale nuclear experiments" which are claimed to be necessary to be sure warheads work properly. Clinton, while still a candidate, promised to support negotiations for a Comprehensive Test Ban. To his credit, President Clinton repeated this pledge in summer 1995, calling for a step "back from the nuclear precipice." In early 1996 the Pope repeated his message that there should be a global ban on testing "without delays".

Seismic waves propagate outward from their source, whether it is an earthquake or underground explosion. The velocity of such waves depends on the character of rock they travel through, but is generally between 4 and 8 kilometers per second. There are several kinds of waves, some compressional (like sound waves in air), others with lateral or up and down motions; others are composites of these. A major earthquake makes the whole Earth ring like a bell. The waves travel from the source both near the surface and on a curved path through the deep mantle of the Earth, and thus reach a distant point at different times. Waves with lateral vibrations are generated by nuclear explosions but not by earthquakes. Earthquakes are more prolonged than explosions, and more poorly approximate point sources. The result is that compressional wave spectra from the two types of sources are quite different. The higher frequency waves distinguish earthquakes from nuclear tests. In 1994 evidence was presented that these factors and some new discoveries greatly simplify the process of distinguishing seismic waves generated by nuclear explosions from those of earthquakes or chemical explosions.

Explosions with yield as little as 50 tons have been detected 1900 miles from the test site using the newer high-frequency (30 to 40 hertz) equipment. It is safe to say that modern seismometers can detect any significant cheating if a Comprehensive Test Ban is accepted. Seismographs at the California Institute of Technology have routinely detected Nevada tests down to 0.1 kiloton. The so-called "secret" test explosions are public knowledge. There might be a problem spotting midget-sized explosions of hydronuclear bombs (9-61). In opposing the Treaty, the nuclear weapons laboratories and the Department of Defense always presented worst-case scenarios to Congress when the results of a test ban were to be debated.

By the year 2000, the major powers stopped testing, except for hydronuclear experiments.

In 1996 the Comprehensive Test Ban was signed, but in 1999 its ratification was rejected by Congress. To the chagrin of some members of Congress, the Duma of Russia did ratify the Treaty (this was in April, 2000).

9-64 Detection of Nuclear Warheads

Both the United States and the Soviets have developed instruments for detecting the presence of nuclear warheads. This capacity is important in verifying conformity to nuclear treaties. The instruments depend on the release of gamma rays during radioactive decay of the heavy metals inside warheads.

In 1989 the Soviets permitted an American team, supported by the Natural Resources Defense Council, to test the guided-missile cruiser Slava in the Black Sea off the coast near Yalta. Using a germanium crystal scintillation counter and an exposure time of 20 minutes, gamma rays corresponding to the energies of uranium-235, plutonium-239, and americium-241 were recorded. The gamma rays had to penetrate 8 cm (3 inches) of steel. The Soviets measured neutron emissions rather than gamma rays. Using a counter of large area (2.5 square meters) in a helicopter 70 meters over the ship, neutrons from the spontaneous fission of plutonium-240 were detected and counted. If allowed to get close enough, nuclear warheads can be detected.

9-65 The Meaning of a Megaton

As we have seen, the unit used to measure the size (really energy, or loosely, power) of nuclear explosions is the equivalent weight of TNT in tons required to release the same amount of energy. Even small nuclear explosions equal many tons of TNT. Consider a hydrogen bomb of energy equal to one million tons of TNT. This is one megaton, a word which rolls so smoothly off the tongue that its meaning is disguised. Let's analyze this term.

If we load 500,000 trucks with 2 tons of TNT each, this is one million tons of the explosive. Bumper to bumper, these trucks would stretch 2,500 miles, the straight distance from Los Angeles to New York! Suppose all this TNT is heaped together into a small mountain, and a one megaton hydrogen bomb is readied far away. Both are exploded. While the total energy liberated in the two cases is the same, the nuclear explosion is more dangerous because of its radioactive products and because X-rays, gamma rays and neutrons are liberated on detonation. The largest bomb of World War I contained 1650 pounds of explosive. The World War II blockbuster contained approximately 5 tons. The Hiroshima bomb was equivalent to around 15,000 tons. Finally, consider a big hydrogen bomb, one of 5 million tons equivalency. When expressed as distance above the Earth's surface, the energy of these bombs compare approximately as follows:

500,000 trucks carry 1 megaton of TNT.

World War I bomb 2 inches
World War II blockbuster 1 foot
Hiroshima bomb One half mile
5 megaton H-bomb 190 miles

This last is as high as the orbit of a satellite! The energy of a single seven-megaton hydrogen bomb is greater than the combined explosive energy of all wars of the human race, including World War II, the Korean war, and the Vietnam War. There are enough nuclear explosives in the world to be equivalent to roughly 13,000 megatons of TNT. Our Earth now has about 6 billion people. The ratio of these figures is around 2.2 tons of TNT per person on Earth! The terrorist bomb which destroyed a federal building in Oklahoma City in 1995 consisting of ammonium nitrate and oil, weighed only about three tons, that is, 0.003 kiloton.

More than two tons of TNT per person on Earth

9-66 Accidents With Nuclear Bombs

The Department of Defense has reported 32 serious accidents with nuclear weapons since 1950, generally in a vague and fragmentary manner. Altogether, at least 1250 accidents took place between 1950 and 1968. Weapons are in storage sites distributed all over the United States and also in foreign countries, as well as on shipboard. They are constantly being moved around. Only two or three accidents involved loss of radioactive materials. In earlier models the plutonium-239 and/or uranium-235 core material were stored separately from the bomb proper (safe configuration), but in modern weapons multiple safety features are considered so reliable that physical separation is not necessary. Various accidents have subjected bombs to extreme stress and damage, so far without any nuclear explosions. However, an unarmed nuclear warhead was subjected to a conventional explosion in a test in the late 1950s at the Nevada test site. The result showed that a small amount of fissile material did undergo fission, releasing radioactivity.

The chain reaction was not self-sustaining. Hydrodynamic testing (9-61) is employed to find out whether accidental detonation of a single explosive cap of a warhead will cause the entire bomb to go off; these are called "one-point safety" or "single-point safety" studies. Such tests started about 1955. The principal danger to the personnel from accidents with nuclear warheads proved to be from combustion of the plutonium-239 or uranium-235 and subsequent inhalation of their oxides in aerosol form.

Some of the accidents involving nuclear warheads are described below.

February 13, 1950. A B-36 bomber on a training mission was flying near Alaska. The engines developed trouble and three of the four had to be shut down. The plane began to ice up and descend. Its nuclear weapon was dropped into the ocean at 8000 feet. On impact, the chemical high explosive detonated in a bright flash. The 17 men on board bailed out, and the plane crashed on Vancouver Island.

July 27, 1956. A B-47 aircraft went out of control near Cambridge, England, and crashed into a storage building which housed three nuclear bombs. Each contained about 8000 pounds of TNT whose function was to implode the fissile material. The four crewmen were killed. The TNT was not ignited by the blazing fuel. Had it exploded, deadly plutonium might have been scattered over a wide area in a nonnuclear explosion.

May 22, 1957. A B-36 bomber was ferrying a hydrogen bomb to an Air Force base in New Mexico. An officer was installing a safety release mechanism preparatory to landing when the plane hit turbulent air, causing the 21-ton bomb to drop unexpectedly, tearing off the bomb bay doors. The bomb was evidently a powerful one, perhaps 10 megatons. It fell 700 feet and the high explosive detonated on impact, making a 25-foot crater. Most of the radioactivity was confined to the crater. There was no fission explosion.

March 11, 1958. A B-47 bomber was flying over South Carolina when a hydrogen bomb somehow became dislodged and fell out. It clipped off the top of a home in the town of Mars Bluff, and on landing the chemical explosive detonated. A few civilians were slightly injured.

January 24, 1961. A B-52 Superfortress began having structural problems. On dropping to 10,000 feet, it was uncontrollable and began to disintegrate over North Carolina. Of the eight crew members, five were able to parachute to safety; the others perished. One of the two hydrogen bombs was ejected and parachuted without damage. The other fell free and crashed into a swamp. Its lithium deuteride ignited and burned with a brilliant red color. The fissile material was never recovered.

December, 1965. In the Pacific 70 miles south of Okinawa, a warplane rolled off the deck of the aircraft carrier Ticonderoga; it held a one-megaton hydrogen bomb. The plane, pilot, and bomb sank in three miles of water. The Navy covered up the event until 1989. The occurrence was politically sensitive since the plane had been patrolling the Vietnam coast, and the ship, carrying at least one nuclear weapon, had been in Japanese ports and territorial waters, contrary to Japanese law.

January 17, 1966. An American tactic during the Cold War was to keep bombers carrying nuclear warheads aloft at all times to signal to the Soviet Union that any attack would mean instant retaliation. In this operation, called Chrome Dome, a B-52 bomber was being refueled in flight and collided with the tanker. Both planes crashed near Palomares, in southern Spain, killing seven of the eleven airmen. The B-52 carried four hydrogen bombs, of which the chemical high explosives of two exploded. This distributed plutonium over a considerable area, requiring 1400 to 1750 tons of contaminated soil and vegetation to be scooped up and sent to the United States for disposal. One of the other two bombs was found on the ground with relatively little damage, and the other was found at 2850 feet in the ocean a few months later after an intensive and harrowing search. The task force consisted of scuba teams, sonar experts, nuclear weapons engineers, underwater photographers, hundreds of sailors, and midget submarines.

Plutonium on the plains of Spain

January 21,1968. A B-52 flying on the Arctic Circle route suffered a fire on board, which was evidently caused by a heater being turned up full blast in the Arctic sky. Six of the seven crewmen ejected and survived. The plane crashed in flames on sea ice near Thule Air Base, Greenland, and exploded. It had just been refueled in flight and had 24,000 pounds of fuel. Plutonium from the four 1.1-megaton hydrogen bombs on board was scattered around the site, requiring the removal of some 237,000 cubic feet of contaminated ice and debris to the U.S. In addition, the area was contaminated with tritium, which came from the booster assemblies and neutron generators of the hydrogen bombs aboard. The first rescue workers to reach the wreck site were Inuit hunters with dog sleds. Several hundred Danes came later from Thule (Greenlanders are Danish citizens). If the bombs had contained insensitive high explosives (not available until 1979), the accidents in Spain and over the Arctic probably would not have resulted in the explosions of the chemical explosive components in the warheads.

Twenty years later evidence began to accumulate that some of the clean-up personnel, both American and Danish, had suffered exposure to radiation, and now had a cancer rate higher than normal. In 1995 President Clinton ordered declassification of millions of secret Cold War-era documents, including those on the Greenland accident. The information reached Copenhagen via Internet immediately, precipitating demands by the Danes for further information, especially that on health effects. Quite a number of Danes who had aided in the cleanup of plutonium from the crash site claimed they were now suffering from extreme fatigue, skin disorders, immune system deficiencies, and premature aging; several had died.

September 19, 1980. A workman accidentally dropped a nine-pound wrench while repairing a Titan II rocket in its silo near Damascus, Arkansas. The tool caused a leak in the pressurized fuel tank. About 8 hours later, fuel vapors in the silo ignited, the resulting explosion fatally injuring one person. The explosion was powerful enough to blow off the 740-ton door of the silo and to catapult the warhead 600 feet away. It was a nine-megaton hydrogen bomb; its high explosive did not detonate. By the end of the decade, the Titan were retired.

We have little reliable information concerning accidents with Soviet nuclear warheads, but their record is probably comparable to our own. There have been persistent reports that in 1972 or 1973 an accident at the Semipalatinsk test site wiped out an entire company of soldiers. A missile with a nuclear weapon exploded near Turnov, Czechoslovakia, in 1983, resulting in many casualties. An explosion occurred in a missile silo of a Soviet submarine, the K-219, in October, 1986, with a 120-man crew. It was probably the high explosive of one of the 32 warheads on board which detonated. The sub was towed by a Soviet merchant ship for two days. During servicing the two reactors, one of them overheated and the automatic controls failed. It was shut down manually, but a sudden change in air pressure closed the latch. The sub took on water and began to sink. The line to the merchant ship was cut. The submarine went down in 18,000 feet of water 600 miles south of Bermuda. Three crewmen were lost. An estimated 90 kilograms (200 pounds) of plutonium was in the bombs and this metal is without doubt slowly dissolving in the seawater. The sea bottom in the area is a reddish clay with strong adsorbing powers for plutonium, and there seems to be little danger of contamination of marine life.

Aside from the incidents noted above with nuclear bombs, there has also been a number of accidents with nuclear systems carried into space. These systems may be either small nuclear reactors or a large amount of a radioactive isotope which on decaying produces heat; in both cases electricity is generated to power satellite operations. At least eight such accidents have been recorded. Two examples are: in 1970, the aborted Apollo 13 mission jettisoned a nuclear-powered generator which fell into the Pacific and was never recovered, and in 1978 a Soviet reconnaissance satellite failed, strewing a swath of radioactive debris across northwest Canada. In no case has an accidental nuclear explosion taken place.

As the year 2000 approached, a problem popularly known as Y2K (for Year 2 Kilos) arose. There was some apprehension that early computers programmed without the complete digits for the current year would be unable to distinguish 2000 from 1900 (along with related problems), and that this might cause unauthorized launching of missiles bearing nuclear warheads. This anxiety was misplaced in that human operation of keys is an essential step in activating the arming of nuclear warheads. In the case of the Russian nuclear armament, whose maintenance has deteriorated, the possibility of unintended launchings was higher. There was a giant sigh of relief as the year 2000 came and there was no significant problem.

9-67 Radiological Warfare and Terrorism

Another horror, fortunately impractical

During World War II three measures considered but not employed were use of poison gas, use of deadly microbial agents, and radiological warfare. The third case was seriously contemplated at least as early as 1941. The idea was to use radioactive fission products to contaminate land or water supplies of the enemy, perhaps by using small bombs to explode large amounts of the materials in solid form. Spread over a city, the materials would force evacuation. Ingestion of as little as 0.1 curie (0.7 mg) per person of strontium-90 would cause incapacitation or death. The reasons these vicious radiological weapons were not developed were technical, not moral. Radioactive decay would liberate enough heat to cause serious storage problems, and the weapons in any case would lose their effectiveness on storage owing to decay of their radioactivity.

But the idea was not dropped until some years after the war. Four one-ton bombs filled with radioactive waste were actually tested in 1949. The results were disappointing from the military viewpoint. In 1958 Teller advocated a cobalt bomb. This would be a hydrogen bomb equipped with a massive cobalt tamper. Its explosion would generate high yields of cobalt-60 (half-life 5.27 years), contaminating thousands of square miles of land for at least ten years. Richard Rhodes, author of two authoritative histories on the development of nuclear weapons, precisely described Teller as "the Richard Nixon of American science—dark, brooding, indefatigable."

During the Korean war serious proposals were made to seal off the peninsula by a line of cobalt-60 or reactor waste products. The closest approach to radiological warfare the world has seen to date is the exposure to fallout of Ukranians and Belorussians near Chernobyl, exposure of Kazakh citizens following the Soviet tests starting in 1949, and the exposure of Marshallese in the Pacific and Americans in the West following American tests.

Today a new kind of radiological warfare is possible, namely targeting nuclear reactors. A reactor with ferroconcrete containment is not easy to breach, but it could be done by a huge bomb guided by global positioning satellites, or by a nuclear bomb. The consequence of bombing nuclear reactors, which house billions of curies of fission products, would depend on variables such as siting near a city, wind, and the weather. Thus there is the possibility of converting conventional bombs into radiological weapons which could contaminate hundreds, perhaps thousands, of square miles.

If a terrorist group decided to attack the U.S. using a cheap but effective weapon, they might well choose a sort of radiological device. Many types are possible. One would consist of dynamite in a barrel of powdered uranium ore or radioactive waste from a nuclear reactor or mill tailings from uranium ore. It could be detonated from a high building in any city, or even in a street vehicle. It would do little physical damage, but its psychological effect would be deep and lasting. Once news got out that radioactivity was involved in the explosion, American fears might create panic. It would be difficult and expensive to clean up after these radiological dispersion devices. Terrorists can have diabolical and morbid talents.

9-68 How Much Weapons-Grade Uranium-235 and Plutonium-239 Exist?

A study to estimate the of the amounts of fissile metals in the world was carried out jointly by Oxford University and the Stockholm International Peace Research Institute (SIPRI). The results for1997 are in the table below:

	Weapons-grade uranium	Weapons-grade plutonium
USA	635 metric tonnes	100 metric tonnes
Russia	1010 metric tonnes	130 metric tonnes
Britain	15 metric tonnes	7.6 metric tonnes
France	24 metric tonnes	5 metric tonnes
China	20 metric tonnes	4 metric tonnes
Totals	**1699** metric tonnes	**247** metric tonnes

The degree of enrichment of uranium in its lighter isotope is variable, so the results are expressed in terms of "weapons-grade uranium equivalent." Production of both substances by all five countries listed has been for the most part halted.

9-69 What To Do with Uranium-235 and Plutonium-239 from Dismantled Warheads?

The lethal legacy of old nuclear warheads from the late Cold War must today be realistically addressed. Aside from disposing of most of our own warheads, we also have a self -interest in purchasing and destroying fissile materials from ex-Soviet countries and South Africa. As many as 40,000 American and Soviet warheads might have to be processed. From American sources, this is expected to yield about 400 metric tonnes of weapon-grade uranium-235 and 88 metric tonnes of plutonium. The warheads from the old Soviet warheads will supply 800 to 1200 metric tonnes of uranium-235 and 50 to 75 tonnes of plutonium. A 1992 report of the National Academy of Sciences labeled this surplus plutonium "a clear and present danger." A Rand study indicated that approximately 60,000 nuclear warheads remain on the global scale as of 1998.

In 1992, the Department of Energy began actively exploring means of consuming fissile materials from warheads. American warheads are dismantled at the same facility where they were assembled, in Pantex, Texas. Approximately 10,500 warheads were disassembled between 1990 and 1997. There is space currently to store 12,000 pits from warheads. The case of the uranium-235 is the simpler one. First the bomb-grade uranium metal (more than 90% U-235) from dismantled warheads is melted and blended with natural uranium (99.3% U-238) or depleted uranium (99.8% U-238). Alternatively, uranium-235 metal can be heated in steam to convert it to the dioxide, which is ground with ordinary uranium oxide. This blending of uranium-235 from both American and Russian bombs furnishes reactor grade fuel, 2 to 5% U-235. Used as fuel in nuclear reactors, perhaps of the breeder type as the Japanese plan to do, it forever eliminates the possibility of again manufacturing warheads from this source. Old timers who lovingly devoted their blood, sweat, and lives to isolating this bomb-grade uranium, which is highly enriched in isotope 235, undergo stormy, mixed emotional reactions at the thought of this blending process. Uranium-233, which is also fissile, can likewise be diluted with uranium-238 to render it unusable in warheads. Plutonium presents a more difficult problem.

Nuclear warheads can truly be destroyed if we really want to.

The question of whether consuming uranium-235 and plutonium-239 in reactors is economical is not the main issue; the chief motive is to get rid of these substances. In addition, it is important that all other countries become convinced that these materials are either irreversibly destroyed or made otherwise unavailable.

Three main techniques have been developed by the Department of Energy for coping with the excess plutonium. They are:

1. Using it as fuel in reactors.
2. Immobilization by incorporating in a glass or ceramic matrix for a geological repository or surrounded by highly radioactive waste.
3. Emplacement in deep boreholes, possibly after vitrification

A fourth method might be to dissolve the plutonium and mix it again with the highly radioactive waste from which it was earlier separated. Late in 1996 the Department of Energy announced that test runs using the first two of the above methods have been chosen in order to see which has fewer problems and lower costs.

Arjun Makhijani, the well-informed and thoughtful president of the Institute for Energy and Environmental Research, supports still another alternative. This is storing the valuable plutonium under international auspices, with constant monitoring. Such a plan would neutralize Russian objections that an expensive energy source is going to waste.

9-70 Destroying Surplus Plutonium Using Reactors

By alloying plutonium-239 with natural or depleted uranium, and converting to the dioxides, the mixed oxides (MOX) can be made. This MOX can be used as fuel in existing light-water reactors if some modifications are made. Breeder reactors can accommodate either oxide or metallic fuel, depending on design. Some breeder reactors can use an alloy of uranium-238 and plutonium-239 directly, that is, in metallic form. The cost of converting heavy-water reactors to accept MOX would be much less than that of light-water reactors. With the latter, about 5% is the maximum concentration of plutonium-239 which could be used without damage. Use of neutron-absorbing substances, such as cadmium, might permit the plutonium concentration to be increased to 7%. A quite different core configuration is essential to consumption of plutonium-rich fuel. If plutonium-rich fuel is consumed in modified reactors, only about 30% of it would be destroyed, but the remainder would be embedded in spent fuel which is dangerous enough to prevent theft. Russia recommended that the Department of Energy employ certain types of high-temperature, gas-cooled reactors which are capable of consuming plutonium so completely that sufficient reduction is accomplished in a single cycle. Large-scale use of plutonium in American reactors can hardly begin before about 2005, and will take at least ten years to complete. A few fuel rods containing MOX, some made in Los Alamos and others in Russia, were sent to the Canadian reactor at Chalk River, Ontario, in 1999 for testing. In January 2000 the Department of Energy announced a decision to convert 17 metric tonnes of plutonium to MOX. Russia has already announced its intention to use excess plutonium as fuel. British Nuclear Fuels and its French competitor Cogéma are bidding for contracts to convert American warhead plutonium into MOX.

Consuming plutonium in ordinary nuclear reactors is not as easy as it appears.

Another problem in converting plutonium from dismantled American warheads into MOX is that most of this plutonium contains gallium, alloyed to about 1%. Perfecting a means of removing this metal will require a few years of research. Traces of gallium left in waste plutonium seems to accelerate deterioration of metals such as zirconium which are used to confine the waste. Gallium does not interfere in vitrification.

Counting all plutonium in weapons, reactors, spent fuel, and waste, our world has on the order of 1300 metric tonnes of plutonium (250 tonnes of weapons grade Pu-239).

There is always the danger of theft of plutonium-bearing materials, particularly when it is weapons grade. Each country having such materials has a strong self-interest in protecting them well. Spent fuel, stored in heavy canisters, is too radioactive and too massive to invite thieves. Weapons-grade uranium-235 and plutonium can be converted to the "spent fuel standard" to make the materials essentially theft-proof and inaccessible. This can be done by converting to the dioxides and running through a nuclear reactor at a certain rate. Enough fission products are formed to afford self-protection. Another technique is to remove some of the spent fuel assemblies from canisters and replacing them with suitably-packaged uranium-235 or plutonium whose level of radioactivity has been greatly increased.

Plutonium from weapons can be consumed in a number of commercial reactors. Mixed oxide fuel is already produced by factories in Belgium (Dessel plant), France (Cadarache and Marcoule), and England (Sellafield). Germany abandoned its plans for a facility owing to political pressures, but nevertheless has 17 reactors which use or plan to use imported MOX fuel. MOX has been successfully consumed in several types of light-water reactors, at least seven in Germany and two in Switzerland. Half of France's 56 reactors are licensed or scheduled to be licensed to use MOX fuel. While most light-water reactors in the United States could not accommodate a full core of mixed-oxide fuel, they could handle a load containing one-third mixed oxide. The cost would be up to two billion dollars. More control rods would be needed. The Canadian CANDU reactors can better accommodate plutonium-rich fuel, and the Canadians have offered to accept a certain amount of mixed oxide fuel. In Russia, only the VVER-1000 light-water reactors could safely consume mixed oxide. The Russians also want to use their BN-600 breeder reactor for this purpose. Each gram of plutonium consumed in a reactor allows about 140 grams of uranium to be left as ore in the Earth for possible use by future generations.

It is profoundly satisfying to nullify the capacity of plutonium to be employed in bombs.

While use of MOX as a reactor fuel has many attractive features, it is much more expensive than low-enriched uranium. Many nuclear experts favor vitrifying plutonium and imobilizing it in boreholes (9-72).

During the 1950s and 1960s several experimental reactors were made in the U.S. which used weapons grade uranium-235 (93%). They were discontinued because of proliferation concerns. But in 1995 physicists at the Technical University of Munich announced plans to build such a reactor at Garching, just outside Munich. It is to be a 20-megawatt reactor, but one of the principal motivations is to use it as a source of cryogenic neutrons in research work.

A consortium of three firms has been proposed to develop a plutonium-disposal system. Fetchingly known as the Isaiah project, the plan is to take over a Department of Energy facility at Hanford, Washington, for mixed oxide production for the abandoned breeder reactors situated there. There are two unfinished reactors which would be finished with appropriate modifications to make them compatible with mixed oxide fuel. One of them would need only slight changes. The consortium would then consume excess plutonium to produce and sell electricity.

The cost and required modifications would probably mean that a great deal of plutonium could not be consumed in reactors in a timely manner, and other ways of disposal are needed.

9-71 Immobilization of Surplus Plutonium

Current immobilization techniques for vitrification or use of ceramics are considered quite satisfactory, but any process can be improved by further research. One option is to convert unwanted plutonium (as oxide) into two-ton glass logs, as is the case with high-level waste, and put them into a geological repository. The glass is compounded with neutron-hungry components, such as boron, cadmium and gadolinium; addition of dangerous fission products is also an option to further reduce the danger of theft. The type of glass for this purpose is about 100 times as durable as that used to vitrify high-level waste. The glass logs would be dangerous and too heavy to move without machinery. All this would require at least ten years to perfect.

There are several proposed variations for vitrification of plutonium. In the Greenfield procedure, the plutonium as dioxide is mixed with glass frit and a neutron absorber, and the mixture is melted and stirred. In a second stage the plutonium-bearing glass is melted with cesium-137 nitrate (the cesium-137, half-life 30 years, is abundant in fission product waste). The resulting glass is cast in canisters, each holding 1660 kilograms. The glass is about 5% plutonium, so that each canister holds 83 kilograms of plutonium. The purpose of the cesium-137 is to act as a radiation barrier for added protection against theft. The second variation is the can-in-canister procedure. The plutonium dioxide is dissolved in molten glass or ceramic matrix with a neutron absorber as before, and cast in small cans. Twenty assemblies of these smaller cans are stacked in a large canister, which is then filled with vitrified high-level waste as a radiation barrier. Each small can holds 2.5 kilograms of plutonium. The can-in-canister procedure is probably the quickest, and some authorities favor it to treat Russia's excess plutonium. The third variation is the adjunct melter procedure, and it resembles the Greenfield method.

Vitrified plutonium could be regarded as a plutonium reserve, helping to alleviate fears of future energy shortages.

Immobilization of plutonium using ceramics also has Greenfield and can-in-canister variations. Plutonium and cesium-137 as their nitrates are mixed with neutron absorbers and the components of a titanate-based ceramic; the combination is heated strongly. After hot compressing and sealing, the cylinders, holding 80 kilograms of plutonium and weighing 660 kilograms, are loaded into a canister, filled with titanium dioxide, welded shut, and emplaced in a geological repository.

Another variation is known as the "storage MOX" way, originating in Germany. The MOX would be fashioned into small ceramic pellets and loaded into zirconium or stainless steel tubes, which are welded shut. The pellets are mixed with neutron-absorbing materials such as hafnium (a by-product from zirconium refining) and spent fuel rods to prevent theft. The filled tubes are then ready to be sent for geological burial. An advantage of the "storage MOX" procedure is that it can accommodate perhaps 15% plutonium, about twice as much as the can-in-canister technique.

9-72 Disposing of Surplus Plutonium in Deep Boreholes

The third possibility is to sequester the plutonium in boreholes 4 kilometers (2.5 miles) deep, and seal them in with clay and concrete. The holes would be filled to half the depth, which would insure that all waste is in bedrock far below any aquifer or groundwater. While theft-proof, such plutonium could conceivably be retrieved using the immense resources of government. The technique would isolate plutonium on a geologic time scale.

There are two variations under consideration, the direct emplacement alternative and the immobilized emplacement alternative. In the first, plutonium oxide or metal is canned in steel and the cans are loaded into 20-foot canisters, each accommodating somewhat more than 40 kilograms of plutonium. The voids in the canisters are filled and the canisters are strung like beads from cables and lowered into the boreholes. The holes are filled with kaolin clay grout, which hardens in place. After making a concrete plug, the hole is filled with the original rock and soil excavated in boring the hole. There is no radiation barrier. In the immobilization emplacement alternative, the plutonium is first fixed in ceramic as described above, shaped into pellets, and emplaced directly without canisters. The material averages about 0.5% plutonium. Kaolin grout fills the voids as before.

Not exactly buried treasure

Any of the above procedures for coping with plutonium-239 would take five or ten years to perfect. Meanwhile, security measures would have to be exercised, especially in view of the developing market of old Soviet weapons-grade uranium-235. Five European countries are beginning to make purchases (Britain, France, Germany, Belgium, and the Netherlands). Mostly, the uranium-235 is to be converted into MOX, but some will be used in experimental breeder reactors. The United States paid $12 billion for 500 metric tonnes of Russian uranium-235, and there are at least 700 tonnes more. Early in 2000, the Department of Energy announced that up to 33 metric tonnes of surplus plutonium will be converted to MOX fuel, and approximately 17 tonnes will be immobilized.

Experience at Los Alamos on the handling of metallic plutonium has given some tips on what not to do in regard to in storing the substance. In one instance, 2.5 kilograms of pure plutonium was put into a steel tube, and the cap was welded in place. This tube was put into a polyethylene plastic bag, wrapped in tape, and this was put into an iron container. On storage more than seven years, the plutonium had oxidized, expanded, and ruptured the inner tube. Examination showed that the cap had been imperfectly welded. The plastic was decomposed by the radiation, liberating hydrogen. This gas formed plutonium hydride, which oxidized quickly. An incident in England was similar. Considering all American nuclear sites, at least 26 metric tonnes of plutonium were stored unsafely; as much as 12.8 metric tonnes in metallic form are at Rocky Flats alone. Some plastic containers bulge from internal gas. Steps are being taken to remedy the matter.

Plutonium pits salvaged from old American warheads are being stored in bunkers at the Pantex plant in Texas. Each pit, clad in stainless steel, is secured by a holding fixture inside a sealed steel container. Old Soviet warheads are being dismantled at Chelyabinsk-65, and their pits from Russian warheads are stored in a warehouse at Tomsk-7; these are two of the formerly secret atomic cities. Protection against theft is weak. Their accountancy system is primitive. They do not use bar codes or portal monitors that automatically record arrival or departure of radioactive materials. Fortunately, Secretary O'Leary of the Department of Energy and Russian Minister of Atomic Energy Mikhailov signed an agreement in 1994 permitting mutual inspection of storage facilities. American assistance and financial aid to the Russians to help in dismantling warheads to the extent of $1.3 billion has been suggested, but Congress approved only $117 million, and under $10 million had been delivered as of the end of 1995.

An American, Corin Cummings, was able to visit Tomsk-7 in 1996. He reported the stresses following *glasnost* and a hail of criticism in the press on account of its privileges. Subsidies from Moscow began to dry up. Still, the city of 100,000 was relatively well off.

9-73 Cleaning Up the Weapons Sites

By the late1980s it became obvious that shoddy environmental practices at American production facilities had resulted in serious contamination of the working areas and surrounding territory. The pervasive contamination resulted largely during the frenzy of the Cold War, when bomb production dominated over all other considerations. The Department of Energy and others made estimates of the cleanup costs to a level judged by radiation from the land, as well as concentration of specified key nuclides. A 1989 estimate was $100 billion, and by 1991 it had doubled. By 1995 the estimate for remediation had risen to $230 billion over 75 years. The true cost will be more. Of 856 sites, the five most contaminated locales are Rocky Flats, Colorado; the Idaho National Engineering Laboratory; the uranium facilities at Fernald, Ohio; the Savannah River complex in South Carolina; and the mammoth facilities at Hanford, Washington. By the middle of 1992, Hanford had again assumed the demeanor of a boom town, owing to an infusion of dollars for cleanup. The map in section 9-8 shows the location of 15 sites. The cleanup will be one of the largest public works in history.

In 1984 one of those citizens' advocacy groups which show democracy in action was formed in the Hanford area. It was called the Hanford Education Action League. During its 15-year life it investigated many issues revolving about nuclear weapons, plutonium, radioactive waste, etc. The League used the Freedom of Information Act to pry out of the Department of Energy papers concerning transport of plutonium, the N-reactor, Hanford's Fast Flux Breeder Reactor and its tritium production, release of radioactive material off-site, and many related issues. A similar organization is the Snake River Alliance, headquartered in Boise, Idaho. This group monitors the Idaho National Engineering and Environmental Laboratory as well as transport of radioactive materials into and out of the state. All of us are indebted to these two organizations.

The facility at Rocky Flats had been so flagrantly violating environmental regulations that its managers would blindfold investigators from the Environmental Protection Agency before leading them through the plant. There was evidence of illegal clandestine midnight burning of waste. In 1989, 75 agents of the FBI, in a blaze of scandal, raided the Rocky Flats site, then being run by the Rockwell International Corp. The violations of environmental standards were so severe that a grand jury found the management guilty to the extent that Rockwell agreed to pay a fine of $18.5 million.

Many felt that Rockwell was let off too easily; in fact the government quashed the grand jury indictment in 1992. When some grand jurors later publicized the case they were threatened with criminal prosecution. One should keep in mind that it was virtually impossible for the assigned tasks to be accomplished by anyone while keeping within the environmental regulations. Once cleanup is finished, Rocky Flats might close down. One technique under consideration is fusing the contaminated soil using a heavy electric current, which would immobilize the dangerous elements as a glass. This would be frightfully expensive.

9-74 Chronology of Events Relating to Nuclear Warheads

1968—At this time the Nuclear Non-Proliferation Treaty was finally negotiated; it became effective two years later. The parties signing on are committed to declare their activities to the International Atomic Energy Agency (IAEA), which has the right and obligation to verify compliance. The treaty provides that the nuclear powers not supply nuclear weapons or technology to countries without them; that nonnuclear countries not undertake to acquire nuclear weapons; and that these nations will accept the IAEA's safeguards to insure that nuclear installations are not used for military purposes. In recent years, the treaty also emphasizes the need for the nuclear-weapons states to pursue negotiations to stop any nuclear arms race. Within a few years 134 countries had signed the treaty after the United States and the Soviet Union had ratified it, but there remained a number of holdouts. The Treaty does not prohibit commerce in plutonium. It does require that separated plutonium be safeguarded. The treaty was extended indefinitely in the spring of 1995. Since the Persian Gulf conflict the IAEA has made commendable progress in asserting its rights and in developing its capabilities to detect undeclared nuclear activities. Inspectors employed by IAEA inspect about 1000 nuclear facilities in the world. There are only about 200 inspectors. The Non-Proliferation Treaty deserves the full support of all countries.

The Non-Proliferation Treaty did more or less succeed for a while in dampening nationalistic fervor for acquiring nuclear weapons, but has come under increasing stress during more recent years. It divides the world into nuclear powers and nonnuclear powers, a double standard. India, for example, has a substantial cadre of highly trained scientists, and clearly feels that the Treaty is discriminatory and paternalistic. Lately, Arab nations and Iran display a growing unhappiness with the Treaty, and some might withdraw unless Israel is more accommodating. Increasingly, leaders of nonnuclear nations are inclined to conclude that proliferation is inevitable, and that it is only a matter of time before one's feared adversaries somehow get nuclear weapons in their arsenals.

Imperfect, but useful

Despite these misgivings, the Non-Proliferation Treaty was extended indefinitely in 1995. Israel, Pakistan, India, and most importantly, China, did not sign. A few other countries have not signed on, but have no nuclear military programs.

1972—The United States and the Soviet Union signed the Anti-Ballistic Missile Treaty, which limits development of these systems. It enhances deterrence and has saved each side tens of billions of dollars.

1974 & 1976—The Threshold Test Ban Treaty and the Peaceful Nuclear Explosions Treaty were signed by the USA and USSR in these two years. While still unratified, their main condition, that underground tests be limited to yields of 150 kilotons, has probably not been violated, despite some claims that it has.

Seismologists hold that the so-called Lg waves, which are tremors propagated inside the Earth's crust rather than along the surface, measure yields within 30%. Another technique is called CORRTEX (Continuous Reflectometry for Radius versus Time Experiments). It requires a hole bored near the explosion site, with a probe inserted and connected to a recording unit. The United States monitors the above treaties using a network of seismic instruments known as the Atomic Energy Detection System.

1975—The American Nuclear Regulatory Commission, descendant of the old Atomic Energy Commission, was founded. Its function is to act as watchdog in regulating the nuclear industry, but not the military branches of nuclear work.

1987—On December 8 the Americans and Soviets signed the Intermediate Nuclear Forces Treaty, another agreement which provided for a reduction of deployed arms. It provides for the retirement of missiles in Europe with ranges of 300 to 3000 miles. The United States and its allies are to give up about 400 warheads, and the Soviets about 1600. The totals represent approximately 4% of the arsenals of the superpowers. The uranium-235 and plutonium-239 of the warheads are to be recycled, and may be used in other warheads; only the hardware (missiles, their trucks, etc.) are to be destroyed. Hopefully, this agreement will open the door to further and more extensive disarmament steps, such as the Strategic Arms Reduction (START) accords.

1990—The last American nuclear warhead, a W88, was assembled.

1992—In July the United States formally declared the end of its nuclear warhead production. The removal of all American tactical nuclear arms from Europe was completed.

1994—In March Russia agreed to shut down its last three reactors producing weapon-grade plutonium; bomb production had already been halted.

1995—With the immediate threat of nuclear war negligible, the American military establishment began to prepare complete archives of the entire subject of nuclear bombs, in all its aspects. The detailed chronicle is supposed to insure that in the future, long after all the veterans of the Manhattan Project are gone, the nation will still be able to maintain adequate defense. The undertaking is known as the Knowledge Preservation Project. Thus a scientific infrastructure is to be erected to underpin a permanent nuclear force.

1996—In order to assure that the expected Comprehensive Test Ban is not violated, still another means of detection of nuclear warhead tests was developed. This was at the Pacific Northwest National Laboratory. It depends on the release of fission product radio-xenon isotopes, principally Xe-133, Xe-133m, and Xe-135, into the atmosphere during tests. If an explosion is suspected, separation of xenon from a sample of air is first performed, and any radioactive xenon is determined using a new type of ultra-sensitive equipment. Even in underground explosions, xenon cannot be fully contained; the extreme pressures push some xenon outside. Xenon from nuclear reactors does not interfere. The technique cannot identify the location of a test, but does supplement other procedures.

1996—The former chief of U.S. nuclear forces (Strategic Air Command) called for a worldwide ban on all nuclear weapons. Gen. G. L. Butler declared that the weapons now have but little military value and that the nuclear powers should agree on permanent global prohibition (more on this issue in 11-7A).

1998—Nuclear affairs in Russia today are handled by the Ministry of Atomic Energy (MinAtom), a giant agency headed by Viktor Mikhailov until early 1998, when he was replaced by Yevgeny Adamov. It is responsible not only for Russia's nuclear arsenal, dismantling those required by treaty, and the remnants of the industrial-military complex, but also privatization and foreign sales of nuclear equipment, including reactors. MinAtom is one of the most powerful bureaucracies in Russia. Mikhailov was weapons-oriented in outlook; his successor Adamov is more inclined toward development of safer reactors and cleanup of the radioactive mess from old weapons programs and Chernobyl.

9-75 Some Final Comments

There is an urgent need for the nuclear powers of the world to rethink the purposes of their most powerful weapons.

Again we see that intensive study of science is not just an idle exercise of the intellect, but of vital importance to all human beings. It can be and is pursued for both the pure joy of intellectual satisfaction and of discovery, or for money, power, and defense, or aggression. Scientists are not nearly as scientific as they like to think. They are only human, and have the same jealousies, irrationalities, fallibility, and other shortcomings as everyone else. We have seen that The Bomb has metastasized from its genesis in 1945 in the USA to several other countries, and threatens to continue doing so. Now with the conclusion of the Cold War between the two nuclear giants, it is conceivable, but unlikely, that a genuine effort to rid our world of all nuclear bombs could begin. So far, few signs of the political will necessary to undertake this task have appeared. In any case, knowledge of how to make the bombs will not disappear. During the time of more than a half century since nuclear bombs were manufactured, their enormous power might have played a role in preventing wars between the major nations, but they have not deterred other conflicts in a very violent world. If you think computers have changed our lives during the past 50 years, just consider what the next 50 years will bring. Also during that fifty-year period, continued advances in studies of radioactivity for peaceful purposes, such as nuclear medicine and insect control, will bring vast gains for the human race, but regrettably, there are still strong tendencies to advance nuclear weapons too.

An example of these tendencies is the possible development of gamma-ray weapons. This possible development consists of first making excited, metastable nuclei, such as those of hafnium, niobium, or thorium. This is done by "pumping" up these nuclei using high-energy photons , and stimulating them with low-energy X-rays. This is said to trigger an immense discharge of deadly gamma rays. Hopefully, these experiments will fail.

An important point sometimes overlooked is that nuclear bombs, of both the fission and fusion types, can be made using uranium-235, with no plutonium-239 at all. Thus if nuclear reactors had never been invented and if plutonium had never been discovered, we would still be plagued with the problem of nuclear weapons. Whatever the opinions of people toward nuclear reactors policy, they should never suggest that shutting them all down will make the world safe from nuclear weapons.

Bibliography for Chapter 9: Nuclear Weapons

Howard Ball, *JUSTICE DOWNWIND: ATOMIC TESTING AT THE NEVADA TEST SITE*, Oxford, 1986.

Brian Beckett, *WEAPONS OF TOMORROW*, Plenum Books, 1983.

Louis R. Beres, *ISRAEL'S SECURITY OR ARMAGGEDON?*, Lexington, 1986.

Paul Boyer, *FALLOUT*, A Historian Reflects on America's half-Century Encounter with Nuclear Weapons, Ohio State University Press, 1998.

William Burr, Thomas S. Blanton, and Malcolm Byrne, *U.S. NUCLEAR HISTORY AND POLICY IN THE MISSILE AGE*, 1955-1968, Chadwyck-Healey, Inc., 1998, *Fiche & Guidebook/Index; cost,* $4200.

William E. Burrows and Robert Windrem, *CRITICAL MASS: THE DANGEROUS RACE FOR SUPERWEAPONS IN A FRAGMENTING WORLD*, Simon and Schuster, 1994.

John Canaday, *THE NUCLEAR MUSE*, Literature, Physics, and the First Atomic Bombs, The University of Wisconsin Press, 2000.

Thomas B. Cochran, William M. Arkin, and Milton M. Hoenig, *NUCLEAR WEAPONS DATABOOK: Vol. I, U.S. NUCLEAR FORCES AND CAPABILITIES*, Ballinger, 1984.

Thomas B. Cochran, William M. Arkin, Robert S. Norris, and Milton M. Hoenig, *NUCLEAR WEAPONS DATABOOK: Vol. II, U.S. NUCLEAR WARHEAD PRODUCTION*, Ballinger, 1987.

Thomas B. Cochran, Willian B. Arkin, Robert S. Norris, and Milton M. Hoenig, *NUCLEAR WEAPONS DATABOOK: Vol. III, U.S. NUCLEAR WARHEAD FACILITY PROFILES*, Ballinger, 1987.

Avner Cohen and Steven Lee, eds., *NUCLEAR WEAPONS AND THE FUTURE OF HUMANITY*, Rowman & Allanheld, 1985.

Avner Cohen, *ISRAEL AND THE BOMB*, Columbia University Press, 1998.

Sam Cohen, *THE TRUTH ABOUT THE NEUTRON BOMB*, William Morrow & Co., New York, 1983.

Michael D'Antonio, *ATOMIC HARVEST: HANFORD AND THE LETHAL TOLL OF AMERICA'S NUCLEAR ARSENAL*, Crown Publishers, NY, 1993.

S. Devkinandan, *HOW CHINA MAY USE THE ATOM BOMB*, New Century Books, Dehli, India, 1974.

Rachel Fermi and Esther Samra, *PICTURING THE BOMB: PHOTOGRAPHS FROM THE SECRET WORLD OF THE MANHATTAN PROJECT*, Harry N. Abrams, Inc., Publishers, 1995.

Philip L. Fradkin, *AN AMERICAN TRAGEDY* (radioactive fallout), University of Arizona Press, 1989.

John G. Fuller, *THE DAY WE BOMBED UTAH*, New American Library, 1985.

Fusion Video, *THE BIRTH OF THE BOMB*, a VCR tape (VHS type) sold by Fusion Video, 17214 So. Oak Park Ave., Tinley Park IL 60477.

Mark Gaffney, *DIMONA: THE THIRD TEMPLE?* The story behind the Vanunu revelation (Israeli nuclear weapons), Amana Books, 1989.

Carole Gallagher, *AMERICAN GROUND ZERO: THE SECRET NUCLEAR WAR*, MIT Press, 1993.

James N. Gibson, *NUCLEAR WEAPONS OF THE UNITED STATES: AN ILLUSTRATED HISTORY*, Schiffer Publishing, Arglen, PA, 1996.

Samuel Glasstone and Philip J. Dolan, *THE EFFECTS OF NUCLEAR WEAPONS*, Superintendent of Documents, U.S. Government Printing Office, Washington, DC 20402.

Hugh Gusterson, *NUCLEAR RITES: A WEAPONS LABORATORY AT THE END OF THE COLD WAR*, University of California Press, 1996.

Khidhir Hamza, *SADDAM'S BOMBMAKERS*, Lisa Drew Books/Schribner, 2000.

Chuck Hansen, *U.S. NUCLEAR WEAPONS: THE SECRET HISTORY*, Orion Books, 1988.

Chuck Hansen, *THE SWORDS OF ARMAGEDDON*, complete record of nuclear weapon development, CD-ROMs covering eight volumes and 2503 pages; e-mail to *sobernado@aol.com* or web site *http://www.uscoldwar.com/*.

Seymour Hersh, *THE SAMSON OPTION* (on Israel's nuclear arsenal), Random House, 1991.

John P. Holdren et al., *MANAGEMENT AND DISPOSITION OF EXCESS WEAPONS PLUTONIUM, REACTOR-RELATED OPTIONS*, National Academy Press, 1995.

David Holloway, *STALIN AND THE BOMB*, Yale University Press, 1994.

Fred Holroyd, ed., *THINKING ABOUT NUCLEAR WEAPONS*, Auburn House, 1985.

David Irving, *THE GERMAN ATOMIC BOMB*, Simon & Schuster, 1967.

Paul R. Josephson, *RED ATOM, RUSSIA'S NUCLEAR POWER PROGRAM FROM STALIN TO TODAY*, W. H. Freeman and Co., 1999.

Peter Kuran, *TRINITY AND BEYOND (THE ATOMIC BOMB MOVIE),* a VCR tape covering testing of nuclear warheads made by American, Soviet, English, and Chinese efforts. Goldhil Home Media, 137 East Thousand Oaks Bl., Suite 207, Thousand Oaks, CA 91360.

J. Carson Mark, *EXPLOSIVE PROPERTIES OF REACTOR-GRADE PLUTONIUM*, Science and Global Security, vol. 4, pp. 111-128, 1993.

Richard Miller, *UNDER THE CLOUD: THE DECADES OF NUCLEAR TESTING*, The Free Press, 1986.

Howard Morland, *THE SECRET THAT EXPLODED*, Random House, 1981.

Robert S. Norris, Thomas B. Cochran, and William M. Arkin, *NUCLEAR WEAPONS DATABOOK*: Known U.S. Nuclear Tests July 1945-December 1985, Natural Resources Defense Council, 1986.

George Perkovich, *INDIA'S NUCLEAR BOMB*, University of California Press, 2000.

Thomas Powers, *HITLER'S SCIENTISTS, Viking, 2003.*

Richard Rhodes, *THE MAKING OF THE ATOMIC BOMB*, Simon & Schuster, 1986.

Richard Rhodes, *DARK SUN: THE MAKING OF THE HYDROGEN BOMB*, Simon & Schuster, 1995.

Nikolaus Riehl and Frederick Seitz, *STALIN'S CAPTIVE: NIKOLAUS RIEHL* and the Soviet Race for the Bomb, The American Chemical Society, 1966.

Jeffery I. Sands, Robert S. Norris, and Thomas B. Cochran, *NUCLEAR WEAPONS DATABOOK*: Known Soviet Nuclear Explosions 1949-1985, Natural Resources Defense Council, 1986.

Robert Scheer, *WITH ENOUGH SHOVELS: REAGAN, BUSH & NUCLEAR WAR*, Random House, 1982.

Stephen I. Schwartz, ed., *ATOMIC AUDIT, The Costs and Consequences of U.S. Nuclear Weapons since 1940, Brookings Institution Press,* Washington, D.C., 1998.

Glenn T. Seaborg et al., *PROTECTION AND MANAGEMENT OF PLUTONIUM*, American Nuclear Society, 1995.

Eric Semler, James Benjamin, Adam Gross, and Sarah Rosenfield, *THE LANGUAGE OF NUCLEAR WAR* (a nuclear dictionary), Perennial Library, N.Y., 1987.

Robert Serber, *THE LOS ALAMOS PRIMER* (First Lectures on How to Build an Atomic Bomb),University of California Press, Berkeley, 1992.

Peter Sharfman et al., Office of Technology Assessment, *THE EFFECTS OF NUCLEAR WAR*, Gale Research Co., Book Tower, Detroit, 1984.

Rebecca Solnit, *SAVAGE DREAMS* (fallout from nuclear testing in Nevada), Sierra Club Books, 1994.

Louis Toscano, *TRIPLE CROSS: ISRAEL, THE ATOMIC BOMB, AND THE MAN WHO SPILLED THE SECRETS* (the Vanunu affair), Carol Pub. Group/Birch, Lane Press, 1990.

Jonathon Weisgall, *OPERATION CROSSROADS: THE ATOMIC TESTS AT BIKINI*, Naval Institute Press, 1994.

Steve Weissman and Herbert Krasney, *THE ISLAMIC BOMB*, Times Books, 1981.

Mason Willrich and Theodore B. Taylor, *NUCLEAR THEFT: RISKS AND SAFEGUARDS*, Ballinger, 1974.

Sources of information on the web:

Energy Department *www.doe.gov*
Images of nuclear tests *www.atomicarchive.com/photos/LANL/index.shtml*
Gallery of U.S. Nuclear Tests: inquire at e-mail *jim@leonard.okgeosurvey1.gov*
Defense Special Weapons Agency *www.dswa.mil*
Los Alamos National Laboratory *www.lanl.gov*
Livermore National Laboratory *www.llnl.gov*
Nuclear bomb explosions, some with video *atomicrocks.com*

Chapter 10: EFFECTS OF NUCLEAR BOMBS

Part I: TARGETING NUCLEAR WARHEADS
Part II: THE PHYSICAL EFFECTS OF NUCLEAR EXPLOSIONS
Part III: THE MEANING OF NUCLEAR WAR

Part I: TARGETING NUCLEAR WARHEADS

ABSTRACT—The principal means—aircraft and missiles—to carry nuclear bombs to their targets are described. Missiles can be launched from land, surface ships or submerged submarines, air, or from satellites. Warning systems are briefly covered. The difference between strategic and tactical weapons is defined, as well as the terms cruise missiles, "smart" bombs, and the global positioning system. Other important concepts, such as payload, throw weight, and circular error probability are clarified. The story of the Strategic Defense Initiative (SDI, alias Star Wars) is presented, as well as its modern modifications with X-ray lasers and orbiting mirrors. Its gigantic costs and effectiveness are analyzed. Some of SDI's latest modifications, such as THAAD, are described.

10-1 Systems to Deliver Nuclear Weapons

During World War II, a B-29 bomber took off from the newly liberated island of Tinian, in the Pacific. It carried a primitive atomic bomb which was dropped over Hiroshima, the first such weapon ever used in war. A few days later Nagasaki was similarly bombed by a nuclear warhead of a different type.

During the time since the end of World War II manned bombers remained a major means of delivering nuclear weapons to their targets in case of war. Of course other means have also been developed. These include land-based intercontinental ballistic missiles, submarine-launched ballistic missiles, and cruise missiles. All of these were developed in exquisite multiplicity by both of the superpowers, the USA and the USSR, at horrendous expense. Our world spends hundreds of billions of dollars each year on what is called "defense," and only a minuscule fraction of that sum on promotion of peace. Even with the end of the Cold War, much of the world remains infatuated with preparations for war.

Hundreds of billions for weapons, crumbs for peace

The arms race comprised both classical weapons and nuclear weapons and the ways to deliver them, in a chimerical marathon seeking security. An extremely abbreviated account of these formidable targeting systems follows; they are diverse, complex, overwhelming, and changing constantly. They encompass not only science and engineering, but also politics and economics. The three main components of delivering bombs are frequently described as a triad; these are bomber aircraft, land-based missiles, and submarine-launched missiles.

10-2 Strategic and Tactical Weapons

The term strategic weapons generally means long-range weapons and their targeting systems which can attack the homeland of an enemy (or supposed enemy). Tactical weapons are those which are for classical battlefield use, that is, short-range systems. Intercontinental missiles of all types and long-range bombers are strategic, while short-range missiles and nuclear artillery are tactical. Theater weapons are mostly tactical; they include short-range ballistic missiles, surface-to-surface and surface-to-air missiles, nuclear land mines, and nuclear depth charges. Tactical weapons are deployed for conflict at sea or on foreign soil. The distinction between the two types of weapons is often vague. Another aspect of military conflict is logistics, the complex discipline of moving troops, weapons, and supplies to the points they are needed. "Counterforce" warheads are designed to hit, with great accuracy, hardened targets such as silos housing bomb-laden missiles. Toward the end of the Cold War, Russia withdrew all tactical nuclear weapons from the other Soviet republics. Of all these republics, only Russia can sustain a strategic nuclear arsenal.

10-3 Two Guidance Systems

The Persian Gulf War (1990-91) provided extensive testing of the so-called "smart" bombs. While there were dramatic successes, so far as accuracy is concerned, there were also many failures, most of which were not publicized. The cost of the smart bomb and missile program was approximately $58 billion. In 1996, about five years after the Gulf War, more of the truth emerged in a General Accounting Office report. It appears that the claims by the weapons manufacturers were "overstated, misleading," etc. These deficiencies were especially prominent in the cases of the F-117 stealth bomber and laser-guided bombs. It turned out that their performance was seriously degraded by rain, clouds, fog, smoke, or high humidity. Information about the war on Iraq was tightly controlled by the U.S. military and this permitted manipulation of information to give distorted impressions. Flying over Serbia in 1999, the Serbs waited until an F-117 opened its bomb-bay doors, when it became visible to Russian-made, low-frequency radar. It was shot down. Doppler radar was found to be capable of detecting the wake of the planes.

A satellite system that determines precise locations on the surface is called Navstar Global Positioning System. The $10 billion complex is a constellation of satellites which was first employed in Panama in 1989, and also to locate minefields in the Iran-Iraq war. It was used even more extensively during the Persian Gulf War in 1991. Its ability to help pinpoint positions of troops, tanks, ships, and targets was of enormous military aid. Each Navstar satellite, 9480 miles high, orbits Earth once every 12 hours and carries an atomic clock (6-39F). It constantly broadcasts a series of signals fixing its position in space at given times. Receivers on ground, synchronized to the satellite's clock, calculate the exact distance to the satellite from the time required for the signal to reach it. Three satellites emitting signals simultaneously permit the receiver to compute its own position within a few feet. Signals from a fourth satellite permit determination of altitude as well. Research refining these systems has continued. There is no reason they could not be adapted to nuclear warheads in targeting specific geographic coordinates. By the time of the attack of Iraq 2003, the precision of guided missiles had been vastly improved.

10-4 Bombers

Aircraft remain popular in military circles to target nuclear weapons because they are familiar and because they have certain advantages over other means. While bombers are not especially accurate, they can be recalled after takeoff, and are versatile enough to attack mobile targets or widely separated targets. Their principal weakness is vulnerability to surface-to-air or air-to-air missiles.

An old standby that is nuclear-capable is the B-52 bomber or stratofortress. It is made in several modifications. Traveling at 50,000 feet, it can fly at a speed slightly slower than that of sound. Typically the B-52 is outfitted to carry 4 to 24 nuclear warheads and is often equipped with Short-Range Attack Missiles, also armed with nuclear warheads. These missiles are supersonic (more than 3.5 times the speed of sound), and can be controlled in flight. Once a missile is launched, it can be made to turn as much as 180 degrees and target another objective. The warhead is between 170 and 200 kilotons yield (type W69). Nearly 200 of these venerable planes were still in the strategic forces as of 1990.

Battleships ten miles high

Another plane equipped to carry nuclear weapons is the FB111. This plane can fly 2.5 times the speed of sound at 36,000 feet, and can carry six bombs or six Attack Missiles.

Funding was approved for the new B-1 series of swing-wing bombers, although on a scale smaller than that first requested. They are said to be capable of allowing intercontinental missions without aerial refueling, to be supersonic, and to have other improved features. They can carry twice the payload as the B-52, and several types of nuclear warheads with yields of 100 kilotons to more than 1 megaton. Some were operational early in 1988, at a cost of more than $280,000,000 each, and rising.

Another aircraft is the B-2 “stealth” or advanced technology bomber. This subsonic plane is covered with a cloth woven from fine graphite fibers, and the surface is then covered with a thin plastic that hardens. This surface absorbs most of radar and infrared radiation which strikes it, and that is supposed to defeat detection, or at least lessens the chances. The plane uses treated fuel which has lower exhaust temperatures and thus emits less infrared radiation. But the upgraded longer wavelength radar is able to detect stealth bombers, and they are visible to the eye in any case. The cost of each plane has proven to be two to three billion dollars, which is about five times the value of its weight in gold. It costs about $500 per minute to keep a B-2 in the air. If they work well, they would threaten exactly those defenses—mobile missiles and command posts—whose safety is the basis of deterrence. But judging from Lockheed’s earlier stealth fighter, the F-117, mentioned above, stealth technology is overblown. British, French, Czech, and Chinese radar systems easily tracked the F-117s. Tests in 1991 disclosed that the B-2 failed routine radar detection. Interest in the B-2 dwindled on Clinton’s election, but with the Republican victories in 1994, the House of Representatives authorized a $443 million down payment to manufacture more planes, even though the military had not requested them. By 1997, 21 planes had been manufactured, with more being planned. Tests in 1995 and following proved that the stealth character of the B-2 degrades when wet, although the planes themselves were not damaged. The materials blister in strong sunlight and become brittle in the cold; a Northrup Grumman Corporation spokesman says these problems have been solved. The stealth technology was developed to penetrate sophisticated Soviet defenses which no longer exist. Up until the battles in Kosovo in

1999, the only use of the B-2 has been to show off to the public at air shows, although its manufacturer maintains that it has demonstrated that it can "project power to any part of the globe within a matter of hours." Two B-2s flew nonstop across the Atlantic and each dropped 16 guided "smart" bombs on targets in Serbia. They also launched cruise missiles. In bombing of Yugoslav tanks and other military targets, the B-2 proved to be creditable, but hardly outstanding. In 2001, they successfully delivered payloads accurately to selected targets in Afghanistan.

Additionally, there are currently a few tactical aircraft capable of carrying nuclear weapons. They can transport bombs of yield up to 1 megaton. As in the other weapons delivered by air, these warheads can be set into various modes: to explode on the ground on impact or be retarded, or in the air at any specified height. As of 2000, the United States had in excess of 1000 nuclear bombs which are not in missiles, that is, are "gravity bombs," to be dropped from planes.

The following quotes from a former Cold Warrior might hold some grim interest. C. L. Novak was a navigator and bombardier on a B-52 plane whose warheads totaled 7.76 megatons yield. Novak wrote:

A few million tons of TNT in just one plane

> I studied, practiced and memorized every aspect of bombing until it became mechanical, emotionless, cold. Going out each morning on alert and running my hands over one-megaton warheads, I was in awe of the unspeakable horror that lay inside such an unremarkable metal casing. But my job was to bomb targets, not debate morality.

10-5 Land-Based Missile Systems

Ballistic missiles are propelled by multistage rockets, which detach and fall. The missiles continue on a trajectory governed mostly by gravity until they fall to their targets. Intercontinental ballistic missiles leave the atmosphere into the vacuum of outer space and reenter in the target area. The boost phase is the time during propulsion; this is followed by the exo-atmospheric midcourse phase, and this by the reentry or terminal phase. The range of modern missiles is more than 7000 miles and their present-day accuracy is 200 meters (about two city blocks). The intercontinental transit time is generally less than half an hour.

The older propulsion systems used liquid fuels, and could not be launched immediately on command. They were plagued with leaks. Modern military rockets employ solid fuels and can be dispatched at once. When quick launching is not important, such as with the space shuttle, liquid fuels (as well as solid) are still employed.

From the military point of view, intercontinental ballistic missiles have the following advantages: capability of delivering nuclear warheads to almost any point on Earth, high accuracy and reliability, safety from interception at reasonable cost, and security from destruction through use of underground silos. The United States had, as of 1984, 1049 land-based intercontinental ballistic missiles carrying 2149 nuclear warheads with a combined yield of more than 1400 megatons.

Amid all this depressing information a more cheerful note appeared after the end of the Cold War. In 1995, the Ed Peyden family bought an old missile silo in Kansas and converted it into their home. It is a cozy, split-level, four-bedroom abode. In Holton, Kansas, a school has been constructed in an unused silo.

The reentry vehicle is the part of a missile in outer space which carries the warhead back into the atmosphere. A heat shield protects it on reentering the atmosphere. Some missiles carry multiple independently-targetable reentry vehicles (MIRVs) which are released one by one; approximately half of U.S. warheads are now on MIRVed missiles. A computer on board controls changes in speed and orientation, controlling thrusters which separate each warhead, set it spinning, and direct it to a preselected target. Newer reentry vehicles are guided on a trajectory. Some vehicles use precision updates from navigational satellites, such as Navstar (10-3), to improve the accuracy of the MIRVs they dispense. All of these have been constructed in many versions, each more sophisticated and expensive than its ancestors.

Modern reentry vehicles are computer-guided to targets.

Offensive missiles generally carry penetration aids, which are devices to increase the probability that a target's defenses can be overcome. These generally involve dispersing chaff to confuse radar and balloons to confound exo-atmospheric sensors. The *payload* of a missile is the weight of its weapons and penetration aids. *Throw-weight* is the sum of weights of the reentry vehicles, boosters for its targeting, and penetration aids. *"Circle error, probable"* or *"circular error probability"* (CEP) is a term used to measure the accuracy of targeting of a missile carrying a warhead. It is the radius of a circle around a target of such size that a weapon aimed at the center has a 50% probability of falling within the circle. Advanced missiles are guided by computer-driven inertial guidance systems updated by receivers and decoders. These are mounted on platforms stabilized by signals computed from the outputs of platform-mounted gyroscopes. The on-board computer calculates position and velocity from the data supplied from accelerometers. The computer also calculates the thrust required for each MIRV vehicle as it is sent to its target.

Payload and throw weight

A brief description of some of the more important land-based missile systems follows. In general, each new missile introduced by Americans has been matched by the Soviets, and vice versa. One should never lose sight of the action-reaction psychology which plays such an important role in driving any arms race.

10-6 Some Land-Based Missiles

The Titan II was the largest American intercontinental missile. It dated from 1963, and has been retired. The Titan carried a single extremely potent (9 megaton) nuclear warhead in its payload of 8275 pounds. It was liquid fueled and sited in a hardened ferroconcrete silo. It was not very accurate (circle error probability around half a mile), but with such a tremendous warhead it would still have been quite effective.

Minuteman II and Minuteman III are intercontinental missiles about half the size of Titan II. They are solid fueled. The warhead of MM II is 1.2 megatons (about 80 Hiroshimas), and its circle error probability is around 1200 feet. The MM III can carry two types of warheads, 170 or 350 kilotons (13 or 27 Hiroshimas); it has two or three independently-targeted warheads (MIRVed) with CEP approximately 600 feet. The range of the two missiles is 7000 to 8000 miles. There are about 600 MM II and 800 MM III missiles. Silo-based Minutemen can survive

Minuteman missiles are accurate and numerous.

almost any attack except a direct hit. They can clear their silos within one minute of the firing order. Maneuverable reentry Minuteman vehicles are available; these can change course by using flaps or wings, which improves accuracy and makes interception more difficult.

The most controversial missile is the MX (for missile, experimental), called the Peacekeeper in a bit of euphemistic mayhem. It is huge (weight at launch, nearly 100 tons; payload 7940 pounds; see sketch), and is MIRVed to carry 10 to 12 warheads, each of 300 kiloton yield. Manufacture of the components is distributed among quite a number of subcontractors. Each warhead can be guided to within 400 feet (the CEP) of preselected targets. In flight, the MX is to be guided by the Navstar system (10-3). The two principal difficulties of the MX are (1) the vulnerability of the Navstar satellites and (2) its basing mode. Many ways to protect or conceal the system have been considered: silos, tunnels, road networks, constant movement on railroads or trucks, in jet aircraft, underwater, on ships, and others. None seems satisfactory. Some MX missiles were operational in early 1988. The weapon is better suited for a first strike than for pure defense.

Several smaller, single-warhead missiles have been developed. The Midgetman weighs 10 or 15 tons and has an adequate range. It can be mounted on a truck and moved often, and so is nearly invulnerable. The Pershing II missile has a 1000-mile range. When it is equipped with extra propulsion stages it is converted to Pershing III, which has an 8000-mile range. These can be launched from a silo or from an armored, mobile carrier. The long range means that Pershing III is a strategic, not tactical, weapon. Deploying 108 Pershing missiles in Europe began in 1984, and this awakened many citizens there to the dangers of nuclear destruction. The MX missiles are counterforce weapons.

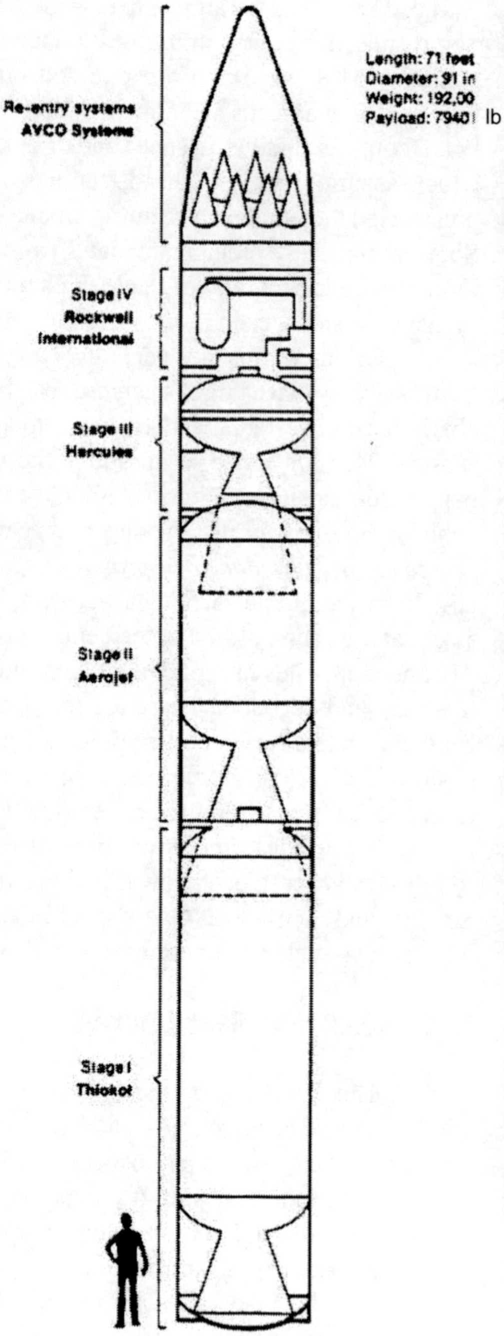

Length: 71 feet
Diameter: 91 in
Weight: 192,00
Payload: 7940 lb
Re-entry systems
AVCO Systems
Stage IV
Rockwell
International
Stage III
Hercules
Stage II
Aerojet
Stage I
Thiokol

MX Missile

An incident during the post-Cold War period confirmed how delicate the situation still is. This was in January 1995, when a Russian radar crew detected a missile of some type moving fast near Russia's northern border. It separated into several parts just as a MIRVed rocket would (10-5). Some of these components seemed to be headed to Moscow. In such a case the protocol required assessment and response within 10 minutes. Alerting orders were sent to Russian submarine commanders. After eight minutes, the several components of the missile fell into the sea. Several hours later the Russians learned that the object was a Norwegian research rocket designed to study the Northern lights. Actually the Russian government had been informed in advance, but word never reached the radar crew.

10-7 Sea-Based Systems

Rocket-carried nuclear weapons can be launched from surface ships of many types or from submarines, either surfaced or submerged. Most reliance is vested in submarines because they are virtually invulnerable, and thus can deliver devastating retaliation against the homeland of a country which has itself embarked on a first strike. Submarines are sleek, silent, and rarely seen, and a single one can carry more nuclear firepower than was used in all of World War II, counting all theaters of war. The American Navy developed the technology of firing missiles from under water during the late 1950s, and the Soviets soon followed suit. But this insulation from the outside world also means the submarine has more tenuous communications contact with its national command, particularly in the chaos of conflict. During the Cold War both superpowers kept a certain number of submarines at sea at all times to insure survivability. They were powered by nuclear reactors. Electrical energy from the reactors also electrolyzed water to give breathing oxygen for the crew.

Launched from under water, missiles were formerly less accurate than ground-based intercontinental ballistic missiles because of uncertainties in position and orientation, but the latest types have greatly improved accuracy, and are practically as precise as land-based missiles. Satellite guidance updates, while in flight, also improves navigation.

In the early 1960s, the United States built a series of Polaris submarines, capable of launching ballistic missiles. Some of these were converted to the Poseidon type of submarines, which until post-Cold War times made up the preponderance of strategic underwater ships. The first of the much larger Trident submarines was deployed in 1981. Fourteen to 24 of these will remain after 1994. The United States had at least 50 attack submarines on duty by 2000. Much attention is given to designing the submarines in a manner which minimizes their noise, the better to avoid detection. Nearly half of all US navy vessels are powered by nuclear reactors. The giant aircraft carrier Enterprise is driven by no fewer than eight reactors.

Poseidon vessels have pressurized-water nuclear reactors for their power plants. Each has 16 missile tubes, these accommodating missiles with either of 50 or 100 kilotons yield. The MIRVed 100-kiloton warheads number 192. These missiles have a range of 3500 to 4500 miles at full payload, and even further if fewer reentry vehicles are carried. Their accuracy (CEP) is around 1200 feet.

Tridents are about twice as big as Poseidons and are also nuclear powered. Trident II missiles carry hydrogen bombs (W88) of very high yield (475 kilotons) and have sufficient range to strike within 400 feet of any target on all continents on Earth. There are 18 Trident submarines currently, each with 24 missiles, and each missile is MIRVed with 8 to10 warheads. Some attack submarines are equipped with cruise missiles. The world now has in excess of 330 nuclear submarines. These systems are the most effective current means of maintaining deterrence, and this will continue into the foreseeable future. But questions always arise, such as: Was Trident II necessary, or was it built only because it was possible?

Trident submarines can send nuclear warheads to any spot on earth.

A recent concern is low-trajectory missiles launched from submarines. If developed, they could reach any site in the United States within 5 minutes, a clearly destabilizing situation. Despite extreme vulnerability to nuclear missiles, the navies of the world are abuilding. The U.S. has a 600-ship goal. All American aircraft carriers, battleships, cruisers, and destroyers are nuclear armed. The missiles are of the surface-to-air, surface-to-land, and nuclear depth charge types. Attack submarines carry nuclear torpedoes.

10-8 Cruise Missiles

During the last stages of World War II, development of rocket-delivered bombs was accomplished. The supersonic German V-2 rocket was jet propelled by combustion of alcohol with liquid oxygen. Subsonic buzz bombs using air and hydrocarbon fuels were also employed. It is from this last class that modern cruise missiles are descended. Their further development in the immediate postwar years was eclipsed by ballistic missiles, but nevertheless the U.S. deployed two types of nuclear-armed cruise missiles in the 1950s. These were large, unreliable, and inaccurate, and were abandoned.

In the 1960s military engineering advances gave birth to miniaturized guidance systems, improved jet engine designs, and lighter nuclear warheads. When an Israeli destroyer was sunk in 1967 by a Soviet-manufactured cruise missile (carrying a conventional bomb), the U.S. accelerated the pace of cruise missile development.

Cruise missiles are essentially jet-propelled aircraft which fly at a rather low altitude, that is, they are not ballistic missiles. Their wingspan is only eight or nine feet, their length is around 18 feet, and their diameter is 20 inches. Some burn hydrocarbon fuels using air and others have solid fuel and oxidizing agents. They are relatively slow (500-600 miles per hour). Their internal guidance systems use gyroscopes and accelerometers. By 1976 tests of air-launched cruise missiles began. They are coupled to computers and receive input from radar. The cruise missiles thus follow trails on digitized maps, allowing them to accommodate to the contours of terrain. As the missile nears the target, a video camera is turned on. Comparing the target's image with a pre-programmed image in the memory permits final adjustment of the course. Thus predesignated targets can be struck with extreme accuracy with a single nuclear (or conventional) warhead. The circular error probability is as low as 100 feet. Their cost is about $1,300,000 each. The sketch illustrates the essential features of a cruise missile. These features made cruise missiles a favorite in the Iraq war (1989-90), as well as later in Serbia.

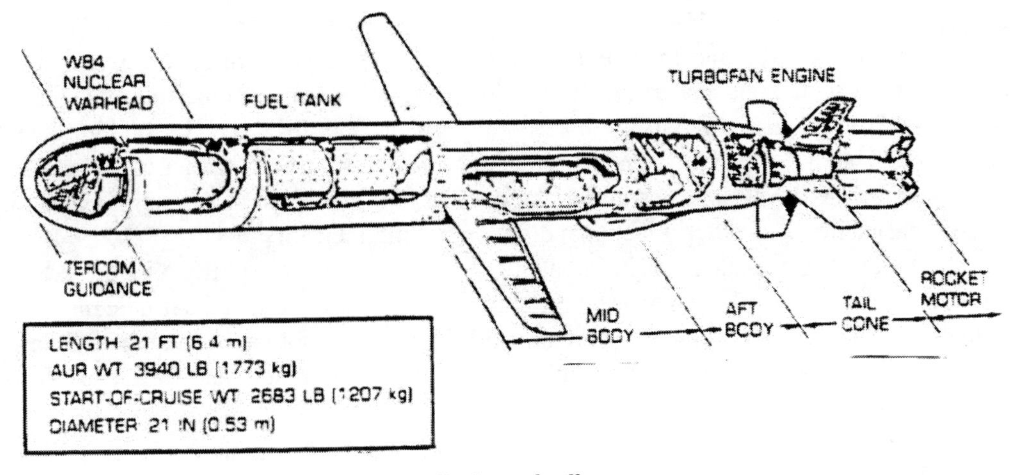

Cruise missile

A cruise missile has a range of up to1500 miles. The throw weight is 240 to 270 pounds, accommodating a warhead of 200 to 250 kilotons (if nuclear). They are relatively small and easily hidden, and hence can confound verification of treaty limits on missiles. Cruise missiles may be launched from the ground, air, or sea. The Tomahawk is in the last category; they can be submarine launched. One of the latest is the "Advanced Technology Cruise Missile," which has a range of around 2100 miles and employs "stealth" (low radar profile) covering. Its principal role will be to hunt mobile targets. Approximately 9000 cruise missiles were scheduled for deployment; in 1984 plans to site 464 of them in Europe were undertaken. With the virtual end of the Cold War, all these plans have been cut back. Long range, intercontinental cruise missiles are under development.

Cruise missles are of many versatile types

During the Iraq War (2003) hundreds of cruise missiles were launched from aircraft carriers; each was guided using the Global Positioning Satellite system. Most missiles proved to be quite accurate. Each cost around $1.3 million.

10-9 Soviet Strategic Forces

Estimates are available of the nuclear forces of the former Soviet Union from a variety of sources. They focused their strategic nuclear strength on intercontinental ballistic missiles. The oldest of these deployed up until recently is labeled the SS-11, while two of the newer ones are SS-18 and the thin-nosed SS-19. Only the SS-18 is currently capable of destroying a hardened silo. The rail-mobile SS-24 has a burn time of only 180 seconds, and this can probably be reduced, making it immune to any Strategic Defense Initiative system.

Some tactical missiles are the SS-4, SS-5, SS-19 or Stiletto, and SS-20; the series goes at least up to SS-27. The SS-19 carries six warheads. The latest of Soviet submarines were in the series known as Typhoon and Delta IV; they are the world's largest underwater ships. Soviet missiles launched from submarines are called SS-N-20,

Soviets more or less matched Americans in all military lines.

etc. The Soviets also used MIRV technology. They too had their cruise missiles. The AS-3 was an air-launched cruise missile. During the 1980s the Soviets dramatially increased their capacity to launch intercontinental ballistic missiles from submarines. They had only 15 to 20% of their submarines at sea at any given time; for the U.S., the figure was 50 to 60%. They followed the trend of replacing one huge warhead with 8 to 10 smaller, more accurate, MIRVed missiles. Since the demise of the Soviet Union, maintenance of the submarine fleet has deteriorated, severely degrading their threat.

In the 1962 missile crisis in Cuba, the Soviets were far from parity with the U.S. in deliverable nuclear bombs. They had a maximum of 44 intercontinental ballistic missiles, while the United States had 56, and an additional 144 submarine-launched Polaris missiles. But Soviet SS-4 missiles in Cuba could reach Washington, and were capable of carrying three-megaton warheads. Khrushchev had to back down. By the period 1975-1980, the Soviets had grown so strong that they could no longer be successfully dictated to and threatened. With the end of the Cold War, the situation changed still another time.

10-10 Comparison of American and Soviet Nuclear Forces

The table below illustrates the strategic nuclear forces of the two superpowers as of the year 1987, when they were at or near maximum. The figures cannot be considered exact, but are nevertheless informative. Cruise missiles and nuclear artillery are not included in the table. In case of hostilities, one would expect that a certain fraction of missiles would misfire, go off target, or otherwise fail.

Comparison of Strategic Nuclear Forces, 1987

Vehicle	*Number*	*Nuclear Warheads*	*Total Yield, Megatons*
United States			
Bombers	361	5,070	1,594
ICBMs	1,000	2,310	1,044
Submarine-launched ballistic missiles	640	5,632	410
Total	2,001	13,012	3,047
Soviet Union			
Bombers	155	1,170	808
ICBMs	1,392	6,846	3,841
Submarine-launched ballistic missiles	928	3,232	1770
Total	2,475	11,248	36,419

In 1987 the Intermediate Nuclear Forces Treaty was negotiated, and it was ratified in 1988; public approval was overwhelming. According to its terms 2695 Soviet and U.S. missiles, with 3107 warheads, in Europe were to be scrapped. The Soviets were required to dismantle three or four times as many warheads as the NATO Powers, and this process was monitored and verified. While this represents only 4% or 5% of deployed warheads, it is the first time armaments have been decreased rather than increased. The warheads and the guidance systems were not destroyed, merely returned to their home installations for storage or recycling.

It is dismaying to note, however, that the Pentagon tried to seek means of subverting the spirit of this new agreement. This was done by lifting the ceilings on nuclear artillery shells in Europe, by nuclearizing the new Army Tactical Missile Systems, and by increasing the nuclear capability of aircraft. But by September 1991 NATO had decided that all tactical nuclear weapons would be removed from Europe. There were more than 2000 such shells in Germany.

10-11 Warning and Intelligence Systems

Each superpower maintained surveillance satellites in geosynchronous orbit to keep the other under constant observation, the idea being to sound the alert if unusual military activity is detected. Such satellites must be considered a stabilizing factor. Photo reconnaissance cameras have been perfected to the point that they are capable of recognizing a 32-inch object from an orbit 100 miles high. The Keyhole satellite ejected film which was recovered from the ocean, a process now obsolete. The sophisticated Closelook satellite has a resolution of 4 inches. Infrared photography can detect heat-emitting objects night and day.

There are Distant Early Warning radar systems which are ground- and air-based. Increasingly sophisticated electronics are employed in the command. One must cope with the false communications and control alarms which warning systems give. The U.S. has laid an extensive array of sonar detectors along its coasts and those of allies to detect moving objects such as submarines. Various instruments have been developed which, dropped into the seas in buoys, detect anomalous magnetic behavior, and thus signal the presence of massive iron objects, that is, submarines. Methods of communicating with distant submerged submarines have been investigated for years without success.

During the later phases of the Cold War, the United States spent approximately $15 billion annually to produce dozens of military spacecraft, and another $5 billion to operate them. There were also satellite systems. These included: The Global Positioning System of 24 satellites; Magnum, satellites to capture foreign telephone communications; Project White Cloud, a system to locate foreign ships exactly; U.S. Satellite Systems, a CIA network to transfer spy data; Defense Satellite Communications System, providing voice and data transmission between bases in the U.S. and those abroad; Fleet Satellite Communications System, a Navy system to link ships and aircraft; Defense Support System, giving early warning of missile launches; Nato III, providing communication between NATO members; Defense Meteorological Satellite Program, providing world-wide weather forecasting service; Keyhole 11, a CIA system providing surveillance photos of foreign nations from space, with a resolution of less than a foot; La Crosse, an Air Force system of satellites giving radar images of foreign countries; Jumpseat, a satellite to capture transmissions of foreign military; and

A smorgasbord of defense programs

Leasat, a Navy communications system. Some of these systems are still in operation. In 1995 Israel launched a spy satellite, the Ofek-3; its resolution proved to be sufficient to read car license plates in Iraq. The fastest plane ever built, the SR-71 or Blackbird, was constructed in the mid 1960s for surveillance. Its speed was 2500 miles per hour at a height of 15 miles. The costs of production and maintenance were so high that each spy photo cost a staggering $1 million. The planes were put in storage, but two were taken out of retirement in 1995 by an act of Congress and a reluctant military was ordered to refurbish them for use in Bosnia, despite their obsolete equipment. Thus another $62 million was dissipated.

10-12 Nonmilitary Satellite Systems

One should not suppose that all rocket and satellite systems are devoted to military purposes. Satellites are routinely employed in worldwide communications, as in telephones and bringing educational television to remote villages. The Search and Rescue Satellite System has already saved the lives of over 200 downed pilots and others in distress; it also locates ships in trouble.

The Global Positioning Satellite system has a multitude of non-military applications. Commercial receivers for GPS signals have dropped drastically in price, some selling for as little as $100. A global air traffic system controlled via satellite is planned. Satellites photograph the surface of the Earth for agricultural crop census, location of minerals, for improving our knowledge of geography and continental drift, and many other purposes. Exploration of our solar system is a prime non-military purpose of rocket systems.

10-13 Nuclear Terrorism and Extortion

On the subject of targeting nuclear weapons, there is one more aspect which should be mentioned, and it is not military. The following scenario is conceivable at some future date. We wake up one fine morning and learn that a mysterious nuclear explosion has taken place in some distant desert or uninhabited island, or in space. No one claims responsibility. Multinational and United Nations investigations shed little light on the event.

Then, about a month later, the White House receives a message that unless a payment of, say, $25 million, is made each month to certain bank accounts in several other countries, an unnamed American city will be demolished or at least seriously damaged by a nuclear bomb. The threatening letter from some mysterious subnational group explains that the component parts of a nuclear device have been smuggled into the target city or elsewhere in the country and there assembled and hidden with enough shielding that detectors of radioactivity cannot find it. Therefore we must pay or suffer the consequences, it is implied.

Instead of extorting monetary tribute, the message might be delivered to, say, Israel, with the demand that unless the Golan Heights area is evacuated in one month, then a city will be destroyed. The possibilities are endless.

With many nuclear scientists from the former Soviet Union out of work and out of funds, the probability of such an event is probably growing greater for the time being.

Witness some of the signs that the matter is becoming threatening: in the fall of 1992, there was an alarm in Germany involving alleged smuggling of 20 kilograms of weapons-grade uranium-235. While that event did not prove true, there had been an attempt to smuggle in some cesium-137 and strontium-90 from Eastern Europe into Germany. Two of the four would-be smugglers were ignorant or careless enough to receive high, perhaps fatal, radiation doses. In October 1993 a Briton, one Norman Derbyshire, was convicted by a German court of trying to sell 80 kilograms (176 pounds) of Russian-made plutonium, valued at $80 million. The U.S. National Academy of Sciences has documented the disappearance of weapons-grade uranium-235 of Russian origin. American officials say there is credible evidence that Iranian front companies have tried to acquire nuclear materials from Kazakhstan. In December 1993 police caught six people smuggling 10 ounces of unspecified nuclear materials from Ukraine to neighboring Moldova. Directly afterwards, 3.3 pounds of radioactive materials were seized in the capital of Moldova.

What could a country do if such a deplorable menace as nuclear extortion actually materialized? If millions of hours and dollars would be spent fruitlessly searching cities for a nuclear bomb, would failing to find one be considered confirmation that the threat was a hoax? Clearly, here we would have a first-class quandary. For the immediate future the danger of a terrorist act such as that described might be considered remote, but after 25 or 50 years or so, the picture could be quite different. No system of safeguards can provide absolute assurance of safety.

10-14 The Strategic Defense Initiative, Alias Star Wars

Disinventing the Bomb?

In 1983, President Reagan delivered a speech in which he requested the scientific community of our country "to give us the means of rendering these nuclear weapons impotent and obsolete." It sounded like a wonderful idea, and immediately won a warm response from the public. A budget of $2 billion was established for fiscal 1985. The proposal, formally, but pretentiously known as the Strategic Defense Initiative or its sterile abbreviation SDI, was inevitably dubbed Star Wars. Actually, a program of considerable size had already been carried out earlier on antimissile missiles. In fact, the concept of using laser beams to disable incoming missiles was investigated in the 1960s, and was abandoned because of the impossible energy requirements and the conclusion that each defense unit would be hundreds of times more expensive than each attacking missile. In a test in 1984 an experimental rocket successfully intercepted an incoming ICBM, and this was proclaimed a triumph of U.S. military technology. Nine years later it became known that the test was a fraud: the ICBM carried an electronic homing beacon to guide the small rocket to its target.

Why did the Strategic Defense Initiative prove so popular with the public? The reasons seem to be composed of several elements. Like Reagan, Americans in general are exceedingly limited in science education, and most are intimidated by the wonders of modern technology. Learning of a system which promises to provide protection from those obliterating nuclear bombs they had been hearing about, naturally it should be supported. In addition, we Americans have long considered ourselves as sort of innocent redeemers of the world, and being able to accomplish almost anything. Reagan's proposal was a masterful political move. He did not bother to consult the defense-science community or America's allies before making the Star Wars speech.

Although the American public supported SDI at the beginning, that endorsement began to drop. As the budgetary deficit and economic distortions became more visible, further erosion of support took place.

10-15 Systems of the Strategic Defense Initiative

Here is what SDI postulates in its various facets. A high-technology complex of space-based stations would be orbited with sophisticated electronic communications and sensors capable of firing laser beams, or possibly particle beams, at any missiles directly after launch, thus disabling them. It is supposed to be the flare in the rockets' exhausts which is detected and which guide the aiming mechanism of the laser. There would be a flotilla of at least 200 platforms, each weighing tens of tons, with laser generators, optical systems, power supplies, and tracking and targeting apparatus. This swarm of technological wonders would orbit for years, always ready to counter any nuclear attack. Later, realizing that space stations would be vulnerable, it was proposed that laser weapons be "popped up" from a submarine just when needed to accomplish the same end, as sketched below.

Guardian angels

To get an idea of the difficulty of the task, consider that the vehicle of a MIRVed missile, around 12 feet in length, looks approximately the same diameter at 3000 miles that a thimble does at 15 miles. If a single warhead is involved (diameter less than 6 feet), it subtends the same angular diameter as a thimble at about 30 miles. And the targets are moving at more than four miles per second. It is really asking a great deal of any system to hit a thimble 15 to 30 miles away while it is zipping by at a fantastic speed.

Hit a thimble 15 miles away?

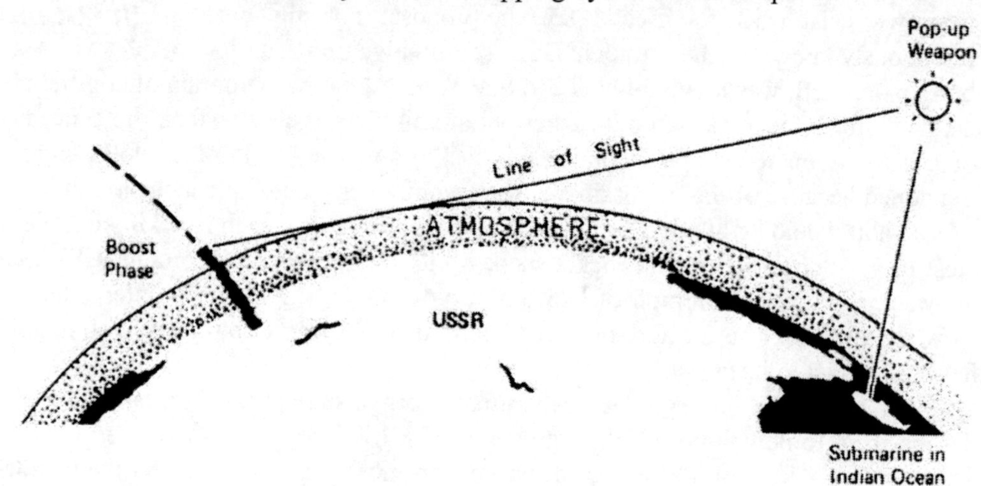

Pop-up version of an anti-missile laser weapon

Another idea presented was to use something called an electromagnetic rail gun to hurl solid projectiles at a missile being launched. Yet another is code-named

Prometheus, a sort of nuclear blunderbuss, blasting out swarms of small metal pellets, which are supposed to wreck decoy missiles, leaving the real ones to SDI lasers. The Pentagon even tested a high-energy rocket fuel based on beryllium hydride; the beryllium oxide produced is known to be highly toxic, attacking the lungs.

Still another idea was to build colossal land-based lasers to radiate beams through the atmosphere to truly gigantic mirrors in geosynchronous orbit, which reflect the beams accurately to other orbiting mirrors, which direct the beams to missiles (see sketch, below). Such beams would travel some 50,000 miles, and would have to be powerful enough to compensate for disturbances by the atmosphere, a major fault. A laser beam made using the reaction of deuterium with fluorine (wavelength 3.8 micrometers) is not absorbed by the atmosphere appreciably, but would be defeated by cloudy weather. Once a weapons system is adopted, it is extremely difficult to cancel it; as late as 1995, we were still spending millions on these chemical lasers for SDI. Other proposed types of lasers are those based on decelerating a beam of free electrons and those based on excited dimers ("excimers"), such as krypton fluoride. With such devices, the designation Star Wars seems quite appropriate. SDI attempts to disinvent the Bomb. It appeals strongly to those who yearn not for a way of preventing war, but a way to return to the prenuclear age.

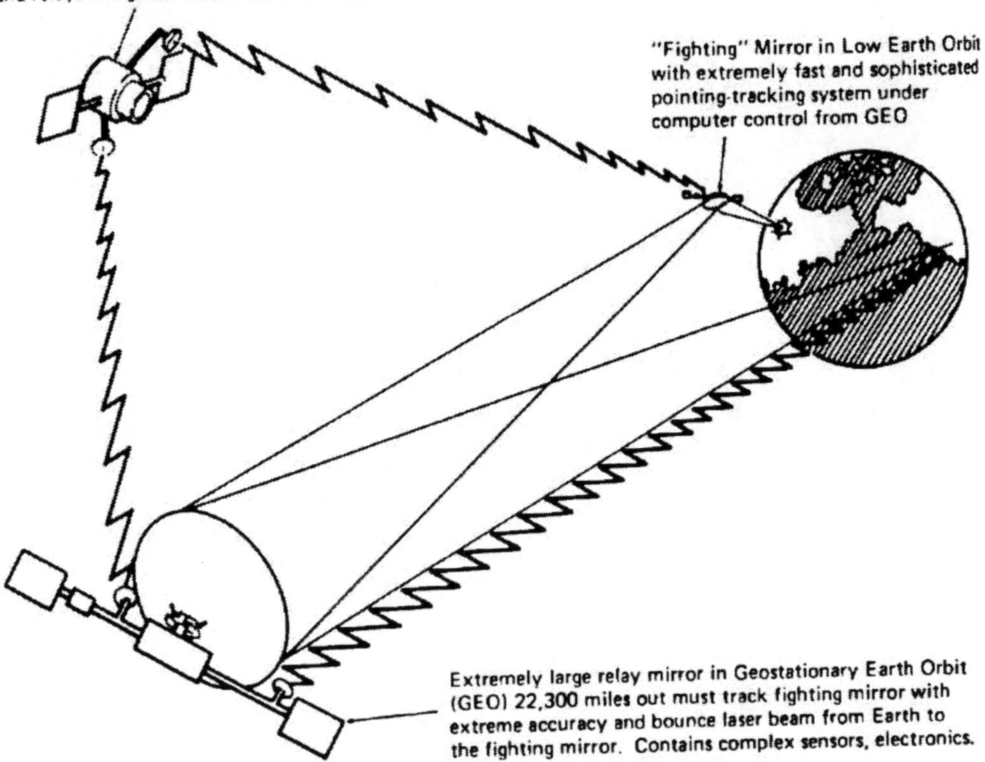

Orbiting mirrors

Nuclear warheads in missiles are shielded against the searing heat generated on reentering the atmosphere. Therefore any laser beam would have to be extraordinarily powerful and accurately aimed to burn through the missile's hull, especially considering that the targets rotate, and thus constantly present fresh surface to the beam. At least 100 million joules of absorbed energy would be required. How could such a laser be powered? The proposal was to use an energetic chemical reaction, such as that of hydrogen with fluorine, to form a gas laser. Mammoth tanks of compressed gases, mounted on massive space platforms, would be required. This idea was pursued through the summer of 1991, when its impracticality was realized, and another concept, the X-ray laser, was proposed.

Instant barbecuing of missiles by laser beams?

Recent research in nuclear explosions by Star Warriors is said to have proven that under the correct circumstances, a nuclear explosion of perhaps 120 kiloton yield, generates X-rays which follow down a metal rod and emerge as a powerful laser beam. The idea was that this beam, on striking a missile, vaporizes its outer surface, disabling it, or at least "thumps" it off course (sketch, below). Each device would have a number of metal rods, separately aimed. The entire space station would be demolished, and an electromagnetic pulse would be generated, endangering spacecraft and communications on land below. Edward Teller convinced science-illiterate Reagan of the feasibility of this scheme. Of course, nuclear X-ray lasers have been almost forgotten owing to poor performance in preliminary tests.

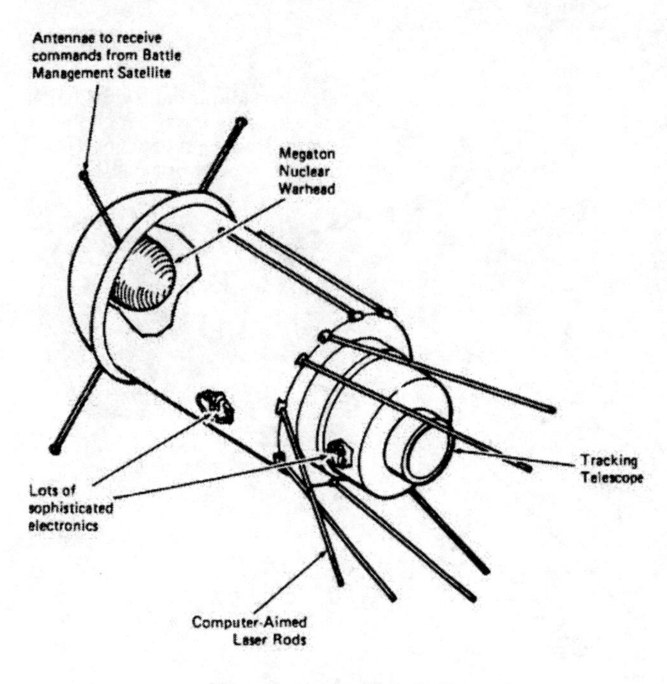

X-ray laser battle station

Still another laser, said to be usable over and over, is known by the catchy acronym FALCON (fission-activated laser concepts). Neutrons from a reactor, after being moderated by a plastic sheet, strike some uranium-235 foil. The charged fission products are expelled and their energy pumps a light-amplifying substance, and a laser beam is later discharged. Such fanciful ideas were actually being pursued in the arms race. The military failed to take into consideration adequately the consequences of a hydrogen bomb of one to three megaton yield at a distance of around 36,000 kilometers (22,500 miles) above the Earth. Such a blast in outer space generates X- and gamma rays which would cause electrons to be emitted from the metal surfaces of most satellites in orbit. This would create high electric fields, perhaps a hundred thousand to a million volts per meter, inside the spacecraft. This electromagnetic pulse (9-29) inside the satellite would damage the electronics of payloads. A space-based battle station requires power. According to the scheme, this power is supplied by a new type of nuclear reactor called the SP100, manufactured by General Electric. It employs uranium nitride as the fuel, and molten lithium metal for cooling. Its total power is 2.5 megawatts, but its electric power is only 100 kilowatts, making it only 4% efficient. It operates at a high temperature, nearly 1100 °C (2000 °F), which is a white heat. The energy from cooling would be emitted largely as infrared radiation, making the battle station a beacon, and therefore highly vulnerable. The cost would be at least $700 million before even a prototype is built. As late as 1991 as many as 100 of these reactors were still on the books. Star Wars would militarize space.

In 1980, NASA launched a gamma-ray spectrometer as part of the Solar Maximum Mission. At once, it began to record unexplained bursts of gamma rays. These were traced to a Soviet spacecraft carrying a RORSAT reactor in a 150-mile-high orbit. It was releasing electrons and positrons, whose mutual annihilation created the gamma rays. The reactor was shut down in 1988. Reactors in orbit are readily detected.

However, Star Warriors seemed to be determined as late as 1992 to orbit RORSAT and Topaz 2 nuclear reactors, which were purchased from Russia. Using a thermionic technique, a field in which Russia surpassed the U.S., the Topaz 2 generates 6 kilowatts of electric power. If this is done, its gamma ray emissions would probably seriously interfere with the operation of the Compton Gamma Ray Observatory, which was launched in 1991. An orbit about 3750 miles high would be necessary to prevent blinding the gamma ray instrument.

The main incentive for the 1991 purchase of Topaz 2 was to use it to power Star Wars space stations. It is ironic that just as the Cold War was winding down, technology from the former Soviet Union would be considered useful in counteracting former Soviet technology, which has become less and less threatening. But such is the military mind.

The Bush (senior) administration continued research to advance the Strategic Defense Initiative, introducing a Space Nuclear Thermal Propulsion program (Project Timberwind). More than $130 million was spent on this venture. In 1992 a classified environmental impact statement was prepared; its secret status infuriated activists. Timberwind is based on an advanced technology called a particle-bed reactor. This type employs half-millimeter fuel particles, each coated with a carbide to serve as neutron moderator. Having so much surface, the particles transfer heat rapidly to the propellant, which is hydrogen. Liquid hydrogen is injected directly into the white-hot reactor, when it expands instantly and provides thrust. A radioactive plume results. Atmospheric testing had been proposed, despite violations of nuclear safety standards. Evidently, little was learned from a 1973 effort by NASA to build a nuclear-powered rocket, costing about $1.5 billion. The Soviets had also wasted much resources on a futile attempt to build a nuclear rocket. By 1999 another type of reactor (Mitee), using lithium-7 hydride as a moderator, was being proposed as a rocket engine for outer space exploration. It too would heat hydrogen (to 2700 °F) and expel it for thrust. It would collect hydrogen from the atmospheres of the largest planets, or even electrolyze water. Such technology would take decades and vast funding to perfect.

It's going to take better ideas than these to build a successful nuclear rocket.

10-16 How Much Would SDI Cost?

The cost of the Strategic Defense Initiative, according to the Department of Defense, was $26 billion for the five years beginning in 1985. This was the initial development phase. By the end of 1992, an estimated $32 billion had been dissipated on SDI. There is very little to show for it. SDI has been funded at about twice the rate as the National Science Foundation. The funds could have been far better spent on researching solar energy, or on our crippling social ills, or in innumerable other, more worthy ways.

In the future, projections are much less clear, but for full development half a trillion dollars, and even a full trillion (the estimate of a recent Congressional Research Service report) have been calculated. This would have amounted to a hemorrhage of red ink. The costs cited were based on continuing the Cold War. As we see today, the end of that madness has resulted in many changes.

10-17 Is the Strategic Defense Initiative Just Another Step in the Arms Race?

Former Secretary of Defense Robert McNamara contends that "any attempt to strengthen deterrence by adding strategic defenses to strategic offensive forces will lead to a rapid escalation of the arms race," and concluded that we cannot have SDI and arms control at the same time. Most observers agree that the surveillance satellites which each superpower maintain in stationary orbit over the other's landmass enhance stability by being able to detect preparations for a first strike. Orbiting a system of attack satellites which could disable the stationary ones would be clearly destabilizing. Soviet military circles began to write about space mines which could cripple orbiting SDI stations. Anti-mine missiles would be next, and then means to cancel their effectiveness, etc.

The road to escalation

A recent report from the Stockholm International Peace Research Institute concluded that the Strategic Defense Initiative promises to hinder nuclear deterrence and induce a renewed arms race on land and in space. Projecting those trends, if they continue, one could envision the heavens enclosing thousands of American orbiting battle stations, mirrors, mines and other weapons, each with its "enemy" counterpart. It has been said that the human race has put much effort into its religions, but weaponry, there's where its heart really lies.

10-18 How to Frustrate SDI

Aside from space mines and antisatellite missiles of various types, there are other ways to render the Strategic Defense Initiative ineffective. One addresses the proposed laser-beam technique of disarming missiles. A laser beam from a battle station travels in nearly parallel rays in the vacuum of space, but is broadened as well as attenuated by the atmosphere. This is especially serious in the case of X-rays. The proposed system would detect and track the flare from attacking rockets and aim the laser beam so that it fires just as the target emerges from the protective atmosphere. Therefore recent advances in propulsion have been made, resulting in short-burn launches (40 to 60 seconds), so that the flare dies out before the missile goes into the vacuum of space (sketch below). This greatly complicates the aiming process.

Another change is to design the attacking missile so that the warhead separates from its propulsion unit, and it alone enters its trajectory in space. This small warhead, approximately five feet across, represents a smaller target. Moreover, it is spinning, and protected with an ablative heat shield.

Still another technique for foiling SDI is the use of decoys. By launching rockets loaded with decoys shaped exactly like real warheads, the detection and firing equipment would be overwhelmed. Reports soon appeared on making both true warheads and dummy warheads capable of evasive action to render them almost invulnerable. These are Maneuverable Reentry Vehicles, or MaRVs. Since neutral atoms of hydrogen in an energetic beam can penetrate deeply into metals, in principle a technique for detecting decoys exists, but this would require another enormous outlay of finance to develop, and could probably be defeated. There is also the possibility of blinding SDI sensors by lasers or flares.

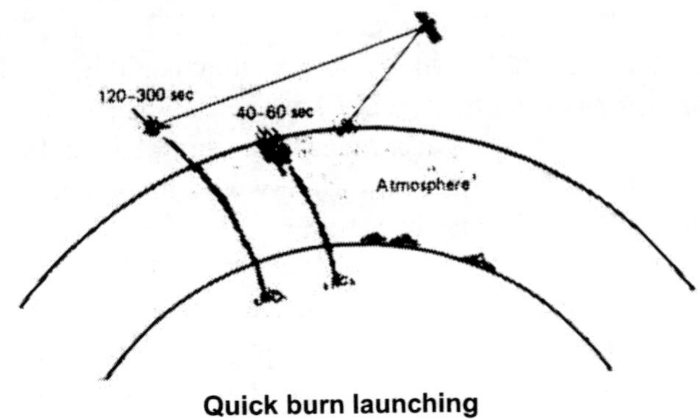

Quick burn launching

The electronics to accomplish the Strategic Defense Initiative are much more formidable than any ever attempted. Their computer codes would run into more than 100 million lines of error-free programming. It would take decades to accomplish this, and the program must function without error the first time, for it cannot be tested reliably under realistic circumstances. A single hiccup in the computer program could result in failure of the command. It should be noted that the Patriot system used in the Persian Gulf War required a modest several-million line computer code. The performance in real war of Patriot was pathetic. Under ideal conditions, such as being alerted in advance, Patriot can bring down missiles on smooth, stable trajectories, but in the Iraq hostilities, of the 44 attempts to hit Scud missiles under unpredictable wartime conditions, all or nearly all failed. This is because the Scuds followed irregular flight patterns. These considerations alone represent a towering, perhaps insurmountable, obstacle.

Just making the software presents crushing obstacles.

Finally, there are three fatal areas which the Strategic Defense Initiative does not address at all. These are the three ways of targeting nuclear warheads by means which do not involve outer space, namely bombers, missiles from submarines, and cruise missiles. In all of these cases, the vehicles are entirely within the atmosphere, and thus protected from overhead Star Wars attack.

10-19 What the Strategic Defense Initiative Does Accomplish

With monumental sums being spent on Star Wars technology, there must be some successes. SDI's battle stations in space would be capable of incapacitating those satellites with easily computed orbits. This could serve to blind the surveillance and observation facilities of an adversary in advance if a first strike were planned.

The development of exceedingly powerful lasers which can project intense beams of visible light or infrared radiation might conceivably be used as anti-aircraft weapons. If they could be made mobile, they could also be used as weapons in classical warfare to incinerate enemy soldiers. Perhaps such lasers and their power sources could be made light enough to be carried by plane, in which case they could be used to set cities, oil tanks, and forests afire. If deployed on battle stations in space, they might be able to accomplish the same task, and to cripple ground-based missiles in a first strike. This form of warfare would involve no radioactivity. Critics call the system the Strategic Offense Initiative.

Laser technology can be empoyed in nonnuclear war.

Suppose, after years of effort and billions and billions of dollars, a system based on the Strategic Defense Initiative is deployed. How effective would it be in case of real hostilities? There is no easy way to answer this question, but considering the many means of thwarting SDI, an estimated 5 or 10% of enemy missiles would leak through at the very least, and probably 50% or more. In order to insure effectiveness, the adversary launches many more missiles with multiple warheads than otherwise. This would insure success. What happens to those warheads which are disabled? They might be fused to explode if over enemy territory, to give an electromagnetic pulse. More likely, they would burn in the atmosphere, spewing plutonium oxide into the environment.

Before accepting the promise of Star Wars, one might well contemplate the words of German Air Minister Hermann Goering at the outbreak of World War II. He publicly stated that not a single enemy bomb would fall on Berlin. He was predictably dead wrong, as politicians so frequently are.

The problem is a little like trying to prevent smuggling cocaine into the United States. It is impossible to seal our land and sea borders tightly enough to throttle all contraband. A cynic once said that a nuclear bomb could be slipped into the United States if it were concealed in a bale of marijuana.

10-20 Advocates of the Strategic Defense Initiative

As mentioned earlier, politicians and much of the American public supported the Strategic Defense Initiative, not for sound scientific reasons, but because it gives a feeling of enhanced security. It should not be surprising to learn that many military circles also support SDI; it is difficult to remember any military program they oppose. The Air Force leadership in particular is buoyant with optimism about the exotic new technologies. Without additional funding specifically for SDI, however, the military is less enthusiastic, for then support would have to come from the regular defense budget.

The rapacity of the industrial-military complex is well known. With presidential favor, the arms lobbyists mobilized their patrons and now SDI has a life of its own. Quick deployment of something in space, whether it works or not, is seen as essential to keep the institutional momentum on track. About 87% of SDI and antisatellite funds was awarded to only ten companies, and these giants make subcontracts with the minnows of the trade. Profits were guaranteed. Jobs were at stake. A contract to Martin-Marietta, an important firm in the industrial-military complex, was made for a nuclear-powered

Who could oppose guaranteed profits and jobs?

laser weapon platform and tracking system. Numerous other defense contracts have been funded. The defense complex at Huntsville, Alabama, began to sparkle with new prosperity from $862 million in SDI contracts. Very little of this high-tech research has helped the United States compete more effectively in the world economy.

10-21 Detractors of the Strategic Defense Initiative

In 1986 the Union of Concerned Scientists polled the members of the American Physical Society concerning SDI. These are the people most competent to judge the scientific merits of the proposal. The results showed that 54% thought SDI was a step in the wrong direction, while 29% felt it is in the right direction. A number of universities accepted SDI contracts to conduct research. While a very few university-based scientists and engineers have become vocally supportive of SDI, 6500 others, representing a majority of professors in the nation's top 20 universities, have declared their opposition and have pledged not to accept any Star Wars funds. A 1987 poll of members of the National Academy of Sciences, generally regarded as the nation's most productive researchers, found 70% opposed to SDI. Nearly all (98%) thought that Star Wars could not protect the United States.

Impartial scientists oppose SDI.

A blue-ribbon panel of physicists, formed by the American Physical Society in cooperation with the Defense Department, prepared an exhaustive study of the Strategic Defense Initiative. They had full access to the classified documents. Their general conclusion, expressed in a cold, 400-page report in April 1987, was that Star Wars is not feasible, that directed-energy defense cannot be built now or in the foreseeable future, and that it is easy and cheap to develop counter measures.

The scientists' opposition was summarized by the eminent physicist Hans Bethe: "Star Wars cannot provide a comprehensive defense against a determined adversary who could overwhelm it with warheads and decoys or circumvent it with cruise missiles and bombers." He said that key elements such as X-ray lasers are not going to work. Others used more piquant language. Astronomer Carl Sagan called SDI zany, unworkable and more likely to ignite a nuclear war than to preserve peace. Former Secretary of Defense James Schlesinger said SDI is entirely unrealistic. He went on: "There is no serious likelihood of removing the nuclear threat from our cities in our lifetime or in the lifetime of our children."

The following is quoted from the Los Angeles Times, July 26, 1989. Barbara Boxer was then a Democratic Representative from California and is now a Senator.

> Opposition to "Star Wars" is based primarily on the assumption of many House members that the United States ultimately will agree to outlaw space-based nuclear defenses in arms control negotiations with the Soviet Union. But supporters agreed that the program must be fully funded for the United States to negotiate from a position of strength.
>
> When Rep. Kyl claimed that Americans currently spend more on pantyhose than on nuclear defenses, Rep. Barbara Boxer sprang to her feet to denounce the weapon. She argued that the Administration has never clearly defined the mission of "Star Wars." "Believe me," she said, "pantyhose is affordable; 'Star Wars' is not. Pantyhose

gives us 100% support; 'Star Wars' does not. Pantyhose has a mission that does not change every day; 'Star Wars' mission has changed from a protective shield to military installations defense to accidental launch protection to 'brilliant pebbles' to terrorist deterrence. The 'Star Wars' [mission] has changed more times than Imelda Marcos has changed her shoes."

Fred Reed, of the Air Force Times, innocently thinking he was writing an obituary of Star Wars, began in these colorful terms: "Star Wars was just flat nuttier than a pecan orchard on fertility drugs. The genial madness of it all wasn't obvious if you focused on its avowed intentions (saving America) instead of its funding, its weirdly shifting proposed technologies and its wacko enthusiasts."

In summer 1994 the General Accounting Office of the U.S. government, reviewing a critical analysis of the Strategic Defense Initiative, exposed outright fraud in earlier tests. In one case a bomb was planted in the target missile to explode by a proximity fuse on an attacking SDI missile, giving a miss the appearance of a direct hit. Some target missiles were heated, making them emit infrared and thus easier to detect. Target missiles were turned sideways in flight, presenting a much larger objective. These deceptions were kept from Congress for ten years, after $35 billion had been spent.

But Star Wars has not yet had a wooden stake driven through its heart. Incredibly, as late as 1993, the Army launched a series of expensive, unnecessary tests of Star Wars missiles from the garden isle of Kauai, Hawaii. These were tests of the Strategic Target System, with the cute acronym STARS. In the first test, an unarmed Polaris missile was fired from Nohili Dunes, a beach area near a cemetery holding the remains of ancient Hawaiians. The target was near Kwajalein Atoll, 2000 miles distant. The tests were to detect and to track these missiles, which mimic a putative Soviet attack, during their 18-minute flight. Up to the first test, $210 million had been spent, without commensurate benefit. More tests were scheduled.

10-22 Other Consequences of SDI

Compared with Europe and Japan, America's enfeebled educational system produces far too few qualified scientists and engineers. If a vigorous Strategic Defense Initiative is undertaken, many of those who do graduate would be absorbed and no longer be available to industry. There have been euphoric allegations by SDI partisans of civilian spinoff from Star Wars research, invigorating the American economy. These claims seem grossly exaggerated. A more likely result will be still further erosion of America's competitive status in the world of commerce.

The Anti-Ballistic Missile Treaty of 1972 permitted each superpower to construct one anti-ballistic missile system. The Soviets chose to construct theirs around Moscow. The immediate American response was to proliferate warheads targeted on that area, whose defenses today could easily be overpowered. Thus installation of an anti-ballistic system resulted in less security for Moscow, not more. The Strategic Defense Initiative would repeat this counter-productivity on a grand scale. The treaty, still in effect, prohibits both the USA and Russia from deploying nationwide defense systems.

Testing SDI has already introduced many thousands of shell and missile fragments into orbit about the Earth. This costly junk travels at fantastic speed, and will stay in orbit for centuries. This debris poses a danger to satellites and spacecraft.

10-23 Why Soviet Opposition to SDI?

Imagine Soviet leaders in the 1980s when they observed Americans investing billions of dollars into something they say is purely defensive. Naturally it had to be investigated closely. When it is seen that this plan, called the Strategic Defense Initiative, can be rather easily overwhelmed by massive attacks and underflown by missiles launched from submarines, cruise missiles and bombers, they conclude that the real objectives are not defensive at all. They are much more sinister, perhaps a camouflage for a first strike. Development of space stations with powerful lasers were, however, well suited to destroy all Soviet surveillance satellites, and perhaps could be used against targets on the ground.

The Soviets felt forced to conclude that Star Wars is a challenge to their security, that is, an offensive weapon. If by some chance SDI had been successful, it would have allowed the U.S. to launch a first strike with impunity, a clearly destabilizing development. The Soviets saw no choice but to maintain deterrence by taking countermeasures. Physicist Roald Sagdeev, director of the Soviet Space Research Institute, said U.S. deployment of SDI would result in a Soviet buildup of long-range weapons. It is known that the Soviets have a crude anti-ballistics missile system; if this is upgraded into their version of SDI, it need not trouble us: they would face the same intractable obstacles as Star Wars (and would look aggressive in American eyes). The Russians evidently agree with a statement by Lyndon Johnson: ". . . [C]ontrol of space means control of the world, far more certainly, far more totally than any control that has been achieved by weapons or by troops of occupation. Space is the ultimate position, the position of total control over Earth."

A Soviet SDI would have seemed aggressive to Americans.

10-24 The Strategic Defense Initiative: the Verdict

The Franck Report, written in 1945 before the first test of a nuclear bomb, contained the following prophetic words: "In the past, science has often been able to also provide new methods against new weapons of aggression it made possible, but it cannot promise such efficient protection against the destructive use of nuclear power. This protection can come only from the political organization of the world." Einstein too, with nuclear weapons in mind, made the durable observation, "There is no defense." We see that today the offense will continue to have the advantage. The hard reality is that we will be sharing our world with nuclear weapons for a long time, a very long time, to come.

National security no longer exists so far as nuclear attack is concerned. It largely faded away during the period 1945 to about 1975 or 1980, and will never return. At the moment, international security doesn't exist either. It will not prevail until we human beings arrange our affairs on Earth to establish a more stable world structure which can control all nuclear weapons.

The Strategic Defense Initiative is a technological extravaganza seeking a unilateral solution to the arms race. The problem is essentially political, and requires a political solution. One side only cannot be secure. SDI gave every incentive to the USSR to build new offensive weapons systems. Abandoning SDI would enhance our security.

The final result would be to lessen our security.

Far from making "nuclear weapons impotent and obsolete," Star Wars stimulated a whole new generation of this Frankenstein ordnance. Pursued vigorously, SDI would cause economic devastation in the U.S., and accelerate industrial decline. It is a financial black hole.

The fantasy of the Strategic Defense Initiative shielding the American people against nuclear weapons is tailor-made for the opponents of arms control and for easily seduced technological minds. Pursuing Star Wars resembles an ailing and desperate cancer patient who seeks an unproven drug such as Laetrile. SDI fosters a dangerous, ghoulish delusion of a space age Maginot line or Great Wall of China. The real issue is hardly SDI itself, but rather our proclivity to hunger for a technological fix for every human folly. It is difficult to escape the suspicion that Star Wars is a result of the anxiety and power needs of men who have dissociated themselves from earthly human compassion for real people.

One fatal flaw in the SDI proposal is its failure to accommodate to the idea that it is just another notch in the arms race, that it stimulates steps to counteract its claimed effectiveness, all this extracting resources from our livelihood to feed still more incredibly expensive and insatiable war machines. It would be a tragedy to permit the sour brine of military theology to become our guidestar.

By 1988, the Star Wars program had been scaled down by eliminating some of its more outlandish objectives. Its admitted goal was changed to protect missile sites, not cities. It became embedded in the American military-industrial complex with a budget of around $5 billion per year. Gorbachev announced, "If the Americans have a lot of money, let them squander it on SDI. We will look for a response along other, asymmetrical lines that will be less expensive by a hundred times, or probably more."

By 1990 still another project within Star Wars had been presented. This one, even more zany than its predecessors, was called "Brilliant Pebbles," and was supposed to consist of up to eight thousand small, high-speed rockets, a veritable constellation, launched from numerous satellites and which destroy incoming missiles by collision. Its cost was $46 billion. Perhaps a better name would be "Loose Marbles." Development of "Brilliant Pebbles" would violate the ABM Treaty. In 1993 SDI was renamed the Ballistic Missile Defense Organization. By 1994, at least $40 billion had been spent on SDI. The whole program can be considered as a gigantic hoax perpetrated on the American people.

In his 1992 election campaign, Bill Clinton promised to "bring a healthy dose of reality to the SDI program." By 1995, this goal had been partially met, but embedded programs still existed. With the Republican Congressional victory of 1994, the specter of Star Wars II was resurrected, despite the discredited status of Star Wars I. Proposals to build one sort of missile-defense system or another continued to be resuscitated through the remainder of the century. They still would waste billions of dollars on a false sense of security.

It is not inconsistent with the above analysis to state that science in all its aspects should be employed in seeking real and genuine defense, to whatever extent possible. But efforts to establish a peaceful world should receive at least equal support. Though the Cold War has ended, various countries are still endeavoring to become nuclear powers (Chapter 9). There is a legitimate mission for a military force to protect the United States in today's world. It is the maintenance of peace in the nuclear age which must be one of our overriding objectives.

10-25 The Sequel

Could there be a Star Wars II ? Certainly there are its advocates. Measures were introduced into Congress in 1995 to set the course to this end. But who are the villains? According to a sponsor of an SDI follow-up, Rep. Curt Weldon of Pennsylvania, it doesn't matter. He says, "If you keep relying on the facts and logic, then we're going to lose this battle." He didn't say which battle. The Pentagon has prepared so many high-quality animated graphics and cartoons showing invading missiles being shot down by anti-ballistic missiles with 100% success that it is hardly surprising that so many Americans believe such a system would actually function as promised by Star Wars propaganda.

Congressional hawks were finally successful in forcing Clinton to agree to a version of Star Wars II, called the National Missile Defense (NMD) system, which Congress approved in April, 1999. This occurred in spite of the absence of any visible adversary, unless one considers North Korea, a weak, impoverished country, to be a viable threat. Thus the venerable fraud continues. A yearly budget of $6 billion was authorized. This new system violates the ABM Treaty. During the past 20 years or so, some advances have been made in defense technology. Computers have been advanced, and radar has been improved.

In the late 1990s, still another pathetic addition to the Star Wars II family of programs appeared. It is called Theater High Altitude Air Defense, or THAAD. Its first six tests resulted in six misses in attempts to intercept incoming missiles. Congress has passed resolutions declaring that an anti-missile system must be deployed at the earliest possible date. This would also violate the Anti-Ballistic Missile Treaty. Senator Helms simply announced that "We will put the ABM Treaty in the dust bin of history." By fall 1999, $55 to $60 billion had been spent on Star Wars, and already $4 billion more has been lavished on THAAD. In fall, 1999, a $100 million test of an interceptor was carried out over the Pacific. Of course it was pronounced by its proponents as a perfect success. The launch time, place, and other data were known in advance to the testers, who also benefit from its financing. A second $100 million test in summer 2000 was so obviously a failure that no claim of success was even attempted.

The new, unproven, antiballistic missile systems which many members of Congress advocate depends on infrared sensors in space in stationary orbit, which are supposed to detect large heat emissions of a launch, and afterwards infrared released by warhead-bearing vehicles. So-called "rogue" nations, meaning Iran, Iraq, and North Korea, are held up as the aggressors. The invading missile emerges from the atmosphere and releases reentry vehicles and decoys. Space-based early warning infrared sensors alert the ground-based radar, which is then supposed to launch interceptor missiles, which somehow distinguishes the bomb-carrying vehicles from the decoys, and maneuvers into position to collide at the speed of 10,000 miles per hour with the targets.

It seems as if no one has addressed the question of why any "rogue" nation would make a nuclear attack on the United States, when they are well aware that they would face swift nuclear annihilation in response.

Actually, if a "rogue" country decided to attack the U.S., it would be more easily carried out by bringing in a weapon of mass destruction by boat, truck, or ship cargo container. It would be less expensive and more difficult to identify the responsible party.

Any country scientifically advanced enough to manufacture ballistic missiles which could send nuclear warheads to the United States would also be capable of making sophisticated decoys to thwart any anti-ballistic missile system. A missile with nuclear warhead, released in the vacuum of space above our atmosphere, could be made to avoid detection using infrared sensors by simply adding an outer layer containing liquid nitrogen. This material is so cold that it would radiate infrared less than one millionth as intense as at its launch temperature. Covering the warhead vehicles with radar-absorbing materials is also a possibility. Dozens of lightweight decoys would accompany a warhead, as well as the opposite, that is, to make the warhead resemble a decoy. Decoys would be warmed to make them radiate infrared to confound detectors. The advantage in these cases is always with an aggressor. For each measure, there would be countermeasures, all this with outrageous costs. In short, it would be Cold War II.

Just after the beginning of a new millennium it appears as if the United States is about to embark on more foolish ventures, disguised as defense. It just isn't right.

PART II: THE PHYSICAL EFFECTS OF NUCLEAR EXPLOSIONS

ABSTRACT—Nuclear blasts affect their targets by radiations (thermal, gamma, neutron), by shock waves, overpressure, dynamic pressure, and radioactive fallout. The origin, extent, and importance of these physical effects are analyzed. Shielding offers some protection. Radioactivity from local fallout is the most dangerous; shock waves and burns also take a heavy toll. Radioactivity induced in soil by neutrons, over- and under pressure, and dynamic pressure are explained.

10-26 Physical Effects of Nuclear Explosions

This Part, which is largely based on the classic analyses of the topic by Glasstone and Dolan (see bibliography), concerns details of the physical effects of nuclear explosions. For readers who are less interested in the quantitative aspects of the subject, this entire Part II may be omitted without excessive loss of continuity.

The principal features of the physical effects of nuclear explosions fall under the headings of air blast and overpressure, the main radiation types (thermal, gamma, and neutron), radioactive fallout, and explosions at the Earth's surface and below water. The electromagnetic pulse may also be classified under the effects of nuclear explosions; it is discussed in 9-29. To understand the meaning of a nuclear war, we should first examine the mechanical and radiative effects of nuclear explosions.

10-27 Thermal Radiation in Air Bursts

As described earlier (9-4), the energy distribution of a nuclear explosion in air is approximately as follows: 50% in the shock wave, 35% as ultraviolet, visible and infrared radiation (mostly the last), 5% as gamma, X-ray, and neutron radiation, and 10% as the radioactivity of the fission products. There are also some alpha and beta radiations, but their range in air is short and their effects are inconsequential in the long run.

When you hold your hands in front of a fire, the skin absorbs the radiation (largely infrared) and its temperature is raised. Similarly, if a flash of radiation from a nuclear explosion strikes a surface, absorption of the energy raises the temperature instantly; and since the intensity is extreme, the temperature jumps proportionately. If the material is combustible (wood, leaves, paper, fabric, rubber, etc.), it is heated above the kindling point if the distance is not too great. The side of a wooden house is scorched over its entire surface within a few seconds. Of course, exposed skin is burned and eyes are damaged even more easily.

The intensity of radiation is diminished by increasing distance, fog, and smoke.

All radiation coming from a point necessarily decreases in intensity or power as it moves outward according to the inverse square law, that is, if the intensity at 1 kilometer is represented by I, at 2 kilometers it is I divided by 2 squared, or I/4. This holds approximately for nuclear explosions except when the target is close. This attenuation of intensity, spreading radiation over an ever increasing area, is of geometrical origin. An additional reason for attenuation is that the air both absorbs and scatters some radiation. Ultraviolet rays are absorbed more readily than visible or infrared light. Dust, fog, or smoke causes further weakening of radiation. The radiation from nuclear explosions above clouds penetrates but little to the land below; if an explosion is below a cloud layer, much radiation is reflected back downward.

Of course, shielding protects a target from radiation. Opaque objects such as hills, houses, concrete, and even clothing provide variable amounts of protection. A target surrounded and covered by shielding is better protected than by shielding which merely intervenes in front; this is because of scattered radiation, which is especially important under hazy conditions. Radiation coming from random directions is sometimes referred to as "skyshine."

The amount of radiative energy which reaches a target from a nuclear explosion depends primarily on three factors: the distance between bomb and target (which also takes into account the altitude); the yield (number of kilotons of TNT equivalence); and the air conditions. Thermal radiation injures living creatures directly and by the secondary effect of fires ignited by the radiation.

When a small nuclear bomb (Hiroshima size, about 15 kilotons yield) is exploded in air, the dangerous thermal radiation is finished in about 0.4 second. But when the yield is very high, say 10 megatons, the dangerous stage of thermal radiation lasts around 20 seconds. Except for the longer-lived fission products, which are responsible for radioactive fallout, the most dangerous radiant emissions of nuclear explosions occur within about one minute.

10-28 Effects of Thermal Radiation

Radiation striking a surface is reflected, absorbed, or transmitted. Only that absorbed is damaging. Dark surfaces absorb most, light surfaces least. In the case of a nuclear explosion, the duration of exposure is short, so the intensity is high, causing surface temperatures to rise rapidly. The Hiroshima bomb was around 15 kilotons yield, and it exploded at an altitude of 1900 feet. The Earth directly underneath (the hypocenter or ground zero) was heated white hot (3000 to 4000°C) by the radiations of all types.

Thin combustible materials, such as dry grass or leaves, paper, and cloth, are raised to ignition temperature. Massive wood is scorched and charred, but not ignited unless it is quite close to the explosion. The higher the moisture content of an irradiated material, the more resistant it is. Limestone, on exposure to nuclear bomb radiations, decomposes and liberates carbon dioxide gas, causing each particle to undergo a mild explosion ("popcorning"). Damp sand behaves similarly. Of the common white fabrics, wool is the most resistant, cotton next, rayon next, and nylon least.

Radioactive energy can char, ignite, decompose, or melt matter it strikes.

The term which measures the amount of thermal radiation a surface receives is the number of joules of energy absorbed per square centimeter. A cotton shirt ignites when this energy reaches 60 J/sq cm. For ignition, newspaper requires 20 J/sq cm and black rubber, 40 J/sq cm.

What is of most interest in connection with thermal radiation is the amount of energy delivered to surfaces by bombs of various yields exploded at a height between 500 and 15,000 feet. The point on the earth directly under an elevated nuclear explosion is the hypocenter or ground zero; the paths from the explosion point to the surrounding land are slanting lines, and their lengths are called slant ranges. A table which gives approximate values of radiant energy received (radiant exposure) per square centimeter for five bomb sizes when visibility is average is given (table 10-50A at the end of this Part). The numbers look cold and unimportant; in fact, they measure death-dealing capacity.

10-29 The Japanese Experience

Studies of the permanent shadows burnt into various surfaces by the flash of the explosions at Hiroshima and Nagasaki permitted location of the exact points of explosion, that is, the hypocenters and heights were determined. Even the diameters of the fireballs could be ascertained. In Nagasaki, the dark components of a polished granite bank fronting absorbed so much more energy than the light colored parts that they were heated to at least 600 °C (a red heat), causing them to expand and pop out. The resulting surface was rough. Green-black ceramic tile on a roof at a slant range of 0.6 mile received around 185 joules per square centimeter for about 4 seconds. This heated it to at least 1800°C, causing its surface to melt and blister. Flash marks were burnt into asphalt, wood, painted surfaces, and fabrics. Radiant exposure of just under 20 J/sq cm caused the black writing on a paper to burn through, but not the white areas. Cotton blackout curtains ignited at two-thirds of a mile.

10-30 Incendiary Effects

Radiant energy from nuclear explosions starts some fires by direct ignition of thin combustible materials, as mentioned above; radiation entering windows can cause internal fires. The shock wave, which arrives several seconds or minutes after the radiant flash, may blow out smaller fires, but they smolder, and often re-ignite.

Firestorms may result under certain conditions of weather, terrain, density of combustible materials, and other variables. They are formed when many individual fires merge to form a convective column of hot gases, drawing still more air inward and upward. Such a firestorm resulted at Hiroshima, but not at Nagasaki. The inward wind at Hiroshima reached a velocity of 30 to 40 miles per hour.

10-31 Exposure to Gamma Radiation

Although very different in general properties, gamma rays (the term will include X- rays in this discussion) and neutrons cause similar biological damage, qualitatively speaking. Both types of radiation are released in dangerous amounts by nuclear explosions, but their range is shorter than that of thermal radiation. High-yield hydrogen bombs release the most dangerous levels of gamma and neutron radiation. In the case of a smaller fission bomb, say of the Nagasaki type (22 kilotons), gamma ray injury is limited to about 2 kilometers, with no shielding.

Fortunately, gamma rays tend to be absorbed by air.

Tests of nuclear weapons have given much grisly data on the dose of gamma and neutron irradiation at varying distances and bomb yields. The figures differ for pure fission weapons and those with much of the energy from fusion. Two tables (tables10-50B and 10-50C at end of this Part) present a few selected gamma ray doses, accurate to within a factor of 2, for both kinds of bombs at varying distance and yield. Again the numbers look harmless, but their meaning is deadly.

10-32 Shielding Against Gamma Rays

Both gamma and neutron radiations are extremely penetrating and shielding is difficult. Even 2 feet of concrete will not prevent a fatal dose of gamma rays from a one-megaton bomb exploding a mile distant. In general, the denser a material is, the better it absorbs gamma rays. A 24-inch thickness of water will reduce incoming gamma rays to one-tenth of their initial intensity. Eleven inches of concrete or 3.3 inches of steel accomplishes the same attenuation. Lead is quite effective. By mixing iron oxide with concrete, the capacity to absorb gamma rays is greatly improved.

Smaller explosions, such as those at Hiroshima and Nagasaki, release 65% of their gamma radiation in the first second. In the case of huge explosions, say 5 megatons, only about 5% is released in the first second. Therefore, in the second case, persons seeing the initial flash could duck behind any substantial shielding within a second or two and greatly reduce their total body dose.

10-33 Exposure to Neutron Radiation

Doses from neutron irradiation under conditions analogous to those described above are generally less than gamma ray doses. High-energy neutrons collide with nitrogen and oxygen molecules in the air and are slowed down. Some neutrons are captured by nitrogen nuclei and form carbon-14. Two tables (10-50D and 10-50E) show approximate values of doses from neutron irradiation from several different bomb yields and distances. Again we face a series of boring numbers, but they conceal power over life and death.

Comparison of the effects of the Hiroshima explosion with that at Nagasaki revealed that the first, which involved uranium-235, released many more neutrons than the second, which involved plutonium-239.

10-34 Shielding Against Neutrons

While shielding against neutrons is more difficult than in the case of gamma rays, it can be accomplished by using the proper combination of materials. A mixture of substances containing both heavy and light elements is best. The light atoms slow down fast neutrons, permitting them to be absorbed by certain other atoms. But this capture of neutrons emits gamma rays, hence the presence of heavy metals. Concrete and damp earth are fairly effective. A 12-inch slab of concrete reduces neutron density tenfold; a second 12-inch thickness reduces it another tenfold, so that only one neutron in a hundred

Shielding against neutrons is more difficult.

can get through. Addition of the strongly neutron-absorbing element boron (as borax) improves neutron attenuation still further.

10-35 Shock Waves in Air from Nuclear Blasts

Although the following discussion is in physical or engineering terms, there is always in the back of our minds a haunting truth: this is not just physics and engineering, but it is our lives and our homes that are at stake.

We have seen that about half of the energy of a nuclear explosion in air is transmitted to the surrounding area via shock waves. These are responsible for most of the damage to living things and structures. An account of the properties of these blast waves follows.

Air at sea level exerts a pressure of 14.7 pounds per square inch (psi). This is normal atmospheric pressure. The speed of sound in this air is 1116 feet per second or 761 miles per hour. When a shock wave is created by a nuclear explosion, it is not mere sound. The mass of air around the bomb site is thrown out at a speed exceeding that of sound, each molecule being a projectile. The shock wave initially travels several times the speed of sound, and gradually slows down to that value. It takes sound 4.73 seconds to go one mile. The supersonic shock wave from a 20 kiloton explosion yield requires about 3 seconds, while that from a 1 megaton explosion yield requires only 1.4 seconds. Looking down from a distance, a shock wave is actually visible, appearing as a bleary shimmer.

The initial speed of a shock wave exceeds that of sound.

Pressure can be either static (as in air at rest) or dynamic (air in motion). In the second case, pressure is higher in the direction of travel than laterally. Air is being compressed at the front of the wave. *Overpressure* is the term used to describe how much the maximum pressure at the wave front exceeds the static pressure of undisturbed air. In the Nagasaki explosion, the overpressure 1.4 miles from ground zero was 3 psi, meaning that the total pressure was 14.7 + 3, or 17.7 psi. Tables 10-50F and 10-50G at the end of this Part give peak overpressures at various distances from ground zero for a 1 megaton explosion at 6000 feet and on the ground.

After a shock wave passes a given point, the air is rarefied and the pressure may fall to a value under the static value of 14.7 psi. The amount less than standard atmospheric pressure is the *underpressure*. It is a sort of negative pressure, that is, negative relative to standard atmospheric pressure. Underpressure results in air being drawn backwards by suction. Another important consequence of underpressure is that directly after the instant of a nuclear explosion, the newborn fission products which have very short half-lives continue to emit gamma rays for several minutes; since this radiation is now traveling through rarefied atmosphere, its intensity is attenuated less than at normal pressure, and is all the more damaging.

Imagine a nuclear explosion a few hundred feet above the ground, a target being some distance away. Radiant energy travels with the speed of light and hits the target almost instantly. The shock wave rushes out in all directions at several times the speed of sound; it hits the Earth at ground zero and is reflected back. Laterally, the

Successive over- and underpressure

wave expands and combines with its reflection. It eventually slows down to the speed of sound. Several seconds are required to hit the target. If there is a fixed observation point, we first observe a high overpressure as the shock wave passes over; it is followed by an underpressure. Both are transient. Overpressures can be high, hundreds or even thousands of pounds per square inch. Underpressures are usually much smaller, being around 4 psi. The magnitude of both depends primarily on the explosion yield and the distance.

When a bomb of 1 kiloton yield explodes 1000 feet above ground, the following peak overpressures prevail: 15 psi at 280 feet from ground zero; 8 psi at 1000 feet; 2.3 psi at 4000 feet; and 1 psi at 6500 feet. Of course, 1 kiloton yield is tiny by modern standards.

Let us state a certain overpressure, say 5 psi; nuclear bombs will generate this overpressure to a distance proportional to the cube root of their yield (energy released). Thus if the yield of a bomb is doubled, the circle of a shock wave of 5 psi overpressure is only the cube root of 2 (which is 1.26) times as large in radius. This says that larger weapons distribute their destructive power less efficiently than smaller ones; two one-megaton bombs cause more devastation than a single two-megaton one.

The height above ground for the most effective (that is, most destructive) nuclear explosion of given yield depends on the nature of the target and whether the attacker wishes to create a cloud of dangerous fallout. There is no single optimum height with regard to blast effects. Hard targets require a low or surface burst. Weaker targets, such as residential territory, can be flattened by higher bursts, which increase the area razed.

Two one-megaton hydrogen bombs are more destructive than a single two-megaton bomb. The term *equivalent megatonnage* has been coined by nuclear strategists to better compare the destructiveness of bombs of differing yields. The equivalent megatonnage is the actual megatonnage raised to the 2/3 power, that is, the cube root squared.

10-36 Dynamic Pressure

There is another term of importance in describing the destructive effects of shock waves: the *dynamic pressure*. It is a more subtle concept than overpressure. Dynamic pressure is the pressure which results from the mass of air which flows behind the shock front. It is a measure of the kinetic energy (the energy of air molecules associated with their motion) of the air behind the shock front. Unlike overpressure and underpressure, which are the amounts above or below atmospheric pressure, dynamic pressure is not relative to atmospheric pressure and cannot be negative.

Dynamic pressure is important because strong winds result from the passage of a shock front. These winds tend to be prolonged. Overpressure is usually exerted for 1 to 3 seconds; the winds resulting from dynamic pressure may last several minutes. This results in a drag force on structures. Depending on shape, some structures are more susceptible to damage by overpressure than by *drag winds* arising from dynamic pressure; for other structures, the opposite is true. While both must be considered in estimating damage, overpressures are generally more destructive. The actual definition of dynamic pressure is one-half the product of the density of air through which the blast wave passes and the square of the wind velocity behind the shock front.

Destructive drag winds result from dynamic pressure.

For overpressure values of 70 psi or more, dynamic pressures are higher; if the overpressure is less than 70 psi, dynamic pressure is lower. Some peak values of overpressure, dynamic pressure, and corresponding wind velocities are tabulated in table 10-50H. Again it should be mentioned that these figures are not just an idle exercise in calculation; they help inform us of the level of destruction we could face.

10-37 Reflection, Refraction, and Pressure Effects of Shock Waves

A shock wave is reflected by the Earth or other solids, or by the surface of water. If the explosion is high in the air, then at points underneath, the overpressure of the shock wave is first felt, followed by its reflection coming up. The shape of a shock front reflected from a flat surface is that of an expanding dome. The reflected wave coming back up is passing through air which has already been shocked by the primary wave, and is therefore heated and pressurized. Under these conditions, the reflected wave is propagated faster than the primary wave front, and can catch up and merge with it. Thus the total overpressure can be much higher than at the primary shock front alone. The merged front is called the Mach reflection region. Because of this effect, the peak overpressure at a certain distance from ground zero may be intensified by exploding the weapon at some altitude rather than at ground level.

Hills reflect shock waves irregularly, sheltering some areas and focusing the waves' fury on others. Areas not in the line of sight to the explosion can nevertheless experience severe shock. A temperature inversion layer in the atmosphere may reflect much of the energy of a shock wave back down. Such reflected waves are capable of breaking windows hundreds of miles from the burst point.

Reflection of a shock wave on a surface results in exerting a pressure on it of more than twice the overpressure; it may be up to 8 times the overpressure, depending on the shape and other factors. This results from the combination of various Mach reflection regions. If the surface is immobile, such as the Earth, a high proportion of the energy is reflected back. If the surface is a wall which is pushed over, only a fraction of the energy is reflected back. The exact value of pressure exerted on a wall depends not only on the overpressure, but also on the angle at which it strikes; there is always a component pressure at right angles to the wall. If a shock wave creates an overpressure component of only 2 pounds per square inch perpendicular to a wall, at first thought this doesn't sound very high. But if the wall is 10 by 15 feet, there are 21,600 square inches, resulting in a minimum total force of 43,200 pounds or 21.6 tons. The actual force might be twice this value. It is exerted for 1 to 3 seconds. It takes a strong wall to withstand these stresses. Drag winds follow.

Reflection of a shock wave from a surface exerts enormous pressure.

At corners, shock waves diffract or bend around a structure, exerting high pressures on the roof and sides. How high this pressure is depends on the overpressure, as well as the size, shape, mass, and rigidity of the structure. It also depends on the size of doors and windows. When these are blown in, air rushes inside and tends to equalize internal and outside pressures, lessening overall damage somewhat. But most of the damage is done before this equalizing effect takes place. Vertical cylindrical objects, such as telephone poles and smokestacks, are curiously less vulnerable to damage than one might expect. The curved surface minimizes diffraction effects. In Hiroshima, many factories were destroyed, but their nearly undamaged smokestacks still stood among the ruins. Nevertheless, those close to ground zero were demolished.

Explosions high in the air tend to dish in the roofs of buildings and autos. Larger buildings, such as multistory steel-reinforced concrete structures, most apartment houses, and wood-frame dwellings are very susceptible to damage from shock waves.

Both the shock front and drag winds from dynamic pressure cause damage. Details of their interaction are complicated. Drag winds last several minutes and can push over poles spared from shock wave damage.

10-38 Structural Damage by Shock Waves

Analyses of the damage to Hiroshima and Nagasaki have revealed a great deal about the damage inflicted on structures of many types. Some Japanese buildings had been built to resist the severe earthquakes which are not infrequent there. Additional studies of damage caused by nuclear explosions were carried out in the Nevada deserts, at Bikini, and by using old ships to be junked.

Among the qualities which affect response to blast are strength of beam materials and joints, resilience of the framework, and elasticity. Smaller residences of masonry or wood are engulfed by the pressure wave and quickly collapse. Masonry walls which bear the load of roofing are easily demolished. Brittle materials fail at low overpressures. Industrial buildings of steel are denuded of roofing and siding, and their frames are twisted. Steel is elastic and strong, and thick steel-reinforced concrete (ferroconcrete) is most resistant.

Residences are most easily demolished; industrial structures are damaged beyond repair.

The 15-kiloton-yield bomb at Hiroshima destroyed many substantial buildings. Nothing useful was left within 1.7 miles of ground zero. Heavy damage extended to nearly 4 miles, and windows were broken 8 miles away. Reinforced concrete buildings which appeared to suffer only superficial damage at first sight were, on closer examination, found to be unsafe and unsalvable. Walls had buckled, roofs had been pushed downward. Most had been ravaged by fire. Some fires were started by radiant heat, but most came from broken fuel lines and containers.

In Nevada, tests measurements of overpressures were made. A summary of the results and effects follows.

- Overpressure of 0.5 to1 psi. Windows broken, depending on size. Bigger windows break more easily. Corrugated steel structures could be repaired.
- Overpressure of 1 to 2 psi. Corrugated steel paneling of industrial buildings buckle. Aluminum siding is pushed in. Buildings not reparable. Wooden siding demolished. Aircraft on ground ruined.
- Overpressure of 2 to 3 psi. Steel-frame buildings severely damaged. Unreinforced brick walls collapsed.
- Overpressure of 4 to 6 psi. Moderate damage to steel-reinforced masonry block houses.
- Overpressure of 6 to 30 psi. Ferroconcrete structures buckled. Most factories and commercial structures collapsed. Railroad cars and trucks completely destroyed.

It should be emphasized that damage estimates cannot be made from overpressure values alone. The dynamic pressure, weather, terrain, and other factors must be considered. In the case of automobiles, trucks, and railroad cars, for example, it is the drag winds which are most important.

The ship U.S.S. Crittenden was exposed to a blast of 200 kilotons yield; the ship was nearly half a mile from the hypocenter. This test was at Bikini in 1946. Very serious damage was done. Ships, being large and slow, are exceedingly vulnerable to nuclear bombs. An aircraft carrier costing $5 billion or $10 billion can easily be sunk by a cheap nuclear bomb.

10-39 Underwater Nuclear Explosions

A number of underwater bursts have been carried out in the Pacific. They generate relatively slow-moving waves in the form of growing circles around surface zero. The waves do not carry as much of the blast energy as one might at first expect. A test with 20-kiloton yield produced waves at least a hundred feet high, but they slackened off rather quickly, and were only about 14 feet high at a distance of half a mile. Conceivably, waves generated by explosions in the ocean could damage harbors and structures near the shore, but would probably not be as destructive as the same warhead exploded in air.

10-40 Radioactive Fallout

Radioactive fallout is one of the more important consequences of exploding nuclear bombs. Earlier (9-18) it was briefly described; a more complete account is given here.

One minute after a nuclear explosion, about 30 billion curies of fission products have been formed for each kiloton of fission (not fusion) yield. These fission products decay by beta and gamma emission. A great deal of the nuclides have extremely short half lives; after 24 hours, the level of radioactivity is 2000 times less than its 1-minute value. Fresh fission products are the most dangerous, primarily on account of gamma emissions.

Dangerous radioactivity also arises from fission products, plutonium, neutron-induced activity, and tritium.

There are two additional sources of radioactivity after a nuclear explosion. One is the induced radioactivity resulting from the absorption of excess neutrons by nonradioactive matter. The other is the unfissioned plutonium-239 or uranium-235. In modern nuclear warheads, 35 to 40% of the fissile metal undergoes fission, and the remainder ends up as plutonium or uranium oxide. The plutonium oxide is far more dangerous to life than the uranium oxide. The level of radioactivity from the plutonium (by alpha decay) is negligible compared to that from the fresh fission products and neutron-induced activity, but it endures much longer. Aside from the three sources of radioactivity listed above, there is still another from hydrogen (fusion) bombs. This is tritium, or hydrogen-3; some of it escapes fusion.

More than 700 kinds of nuclides are formed on fission. In the case of warheads which are predominantly of the fusion type, huge numbers of surplus neutrons are released, and these react with the various elements in the weapons materials, the air, and earth. These reactions produce new radioactive nuclides, and the radiation from these sources may be dangerous.

In a high air burst the fireball does not touch the Earth. The weapon materials are all vaporized and carried upward by convection. They condense to exceedingly fine particles which take years to settle. This is *global fallout* and it is distributed worldwide (9-18). In the explosion of smaller bombs at a height, such as at Hiroshima and Nagasaki, the fireballs did not touch the ground, and essentially all of the fallout was global, that is, carried upward and away. There was a small amount of neutron-induced radioactivity on the ground.

The fireballs of hydrogen bomb explosions in the atmosphere always produce global fallout, and those which touch the Earth also produce fallout which is deposited on the surface downwind within several days. The second type is called *local fallout* (or *early fallout*). The particles consist of soil materials which were fused and vaporized, along with fission products and other bomb materials. In addition, there is a great deal of neutron-induced radioactivity. There is a spectrum of particle sizes, from microscopic up to several millimeters, like sand. Much of fallout particles consist of glassy spheres. When steel towers were used to hold a test bomb several hundred feet in the air, some of the fallout particles were black since they held magnetic oxide of iron. The larger particles settle down rather quickly, within about 24 hours, and become local fallout. This material is carried downwind, and is the most dangerous of all fallout. Roughly 65% of the total radioactivity appears as local fallout.

Local fallout consists of particles of fission products mixed with materials from the Earth.

The fission products are beta and gamma active; the beta particles cannot travel far in air. The beta activity does little harm unless the materials are ingested by breathing dust or taking contaminated food or water, or fall onto leaves or animals and irradiate their surfaces on direct contact. It is mostly the gamma radiation we have to worry about. The number of rads measured is nearly equal to the number of rems.

10-41 Global Fallout

Nearly all of the fission products from air bursts which do not touch the Earth, as well as about 35% of the fission products from surface bursts, are carried upward into the atmosphere as fine particulate matter. The troposphere is the lowest stratum of atmosphere and it carries most of the clouds; the stratosphere is just above. Both are invaded by the radioactive materials which are then circulated around the globe. The fraction in the troposphere is largely washed down to Earth by rain during the first month. The material in the stratosphere mostly stays there and decays harmlessly.

10-42 Local Fallout

The fireball of a nuclear explosion which touches the ground vaporizes soil to an extent depending on yield and height. As the fireball cools, the fission products and soil materials (which exhibit induced radioactivity) condense to particulate matter. The more refractory components condense first; the more volatile components condense last. This gives rise to what is called fractionation: different radiological properties for

Fallout is not uniform.

near and far fallout. The local fallout is carried downwind and settles in an elongated area of several thousand square miles. That which settles nearest to ground zero is most dangerous, especially during the first 24 hours.

The local fallout exposes everything in its path to radiation. There is an approximate rule of thumb which permits one to estimate exposure rate. If the dose rate in rads per hour is measured at a certain spot one hour after the explosion, then at 7 times one hour, that is, 7 hours after the explosion, the dose rate will be about 10 times smaller. After 7 times this (7 x 7 = 49 hours), the dose rate is another 10 times smaller, that is one-hundredth of the 1-hour rate. After 7 x 7 x 7 = 343 hours, the rate is still another10 times less, that is, one thousandth the 1-hour rate. This rule is accurate to within 25% for two weeks and to within 50% for 6 months. Tabular and graphical data are available for many other cases.

10-43 Idealized Fallout Patterns

Each nuclear shot in the atmosphere results in its own distribution of radioactive material. The fallout pattern depends on the explosion yield, its height, the type of ground around the hypocenter, the wind direction and velocity, and other factors. If rain or snow falls through a cloud of fission products and other debris, a large fraction of the radioactivity is scavenged out and brought to Earth in irregular patterns. Despite these variables, certain gross features can be distinguished.

Fallout patterns depend on many unknown variables.

Our knowledge of fallout patterns is incomplete. What we know comes mostly from studies of tests of hydrogen bombs in the Pacific (marine conditions) and tests of smaller bombs (below 100 kilotons) in Nevada (desert conditions). These analyses have led to mathematical models of fallout patterns. An idealized fallout model is probably the best to date, and requires computer programs which can accommodate wind velocity and other variables. Applied to wind, the term shear means different velocity at each altitude. In idealized fallout patterns, no wind shear and no physical obstructions are assumed. The results are in the form of a map with contours representing the boundaries of radiation of specified levels (either as rate in rads per hour or as total accumulated dose in rads). The highest activity is found near ground zero. The fallout is driven by wind into a very elongated ellipse; the faster the wind is, the more elongated is the ellipse. The figure (page 584) shows the fallout pattern for an explosion of 2-megaton yield (half from fission, half from

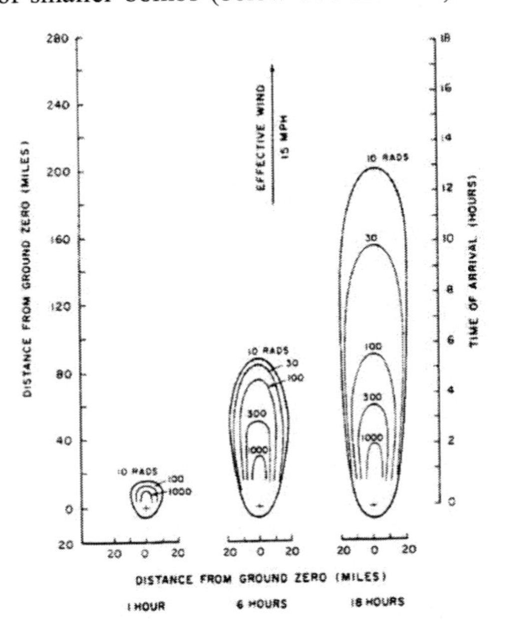

Total-dose countours from local fallout, idealized (2-megaton yield, 50% from fission, surface burst)

fusion) and a wind velocity of 15 miles per hour. It is in terms of total accumulated dose, not dose rate. The three sets of contours correspond to 1, 6, and 18 hours after explosion.

The degree of radioactivity depends on the fission yield, not the fusion yield.

While only a few selected contour lines are drawn in, corresponding to a few dose levels, one can imagine a line for any specified dose. Consider a point 20 miles downwind. It receives some irradiation from the flash, but no more until the first fallout arrives. In 1 hour, the first fallout begins to arrive. After 6 hours the total dose has reached more than 1000 rads, and after 18 hours it is more than 2000 rads. The dose accumulates slowly after that; the dose rate falls off because of radioactive decay of the fission products.

10-44 Real Fallout Patterns

The hydrogen bomb test, called Bravo, of March 1, 1954, on one of the islets near Bikini Atoll in the Pacific (9-19) was of 15-megaton yield, the most powerful ever exploded by the United States. The bomb was only 7 feet above the coral reef. The fallout was blown by a gentle wind for several hundred miles. The map (below) shows the measured total doses within 4 days.

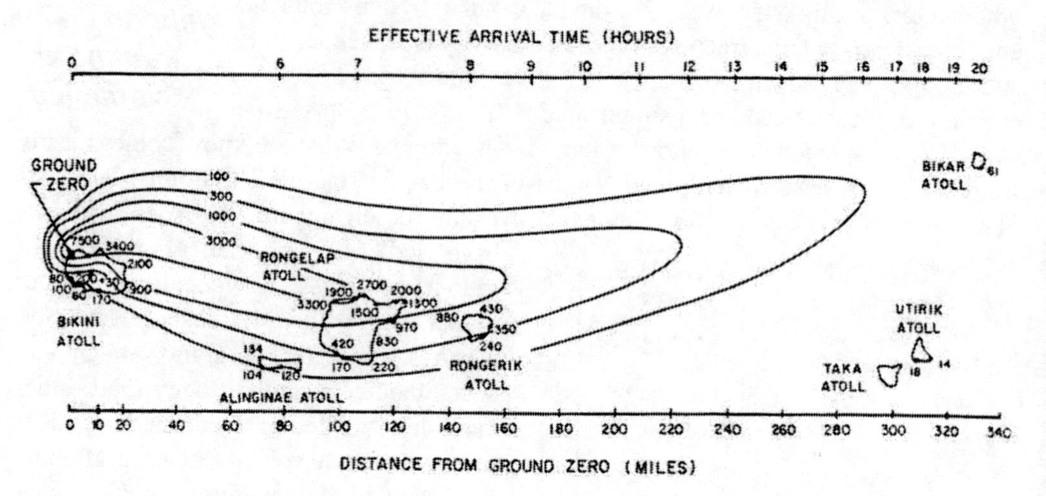

Real fallout pattern from the 15 megaton Bravo test at Bikini (the numbers are total doses in rads within four days)

An area of about 7500 square miles received enough radiation to be fatal in the 4-day period. The total doses on the map pertain to maximum exposure to persons without protection. As of year 2000 it is still not entirely safe to return to Bikini. The two most important fission products which remain in dangerous amounts are cesium-137and strontium-90; there is also some plutonium.

The irregularities of real fallout patterns are further illustrated by two of the Nevada tests of the 1950s. The yields were comparatively small (12 and 43 kilotons) and each was on a 500-foot tower. The patterns (below) are also shown (dose rates 2 hours after detonation).

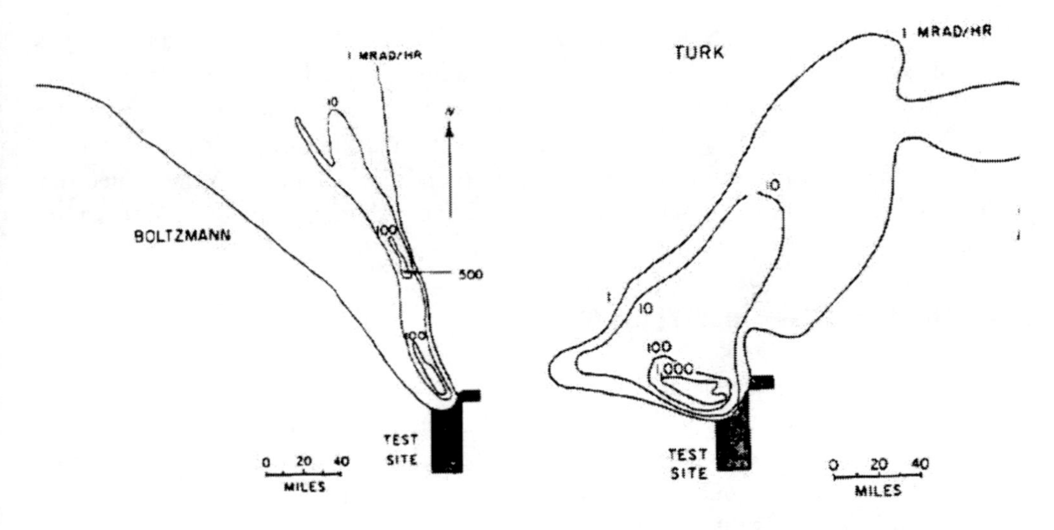

Pattern of fallout, Boltzmann shot
12-kiloton yield

Pattern of fallout, Turk shot
43-kiloton yield

Note the extreme irregularities. The fallout from the smaller shot formed hot spots some 60 miles from ground zero. These are unpredictable, and result from shifting wind direction and speed, obstacles presented by the terrain, and other factors. When wind shear exists, fallout patterns take on a double or triple lobed character. Explosion of many bombs on the surface can thus cover most surface of a large area with lethal fallout.

10-45 Neutron-Induced Radioactivity

We have seen that the neutrons released from nuclear explosions interact with the chemical elements of the air and ground to produce many radioactive nuclides. The effect is moderate in the case of fission bombs, but with hydrogen bombs, in which many more surplus neutrons are discharged, the neutron-induced activity can be up to 40% of that of the fission products themselves.

Probably the most dangerous radioisotope formed in this way is sodium-24. Sodium in Nature is sodium-23, and occurs everywhere. All soil contains some sodium-23, and seawater is about 2.8% salt (sodium chloride). The sodium-24 resulting from absorption of a neutron by the sodium-23 nucleus has a half-life of 15 hours. In its decay, both beta particles and gamma rays are emitted. Moreover, sodium is a necessary element for both plants and animals, and it quickly enters the food chain.

Soils also contain traces of manganese, zinc, and other essential elements. The first on neutron activation yields manganese-56 (half-life 2.6 hours) and the second yields zinc-65 (half-life 244 days). Fortunately these are formed in tiny yields.

Carbon-14 results from the action of excess neutrons on the nitrogen of the atmosphere. The total amount of carbon-14 produced by all atmospheric explosions up through 1963 has been variously estimated at 1450 to 4300 kilograms. This represents an increase of 2 to 5% in the world's carbon-14 reservoir. It is in

The average human body today is subjected to a dose of about 10 millirems per year from its carbon-14 content.

the form of carbon dioxide. Somewhat more than half of that has dissolved in the oceans. Nevertheless, some of this carbon-14 is assimilated into the food supply via green plants, and thus its radioactive decay (half-life 5730 years) inside our bodies contributes a little to somatic and genetic damage. This will continue for thousands of years.

There are still other elements in the environment which on exposure to neutrons produce radioactive forms, but their half-lives are all very short, and relatively little danger is presented.

10-46 Injuries by Nuclear Explosions

There are four principal ways in which nuclear explosions may injure human beings: blast and shock effects, thermal radiation, gamma radiation, and radiation from fallout. There are also secondary sources of injury, including burning from fires, damage by objects hurled by the blast, and being hurled bodily for some distance. Biological damage by radiation was discussed in Chapter 5.

Our knowledge of the effects of nuclear explosions on people stem mostly from the events at Hiroshima and Nagasaki, but also from test explosions and their effects on animals. In addition, information from ionizing radiation comes from many other sources, such as the accident at Chernobyl (Chapters 5 and 7). Imagine circles on a map of Hiroshima centered at ground zero. The first circle has a radius of 0.6 mile; 86% of the people in this area died at once. In a ring between this circle and a larger one with radius 1.6 miles, 27% of the people died at once. Outside of that, up to 3.1 miles, only 2% of the people died. Altogether 68,000 people died at once, and many more perished later. About 30% of those who perished had received lethal doses of radiation, even though death may have been caused by the shock wave, a flying or falling object, or fire.

10-47 Blast Effects on the Body

Blast injuries fall into two types, direct and indirect. The first results from the extreme pressure effects of the shock wave. The second results from flying objects. When a human being is engulfed by a shock wave, the diffraction process instantly subjects the body to intense pressure, as in the case of any other object. Later the victim is subject to drag winds, and might be thrown some distance. Compression and decompression of the body causes hemorrhage of the lungs and rupture of abdominal organs, such as the spleen. Subsequently, the lungs accumulate fluid and suffer edema. An embolus can form in the blood vessels, resulting in quick death. Surprisingly, cases of eardrum rupture are relatively rare. A person near a wall experiences greater bodily damage from a shock wave than from one farther away. This is because of the more than doubling of overpressure on reflection.

10-48 Burn Injuries

Clothing provides partial protection from flash burns.

Exposure of human skin, either directly or through clothing, to the thermal radiation from a nuclear blast causes flash burns. Not including gamma and X-rays, the radiation consists of the ultraviolet, visible, infrared, and microwave regions of the spectrum. The least severe burns (first degree) are superficial but painful, but no scars result. More severe burns (second degree) form blisters, redness, and scabbing. No scars result unless there is infection. The most severe burns (third degree) destroy nerve endings, so pain is felt only at the edges of the wound. They take several weeks to heal and often become infected. Scars always result, sometimes keloid. If a relatively large area is burned, the decomposition products of the skin, on entering the bloodstream systemically, may cause vomiting and sickness.

The experience of Hiroshima and Nagasaki showed that even thin clothing protects the skin from flash burns to some extent. Light areas of fabric absorb less radiation than dark. There were many cases in which designs in fabric were tattooed onto skin. Radiant exposures of unprotected skin of 18 to 25 joules per square centimeter generally cause second-degree burns. First-degree and third degree burns involve lower and higher radiant exposures, respectively. Second-degree burns over 30% of the human body are generally fatal without prompt treatment.

Permanent eye injuries from the explosions in Japan were rare. There were many cases of temporary blindness, but within several hours, sight returned to normal. This flash blindness is caused by bleaching of the retinal light-sensitive pigments. Retinal burns, on the other hand, cause permanent eye injury. They can be produced even at great distances by staring at an atomic fireball.

10-49 Determination of the Yields of Nuclear Explosions

There are nine methods of establishing the yield of a nuclear explosion. Most were developed by detailed studies of such explosions in air, starting with the very first, and continuing through those up to1963 (when atmospheric tests were banned). The data permit calibration scales to be drawn up. Some of these methods are:

- Radiochemical measurements. This technique, probably the best, depends on analysis of the debris from the explosion. The results tell us what fraction of the fissile elements underwent fission, and knowing their initial mass, permit calculating the yield.
- Thermal radiation. The depth and character of wood charring at a known distance from the explosion can give a good estimate of yield. Studies of various kinds of wood exposed to radiation from explosions of known yield, and in laboratory furnaces, furnish the necessary data. The cypress on a shrine in Hiroshima was charred, and two analyses of the data gave the yield as 14 and 15 kilotons, respectively.
- Gamma ray-induced thermoluminescence. Gamma rays excite certain atoms in roof tiles and similar ceramics, and later heating causes the stored energy to be emitted as light. Measurement of this light intensity gives enough data, using reliable calibrations, to calculate the yield of nuclear explosions.
- Neutron measurements. Neutrons from nuclear explosions induce radioactivity in a number of common elements. Some of the sulfur, used in bonding insulators to utility poles, was converted to radioactive phosphorus. Measurement of its level of radioactivity permitted determination of the blast yield at both Hiroshima and Nagasaki.
- Blast wave observations. Measuring the shock overpressure change as a function of time can be employed to estimate blast yields. Three parachute-retarded canisters containing shock wave-measuring devices were dropped over Hiroshima and furnished enough information to estimate the yield of the atomic explosion

- Theoretical calculations. Computerized weapon-design codes produce reliable estimates of yield. This method failed for the Hiroshima bomb, since no other bomb of its design had been exploded.

10-50 Tables of Data for Nuclear Explosions

Table 10-50A
Radiant exposures at varying distance and yields (for section 10-28)

Yield (kilotons)	Slant Range (miles)	Radiant Exposure (J/sq cm)
10	1	42
	1.5	16
50	1	210
	1.5	75
	2	50
	4	15
100	2	85
	3	33
	4	17
500	3	170
	4	67
	6	30
	7	17
1000	4	170
	5	100
	7	33
	10	13

Table 10-50C
Gamma ray dose from bombs with 50% of energy from fusion (for section 10-31)

Yield (kilotons)	Slant Range (miles)	Dose (rads)
200	0.85	7,000
	1.14	1,000
	1.42	250
500	1.14	3,000
	1.42	700
	1.70	100
1,000	1.14	10,000
	1.70	300
	2.00	65
5,000	1.70	8,000
	2.27	300
	2.56	65

Table 10-50B
Gamma ray dose from fission bombs (for section 10-31)

Yield (kilotons)	Slant Range (miles)	Dose (rads)
10	0.57	3,000
	0.71	900
	0.85	280
	1.14	40
50	0.71	6,000
	0.85	2,200
	1.14	270
	1.42	40

Table 10-50D
Dose from neutron irradiation, fission bombs (for section 10-33)

Yield (kilotons)	Slant Range (miles)	Dose (rads)
10	0.57	4,000
	0.85	200
50	0.71	3,000
	0.85	800
	1.14	65

Table 10-50E
Dose from neutrons from bombs with 50% of energy from fusion (for section 10-33)

Yield (kilotons)	Slant Range (miles)	Dose (rads)
200	0.85	3,000
	1.14	250
500	0.85	8,000
	1.14	750
	1.42	65
1,000	1.14	1,500
	1.42	120
	1.56	30
5,000	1.14	7,000
	1.42	650

Table 10-50H
Overpressures, dynamic pressures, and wind velocities (for section 10-36)

Overpressure (psi)	Dynamic pressure (psi)	Wind Velocity (mph)
200	330	2,078
100	123	1,415
20	8.1	502
10	2.2	294
2	0.1	70

Table 10-50F
Overpressures from a 1 Megaton Explosion at 6000 Feet (50% of energy from fusion) (for section 10-35)

Distance from ground zero (miles)	Peak Overpressure (psi)
1.8	20
2.5	12
2.7	10
4	5
7	2
10	1

Table 10-50G
Peak Overpressures from a 1 Megaton Explosion on the Surface (50% of energy from fusion) (for section 10-35)

Distance from ground zero (miles)	Peak Overpressure (psi)
2	12
3	5
5	2
8	1

PART III: MEANING OF NUCLEAR WAR

ABSTRACT—An all-out nuclear war which might have occurred during the Cold War would probably not have extinguished the human race, but this is the most auspicious statement it is prudent to make. The level of destruction would be beyond imagination. Such a war could become possible again, and can be prevented only by deep changes in our thought and actions. The effects of bombs on cities is detailed, and the long-range consequences of nuclear fallout outlined. Some relevant natural catastrophes are described. A possible nuclear winter and destruction of the ozone layer, and their aftermath, are summarized. An analysis of the possible genetic effects is presented. The futility of civil defense is shown. Finally, a possible grim scenario of the life of survivors is painted.

10-51 Introduction

A great deal has been written about the consequences of all-out nuclear war, much of it based on speculation and emotionalism. Here an attempt is made to outline the tragedy of nuclear war, with the emotional factor toned down to some degree. Since we are talking about billions of human lives and survival of civilizations, emotional views cannot and should not be totally avoided; indeed, appeals to passion are not lacking in the following pages. Despite the unprecedented horrors of nuclear apocalypse, it would not mean the end of the human race.

In 1986 there were in excess of 69,000 nuclear bombs in our world (not all operational). Suppose the average yield was one megaton (compared to which the Hiroshima bomb was a firecracker). Then the total would be very near the amount of explosive power which existed in our world during the late stages of the Cold War, 69,000 megatons. All the wars in the history of humanity, including the two atomic bombs used against Japan, the Korean and Vietnamese wars, and all others since, total only 6 or 7 megatons. Thus the world had enough nuclear weapons for nearly 10,000 times this total. Think of it, if only a quarter of this were expended in a war, it would still be 2,500 times the total of all wars of the past!

Too much firepower

Imagine all the world's wars over and over, 2,500 times! This would not be spread over centuries, but within a short time. Moreover, it is not just the explosive power of nuclear weapons; the radioactivity and other effects must also be included. The very concept makes one giddy. If a real nuclear war ever comes, it would be such an utter and unmitigated disaster that an expression like international suicide pact would be more precise. But for lack of a better term, let us continue to use the term nuclear war, especially considering that there would probably be survivors.

The wars of the past, usually justified by both sides as for a noble cause, have been cruelly bloody and the suffering has been beyond description. The word "valor" was often invoked; today this sounds quaint. But even in modern times such classical wars take place, for example the one that was recently devastating Iran and Iraq (1980-1988). Even in nonnuclear terms the modern electronic battlefield involves push-button annihilation, screeching armor-piercing, uranium-tipped shells, outer-space rockets, and laser weaponry. With the wholesale introduction of nuclear weapons in the form of artillery and MX or SS-20 missiles, the dimensions have inflated to encompass the world, and the stakes would include human civilizations in the northern hemisphere.

The response of both superpowers during the Cold War to the threat of a real war was primarily of military character, not negotiation. The American military established a vast nerve center for the U.S. (and Canadian) defense systems called NORAD (North American Aerospace Defense Command). It is in an enormous cave system carved from solid granite in Cheyenne Mountain near Colorado Springs; the author made a tour of these facilities in 1990. Warning systems feed information into NORAD's computers from satellites, stations in the Arctic and on the coast at Cape Cod, and other sources. Another data-processing center is at the Strategic Air Command in Omaha, and there are still more military command centers elsewhere. The Russians, though nearly bankrupt, have parallel systems, and had enough old-fashioned military power to launch punishing attacks on Chechnya in 1999 and following.

10-52 Possible Scenarios for Start of Nuclear War

Wars from ancient times up to the present have brought indescribable agony to millions of human beings, but knowledge of this has never inhibited outbreak of new hostilities. It is widely appreciated today that any nuclear conflict would be far, far worse, but there is no evidence that the human race has changed its way of thinking about war in any significant way. Psychopathic addiction to war is so deeply ingrained that one can only conclude that thermonuclear war is a distinct possibility. No rational world leader would launch a nuclear war; but, regrettably, history has shown that irrational (or subrational) leaders frequently come to power, and some of these have a ruttish hankering for war. Moreover, the use of nuclear bombs in 1945 in warfare makes the next use easier; precedent greases the path.

The human race is not too wise to fight nuclear wars.

There are quite a number of ways in which one can imagine how a nuclear war could begin. Some of the possibilities are listed below and are then described briefly; to some degree they overlap.

A. Deliberate first strike
B. War by accident
C. Launch on warning
D. Limited nuclear war
E. Escalation of conventional war
F. Nuclear war between third-world countries

Aside from the above, there are undoubtedly other unforeseen ways. Nuclear war is not un-thinkable, but rather unknowable. Any real nuclear war would involve rational and irrational people, failure of communication and equipment, bad weather, panic decisions, and unpredictable accidents, and could result in the deaths of tens of millions in the first few hours. While as of 2000 there has been only one superpower, politics and military power are always in flux, and in a few generations we could be back to the status of another old Cold War.

First Strike—Military leaders of each superpower spent a great deal of time and energy during the Cold War worrying about the other side, in a seemingly cool and rational manner, launching a deliberate first strike. The probability of such a nuclear war has dropped off since the end of the Cold War and the emergence of the United States as the sole superpower. In any case, such a prospect is of very low probability, not because of humanitarian concerns, but because of the deterrence afforded by a retaliatory second strike.

War by Accident—Nuclear weapons are being incorporated to a higher and higher extent into conventional military institutions; they are becoming more sophisticated; and increasing numbers of people and nations have access to them. Nuclear artillery shells are especially numerous. The superpowers had grown to rely on computerized warning systems and being on hair-trigger alert. If China grows into a superpower, the old Cold War could begin anew. Nuclear powers of intermediate strength, such as Great Britain and France, could conceivably be accidentally drawn into conflict. Fortunately today, the probability is low.

Stresses and psychological pressures arising from a minor conflict, such as might well occur in, say, Taiwan, could conceivably launch the U.S. and China on a collision course. If one side had aggressive, hawkish leadership, that side, to demonstrate resolve, might explode a one-megaton warhead high over the landmass of the other in order to generate an electromagnetic pulse. This warning shot would cripple much unprotected electronic circuitry. The leaders of the other country could be pressured into authorizing what they consider to be a retaliatory measure, namely exploding two still more powerful warheads in space over the adversary. But one of these might be accidentally too low on explosion, causing an atmospheric shock wave and extensive damage. As judgment becomes clouded by the building passions, each antagonist would mobilize to a full alert status. Ultimatums are sent and ignored. Thus the lethal escalation rapidly sets in. The destruction of an Iranian airbus over the Persian Gulf in July, 1988, by missiles from an American warship despite a sophisticated Aegis radar system, illustrates the sort of episode which could serve as a trigger.

Limits quickly vanish on use of nuclear weapons.

Launch on Warning—Even with one superpower and several other countries deploying nuclear weapons in their various modes of attack, the systems become too complicated for human crews to handle under emergency conditions. This must result in greater dependence on computerized discharging sequences, keyed to fire under attack. After all, the time required for intercontinental ballistic missiles is only 15 to 30 minutes, and for submarine-launched missiles even less. All participants would be operating under the anxiety that their weapons would be destroyed before they could be fired, creating the "use 'em or lose 'em" syndrome. This might be described as a form of electronic nuclear roulette.

Limited Nuclear War—Still another avenue to conflagration is the idea of limited nuclear war. A standard doctrine of the North Atlantic Treaty Organization called "flexible response" (about 1960 to 1988) was that if the Warsaw Pact powers invaded western Europe using their allegedly superior conventional weapons, then American forces would use nuclear weapons for their defense. This first-use of nuclear weapons had as its basis the unlikely assumption that the Soviets would not respond in kind and would withdraw on terms favorable to the West. The danger in this case would extend, fortunately to a lesser degree, to any comparable political status in the future, such as a standoff between the United States and China.

Many military and other experts severely criticize this concept of limited nuclear war. The risk that the confrontation would expand in an uncontrolled fashion is enormous. Former Secretary of Defense Robert McNamara says that the threat of first use "has lost all credibility as a deterrent on an incredible action." Such a limited first use of nuclear weapons in Europe would very likely not stay limited long, and the question would boil down to this: Is the United States actually willing to risk the sacrifice of American cities to save Europe? Very few people would answer yes.

Such a war, supposed to be limited, would almost certainly not be containable. The Soviet Defense Minister said in 1981: "Could anyone in his right mind speak seriously of any limited nuclear war? It should be quite clear that the aggressor's actions will instantly and inevitably trigger a devastating counterstroke by the other side."

Probably it is the so-called tactical nuclear weapons which are most likely to be used without authorization. Most of these are nuclear artillery. They are widespread and available to lower-level officers. Their power is approximately that of Hiroshima-sized bombs. It is difficult to understand how use could be limited to just one.

It is instructive to examine the Soviet-American crisis of 1962 in which the immediate issue was the emplacement of Soviet missile bases in Cuba. President Kennedy was said to have presented an ultimatum: We have to have a commitment by tomorrow that those bases will be removed or we will take them out ourselves (recent documents reveal that his stand was much more diplomatic). Soviet Ambassador Dobrynin brought up the matter of American nuclear missiles in Turkey, much closer to the USSR than Cuba is to the USA. The American government was adamant: no deal was to be made. The Soviets were stared down and removed the missiles. Later Kennedy wrote that he had expected war, characterizing the crisis as "a confrontation between the two giant atomic nations . . . which brought the world to the abyss of nuclear destruction and the end of mankind." He appeared to be willing to risk that possibility to gain a transient advantage. It should be noted that American missiles in Turkey, as well as in Norway, were removed several months later.

Escalation of Conventional War—There are several types of scenarios which might fall in this category. One is the "back-to-the-wall" concept. Just suppose, for example, that the Islamic powers settled their differences for a while, and united to crush Israel militarily. The Israelis would of course defend themselves as best possible. The superpowers and others would be fully alerted. Now if the Israelis find that they are being defeated and their backs are to the wall, so to speak, they would naturally employ their ultimate weapon. Although Israel has not tested any nuclear bomb, most knowledgeable observers believe that Israel could nevertheless employ their stock of weapons successfully. Who knows where this kind of war could lead? In any case, a country with nuclear weapons which is losing a conventional war would be under overwhelming pressure to escalate.

When one's back is to the wall, anything goes.

Nuclear War Between Third-World Countries—National passions shift in time, but blood-enemy rancor can endure for decades (witness Kosovo, Israel-Palestine, etc.). India and Pakistan might also be classified in this way. They have already fought several wars. In 1998, India exploded a series of nuclear bombs in tests (9-47), and reportedly has manufactured many more. Pakistan followed suit at once. In less than half a century, both countries will probably have a stock of nuclear bombs of several types.

It is not hard to imagine a scenario in which still another armed conflict between India and Pakistan arises, and now it could escalate into the nuclear phase. With the carnage of tens of millions of deaths exhibited on television screens worldwide, this object lesson just might stimulate other nuclear powers to seriously reconsider their policies.

10-53 Limited Nuclear Attack

Here we consider the world with two major superpowers, such as existed from about 1958 to 1990. The only other credible repetition of this situation in the near future is the case in which China grows to become a true superpower.

A computer analysis of a limited nuclear attack on the United States by the Soviet Union was commissioned by the Federal Emergency Management Agency, and its report was completed in 1983. It assumed that about 1% of the Soviet nuclear arsenal (85 warheads of 550 kilotons each and 154 warheads of 200 kilotons each, totaling about 78 megatons yield) had targeted oil fields, refineries, ports, and of course retaliatory facilities and a few other critical installations. Such studies which are made public always assume a Soviet attack on the USA, never the reverse.

The conclusion was that about 8% of the population would be killed at once and approximately 60% would perish within two years, mostly from starvation. With the loss of our liquid fuel supplies, the standard of living for the survivors would drop drastically, perhaps to medieval levels, for years.

Suppose now that an attack on the USA used 25% of the Soviet arsenal (2000 megatons). The primary targets would be not only the fuel reserves but also missile silos in the Midwest. Bases in Montana, North and South Dakota, Wyoming, Kansas, and Arkansas would be nullified. Since the targets are hardened, ground bursts would be necessary, and therefore deadly clouds of fallout would drift downwind. An estimated 10% of the American population would succumb immediately, a relatively low level owing to the small population in these areas. Within two years the death toll would climb to a level higher than the case described above. Death from radiation sickness would be slow and unbearable. Survivors would be weakened and scarred.

The 10% killed at once is only the beginning.

In order to destroy a missile silo, an overpressure of more than 1000 psi is necessary. This means that a 1-megaton warhead would be exploded at or under the surface, making a large, evil cloud of fallout unavoidable. More likely, still more powerful warheads (5 megatons) would be used.

An attack on the European part of the Soviet Union would have comparable results. Most analysts believe that these limited war scenarios have minimum validity in any case, since they would not remain limited long; they stay limited only in an imaginary world.

10-54 Calamitous Thermonuclear War

The occurrence of a nuclear war is itself the point of overwhelming importance, not how it started or who fired the first shot. Imagine that one of the scenarios outlined earlier, or another as yet unforeseen, begins to unfold in our nuclear-tinderbox world. After a period of frenzied communications by frantic political, diplomatic and military leaders, patience is exhausted, and mutual views in terms of demonic stereotypes prevail. The situation rapidly deteriorates. The principals undergo an emotional meltdown and disconnect their souls. The doomsday machine begins its fatal curse, cascading into war.

Once it is understood that reason has been abandoned and that views compatible with irrationality dominate, war becomes inevitable; what would happen then? Each power would see that priority targets such as the major political and military leadership of the enemy are annihilated at once, with simultaneous attacks to decapitate all command, control, and communication facilities. Other targets would be as many missile-launching sites as possible.

Events take place so rapidly that one might think the gods were playing yo-yo with the Earth.

All this means the extermination of the capital cities and obliteration of various army, navy, and air force headquarters. Some of these are deep underground, which attracts exceedingly powerful nuclear warheads (maybe 5 or more megatons) exploded on or under the surface. Surviving missiles would be launched from silos or from submarines; some bombers would probably come through to participate. Such classical concepts as the "front lines" would have no meaning. Many warheads exploded in space above the American and Asian landmasses produce electromagnetic pulses which paralyze all but the best protected communications; this damages much of each nation's communication nervous system and electric grids. It leaves the populace in the dark about events until it is too late. Once some news, however fragmentary or inaccurate, is received by each power concerning their fatalities, additional attacks continue on the industrial backbone and ports (especially those with submarine facilities) of each side. Other likely targets are airfields with nuclear-capable planes, military depots, and tank storage yards. Finally, the cities themselves are extinguished. All this occurs within several days. History shows that decisive wars are fought to the bitter end; there is no reason to think that this one would be an exception. Admiral Hyman G. Rickover, largely responsible for nuclearizing submarines, put it this way in 1982:

A rampage of annihilation beyond belief

> When a war starts, every nation will ultimately use whatever weapon has been available. That is the lesson learned time and again.

Each belligerent in an all-out war would run out of worthwhile targets before the adversary runs out of bombs; this would almost certainly not inhibit use of all stocks on hand.

In a modern society, cities and institutions are interdependent. When Hiroshima was demolished, a certain amount of help and relief was brought in from the outside. When most cities in a country are simultaneously shattered, no such aid is forthcoming, making matters all the worse.

10-55 Destruction of Cities

War game experts began exploring how most efficiently to devastate cities and other targets as early as 1950, maybe even before. Each potential target was studied. As more bombs became available, the target lists were extended, until smaller and smaller cities were included.

Explosions at a height minimize fallout, but maximize blast and radiation effects. Ground-level bursts have fewer fatalities from blast and direct radiation, but maximize deadly fallout. It seems that yields of 1 to 3 megatons per million inhabitants does the job economically. A city of 100,000 would need only a single 50 kiloton burst to be expunged, while larger cities would require 1 to 15 bombs in the megaton range, some exploded high and others on the surface. A spread-out city such as Los Angeles might require 20 or so 1-megaton warheads for total pulverization, although only two would incapacitate the city. Hydrogen bombs provide a cheap means to kill; a single warhead destroying 10 million people comes out to cost only about 12 cents per death.

Contingency plans are ready for destruction of cities and other targets.

Neither side would target cities merely to incinerate their populations, at least at the beginning of hostilities. But this hesitancy would evaporate if one side suffered loss of a city or two. Neither side would refrain from nullifying enemy cities and their inhabitants if military, economic, or political targets are centered there, which is so often the case.

The sketches below illustrate the explosion of 1-megaton warheads on a large city. In both cases, 50% of the energy is from fusion, meaning that the weapons were hydrogen bombs. One is programmed to explode at 6000 feet and the other on the surface. From ground zero in each case, an expanding circle of overpressure is caused by the blast; the circles in the sketches show the values of peak overpressure at several distances from ground zero. The blast not only kills directly; it also collapses buildings on their occupants, hurls broken glass as projectiles, and causes many fires from broken gas pipes or spilled fuel. Immediately afterward, the fiery hurricanes resulting from drag winds caused by dynamic pressure augment the destruction. In some cases a firestorm develops in the rubble, scorching all that remains. Probably more people die from fire than any other single cause. Of course, there are also the effects of radiant energy, neutrons, gamma rays and X-rays, and radioactive fallout. An intangible corollary is the psychological effect. The total effect is utterly demoralizing on the survivors (and there are survivors in the outskirts of the city).

Obviously, maximum destruction occurs at ground zero in both cases. A blast at 6000 feet causes an overpressure of at least 20 psi up to nearly 2 miles from ground zero, wrecking all structures, even reinforced concrete. Drag winds of around 500 miles per hour complete the destruction. At a radius of 4 miles, the overpressure is 5 psi, enough to push over steel-reinforced block structures; winds of 170 miles per hour follow, crushing much of that which remains. Even out to 10 miles from ground zero the overpressure amounts to 1 psi, enough to seriously damage most houses, and even here the wind has a velocity of 50 miles per hour.

The gamma ray doses caused by air blasts in general are lethal only at rather close range, in which case death results in any case from shock effects. In the present case, a 1-megaton explosion at 6000 feet, the dose is 65 rads at a slant range of 2 miles (table 10-50C); the dose from neutrons is even less. But the radiant energy absorbed is in excess of 600 joules/square centimeter. This is enough to melt or vaporize most substances and ignite all combustible material. Up to about 3 miles, tile is melted, and at 5 miles, with radiant energy of 100 joules/square centimeter (table 10-50A), everything which can burn ignites.

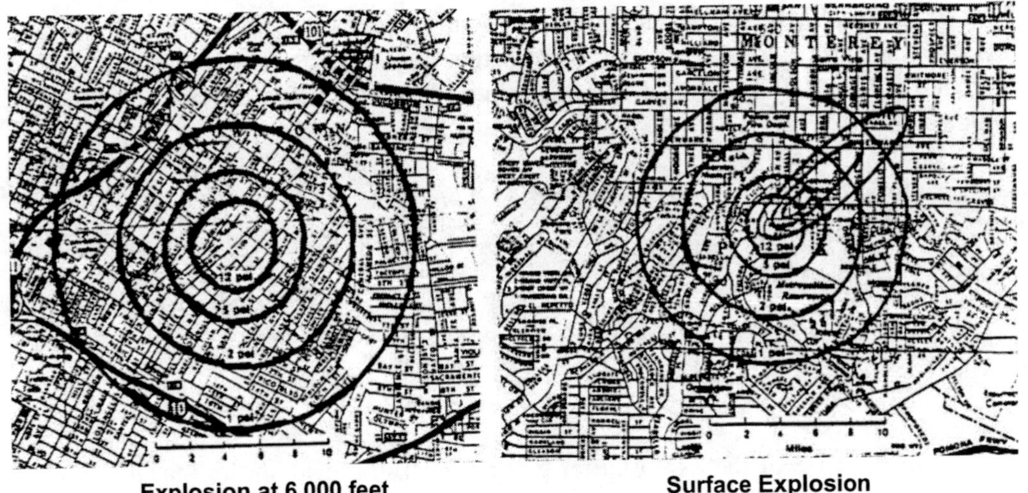

Explosion at 6,000 feet **Surface Explosion**

One Megaton Nuclear Blasts Over a City

Human skin exposed to this radiant energy is burned to a degree which depends on the amount of energy absorbed. This in turn depends primarily on bomb yield, slant range, and skin pigmentation. Roughly speaking, radiant energy absorption of 8 to 12 joules/square centimeter causes first degree burns, 18 to 25 joules/square centimeter second degree burns, and above 25 joules/square centimeter third degree burns. According to the experience in Hiroshima and Nagasaki, about 25% of the victims suffered flash burns. In the present case of a 1-megaton bomb exploding at 6000 feet, third degree burns would be inflicted upon all exposed people up to about 6 miles (table 10-50A).

The surface explosion has a more restricted shock range. It results in a crater 200 feet deep and a thousand feet across, with a ring of radioactive dirt extending another thousand feet. The overpressure resulting from the blast does enormous damage, as well as the drag winds, radiant energy, and gamma and neutron irradiation. But another contribution to lethality is the cloud of fallout, which forms in the mushroom stem and head and is deposited downwind. In addition, the excess neutrons released into the soil form dangerous radioactive nuclides, such as sodium-24. Some of this material is lofted into the mushroom cloud or its stem, and becomes a part of the local fallout. That remaining in the ground is readily dissolved by rain water. Thus sodium-24 contributes to the exposure of survivors. The crater also contains deadly plutonium-239 and tritium; these, along with cesium-137 and strontium-90 render the area deadly for many decades. Two words summarize all these factors: misery and death.

10-56 Immediate Fatalities in a Large City

Let us analyze the effects of the two 1-megaton hydrogen bomb explosions on a city of several million, one exploding at the height of 6000 feet and the other on the surface. The effects depend on many factors, such as whether it is windy, night or day, clear or rainy or snowy, winter or summer. Estimates of fatalities and injuries in the two cases have been made, but must be increased or decreased, depending on circumstances.

In the case of the air burst, the map with overpressure rings above divides the worst damaged area into four zones, namely those with peak overpressure limits of 12, 5, 2, and 1 psi. There is no local fallout or crater. The table below assesses the fatalities within a day or so.

Distance from ground zero	Overpressure at limit	Population	Fatalities
0–2.5 miles	12 psi	200,000	200,000
2.5–4 miles	5 psi	500,000	250,000
4–7 miles	2 psi	500,000	25,000
7–10.5 miles	1 psi	700,000	few
	TOTAL	1.9 million	475,000

In the case of the explosion at ground level, the map shows that the rings of limiting overpressure are smaller. The table below estimates the immediate fatalities.

Distance from ground zero	Overpressure at limit	Population	Fatalities
0–1.7 miles	12 psi	70,000	70,000
1.7–2.7 miles	5 psi	130,000	130,000
2.7–4.7 miles	2 psi	400,000	20,000
4.7–7.4 miles	1 psi	600,000	few
TOTAL		1.2 million	220,000

Thus we see that the air burst kills about twice as many people as the ground burst, so far as immediate deaths are concerned. The ground burst razes everything within about 0.6 mile. At 1.3 miles, a few reinforced concrete shells remain. At the 2 psi ring, some structures are not completely destroyed, but no one remains alive, and nothing of value is left. The explosion at 6000 feet causes burns and injuries at a longer range than the ground blast. In the above case, the two explosions kill about half of the population within the sets of overpressure rings, and half of the rest are seriously injured. In an actual war, more than two warheads would be used, insuring that virtually all inhabitants die or are incapacitated.

Surface explosions kill fewer by flash and shock, but kill more by fallout.

In 2002 the Natural Resources Defense Council analyzed the effects of a puny nuclear bomb with a yield of only one kiloton (that is, 1000 tons of TNT equivalency) exploding in Times Square, New York City. The investigation was carried out via computer modeling. The blast would ruin everything within a city block in every direction, killing an estimated 20,000 people within seconds. Most within a quarter mile would die of radiation sickness. These two factors would cause a total of perhaps a quarter million fatalities. Unshielded people up to half a mile away would receive a radiation dose sufficient to cause death within a few days. A small mushroom cloud of debris would form, much of it drifting back, injuring or dooming any survivors.

10-57 Local Fallout

Explosion of either of the 1-megaton hydrogen bombs described above creates around 30 trillion curies of radioactivity within one minute. After 24 hours, this decays to15 billion curies. In the case of the air burst, when the fireball does not touch the Earth, nearly all of the radioactivity is carried up into the troposphere and stratosphere, where it circulates around the Earth (global fallout) in a band of more or less fixed latitude. Most of the fission products in the stratosphere stay there until they decay; the material in the lower troposphere is washed down by rain. But in the case of the surface explosion, much earth is vaporized and carried up into the mushroom cloud and its stem. On cooling, particles of lethal solids begin to fall in less than an hour; they are carried downwind, and reach the surface as local fallout. Local fallout is generally considered to be that which is deposited within 24 hours.

Idealized and real fallout patterns were shown earlier (10-43 and 10-44).

10-58 Moderate to All-Out Nuclear Exchange

Only nuclear war which is limited, implausible as it is, has been considered so far. One can imagine all levels of hostilities from limited war to all-out war, in which warring powers use as much of their arsenals as possible. Here we consider the case of two superpowers.

A moderate nuclear war might involve a sum of about a third of the world's warheads, totaling around 13,000 bombs and 4000 megatons total yield. An all-out nuclear war would involve perhaps 24,000 bombs and 10,000 megatons yield. Each superpower has reserves of fissile materials which are three or four times that total in their weapons, and some of these stockpiles could be incorporated into additional deliverable weapons, given lead time. Probably the worst which would happen in the foreseeable future in the event of a cataclysmic war is that each superpower would be scourged with 5300 megatons. There are so many unknowns and unpredictable factors that only an informed guess can be made.

One of many possible distribution patterns of warhead yields and numbers striking each superpower is shown in the following table (some figures are rounded):

	Surface		Air		
Yield (kilotons)	Number of Warheads	Yield (megatons)	Number of Warheads	Yield (megatons)	Total Yield (megatons)
50	550	28	600	30	58
100	1.200	120	1,300	130	250
200	500	100	800	160	250
300	900	270	1.200	360	630
500	1,200	600	1,500	750	1,300
1,000	1,000	1,000	1,300	1,300	2,360
5,000	75	375	0	0	375
TOTALS: (rounded)	5,425	2,500	6,700	2,700	5,200

Somewhat more than half of the warheads could be expected to explode in the air and the remainder on the surface. If nearly all of these were targeted on the United States (the 48 contiguous states, that is), the land would be pockmarked with perhaps 5400 surface explosions to crush missile silos and to erase numerous other prime military facilities, as well as industries and cities. Missile launching sites such as Malmstrom, Grand Forks, Ellsworth, Warren, Whiteman, Little Rock, McConnell, and Davis-Monthan would be targeted. (Some of these launching sites have now been decommissioned). Many overpressure zones would overlap whenever multiple warheads attacked a single large target. Local fallout patterns would also overlap, and spread downwind, often being split into irregular forked tongues by wind shear.

A number of competent physicists have analyzed nuclear-war scenarios. A recent study carried out at Livermore National Laboratory postulates a war in which the United States suffers attack by about 4000 nuclear weapons, totaling 3000 megatons, 1900 megatons of which are surface bursts. The weapons are hydrogen bombs in which half the energy comes from fission. These figures are realistic and more or less in line with those assumed earlier. The attack occurs in summer on a population mostly unsheltered; some would be partially protected in homes, buildings, and basements, and would thus incur lower exposures.

How many Americans would perish in a massive attack?

The Livermore calculations showed that approximately 98 million deaths would occur promptly (blast, fire, collapse of buildings, etc.) and up to 13 million more fatalities would result from the first 48 hours of exposure to fallout. The map above is reproduced from the authoritative Livermore paper. The numbers inside the contours measure exposure in sieverts, that is, in hundreds of rems (see 5-5). Note that only ten bombed areas appear on the map; if all were drawn in, clarity would be lost from overlap. Remember that 450 rems (4.5 sieverts) is considered the median lethal dose (it might be lower). One should keep in mind that all these appraisals are fraught with enormous uncertainties, but the above figures are probable minimum values; actual areas might be twice these values, or less likely, half. Corresponding devastation would be wreaked on each side.

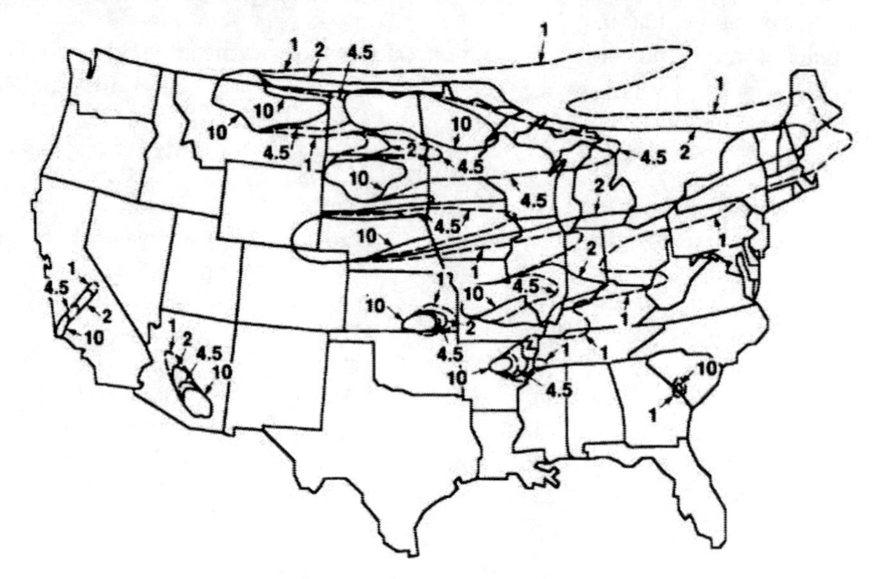

Fallout pattern for only ten bombing areas in an attack on the United States; the numbers are exposures in sieverts (hundreds of rems)

The Livermore studies indicate that fallout stays in the landmasses of the belligerents to a greater degree than formerly thought, and thus the survival rate is higher than previous estimates. There would be many survivors. Remote mountain areas, inhabited by a few flinty souls, would be least affected.

A World Health Organization study in 1984 estimated that a global war of 10,000 megatons yield could immediately cause 1.1 billion deaths from blast, fire, and radiation, and a like number of severe injuries. Long-term biological effects are not included here.

10-59 Targeting Nuclear Reactors

Suppose then in a mindless, all-out nuclear war each side comes to the conclusion it must dispatch enemy civilians on as great a scale as possible; considering war psychology of the past, this does not seem unlikely. One way to do this is to bombard giant nuclear reactors with fission or hydrogen bombs.

A billion-watt (1000 megawatt) nuclear reactor contains approximately 5 billion curies of radioactive materials. Much of this material, but not all, would be a few months old, and the short-lived nuclides would have largely decayed. Explosion of a 1-megaton hydrogen bomb liberates around 30 trillion curies, but the abundant short-lived fission products decay so fast that after 24 hours the total is down to 15 billion curies. If the bomb destroys the reactor, the mixture of the two sources of radioactivity represent the most potent and fatal weapon known. Many such reactors are near cities of great size. Generally nuclear reactors have spent fuel rods in storage in nearby pools. If the radioactivity in this source is also dispersed, the disaster would be all the more horrendous. Depending on wind and weather, a single such incident could create a first-class catastrophe.

Don't think the horror would prevent this.

Although the contribution of the fission products in the waste from the reactor to the dose rate is lower at the start, it is much more prolonged owing to the large amounts of accumulated long-lived nuclides. After about four days, the dose rates from the two sources are roughly equal. After five years, the dose rate from the reactor debris is around 200 times the rate from the bomb debris. The worst nuclides are cesium-137 and strontium-90. Large areas could be made uninhabitable for many decades.

Since the terrorist suicide attacks of American buildings on September 11, 2001, considerable attention has been given to similar attacks by large aircraft. Light planes could not pierce the thick ferroconcrete containment domes, and thus would probably not be chosen by terrorists unless they could be loaded with explosives and detonators, and even in this case could only blow a hole in the containment. But a large skyliner with its fuel tanks nearly full would probably go through and strike the massive shield, a ferroconcrete structure 9 to 10 feet thick (see description in 7-4G). The impact with the containment would absorb much of the kinetic energy of the plane, and even at worst there would probably not be enough left to rupture the part of the exposed top of the steel core. Its connecting lines could be broken off, resulting in a steam explosion in which some radioactive substances would be carried outside.

The cooling system could be disabled, resulting in an incident resembling that at Three Mile Island. On-site guards could not prevent such an attack unless they had sufficient warning and anti-aircraft guns and the training in their use. These measures would probably not be effective. Interception by military aircraft, given sufficient notice, might be able to down the plane on its way to the reactor. The new Pebble Bed Modular Reactors do not have containments, and so would be most vulnerable.

A greater danger could arise from warplanes carrying bombs. This technique was employed by Israel to destroy a just-built reactor in Iraq in 1981 (see 9-52). It had not yet been turned on so relatively little radioactivity was scattered about. The first planes blasted holes in the containment and those following dropped bombs through the holes. The reactor was utterly destroyed. Conceivably, a group of such planes might be able to attack coastal American reactors, but the logistics would pose almost insuperable difficulties for the terrorists. Attacks on nuclear reactors using nuclear bombs would have the most dangerous consequences imaginable.

Spent fuel rods are stored inside the containment of many reactors. They are in pools filled with water. Loss of the water could expose the fuel rods, and if the temperature became high enough, the zirconium cladding could ignite. The probability of this consequence is quite low. The large amount of radioactivity in the spent fuel (several times that in the core) would represent serious, alarming danger. Nearly all reactors have older spent fuel in storage outside the containment structure, and this is readily vulnerable to a suicidal terrorist piloting a plane. The possibility of releasing enormous levels of radioactivity from such attacks cannot be simply ruled out.

10-60 Some Natural Cataclysms

The accounts following provide us with some relevant information concerning catastrophic events which have strongly affected our world, and which might guide our thinking about nuclear war in some respects.

In 1883 the volcano Krakatoa, between Java and Sumatra, erupted in one of the mightiest explosions known. A rough estimate of its energy is 1000 megatons. It injected so much dust into the upper atmosphere that the Earth experienced a cooling effect as the sunlight was blocked. Sunsets worldwide were colored spectacularly for nearly three years. The explosion of Mount Tambora on the island of Sumbawa, which is also in Indonesia, in 1815 was much larger. Recently, evidence has been accumulated that the huge volcanic eruption in Iceland of 210 BC darkened the skies over the Eurasian land mass to the extent that extensive starvation occurred in China.

In 1980, L. W. Alvarez and his son Walter Alvarez and their coworkers analyzed a finger-thick, pinkish clay layer first identified near a medieval town in northern Italy, but then was recognized in many sites over the world. This clay was found to have an extraordinarily high content, compared to ordinary clays, of iridium (a metal resembling platinum and other noble metals). The clay layer was deposited at the boundary between the Cretaceous and Tertiary Periods 65 million years ago, just the time at which the dinosaurs suddenly became extinct. The scientists proposed a theory in which an asteroid, or possibly a comet six to eight miles in diameter, came screaming down from outer space and collided with the Earth at that time. In 1993 the theory was refined and extended on the basis of new evidence. The energy of the impact was estimated at 100 to 200 million megatons, thousands of times more than the world's nuclear arsenals combined at their peak. Most of this energy was absorbed about 15 miles deep inside the Earth. The event raised a global dust cloud which eventually snowed down to form the thin clay layer from vaporized stone. The asteroid was evidently relatively rich in iridium. The sunlight was obstructed so thoroughly that winter conditions for a prolonged period came to pass. This resulted in the breakdown of food chains supporting the dinosaurs, leading to their extinction. Approximately 70% of all animals disappeared. Some mammals, which had newly evolved, survived. The uncharacteristic worldwide distribution of so rare a metal as iridium is difficult to explain in any other way than extraterrestrial.

Strong support for this theory lies in the isotopic composition of the iridium in the clay layer. Iridium has only two stable isotopes, mass numbers 191 and 193. Iridium from meteorites (which are part of our solar system) and also ordinary iridium from our Earth consists of these in the ratio 168 atoms of the heavier isotope to 100 of the lighter one. The ratio in the iridium from the clay is the same, indicating that the asteroid which fell on Earth was from our solar system, not one from far outer space. Soviet scientists found similar results with rhodium, another metal in the platinum family. It is known that some asteroids (which exist mostly between Mars and Jupiter) cross the Earth's orbit at rare intervals. Geologic evidence is that our Earth has taken a major hit at least 139 times during its history.

Nuclear detectives unravel disappearances of 65 million years ago.

Spectacular evidence supporting the impact theory came in the early 1990s. A search for the site of the asteroid impact was under way. Geochemist Alan Hildebrand, a specialist in cosmology, ran across some droplets of glass in the iridium-bearing clay in Haiti. This bed was up to half a meter thick. Physical examination disclosed a type of striations which are known to be formed by the shock of intense impact, such as in a meteorite falling to Earth or a nuclear explosion. The globules of glass were so large that they were probably formed not too far away. The age of these specimens, as determined by the reliable argon-39/argon-40 method (6-3), proved to be 65.06 million years, within 0.18 million years. A rich deposit of glass beads was unearthed near the Gulf in northeast Mexico. Similar glass droplets were found in Texas. Moreover, studies of carbon-12 and carbon-13 taken from the layer marking the end of the Cretaceous Period 65 million years ago have indicated that global forest fires occurred. In photosynthesis, plants utilize carbon-12 more efficiently than carbon-13, and thus atmospheric carbon dioxide tends to become somewhat enriched in the heavier isotope. The exact ratios are recorded in the fossilized shells of that time. The data show that right after the collision of the asteroid with the Earth the proportion of carbon-13 dropped suddenly around the world, a sign that extra carbon-12 was added to the atmosphere. This is evidence of worldwide burning of biomass at that time.

Having picked up a clue, Hildebrand examined all records of possible crater sites in the Caribbean area, and learned that ten years earlier a geophysicist had stumbled across a gigantic circular crater on the north coast of the Yucatan peninsula, near Chicxulub. It is about 145 miles in diameter, and its outline was clear via radar from the space shuttle Endeavour. While situated on the coast today, the site was inland 65 million years ago. A geologist from the U.S. Geological Service found many glass globules, some from drill holes, in the Chicxulub crater which had shock striations. Using the same argon-39/ argon-40 dating technique, these proved to be 64.98 million years old, within 0.06 million years. This close match, which shows the two samples are of the same age within the tiny experimental error, convinced even the skeptics that the asteroid impact hypothesis might very well be true. Additional supporting evidence came in 1997 when an international geological team recovered three core samples from the ocean floor off the Florida coast, 8,500 feet deep, and found the unmistakable signature of an asteroid impact. The deepest core material contained the remains of numerous life forms, but above that was a layer of small green glass pebbles, believed to have been formed by the asteroid impact. Above that was a layer of the iridium-bearing material from the vaporized asteroid body itself, and the next higher stratum held fossils of new life forms. There is evidence found recently of another huge meteoritic impact 145 million years ago, this one in southern Africa. The Morokweng crater thus formed is about 70 kilometers wide.

One competing theory is that the oxygen content of the air, estimated at 35% 62 million years ago, slowly dropped, finishing off the dinosaurs by respiratory distress. Another is that the heat from the meteorite impact decomposed limestone, yielding carbon dioxide in quantity sufficient to cause excessive heating of the atmosphere by the greenhouse effect (4-31), the high temperatures causing extinction of the dinosaurs. Oxides of nitrogen from the blast heat would have caused terribly acidic rain. Field work at the impact site disclosed that it is extraordinarily rich in sulfur. This element would have been burned to sulfur dioxide, adding to the lethally toxic atmosphere. A supplemental consequence of meteoritic impact might have been the triggering of massive volcanic eruptions, which over thousands of years completed extinction of the dinosaurs. There is evidence that the dinosaurs were dying off anyway, and the asteroid impact was just the coup de grace. Those who doubt the impact theory point to massive volcanic eruptions, such as the one of Mt. Tambora in Sumbawa, Indonesia (then Dutch East Indies), in 1815, which sent an aerosol cloud of sulfur dioxide into the stratosphere, leading to worldwide cooling and crop failures. One result was summer snow in New England, and continuing frosts through August. Material from the Earth's mantle contains iridium at about the same level as meteorites. French scientists have given evidence that a shower of huge meteorites fell into the Pacific 65 million years ago. The matter has not been settled in its entirety. There is a certain minuscule probability that another asteroid, maybe as small as three miles across, will collide with our Earth, inflicting calamitous damage, and conceivably imperiling millions or billions of human lives.

An asteroid impact is not the only cataclysmic event which has caused mass extinction of life on Earth. Evidence published in 1999 has given good evidence, based on radiochemical analysis of basalt and other igneous stones from eastern United States, South America, and Europe that massive volcanic eruptions took place about 200 million years ago. This volcanism occurred in the immense continent known as Pangea, dividing it and permitting formation of the Atlantic Ocean. Millions of square miles were covered with basaltic flows. Many life forms were wiped out. There was another such volcanic frenzy 250 millions of years ago, killing more than 75% of all species of life. This was before the age of the dinosaurs. In this case, molten lava poured in Siberia, forming a layer a mile thick and covering an area half that of Australia. This is known as the Permian-Triassic extinction. Several other smaller such catastrophes are also known to have taken place.

10-61 Nuclear Winter

In the years after 1980, several teams of scientists began to explore the idea that a cataclysmic nuclear war could loft not just dust, but also smoke particles, into the upper atmosphere in sufficient quantities to bring on an artificial winter, dubbed nuclear winter. A number of quantitative studies on this point have been carried out. Despite enormous uncertainties, the general conclusion is that such an event is not impossible. If true, an entirely new threat to populations far removed from belligerent countries would be encountered. The concept of a nuclear winter had been completely overlooked by the Pentagon.

Winter in the summertime maybe just could take place if enabled by the immense energy of many nuclear bombs.

A war between superpowers would be largely confined to the northern hemisphere, mostly between 30 and 70 degrees latitude. The amount of dust raised up into the upper regions of the atmosphere is proportional to the total energy (megatonnage) of the explosions. An estimate of the amount of dust involved is around 300,000 metric tonnes per megaton nuclear yield; this totals more than a billion metric tonnes for the estimated worst-case war (10,600 megaton total yield, less than half expended as surface bursts). Of this dust, approximately 8% is fine enough (below a millionth of a meter) to remain suspended for some years, although that in the troposphere would be slowly rained out.

Fires and their smoke are more difficult to quantify. Many hundreds of urban conflagrations and voracious firestorms would create huge amounts of particulate smoke and soot within a short time (a few days). The buoyant plumes from fires consuming above-ground fuel reserves, mostly oil but much coal, contribute a large share of particulate matter to the smoke. Two-thirds of global petroleum in vulnerable storage is concentrated in as few as 200 sites. Unchecked forest fires are another factor. Finally, trees killed by fallout become dry within a few months, and are very susceptible to fire, giving additional smoke emissions. All of these events occurring within a few weeks is the factor which might cause blotting out sunlight for some time. If it develops, the temperate zone and maybe other sections of our planet would suffer severe degradation of the environment.

A nuclear winter would be limited mostly to the northern hemisphere.

At the worst, sunlight levels could be reduced to as little as 1% of normal in regions covered by the initial dust and smoke clouds, and to about 50% over larger areas. Plumes of black smoke coalescing into an opaque shroud girdling the globe would cause continental temperatures in summer to decrease by 10 to 20 Celsius degrees (18 to 45 Fahrenheit degrees), but cooling would be much less near the oceans. A fall of only 5 Fahrenheit degrees is enough to greatly impair wheat yields, and a fall of 13 °F virtually stops agriculture. Temperatures at night could fall below freezing. Some of the smoke would probably leak across the equator. While uncertainties abound, the great black cloud would probably interfere with the monsoons, bringing about drought.

A drop of only a few degrees in temparature is very serious.

A nuclear winter during the agricultural growing season would inflict the worst damage; it would be much less dangerous in winter. Livestock would be largely wiped out. Human well-being depends sensitively on agriculture, and such perturbations of the climate could result in the deaths of more than a billion from famine on continents where no nuclear bombs exploded. Thus the bleak aftermath of a nuclear war would resemble famine in a vast desert in much of the world. How likely is a devastating nuclear winter in the event of all-out nuclear war? The most knowledgeable authorities are divided. It is not certain that a nuclear winter would come to pass, but it might. The basic mechanisms of such a disaster have been reaffirmed through several authoritative international assessments.

But a nuclear war would form oxides of nitrogen at unprecedented levels. A nuclear explosion in air generates a sphere of plasma around the fireball; on cooling, the oxygen and nitrogen components, as free nuclei or ions, form abundant yields of nitric oxide (formula: NO). This compound is also formed in the ionized air outside the fireball. Finally, the shock wave itself heats air sufficiently to form still more oxides of nitrogen. From each megaton yield of nuclear explosive, between 3000 and 5000 metric tonnes of nitric oxide are produced. Most of this is carried up into the stratosphere quickly; the rest slowly diffuses everywhere. The newer, lower-yield nuclear weapons are less damaging to the ozone layer than the older ones. Nitric oxide is oxidized slowly to nitrogen dioxide (NO_2) by oxygen, but it makes no difference: NO_2 is converted back to NO by the atomic oxygen in the upper atmosphere.

If the total yield in a nuclear war is 10,600 megatons, nearly all of which would be exploded in the atmosphere, the amount of nitric oxide formed would be between 30 and 50 million metric tons, more than 5 times the natural amount. As best can be determined, this would slowly work its way around in the stratosphere, devouring ozone. It would take six months to a year for the ozone layer to reach its minimum concentration, and another 8 or 10 years to build back up to near normal levels. The degree of depletion at the worst would be 20 to 60%. Just as the nuclear winter was fading, the effects of ozone depletion would begin.

Nitrogen oxides formed in air by nuclear explosions would ravage the ozone layer.

And what would be the results of depletion of the ozone layer? They would be far-reaching. They include:

- The increased ultraviolet radiation reaching the surface would cause severe sunburn in the northern temperate zone. Sunburn might occur with 10 minutes of exposure. Damage to crops would also result.
- In humans, an increase of skin cancer of about 10% would be expected. This is basal cell carcinoma, not the more dangerous melanoma.
- Human eyes are injured by excessive ultraviolet. Painful inflammation of the cornea (conjunctivitis and photokeratitis) are possible consequences, sometimes leading to blindness. Cataracts are also possible.
- Many aquatic ecosystems would suffer irreversible damage from the higher ultraviolet radiation.
- Terrestrial life cycles would also be damaged. In particular, quite a number of agricultural crops, such as beans, tomatoes, peas, and others would be scalded.

One cannot be certain that the calamitous nuclear war referred to above would actually result in a nuclear winter and serious depletion of the ozone layer. But it does seem that nuclear winter is possible, even likely, and that ozone depletion is probable.

10-62 Disease and the Survivors

Survivors of a nuclear attack would be in pitiable condition. Imagine the shock, the lack of information, the frustration. At least half of those still living after an attack would be seriously injured. Those able to search the ruins for their family members must of necessity ignore the pathetic cries of the wounded. The world has already seen this at Hiroshima and Nagasaki, and also after nonnuclear bombings.

Even if existing medical facilities were not destroyed, they would be utterly insufficient, totally overwhelmed. Survivors would soon face the rigors of inadequate food and water, and speedily become further demoralized. Some force themselves into shelters, only to find them overcrowded and hopeless. The unburied dead prove to be especially disheartening.

After some time, the first signs of disease appear. Dysentery, food poisoning, meningitis, and disorders which had been almost eliminated, begin to reappear. In the weakening physical condition of the survivors, infectious hepatitis, septicemia, and pneumonia materialize. After a month or so, there are cases of diphtheria, typhoid, and cholera. Tuberculosis cannot be far behind. Hemorrhage, often accompanied by infection, would be a common cause of death. Many Americans, accustomed to living under hygienic conditions and depending on antibiotics, have weakened immune systems. Anguish, suffering, illness, and death are the order of the day.

Old diseases begin to emerge among the survivors.

The Hiroshima experience has given evidence of the extreme sensitivity of fetuses to radiation (gamma and neutron). While accurate figures are lacking, fetal mortality (mis-miscarriage and stillbirth) up to 23% was noted. Of those born alive, small head size (microcephaly) was often observed, generally accompanied by mental retardation. A study was conducted in 1972 of 388 children born to women whose exact whereabouts could be established at the time of the explosion. Of these, 48 showed microcephaly.

The dwindling numbers of survivors, some months later, are of course aware of cancer. Just the word inspires dread. We saw earlier (Chapter 5) that ionizing radiation causes a rise in the cancer rate. The radiation may be gamma rays directly from a nuclear explosion, or indirect gamma or beta radiation from fallout. By altering the DNA of various somatic tissues, the uncontrolled growth of a cancer may appear sooner or later.

Exposure of human beings to doses of 30 to 50 rads leads to a great increase in noncancer deaths. Massive bone marrow damage was a leading cause of death for many in Hiroshima who survived the blast. The immune system is crippled and death arises from infection or aplastic anemia. A dose of 100 to 200 rads causes temporary sterility and suppresses menstruation for 2 or 3 years, and sometimes causes cataracts in addition.

In summary, most survivors of the holocaust have a bleak future whose mark is hunger, disease, and death.

10-63 Genetic Effects

One of the most frightening consequences of a nuclear war is possible genetic effects, the indelible imprinting of DNA with altered codes. Gamma rays affecting the DNA of somatic tissue such as skin or muscle act as a carcinogen, causing cancer at a later date. Gamma rays affecting the genetic DNA of chromosomes can act as a mutagen, that is, causing mutations. Survivors of Hiroshima and Nagasaki were exposed to up to 250 rems, in some cases more. A search for mutations in the descendants of these people have not shown any statistically valid increase in the natural mutation rate. But the use of sophisticated analytical techniques in 1987 did reveal a specific gene alteration in somatic cells. The mutated genes are stably integrated into the cells, and the extent of alteration depends on the radiation dose. The results provide a way to determine past exposure doses by analysis of blood samples.

The above studies also gave a better estimate of the amount of acute gonadal irradiation required to double the natural mutation rate: 156 rems (earlier estimates ranged from 16 to 250 rems). Conceivably, new hereditary diseases could appear in the gene pool. The human race is already afflicted with at least 4000 genetic disorders, such as hemophilia, sickle-cell anemia, albinism, phenylketonuria, galactosemia, and Wilson's disease. It is not known what fraction of these arose from natural background radiation, or perhaps have always been with us. Somewhere around 2 or 3% of babies born today have visible hereditary or congenital defects.

What would the situation be, say, 100 years after the nuclear debacle? Only the crudest estimate can be made of the number of persons likely to suffer genetic defects attributable to the irradiation of their ancestors. In the northern hemisphere, it might be an increase of up to 3% of the population, amounting to some tens of millions of people. The great bulk of such effects would be insignificant. Infants born with gross abnormal abnormalities, representing a sort of human weed, would perish, either naturally or otherwise. It is highly unlikely but conceivable that radiation, from the outside or from food-ingested fission products, could reshuffle certain crucial subunits in those genes which control the development of the human brain, resulting in a mutant outwardly no different than the parents, but mentally inferior, or, less likely, superior. We human beings are vain enough to believe that we are the end product of evolution; maybe that is not the case.

A few true mutations would probably result.

In summary, we can only say that the future of the human race, in the event of nuclear war, cannot be predicted from the genetic point of view. It is worth noting that genetic damage has never been shown to be reversible.

10-64 Civil Defense

The protection of civilians in the event of nuclear war, which is the most sweeping meaning of the term civil defense, is a topic which most have mixed feelings about. On the one hand, since we see that nations seem to have little genuine interest in preventing war, the people should support every measure which increases their survival. On the other hand, every civil defense measure can be viewed as a means intended to make nuclear war winnable and survivable, and therefore to make such a war more likely.

The first thought, to protect the urban populations if a nuclear attack comes or is even threatened, is to get them out of the cities. Various evacuation plans have been studied and abandoned. Any strategy designed to remove millions, or even thousands, of civilians from cities or towns in a short time is just impossible. Like trying to predict earthquakes, one false alarm decreases faith in all other efforts. Imagine the jammed highways and roads even during normal times; one breakdown or accident clogs the traffic. And even if many do escape into the countryside, how do they live for the time necessary? How do they know where to go to escape fallout? One should expect little or no protection by anti-ballistic rocket systems such as SDI (sections 10-14 to 10-24).

The other possibility is blast and fallout shelters. The Reagan administration called for a $4.3 billion program in 1982 for a civil defense program over a seven-year period. The sponsors and supporters of the program claimed that in the event of all-out nuclear war, 80% of the American population would survive. The program met incredulous opposition from many sides, and has never been implemented except for a few signs directing civilians to go to certain basements in case of attack.

The costs of building an effective civil defense system of fallout shelters and stocking them adequately would be hundreds of times higher than the $4.3 billion figure. Costs of real estate alone would often be the most expensive item. The units would have to be stocked with food, water, sanitation facilities, beds, and medicinals. They would have to be supplied with ventilation systems. Containing valuables, they would have to be guarded. Once full of people, many injured by radiation, burns, or otherwise, they would become centers of epidemics. Not knowing the dose of radiation received would add to the trauma. Blast shelters would not save their inhabitants from fire storms. A period of confinement of some weeks would be necessary, after which the people emerge into a world of unimaginable deprivation, and most would perish anyway.

Large-scale civil defense is simply not feasible.

Hardline conservatives claimed that the Soviets were building an extensive shelter system and hardening industrial installations. There is essentially no confirmation for this. Even the CIA said, "There is little evidence of hardening of economic installations." Switzerland, while staying neutral and watching its quarrelsome neighbors battle each other time and time again, has constructed underground shelters which can accommodate tens of thousands of its citizens, and more shelters were under construction until recently. Sweden has a few mountain shelters, and China has also burrowed a system of shelters of modest size.

Just the same, there is no reason why one should not know something about shelter from fallout. The "protection factor" or "shielding factor" of any shelter is the number of times the intensity of radiation (generally gamma) is attenuated. A protection factor of about 50 is given by two feet of earth or 16 inches of concrete; a dose rate of 1 rad/hour is reduced to 0.02 rad/hour. Assuming no blast damage, an ordinary house gives a protection factor of 3 to 5, and a basement a factor of 15 to 20. A brick house affords a protection factor of around 50, and an earth-covered trench a factor of 100. Subway tunnels would be safe. In these cases it is assumed that no fallout dust has blown inside; one should remember that like snow, dust is wind-driven. All in all, one must conclude that a successful shelter program is utterly impractical for an entire population.

Protection factor is the number of times the intensity of radiation is reduced by a structure.

Prisons afford an ironic twist to the shelter issue. The most hardened criminals are incarcerated in the most secure penitentiaries, that is, the sturdiest, with thick steel and stone. These features make prisons first class fallout shelters. Thus the cruelest criminal elements would be among the most likely to survive.

During the past few decades, a nonnuclear explosive of a new kind has been developed. This is the fuel-air explosive. An aerosol cloud of a gas, such as propylene oxide, is released into the atmosphere just above the ground. Several such clouds might be generated side by side. On ignition, the explosion has the energy up to that of a small nuclear bomb. People in shelters would suffer sufficient lung damage to suffocate.

10-65 Additional Long-Range Effects

A few additional complications are described below:

• Agriculture and Fresh Water—As mentioned earlier, a 5300-megaton attack on the USA would cover 7% or 8% of the land with fallout giving a 450-rad dose in 48 hours. All agriculture would be stopped in the afflicted areas until enough time passes to allow the dose rate to decrease greatly; this would be years, in some areas decades.

Nuclear explosions yield fission products representing many elements. Fallout containing these radioactive nuclides, when deposited on plants, irradiate their leaves and often leads to the death of the plant. But only a few elements are taken up by the roots of plants and become incorporated into our food.

For hydrogen bomb explosions, each megaton yield forms billions of curies of fission products, most of them with short half-lives. Each megaton of yield produces 11 million curies of strontium-89 (half-life 50.6 days), 80,000 curies of strontium-90 (half-life 28.5 years), and 130,000 curies of cesium-137 (half-life 30.0 years). All of these are taken up by plants, but the last two are the worst because of their longer half-lives. These factors make agriculture hazardous in affected areas, and drives survivors to areas of lower contamination.

Fresh water reservoirs would be seriously polluted with fallout, and this would persist for some years. Rainwater right after the attack would be deadly. Underground water would be much slower to be dirtied by fallout, but would be unavailable to most. Safe drinking water could be prepared by distillation. Use of a home water softener removes strontium.

• Insects—Since insects are very resistant to irradiation effects, one could expect huge populations a few weeks or months after the destruction of cities.

• Neurosis—The extraordinary stresses among the survivors is certain to cause mental disturbances in many cases. And little or no treatment would be available.

• Economy—The post-war economy would revert to something resembling that of the dark ages and finally evolve into a form not now predictable.

10-66 Survival of the Human Race

There has been much loose talk about the human race extinguishing itself in a nuclear holocaust. How likely is it? We should base our opinions on the best evidence available.

The Federal Emergency Management Agency in 1979 estimated the number of casualties expected from a 6500 megaton attack on the United States. This total yield is higher than the 5300 megatons assumed above, but nevertheless the report gives an idea of what to expect. Adjusted to the present population of the United States, the results are that some 155 million people would die from blast and fallout, and millions more would be injured. Blast effects and fire would account for around 64% of the fatalities, and irradiation fallout around 28%. Somewhere between 60 and 90% of urban populations, counting cities of 50,000 or more, would perish. Considering the disruption of transportation and contamination of foodstuffs, survivors would face starvation. In addition, the post-attack chaos and lack of medical and hygienic facilities would claim a dreadful toll. A catastrophe of the same dimensions would have been expected in the USSR and Europe had such a war occurred in the period 1970 to 1990, roughly speaking.

A 6,500-megaton attack on the U.S. might kill 155 million people at once, and millions more eventually.

An analysis from the Livermore National Laboratory shows that the great bulk of local fallout would stay in the lands of the belligerents. The most deadly portion of the fission products evidently does not spread out as much as formerly believed. Thus an attack on the United States would result in relatively little fallout blowing into Canada or Mexico. Similarly, fallout in the USSR would have been mostly confined within its borders. The global fallout stays for the most part in the stratosphere, and thus, while there would some backlash to damage other countries, it would not cause wholesale slaughter. Only the small fraction leached by rain from the troposphere comes to Earth.

Fortunately, local fallout does not spread out much, and thus kills fewer than the maximum possible.

The above conclusion is not in conflict with the nation-wide spread of fission products during the tests in Nevada during the 1950s. Imagine a progressive series of nuclear explosions, starting with a ground burst, another slightly above ground, the third still higher, etc., until the explosions are so high the fireball does not touch the Earth. The ground burst ejects heavy local fallout, mostly confined to several hundred miles. With rising height of burst, the proportion of local fallout decreases, and the proportion of global fallout increases. Most of the tests of the 1950s were below a height of 1500 feet, and thus were intermediate. Fallout covered the country, but in far-from-lethal quantities, except for the unfortunate few who contracted cancer as a result of the tests. Such cancer cases in survivors of a war would be far, far more numerous.

Considering a calamitous war in which approximately 5300 megatons are exploded in the air in the northern hemisphere, a huge quantity of fission products enters the stratosphere as global fallout. The best estimates of the average radiation dose to human beings, counting this source alone, are rather small. Over a 50 year period, those surviving in the northern hemisphere would receive about 15 rads each (in addition to dose from local fallout much earlier), and those south of the equator only half a rad.

While this outcome would spare millions of innocents from death by irradiation, the nuclear winter, ozone layer depletion, and other such consequences would not. Various estimates have been made of the number of people who would die in a cataclysmic nuclear war of the magnitude mentioned. The world population is

The good news is that the human race would not become extinct.

somewhat more than 6 billion souls, mostly living in the northern hemisphere. Bleak estimates, fraught with imponderable uncertainties, are that between 2 and 3 billion would perish (which is almost beyond imagination), still leaving more than 3 billion alive. These survivors would be the citizens of nonbelligerent nations (Japan, South America, Canada, Africa, etc.), gritty farmerfolk of remote areas of belligerents, and most of the peoples of the southern hemisphere. It seems fairly certain that the human race would not become extinct. Our planet would not become a radioactive desert in its entirety; only parts of the northern hemisphere would suffer that grim fate. Some studies indicate that most of the population of the northern hemisphere would die.

The above analysis might have understated the consequences of an all-out nuclear war. After all, there are endless pathways between cause and effect, and complicated interconnections between the various life forms on Earth. One can make a case that the description above is only an optimistic scenario, not the worst.

But that isn't all. Suppose, as seems likely, that the human species manage to avoid an all-out nuclear holocaust for the present, but at the same time refuse to change our way of thinking about matters of war and peace. Imagine that this precarious accord prevails for 50 or 100 years, and that during this time we (most of the human race) continue the patterns of the past, that is, devote a very high fraction of our energies to more and better nuclear weapons, more certain delivery systems, and more efficient means of rubbing out those we regard as enemies. Then, if or when a holocaust comes, it very well might eradicate this remarkable, but mad, species from our Earth. If so, we would not evolve again. The entirety of the human species would be but a hiccup in the history of the galaxy. The ocean waves, tortured by energy, would continue to pound a planet without human beings, eon after eon.

The bad news is that we might eradicate our species in the future.

10-67 Trial by Fire

How can words capture the events of a real nuclear war? Words at best can only convey the blueprint, the contours of the occurrences. Without examining the rights and wrongs, let us try to register snatches of the image of possible happenings. This could have occurred during the long Cold War, or it could happen again in the future if the human race is unwise enough to allow our world to develop into a system of rivalry between two or more superpowers, which is the assumed case described below.

As in the past, opposing nations frequently allow small differences to become magnified and become enemies. With rising passions and hostilities, there are numerous ways in which hostilities could start (10-52). Within hours, silos are emptied, their accurate and ruinous missiles are launched to destroy silos in enemy country (use'm or lose'm). Cruise missiles, submarine-launched missiles, and bombers carry out the gruesome roles they were made for. Monstrous warheads, hydrogen bombs of 1 to 5 megatons, crumble underground military headquarters by surface and earth-penetrating hits. Capital cities are extinguished with multiple one-megaton explosions, leaving lava plateaus. The fireballs, radiant with terror, incinerate everything. Priority targets, such as industry, transportation facilities, and fuel depots are blasted into oblivion. Many cities, being near industries, are erased unavoidably. Uncounted hundreds of thousands of innocent lives are snuffed out, many with no knowledge of the reasons. Older communication facilities had already been suppressed through electromagnetic pulses, but news of the expanding war gets through. Some missiles are bound to malfunction, hitting land at random.

City populations become panic stricken even before the first of several one-megaton warheads explodes in the air high above or on the surface, inflicting unprecedented carnage. Don't think for a minute that officialdom—civil service, the military, police, firefighters, bureaucrats, medical personnel—will sacrifice whatever chance there might be of survival for themselves and their families. Many leave their posts, and who could blame them? Pentagon personnel, being first to learn of incoming missiles, are the first to bolt in bedlam. There is total paralysis of authority. Fleeing in panic and feral fear, traffic jams never before seen clog all roads, only to be cudgeled by a fatal air blast. Bodies are roasted and mangled. People are squashed like bugs; some are thrown bodily by drag winds and hurt beyond repair. Streets become so littered with rubble that only movement on foot is possible. Many firestorms are started and the infernos char the rubble, along with the few persons who have endured so far in makeshift shelters.

In a real attack, most officialdom would desert.

Unlike past disasters, which were more localized and assistance from outside could arrive, the present tragedy encompasses whole countries, and the wounded are without help. Pernicious fallout lacerates town and country alike. No one comes in to succor the casualties, there are no physicians or nurses or hospitals, there are no antibiotics. Even that primitive ritual of burying the dead cannot be fully carried out.

Inevitably, a certain number of city dwellers manage to escape to safety, carrying some hastily-assembled survival gear. Very few stop to aid the injured, despite their piteous cries. Those refugee families with civilian-band radios have a distinct advantage. Many carry guns, and conflicts over water and food claim more lives. Some evacuees, being aware of wind-driven fallout, are able to select less dangerous routes. Within a few days the signs of fatal radiation exposure appear in many of the fleeing people: nausea, diarrhea, and slow, horrible deaths as their lives are leached out.

Eventually quite a number of people manage to reach areas where they think survival is possible. Fearing surface water is contaminated, they look for wells, springs, and water mains. Their arrival at farms is met with hostility, and again battles break out. One group wins out, but not for long, for their blood streams are invaded by microbes, and infectious sickness reigns. The land swarms with flies and cockroaches.

In the end it is gangs of teenagers who prove most adept at survival. Hardened criminals who survived in their prison shelters make up a subgroup. With no farming skills, most eventually succumb. But human beings are amazingly resourceful and tough and, if young and healthy, are hard to kill. Some would come through.

In quite a number of small-town food warehouses, bands of youths set up a regime of sorts, cruel, dictatorial, and merciless. If the skies begin to blacken as a nuclear winter builds up, it is these who live through it. There would be many other survivors in remote villages and valleys scattered over areas west of the Mississippi, and corresponding numbers in other lands. Millions of people south of the equator live on with little immediate danger from the wars in the north.

Most in the north emerge into a world largely stripped of the fruits of human civilization. Food and water sources become scarce or questionable. There are no industries or government. Since the electric generators had been destroyed or soon run out of fuel, there is no radio, no television, no electric lights. Transportation suddenly drops to a primitive level. Medical care practically disappears. The great universities and research institutes are gone. Many religious edifices and institutions are severely damaged or ruined. The libraries and museums and hospitals are ashes. It becomes clear that nuclear weapons are much too dangerous to use in war. There are no winners in such a war, only losers.

Almost nothing is left.

Certainly the human race does not deserve this fate. We parents who love our families; children who love their parents; our dearest friends; the loveliness of Nature; centuries of human accomplishment; are all these to be sacrificed in a week? There is a possibility, some say a probability, that they will. Wars are not natural disasters; they are made by human beings. The idiocy of all-out nuclear war can be summed up as follows: The purpose of all those nuclear weapons in the first place was to defend all we hold dear; yet the result of such a war would be to destroy all we wish to preserve. Only we human beings can safeguard peace.

No nuclear holocaust is in sight currently, in the early years of the third millennium. But we should keep in mind that in 50 or 100 years, or maybe beyond that time, more Cold Wars, even hostilities, could well break out again, since the fundamental causes have not been addressed. There is simply no way to disinvent the bomb.

It would be well to keep in mind a wise statement of Dr. Martin Luther King, Jr. (1963): "Our scientific power has outrun our spiritual power. We have guided missiles and misguided man." Perhaps this type of sentiment can help steer the human race in the direction of abolishing the threat of nuclear weapons.

Bibliography for Chapter 10: Targeting Nuclear Bombs, Their Physical Effects, and the Meaning of Nuclear War

Desmond Ball and Jeffrey Richelson, *STRATEGIC NUCLEAR TARGETING*, Cornell University Press, 1986.

Robert M. Bowman, *STAR WARS: DEFENSE OR DEATH STAR*, Institute for Space and Security Studies, 1985.

William J. Broad, *TELLER'S WAR: THE TOP-SECRET STORY BEHIND THE STAR WARS DECEPTION*, Simon & Schuster, 1992.

Committee for the Compilation of Materials on Damage Caused by the Atomic Bombs in Hiroshima andNagasaki, *HIROSHIMA AND NAGASAKI: THE PHYSICAL, MEDICAL, AND SOCIAL* EFFECTS *OF THE ATOMIC BOMBINGS*, translated from the Japanese, Basic Books, 1981.

Frances FitzGerald, *WAY OUT THERE IN THE BLUE*, Reagan, Star Wars, and the End of the Cold War, Simon & Schuster, 2000.

Herman Kahn, *ON THERMONUCLEAR WAR*, 2nd ed., Princeton University Press, 1961.

Michio Kaku and Daniel Axelrod, *TO WIN A NUCLEAR WAR*, South End Press, 1987.

L. Douglas Keeney, *THE DOOMSDAY SCENARIO*, (detailing the effects of a nuclear attack on the U.S.), MBI Publishing Co., P. O. Box 1, Osceola, WI 54020.

Julius London and Gilbert F. White, eds., *THE ENVIRONMENTAL EFFECTS OF NUCLEAR WAR*, American Association for the Advancement of Science, 1984.

National Academy of Sciences, Committee on the Atmospheric Effects of Nuclear Explosions, *THE EFFECTS ON THE ATMOSPHERE OF A MAJOR NUCLEAR EXCHANGE*, National Academy Press, Washington, DC, 1985.

Rosy Nimroody, Director, *STAR WARS: THE ECONOMIC FALLOUT*, Ballinger, 1987.

Jeannie Peterson, ed., *AFTERMATH: THE HUMAN AND ECOLOGICAL CONSEQUENCES OF NUCLEAR WAR*, Pantheon, 1983.

Carl Sagan, Paul R. Ehrlich, Donald Kennedy, Walter Orr Roberts, et al., *THE COLD AND THE DARK: THE WORLD AFTER NUCLEAR WAR*, Norton, 1984.

Paul B. Stares, *THE MILITARIZATION OF SPACE*, Cornell University Press, 1985.

John Tirman, ed., *EMPTY PROMISES: THE GROWING CASE AGAINST STAR WARS*, The Union of Concerned Scientists, Beacon, 1986.

Yevgeni Velkkhov, Roald Sagdeev, and Anredi Kokoshin, *WEAPONRY IN SPACE: THE DILEMMA OF SECURITY*, Imported Publications, Inc., 1987.

N. Wade, *A WORLD BEYOND HEALING: THE PROLOGUE AND AFTERMATH OF NUCLEAR WAR*, W. W. Norton, 1987.

Lord Zuckerman, *STAR WARS IN A NUCLEAR WORLD*, Vintage Books, 1987.

Chapter 11:
ARMS RACES AND THE AFTERMATH OF THE LATE COLD WAR

ABSTRACT—After the political tectonic convulsions in the old USSR in 1990-91, the Cold War gradually expired, presenting the world with golden new opportunities. The futile pursuit of national security in the nuclear age, another name for the Cold War, is detailed, as well as its enormous costs. The slow demise of the Cold War is chronicled. Thousands and thousands of nuclear warheads did not bring security; in fact, the opposite was true. Many politicians, in both the USA and Russia, still do not grasp this point. Nuclear bombs cannot be disinvented, and this presents the world with a staggering challenge for the new century. The nature of military deterrence is examined, as well as its limitations. A strong Comprehensive Test Ban Treaty would enhance our security, and failure to attain full agreement is analyzed. No one would "win" a nuclear war, and the concept of prevailing in such a conflict is shown to be an illusion. The terms of the Strategic Arms Reduction Treaties are briefly outlined. The immense gains of economic reconversion to a truly peaceful recovery are emphasized. Steps taken to maintain military strength far in excess of current American needs are summarized, including modern nuclear weapon developments and proliferation. Attention is drawn to the dangers presented by un- and under-employed Soviet nuclear scientists, including smuggling of bomb materials, and also to the fate of nuclear weapons in Ukraine, Belarus, and Kazakhstan. Finally, a note on the responsibilities of the remaining super power—the USA—is presented.

11-1 Dimensions of the Cold War

The amount of written literature on the late arms race is truly vast. Quite a number of persons spent their entire professional lives in analyzing the Cold War. Any short discussion of the arms race, such as this chapter, is certain to be burdened with opinion; what to select or omit is itself an editorial process. Necessarily, therefore, this chapter is an incomplete treatment of the subject.

Professionals sometimes seem to feel that only they can make a wholly informed judgment on the matter, but you don't have to follow every nuance to be active, constructive, and have a say. It is best not to be overawed into submission by esoteric science and dazzling gadgets. After all, government experts had made contingency plans to deal with every conceivable twist and turn of the arms race except one: winning the Cold War. Arms races and other issues of war and peace are too important to leave to just the military, diplomats, governments, or scientists. Looking back, it is apparent that the leaders of both sides were generally bunglers, ignorant of the history of the people on the other side, and irrationally preoccupied with global games camouflaged in a cloak of "national security." Many delighted in constructing ideological scarecrows and in squelching any suggestion for chilling the hostilities. Actually, several opportunities came up for ending the Cold War, such as Krushchev's visit to the United States in 1959, the time the test ban treaty was signed in 1963, and again in 1973, with détente.

Sometimes officials of one government or another accused peace activists of being "radical." The truth is that development of nuclear armaments was the most radical change in human history, and the peace activists are trivial in comparison. About one half of American scientists were engaged in so-called defense work during the 1980s. Of all funds for research and development in the United States, 50% was spent on defense in 1981. This figure had risen to 70% in 1987. But by 1993, two or three years after the political tsunami which caused the Soviet Union to collapse, it had dropped to 59%.

The late, unlamented arms race, which was a form of mental menopause, still has after-effects on each and every American every day, mostly negative. Its aftermath intrudes into our well being and livelihoods and robs us of the good life. Even today, the budgets which are set up to finance defense are too high for a pay-as-you-go basis. We are still passing unprecedented costs on to our descendants. The Cold War, counting both sides, has cost at least 10.5 trillion dollars. This sum is roughly twice the national debt. The magnitude of the costs was formerly treated as a military secret and was kept from public knowledge. Somewhat less than 10% of the funds went for nuclear warheads and related matters; the rest was spent on bombers, intercontinental ballistic missiles, nuclear-capable submarines, command and control systems, air defenses, etc., in addition to salaries. When the accounting is made in this way, it becomes doubtful whether nuclear weapons are cheaper than conventional ones.

Our children will pay.

Lev Altschuler, 84 years old in 1997, is regarded as one of the Grand Old Men of the Soviet nuclear weapons effort. His son Boris has calculated Cold War expenditures of each side in terms of what he called "national income," which is about twice the gross domestic product. He concluded that the Soviets spent about 50% of the national income, compared to the American value of about 12%. That 50% figure, being so high, was one of the main reasons for the collapse of the Soviet Union.

The end of the Cold War has presented us with a unique opportunity to attain a level of prosperity which could make us gasp. Just think, all those resources going into peaceful ends. Something like this took place to a small degree during the later Clinton years. One idea is to have a new "cold war," that is, a war against the common cold, which has afflicted humanity for thousands of years. Similarly, Europe might be standing on the brink of enormous affluence, despite such conflicts as the one in the former Yugoslavia.

Probably the only sure way to avoid arms races and wars is through a single world government, and even then civil wars could break out. The human race is nowhere near the level of civilization and education necessary to adopt such a system. If intelligent aliens from a distant galaxy had visited our Earth during the Cold War years and had made a study of our history, they would have to be forgiven for concluding that the arms race was a virulent case of collective mental illness and that earthlings are hopeless and impossible, and psychologically addicted to war; such beings would also have noticed that our species has enormous potential. Yet, war is not an innate component of human nature. It is learned. Other dreadful institutions, such as slavery and dueling, have nearly disappeared. One of the tasks we have is to convince our leaders and friends that more and more nuclear weapons and rocket systems do not bring greater security.

Nuclear weapons are here to stay. It is difficult to imagine the circumstances, realistically speaking, in which a superpower, once having a taste of this magic power, will voluntarily relinquish all its nuclear warheads, although at least one country has done so, South Africa (9-49). The techniques used to manufacture nuclear warheads cannot be forgotten and cannot be disinvented. Fundamentally, arms races and wars are the consequence of failure of agreement on crucial political issues of the world; but in the nuclear age, arms are part of these crucial issues, and contribute importantly to the problem. Up until about 1990, the antagonists were in a condition of stalemate, a low form of truce, maintained precariously. The two superpowers, it seems correct to say, had become rogue elephants, or maybe dinosaurs, on the political scene, infringing treaties, littering the landscape with radioactive debris, and stockpiling the most formidable power keg the Earth has ever seen. The arms race was driven by many ignoble forces, including fear, ignorance, arrogance, and greed, among others.

Nuclear bombs cannot be disinvented.

11-2 How It Started and Persisted

Wars are probably of tribal origin, in the misty domain of prehistory. Some say war is in our genes; this is unproven, and war is probably a learned human activity. When city-states developed, conflicts became better organized, and a warrior caste emerged. There has been a steady development in weapons and their lethality: clubs, spears, bows and arrows, crossbows, guns, poison gases, and a myriad of other devices. In more modern times, with the incorporation of science into arms races, the advances, if that is the proper word, have been ever faster and deadlier.

The development of nations or nation-states accelerated conflict dramatically. Each nation, often unified by race, religion, and language, felt determined to maintain its sovereignty. When a nation perceived that its rivals were arming, naturally it had to arm too. The dreadful fate of past defeated nations stimulated still more powerful defenses, but defense and offense are intertwined. Much of human history became one long and sad record of addiction to war and conquest.

At the start of World War I, there were approximately 50 independent countries in the world; this figure does not include colonies. Through the interplay of complex political and economic forces, they tended to associate into loosely allied groups. When World War I ended, one group of allies included England, France, Russia, Italy, the U.S., Japan, China, and others. On the other side were Germany, the Austro-Hungarian Empire, and Turkey. These alliances are fickle; by the time of World War II, several shifts had occurred. On the one side were England, France, the Soviet Union, the U.S., and China, while on the other were Germany (incorporating Austria), Italy, and Japan. Both sides had minor satellite powers. Still other shifts occurred in the Korean and Vietnam Wars. Each conflict fertilizes the seeds of the next, driving the arms races to new heights. Some arms races during the past 200 years have simply petered out, without ending in conflict.

Up until the time nuclear weapons were used in war in 1945, more arms and raw military power did indeed increase the security of a nation, provided it could keep its aggressive drives in check. The idea that the more weapons we have the safer we are has been thoroughly ingrained in all military organizations and has been transferred to nuclear weapons.

The word propaganda has a negative image within each country; it is something foreigners make. But the propaganda machines of every nation pour out copious, billowing words of propaganda, both official and unofficial. Many of us can look back on propaganda of World War II, with its scorched-earth rhetoric, and recognize it for what it was, but still remain blind to today's propaganda. Most Americans who examine cartoons which demonized the Japanese during World War II are today embarrassed, and are also ashamed of the internment of Americans of Japanese origin, a consequence of intense propaganda and its wretched rhetoric. The ability of governments to manufacture war psychology was summed up by Hitler's right arm, Hermann Goering: "Why of course the people don't want war. . . . It is the leaders who determine policy, and it is always a simple matter to drag the people along. . . . All you have to do is tell them they are being attacked and denounce the pacifists for lack of patriotism and exposing the country to danger. It works the same in any country." Starting four or five years after the end of World War II, the Cold War began between the United States and the Western Bloc on the one side, and the Soviet Bloc on the other side. It lasted about 40 years. During some of this time, China's participation imparted a complicating triangular aspect to the conflict. During those years, American propaganda disparaging everything Soviet was in full force. The Soviets reciprocated in kind, sometimes with less vitriol, sometimes more. Propaganda always identifies virtue with self interest. Such passions generally thwarted reasoned analysis of the arms race. It is well to keep in mind that persistent vilification of any one nation by another serves arms races and similar lunatic behavior.

Propaganda? Not us! Only them!

After World War II the Soviet Union felt threatened by American nuclear arms, and thus believed it must develop its own. The "balance of terror" which resulted was not stable, and evolved into "deterrence" and "mutual assured destruction" (which has the creepy acronym, MAD). Deterrence and mutual assured destruction existed as facts during those years, regardless of policy. During the Cold War, both superpowers had their missiles constantly poised to strike instantly, something like a reflex action. One of the driving forces was defense spending as an economic engine (ignoring the long-range consequences), with more impetus from interservice competition and industry promoting new technologies. MAD remains an invitation to proliferation, fueled by possession of nuclear warheads.

All nations employ and exploit their science and scientists in the quest for new weapons systems, always justified in the name of national security, never in the name of international security. This situation results in massive propaganda and enthusiastic support of arms races by nearly all military personnel and many civilians, some to the point of near veneration of weapons systems, and in certain cases with ghoulish glee. This endures despite our knowledge from long experience that survival comes through cooperation rather than conflict.

11-3 Deterrence and Pursuit of National Security

History is rife with the conquest of one power by another, sometimes resulting in the defeated nation being absorbed, or disappearing through genocide. For example, after the Romans conquered Carthage in the Punic Wars, all the inhabitants of that unfortunate metropolis were put to the sword (except for a few who were enslaved), and the city was burned and its site was plowed. Such atrocities have strengthened the determination of nations to defend themselves militarily. As we approach modern times, we find that all powers assert that their arms are purely defensive, not aggressive. The adversary of each does not see it that way. Arms races and all which goes with them lead to cynical negotiations, excessive manufactured propaganda, and genuine fear of attack. Each power feels the need to spy on its adversaries (or even its allies) and to counter their every "defensive" step, which is seen as offensive. This pattern persists to this day, although currently, with American military ascendancy, in a somewhat muted form.

After the advent of nuclear weapons, which are a principal fulcrum in modern history, most military strategists considered these awesome developments as just an extension of conventional systems. With only two main sides, the USA and the USSR, the race was malignant enough, and the nuclear capabilities of England, France, and China complicated the situation and made the balance even more delicate. With the outlook for a future with still more nuclear powers, one might feel driven to despair. The human race is simply not mature enough to cope competently with nuclear weapons. At times it seemed that the arms race was so dangerous and irrational that the world's decision makers were either insane or evil, although this is not really true. The most important principle in preserving the peace under current political conditions was *deterrence*. According to this concept, each side was supposed to convince the other that a nuclear attack would bring on devastating retaliation. Thus each side held the population of the other hostage. Deterrence rests at least as much on perception as on reality. The U.S. announced that even certain conventional (nonnuclear) attacks would elicit a nuclear response. In 1982 the Soviets proclaimed, concerning nuclear weapons, a no-first-use policy. During the dying throes of the old Soviet Union, the new Russia reversed this policy. American law requires any first use of such weapons to be authorized by the President, and it is very similar in Russia. The whole concept of deterrence depends on responsible and sensible leadership.

It's enough to make the gods grieve.

In accordance with the principles of deterrence, the military establishments of each superpower were charged with responsibility for producing safe, secure, effective, and reliable nuclear weapons. They spent billions on innovation and modernization. Yet, the old versions function dependably. There have been virtually no failures of well-understood bomb designs. From a rational viewpoint deterrence is achieved by each side when they own just enough warheads to destroy the adversary as a functioning society. Thus the threat to use nuclear weapons is supposed to be to prevent their use. Various estimates have been made of the minimum number of warheads which would achieve deterrence. Admiral Burke as early as 1957 stated that 720 warheads or their equivalent on invulnerable Polaris submarines would suffice to deter Soviet attack; the U.S. already had about six times that number. Secretary of Defense McNamara argued that 400 megatons of nuclear explosive power would be enough to deter the Soviets; the U.S. already had 17,000 megatons. The assessment of the American arsenal to achieve deterrence falls between 1000 and 2000 modern warheads, according to a 1992 study by

Deterrence does not demand superiority or even equality in nuclear weapons.

the National Academy of Sciences. A later study, in 1997, put the number at 1000 or less. Hans Bethe, director of the theoretical physics division at Los Alamos on the Manhattan Project, suggested that the U.S. and Russia could safely cut their arsenals to as few as 100 warheads. After all, these numbers of bombs when strategically used are sufficient to terminate even a superpower as a functioning society. Thus deterrence requires neither superiority nor even equality in nuclear weapons. Each Trident submarine carries as many as 240 warheads, and so four might be sufficient for adequate deterrence. One of our constant goals should be to aim for the smallest practical number of nuclear warheads.

A numerical comparison of warheads owned by various powers evades the essential point once a certain minimum number is reached. While there is some credibility in deterrence (after all, there has been no nuclear war since 1945, that is, each side during the Cold War was deterred), and deterrence will be world policy for a long time, it is inadequate as a permanent defense posture. The reasons for this include:

- Deterrence depends for its success on rational people in control of governments. History reveals that irrational persons do at times come into control of governments. Such individuals are not likely to be deterred by any threat, even the destruction of their own countries. Moreover, even normally rational people can become engulfed by a war frenzy, and behave dangerously.
- A balance based on deterrence still permits, indeed encourages, tremendous expenditures of resources on more and more sophisticated weapons systems. Greedy and experienced elements of military-industrial complexes easily manipulate enmity to award arms contracts to themselves. Deterrence thus resembles a narcotic: it takes stronger and stronger doses to make it work, and in the end it doesn't work at all.
- To be successful, deterrence must maintain and constantly renew credibility of retaliatory capacity. The required level of instilled fear needs constant reinforcement by reiteration. Any Cold War environment justifies saber rattling and encourages opportunistic politicians to make bellicose pronouncements. Appearance of lack of resolve might erode deterrence. Each side is obliged to publicize its resolve over and over. The process promotes ever more forceful arms buildup, which has a positive feedback, dangerously decreasing stability.
- The precarious equilibrium based on deterrence stimulates macho expressions such as "peace through strength," "number one military power," and "win and survive a nuclear war." So long as such unrealistic doctrines prevail, there can be little chance of accommodation and defusing of hostilities.
- The necessity for credibility of devastating retaliatory capacity leads to gross overkill potential. This makes every new weapons system, feasible or not, irresistible to arms racists. Moreover, the destructive power of an arsenal of nuclear bombs is so great that it could not be used in most circumstances, but this cannot be admitted because that would lessen the credibility of a nuclear threat in the eyes of potential enemies.
- Deterrence induces incessant propaganda. This takes the form of vilification of the adversary, claims that the other side is ahead, "missile gaps," "windows of vulnerability," and the like. The effect is to increase arsenals far beyond deterrence levels.
- While deterrence manages hostilities to some degree, it provides no basic or lasting resolution of the conflict.

Even in the year 2003 many analysts continued to advocate a robust nuclear deterrent as an essential component of American defense. Thus John Foster, the former director of the Livermore National Laboratory, is representative of those who continue to advocate diversified and survivable nuclear weapons, numbering around 7000. He believes that they should be of many types, deployed in a variety of ways. He considers the Trident submarines as the original, invulnerable stealth platforms, and that they make the world a safer place.

In the end, during the late Cold War, deterrence utterly failed in setting rational limits on military power and indeed fueled the insatiable arms race. Nuclear weapons are unlike conventional weapons because they do not require superiority or equality to maintain deterrence. Understanding this point is part of Einstein's meaning about "new ways of thinking." Nuclear munitions have brought about qualitative changes with volatile overtones which are not yet well understood or complete.

Deluxe bomb shelters

A revealing event in 1958 showed the lack of confidence by Congress in the effectiveness of deterrence. This was the secret construction (open secret, that is) of an underground bunker in West Virginia which was built and maintained at a site more than 40 miles from Washington. The objective was to serve as accommodations for Congressional personnel in case of a real emergency. It cost about $14 million and has been reported to sleep 800 people. In a telling move inspired by the end of the Cold War, the government gave up its lease of the land on July 31, 1995, and the present proprietor plans to convert the bunker into a tourist attraction, or even a casino. A smaller bunker was constructed in the Blue Ridge Mountains in Virginia for the President and other high-ranking officials.

Defense intellectuals have developed their own arcane and hermetically sealed vocabulary and language. Those who do not share these terms are considered unprofessional. Physicians must distance themselves somewhat from suffering or they will experience emotional burnout; professional nuclear analysts similarly use euphemisms to conceal true meanings. Thus "collateral damage" means mass killing of civilians and "sub-holocaust engagement" means incineration of many cities, but not all.

We should not overlook nonnuclear developments in modern warfare. Biological warfare is often discussed, and would probably be effective against peoples with low standards of public hygiene. Chemical warfare, employing nerve gases and other horrors, would most likely be effective against all populations. Just because war gases were not employed during World War II does not mean that the same will apply to nuclear weapons in any future conflicts.

By late 1992, the winding down of the Cold War had inspired an atmosphere in which nuclear arsenals could begin to be dismantled. Between the USA and those shards of the old Soviet Union which had nuclear bombs, perhaps 40,000 to 50,000 warheads might be retired. Nuclear weapons began to retreat from the conscious thoughts of many Americans, and interest in all things nuclear began to dwindle.

Research in the United States was being contemplated for a while with the objective of developing a probe to detect nuclear materials or activities in countries aspiring to develop nuclear weapons. The idea was that a sensitive gamma ray detector was to be built into a monitor a few inches in diameter, and large numbers of these were to be distributed in the suspect areas by spies, parachute, or other means. On being turned on by a radio signal, an antenna transmits a brief message to a satellite, identifying any characteristic gamma rays from certain isotopes of uranium, plutonium, etc. Such techniques are not really reliable.

11-4 Measures and Countermeasures

One can reflect on the Warsaw Pact powers deciding in the 1950s to increase the numbers of their army tanks because such an expensive step was supposed to enhance their security. When this step materialized, it stimulated the North Atlantic Treaty Organization powers to respond with various countermeasures, and in 1981 plans to deploy neutron bombs were announced. Of course, the Soviets soon built their own neutron bombs. American pressure on the European allies resulted in permission to install 108 Pershing missiles and 464 ground-launched cruise missiles; the first of these became operational in 1983. The Soviets deployed still more SS-20 missiles in equally threatening postures. The positioning of the Pershings was claimed not to be a response to the original SS-20s, but because of a "gap in our own nuclear response capability." Both sides seemed to feel that no matter how many weapons or how deadly a weapons system is, it is never enough. Both sides seemed more interested in blaming the other for failure than in achieving success.

Each armaments step by one superpower stimulated a similar step by the other.

Another consequence of Warsaw Pact tank proliferation was the development of TOW (tube-launched, optically-tracked, wire command-linked) guided missiles by the NATO powers, and subsequently by the Soviets. These missiles are available in great abundance, and are deadly accurate. Many have depleted uranium metal (4-20) tips in the form of shaped charges; on impact with a tank, the kinetic energy is high enough to melt a hole through the steel, permitting the charge to detonate inside. Anti-tank artillery shells also are equipped with uranium tips, and some tanks have a layer of depleted uranium armor. These weapons and smart bombs represent steps toward making tanks obsolete, so far as the major powers are concerned. The Phalanx weapon also fires depleted uranium projectiles. About 320 tons of this uranium was left scattered around Iraq after the first Persian Gulf War, and about 2000 tons the second up to 2004. Military aircraft fire smaller rounds with uranium tips. The trend today is to manufacture more depleted uranium ammunition and armor, much of it hardened by alloying with 2% molybdenum or zirconium. There are several American manufacturers of uranium ordnance. At least 100,000 five-inch uranium charges have been test-fired, creating another low-level waste area to be cleaned up. In the Aberdeen Proving Ground in Maryland, 70,000 kilograms (77 tons) of uranium projectiles have been fired. Some has been unwisely sold to at least ten foreign powers, a number of them quite unstable, and it could be that someday American service personnel will be their targets.

The Persian Gulf wars provided a demonstration of the effects of uranium metal in projectiles and armor. A uranium projectile makes a smooth round hole in the target tank and explodes inside, and is incredibly effective. At least 1400 Iraqi tanks were destroyed in this way. In a number of cases, American tanks were hit by "friendly fire." There are reports that in a few cases, Iraqi fire penetrated American tanks, causing their depleted-uranium ammunition to explode, and injuring American tankmen with uranium shrapnel. There were at least 30 surviving American soldiers in 1995 whose bodies hold numerous uranium shrapnel fragments, easily seen by X-rays, but too numerous and too small to permit complete removal by surgery. The urine and semen of these men contain traces of uranium. In some cases, respiratory and kidney problems (nephritis) from chemical toxicity of uranium have resulted. Some of the soldiers manage to live normally, have married, and have fathered at least 23 children, all without any birth defects. After years of exposure to the faint radiation from the slightly radioactive depleted uranium (specific activity, 0.46 microcuries per gram) and its accumulated disintegration products, a certain number of cancers is expected. Often the uranium ignites on striking a target and generates a black cloud of particulate uranium oxide. Some of the tanks were shipped back to the U.S. and buried in a disposal site for radioactive waste. Many soldiers did not know that the material is radioactive and picked up fragments to wear as decorative pendants. The problem has been complicated lately by the introduction of depleted uranium from another source, namely that depleted of most of its uranium-235 content not by physical separation from uranium-238 by gaseous diffusion of uranium hexafluoride, but by causing the uranium-235 content to fission in reactors. This leaves uranium-238 depleted of most of the uranium-235, but the final depleted material contains traces of plutonium and other transuranium elements. This renders the material more radioactive and therefore more hazardous, and also enhances the psychological opposition on the part of its detractors.

Poisoning by uranium is reminiscent in some ways of toxicity of Agent Orange during the war in Vietnam. Depleted uranium is one contributor to Gulf War Syndrome. Perhaps tungsten could be used instead of uranium in these heavy artillery shells. Some observers feel that the use of depleted uranium in military projectiles should be prohibited internationally, classifying it in the same way as war gases,

Thousands of deployed nuclear warheads were not mere symptoms of international tensions and distrust, they were part of the problem, making an important contribution to accelerating the spiraling arms race. It is sometimes stated that wars are fought to bring profit to a few arms merchants. There is a certain truth to this; taking the profits out of war and preparation for war would help in the peace process. But this would not suffice. The problem is more deep-seated.

One blunder which fired up the arms race anew was Reagan's deliberate decision in 1986 to break one of the few treaties which put some brakes on weapons escalation. This was the second Strategic Arms Limiting Treaty, or SALT II. It was knowingly violated by exceeding the number of allowed B-52 bombers equipped to carry cruise missiles. The treaty established crucial limits on powerful and destabilizing weapons systems, limited the total number of missiles and bombers, and embodied several other limitations and prohibitions to tame the arms race. Continuation of SALT II would have prevented the Soviets from building a new land- and sea-based missile system, forced them to dismantle existing systems to compensate for new ones, and prevented them from building a new submarine counterforce capability. Afterward, these limitations were no longer in force. The Soviets felt obliged to examine our capabilities, not our alleged intentions.

The Reagan administration deliberately violated the SALT II agreement.

Another irritant spurring Cold War hostilities was a Soviet radar station being built near Krasnoyarsk, in south central Siberia. It consisted of a transmitter and a receiver, the latter 30 stories tall. The facility could have provided anti-ballistic missile guidance and early warning of missile attack, and thus violate the Anti-Ballistic Missile Treaty of 1972. The Soviets maintained that it was designed to track spacecraft, which was not covered by the treaty, and pointed to its vulnerability to attack and lack of protection against electromagnetic pulses. An on-site inspection team by American Congressmen and their staffs concluded that while the Krasnoyarsk radar was not intended as part of an ABM system, it could have been an early warning radar, violating the letter of the treaty, but not its purpose. The USSR offered to stop the construction if the United States would drop its plans to upgrade its radar stations in Great Britain and Greenland, which are evidently prohibited by the ABM treaty. [The Treaty states that "each Party undertakes not to transfer to other States, and not to deploy outside its national territory, AMB systems or their components limited by this Treaty."] Both sides have attempted to circumvent the arms control process to their unilateral advantage. Finally, the Soviets did stop construction and announced their willingness to dismantle the equipment at Krasnoyarsk in a way which the United States could verify.

11-5 First Strike

The nature of nuclear weapons gives a tempting advantage to a power which strikes first. Such an attack, if carefully planned, could eliminate much retaliatory capability. Up to the period 1960-1965, it was possible to imagine a scenario in which one superpower could effectively disarm the other by a sudden, deadly nuclear missile attack. In later stages of the Cold War, with the deployment of submarines equipped with plentiful warheads, second-strike retaliation was certain. Some bombers would also have survived. Nevertheless, military thinking seems to be obsessed with the idea of a first strike by an opponent, even though such an attack would mean suicide.

Preparations for a first strike could not be hidden.

In a Cold War scenario, acquisition of additional weapons systems by one power is construed as first-strike capability by the other, and thus justification for additional countermeasures. But a first strike would require coordinating tens of thousands of military personnel under conditions of absolute secrecy, a feat virtually impossible to conceal. If detected, it might lead to a preemptive "retaliation in advance," despite deadly backlash (widespread radioactivity, nuclear winter, destruction of the ozone layer, etc.; see Chapter 10-III).

The degrees of effectiveness of the two superpowers' nuclear capabilities were not equal. A first strike by the U.S., using the MX and Trident D-5 missiles, might have eliminated more than 90% of land-based Soviet missiles. The Soviets had about two-thirds of their missiles based on land, whereas only about one-fifth of American missiles were land-based. The Soviets were more vulnerable and therefore more fearful. Such an imbalance led to hair-trigger alertness by both parties. Leaders on each side might have felt that they could not communicate with their missilemen, submarines, and pilots in time. A helpful step would have been to de-alert warheads by removing the fissile materials from each assembly, or other means. This would have provided valuable time for checking any order to launch. Such ideas were simply ignored.

11-6 Cold War Costs

In 1985 a Washington-based peace group, the Coalition for a New Foreign and Military Policy, published an analysis of the monetary costs of America's defense expenditures. Each American household paid about $2700 per year on the arms race. The expenses were broken down into categories of direct national defense (border defense and second-strike weapons), containment of the Soviet Union, Third-World military intervention (the single largest item, 45% of the total), and overhead. The grand total came out to be $306.7 billion for the year 1985, or $1,250 per citizen. Expenses for each American soldier averaged $434,000 during the year 1985. World expenditures on arms were about $930 billion in 1987.

Each American household paid about $2,700 per year on the arms race.

Just consider these sums: $306.7 billion per year is the same rate as $583,000 per minute, or $9725 per second. With every tick of the clock, another $9725. In the same year, the United States was going into debt at the rate of $381,000 per minute or $6350 per second; this staggering figure is not based on total expenditures, but only the excess of expenditures over revenues. Interest payments were growing correspondingly. In 1986, interest payments on the deficit (total deficit, not just military) were $230 billion per year, or $437,000 per minute.

The 1995 U.S. military budget was approximately $263 billion. President Clinton proposed a figure of about $254 billion for fiscal 1997 (the Senate voted to increase this by about $15 billion, a sum which the Pentagon did not request, and the final budget was $269 billion.). Corresponding budgets for other countries for the same time are, according to the Center for Defense Information: Russia, $63 billion; Japan, $54 billion; France, $41 billion; Great Britain, $35 billion; Germany, $34 billion; and China, $29 billion. At present a great deal of the military budget goes indirectly to keep the price of gasoline low; therefore a large reduction of the military budget would depend on our adoption of energy policies based on self-sufficiency (4-29). Worldwide military expenditures reached a maximum in 1987 at $1.3 trillion (1994 dollars). They declined to $840 billion by 1994, with the American budget making up about 36% of the world's total.

The U.S. military budget recommended by Congress from 1995 to 2000

Year:	1996	1997	1998	1999	2000
Budget (billions of dollars):	265	267	269	272	274

The above figures are actually too low. If the total military budget includes such items as the Department of Energy's share of nuclear weapons costs, pensions and benefits for veterans, and the defense-related component of interest, the sum comes out to be around $400 billion per year, or $4700 for each household. In 1980, 50% of American research and development expenditures was military; by 1988 it had reached 78%. Not being willing to tax ourselves adequately, the Reagan administration borrowed both domestically and from abroad. The awesome increase in debt exceeded $1,800,000,000,000 (1.8 trillion dollars).

Most of us would be willing to cut our standard of living to the bone if such expenditures would bring genuine security. There is the crux of the matter. During the period 1946 to 1980 we spent approximately $2 trillion on defense. If such expenditures had really been effective, we would not feel the need for such high military budgets today.

The arms race was robbing the U.S. economy. Funds which might have been invested to modernize and increase productivity went into weapons. By devouring capital the arms race lowered our health care, deprived our children, diverted funds from education, starved our poor, eroded our well being; in short it damaged the very values in our country it is supposed to save. A corresponding situation prevailed in the Soviet Union, but was even worse. We should consider that the inane, insane arms race hurt each of us every day, costing us time and treasure. But the run-away costs will not be curtailed until enough American citizens free themselves from Cold-War doctrines which have throttled common sense.

A comprehensive, richly documented audit of the costs of the frenzied American nuclear weapons program during the period 1940-96 was published in 1998 (see S. I. Schwartz, Bibliography at end of chapter). The conclusion was that the total was at least $5.5 trillion, a galactic number. This does not include the cleanup costs of around $300 billion. One way to visualize the enormity of this total, $5.8 trillion, is to imagine one-dollar bills stacked up. Counting 200 bills to the inch, the total comes out to be 458,000 miles, which is the distance from the Earth to the Moon and back!

11-7 The Comprehensive Test Ban Treaty

Background of the Treaty—The Limited Nuclear Test Ban Treaty of 1963 prohibited nuclear tests in the atmosphere, in the ocean, and in outer space. Even though some smaller powers did not sign, most observers feel that the treaty has been stabilizing and slowed the arms race. Proposals for a Comprehensive Test Ban Treaty to halt all further testing were considered soon afterwards. The Soviet Union unilaterally stopped all testing in 1985 on the fortieth anniversary of the destruction of Hiroshima, but resumed a year and a half later because of continued American testing. In October 1992 President Bush, senior, ordered testing stopped for nine months. (More on the Comprehensive Test Ban Treaty is in section 9-63).

The Soviets agreed in 1986 to permit the United States to establish a broad seismic monitoring network inside its borders in exchange for a like American arrangement. The Americans in the Soviet Union who monitored Soviet tests were not supported by our government, but by a private group, the Natural Resources Defense Council. It was a lonely, under-financed, and widely ignored effort to make compliance with a comprehensive test ban feasible.

Test explosions of military significance cannot be concealed.

Underground tests were limited to a yield of 150 kilotons by the Threshold Test Ban (which though unratified was observed by both superpowers). Advances in seismology permit detection of underground blasts anywhere as small as 0.1 kiloton, so a Comprehensive Test Ban would be verifiable. It is also possible to easily distinguish between earthquake tremors and nuclear explosions. A total test ban alone would not insure lasting peace. It would retard the development of some new kinds of nuclear weapons. To the extent that it impairs defense, if any, such impairment would affect all powers equally.

A wide variety of powerful elements in American society opposed a Comprehensive Test Ban. These included the Department of Defense and parts of the Department of Energy, the National Security Council, the Defense Nuclear Agency (in 1996 renamed Defense Special Weapons Agency), most of the military-industrial complex, and more. Robert Barker, a former assistant Secretary of Defense, held that "we will never be finished" testing. Former Assistant Secretary Richard Perle opposed any test ban whether it could be verified or not. Edward Teller strenuously opposed a ban. As late as 1996, the Republican Party Platform, preparing for the fall election, inserted the opinion that continued nuclear weapons development and testing are required for national security. Former Secretary of Defense James Schlesinger claimed the "confidence in the reliability of the stockpile will inevitably, ineluctably, decline" in the absence of testing. He was rebutted by Richard Garwin, chairman of the State Department's advisory board on arms control, and one of the most highly respected science advisors and nuclear weapons experts. Garwin pointed out that warheads are being inspected more frequently than ever, that their longevity estimates are actually rising, and that the warhead makers in the nuclear laboratories "have as much confidence in the stockpile as they ever did, and probably more." Many of the unemployed weaponeers of the former Soviet Union look for any reason to keep making their bombs.

Still, the United States is committed officially to the idea of a total ban, as stated in the preamble to the Limited Test Ban of 1963. Glenn T. Seaborg, Nobel Laureate chemist who was codiscoverer of plutonium and was former chairman of the Atomic Energy Commission, strongly supported a total test ban. He feared the nuclear warheads of the future will be a "dangerously destabilizing development," and believed that the world would be far better off today if a total test ban had been agreed upon in 1963, when the opportunity was ripe.

The weaponeer community in the United States, in general, avidly opposes a Comprehensive Test Ban. Centered in Los Alamos and Livermore, these warrior-scientists take great pride in their skill in designing new nuclear weapons; it is their heartbeat. Apparently the nuclear warhead producers believe that more and more research and testing should go on endlessly. They appeared to accept without question that their work refining bombs would somehow actually insure that they would never be used in war. They have developed extensive computer programs capable of modeling the dynamics of bomb detonation. Some of them claim that the newer designs are of such fragile sophistication that continued testing is required; if true, it places an unwarranted power over national policy in their hands. When questioned about their roles in building nuclear warheads, one bomb designer answered: "We're in an interim solution until the politicians and social scientists figure out a better way of organizing the world. Until then, this is the best way to keep the peace." Another common view is: "If you get rid of nuclear weapons in the current political environment, you make the world safe for conventional war."

The principal factor which broke the weapons designers' spell and finished their dominant role in defense policy was the end of the Cold War. Other contributing factors to changing the status quo were: the rise of talented antinuclear activists and campaigns publicizing the dangers of huge numbers of threatening warheads; increasing realization by many world leaders of just how dangerous our world had become; devastating blunders and statements by high administration officials; and the withdrawal by a number of influential members of the nuclear weapons community from their positions and in some cases swinging to the other side. An example of the last category is a former weapons designer, Theodore Taylor, who pointed out that testing an occasional stockpiled warhead by underground explosion cannot reveal reasons for any failure. The principal way to assure reliability is by periodic dismantlement, replacement of faulty components, and reassembly.

In early 1995 a prestigious panel recommended that all weapons design be conducted in Los Alamos and Sandia National Laboratories, leaving the Livermore laboratory free for other investigations. Energy Secretary O'Leary was said to favor this change. But later in that year the President decided to keep all three Laboratories active in warhead design and research.

Why a Comprehensive Test Ban? Succinctly, one of its objectives it is to retard, perhaps even halt, the evolution of the any threat of nuclear warhead development by Third-World countries, and thus to contribute to our safety and survival. Knowledge of the procedures for manufacturing nuclear warheads is permanent. Bombs can be monitored, remanufactured, and be kept thoroughly reliable. A Comprehensive Test Ban is central to aborting any future arms races. Pressures resulting in arms races are persistent and a Comprehensive Test Ban would help resist a new one, such as is possible between the USA and China during the next few decades. A more assertive China would mean that nuclear weapons could become still more important as the currency of power. In 1996 China did make an important concession by announcing that it would not insist on the right to conduct "peaceful" nuclear tests.

A Comprehensive Test Ban would enhance our security.

Aside from Pakistan, India sees China as an antagonist in nuclear arms, and both rivalries generate difficulties for a CTB. In 1996 India announced its intent not to sign any Comprehensive Test Ban "because it does not require the five declared nuclear states. . . to pledge to get rid of their stocks of nuclear weapons." Indeed, India did veto the draft treaty at the meeting of the 61-nation Conference on Disarmament. India regards the treaty as being asymmetrical and that it would handcuff their defense options. This veto is ironic in that Jawaharlal Nehru in 1954 urged the United States and Soviet Union to stop testing nuclear warheads. The United Nations General Assembly voted overwhelmingly in September1996 to pass the Comprehensive Test Ban Treaty. Pakistan warned that it will not comply unless India does. It is not yet clear how serious an obstacle India's decision will be.

It is difficult to avoid the suspicion that India aspires to become a great nuclear power. Rapid reduction of nuclear arsenals by the five big nuclear powers would aid in convincing India not to develop such an arsenal, and thus would contribute to world safety. In early fall 1996, at the 51st session of the United Nations General Assembly, the long-fought battle almost ended with the signing of the Comprehensive Test Ban. As promised, India refused to sign on, meaning that the treaty cannot take effect formally. The ban applies to so-called peaceful nuclear explosions, and presumably to hydronuclear bombs (9-61).

The development of intricate but reliable computer modeling of nuclear bombs and their action is a reality, but is no panacea. If these simulations are genuinely dependable they will permit continued manufacture of many types of bombs just as though actual testing were carried out. Employing computer simulations, the present nuclear nations, as well as each those aspiring to attain that status, can keep on manufacturing, remanufacturing, and modernizing all the warheads they want in a make-believe fashion, and not violate a CTB. The goal of a world free of these horrors would be as distant as ever. A ban on production is also required. An important note concerning this matter was issued by the Canberra Commission on the Elimination of Nuclear Weapons in 1996, namely: "The proposition that nuclear weapons can be retained in perpetuity and never used—accidentally or by decision—defies credibility." During Bill Clinton's quest for the presidency, he promised an international test ban by 1996, and this was accomplished. Opponents of continued testing during the Clinton presidency point out that resumption of testing would undermine U.S.-led international efforts to curb nuclear-weapons production by emerging nuclear powers. As of 1993, nearly two billion dollars per year was still being authorized for testing. Clinton declared a temporary ban, effective until any other country carried out tests. After this development, France responded with a test ban of its own. But in June 1995 the Pentagon began requesting permission to carry out a series of "small-scale" blasts, those with yields of 300 tons (0.3 kiloton), but with a margin of error permitting yields up to 500 tons (see hydronuclear bombs, 9-61). If these are "small," one might keep in mind that the terrorist explosion in Oklahoma City in April 1995 was equivalent to only about 3 tons of TNT in yield (0.003 kiloton). The experiments the military wishes to undertake are touted as guaranteeing reliability of American warheads, but this can be done in other ways. If started, other nations would feel encouraged to do their own low-level testing, and any CTB would wither. So far, no recent President has agreed to further tests.

Our military, and especially its nuclear segments, should be encouraged to accept that the Cold War has really ended and to break free from the old habits and attitudes of nuclear weapon production and possession. General G. L. Butler, who has spent decades studying the consequences of exploding nuclear warheads during war and in every aspect of American nuclear policies, announced his support in 1996 for abolishing all such weapons from Earth. He has not gained powerful support for these views; instead he has been criticized by Cold War hangovers who claim the general is naïve, dangerously delusional, and even ill informed. Butler said, "Nuclear weapons play on our deepest fears and pander to our darkest instincts. They corrode our sense of humanity, numb our capacity for moral outrage…" The statement that nuclear weapons cannot be disinvented is true, but it does not automatically follow that they cannot be eliminated. Such a defeatist idea assumes that the human race is incapable of rational solutions to any important problem and that technology is beyond control. Another officer who favors gradually eliminating all nuclear warheads is Admiral Noel Gayler, U.S. Navy (Retired). Here is another arena where bold and creative thinking is desperately needed.

A durable voice for a peaceful world is that of Prof. Hans Bethe. At age 90 in 1997, and disturbed by continuing theoretical and other research to make still more sophisticated nuclear weapons possible, he wrote President Clinton a letter which had the following words: "The time has come for our nation to declare that it is not working, in any way, to develop further weapons of mass destruction. Further, it is our own splendid weapons laboratories that are, by far and without question, the most likely to succeed in such nuclear inventions. Since any new types of weapons would, in time, spread to others and present a threat to us, it is logical for us not to pioneer further in this field."

Rejection of the Comprehensive Test Ban Treaty by the Senate—Obstructionists in the American Senate threatened to throttle ratification. By 1998, 147 countries had ratified the pact, but the United States had not. This was mostly because one reactionary senator, namely Jesse Helms, chair of the Foreign Relations Committee, had refused to schedule hearings. He kept the treaty bottled up for two years and then sprung it on the Senate only when its defeat was certain.

Disgraceful behavior in the Senate

On October 13, 1999, a vote on the Comprehensive Nuclear Test Ban Treaty (CTBT) finally took place. Ratification was defeated. The treaty had been signed by 152 countries, including the U.S. To take effect, it had to be ratified by the 44 countries which have nuclear reactors, and 26 had done so. The American Physical Society called the treaty an important advance in reducing the danger of nuclear arms, and 32 Nobel Laureates in physics approved ratifying the treaty. The American Geophysical Union and the Seisomological Society of America stated they are confident that the worldwide monitoring system can meet the treaty's verification goals. More than fifty years earlier President Eisenhower noted that proliferation of nuclear weapons posed the greatest threat to our national security. It would have taken a two-thirds majority (67 votes) in the Senate to pass, but the count was 51 against to 48 in favor. The vote was mostly along party lines, all the negative votes being Republican. The Senate vote would be partially responsible for any renewed testing by China and other powers, their developing MIRVed missiles to threaten cities in the United States, and continued Cold War. It has been about 80 years since the Senate rejected a major international treaty, namely the Treaty of Versailles, whose passage would have made the United States a member of the League of Nations.

In a report (2002) the American National Academy of Sciences stated that there were no serious flaws in the Comprehensive Test Ban Treaty.

This undermining of American leadership in the global arena has hastened unraveling of arms control policies world-wide and alarms have begun to appear. President Clinton, obviously angry, said the vote represented "partisan politics of the worst kind." This might be true, but Clinton had not lobbied for the treaty in a vigorous manner. But Clinton asked further: "Are we more secure because other countries are not testing nuclear weapons…? I believe we are."

The director of the Arms Control Association called the vote "a tragedy and a disaster for America's long-standing efforts to prevent nuclear proliferation." Sen. Biden labeled the vote "a fundamental U-turn in America's 50-year policy of seeking global arms control." United Nations Secretary-General Kofi Annan voiced his regret at the decision. Foreign ministers of Russia and western European countries declared they were "very concerned," or "deeply disappointed," or that the vote was "a serious blow to America's political and moral authority." In particular, German Defense Minister Scharping labeled the decision "absolutely wrong" and "highly regrettable." British defense analyst Andrew Brooks said "The perception here is one of disbelief... This is the chance for the biggest superpower to freeze the nuclear mechanisms and [it is] behaving like a small child." The President of the Los Angeles Physicians for Social Responsibility said "The Senate's historic blunder sends a dangerous signal to those states who seek to acquire and further develop nuclear weapons."

Russia's President persuaded his country's parliament, the Duma, to ratify the Comprehensive Test Ban Treaty in April, 2000.

Countries which have abandoned their nuclear weapon programs, such as South Africa, Brazil, and Argentina, have done so in part because they trusted the United States to lead in cooperative efforts to rein in nuclear weapons. Such developments will be less likely now.

Systems to monitor a successful CTBT had been 40 years in the process of construction at the time of the vote. It was not complete, but was to consist of 321 seismic, infrasound (low-frequency sound in the atmosphere, detectable at great distances), hydroacoustic (undersea, detectable at great distances), and radionuclide sensors to be located in 89 countries and Antarctica. Detection of short-lived radioactive xenon isotopes by sniffing the atmosphere provides indisputable evidence that a nuclear warhead has been tested. Despite Republican claims that the detection system could be evaded, in truth, even at an incomplete stage, the system worked very well. For example, it readily detected the small underground nuclear tests of India and Pakistan in 1998. In underground tests, some xenon always leaks out into the air.

Even though incomplete, the detection system was successful.

The xenon isotopes mentioned are Xe-133 and Xe-135. Some xenon is always released by nuclear reactors, but explosion of a bomb creates the isotopes in a ratio of Xe-135/Xe-133 which is 10,000 times greater than in the case of xenon from reactors. The technique readily detects any test of military significance.

Additionally, had it passed, the treaty would have banned all nuclear test explosions worldwide, authorized on-site inspections of suspect areas, and required notification by countries of scheduled explosions using conventional explosives above a certain high limit. It would not limit the type or yield of bombs, or the size of nuclear arsenals. It would not even prohibit improvement, production, or deployment of nuclear weapons, but would not allow any signatory to resume testing even if it feels its stockpile is unreliable (the U.S. rejected this section in advance). The CTBT would be entirely concerned with research and development by prohibiting all tests of nuclear bombs involving explosions.

Senators opposing the CTBT resorted to inaccurate statements and exaggerations. Sen. Kyl claimed "it was a bad treaty that would have jeopardized America's security," when quite the opposite is true. Kyl and others referred to the treaty as fatally flawed. No treaty is perfect, but the CTBT was not fatally flawed. It contains clauses designed to correct any defects. Opponents of the treaty asserted, with enthusiasm but without experience, that continued testing is essential to reliable nuclear warheads. Kyl even brought out an old, discredited argument that a country could make a nuclear test in a huge spherical underground cavern, and that this would "decouple" the nuclear noise, thus evading detection. He even said it "is technologically simple to achieve." In truth, decoupling is expensive, unproven, and has never been accomplished even by the U.S. or Soviet Union. For an inexperienced minor country to accomplish this to advantage is simply preposterous.

Continuing, Kyl said "Testing has been essential to maintaining our arsenal." It is not true that the United States has depended much on testing to detect problems in nuclear warheads. In stockpiled weapons between 1958 and 1993, about 830 defects were found, but fewer than one percent were discovered via testing. Only one test out of 387 conducted since 1970 was for the purpose of finding age-related problems. Only 11 tests of the 387 were carried out to ensure reliability. The main reason for testing is to develop new types of warheads.

11-8 Prevailing in a Nuclear War

During the 1980s, there was much frightening talk by extremists about "prevailing" in a nuclear war. Secretary of Defense Weinberger in 1981 spoke of "prosecuting a global war with the Soviet Union." In 1982 the Pentagon's annual Defense Policy Guidance Statement began with the declaration: "The United States nuclear capabilities must prevail even under the condition of prolonged war." A later Pentagon statement, concerning the expanding nuclear capability, reads that it is "intended to enable the United States to regain nuclear superiority over the Soviet Union within this decade. The Administration intends to build a capacity to fight nuclear wars that range from a limited strike through a protracted conflict to an all-out exchange." One of Reagan's arms-control advisers, Colin Gray, wrote:

Some conservatives think we can "win" a nuclear war.

> The United States should plan to defeat the Soviet Union and to do so at a cost that would not prohibit U.S. recovery. Washington should identify war aims that in the last resort would contemplate the destruction of Soviet political authority and the emergence of a postwar world order compatible with Western values.

But President Carter said in 1977: "Nuclear war cannot be measured by archaic standards of 'victory' or 'defeat'." Even Richard Nixon rejected the idea of victory in a nuclear war, concluding in his book *Real Peace* that peace is "the only option."

Think tank analysts are constantly talking in terms of "acceptable" losses involving tens of millions of lives. The idea that incinerating a hundred cities is acceptable is beyond belief. There is no reason such analyses should not be carried out; indeed, maybe inquiry and reflection along these lines will bring an element of sanity now lacking in some circles. Certainly a higher measure of rationality on the part of all nuclear powers is in order. Of the nuclear pioneers, it was Leo Szilard who retained the most rational ideas about the nuclear arms race, but he became less and less influential.

One of the purposes of any government is supposed to be the protection of its citizens. Nuclear arms have weakened this self-evident tenet. During the Cold War decades, a form of seeming collective insanity, the nuclear powers were in greater danger than ever before in their history. The pursuit of security through nuclear weapons resulted in the highest jeopardy ever to the populations of countries which depend on these arms. One can reasonably doubt the judgment of the military and political leaders, claiming to be realistic, who have helped to bring this situation to pass. Today, with the demise of the Cold War, we can all breathe a little easier. But the fundamental political structure of the world is unchanged, and a Cold War or something similar could return within a generation or two unless we purposefully take effective measures to avoid it.

The corrosive effects of Cold-War psychology can be seen in American treatment of that gentle democracy, New Zealand. In 1985 Wellington banned all nuclear-powered or nuclear-armed ships from the harbors of the island nation. Although few vessels were involved, the United States retaliated by imposing a quarantine. New Zealand temporarily ceased being an ally. The Pentagon stopped joint training exercises, logistic support, sharing of intelligence, sale of most arms, and high-level political contact. This childish behavior was repaired in 1991.

While Congress has moved to cut the American stockpile of nuclear bombs in half, billions of dollars have been allocated to research and to advance new types of weapons. Weapons laboratories are scrambling to find new ways to justify their existence.

In 2003, President George W. Bush, in his wretched obsession with Iraq, came close to threatening preemptive nuclear attack on its unproven nuclear and other means of mass destruction. He described possible use of nuclear "bunker busters" for deeply buried targets. For the U.S. to breach the barrier to use of such weapons would lump them with ordinary munitions. Such a deplorably irresponsible attack would pit the Arab and Islamic world against the U.S. far into the future. Other nuclear powers would feel entitled to use their nuclear warheads to help win their own local skirmishes. Nations considering making their own nuclear bombs would accelerate their efforts. The world, already as dangerous as dancing in a minefield, would become even more hazardous.

At the urging of the Bush regime, the Senate Arms Services Committee voted in May 2003 to repeal the Spratt-Furse Amendment which banned research and development in the area of low-yield nuclear warheads. More funds were directed to bring the Nevada Test Site up to date. These are powerful, distressing signs which prompted Mayor Tadatoshi Akiba of Hiroshima to write:

> This clear indication that the United States intends to develop small nuclear weapons raises the horrifying specter that nuclear weapons will actually be used. As mayor of the A-bombed city, Hiroshima, I am outraged by the barbarism that has led you not only to attack Iraq, killing or injuring thousands of innocent Iraqi citizens, but also to develop new nuclear weapons. You are trampling viciously on the hopes of the vast majority of people around the world who seek peace and, on behalf of the residents of Hiroshima, I vehemently protest.

Military strength is only one facet of security. National security depends as much or more on features such as a healthy population and environment, an educated electorate, and a just society. The most threatening perils include pollution, illiteracy, drug abuse, wasting scientific talent in the military-industrial complex, corporate greed, possibly the greenhouse effect, depletion of the ozone layer, poor energy policies, and over-population. Military leaders err in thinking that the perils mentioned can be dealt with by higher military budgets.

11-9 Ground Wave Emergency Network

Another of the tentacles of the late Cold War which was still alive and well in late 1993 is the Ground Wave Emergency Network (GWEN). Born during the Reagan era, it represents a desperate attempt to maintain communications between military bases and perhaps between bases and certain submarines at sea after a massive nuclear attack on the United States. A series of electromagnetic pulses during such an attack would incapacitate most ordinary communications.

GWEN consists of a series of radio towers spread over the country which could survive electromagnetic pulses. It is supposed to link military bases using low-frequency (150-175 kilohertz) radio waves which travel just over the ground. Construction was halted in 1990 so the National Academy of Sciences could investigate health risks. No evidence was found of any risks (no studies had been made), and the military poised itself to renew construction.

So far at least 54 relay towers have been built, and more are planned. The cost has been at least $235 million and $12 million more was ready to be authorized; these expenses are relatively small. No one seems to have the responsibility of asking why the project should be continued, given the obsolete assumptions on which it was based. It is known that newly installed fiber optic systems are immune to the electromagnetic pulse, and thus GWEN is redundant, but like so many other military ventures, GWEN has mindlessly taken on a life of its own.

Another project which could be stopped without harming our security

11-10 The Slow Death of the Cold War

Old habits are tenacious. As late as 1992, the proposed American military budget included the following requests:

- For plutonium processing at Savannah River's F-Canyon, $103.6 million.
- Reprocessing at the Idaho Chemical Processing Plant, $231.4 million.
- Upgrading the same plant's uranium extraction facility, $40.8 million.
- For restart and operation of the K Reactor (for tritium production) at Savannah River, $553.2 million.
- For the New Production Reactor, $66 million. This project still has $125 million left over from previous funding.
- For nuclear weapons testing, $186.4 million.
- The United States in 1994 was spending billions of dollars on its strategic nuclear forces.

The Cold War died hard. In 1992 American U-2 spy planes still patrolled the borders of the former Soviet Union. One of them flying from Japan crashed near Korea. B-52 bombers still crisscrossed the globe. Most of these practices had died down by

1994. In 1995 the U.S. military budget was still $270 billion, of which $28 billion was spent on intelligence alone. Despite the end of the Cold War, many important aspects of American policy are still embedded in Cold War psychology. Both first-strike and quick second-strike facilities are in place.

Nevertheless, the end of the Cold War has brought some changes. For 42 years the Strategic Air Command had planes laden with nuclear bombs airborne or on alert. In 1991, the practice was finally wound down. Mobile versions of the MX missile and other ICBMs were canceled. NATO slashed nuclear weapons by 80%, leaving only 700 warheads in Europe. In 1991 the United States announced intent to eliminate unilaterally all of its ground-based tactical nuclear weapons in Europe and Asia, and to remove all such weapons from the Navy's surface fleet. As the Soviet threat faded, the START agreements would allow building down even the strategic weapons. The final numbers are not yet certain, but some experts advocate about 1000 warheads for each side. However, as of 1996 several nuclear powers continue to patrol the seas using submarines; there is no good reason why this practice could not be halted as well.

A large number of targets has been eliminated from U.S. nuclear war plans, the result of a two-year study. The list comprised more than 20% of the approximately 8500 Soviet Bloc targets, and could be extended greatly with safety. One senior Pentagon official, describing the original list, said "With all the weapons they had, they [military planners] seemed to have targeted almost every telephone pole and Communist Party headquarters out in the sticks."

With the end of the Cold War, the United States plans to dismantle perhaps 20,000 nuclear warheads. By 2003 about 3500 warheads were left. The plutonium from these weapons is stored at the Pantex plant in Texas. Approximately 1500 warheads are being taken apart each year. The spherical plutonium pits are put in argon-filled stainless steel containers, which are welded shut and stored in earth-covered warehouses. Storage of this plutonium, rather than converting it to mixed oxide for reactor fuel, could be perceived by other nations as the U.S. keeping open the option of another arms race.

The U.S. has agreed to purchase 550 tons of highly enriched uranium taken from Russian warheads at $10,000 per pound over the next 20 years. This material will eventually be used as fuel in nuclear reactors, or will be vitrified and buried.

11-11 Nonnuclear Military Budget; Hot War in Afghanistan

Keeping the Military Budget Under Control—There are still abundant means for reducing non-nuclear military expenditures. Department of Defense experts might study the programs mentioned below and decide which can be deleted entirely or diminished in scope with little effect on American security. These are items associated with the Cold War with the Soviets, not those dealing with Third-World powers or stateless terrorists today. The Navy P-7 patrol plane, the Army Sgt. York antiaircraft gun, and the A-12 attack plane have already been canceled. Weapons programs canceled (1992-1996) include the Tri-Service Stand-off Attack Missile ($2.1 billion) and the Comanche helicopter ($2.1 billion). The Aegis destroyer program has been slowed. The most expensive weapons systems which might be eliminated or greatly reduced include the following: the multi-billion dollar B-2 bomber program; the $2.2 billion C-17 cargo jet; the F-22 Advanced

Tactical Fighter (trimmed 10% in 1994); the $2 billion Seawolf attack submarine; $15 billion for a new aircraft carrier and four new destroyers; the proposed huge Air Force complex at Crotone, Italy; the Ground Wave Emergency Network; the Titan IV launch rockets; the stealth Tri-Service Surface-to-Air Missile; the $1.1 billion order for 24 Trident II (submarine) D-5 missiles; as well as many sections of the CIA, the National Security Agency, and the Defense Intelligence Agency. What is left of the Strategic Defense Initiative, such as the anti-missile defense program, now costs more than $4 billion annually, and its proposed successor, the National Missile Defense program, could be deleted with profit for reasons presented in Chapter 10-I. Much of the savings accomplished could be well used to enhance the health and welfare of American veterans of World War II, the Korean War, the Vietnam War, the Persian Gulf War, and others.

One consequence of a reduced budget is to force technological innovations. Computer-driven, high-speed drones, made possible by microprocessors, can turn at angles no human could survive, and will be able to outmaneuver such proposed fighter planes as the F-22. Unmanned bombers have already been deployed. The power of satellites and unmanned planes in reconnaissance was demonstrated during the Persian Gulf War and Afghanistan War. Computer networks collecting data from a constellation of surveillance systems are drastically changing the nature of war. To be sure, the older equipment—tanks, subs, aircraft carriers, aircraft—will still be effective against any likely adversary for a few decades.

Some might feel that if the above suggestions for reduced armament were actually carried out, it would leave the U.S. vulnerable. It is recognized that the world today is a tough neighborhood, and that if we were to disarm too much it would leave us susceptible to attack. There is no proposal made here to disarm to this extent. Excessive armaments are part of the problem. The intent is to reduce armaments just to the level needed to deter. Certainly American armed forces should not be handicapped. Another madman like Hitler could come along at any time.

The major wars involving the United States during the 20th century are World War I, World War II, the Korean War, and the Vietnam War. American servicemen and women fought bravely and valiantly, and many paid the supreme sacrifice. We are all deeply indebted to them, and rightly honor them at every opportunity. The main objective of the critique here is to make such wars unnecessary in the first place, especially in the nuclear age.

Terrorist Attacks on the USA and their Aftermath—The above points are suggestions to study the various programs, not to eliminate all of them. After all, our world is still a dangerous place, and at this stage of civilization, we must keep our defenses up. These points were brought home by the terrorists attacks of September 11, 2001. During the war in Afghanistan directly afterwards, the B-2 bombers played a modest role. The older B-1 bombers, retrofitted to deliver classical bombs rather than nuclear, functioned well despite their much-maligned reputation. Flying at supersonic speed from the island of Diego Garcia with precision-guided bombs, B-1 bombers dropped many tons of bombs on Taliban and Al Qaeda targets. Without air defenses in Afghanistan, it was relatively easy. The introduction of precision-guided bombs in large numbers (60% of the total) changed the nature of modern warfare. Afghanistan, with its inhospitable terrain, mountains, and caves, was not much different from the way Genghis Kahn found it in the 13th century. In the past the Afghans had beaten back British and Soviet invaders, but they could not stand up against Americans whom they rarely saw, an enemy who seemed to be able to destroy one selected house among many, or to target a single truck moving along a trail. They seemed to be powerful beyond comprehension. Americans suffered only a very few casualties. Moreover, there were drone spy planes which could select targets, bathe them with laser light, and send their exact location to bombers using Global Positioning Satellites. No country had ever before performed a series of such feats. It seemed to be a turning point in the nature of modern warfare.

Terrorist Danger of Nuclear Bombs—The level of danger to the U.S. from attack by a national state is relatively low. If, for example, North Korea were able to manufacture nuclear bombs and use one or more to attack any part of the USA, it would be only a matter of hours before the country of the aggressor would be essentially vaporized by American retaliation. Thus, such an act would be deterred. The real danger is not such an attack, but rather that essential parts of nuclear warheads would be sold to terrorists, who would use them for the same purpose. Since these are subnational groups without a fixed homeland, how would they be deterred? This is a problem as yet unsolved.

11-12 Strategic Arms Reduction Treaties—START I and II

During the 1980s the United States and the Soviet Union negotiated the first of two Strategic Arms Reduction Treaties. The numbers of warheads left under START-I, 8556 for the USA and 6449 for Russia, were down from 10,000 to 12,000 before. Under START II, the numbers would be reduced to 3500 for each side if it is ever fully ratified. Of the respective totals, up to 1750 could be carried by submarines by each side. The United States had 50 or so nuclear attack submarines by the turn of the new century. START II is supposed to be in effect by 2003. It was not until 1996 that the U.S. Senate ratified START II, by which time the Russian Duma had not acted. Russia's President Putin managed to prod the Duma into ratifying START II in 2000. Passage was, however, conditional on the U.S. not deploying a National Missile Defense system; if this is done, Russia will withdraw from START II.

Unfortunately, the numbers for START II above are a bit deceptive. According to the terms, both sides agreed to eliminate giant multi-warhead missiles, such as the U.S. Peacekeeper and Russian SS-18. The 3000-3500 figures are for deployed warheads only. When the reserve stockpiles and tactical cruise missiles are included, the U.S. stockpile was closer to 8500 weapons in 2003. As a consequence of post-Cold War economic austerities, the Russian military received only 17 combat aircraft in 1995, compared with the Soviet figure of 550 in 1990. If agreement to a START III treaty can be made, it would probably reduce the two nations' stockpiles to around 1500 to 2500 warheads each.

In late 1998, the Russian military was able to find funding in their anemic economy to construct ten nuclear-capable missiles of the Topol-M type. These are single-warhead missiles with a range of about 6,200 miles. Forty more such missiles were scheduled to be finished by the end of 2000. Their manufacture does not violate the START treaties.

By 1997 advances in computer-driven procedures permitted retargeting and launching as many as 600 missiles in half an hour. The nuclear strength of the United States is excessive for any conceivable requirement of deterrence.

11-13 Economic Reconversion

With the winding down of the Cold War, the U.S. economy faced new challenges and opportunities. The main problem is to convert our economy back to a peacetime basis. The displacements accompanying this measure would necessitate a jobs program for some workers to minimize prolonged, massive unemployment. We can take heart in a dynamic historical quality of the United States: at irregular intervals, as circumstances demanded, our country has introduced qualitative changes, such as the income tax, the New Deal, Social Security, Medicare, and defense measures as the Manhattan Project. Another successful undertaking was the "GI Bill" after World War II to provide for education of returning military personnel; its impact on the country was uplifting. Now is the time for still another great initiative.

Piecemeal, local efforts are insufficient: a national program with overall planning is required for real economic reconversion. Present federal contracting procedures could be used for clearly defined programs, funds being transferred from the budgets of the Department of Defense and the nuclear weapons portion of the Department of Energy. Various government entities would cooperate, such as the National Science Foundation, and Departments of Transportation, Commerce, Health, Education, and Welfare, and others. A Department of Defense about one-third its Cold War size would seem to be adequate. Perhaps some ideas can be adapted from the successful changes of the economies of Japan and of Germany from those of World War II to the postwar years.

Dollar for dollar, non-military spending creates more jobs than military expenditures do owing to the less capital-intensive nature of civilian products and to lower salaries. The Worldwatch Institute estimates, for example, that $1 billion spent on guided missiles yields about 12,100 jobs, but the same amount spent on local transit equipment would create 28,900 jobs, which is more than twice as many.

Farewell to arms

Restructuring of certain aspects of taxation would accelerate economic conversion, especially the jobs program part. One of the most important policy changes is restoring the tax levels deemed as fair up to about 1980, the start of the Reagan-Bush era. During recent times, the wealthiest one percent of taxpayers have paid around $80 billion less each year than in 1977.

World War II and the Cold War poured at least one trillion dollars into California, which became the major focus of the defense industry. The state's wealth from these sources and others grew steadily until the end of the Cold War caused its artificial heart to falter. A prolonged recession set in.

Beginning in World War II, the United States built up a series of national laboratories. While some of them, such as the Jet Propulsion Laboratory and the National Institutes of Health. are purely non-military, most of them owe their origin to the Cold War. These are operated by the Department of Defense, NASA, the Department of Energy, or other agencies. Examples are the Los Alamos National Laboratory, Lawrence Livermore

National Laboratory, Sandia National Laboratories, Argonne National Laboratory, Idaho National Engineering Laboratory, Oak Ridge National Laboratory, and the Savannah River Laboratory.

With the end of the Cold War, the personnel of those Laboratories which depended on ever more weapons development underwent a soul-searching crisis. In general, the Laboratories' scientists are accomplished and conscientious men and women of the highest caliber. Their brain power must not be lost. To direct their awesome talents toward peacetime needs is one of our most important challenges.

Examples of the type of problems in which their skills can be used are the following. Obviously, the stewardship of the remaining warheads must be supervised. The dismantling of old bombs and the disposition of their plutonium-239 and uranium-235 will occupy many. The cleanup of nuclear sites such as Rocky Flats, Hanford, and Savannah River will occupy thousands. Nascent technologies such as mapping the human genome, use of the wonders of nuclear medicine such as PET (6-25) and SPECT (6-26) in addressing disorders such as Parkinson's and Alzheimer's diseases, paranoia and other mental diseases are of top precedence. Narcotics addiction in the United States is another problem needing new approaches. The enhancement of our country's economic competitiveness is a matter of priority. Development of new types of batteries for electric vehicles, of alternative energy sources, and environmental protection measures are examples of the possibilities. Building the nonmilitary economy can be accomplished using procedures similar to those used to build the military, in some cases.

Someday we Americans will look back on the long nuclear arms race much as we now look back on the Crusades, a futile, wasteful, dangerous activity driven by fanaticism.

It would be a shameful folly to permit the historic opportunity of the complete end of the Cold War to be squandered away, but that is a distinct possibility. To date, a comprehensive, national/international program has not figured prominently in any political leader's agenda.

11-14 Post-Cold War Nuclear Weapon Programs of the United States

In 1993 the Department of Energy began holding hearings on the environmental assessment of the planned nuclear arms program for the post-Cold War period, mostly during the 21st century. Called Complex 21, it tried to establish the number and kinds of warheads the United States might need on a long-term basis. While the exact number of warheads estimated was not announced, indicators point to an aggregate of about 6000. This number would require continued processing facilities and a tritium production reactor, and would cost billions of dollars per year. The number 6000 seems to be far too high; a lower number would appear to be adequate for the task. One thousand warheads would require no new production facilities, and no new tritium production would be needed for years since tritium recycled from dismantled warheads would be sufficient. Under the Strategic Arms Reduction Treaty (START II), Washington planned to pare its nuclear arsenal to 3,700 warheads by 1997. In December 1994 the treaty was ratified by the United States, Russia, Belarus, Ukraine, and Kazakhstan. The Air Force has begun dismantling 241 Minuteman II missile silos.

Under the terms of START II more than 300 missiles had to be removed from silos in South Dakota and Missouri. Many of these are of the Minuteman II type. The newer Peacekeeper and Minuteman III missiles, numbering more than 500, will be kept longer. The empty silos are being filled with sand and their massive launch chambers are welded shut. All will be covered with seven feet of topsoil.

The durability of addiction to weapons development was illustrated again late in 1994 when the national laboratory at Livermore requested funding for a giant laser, capable of delivering an enormous wallop of energy (1.8 megajoules). This project, the National Ignition Facility, with a budget of $4.5 billion, would construct lasers to initiate nuclear fusion. The announced budget was known in advance to be a gross underestimate; indeed, by 1999 it had overrun its supposed cost by $350 million. The work is claimed to be crucial to maintain proficiency in hydrogen bomb physics, and to replace underground test explosions. It would keep dozens of weaponeers employed for a decade, and maintain a robust nuclear weapons program. Conceivably, it might also be useful in controlled fusion (7-38) or in pure fusion bombs (9-36). A typical experiment would blast a centimeter-long pellet consisting of deuterium and tritium in a specially-shaped cavity (called a *hohlraum*) with 192 lasers. In any case, such a program would tend to undermine efforts to ban nuclear weapons testing by other countries. Nevertheless, it was approved by the Department of Energy in the fall of 1994, with a $900 million down payment. Congressional approval of the funds followed and the Department of Energy broke ground for construction in May 1997. Critics (such as Peace Action) of the National Ignition Facility, or NIF, were quick to dub the acronym as that of Nuclear Insanity Forever. The French are similarly building a gigantic laser complex near Bordeaux. Like its American counterpart, it will focus numerous laser beams on a kernel containing deuterium and tritium. Construction of this dangerous toy also started in May 1997.

In April 1997 Hans Bethe, who was a major spokesman for nuclear sanity all during the Cold War, wrote President Clinton urging that the weapons laboratories be prohibited from engaging in any research designed to create “new types of nuclear weapons . . . such as a pure fusion bomb.” Clinton’s response quoted the preamble to the Test Ban Treaty to the effect that no new type can be developed without testing, which is prohibited by the Treaty. Any work which does not involve testing is not prohibited, however, and this point should be addressed.

Cold War Lite

In spite of the formal end of the Cold War, as late as fall, 1994, both the USA and Russia were still practicing count-down procedures to launch nuclear-tipped missiles; old habits die hard. This nonsense might be termed Cold War Lite.

In September 1994 an incident some think of as amusing took place near Moscow. The electricity was turned off at the Strategic Rocket Forces command for more than an hour for failure to pay an outstanding $645,000 electricity bill. In early 1997 at the Impulse State Scientific Production Association in St. Petersburg, 900 scientists and engineers who maintain the command and control of Russia’s vast nuclear weapons system went on strike. They had not been paid in eight months. The government finally paid its arrears.

The U.S. government spent $4.4 billion on nuclear weapons in 1994. Viewing nuclear weapons as the cornerstone of national security policy, production of new bombs to replace older models is planned to resume in 2003. This task requires training of additional technicians, and some worry that the funding is insufficient. Conservative circles have made the claim that weakening the U.S. nuclear arsenal further would undermine international confidence in its deterrent value. Department of Energy officials announced in fall 1997 that an extra $5 billion will be required during the next ten years to maintain our nuclear stockpile, raising the estimated cost above $40 billion. This level of expense exceeds the price tag during the Cold War.

By the time the year 2000 arrived, advances in the effectiveness of "smart bombs" had added a new dimension to deterrence. Some of these are precision-guided cruise missiles carrying half-ton bombs, and others are called air-to-surface standoff weapons. Hypersonic missiles can effectively attack moving targets. Unmanned aerial vehicles are able to loiter over battle areas. High-power microwave weapons and miniature warheads holding modern super-high explosives, with several times as much power as earlier explosives, have been developed. These factors mean that less deterrence value needs to be placed on nuclear weapons.

There are approximately 73,000 people working at 11 nuclear weapons plants, more than half maintaining the arsenal. The Science-based Stockpile Stewardship Program was devised to maintain the safety and reliability of the reduced nuclear weapons arsenal in the absence of further testing. This program is funded at about $4.5 billion or $5 billion per year, which is nearly the same as the Cold War level, and far exceeds the amount required to maintain our nuclear arsenal. The K reactor at Savannah River in a South Carolina pine forest, on cold standby, has a crew of 400 in case orders to resume producing tritium come. Workers at Rocky Flats had so little to do in 1994 that they set up a volleyball court. The court was eventually moved to a security area to prevent visitors from getting a bad impression.

Secret volleyball

In 1994 the conservative Center for Strategic and International Studies and the more liberal Center for Defense Information independently concluded that 1000 nuclear weapons would be sufficient. A knowledgeable expert, physicist Sidney Drell, director of the Stanford Linear Accelerator, argues that 1000 to 1500 warheads are sufficient. New wars generally begin using the same types of weapons as in the last. Since World War II ended with city-shattering nuclear bombs, such warheads were upgraded and made more powerful. But modern bombs, especially the thermonuclear types, are too powerful to be used; they cause far more destruction than necessary.

In 1996 the Clinton Administration was seriously discussing a dangerous new departure in policy, namely production of tritium in civilian reactors. This would violate a long-standing national policy. The idea is to manufacture tritium in a Tennessee Valley Authority reactor named Watts Bar. For years the United States has tried to dissuade other nations from using civilian reactors for military purposes, so the idea is especially absurd. In addition, the Administration is continuing redesign of hydrogen bombs, upgrading and replacing such warheads. This work focuses on the B-61 carried by planes, the W87 (for MX missiles), and the W76 and W88 warheads for Trident missiles, launched from submarines. The report on this topic, with the innocent title "Stockpile Stewardship and Management Plan," was pried loose from the Energy Department by a lawsuit filed by the Natural Resources Defense Council. It violates the spirit if not the word of the Comprehensive Test Ban.

In Los Alamos, existing nuclear warheads are being remanufactured at the T-55 facility. Others warheads, such as the B-61 tactical weapon, are being modified to resemble the Mod-11 version, a ground-penetration bomb. Under the "Stockpile Stewardship and Management Plan," announced in May 1996, a series of weapons-related initiatives are to be undertaken. These seem to skirt the very limits of all agreements to stop new nuclear weapon programs.

The following programs are typical of new military developments:

- The Submarine-launched Ballistic Missile Warhead Protection Program, under which W76 warheads, the type which is most numerous in the arsenal, would be upgraded to a newer kind similar to the W88.
- W87 Refurbishment, under which the warheads in the MX missiles would be overhauled. The W87 has the most complete safety features in the stockpile. To accomplish the announced objectives would require expansion of the already swollen weapons infrastructure.
- B83 Improvements under which this megaton warhead, carried by B-2 bombers, would have its accuracy improved when launched at low altitude.
- New /Reentry Vehicles, developing new materials of construction.
- New Submarine-Launched Ballistic Missiles, under which an innovative design would be tested. This would violate a "no new delivery" system pledge.
- Others include: A new ballistic missile submarine; a bomb impact optimization system; a strategic target-changing system; a means of identifying hardened buried targets; and others.
- Shortly after George W. Bush became president in January, 2001, he began to advocate a new generation of nuclear weapons for the purposes of deterrence and also "wartime roles," "preventing catastrophic losses in a conventional war," that is, first use, "providing unique targeting capabilities" (such as deep underground weapons), and "enhancing U.S. influence in crises." The new president seems to be taking advice from unregenerate initiates in the nuclear priesthood who are desperately searching for ways of legitimize nuclear weapons and their use. The new National Security Strategy contains phrases such as " preemption" and "defensive intervention."
- The new president's budget includes $4 million to fund new conceptual designs of nuclear bomb pits and about $220 million increase for production of new plutonium pits at Los Alamos.
- Biological weapons, as mentioned above, and chemical weapons can be regarded, as Jonathan Schell elegantly worded it, the "ugly little sisters of the family of mass destruction."

11-15 Proliferation

Adapting to new realities

With the Clinton Administration, a new policy toward the spread of nuclear weapons began to emerge. It conceded that a fact of life is that some Third-World nations will acquire nuclear arms one way or another. The change of guidelines focused on how best to accommodate to this transformation. According to the new concept, the U.S. will stop trying to persuade India and Pakistan, as well as some other countries, to abandon their nuclear weapons program, but rather to limit the numbers of warheads severely. To enhance American capabilities to cope with this new reality, military intelligence would be improved (locating sites of nuclear installations, etc.), developing deep-penetrating nonnuclear bombs with modern precision guidance, and other measures. The good offices of the United States are to help these two antagonists to develop fail-safe command and control systems to lessen chances of conflict.

The Clinton Administration announced in 1994 that plans to counter the spread of nuclear weapons to Third World countries do not include preemptive strikes at nuclear facilities.

Lessons which we should learn from the long and debilitating Cold War include the following. When countries allow unbridled rivalry to dominate their policies, the primary purpose of governments (ostensibly promotion of the welfare of its citizens) becomes submerged in nebulous concepts such as "national security." Just recall the legacy the Cold War left to our children: an astronomical national debt; fantastically expensive weapons systems, now slowly decaying in the absence of expensive maintenance; nuclear environmental pollution on a grand scale; and a distorted social structure.

The comments on proliferation by Gen. Leslie Groves, who led the military aspects of the Manhattan Project, and written two months after the bombing of Hiroshima, are quoted below:

> If we were truly realistic instead of idealistic, . . . we would not permit any foreign power with which we are not firmly allied, and in which we do not have absolute confidence, to make or possess atomic weapons. If such a country started to make atomic weapons we would destroy its capacity to make them before it has progressed far enough to threaten us.

No American president took Groves' advice seriously until George W. Bush in 2003 in his confrontation with Iraq. Action such as that advocated by Groves is doomed to failure in the long run.

11-16 Ex-Soviet Scientists and Their Bombs

At the end of World War II in Europe, hundreds of German scientists found themselves without employment. Many of them ended up in the Soviet Union or in the United States, joining their compatriots who were captured at the end of World War II. They contributed heavily to the Cold War. Paralleling this to some degree, in 1991-92, Soviet scientists working on nuclear weapons and rockets were suddenly transformed from a pampered elite class into an un- or underemployed class. The old Soviet Union had several hundred thousand scientists, engineers, and technicians in this military work. Of these, perhaps 2000 had top-secret expertise in nuclear warhead design, and 5000 more worked in uranium enrichment and plutonium processing. By 1993 economic pressures were forcing many ex-Soviet scientists to consider emigrating, some as nuclear mercenaries. Moneyed bidders for their services were available, including Iran, Libya, and Iraq.

Most scientists, including those in the former Soviet Union, prefer non-military work. The Russians have formed two groups, the first International Solidarity Association with one headquarters in the U.S., and the second is called Mucatex, headquartered in Russia. They have had some success in placing Russian professors, in contracting for design syntheses of organic compounds in Russia, and in arranging for other services there. At least 50 contracts have been made in the U.S., Canada, Denmark, Korea, Taiwan, and Israel.

The most worrisome development is that Soviet-made nuclear warheads would somehow be acquired by Iran, Libya, Iraq, Pakistan, or North Korea. There have been lurid rumors of such negotiations or even actual sales at Mideast arms bazaars, which are a kind of international garage sale on a cash-and-carry basis. Tactical nuclear artillery shells, being relatively small, would be easiest to smuggle. If this develops, it would be a strongly destabilizing influence. Soldiers guarding old Soviet warheads and rockets are said to receive their pay irregularly, and sometimes not at all. They have to sell small arms and ammunition to live. One can't help but wonder what would happen if a generous offer were made to buy nuclear artillery shells. Fortunately, by the year 2000 the economic status of the ex-scientists and technicians had improved.

International garage sales of nuclear parts

In 1991 Congress earmarked $400,000 to help Russia dismantle much of its stockpile of nuclear warheads. That sum is insufficient for such an important task. It is not unreasonable for Russia to ask that the United States accelerate its own dismantling program simultaneously. In 1992 the U.S. and Western Europe agreed to contribute toward a science center to aid the Russian government in creating non-military employment opportunities, especially for scientists with weapons expertise. There is clear self-interest in keeping these experts from emigrating. For the period 1994-98, American support for Russian science amounted to about $42 million, much of which reverts to the U.S. Belarus has already made significant steps toward nuclear disarmament. It might have been the huge doses of radiation from Chernobyl which neutralized any opposition to this action.

11-17 Smuggling Ex-Soviet Nuclear Bomb Materials

A few years after the disintegration of the Soviet Union, employees of the huge nuclear enterprises had lost many of their privileges and were increasingly desperate. This was an important factor in a series of apparent attempts to smuggle valuable nuclear materials out of Russia for sale to foreigners. Russia has hundreds of tons of plutonium-239 and uranium-235; according to a U.S. General Accounting Office estimate, the total is around 1400 metric tonnes. Following are some of the developments from the primary transit routes, mostly through Germany.

In 1992, 1.7 kilograms of 90% pure uranium-235 was stolen from the Luch Scientific Production Association in Russia. In 1993 two seamen stole 1.8 kilograms of highly enriched uranium from a naval storage site in Arctic Russia, and a few months later three naval officers stole 4.5 kilograms of the same type of material from submarine reactor assemblies in Murmansk. Police found three kilograms of highly enriched uranium in a St. Petersburg icebox. In May 1994 German police raided businessman Adolf Jaekle's garage in Tengen, near Munich, and found six grams of plutonium-239. The business cards of two Russian scientists from Moscow's Kurchatov Institute were found in Jaekle's apartment, as well as notes implicating Iraq. Analysis of the material disclosed an extraordinarily high plutonium-239 content, 99.7%. This means it was a laboratory standard painstakingly enriched for study of the properties of nearly isotopically pure Pu-239. Only Russia produces such a grade, and this is done in the formerly secret city of Arzamas-16. This evidence comes from determination of the isotopic make-up of the material, as well as the presence of traces of other elements. In August 1994 German officials arrested two Spaniards and a Columbian in a third raid. They confiscated about 265 grams of plutonium dioxide in a suitcase on a flight from Moscow. It was mixed with 210 grams of uranium oxide. Mixed oxides of this type are used as fuel in certain reactors. Eight months later, the magazine Der Spiegel claimed the plutonium seizure was a setup perpetrated by German intelligence right in the middle of a federal election. This indeed proved to be the case. It turned out that German intelligence had set up a complicated sting operation. The three men were sentenced to six years imprisonment, less than the maximum of ten years because of the entrapment angle.

Later in 1994 there was a series of other such incidents. Bavarian police arrested six people for smuggling one gram of uranium-235 from Russia. It proved to be 87% pure, but contained traces of uranium-232 (half-life 70 years). This lighter isotope of uranium does not exist in nature, and so must have been made by reprocessing spent fuel and enriching the product. Russia is the only known country which carries out this operation. Still another black marketeer was captured in Germany with more than 300 grams of weapon-grade plutonium-239. There was evidence that this was part of four kilograms of illicit plutonium to be sold for $250 million. The Germans stated they had laboratory tests proving Russian manufacture of the plutonium. Still later German authorities seized 900 grams of lithium-6, which is used in hydrogen bomb production. Toward the end of August 1994 Russian security officials themselves recovered more than ten kilograms of stolen uranium. This material turned out to be ordinary uranium-238, which can be purchased openly in many countries. Two unemployed men foolishly thought they could sell the material for millions. At the end of September four Slovaks were captured while trying to smuggle 750 grams of uranium-235 across the Hungarian border. In October Turkish police arrested an Azerbajani who was trying to sell enriched uranium. In December 2.8 kilograms of weapons-grade uranium-235 was seized from a car by Prague police, who had been tipped off by Interpol. The material proved to be 87.7% U-235, and to be in the chemical form of the dioxide. Traces of U-232 and U-236 were found in the material, but its exact origin is still uncertain. Four men were arrested, three of them former Soviet citizens. In spring 1995 nine people were arrested in Slovakia smuggling in 110 pounds of uranium.

The fissile material which poses the most acute problem is uranium-235. It is much more abundant than plutonium, is far less radioactive, and is simpler to convert into a nuclear warhead using the gun-assembly technique. Some reactor fuel rods for Russian submarines, fresh and not yet used in a reactor, were stolen from the Northern Fleet on at least two occasions.

Loose nukes?

Several couriers have inadvertently died from radiation exposure incurred during smuggling body-packed radioactive materials, according to German investigators. Nevertheless, the seepage of nuclear materials from Russia is expected to continue. It is evidently possible to hire pilots to fly contraband material from Moscow to Leipzig, avoiding all customs. In 1997 Russia's Gen. Lebed claimed on American TV that about 100 nuclear bombs small enough to be carried in suitcases had disappeared from the accounting system, and he suspects they have been stolen. His political opponents rebut the assertion and point out that Lebed is merely trying to boost his waning political image.

All of this is only the start. While some of the cases mentioned above are probably scams of one sort or another, we must consider that with huge supplies of nuclear materials, deteriorating security, possible enormous profits, and the desperation in Russia, where nuclear physicists are eating in soup kitchens, more and more such attempts are expected. It is impossible to determine how much contraband has been successfully sold. Some consider the situation to be the gravest threat to the security of the U.S. today. Even if the amount of plutonium is insufficient for a warhead, the material can still bring a substantial price. This is because countries such as Iran or Libya covet small amounts to develop skill in handling the element and other highly radioactive materials, studying its chemical properties and consequent separation aspects, and to gain experience in using remote control procedures and establishing safety standards. In spite of all these developments, the problems have so far been more smoke than fire.

Look for growth in this illegal business

But there is one note of optimism. In December 1994 the United States and Russia completed a secret operation to safeguard the most vulnerable uranium-235 and plutonium-239 in the Kurchatov Institute in Moscow. This complex has tons of weapons-grade nuclear metals, has weak inventory controls, and other shortcomings. An agreement to conduct a similar operation at Obninsk, site of a research breeder reactor, was undertaken. The cost to the United States in this program is best considered a form of relatively inexpensive insurance against illicit nuclear proliferation. The storage chambers are equipped with infrared sensors to detect body heat, which would turn on cameras. Infrared sensors detect movement. By the end of 1995 the system was in place; the Russians can similarly check on uranium-235 in Idaho.

11-18 Nuclear Terrorism

With illegal nuclear materials becoming available on the black market, it is only a matter of time before some subnational group acquires sufficient materials for assembling a nuclear bomb. Even worse, a bomb ready to use could conceivably be sold. Any number of organizations feel motivated to first conduct an unannounced demonstration nuclear explosion in a desert, in a boat at sea, from a plane, or otherwise. This done, warnings by terrorists could be issued to the governments of the United States, Europe, or Japan, and then could be carried out. Capitol cities such as Washington or commercial cities such as Frankfurt would receive demands to pay tribute or suffer destruction. What could be done in cases of such extortion?

A subnational terrorist group such as Al Qaeda might be successful in building a nuclear bomb by using the gun assembly technique (which is much easier than the implosion technique). This assumes that sufficient contraband weapons-grade uranium-235 could somehow be procured. A team with many specialists would be required. At least one person who is expert in each of the following disciplines would be necessary: physics of chain reactions and neutron generation; chemistry of uranium and many other materials; metallurgy; chemical high explosives; counters for radioactivity; radiation health; electrical circuitry; hydrodynamics; and others. Of course, if greater risks are acceptable, corners could be cut. It is probably easier to construct a workable bomb from such raw materials that to steal one and disarm its permissive action link (9-20).

One of the easiest ways to smuggle a nuclear bomb into the U.S. would be in a shipping container. Nearly 50,000 such containers enter our country every day, bringing in all kinds of cargo. Only a small fraction is opened for inspection and few are X-rayed. Many containers are carried on river boats deep into the interior. Uranium-235 emits a much lower level of X- and gamma-rays than plutonium, and is thus more difficult to detect. We are more vulnerable to a disastrous sneak attack than most of us imagine.

Another option, frequently mentioned in the press, is for terrorists to use ordinary dynamite placed in a barrel, surrounded with finely ground uranium ore, mine tailings, or other radioactive material. This would be a second type of "dirty bomb," also called a radioactivity dispersal device. Exploding such a device in any city would do little physical damage, but as soon as the radioactive nature of the dust is announced, it would come close to causing panic. Cleanup costs would be fantastic. This is a sort of psychological warfare.

Such scenarios were unthinkable up to about 1990. Today they are becoming increasingly credible. After the terrorist attacks on the twin towers of the World Trade Center in New York City on September 11, 2001, the danger of renegade organizations acquiring nuclear warheads or fissile metals in kilogram quantities was elevated another notch.

11-19 Current Sales of Conventional Arms to the Developing World

After the Cold War ended, expenditures on armaments dropped significantly. Nevertheless, sales of conventional weapons of destruction are still awesome. In 1991, the United States was by far the biggest seller of weapons and other military goods, the value being $14.2 billion. The fragments of the old Soviet Union, with their shell-shocked economies, sold about $5 billion worth. Britain sold $2 billion worth, Czechoslovakia $600 million, Germany and France $400 million each, and Belgium, China, and Spain $300 million each. The whole issue of killing for profit needs to be challenged.

In 1986, of all conventional arms sold to Third-World countries, the Soviet Union was responsible for about 57% of them, and the U.S. only 9%. By 1992, the Russian share had fallen to 6%, and the American share had risen to 57%.

Just consider the results of sales of conventional arms to less-developed nations. Witness the consequences in El Salvador, Guatemala, Yugoslavia, Somalia, Iraq, Iran, Angola, Rwanda, Algeria, and others.

11-20 Russian Nuclear Businesses

Aside from selling nuclear reactors, the Russian Ministry of Atomic Power and Industry has founded the Chetek Corporation. This firm advertises incineration of any toxic waste by underground explosion of nuclear bombs. The intent is to use the huge voids from old tests on the Arctic island of Novaya Zemlya. Disposable materials include war gases from Iraq, industrial toxic waste, decommissioned reactor parts, and retired nuclear weapons. The company promises "total safety." The charge is $300 to $1200 per metric tonne, depending on the nature of the waste; about 1000 tonnes of waste is estimated to be incinerated per blast. Conditions of weapons-test treaties must be addressed.

Russia also seems to be gearing up to compete with the French and English in the business of reprocessing spent fuel elements. The country is expanding these operations as a means of earning foreign capital. The unfinished reprocessing plant at Krasnoyarsk, which had been allowed to languish unattended for several years, has evidently been completed. Customers might include some of the former Soviet satellites, Germany, and South Korea.

Cash-starved ex-Soviets also consider selling many products. At a recent scientific conference Americans were asked discreetly whether they were interested in buying spy-satellite photographs of the United States! SS-18 missiles, without the nuclear warheads, were also said to be offered.

Want to buy an old Soviet photo of your area?

11-21 Nuclear Weapons and the Ex-Soviet Republics

In the vortex of history, the economy of the Soviet Union melted down in 1990-92. There is no history-based textbook on dealing with a crumbling nuclear superpower. Technically autonomous today, 11 of the 15 republics have formed a loosely-knit Commonwealth of Independent States. During Soviet times, nuclear weapons were stored in every Republic, but as the empire collapsed, they were moved into four: Russia, Ukraine, Belarus, and Kazakhstan. All four of these countries have ratified the Non-Proliferation Treaty, and they have agreed that eventually Russia will accept nearly all of the nuclear warheads. Estimates by the Arms Control Association of the numbers of nuclear warheads left in Russia, Belarus, Ukraine, and Kazakhstan in 1993 were:

	On intercontinental Ballistic Missiles	*On Submarines*	*On Bombers*
Russia	3,817	2,492	428
Ukraine	1,240	0	0
Belarus	81	0	0
Kazakhstan	1,040	0	370
TOTALS	6,178	2,492	798

By fall 1996 the last missile in Belarus, along with its bombs, had been returned to Russia. Ukraine began selling Russia excess bombers and missiles in 1995, not for cash but for oil and gas. As of the end of 1995, 48 SS-19 missiles were sold. Russia is planning on purchasing back additional Tu-160 Blackjack and Tu-95 Bear aircraft. Both Ukraine and Kazakhstan have been slowly returning their nuclear bombs to Russia. In any case, Russia keeps control of the launch codes.

The second Strategic Arms Reduction Treaty agreement of 1992 mandates a two-thirds reduction in the strategic nuclear arsenals of the U.S. and Russia by 2003. At that time each power, according to the schedule, can have up to 3500 strategic nuclear warheads. Most multiple-warhead missiles based on land will also be retired.

11-22 Ukraine

The policies of Ukraine on nuclear weapons illustrates the grip which these terrifying bombs have on a nation's psyche. This newly-independent country inherited an atomic arsenal sufficient to catapult it into third place in the world's powers so far as numbers of warheads are concerned, and thus getting ahead of France. Although most of the bombs have security codes held in Moscow, which prevent their use for now, Ukraine probably has sufficient know-how to reconfigure them and make them operable.

Still traumatized by Chernobyl, the Ukrainian Parliament in early fall of 1991 showed strong sentiments towards returning all nuclear arms to Russia. By December the message was an intention to become "neutral and nonnuclear." In March 1992, the Ukrainian president began to express doubts about Russia's security arrangements and shipments to Russia were stopped. This development precipitated a case of nuclear jitters in diplomatic circles, which endangered recognition of the newly-emerged Ukrainian state. At once a fresh commitment to return the arms was made. An agreement to this effect was signed in April, and all tactical nuclear warheads were shortly sent to Russia except for those aboard warships in the Black Sea. Ukraine's intent to become nonnuclear was reaffirmed in May.

A year later, an ominous change had taken place. In June 1993 the Prime Minister and a large block of parliamentarians opposed surrendering weapons without hard security guarantees and monetary compensation. While Russia, Belarus, and Kazakhstan early ratified the START I treaty, Ukraine waited until November 1993; the treaty provides for dismantling warheads. An element of national pride had entered the picture. Hints were circulated that bypassing Russian code controls over the weapons and launching them were within his country's competence. This point might be in doubt given that the weapons are deteriorating from lack of maintenance. American Defense Secretary Aspin went to Kiev to try and persuade Ukraine to give its nuclear arsenal to international control for storage and dismantlement. In July the Parliament voted to declare ownership of all weapons on Ukrainian soil. In this on-again, off-again decision-making process, President Kuchma declared in October 1993, according to a deal sweetened by an American subsidy of $330 million, that he wants to get rid of the weapons, but other officials insisted on keeping some of them for 10 or 20 years. By January 1994 Ukraine had agreed to send its entire nuclear arsenal to Russia for dismantling, and this was reaffirmed in the fall. Ukraine evidently wanted it both ways. The allure of the nuclear genie was subdued in this case; by June 1, 1996, Ukraine had sent the last of its nuclear warheads to Russia. Part of the agreement was that Russia would supply nuclear fuel since Ukraine has a pressing problem in its severe energy shortage. Altogether, American aid totaled more than $900 million.

11-23 Kazakhstan

Of the former Soviet Republics, Kazakhstan is exceeded in area only by Russia, and holds the site of the Semipalatinsk nuclear testing grounds. With the stirrings of *glasnost* in 1990, Kazakh citizens became free to express their feelings. They felt a deep sense of betrayal on account of the lies they had been told about the nuclear tests. The

Nevada/ Semipalatinsk movement (page 482) proved to be strong enough to contribute importantly to stopping further Soviet nuclear tests. It emphasized how similar the fates were of Kazakhs (9-25) and American downwinders (9-31) in Nevada, Utah, and Arizona, and of Pacific Islanders (9-19), as well as still others. In August of 1991, with a degree of independence, Kazakh President Nazarbayev closed the Semipalatinsk testing range. By that fall, Kazakhstan was demanding control of all nuclear weapons in its territory, and turning the country into a nonnuclear republic. It has begun to export old Soviet uranium reserves to raise badly-needed funds. Like Ukraine, the Kazakhs were at first divided about which policy is in their own best interests. But the country did ratify the Non-Proliferation Treaty, action which occurred during a visit by Vice President Gore in December, 1993.

No more nuclear testing here!

In 1994 President Nazarbayev visited President Clinton in Washington. One result was an agreement that Kazakhstan will send most of its 1410 nuclear warheads on missiles and bombers back to Russia, and destroy the rest. The SS-18 intercontinental missile silos are to be dismantled. The United States will contribute nearly $400 million to aid these steps.

Another provision was that in 1994 the U.S. could purchase about 600 kilograms of uranium-235 from Kazakhstan. This material had been manufactured to fuel reactors of warships and submarines, and could also be used in warheads. It had been manufactured at the Ulbinsky fuel fabrication complex in Ust-Kamenogorsk, Kazakhstan. It was stored in the remote region of Ulba in several chemical forms: metal, dioxide, and hydrated oxide. Under top-secret security, American Air Force C-5A cargo planes collected the material into 456 containers for the flight to the United States. The material was sent to Oak Ridge. The entire operation was overseen by the United Nations' International Atomic Energy Agency. It was perceived as a diplomatic coup since Iran had sent purchasing agents in 1993 who tried to buy some Kazakh uranium-235, apparently without success.

During Soviet times Kazakhstan was the source of beryllium ores. Beryllium plays an important role in manufacturing neutron initiators, neutron reflectors, and other parts of all nuclear bombs. Today the Kazakhs, pressed for hard currency, sell their beryllium to the West.

In 1996 the Kazakhs began cooperation with the Department of Energy in a program designed to locate dumping grounds of nuclear waste all over the steppes. Much of this waste, which stems from Soviet times, is in unregistered sites. The search will take place using the Airborne Multisensory Pod System, which consists of multiple sensing instruments attached under the wings of aircraft. They use photography, radar, and infrared and other sensors. At the same time, a search for mineral deposits will be made.

11-24 One Superpower

One nation—the USA—is dominant today, and this is a sobering responsibility. This should mean that we behave as an equal partner in the family of nations, not the "top dog." Strengthening the United Nations would be preferable to a Pax Americana. While U.S. military forces were shaped for conflict with a superpower, the end of the Cold War permits a smaller, more flexible, and less expensive military establishment. Let us seize this opportunity, and do so safely.

This will be a gargantuan task. Powerful elements in American society today oppose any lowering of the number of our nuclear weapons; a mirror image of this situation exists in Russia. In 2001 the U.S. still had the following nuclear weapons in its arsenal: 5400 warheads loaded on intercontinental ballistic missiles; an additional 1750 nuclear bombs ready to be launched from bombers or cruise missiles; another 1670 tactical nuclear warheads; and an estimated 10,000 more nuclear warheads stored in bunkers around the country. About 500 warheads remain targeted on the Moscow alone. The 192 warheads on the missiles carried in a single Trident submarine could cause more than 50,000,000 casualities. The Russians retain at least the same numbers, but theirs are poorly maintained, and increasingly unreliable.

While the end of the Cold War has brought a higher level of security to the world, this benefit is being eroded by the spread of nuclear capability to other countries, and by the development of miniature warheads. Regrettably, our world will have nuclear bombs for many years to come.

Bibliography for Chapter 11: Arms Races and the Aftermath of the Late Cold War

Barry M. Blechman, Ed., *PREVENTING NUCLEAR WAR*, Indiana University Press, 1985.

Helen Caldicott, *MISSILE ENVY: THE ARMS RACE & NUCLEAR WAR*, William Morrow, 1984.

COLD WAR, A series of VCR tapes, CNN, Warner Home Video, 6 Commercial St., Hicksville, NY 11801.

Daniel Ford, *THE BUTTON*, Simon & Schuster, 1985.

Hugh Gusterson, *NUCLEAR RITES: A WEAPONS LABORATORY AT THE END OF THE COLD WAR*, University of California Press, 1998.

David Hafemeister, ed., *PHYSICS AND NUCLEAR ARMS TODAY*, American Institute of Physics, 1991.

International Physicians for the Prevention of Nuclear War, *PLUTONIUM: DEADLY GOLD OF THE NUCLEAR AGE*, The Institute for Energy and Environmental Research, 6935 Laurel Ave., Takoma Park, MD 20912.

Robert Jervis, *THE MEANING OF THE NUCLEAR REVOLUTION*, Cornell University Press, 1989.

Roman Kolkowitz, ed., *THE LOGIC OF NUCLEAR TERROR*, Allen & Unwin, 1987.

Richard N. Lebow, *NUCLEAR CRISIS MANAGEMENT*, Cornell University Press, 1989.

Stuart Leslie, *THE COLD WAR AND AMERICAN SCIENCE: THE MILITARY-INDUSTRIAL COMPLEX AT MIT AND STANFORD*, Columbia University Press, 1993.

National Academy of Sciences, Committee on International Security and Arms Control, *NUCLEAR ARMS CONTROL*, National Academy Press, Washington, DC, 1985.

Office of Technology Assessment, *PROLIFERATION AND THE FORMER SOVIET UNION*, Government Printing Office, Washington, DC, 1994.

Ronald E. Powaski, *MARCH TO ARMAGEDDON; THE U.S. AND THE NUCLEAR ARMS RACE*, Oxford University Press, 1987.

Jonathan Schell, *THE FATE OF THE EARTH*, Knopf, 1982.

Jonathan Schell, *THE GIFT OF TIME: THE CASE FOR ABOLISHING NUCLEAR WEAPONS NOW*, Henry Holt, 1998.

Stephen I. Schwartz, ed., *ATOMIC AUDIT*, Brookings Institution Press, Washington, D.C., 1998.

Kosta Tsipis, ARSENAL: UNDERSTANDING WEAPONS IN THE NUCLEAR AGE, Simon and Schuster, 1983.

WORLD ARMAMENTS AND DISARMAMENT, SIPRI Yearbook 1992. Oxford University Press, 200 Madison Ave., New York, NY 10016.

Chapter 12: WAYS TO PEACE

Part I: A CLASSICAL VIEW OF THE WORLD PEACE SCENE
Part II: A NEW WAY OF THINKING ABOUT PRESERVING PEACE

Part I: A CLASSICAL VIEW OF THE WORLD PEACE SCENE

ABSTRACT—The advent of nuclear weapons and their missiles poses one of the greatest threats in human history. Old political structures are inadequate. The religions of the world have not brought peace. It is essential that new modes of thought be invented and applied. Clear, profound, creative thinking is intensely needed. Some ways to cope with these problems at the international level, national level, and personal level are offered. Scientists have a special role to play. The magnitude of the dangers can transmute ancient national security concepts.

12-1 Inadequacy of Present Policies

The hammer of history has pounded human society into its present nation-state political system, resulting in endless arms races and wars. Ideally speaking, a world government would be the way to prevent this mindless behavior, but that development is not in the visible future, and we don't have time to wait. The development of nuclear weapons has made the world more precarious than ever. The AIDS pandemic is also exceedingly dangerous, but in an entirely different way. Peace in the nuclear age is among the most critical issues of our time.

All those nuclear warheads and missiles have most certainly not brought us more security. We can be comforted by the demise of the Cold War in the period 1989-92, but the fundamental causes of conflict have not disappeared. The Cold War savagely scarred nearly half of the twentieth century, and we have paid dearly for it, and will continue to pay. Moreover, the war mindset remains unchanged in vast numbers of people. It does not seem unreasonable to urge public introspection, during the early years of the new millennium, about the state of human convictions, where we have been, and where we are going.

It is time to entomb the wretched bombast to the effect that to preserve peace we must constantly prepare for mighty wars; we might as well include with it the intellectual sludge and seminal silliness we heard so much of during the Cold War. The institutionalized mentality of war played a strong role in promoting the Persian Gulf War, which began in 1990, and its progeny twelve years later and following. Many small wars have occurred or are still in progress, for example, in Afghanistan, Somalia, Rwanda, El Salvador, Yugoslavia, and others.

The present world structure leads sane people to insane action. Stockpiling nuclear weapons is insane, but is done by sane people. The threat to our world comes from normal people. Some claim that scientists are responsible, holding them to higher moral standards than others. In fact scientists are no more or less ethical than others; they too contemplate killing millions or even billions, as well as creating a more nearly ideal world. Warrior-scientists of the world still participate in the madness of designing new nuclear warheads. To allow present policies to drift along without a conscious endeavor to seek a more peaceful world is the route to ultimate disaster. Classical wars were merely irrational; nuclear wars are demented.

If we—meaning people and government—fail to make a calculated effort for peace, we will eventually drift into war.

Excessive militarism will be the death of us yet unless it is successfully challenged. The bombs are the symptoms of our problems, and while not the primary cause, they aggravate them. Taking all profits from warfare would be a mighty contribution toward peace. Many of us have grown accustomed to nuclear weapons, and some even seem to see them as a sort of idol demanding sacrifice. It is too idealistic to plan a world free of enmity and rancor; the best we might be able to manage is for the various national, religious, and ethnic groups to refrain from waging nuclear war, even though their mutual hatred and fears continue. It is the infernal spiral toward war which must somehow be neutralized. After all, we have a duty to reason and civilization.

The religions of the world have failed to maintain peace, and show no greater promise for the future. Conflicts occur equally between those of different religions and between different segments of the same religion. Bishop Leroy Matthieson of the Catholic diocese of Amarillo, Texas, where final assembly of thousands of nuclear bombs was carried out, appealed to the workers, asking them "to consider what they are doing, to resign from such activities, and to seek employment in peaceful pursuits." This was in 1981. About the same time, Archbishop Terrence Cardinal Cooke in New York was describing nuclear weapons as tolerable, and he added that those who produce them "can do so in good conscience." Christians have gladly shot other Christians; Muslims happily cut the throats of other Muslims. Experience demonstrates that religion does not diminish the neurotic zest for war.

Peace today rests on deterrence, an inherently unstable situation (8-3). To change mutually assured destruction into mutually assured survival will require new modes of thought and new ideas. One such idea which merits widespread support is the concept that our world has become a planet with interconnected life-support systems. Absolute values of sovereignty are obsolete. Einstein, with nuclear weapons in mind, stated this clearly when he said: "The basic power of the Universe cannot be fitted into the outmoded concept of narrow nationalism."

Most peace movements of the past have not struck at the causes of war at its roots. If a movement against militarism is to make any progress in the foreseeable future, it has to broaden both its sights and its support. Opposition to a particular weapons system is not enough. National and international priorities will have to be redirected to address those who suffer most from unjust and undemocratic distribution of human and material resources. Movements born out of fear of devastation can be reborn by acting on a commitment to change.

12-2 Steps Toward Peace: The International Level

Arms Control, Disarmament, and Détente—The drive of countries to arm themselves is so strong that attempts to forge disarmament treaties in the past have mostly failed. While arms control has fared a little better, it is still no panacea. Arms control agreements have helped keep competition within manageable limits, have helped contain the costs, and helped maintain a relatively stable balance of power. The period of détente between the superpowers of the 1960s and early 1970s permitted the ban on warhead testing in the atmosphere, the Threshold Test Ban Treaty, and others. These are positive, but insufficient measures.

While insufficient, arms control does buy time.

Comprehensive Test Ban—An agreement to halt all tests of nuclear warheads would be a giant step toward peace (8-7). It would not be difficult to monitor. A total ban would prevent the development of new nuclear weapons except at the design and computational level. The Soviets unilaterally observed a test ban for a year and a half, but the American government refused corresponding restraint. If we cannot even agree on preliminary steps such as this, more advanced agreements are hardly possible. This world has too many warheads already, and a total test ban would enhance our security. The natural decay of tritium, with a half-life of 12.3 years, means that hydrogen bombs and tritium-boosted fission bombs become increasingly disabled without maintenance; this presents us with a sort of automatic partial disarmament. (More on the Comprehensive Test Ban Treaty is in sections 9-63 and 11-7).

Centers to Reduce Nuclear Risk—Suppose the United States, in cooperation with other nuclear powers and the United Nations, established a series of peace centers along the lines of a university graduate school or think tank. The organization would cost relatively little when compared to expenditures for armaments. It would have facilities in quite a number of countries. The world's best minds would be encouraged to study the origins of war and of conflict resolution, the psychology of arms races, and the roots of human behavior. Studies would cover social, historic, ethnic, and ethical aspects, and all else which makes the human race so quick to reach for the gun. Studies aimed at reducing the nuclear threat, to be realistic, would require deep, almost oracular, political insight, understanding the psychology of rivalry, and immense wisdom. Results from the studies would be used as resource material by governments and educational facilities. One should not expect too much from such peace centers, or existing arms-control think tanks, etc. The roots of much conflict stem from many sources, including unjust economic status, overpopulation, competition for natural resources, and other deeply-implanted causes. Opposition to recommended moves would be fierce. In 1984 the Senate overwhelmingly recommended establishment of nuclear risk reduction centers in Washington and Moscow, but today one hears little of this action. In spite of this apathy, there is at least some chance that a sincere, well-financed series of study centers would come up with the spark to activate the world to make conscious steps aimed at maintaining peace.

Travel Experience for Political Leaders—A modest step to expedite mutual international understanding and to lower animosity would be to encourage each of our high national leaders, say all members of Congress, cabinet members, and other ranking persons, to visit and explore Russia and China and perhaps some other countries. This could be done after elections but before taking office, where feasible, and periodically afterward. Reciprocal visits by their foreign counterparts could also take place. Learning to see how the common people of each country live would contribute somewhat to world stability. In 1958, Sen. John Stennis, a conservative from Mississippi, visited the Soviet Union, and for the first time began to doubt that Russia plans an attack on the U.S. Such a comment is typical of the observations of other members of Congress.

Conservatives are certain to label such trips as junkets, as if going to Moscow could be so classified.

Role of Scientists—As the renowned American scientist Linus Pauling has pointed out, almost all great world problems have significant scientific components. A special obligation therefore falls on to the shoulders of scientists in today's world to help citizens and world leaders to understand and cope with modern weapons, origins of war, hostility, racism, poverty, population pressures, and many other such problems. Moreover, any steps taken toward expanding science education all over the world are steps in the right direction. Many scientific organizations would contribute their services.

Abolition 2000—An idealistic movement called Abolition 2000 was a global network of over 2000 organizations founded in 1995. Its goal was to win an international treaty to abolish all nuclear weapons by the year 2000 or shortly thereafter. Here's a wish that it had been a success. At the least it was a force to reduce the number of nuclear warheads in our world.

The U.S. is committed on paper to the goal of general disarmament. Article VI of the Non-Proliferation Treaty (1968) commits the United States to pursue negotiations in good faith, concerning nuclear weapons, on a treaty for "general and effective international control." This section was repeated in 1995 in a revision of the Non-Proliferation Treaty. General Butler's call for abolishing all nuclear weapons from Earth (11-7A) is closely related.

Much of the world is still in the thrall of nuclear weapons even though the Cold War has ceased. There is today no nation in the world which is a military threat to the United States the way the Soviet Union once was. By ending the practice of keeping American and Russian ballistic missiles on high nuclear alert, both land- and sea-based, we might begin to create the atmosphere necessary for serious consideration of eliminating all nuclear warheads on Earth.

12-3 Steps Toward Peace: The National Level

Reduce the Defense Budget—Once an administration is convinced that present military expenditures surpass the need to maintain deterrence, it would be feasible and safe to reduce the budget by, say, 5%. The risks in this action are minimal; the benefits would be enormous, especially if it could be repeated several times. Reduction of armaments funding is not just emotionally appealing; it is also sensible and practical. In any case, the proposed series of reductions would be vastly safer than continuation of constantly increasing military expenditures.

The present American arms budget is still far in excess of need.

Just as development of a new arms system by one side generally goads the other into behaving likewise, so also a step to lessen armaments is sometimes reciprocated. Thus, during the Cold War, the U.S. decision not to orbit nuclear weapons (1962), to cease testing warheads in the atmosphere (1963), to reduce production of weapons-grade uranium-235 (1964), and to cease production of biological weapons (1969) all served to spark Soviet reciprocation. In some cases the informal agreements were fortified by treaties.

Moderate the Military-Industrial Complex—This step corresponds to the one described above, but directly along military lines. For example, the U.S. could shut down or not start operation of the nuclear reactors which produce tritium above the level needed for research.

Announce a No-First-Use Policy—The United States has consistently taken the position that we might employ nuclear weapons in a classical war, such as an invasion of western Europe. Apparently, this threat is supposed to buttress an element of deterrence. An announced policy that we would not be the first to employ nuclear weapons, with the possible exception of our own territory (as in repelling an invasion), would give a small boost to convincing others of our peaceful intentions. When Sakharov visited the first President Bush, he was shown a photo of the President's family. Bush said "Here's the guarantee that we'll never use nuclear weapons first." Sakharov answered "If you'll never make first use of nuclear weapons, you should announce that publicly, and write it into law." Russia would also be expected to re-instate its no-first-use policy.

Cancel Steps Which Bolster Arms Races—If the remnants of the Strategic Defense Initiative and its descendant, the National Missile Defense program, were terminated, our security would not be lessened. The economic savings would be billions of dollars; this step alone would provide funding for the peace centers. Canceling the B-1 and B-2 bomber programs, safe now that the Cold War is finished, would save more billions. Another project which could be called off with profit is the Atomic Vapor Laser Isotope Separation project (6-6); it has, in fact, been put in cold storage. The end of the Cold War also means steadily adapting many bureaucracies to the new realities, for example amending the old Atomic Energy Act. It means less justification for using national security as a talisman for concealing government activities from taxpayers. It means doing all we can to see that the Commonwealth of Independent States and China also adapt fully to the new status. And it means that the nuclear powers and United Nations should do all possible to see that a new spirit of nonnuclear capability starts to hearten the spectrum of countries which aspire to nuclear arms (Iran, Libya, North Korea, and a few others).

Some say we need huge military expenditures to provide employment; if true, what does this say about the true nature of capitalism?

Winding down excessive military undertakings would bring certain stresses and dislocations into our economy. A point of premier significance is that each million dollars spent on military work provides much less employment than the same sum spent on civilian projects. We can make specific plans to accommodate workers displaced by conversion from militarism.

Announce a No-New-Nuclear-Weapons Policy—Stop sub-nuclear testing and related work. Ratify the Comprehensive Test Ban treaty. Tailor national policies toward waging peace.

12-4 Steps Toward Peace: The Personal Level

All the great movements of history have begun with individuals. Working first with a few, and then with many, a grass-roots effort expands until it resonates among the masses and affects the course of events. You **can** make a difference. It takes a personal commitment.

Inform Yourself—One early step any person needs to take to make a difference in national nuclear policies is to learn a few basics about nuclear energy and weapons. It is not necessary to fully master the mathematics and all those mind-embalming details of reactors, bombs, rads, rems, and the rest, but at least some understanding should be gained. The most important of the technical aspects to be understood are the immense power and destructiveness of nuclear bombs, the nature of radioactive fallout, and the accuracy of missile systems. The real stumbling blocks are political and educational. Many folks are reluctant to learn about these gloomy matters, but in view of their dominance over our future, we have no choice but to face up to the dangers. Doing nothing is the road to ultimate obliteration; it is to acquiesce in our own ruination. Prevention of nuclear war as the priority item in the national agenda can come only after it becomes one of the highest priorities in the personal agenda of our citizens.

A second point should be made concerning national energy sources. A dedicated effort to develop non-polluting, renewable energy sources (solar, wind, geothermal, biomass, etc.; see Chapter 4) would make full employment easier as well as reduce dependence on foreign sources.

Join With Others—There are many groups around the country devoted to nuclear and peace issues. It is neither radical nor extremist to oppose nuclear bombs and to want to change nuclear policies. Associating with others in organizations which study the issues is a good way to learn, and to help others to learn. The problems are so large and complex that we need the input of many thinking citizens. Listen to how others react and feel about nuclear weapons, matters of war and peace, the industrial-military complex, and more.

Politics—Although politics is considered a dirty word by many, there is a constructive aspect to it. Actually, constructive politics is about the only vehicle for significant progress. It would be good if we citizens made all candidates for public office state their views on nuclear issues even if the exertion makes their brains creak. The subject should be discussed in the marketplace. By writing our Senators and Representatives, we can exert some influence. Each of us has creative urges now and then, and what higher gratification is there than to help make our world a safer place? Our task is somehow, in some way, to make our leaders and citizens deeply aware of the cataclysmic peril of any nuclear arms race. It will be a long and difficult task to interrupt the drive of history, considering how deeply weapons are embedded in the human psyche. To institutionalize peace rather than war will require supreme statecraft. It might be hopelessly idealistic, but one can make a case that a world free of nuclear weapons is a human right.

In its constructive sense, politics is a valuable vehicle for change.

Education—Quite a number of school boards have approved teaching "nuclear peace." This is the case in California, New York, Illinois, Massachusetts, Wisconsin, and others. The subject is introduced at a number of levels and no one view is presented; many opinions are covered. The main idea is to teach what nuclear bombs are, their effects on Hiroshima and Nagasaki, and something about the health effects of radioactivity. It requires perceptive discretion on the part of the teachers. Inevitably, a few persons oppose the whole idea, claiming that education for peace is un-American or worse. It is difficult to believe, but a parents' group in Guinnett County, Texas, actually tried to censor out discussion of nuclear war (as well as evolution and other topics) from the school curriculum.

At the university level, many courses with names like "Perspectives on Nuclear War" are available. A typical course covers: atoms and nuclei, energy from fission and fusion, the effects of nuclear explosions, medical and ecological aspects of nuclear attack, psychological resistance to confronting the issue, war mentality, arms control, disarmament, and negotiation techniques.

Resources are abundant. Peacekeeping computer programs are available. VCR tapes can be purchased on peace breaking out, on arms races, and on what you can do. Summer programs on peace studies and global peace tours have been arranged.

12-5 Some Intractable Problems

A series of difficult situations arise from the nation-state political structure of the world. One example is American defense. Being sandwiched between two oceans east and west, and between non-aggressive countries north and south, we have little to fear from conventional attack. Even another Pearl Harbor could be contained by our own conventional forces, especially considering smart bombs and all the rest of modern weaponry. Terrorism is a recent problem. Only a nuclear attack could deal a highly devastating blow. This would argue that we should support world disarmament in nuclear warheads, as we have committed ourselves on paper. But the mindset of the American military, and that of perhaps the majority of the people, is to keep the nuclear option open for defense. So long as the position if the United States is along these lines, we should not be surprised that other powers adopt a similar policy.

Another problem with no apparent solution is that of smaller states which feel threatened by larger neighbors. One example is Pakistan vis-a-vis India. Another is Israel, surrounded by hostile Arab powers. It is going to require some first-class diplomacy to reconcile these positions.

12-6 Scientists and Peace

After World War II the Federation of American Scientists (section 3-15) began a program on education of political leaders about nuclear matters. This small group exerted considerable influence, which continues till this day. A number of other such organizations have been formed; two of the most prominent are the Union of Concerned Scientists and Physicians for Social Responsibility. But compared to the industrial-military complex, their efforts are puny. University scientists earn their recognition primarily from research and secondarily from teaching. There is little encouragement and no financial support for undertaking arms-race educational studies, with its sparse professional rewards. A post-Cold War, international program whose goals include studying the radioactivity from old nuclear explosions around the world is called Radioactivity from Nuclear Test Explosions, or RADTEST. Its member nations are the USA, Russia, China, Kazakhstan, France and the U.K. Its objectives are to determine the radionuclide inventory at the world's test sites, make dose reconstruction studies of human exposure, and many related tasks. Addresses of the above-mentioned organizations are given in Appendix IV.

More than half of American physical scientists worked for the industrial-military complex during the later stages of the Cold War. This is not because their minds are martial; with a few exceptions, they are peace-loving folks. Rather, it is because that is where the jobs are, and they have families to support. A few scientists and engineers, those with sufficient moral energy, refuse to accept war-oriented work, and still generally earn a decent living.

Like others, most scientists go where the money is.

Whatever, scientists should not remain indifferent to the consequences and objectives of their work. We should encourage all of them to devote at least some of their time toward restructuring national and global priorities so as to favor a world free of any nuclear threat.

12-7 Opinions of Two Military Commanders

Our times demand bold, imaginative, and daring innovation, not the timid, crippled thinking of the past, which puts a higher priority on national sovereignty than on national survival. Some military and many political leaders consider themselves "realists," and scorn any plan to control and reduce nuclear arsenals as "impractical," "extreme," or "radical." Lest we think that all military brass are blustering hawks, read what two mature generals have written on peace in the nuclear age. Some quotes are below:

Is common sense radical?

> Every gun that is made, every warship launched, every rocket fired signifies, in the final sense, a theft from those who hunger and are not fed, those who are cold and are not clothed. This world in arms is not spending money alone. It is spending the sweat of its laborers, the genius of its scientists, the hopes of its children . . . This is not a way of life at all in any true sense. Under the cloud of threatening war, it is humanity hanging from a cross of iron.
>
> —President Dwight Eisenhower, 1953

> The era of armaments has ended and the human race must conform its actions to this truth or die.
>
> —President Dwight Eisenhower, 1956

> The great question is . . . can war be outlawed in the world? If so, it would lift at one stroke the darkest shadow that has engulfed mankind from the beginning. It would not only remove fear and bring security . . . it would produce an economic wave of prosperity that would raise the world's standard of living beyond anything ever dreamed of by mankind.
>
> You will say that although the abolition of war has been the dream of man for centuries, every proposition to that end has been promptly discarded as impossible and fantastic... But that was before the science of the past decade made mass destruction a reality.
>
> There must always be one to lead, and we should be that one. . . . We should now proclaim our readiness to abolish war in concert with the other great powers of the world. The result might be magical.
>
> —General Douglas MacArthur, 1955

> Global war has become a Frankenstein to destroy both sides. No longer is it a weapon of adventure—the shortcut to international power. If you lose, you are annihilated. If you win, you stand only to lose. [War] contains now only the germs of double suicide.
>
> —General Douglas MacArthur, 1961

12-8 A Lesson for Leaders

The Peace Memorial Museums and Parks in Hiroshima and Nagasaki afford indelible lessons for all who have leadership roles in human society. Visits by influential political leaders the world over are urgently recommended. The author's visits convinced him that the human race was living on the verge of doomsday during all those Cold War years. The Atomic Dome (pictured as a negative) has been fenced off and kept as a reminder of the folly of war. Such an empty, ghostly image symbolizes our world if the human race is senseless enough to engage in nuclear world war.

Visiting the Peace Memorial Museums, which sear one's soul, would help bring home to political leaders that nothing, no passing passion, no threat, no rivalry, nothing at all justifies a nuclear war. Sometimes one suspects that certain politicians, such as those Senators who blocked ratification of the Comprehensive Test Ban treaty, have delusions of adequacy, cling obstinately to obsolete notions, and can barely cope with reality. The Peace Parks wipe away the cosmic blasphemy of assuming a nuclear war with an enemy du jour is winnable.

12-9 Thinking Anew

No cute new idea will magically serve as a vaccine against war. A world structure which puts the highest priority on avoiding nuclear war can come only when the movers and shakers of the world really wish it. Such leaders arise when most of the common people demand it, when the meaning of the unpalatable alternative to peace becomes clear to millions. The bomb will never be uninvented; we are stuck with it forever, and must learn to live with it. "Just try to forget me!" you can hear the derisive nuclear demon shrieking. The only way to silence this monster is to achieve a world without nuclear weapons. If such a world is a human right, it must be earned. Our species is actually capable of living without war.

The arms race, between the two superpowers at least, has been largely tamed by the great political developments of 1990-91 in the Soviet Union, events of virtually tectonic magnitude. The threat remains that hostilities can slowly build up again, perhaps with China replacing the old USSR. In any case, smaller cold wars, such as between India and Pakistan, are smoldering. The bloody disintegration of Yugoslavia demonstrated once again that the human species remains shortsighted and can be pretty vicious, despite its potential for majestic and exalted achievements. More such wars are almost certain, with the use of nuclear weapons eventually possible, some think even probable.

No permanent progress can be made until the great political, economic, and military leaders themselves become convinced that danger from an uncontrolled arms race is real and immediate, and that a nuclear war would destroy the superpowers and their satellites as functioning societies. Presidents, prime ministers, field marshals and generals, dominant industrial leaders—in short the power elite which runs the world—generally talk peace, but their budgets ordinarily indicate other convictions. Einstein remarked that "mere praise of peace is easy but ineffective. What is needed is active participation in the fight against war and everything that leads to it." Here are the words of the accomplished and compassionate author, Jonathan Schell, concerning abolition of nuclear weapons (1999):

> What I've called the Gift of Time is running out very, verey quickly. We are walking in slow motion without knowing it into a new world of nightmare. This seems to be what defines this particular moment. The end of the Cold War gave us the greatest op-poprtunity, since the invention of nuclear weapons, not just ot control them, not just ot reduce them, not just to stabilize them, but to actually get rid of them. That opportunity remains today, but time is running out. We have the opportunity. We see the danger. What we need is action.

Can you imagine the results if we could find a way of mobilizing for peace as vigorously as for war? For example, remember the energy and money we put into developing nuclear weapons for all conceivable conditions and uses. Tests have been carried out with every variation you can think of. Consider the fission, fusion, and neutron bombs, the multitudes of rockets of elaborate equipment to guide them, the bombers and submarines, warning systems, the Strategic Defense Initiative, and the rest, all lovingly crafted. No country, no alliance, has ever made efforts this vigorously for peace. Somehow, the human race is willing to spend thousands of times more for weapons than for peace efforts, as if the risks of nuclear war are somehow less dangerous than the risks of nuclear disarmament.

Consider that during the recent Persian Gulf War (1990-91), when the Administration quickly found $45 billion to promote hostilities while our educational and health infrastructures at home were withering. One might say that bombs kill twice, first when their manufacture extracts sustenance from our lives, depriving our citizens of necessities, and second when they are employed to kill our supposed enemies. The principal nuclear powers have no intention of giving up reliance on these weapons.

Avoiding nuclear war in the next few decades will mean peaceful coexistence. Some far-right critics have attacked the concept of peaceful coexistence, but have never suggested an acceptable alternative. There is in fact no sane alternative to peace. It is time to cry out for humanity to exert all its resourceful intelligence and verdantly inventive ingenuity to solve the riddle of our compulsive wars. If we disarm unilaterally, we would probably be conquered; if we arm to the teeth, wars break out anyway. It's time to choose the third path: a deliberate, exhaustive, lavishly-financed search for a peaceful way to run our world. A nuclear war would represent blind, brutal calamity, with no meaning, just suffering and death. While the human race would survive, failure to engrave its lessons in the hearts of those who pull through would, after a difficult recovery, result in their simply beginning preparations to do it again. Indeed, one can make a case that the easy part is over, when only a few nuclear powers existed in a global environment of Cold War. What will life be like after a century or two, when many nations have nuclear arms?

We must find the third path.

The final word is: If a nuclear war is to be avoided, it will have to be by adopting policies which we might as well embrace now.

> Peace in the world requires that we recognise the real enemies of mankind and work to vanquish them. These enemies are war, ignorance, disease, poverty, hunger, the pollution of the environment, the wasting and ruination of the world's resources by militarism.
>
> —Ava Helen Pauling, 1975

Bibliography for Part I

Joseph Rotblat, *A NUCLEAR-WEAPON-FREE WORLD*, Westview Press, 1993.

Jonathan Glover, *HUMANITY—A MORAL HISTORY OF THE TWENTIETH CENTURY*, Yale University Press, 1999.

Maurine Doerken, *ONE BOMB AWAY—CITIZEN EMPOWERMENT FOR NUCLEAR AWARENESS*, A.W.O.L. Ink Productions, 12381 Wilshire Blvd., Suite 205, Los Angeles, CA 90025, 2002.

Author's Note on Part II

Einstein, in response to the threat of nuclear arms, urged humanity to think in new ways. In Part II of this chapter, Prof. Wilson outlines one of these possible new ways. It gives us an idea of what kinds of measures we must undertake to maintain world peace. This will be no easy task. Merely dismissing such proposals as "impracticable" is not sufficient; a good case can be made that it is the existing political structure of the world which is impracticable. To be useful, constructive criticism of all new proposals and analyses are essential.

Part II: A NEW WAY OF THINKING ABOUT ACHIEVING AND PRESERVING PEACE

by Raymond G. Wilson
Emeritus Associate Professor of Physics, Illinois Wesleyan University

ABSTRACT—There is probably no issue in the history of humankind about which more words have been written and argued, over a fifty-nine year period, than nuclear war/nuclear peace, and with such meager results. Regarding nuclear weapons, the only true weapons of mass destruction, for mankind so little has been accomplished it is intellectually infuriating, especially after the unheeded warnings by highly respected individuals such as Einstein and Eisenhower. In their time, when world forces were in opposition, there was little opportunity for anyone to really lead, to point the way to a world in which peace would be truly possible. They warned of the direction we were heading. Others tried to show how that old habitual way could be altered. One perhaps unlikely person was J. Robert Oppenheimer, "father" of the two nuclear bombs which brought about the deaths of more than 270,000 people in Hiroshima and Nagasaki.

12-10 Why a Solution to the War Problem Is Necessary, and Possible

Most people in the world have no conception of the enormity of the effects of nuclear war. Why? Greatly because the United States government did not reveal the truth about these effects for some thirty years following 1945. Since "the people" have not learned, regrettably, they may only learn if one or more nuclear bombs are used again. Most of the world has not yet understood the possible obliteration of many millions of people within twenty-four hours. Our brains are too meager for such immensity.

Consider the following: It must be true that in a peaceful world without the conventional weapons of war, without tanks, missiles, bombers, warships, there would be no need for weapons of mass destruction. Regrettably, the converse is not true. In a world without weapons of mass destruction, unless the world changes, there would still be conventional weapons and wars and arms races, eventually leading again to the development of efficient techniques for killing hundreds of thousands of people, so-called, "mass destruction," treating people like matter.

If it is not a fallacy that our goal truly is nuclear disarmament, ridding the world of the "terror bomb" and the main new tool of a WW III, then we should put full effort into the simpler but crucially essential problem of eliminating the need for conventional weapons of war: put full effort into solving regional disputes, the Balkans, the Middle East, Africa, South and South East Asia, the Korean peninsula, and elsewhere; and putting full effort into solving the inequities between the have-nots and the haves. Eliminate the "justifiable" causes of international conflict.

There is evidence that world resources necessary to solve these problems are actually available but for more than 59 years have been diverted into the continuous creation of new weapons and weapon systems rather than toward the creation of a world at peace.

The single, small and primitive Hiroshima bomb destroyed a city of 300,000 and claimed more than 140,000 lives by the end of 1945 and 200,000 by 1950. Nagasaki brought the total deaths to well over 270,000. Both Hiroshima and Nagasaki and their people were instantaneously seared, charred, and vaporized.

It was as if a Richter-10 flaming earthquake came down upon them from the Gods. And afterwards the nuclear radiation began its dirty, deadly, silent, and prolonged massacre.

Averaged over the 50 years following WW II, the world's military industrial complexes created an arsenal equivalent to making 70 Hiroshima A-bombs every day of every one of those 50 years. Seventy on each of those 18,000 days.

Just one of those 70-bomb days could yield 9,800,000 killed in a new war, 70 x 140,000. The World has been most fortunate in one sense.

The world arsenal just referred to is the equivalent of about 50 years x 365 days/year x 70 Hiroshima A-bombs/day, or approximately 1,280,000 Hiroshima A-bombs. Only two were ever used. Is there anything wrong here? Talk about wasted resources! (Total warheads built, from1945 to 2000, more than 128,060.[1])

The people of the world plead for peace, plead for an end to the killing, destruction, and suffering, and their leaders cannot achieve it; and national governments ox-walking to reduce nuclear arsenals is not the way.

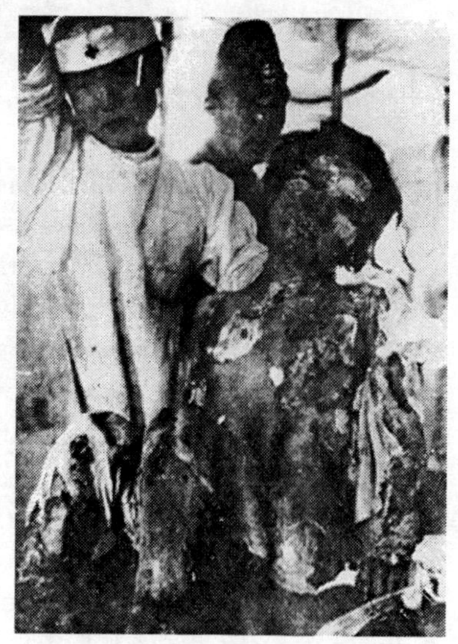

Nagasaki, 14-year-old girl, one of the 270,000 killed.

I shall explain here how world resources could be used: to achieve world peace with justice, fairness, and great benefits for everyone and threats to no one, and to remedy the regional tensions and devastation that permeate much of the less developed world. This can be done at no additional cost. Only once before was a similar task attempted, the Marshall Plan, bringing some relief from the devastation of WW II to selected friends of the western Allied world, while creating an economic boom in America.

Rather than the myopic focus mainly on nuclear abolition with its nettlesome concerns of nuclear breakouts and nuclear terrorism, we should develop the courage to aggressively follow a path which circumvents and defuses rogues' continuous regional threats, terrors, and wars. The world initiatives for action need to be taken away from the gangster rogues' and their dictatorial suicidal commands and directed toward peace for all those less developed nations which are ready for peace, ready for the promised advances of the 21st century. One country tests a bomb, sends a missile over a neighbor, or develops nuclear technology and the world's developed nations have fits for the next several months, and move to increase military spending, to create a missile defense system, which would likely be permeable. Effective proactive amelioration seems an activity unknown in the developed world; the tendency is always to be militarily reactive.

There need be no technical problems to achieve a world without threats. It is only socio-political-ideological problems, in people's minds, which prevent world peace.

Is it true that for some 200 years there has not been a war between truly democratic nations? Is it true that such nations don't even prepare for war with one another? Hence, is it not understandable, the worrisome situation of nuclear capability in nations without democracy? Is the creation of democracies the long sought expedient to world peace? Would war be unlikely if there existed democratic Iraq, Iran, North Korea, Pakistan, Palestine, and Rwanda, and indeed, would living conditions in those nations be improved?

12-11 Background

In the Cold War year of 1981 the U.S. defense budget in total increased to considerably more than US$300 billion per year. We were led to believe that the U.S. would win this confrontation even if the world detonated all 18,000 MILLION TONS [2] of "nuclear TNT," in a WW III thermal and radioactive holocaust. It would have been comparable to the destruction wrought by several thousand WW IIs. What folly! But some people had no fear; the expected "rapture" to heaven would save them. "We should not mistake for laws of God or nature the cultural values of the world's most unstable systems."

No nation's leader, and probably very few active U.S. generals, have ever witnessed a nuclear explosion above ground. Still, it is easy for many to consider a nuclear bomb to be a useable weapon of war; after all, in 1945 the Allies had actually used two, which many believe ended that war. Even during the nuclear tests in the South Pacific, congressmen, invited to witness the tests, were located so far away (for their safety), that many came away unimpressed. "Like a giant firecracker," one said. In Nevada, G.I.s advanced under the mushroom clouds to test themselves at radioactive ground zero.

Imagine the hottest clear day of the year. Remember walking out into the sunlight and being amazed, that even at a distance of 93,000,000 miles, how hot the radiation of our sun really was? The surface temperature of the small primitive Hiroshima atomic bomb was 1000 Celsius degrees hotter than the Sun's. It hung in the air only 300 yards, 0.17 mile, above the people of Hiroshima. Were some people vaporized? Today's average weapon yield is ten times the Hiroshima bomb; some warhead yields can be 500 times greater.

Do American legislators ever confront the question, "Why does the United States have 'enemies' in the world?"

Since 9/11/2001 some United States legislators are asking what went wrong. But what was actually done was to increase the military spending by $100 billion. It would be fascinating to survey all congressmen: Reasons why you think people hate the United

States. Do legislators understand? Are they capable of learning? Will they ever try?

By 2004, more than 23 million killed by nonnuclear wars since 1945; the United Nations incapable of, or always too late at, ending wars. The world average production rate of nuclear weapons for 50 years the equivalent of 70 Hiroshima bombs per day every day of every year since 1945. Something was terribly wrong with the world!

It became clear to many that nuclear weapons were only a symptom of an all-pervasive cancer of the spirit of the world. Some Japanese have an expression for this period of human history in which we find ourselves; they call it "the era of nuclear madness." It's far from over.

More than 400,000 war deaths per year since 1945: Shall the chaos of the world continue to its end?

12-12 Oppenheimer's Conjecture on World Peace

J. Robert Oppenheimer, father of the atomic bomb, conjectured[3] in 1946 that

> (W)ars might be avoided by: universal disarmament; limited national sovereignties; provision for all people of the world: of a rising standard of living, better education; more contact with and better understanding of others; and equal access to the technical and raw materials which are needed for improving life.

Though impossible to implement in 1946 (Stalin had other plans.), most of what Oppenheimer meant I believe is fully realizable now. There can be peace, justice, prosperity, and fairness for all nations, as you shall see.

Even after the brutality of three and a half years of WW II imprisonment by the Japanese Army in Borneo author Agnes Newton Keith believes a peaceful world could be achieved:

> "I believe that:
> While We have more than we need on this continent,
> and others die for want of it, there can be no lasting peace.
> When we work as hard in peacetime to make this world decent to live in,
> as in wartime we work to kill, the world will be decent,
> and the causes for which men fight will be gone." [4]

Let us examine one way it could be done.

At the height of the Cold War America was militarily preparing for a two-hemisphere WWIII with annual "defense" budgets in excess of $300 billion. The rest of the World was spending approximately an equivalent amount, thus totaling $600 billion; some said more, $1000 billion. With the end of the Cold War, the end of the Soviet Union, and with an understanding of the size of the unused world nuclear arsenals; a rational proposal in 1990 could have easily been for the defense budgets of the United States, United Kingdom, France, Russia and China to be cut in half; with appropriate caution, not abruptly, but promptly. You may not understand that if you do not comprehend the size of present world arsenals. Such a cut is not all that is required.

Current and projected U.S. annual military budgets, of $400 billion[5] make it seem that an "arms race" continues. Certainly the taxation for arms will continue. Someone must pay.

There is a further aspect of military spending that is essential to understand. In the early 1980's the U.S. expenditures for ALL PHASES of creating useable new facilities, new weapons, and new weapons systems was about $150 billion annually; i.e., using up about (at that time) half the U.S. military budget.

I have referred to Oppenheimer's conjecture. Here is mine:

> After some 45 years studying world affairs, I have come to the firm belief that in contrast to past policies, if a nation wishes to be at peace, the most effective use of any nation's "defense" budget is, not resorting to murderous war, but by some safe and equitable means, the proactive conversion of existent or potential enemies into friends, all working for a peaceful world with justice and fairness for all.

Today, consider the semi-conversions between Russia and the United States, Egypt and Israel, China and the United States. How much better off could all have been if military spending had been cut in half, if the goals were peace instead of conflict? Consider what might have been, early on, had a proactive approach to peace been taken in the Middle East and the Islamic World. We ask, could such conversions be done, again, and repeatedly, between Israel and Palestine, the United States and Iraq and Iran, Pakistan and India, the U.N. and the Democratic Peoples' Republic of (North) Korea. Fifty-nine years ago the United States was engaged in brutal and deadly warfare with Japan. What happened over the past 59 years to all but eliminate the bitter hatreds of those earlier years? Can it happen again in today's world?

If the aforementioned "conversions" are possible, and historical evidence seems to show it so, then it is implied that if not threatened by war or terrorism, the United States and other nations of the Developed World could make available, half their military budgets annually, totaling well more than US$300 billion, to eliminate war and threats of war throughout the World. If the Developed World is not threatened. The members of the U.N. General Assembly need to consider what they wish for their nations in the 21st century, continued strife or amazing improvements in living conditions, in their nations, without war.

We will show that additional sources are also available to raise the total to at least US$330 billion annually, which, if administered properly for some 20 to 25 years, could be used to bring about the following for all nations that abide by the U.N. Charter and all Covenants:

1. The virtual elimination of the possibility of nuclear war.
2. In the developed world: control of illicit drugs and narcotics; immensely improved international trade in peacetime goods; the extreme reduction of unemployment, budget deficits, and national debts.
3. In the less-developed world: the near elimination of malnutrition, disease, poverty, slavery, illiteracy, rights deprivation, neo-colonialism, and indebtedness.
4. Establish stringent procedures for the elimination of modern conventional warfare between nations and within them.
5. Curtailment of the refugee problem.

If the program to be described here had been implemented when the threats of the Cold War ended we feel that the terrorisms of the past decade would not have occurred. Some $3,000 billion ($300 billion/year for 10 years) would have been at work on items 1-5 above.

It was some satisfaction to learn that physicists Philip Morrison and Kostas Tsipis had separately come to the same conclusion, that something of the order of US$300 billion annually could be available to remedy many or most of the world's most pressing problems.[6] US$300 billion represents some 7 to 10 times what the less developed world receives now. Perhaps more. Considering how present nation-to-nation aid money is often wasted, our recommendations mean that $300 billion could in effect be much more than 10 times present aid. This proposal might be considered to contain the honest and objective peace dividend for all nations. It does not require "world government" and you will be able to see that great benefits would accrue to all nations willing and able to participate.

Greater security for all nations can be obtained by worldwide reduction of the weapons of our "enemies," rather than increasing arsenals everywhere, as we are doing, and as has been done for past centuries. Nations which truly abide by the intentions of the U.N. Charter pose no malicious economic or military threats to their neighbors. Implementing Oppenheimer's conjecture will make it seem that more than US$300 billion each year is eliminating military and economic threats, while peace and justice advance throughout the world, a great bargain.

I believe the following steps based upon Oppenheimer's conjecture can bring us to a peaceful world, if nations only have the hindsight, foresight, and courage to try. There will be political nay-sayers but they have not dedicated their last twenty-five years in the search for true world peace.

12-13 Steps Which Would Be Required

Step 1. Direct aid from developed world nations to the less developed world must end. This kind of money is usually tied to undesirable long-term neo-economic/political/military obligations, and, often in the receiving nation, environmental and social abuse, political and financial corruption. This money stays where it was, in the taxpayer's nation. This is the additional $30 billion, that becomes available, creating a total resource of about $330 billion annually.

Lech Walesa, former president of Poland, says that the United States wasted billions of dollars in aid to formerly communist Eastern European nations in the 1990s because there was no procedure in place to distribute the money. Step 1 remedies this immediately.

Other examples of corrupted programs come to mind: The Alliance for Progress of the Kennedy administration, and the Caribbean Basin Initiatives of the Reagan years.

There are some nations that can maintain efficient and non-political aid programs, Sweden and Japan come to mind but the aid they provide, though valuable, is a single drop in the bucket when one understands the immensity of vital world problems to be solved. Hundreds of billions of dollars will be necessary. We will show that there is a better way.

Step 2. The U.N. aims at obtaining in the less developed world, democracy and self-sufficiency in six areas: 1) food production, 2) housing, 3) health care, 4) economic means, 5) civilian security, and 6) education to support items 1-5.

Annually, US$330 billion in aid from the developed nations will be distributed by the U.N. using new procedures. What are these new procedures?

Each Developed Nation annually deposits with the U.N., "credit chits" in amount equal to half their true military budget; the money actually remains in the Developed Nation's treasury, until payout is due. There will be great advantages to all nations who make payments into this program, and considerable disadvantages to those who can, but do not. The more chits deposited, the greater value accrues to the depositor, as will become obvious.

Who gets the "chits"? Dictatorships steal a nation's most valuable resource, its future, embodied in its young people. Dictators, for their own selfish gain, with lies, propaganda and indoctrination, often provide death as the fate of the young ones. Dictators never exert honest efforts to achieve peace. They and their nations are disqualified as "chit" recipients.

It is regrettable that, for example, the two-democracy type relationship of Canada and the United States does not exist in 2004 between India and Pakistan, North and South Korea, China and Taiwan, Iran and Iraq, Israel and its neighbors. Were these pairs all democratic there would be less war danger in the world. Historical evidence indicates that true democracies do not wage war against each other; true democracies do not even prepare for war with one another.[7]

Thus, for nations of the developing world, which are verifiably evolving toward democratic rule by non-discriminatory consensus, the U.N. makes these funds available on the basis of solicited application of their development proposals, verifiable need, and guarantees against misuse or corruption. These funds may only be utilized for social and economic development, the six specific U.N. self-sufficiency goals, above.

The development proposals submitted to the U.N. by developing nations are carefully evaluated, in terms of the proposed societal, cultural, economic, and environmental impact, and protection against abuse and corruption. Is the nation verifiably moving toward true but self-defined and equitable nondiscriminatory democracy? Does the proposal truly represent the desires of a great majority of the people? Will minority rights be protected? What proof, what evidence, what tests support the proposition? The U.N. may wish to reject certain proposals or return the proposals for corrective improvement.

When a proposal is accepted and funded, the U.N. awards the amount in "Developed World credit chits" for peacetime goods and services. The chits must make their way back to their origin nation within two years of issue, and may pass through several nations, all on the approved list of democratic nations which abide by the U.N. Charter and all Covenants.

Developing nations which abide by the U.N. Charter and all Covenants, and which are funded, can expect constant on-site verification and audit by U.N. inspectors and visitors who will have the responsibility to see that the credit chits are used exactly as originally proposed.

The U.N. will not make such grants to nations where war is likely or where violations of rights: gender, religious, human, or ethnic are active or likely. Repressive and military governments and martial law governments will not qualify for funding or participation in this program, nor will any nation, regardless of its size, including the United States, which is not fully participating and cooperating in the worldwide elimination of: armaments of war, nuclear weapons, terrorism, and illicit drugs. Preference in the allocation of development funds will be given to those nations that:

1. are able to demonstrate a continuing reduction or lack of "war armament,"
2. are part of a multination cooperative regional development, and
3. have instituted U.N. recommended educational programs designed to lead their nations into the 21st century, not indoctrinate for the furtherance international disputes and terrors.

When the chits arrive back in the nation of origin they do not go to the national treasury. They go to the nation's suppliers of peacetime goods and services, thence cashed in at the treasury, thus enhancing productivity and employment in the original nation of chit origin.

Each nation will keep a trained national militia suitably equipped for national and international disasters, not war, and for maintaining civil order in times of need. The U.N. General Assembly must play a major role in controlling all transfers of war weapons between nations, with the aim of reducing them to zero, never sponsoring an increase, never supporting new weapons creation and expense. With the military burden gone in the less developed world, great changes could be obtainable in twenty years rather than 200.

Step 3. At present, not all nations wish to live in peace with their neighbors. For a temporary period, there must be assembled, trained and integrated, a U.N. multinational armed force, the principle function of which shall be to immediately aid any nation which abides by the U.N. Charter and all Covenants when it is physically abused or attacked by another. U.N. Charter Articles 41 and 42 speak to this. The aggressor, clearly violating their signed obligations under the U.N. Charter, will be penalized, shall pay the Multinational Force costs and reparations; and possibly experience an enforced governance change toward democracy. The weapons they lose in warfare will not be allowed to be replaced, a step which should cause great hesitation about even considering armed aggression.

> Henceforth every nation's foreign policy must be judged at every point by one consideration: does it lead us to a world of law and order or does it lead us back toward anarchy and death?
>
> —Albert Einstein

Step 4. Each developing nation should insist on themselves creating "added value" to their natural resources, rather than shipping only raw and crude materials abroad for processing: phosphates, copper, chromium, aluminum, diamonds, uranium, oil, minerals, etc. By this means considerably greater "wealth" is created in each developing nation, and will allow them much greater economic power for importation of necessary goods from abroad, exports from developed nations. But each democracy-oriented developing nation shall decide for itself, and have the power to decide for itself, what ultimate relationship with outside agents best fits its needs. They will ask, "Truly, who have been our friends? Who can we trust?"

By this new policy the destiny of the Developing World shall be molded by their own hands, free from exploitation by outsiders. This can be a rewarding challenge. It becomes their responsibility. Can the leaders of nations of the developing world work together to make the 21st century their century? They should consider the especially appropriate example of Japan in the period 1945 to 1970, a mountainous nation, poor in natural resources, socially and physically destroyed by war but in many ways recovered in 25 years. Their greatest resource is their people, something that their old military government failed to understand. After 1945 a democratic Japan accomplished a great deal with help from its democratic friends.

Even the small nation of Rwanda, racked with genocide and chaos in the 1990s, could form a democratic nation at peace with itself, Hutus and Tutsis working together. They would need help from outside sources, and freedom and protection from outside political interference. This is exactly the solution we propose.

Not all nations are ready for economic changes within a democracy, and can be duped into errors. The contrasts between North and South Korea stand out. If North Korea had a democratic government aid from outside would not have been wasted as it has in military spending. Some years after WW II Japan managed to regain control of its wealth-producing capabilities, and did not relinquish it to the victors. In the early 1950s Japan was invited by Joseph Stalin to join with him and the Soviet Union in the great developments that lie ahead. Wisdom prevailed. The knowledge of all the United Nations is available to help the developing world; they need only ask. I have great fears that the people of North Korea are being led into a catastrophic disaster, while their leadership asks to be guaranteed the right to do just that.

Step 5. To further assure and advance self-determination, development, and confidence for the people of all nations it is necessary to establish government and private international exchange programs involving 10,000 to 50,000 people per year: students, teachers, workers, farmers, artists, government officials, scientists, athletes and upper-bracket bureaucrats; for the purpose of finding creative new approaches to cooperation and development for mutual and world benefit.

The "Sister Cities Program" should be greatly expanded to include the poorer nations of the world. Does Timbuktu (in Mali) have a sister city in the Developed World? Does your town have a sister city in the Third World? Important question: Why not? Shall we soon be able to have sister cities in North Korea? How about P'ungsan in the DPRK (North Korea)?

Step 6. The U.N. needs to decide when and how it can intervene in the internal affairs of a "nation." The U.N.'s inability to act over past years has sanctioned the deaths of millions. It needs to come to grips with the fact that the U.N. actions, which were possible in 1946, are woefully inadequate and much too late for events of the modern electronic and high-speed world. The Cold War has ended; much more U.N. activity without vetoes should be possible. What shall be done about civil wars? How many need to be killed, imprisoned, or tortured, before the U.N. shall act? 10,000? 100,000? 1,000,000? What will be the 2005 year-end death toll in the Sudan? What shall be the limit before a nation is dismissed from the U.N. until its leadership is replaced, perhaps by the U.N., and the people govern? Clearly, under the world conditions being proposed, modern-day democratic nations, such repression and civil wars are highly unlikely. Where is the voice of the U.N. General Assembly in all this? What is "world opinion" about the possibility of world peace and prosperity?

Developing nations, yielding their military burden, must have assurances that they will be quickly and adequately protected by the strongest powers of the world. North Korea needs to understand what changes they need to make to receive assurances and protection against attack by a more powerful nation. "Minds more wise," not pre-programmed bureaucrats, must speak to U.N. Charter revisions. Because all nations are not equal there should be special rules to apply to emerging, developing nations for the protection of their people from corrupt governance and from powerful outside political and exploitive influences.

U.N. Secretary-General Kofi Annan is right on target with what Time magazine labeled "Kofi Doctrine," urging world intervention to stop massive human rights violations, but the doctrine falls far short without the complete and essential ameliorative steps we are proposing here.

12-14 Implementation

This proposed activation of Oppenheimer's conjecture is sometimes criticized as being too futuristic and difficult to implement. But there are no technical implementation difficulties, only those difficulties in people's minds. The necessary, minds more wise, must be found.

If the Baruch proposal had been accepted, how would it have been implemented? How was the Marshall Plan carried out? The Manhattan Project? Similar implementation procedures could be employed here.

Yes, war is much easier to implement; we're all set up for it. We are not, however, set up to implement world peace.

12-15 And In Our "Developed" World

Each year this program will see returned to the nonmilitary economies of the developed nations, in total, more than US$ 330 billion! It is money most of which ordinarily would have been spent for non-wealth-creating new military weapons and systems. It has been remarked that, "Dollar for dollar, nonmilitary spending creates more jobs than military expenditures do, owing to the less capital-intensive nature of civilian products and lower salaries." Worldwatch Institute provides estimates as examples; similar estimates can be found among 1981 data from the New York Council on Economic Priorities. Hence, this program we propose should greatly reduce unemployment in any nation adopting it.

With nations in full peacetime production and without threats of war, national debts should be fairly easily paid off. What effect would a thriving well-managed economy have on social problems? Would it make them solvable?

Oppenheimer's conjecture implied that an exchange could be made:

1. With self-sufficiency and self-defined but true democracy in the developing world and the virtual elimination there of poverty, illiteracy, malnutrition, disease, neocolonialism, rights deprivation, indebtedness, and slavery;
2. The entire world could have full economic recovery, elimination of the possibility for international nuclear catastrophe, and the practical elimination of war. In a world at peace the refugee problem is solved. The killing stops.

The basic tool is incentives, not sanctions; rewards, not penalties. Everyone benefits, as Oppenheimer must have known they could.

Consider, compare, what the 3,500,000,000 people of the developing world do not have, and who is capable of supplying it! There are abundant opportunities for all!

Morrison and Tsipis, in their book[6], *Reason Enough to Hope*, explore some of the problems facing the world should the impoverished billions of people be brought online to also benefit as we have from "the good life." Food and energy needs, and overpopulation are likely to present many difficulties. Food requirements and overpopulation are of course linked. However, in any nation of fixed area which has made development advances in the last century without going to war, I think you will find that though population has increased, family size has decreased. I might be wrong in this conjecture but I think not. In the Japan of 100 years ago large families would not be uncommon especially in rural areas, families with four to eight and more children. It seems hardly conceivable, doesn't it, in Japan, where now the ideal family will have two children, one girl, one boy? If food, education, health care, and economic opportunity are available, parents in a democratic society should be rather quick to learn that a family of four will probably do better all around in contrast to a family of ten. Consider China also, with its desires for one-child families.

Most impoverished nations, at present, do not have the capability to fully utilize all their arable land. Implementation of our proposal would change that. Appropriate agriculture with U.N. help can squeeze the maximum benefits annually out of lands considered not fruitful. Ichiro Kawasaki in his book[8], The Japanese Are Like That, remarked that the entire nation of Japan has always had less good farm land than all of mountainous Kentucky. And yes, we do recognize that unlike Kentucky Japan does have the world's oceans as a food source also. The oceans and seas are free.

Some less advantaged nations are in dry climates, hindering agriculture. Potential farm areas of India are dry and dusty. Annually, neighboring Bangladesh is flooded with fresh water from monsoons and mountainous run-off. That could be changed. The dry plains of the middle United States and Canada could be fed by a fresh water Hudson Bay, if the bay or parts of it could be desalinized. (It was once seriously proposed to dam the north end of Hudson Bay from Southampton Island to Cape Wolstenholme and gradually pump the heavier salt water from the bottom of the Bay out into the Hudson Strait, thus gradually desalinizing Hudson Bay.) What would Canada charge for that fresh water? International foresight and cooperation could make such projects feasible.

Appropriate energy technology can serve the needs of developing nations. Fortunately many such nations are in areas where winter heating needs may be small. Until recently Japanese homes had minimal heating. On the African continent hydroelectric power and solar electricity seem to be rather likely energy sources. The indigenous people supply the labor at a good salary, the developed world supplies the knowledge, teaching, and technology. We should not overlook nuclear power; there are safe power reactors. Radioactive waste remains a solvable problem. With IAEA oversight reprocessing of spent fuel elements need not be a problem.

Perhaps the greatest danger in our proposition might be the personal avarice of those we are trying to help, just as it has been dangerous among nations and industries. A major component of this proposal is to exactly set in place solutions to all the above problems.

Shortly after WWII Senator Vandenberg told Truman that if he expected American taxpayers to finance a military buildup in the aftermath of the war's sacrifices he would have "to scare the hell out of them." They did a very good job, continuing to 2004.

But Eisenhower warned us in his farewell message, "America's leadership depends, not merely upon our unmatched material progress, riches and military strength, but on how we use our power in the interests of world peace and human betterment . . ." ". . . we have been compelled to create a permanent armaments industry of vast proportions . . ." ". . . We annually spend on military security more than the net income of all United States corporations . . ."

Eisenhower saw what was coming: ". . . In the councils of government, we must guard against the acquisition of unwarranted influence, whether sought or unsought, by the military-industrial complex. The potential for the disastrous rise of displaced power exists and will persist." ". . . We must never let the weight of this combination endanger our liberties or democratic processes."

It becomes as simple as this example. We have a choice in these nations "under God." Which do you prefer: $80 billion spent to support U.S.-Japan military activities in Japan, Okinawa, and elsewhere in Asia, in anticipation of conflict which may never occur, and more billions for the U.S. Space Command to achieve 'full spectrum dominance' and superiority in space weapons; or $80 billion to eliminate the threats of wars in Asia while simultaneously enhancing the lives of destitute, distressed, and sometimes oppressed people, bringing them much better life opportunities, and steering $80 billion into peacetime production and services from the Developed world?

12-16 Justification

Does the Developed World have any responsibility for the conditions of poverty, starvation, slavery, disease, displaced refugees, rights deprivation, and illiteracy, etc., as they now exist in the former colonial and less developed world, in Africa, in Asia, in Latin America? Hence, does the Developed World have any unfulfilled moral obligations to the former colonial world?

Many believe it does. Whether or not you agree, the past half-century of Developed World taxation for military defense purposes, in preparation for a Nuclear WW III holocaust, clearly shows that, if the developed world is not militarily or economically threatened, then it can afford to meet its obligations to the less developed world. The proposal is for US$330 billion per year for 20 to 25 years to meet this obligation, while simultaneously ending wars and alleviating international hostilities and the need for armaments. It is not expected that international or national conflicts will vanish, but that procedures will be in place, early, for rectification without resort to murder on the grand scale. Wiser minds, which we must find, can see to that.

There need be no problem with verification or with guarded conversion of fissionable nuclear material and the chemical, biological and other tools of war; these are solvable human problems, and not problems of technology. Mankind can make all nuclear weapons unusable easily within a few years if there is a genuine wish to do so. From the catastrophes at Hiroshima and Nagasaki some of us have learned it is most imperative that the world verifiably rid itself of all nuclear weapons. Though some nuclear disarming is underway there still remain the real fears concerning proliferation, nuclear breakouts and terrorism, and our "new enemies." The danger continues, as Oppenheimer in 1946 recognized it would; "nuclear weapons can be very effective." There still remain at the start of the 21st century some 30,000 deliverable nuclear warheads.

Oppenheimer's conjecture represents one certain way for the elimination of international war for all people of the Earth. It is also probably the only method, for decades or centuries to come, by which people of the less-developed world, in peace, can become their own masters, can create the path to their own destinies as so many other nations have. This is not a threat to the Developed World. Peace with justice is preferable to war, anytime.

> Traveler, there is no path; paths are made by walking.
>
> —Antonio Machado

If the "STEPS" we have been proposing would be put in place, then violence and warlike activities throughout the Less Developed World would only be self-defeating; they would come to an end. When regions and nations are at peace, they advance. Look! See!

For those Less Developed nations which repeatedly blame America and international capitalism for all the ills of the world, all the troubles in their nations, here is their chance to successfully move into the future without necessarily being sucked up into commitments and obligations to Developed World Powers, the World Bank, and the International Monetary Fund. How many leaders of less developed nations are willing to put their people first, rather than their military? How many will build schools and hospitals, homes and farms, rather than nuclear fortresses and glorious palaces and monuments? Which leaders of the developing nations will become immortalized as the ones who led their nation to the "New World," rather than as the ones who kept them chained to the past?

There can be a peaceful world with justice for all if both Developed and Less Developed nations have the hindsight, foresight and courage to view the world in new ways.

12-17 Conclusion: World Peace is Possible Now

Nowhere in this essay has World Government been proposed, but perhaps every ten years all nations should formally renew their pledge to all the world peace goals of the United Nations. One should reread the first articles of the U.N. Charter. What are its goals to which all have freely given their signature of obligation?

Oppenheimer's conjecture leading to this solution of the war problem does not incorporate revenge, penalties, or punishments for past deeds. But then who is not guilty for some past actions? What nation has not killed in war? What nation has not enslaved or tortured in times past? Instead of dwelling there, all people start from now and move forward. For the past 70 years some might refer to this kind of proposal as futuristic. It does direct the World's fate toward a future of peace, and suddenly, that future is now.

Oppenheimer's conjecture: Impossible to implement in 1946, fully realizable now.

> The most effective use of military budgets is, not resorting to murderous war, but the proactive conversion of extant or potential enemies into equal and cooperative friends, all working for a peaceful world with justice and fairness for all people and all nations. We have shown how this can be done.

Our problem is the destiny of humanity on Earth. Understand, our "STEPS" comprise a "complete procedure." Fifty-nine years of small incremental steps, ox-walking, sometimes forward, sometimes backward, has not worked. Our recommended "STEPS," with all their checks and balances, safeguards and assurances, will work; they will withstand any tests, if all the procedures of the "package" are understood. Checking with the principal authorities who deal with questions of the fate of humanity will provide assurance that these "STEPS" will work.

The people of the world, especially people of regional conflicts, plead for peace, plead for an end to the killing, destruction, and suffering, and their leaders, because of greed, ideology, and isolated ignorance, will not achieve it. We have shown how it could be done.

Indeed, in 2001, the World Bank and the United Nations have stated how reasonable our suggested plan is:

> Afghanistan needs about $9 billion during the next five years to rebuild after 20 years of war, the United Nations and World Bank have calculated.
> *(www.cnn.com/2001/WORLD/12/21/gen.eu.afghan.donor/index.html)*

That is only $1.8 billion per year, only 0.45% of the US Annual $400 billion Military budget. And half of this cost is to be contributed by all other developed nations. Why was the $9 billion not used first instead of destruction? By April, 2004, donors had already pledged $8.2 billion. (There, you see how easy it might be to get the resources? How much will be wasted or stolen by corruption and greed? Some Afghan regional lords were asking for about $25 billion. Guess how it would be spent.)

Should there be any doubts in the minds of people of the earth as to the desires of the United States for world peace with justice and fairness for all nations, proposal of this plan by the United States government to the United Nations would put such doubts to rest. It would renew the faith of many Americans in their own government, that it is not imperialistic.

How altruistic and honest about peace are nations willing to be? For 200 years there has not been a war between truly democratic nations.

(M)an will occasionally stumble over the truth, but usually manages to pick himself up, walk over or around it, and carry on.

—Winston S. Churchill

He that will not apply new remedies must expect new evils; for time is the greatest innovator.

—Francis Bacon

Some people see things as they are and ask why; I dream things that never were and ask why not?

—Robert Kennedy

Raymond G. Wilson is an Emeritus Associate Professor of Physics at Illinois Wesleyan University. In addition to teaching about nuclear war issues for 45 years, he has been a somewhat regular visiting scholar to a Hiroshima University which lost 352 women students and faculty on August 6, 1945. With Akiko Wilson he is co-director of the Hiroshima Panorama Project in the United States. Wilson guides an annual workshop, "Hiroshima and Nagasaki for College Teachers." He is the author of the 1995 book, "Fourier Series and Optical Transform Techniques in Contemporary Optics: An Introduction," John Wiley and Sons.

Bibliography for Part-II

Bulletin of the Atomic Scientists, Vol. 56, Mar/Apr, p. 79, 2000.

Sivard , Ruth Leger, *WORLD MILITARY AND SOCIAL EXPENDITURES*, 1996, 16th Edition, p.20, World Priorities, Washington, D.C., 1996. (Actually the world's maximum nuclear arsenal—in terms of total megatonnage—was reached in 1960 when it peaked at about 23,000 megatons or so. The DOE report RDD-6, *RESTRICTED DATA DECLASSIFICATION DECISIONS 1946 TO THE PRESENT* lists the 1960 U.S. arsenal at 20,491.17 megatons. Add to that an estimate of Soviet and other nation's megatonnage to get to about 23,000.)

Oppenheimer, J. Robert, *THE INTERNATIONAL CONTROL OF ATOMIC ENERGY*, Bulletin of the Atomic Scientists, Vol. 1, June, p. [1-5], 1946. Reprinted in *THE ATOMIC BOMB*, H. W. Wilson Co., New York, 1946.

Keith, Agnes Newton, *THREE CAME HOME*, Little, Brown and Company, 1947.

Center for Defense Information, Feb. 5, 2002.

www.cdi.org/issues/budget/FY03Discretionary-pr.cfm also, Friends Committee on National Legislation, Washington Newsletter, No. 665, April, 2002, p. 2.

Morrison, Philip, and Kostas Tsipis, *REASON ENOUGH TO HOPE*, MIT Press, 1998.

Weart, Spencer, *NEVER AT WAR—WHY DEMOCRACIES WILL NOT FIGHT ONE ANOTHER*. Yale University Press, 1998.

Kawasaki, Ichiro, *THE JAPANESE ARE LIKE THAT*, Charles E. Tuttle Co., 1955.

General References

Galtung, Johan, Carl G. Jacobsen and Kai Frithjof Brand-Jacobsen, *SEARCHING FOR PEACE: THE RAOD TO TRANSCEND*, 2nd Edition, Pluto Press, London, 2002.

Glover, Jonathan, Humanity, *A MORAL HISTORY OF THE TWENTIETH CENTURY*, Yale University Press, New Haven, 1999.

Kawade Shobo Shin-Sha's Editorial Staff, *DEAD SPEAK OF WAR*, Masaru shimizu, Kawade Shobo Shin-Sha, 2-32-2, Sendagaya, Shibuya-Ku, Tokyo, Japan, 1983.

Shonno, Naomi, *THE LEGACY OF HIROSHIMA: ITS PAST, OUR FUTURE*, Kosei Pub. Co. (Tuttle) Tokyo, 1986.

Hiroshima Peace Memorial Museum, *THE SPIRIT OF HIROSHIMA: AN INTRODUCTION TO THE ATOMIC BOMB TRAGEDY, 1999*. Hiroshima Peace Memorial Museum, 1-2 Nakajimacho, Nakaku, Hiroshima City 730-0811, Japan.

Rotblat, Joseph, and KONUMA, Michiji, Eds., *TOWARDS A NUCLEAR-WEAPON-FREE WORLD*, Proceedings of the Forty-Fifth Pugwash Conference on Science and World Affairs, World Scientific, Singapore, 1997.

Fig. 3-10D: Author with replica of the Nagasaki bomb at Trinity site, July 16, 1995

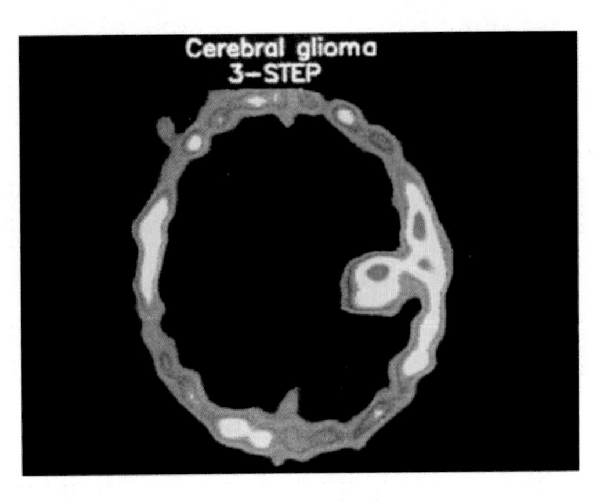

Fig. 6-19-1: Three-step technetium-99m image of cerebral glioma

Fig. 4-29B: Stamp boosting solar power

Fig. 5-24: Promoting alertness to breast cancer

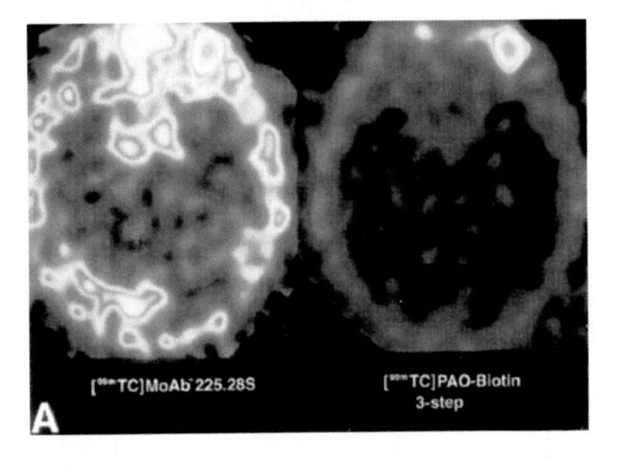

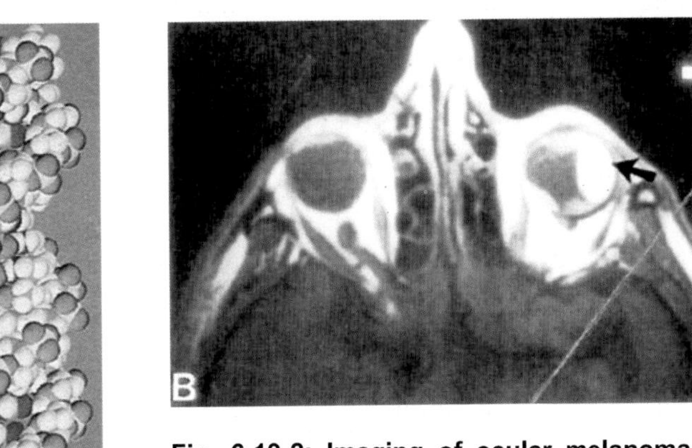

Fig. 6-19-2: Imaging of ocular melanoma. Arrow in image B shows the tumor. Left image in A was made using a monoclonal antibody bonded to Tc-99m; the one on the right used the three-step technique

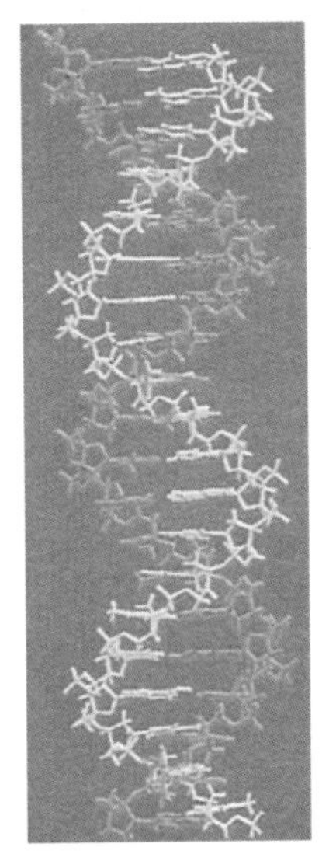

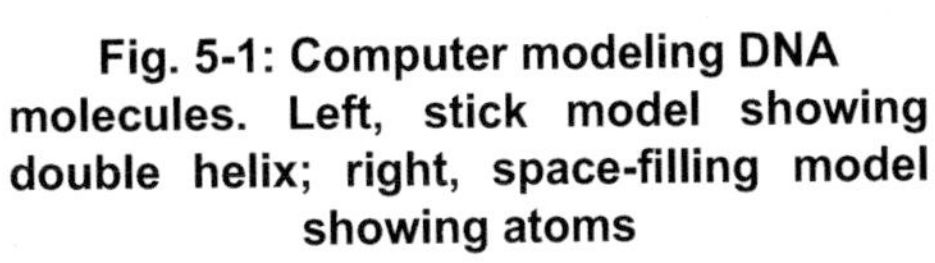

Fig. 5-1: Computer modeling DNA molecules. Left, stick model showing double helix; right, space-filling model showing atoms

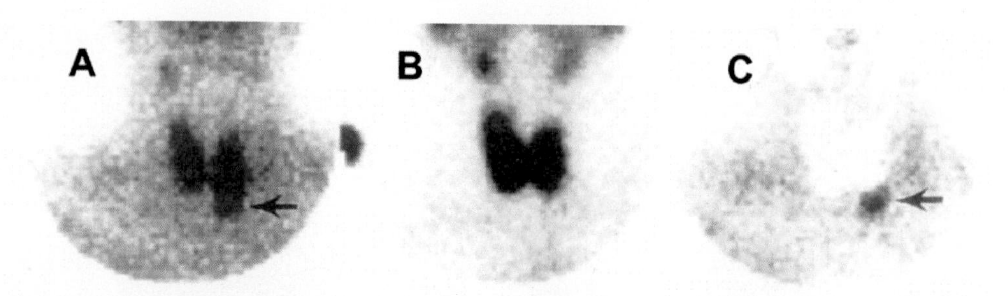

Fig. 6-23: A. Thyroid and parathyroid glands (arrow) imaged using thallium-201; B. Same imaged using technetium-99m; C. After normalization of the densities and computer subtraction, the thyroid images cancel, leaving the parathyroid gland (arrow) visible

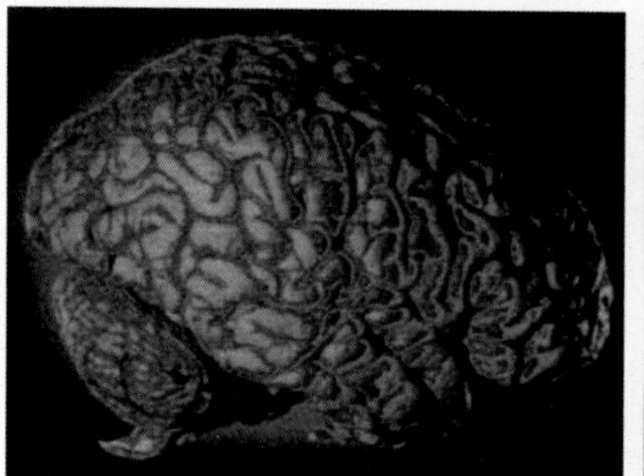

Fig. 6-25A: The human brain

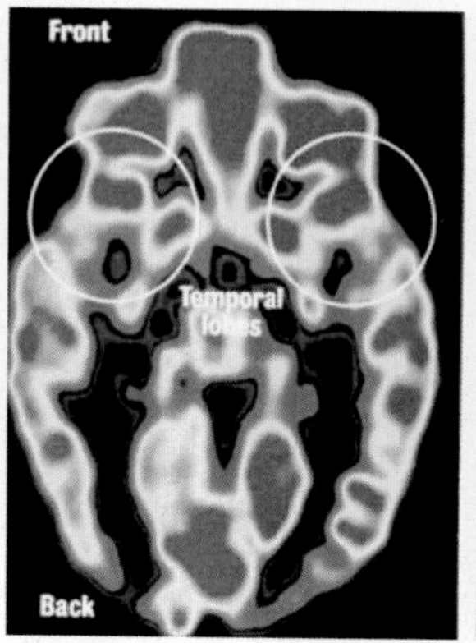

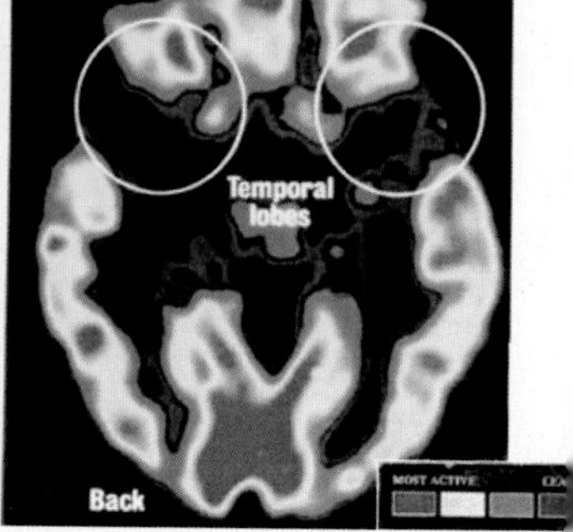

Fig. 6-25F: PET Scans of brains of normal and abused children (see text for explanation)

Fig. 9-30: The Grable shot. Nuclear artillery shell (yield 15 kilotons) detonated at 524 feet, Nevada Test Site, 1953

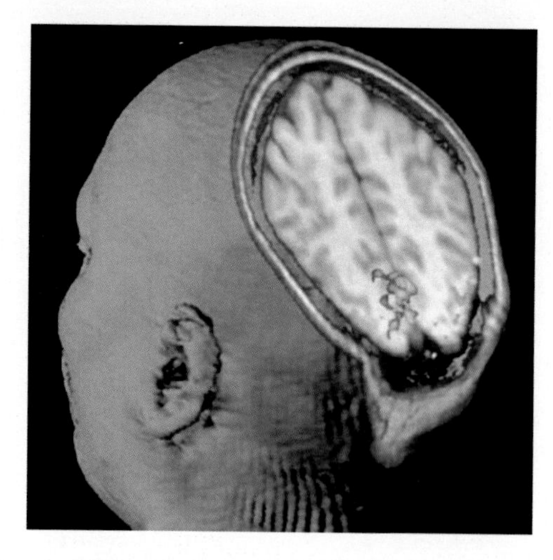

Fig. 6-39B: magnetic resonance tomograph of the brain. It was made during stimulation using visual images. The red areas are in the visual cortex

Periodic Table of Elements

1 H Hydrogen 1.0079																	2 He Helium 4.00260
3 Li Lithium 6.94	4 Be Beryllium 9.01218											5 B Boron 10.81	6 C Carbon 12.011	7 N Nitrogen 14.0067	8 O Oxygen 15.999	9 F Fluorine 18.99840	10 Ne Neon 20.179
11 Na Sodium 22.98977	12 Mg Magnesium 24.305											13 Al Aluminum 26.98154	14 Si Silicon 28.086	15 P Phosphorus 30.97376	16 S Sulfur 32.06	17 Cl Chlorine 35.453	18 Ar Argon 39.948
19 K Potassium 39.098	20 Ca Calcium 40.08	21 Sc Scandium 44.9559	22 Ti Titanium 47.9	23 V Vanadium 50.941	24 Cr Chromium 51.996	25 Mn Manganese 54.9380	26 Fe Iron 55.847	27 Co Cobalt 58.9332	28 Ni Nickel 58.7	29 Cu Copper 63.546	30 Zn Zinc 65.38	31 Ga Gallium 69.72	32 Ge Germanium 72.59	33 As Arsenic 74.9216	34 Se Selenium 78.96	35 Br Bromine 79.904	36 Kr Krypton 83.80
37 Rb Rubidium 85.4678	38 Sr Strontium 87.62	39 Y Yttrium 88.9059	40 Zr Zirconium 91.22	41 Nb Niobium 92.9064	42 Mo Molybdenum 95.9	43 Tc Technetium (98)	44 Ru Ruthenium 101.07	45 Rh Rhodium 102.9055	46 Pd Palladium 106.4	47 Ag Silver 107.868	48 Cd Cadmium 112.40	49 In Indium 114.82	50 Sn Tin 118.69	51 Sb Antimony 121.75	52 Te Tellurium 127.6	53 I Iodine 126.9045	54 Xe Xenon 131.30
55 Cs Cesium 132.9054	56 Ba Barium 137.3	57-71 * See Lanthanide Series	72 Hf Hafnium 178.49	73 Ta Tantalum 180.95	74 W Tungsten 183.85	75 Re Rhenium 186.2	76 Os Osmium 190.2	77 Ir Iridium 192.2	78 Pt Platinum 195.09	79 Au Gold 196.9665	80 Hg Mercury 200.59	81 Tl Thallium 204.37	82 Pb Lead 207.2	83 Bi Bismuth 208.9804	84 Po Polonium (209)	85 At Astatine (210)	86 Rn Radon (222)
87 Fr Francium (223)	88 Ra Radium 226.0254	89-103 • See Actinide Series	104 Rf Rutherfordium (261)	105 Db Dubnium (262)	106 Sg Seaborgium (266)	107 Bh Bohrium (262)	108 Hs Hassium (265)	109 Mt Meitnerium (266)	110 (269)	111 (272)	112 (277)	113	114 (289)	115	116 (289)	117	118 (293)

* Lanthanide (*Rare-Earth*) Series

57 La Lanthanum 138.905	58 Ce Cerium 140.12	59 Pr Praesody-mium 140.9077	60 Nd Neodymium 144.2	61 Pm Promethium 147	62 Sm Samarium 150.4	63 Eu Europium 151.96	64 Gd Gadolinium 157.25	65 Tb Terbium 158.9254	66 Dy Dysprosium 162.5	67 Ho Holmium 164.9304	68 Er Erbium 167.26	69 Tm Thulium 168.9342	70 Yb Ytterbium 173.0	71 Lu Lutetium 174.97

• Actinide Series

89 Ac Actinium (227)	90 Th Thorium 232.0381	91 Pa Protactinium 231.0359	92 U Uranium 238.029	93 Np Neptunium (237)	94 Pu Plutonium (244)	95 Am Americium (243)	96 Cm Curium (247)	97 Bk Berkelium (247)	98 Cf Californium (249)	99 Es Einsteinium (252)	100 Fm Fermium (257)	101 Md Mendelevium (258)	102 No Nobelium (259)	103 Lr Lawrencium (260)

In the squares, the atomic number of each element is given first, then the chemical symbol, name, and atomic weight (mass). Parentheses around the last number indicate that it is the mass number of the isotope with the longest known half-life. Numbers 113 and 117 (shaded) have not yet been discovered. Elements beyond number 109 had not been named as of the date of this publication.

PROPERTIES OF SELECTED RADIONUCLIDES

Half-lives are from Browne and Firestone (see Preface); specific activities were calculated using them. Complete information is available at Web Site http<// necs01.dne.bnl.gov/CoN/index.html> Abbreviations: mCi = millicuries; μCi = microcuries. Alpha and beta decays are generally but not always accompanied by gamma emission.

Atomic number	Element	Mass number	Decay mode	Half-life	Specific activity
1	Hydrogen, H	3	beta, no gamma	12.3 years	9630 Ci/g
5	Boron, B	8	positron	0.77 second	1830 trillion Ci/g
6	Carbon, C	11	positron	20.4 minutes	837 million Ci/g
	Carbon, C	14	beta, no gamma	5730 years	4.455 Ci/g
7	Nitrogen, N	13	positron	9.97 minutes	1.45 billion Ci/g
8	Oxygen, O	15	positron	122 seconds	6.16 billion Ci/g
9	Fluorine, F	18	positron	109.8 minutes	95 million Ci/g
11	Sodium, Na	22	positron	2.60 years	6260 Ci/g
	Sodium, Na	24	beta	14.66 hours	8.9 million Ci/g
15	Phosphorus, P	32	beta, no gamma	14.28 days	285,700 Ci/g
19	Potassium, K	40	89% beta 11% electron capture	1.28 billion years	6.94 μCi/g
20	Calcium, Ca	41	electron capture	103,000 years	0847 Ci/g
24	Chromium, Cr	51	electron capture	27.7 days	92,500 Ci/g
27	Cobalt, Co	60	beta	5.27 years	1130 Ci/g
29	Copper, Cu	67	beta	61.9 hours	756,000 Ci/g
31	Gallium, Ga	67	electron capture	78.3 hour	598,000 Ci/g
36	Krypton, Kr	81m	gamma	13 seconds	10.7 billion Ci/g
	Krypton, Kr	85	beta	10.72 years	393 Ci/g
38	Strontium, Sr	89	beta	50.6 days	29,000 Ci/g
	Strontium, Sr	90	beta	28.5 years	139.5 Ci/g
39	Yttrium, Y	91	beta	58.5 days	24,500 Ci/g
42	Molybdenum, Mo	99	beta	65.9 hours	480,000 Ci/g
43	Technetium, Tc	98	beta	4.2 million years	0.87 mCi/g
	Technetium, Tc	99m	gamma	6.01 hours	5.27 million Ci/g
	Technetium, Tc	99	beta	213,000 years	0.017 Ci/g
44	Ruthenium, Ru	105	beta	44 hours	6.73 million Ci/g
45	Rhodium, Rh	105	beta	35.4 hours	843,000 Ci/g
49	Indium, In	111	electron capture	2.81 days	19,000 Ci/g
52	Tellurium, Te	132	beta	78.2 hours	304,000 Ci/g
53	Iodine, I	123	electron capture	13.2 hours	1.93 millionCi/g
	Iodine, I	125	electron capture	60.1 days	17,500 Ci/g
	Iodine, I	129	beta	0.7 million years	177 μCi/g
	Iodine, I	131	beta	8.04 days	124,000 Ci/g

Atomic number	Element	Mass number	Decay mode	Half-life	Specific activity
53	Iodine, I	133m	gamma	9 seconds	9.4 billion Ci/g
	Iodine I	133	beta	20.8 hours	1.13 million Ci/g
	Iodine, I	134	beta	52.6 minutes	445,000 Ci/g
	Iodine, I	135	beta	6.55 hours	3.5 million Ci/g
54	Xenon, Xe	133m	gamma	2.19 days	449,000 Ci/g
	Xenon, Xe	133	beta	5.24 days	188,000 Ci/g
	Xenon, Xe	135	beta	9.10 hours	2.55 million Ci/g
55	Cesium, Cs	134	beta	2.06 years	1300 Ci/g
	Cesium, Cs	136	beta	13.16 days	73,000 Ci/g
	Cesium, Cs	137	beta	30.0 years	7.0 Ci/g
	Cesium, Cs	138	beta	32.2 minutes	42.3 million Ci/
	Cesium, Cs	139	beta	9.27 minutes	146 million Ci/g
56	Barium, Ba	139	beta	82.9 minutes	16.3 million Ci/g
	Barium, Ba	140	beta	12.75 days	73,200 Ci/g
57	Lanthanum, La	140	beta	40.27 hours	556,000 Ci/g
58	Cerium, Ce	141	beta	32.5 days	28,500 Ci/g
	Cerium, Ce	144	beta	284.9 days	3190 Ci/g
59	Praseodymium, Pr	145	beta	5.98 hours	3.6 million Ci/g
60	Neodymium, Nd	147	beta	10.98 days	80,900 Ci/g
61	Promethium, Pm	147	beta	2.623 years	928 Ci/g
77	Iridium, Ir	192	beta	73.83 days	9200 Ci/g
81	Thallium, Tl	201	electron capture	73.2 hours	213,000 Ci/g
82	Lead, Pb	210	beta	22.3 years	76.3 Ci/g
83	Bismuth, Bi	210	beta, no gamma	5.01 days	124,000 Ci/g
	Bismuth, Bi	212	64% beta	60.5 minutes	14.7 million Ci/g
84	Polonium, Po	210	alpha	138.38 days	4493 Ci/g
86	Radon, Rn	222	alpha	3.825 days	154,000 Ci/g
87	Francium, Fr	223	beta	21.8 minutes	38.7 million Ci/g
88	Radium, Ra	226	alpha	1600 years	0.99 Ci/g
	Radium, Ra	228	beta	5.76 years	272 Ci/g
89	Actinium, Ac	227	beta	21.77 years	72.3 Ci/g
90	Thorium, Th	32	alpha	14.1 billion years	0.109 μCi/g
90	Thorium, Th	234	beta	24.1 days	23,000 Ci/g
92	Uranium, U	233	alpha	159,000 years	9.65 mCi/g
	Uranium, U	234	alpha	245,000 years	6.23 mCi/g
	Uranium, U	235	alpha	704 million years	2.16 μCi/g
	Uranium, U	236	alpha	23.4 million years	64.7 μCi/g
92	Uranium, U	238	alpha	4.468 billion years	0.336 μCi/g
92	Uranium, U	239	beta	23.47 minutes	83.5 million Ci/g
93	Neptunium, Np	239	beta	2.355 days	232,000 Ci/g
94	Plutonium, Pu	238	alpha	87.7 years	17.3 Ci/g
94	Plutonium, Pu	239	alpha	24,110 years	0.0620 Ci/g

Atomic number	Element	Mass number	Decay mode	Half-life	Specific activity
94	Plutonium, Pu	240	alpha	6540 years	0.228 Ci/g
	Plutonium, Pu	241	beta	14.4 years	103.0 Ci/g
	Plutonium, Pu	244	alpha	83 million years	17.6 μCi/g
95	Americium, Am	241	alpha	432.7 years	3.43 Ci/g
96	Curium, Cm	244	alpha	18.11 years	80.9 Ci/g
98	Californium, Cf	252	97% alpha	2.64 years	537 Ci/g
			3% spontaneous fission	85.5 years	
99	Einsteinium, Es	252	78% alpha	472 days	1100 Ci/g
			22% electron capture		
100	Fermium, Fm	257	alpha	100.5 days	5050 Ci/g

PHYSICAL CONSTANTS AND DATA

Energy

1 calorie = 4.184 joules (J)

1 joule = 6.2415 x 10^{18} electron volts (eV)

= 6.2415 x 10^{12} megaelectron volts or million electron volts (MeV)

1 atomic mass unit (amu) = 931.5 megaelectron volts (MeV)

1 watt-hour = 60 watt-minutes = 3600 watt-seconds = 3600 joules

1 kilowatt-hour = 3,600,000 joules

1 British thermal unit (Btu) = 1054.35 joules

1 ton (short ton, 2000 pounds) of TNT on exploding liberates1 billion calories or 4.18 billion joules

Power

1 watt = 1 W = 1 joule/second

Common multiples:

1 kilowatt = 1 kW = 1000 watts

1 megawatt = 1 MW = 1 million watts

1 gigawatt = 1 GW = 1 billion watts

MWth = total energy in megawatts produced if all appears as heat

MWe = energy converted to electricity, generally about 1/3 of MWth.

1 kilowatt-hour/day = 41.67 watts

1 horsepower = 746 watts

Mass of atomic components

proton = 1.00728 amu = 938.3 MeV

neutron = 1.00867 amu = 939.6 MeV

electron = 0.00054858 amu = 0.511 MeV

Conversions

1 kilogram = 1000 grams = 2.2046 pounds

1 metric tonne = 1000 kg = 1 megagram = 2204.6 pounds

1 short ton = 2000 pounds = 0.9072 metric tonne

1 long ton = 2240 pounds = 1.0162 metric tonnes

1 pound = 453.6 grams

1 gallon (U.S.) = 3.785 liters

1 Gray = 100 Rads

1 Sievert = 100 Rems

deg C = $\frac{5}{9}$ (deg F -32)

Constants

Velocity of light (c) = 2.997925 x 10^{8} meters/second (m/s)

Avogadro's number = 6.02204 x 10^{23} particles/mole

Some temperatures

	degrees C	*degrees F*
melting point of ice	0	32
boiling point of water	100	212
melting point of lead	328	622
melting point of gold	1064	1947
melting point of iron	1535	2795
melting point of platinum	1772	3222
melting point of tungsten	3410	6170
surface of the sun	5500	9932
center of sun	15 million	27 million (approx.)
nuclear explosion, fission	40 million	72 million (approx.)
nuclear explosion, fusion	100 million	180 million (approx.)

Elemental Composition of the Earth's Crust

This means from 25 miles deep outward, including the atmosphere. Only the ten most abundant elements are listed; units are per cent by weight.

Rank	*Element*	*Percent*
1	Oxygen, O	45.6
2	Silicon, Si	27.3
3	Aluminum, Al	8.36
4	Iron, Fe	6.22
5	Calcium, Ca	4.66
6	Magnesium, Mg	2.76
7	Sodium, Na	2.27
8	Potassium, K	1.84
9	Titanium, Ti	0.63
10	Hydrogen, H	0.14

Metric prefixes

E	exa	$= 10^{18}$	= 1 quintillion
P	peta	$= 10^{15}$	= 1 quadrillion
T	tera	$= 10^{12}$	= 1 trillion
G	giga	$= 10^{9}$	= 1 billion
M	mega	$= 10^{6}$	= 1 million
k	kilo	$= 10^{3}$	= 1 thousand
c	centi	$= 10^{-2}$	= 1 one-hundredth
m	milli	$= 10^{-3}$	= 1 one-thousandth
μ or mc	micro	$= 10^{-6}$	= 1 one-millionth
n	nano	$= 10^{-9}$	= 1 one-billionth
p	pico	$= 10^{-12}$	= 1 one-trillionth
f	femto	$= 10^{-15}$	= 1 one-quadrillionth
a	atto	$= 10^{-18}$	= 1 one-quintillionth

Rate of radioactivity decay

Two forms of the logarithmic equation which describes the rate of radioactivity decay are:

$$\ln\frac{A}{A_0} = -\lambda t \quad \text{and} \quad \log\frac{A}{A_0} = -\lambda\frac{t}{2.303}$$

In the first equation "ln" is the natural logarithm (base e) and log is the ordinary logarithm (base 10). The level of radioactivity, or simply activity, is A and the initial activity is Ao (the small zero meaning at time zero). The letter t is the time in any specified units. The half-life, the time at which is A/Ao is ½, is represented by $t_{½}$. The Greek letter lambda (λ) is the decay constant, and is given by

$$\lambda = \frac{\ln 2}{t_{1/2}} = \frac{2.303 \cdot \log 2}{t_{1/2}} = \frac{0.693}{t_{1/2}}$$

The activity A may be in curies, millicuries, becquerels, etc. The equations are valid if the units of decaying substance in grams, kilograms, ounces, pounds, number of atoms or moles, etc. are substituted for activity.

For illustration, let us choose iodine-131, whose half-life is 8.04 days. If we start with 100 curies of I-131, how many curies will be left after 44 days?

First let's make an approximate calculation. After 1 half-life, half of the original 100 curies decays away, leaving 50 curies. After a second half-life, 25 curies remain. In thus following this process, we find that after 5 half-lives (40.2 days), 3.125 curies is left, and after 6 half-lives (48.24 days, more than the specified 44 days) 1.56 curies is left. Thus the answer we are seeking must be between 3.125 and 1.56 curies of I-131.

To carry out an exact calculation, we choose the equation with ordinary logarithms above. For this we need the value of the decay constant λ, which is

$$\lambda = \frac{0.693}{8.04} = 0.0862\ d^{-1}$$ (d is days; d^{-1} is reciprocal days, or per day)

Since $A_0 = 100$ Ci,

$$\log\frac{A}{100} = -0.0862\ d^{-1} \times \frac{44}{2.303}\ d = -1.647$$

Taking the anti-log,

$$\frac{A}{100} = 0.0225$$

and

A = 2.25 curies after the 44-day period. Note that this is between the limits estimated above, 3.125 and 1.56 curies.

SOME ORGANIZATIONS IN THE NUCLEAR FIELD

Alliance for Nuclear Accountability
Information on U.S. nuclear weapons complex
Web site *www.ananuclear.org*

American Nuclear Society
555 North Kensington Avenue
La Grange, IL 60525
Tel. 202-328-0002, fax 202-462-2183

Bulletin of the Atomic Scientists
6042 South Kimbark Avenue,
Chicago, IL 60637
Tel. 773-702-2555, fax 773-702-0725

Center for Defense Information
1779 Massachusetts Avenue, N.W.
Washington, DC 20036-2109
Tel. 800-234-3334

Citizens Against Nuclear War
1201 16th Street, N.W., Suite 234
Washington, DC 20036

Coalition for a New Foreign and Military Policy
120 Maryland Avenue, N.W.,
Washington, D.C. 20002

Committee for Nuclear Responsibility, Inc.
P. O. Box 421993
San Francisco, CA 94142

Committee to Bridge the Gap
1637 Butler Ave., # 203
Los Angeles, CA 90025
Tel. 310-478-0829

Educational Foundation for Nuclear Science
(Publishers of Bulletin of the Atomic Scientists)
5801 South Kenwood Avenue
Chicago, IL 60637, Tel. 312-363-5225

Federation of American Scientists
307 Massachusetts Ave., N.E.
Washington, D.C. 20002
Tel. 202-546-3300

Global Network Against Weapons and Nuclear Power in Space
P. O. Box 90083
Gainesville, FL 32607
E-mail: globalnet@mindspring.com

Health Physics Society,
8000 Westpark
Suite 400, McLean VA 22102

Institute for Energy and Environmental Research
6935 Laurel Avenue, Suite 204
Takoma Park, MD 20912
Tel. 301-270-5500

Institute for Space and Security Studies
5017 Bellflower Court
Melbourne, FL 32940

International Atomic Energy Agency
Publications
P. O. Box 433, Murray Hill Station
New York, NY 10157

International Physicians for the Prevention of Nuclear War
126 Rogers Street
Cambridge, MA 02142-9920

Los Alamos Historical Museum, 1921 Juniper Street
P. O. Box 43
Los Alamos, NM 87544-0043
Tel 505-662-6272

National Council on Radiation Protection and Measurements
7910 Woodmont Ave.
Bethesda, MD 20814

Natural Resources Defense Council
40 West 20th Street
New York, NY 10011
Tel 212-727-2700, fax 212-727-1773

Los Angeles office:
6310 West San Vicente Blvd.
Los Angeles, CA
Tel. 323-934-6900

Northwest Environmental Advocates
408 S. W. Second Avenue, Suite 406
Portland, OR 97204
Tel. 503-295-0490

Nuclear Age Peace Foundation
1187 Coast Village Road, Suite 1
Santa Barbara, CA 93108-2794
Tel. 805-965-3443, fax 805-568-0466

Nuclear Free America
325 East 25the Street
Baltimore, MD 21218

Nuclear Information and Resource Service
1424 16th Street NW, Suite 404
Washington, DC 20036
Tel. 202-328-0002

Nukewatch, The Progressive Foundation
P.O. Box 649
Luck, WI 54835-0649

Office of Nuclear Safety-DOE
Washington, DC 20545

Peace Action (formerly Sane/Freeze)
1819 H Street, NW Suite 420
Washington, DC 20006-3603
Physicians for Social Responsibility
1875 Connecticut Avenue N.W., Suite 1012
Washington, DC 20009
Tel. 202-667-4260
California office: Tel. 213-386-4901, ext. 112
3250 Wilshire Blvd., Suite 1400
Los Angeles, CA 90010

Radioactivity from Nuclear Test Explosions (RADTEST)
Executive Director
Department of Physics, San Francisco State University
San Francisco, CA 94132
Tel 415-338-1659

Snake River Alliance
P.O. Box 1731, Boise, ID 83701
Tel. 208-344-9161

Southern California Federation of Scientists
3318 Colbert Avenue, Suite 200
Los Angeles, CA 90066
Tel. 213-390-0306

Stevenson Program on Nuclear Policy
University of California, Santa Cruz
Santa Cruz, CA 95064

Stockholm-International Peace Research Institute (SIPRI)
Bergshamra, S-17173
Solna, Sweden

The Society of Nuclear Medicine
136 Madison Ave.
New York, NY 10016-6760

Union of Concerned Scientists
2 Brattle Square
Cambridge, MA 02238
Tel. 617-547-5552

U.S. Council for Energy Awareness
P.O. Box 66103, Dept. FD02
Washington, DC 20035

U.S. Department of Energy,
Office of Public Affairs
Washington, DC 20585

U.S. Environmental Protection Agency,
Office of Radiation Programs
401 M Street SW, MC ANR-458,
Washington, DC 20460

U.S. Nuclear Regulatory Commission
Washington, DC 20555

Winston Foundation for World Peace
P.O. Box 351,
Kenmore Station
Boston, MA 02215

World Nuclear Directory
C. W. J. Wilson, Ed., Sixth Edition
(A guide to organizations and research in nuclear energy)
Longman, Essex, United Kingdom

JOURNALS AND PERIODICALS

A selected few of the of thousands of works on nuclear subjects are listed at the end of the appropriate chapters. Some less specialized journals and periodicals are identified in the separate list below.

ATOMS & WASTE, Don't Waste Us, Inc., 2311 15th Street NW, #101, Washington, DC 20009.

BULLETIN OF THE ATOMIC SCIENTISTS, 6042 So. Kimbark Ave., Chicago, IL 60637.

NUCLEAR NEWS, American Nuclear Society, 555 North Kensington Avenue, La Grange, IL 60525.

NUCLEUS, Union of Concerned Scientists, 26 Church Street, Cambridge, MA 02238.

PHYSICIANS FOR SOCIAL RESPONSIBILITY QUARTERLY, Williams & Wilkins, Publishers, 428 East Preston Street, Baltimore, MD 21202-3993.

RADIOACTIVE WASTE CAMPAIGN REPORT, 625 Broadway, 2nd Floor, New York, NY 10012-2611.

SPACE AND SECURITY NEWS, Institute for Space and Security Studies, 5115 Highway A1A South, Melbourne Beach, FL 32951.

THE NUCLEAR MONITOR, Nuclear Information & Resource Service, 1424 16th Street NW, Suite 601, Washington, DC 20036.

ABOUT THE AUTHOR

James C. Warf earned his B.S. degree in chemistry at the University of Tulsa, Oklahoma, and Ph.D. degree in inorganic chemistry at Iowa State University. He served as a Group Leader on the Manhattan Project from 1942 to 1947. This was a branch of the Manhattan Project at Iowa State, whose director was F. H. Spedding. It was under the administration of the Metallurgical Laboratory at the University of Chicago, whose over-all director was Enrico Fermi. Dr. Warf headed analytical chemistry section and part of the inorganic chemistry section. He also worked at the University of Chicago and Oak Ridge. He holds patents on extraction techniques which later evolved into the PUREX process for separation of plutonium. Dr. Warf was a founding member of a group which later developed into the Federation of American Scientists. After a year's research on a Guggenheim Fellowship in Switzerland, he went to the University of Southern California where he has been Professor of Chemistry since 1948, and now is Professor Emeritus.

Professor Warf has had a long-time interest in science education in Indonesia and Malaysia. He lived a cumulative total of nearly nine years there, and has written six chemistry books in Indonesian or Malaysian. He spent a sabbatical year in Vienna, and has traveled in 50 countries, frequently giving lectures. He was a consultant at Jet Propulsion Laboratory, working on the life-detection system of the Viking probes to Mars, which used carbon-14. He has testified at hearings by Congressional subcommittees concerning the N Reactor and the proposed atomic vapor laser isotope separation facility.

Professor Warf has been a Research Associate, Program on Nuclear Energy, University of California, Santa Cruz, and a Chair of the Southern California Federation of Scientists. He has been a consultant at Los Angeles County-USC Hospital's nuclear medicine division regarding radioactive isotopes of platinum, used in cancer research. In 1994 he traveled to Semipalatinsk, Kazakhstan, with a team investigating the former Soviet nuclear warhead test sites and health problems resulting from radioactive fallout. In 1996 he inspected the Experimental Breeder Reactor and its proposed system of reprocessing spent fuel in Idaho for the Department of Energy. With more than 60 years experience in the chemistry of radioactive materials, Professor Warf wrote *ALL THINGS NUCLEAR*, first edition, a general account of all manifestations of radioactivity and other nuclear properties. In 2001 he received a Distinguished Professor Emeritus Award from USC. He has been a reader in chemistry since 1967 at Recording for the Blind and Dyslexic.

INDEX

A

B

C

D

E

F

G

H

I

J

K

L

N

O

Q

R

T

U

V

W

X

Y

Z